World Communications

new horizons/new power/new hope

Our high-quality publications
designed for an international audience
of decision makers around the world
appear at selected intervals
when the need arises
for exposition and analysis

LE MONDE ECONOMIQUE **WORLD AIR TRANSPORT IN THE JET AGE**

THE WORLD TELECOMMUNICATIONS IN THE SPACE AGE

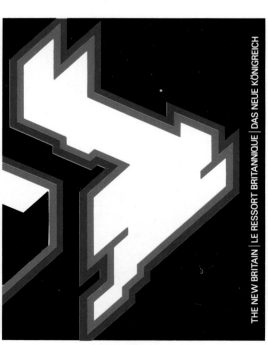

THE NEW BRITAIN | LE RESSORT BRITANNIQUE | DAS NEUE KÖNIGREICH

LE MONDE ÉCONOMIQUE
FONDÉ   EN 1945

INTERNATIONAL PUBLICATIONS

GASTON LIONEL FRANCO
Editor and Publisher (Founder)

The concept of "Le Monde Economique" series of international publications was developed from a weekly magazine founded in 1945 by G. L. Franco. The first of these, "A World in Fusion", published in the 1950s in several languages, was prefaced by Jean Monnet. This great and selfless internationalist, founding father of the European Economic Community, took a keen personal interest in these attempts to communicate worldwide on subjects of great international significance. The emphasis was then, and remains to-day, on the application of modern technology and its impact on the future of mankind. "The Promises of Air Transport", also published in the fifties, followed "A World in Fusion". Then came "Jet Age" and "Telecommunications in the Space Age", both in the sixties, and now "World Communications", bearing the same stamp and purpose. These publications were interspaced with books dealing with economic and industrial issues, and with the development of regions and countries, of which "The New Britain" is the most representative. The object is always the same: to inform, to interpret, to stimulate thought and to promote understanding and the interchange of ideas.

THIS IS A GASTON LIONEL FRANCO PUBLICATION PRODUCED IN COOPERATION WITH ISTITUTO GEOGRAFICO DE AGOSTINI NOVARA - ITALY - TEL: INT'L + 39-321-471201 - TELEX: 200290 WORLD COMMUNICATIONS PUBLICATION PROJECT MANAGERS NOVY EDDISON & PARTNERS: I FRAYSLEA, UXBRIDGE, UB8-2AT UNITED KINGDOM-TEL: UK (0895) 57791-INT'L + 44-895-57791

The purpose of this book is to acquaint decision makers in this vast and complex area of modern communications with the benefits that accrue, nationally and internationally, from the application of the combined technologies of the computer and telecommunications.

The book is designed to provide useful information for those who are concerned with development, investment priorities, choice of system, facilities sharing, international cooperation and other major issues.

The reader will find three threads running through the book: a) the development of "communications"; how they have been changing and where they are going, b) the effect of those developments on the availability, transmission, manipulation and use of "information", c) the consequences, social and cultural as well as economic, and their impact on life style, corporate and personal, in the work place and at home, on production and distribution, on services and controls, in industrialized and developing countries.

The application of modern communications technology, with its electronic highways, frequency architectures and intelligent terminals, is a challenge for all of us. Governments, societies, families and individuals are all involved in this emerging Information Age.

Electronics, often considered de-humanizing, can actually feed, simplify and streamline the creative process, and thus enhance the human values. To adapt it to our needs must be our goal.

The language used in this book, and the illustrations, selected to be meaningful to the non-specialist, should help to perceive and appreciate the new horizons, the new power and the new hope related to the breath-taking developments in communications.

Le but de cet ouvrage est de mieux faire connaître à ceux qui assument des responsabilités dans la prise de décisions, les énormes avantages qui découlent de l'application des technologies combinées de l'informatique et des télécommunications, à l'échelon national et international.

Il a été conçu pour informer utilement ceux qui sont concernés par le développement, la priorité des investissements, le choix et le partage des systèmes, la coopération internationale et autres questions d'importance majeure.

Trois thèmes fondamentaux se retrouvent le long de ces pages : a) le développement des « communications », leur évolution et leur avenir, b) les effets de ce développement sur la disponibilité, le traitement et l'utilisation de « l'information », c) les conséquences sociales, culturelles et économiques, et leur impact sur le style de vie individuelle et collective, sur les conditions de travail et les activités domestiques, sur la production et la distribution, sur les services et les contrôles, dans les pays industrialisés et dans les pays en développement.

L'application de la technologie moderne, avec ses voies électroniques, ses architectures de fréquences et ses terminaux intelligents, est un défi lancé à chacun. Gouvernements, sociétés, familles et individus sont tous concernés par l'avènement de l'ère de l'information.

L'électronique, souvent considérée comme « déshumanisante », peut désormais nourrir, simplifier et dynamiser le processus créatif et, par là même, renforcer les valeurs humaines. Maintenant, il s'agit de l'adapter à nos besoins.

Le langage utilisé, choisi pour ne pas rebuter le non-spécialiste, et les illustrations de cet ouvrage permettront de mieux prendre conscience des nouveaux horizons, du nouveau pouvoir et du nouvel espoir que laissent entrevoir les développements inouïs des communications.

La finalidad de esta obra es que los responsables de adoptar decisiones conozcan mejor las enormes ventajas derivadas de la aplicación de las tecnologías combinadas de la informática y las telecomunicaciones, a nivel nacional e internacional.

Se ha concebido para proporcionar información útil a los interesados en el desarrollo, la prioridad de las inversiones, la elección y la compartición de los sistemas, la cooperación internacional y otras cuestiones esenciales.

En estas páginas se recogen tres temas fundamentales: a) el desarrollo de las "comunicaciones", su evolución y su futuro; b) los efectos de ese desarrollo sobre la disponibilidad, el tratamiento y el uso de la "información"; c) las consecuencias sociales, culturales y económicas, y su impacto sobre el estilo de vida, individual y colectiva, las condiciones de trabajo y las actividades domésticas, la producción y la distribución, los servicios y los controles, tanto en los países industrializados como en desarrollo.

La aplicación de la tecnología moderna de las comunicaciones, con sus vías electrónicas, sus arquitecturas de frecuencias y sus terminales inteligentes, es un desafío para todos, pues la nueva era de la información afecta a los gobiernos, las sociedades, las familias y los individuos.

La electrónica, calificada a menudo de "deshumanizante", podrá alimentar, simplificar y dinamizar el proceso creativo, realzando así los valores humanos, y debemos adaptarla a nuestras necesidades. El lenguaje utilizado y las ilustraciones de esta obra permitirán conocer mejor los nuevos horizontes, el nuevo poder y las nuevas esperanzas que ofrece la increíble evolución de las comunicaciones modernas.

Gaston Lionel FRANCO

NOWLEDGEMENTSACKNOWLEDGEMENTSACKN

We should like to thank for their invaluable co-operation and support, Messrs:

Richard E. Butler, *Secretary-General of the International Telecommunication Union*,
Werner G. G. Wolter, *Chairman, ITU World Telecommunication Forum Management Committee*,

and to acknowledge the contributions and the helpful guidance and discussions with the following personalities, named in alphabetical order:

Avv. Giovanni Agnelli, *Presidente Gruppo FIAT* ▪ Rand V. Araskog, *Chairman, President and Chief Executive, ITT Corporation* ▪ Richard G. Barker, *3M Company* ▪ Warren R. Bechtel, *Western Union Corporation* ▪ Norbert R. Berg, *Deputy Chairman, Control Data Corporation* ▪ Theodore F. Brophy, *Chairman and Chief Executive Officer, GTE* ▪ Charles L. Brown, *Chairman of the Board, American Telephone & Telegraph Company* ▪ Jean-Pierre Brunet, *Président-Directeur Général, Compagnie Générale d'Electricité* ▪ Carlo Camerana, *Telettra SpA* ▪ J. Walton Cannon, *AT&T Communications* ▪ Juan C. Cappello, *Vice President ITT Corporation* ▪ Robert E. Cattlin, *General Manager, Teleport, the Port Authority of New York and New Jersey* ▪ Pierre Chavance, *Administrateur-Directeur Général, CIT-Alcatel* ▪ Ronald D. Coleman, *Senior Vice President, Law and Corporate Development, Direct Broadcast Satellite Corporation* ▪ Benjamin M. Compaine, *Executive Director, Program on Information Policy Research, Harvard University* ▪ Robert C. Cooper, *The Western Union Telegraph Company* ▪ Yvan S. Coscas, *Communications Consultant* ▪ Jacques Darmon, *Directeur Délégué, Directeur de la Branche Communications, Thomson-CSF* ▪ Dr. Lee Davenport, *Consultant* ▪ Jean Delpit, *Directeur à la Direction Générale, CIT-Alcatel* ▪ Claire DeNatale, *Manager Marketing Communications, GTE* ▪ Dr. Jochen Detig, *Siemens AG* ▪ James S. Doyle, *3M Company* ▪ Robert W. Duncan, *President International Operations, Control Data Corporation* ▪ Professor Roger T. Eddison, *Partner, Novy Eddison & Partners* ▪ Peter F. Eder ▪ Steven A. Erenburg, *Director Telecommunications and Electronics, ITT Corporation* ▪ Robert M. Flanagan, *Chairman of the Board and Chief Executive Officer, Western Union Corporation* ▪ Herbert I. Fusfeld, *Director, Center for Science and Technology Policy, New York University* ▪ Edward J. Gerrity, *Senior Vice President, ITT Corporation* ▪ Frederik W. Gibbs, *Executive Vice President, ITT Corporation* ▪ Alain Gomez, *Président-Directeur Général, Thomson* ▪ Edgar A. Grabhorn, *Arthur D. Little, Inc.* ▪ Jean-François Guichard, *CIT-Alcatel* ▪ John W. Guilfoyle, *Executive Vice President, ITT Corporation* ▪ Allan J. Huber, *Executive Vice President, Electronic and Information Technologies Sector, 3M Company* ▪ Alan B. Kamman, *Vice President, Arthur D. Little, Inc.* ▪ Dr. Karlheinz Kaske, *President and Chief Executive Officer, Siemens AG* ▪ H. E. Dr. Alawi Darweesh Kayal, *Minister of Posts, Telegraphs and Telephones, Kingdom of Saudi Arabia* ▪ Yasusada Kitahara, *Executive Vice President, Nippon Telegraph & Telephone Public Corporation*

■ Dr. Koji Kobayashi, *Chairman and Chief Executive Officer, NEC Corporation* ■ John B. Lawrence Jr., *Senior Editor, GTE* ■ Lewis W. Lehr, *Chairman and Chief Executive Officer, 3M Company* ■ Michel Lescœur, *Délégué Général, Syndicat des Industries du Téléphone, du Télégraphe et de leurs Applications Télématiques, France* ■ Ambrose J. Linnen, *AT&T Communications* ■ John W. Linz, *AT&T International* ■ Francine Londez, *Thomson-CSF* ■ Dr. Horst Edgar Martin, *Siemens AG* ■ Dipl.-Ing. Hans Otto Matt, *Siemens AG* ■ John McLaughlin, *Vice President & Executive Director, Program on Information Policy Research, Harvard University* ■ Gorman D. McMullen, *Director, United States Independent Telephone Association* ■ Bruno Zuccardi Merli, *Vice Direttore Generale, Telettra SpA* ■ M. Mili, *past Secretary-General of the International Telecommunication Union* ■ Warren P. Miner, *AT&T International* ■ William C. Norris, *Chairman and Chief Executive Officer, Control Data Corporation* ■ Peter A. Novy ■ Tom O'Connor, *Western Union Corporation* ■ Anthony G. Oettinger, *Chairman, Program on Information Policy Research, Harvard University* ■ Raffaele Palieri, *Amministratore Delegato e Direttore Generale, Telettra SpA* ■ Georges Pebereau, *Président-Directeur Général, CIT-Alcatel* ■ Gerald D. Pint, *Group Vice President, Electrical Products Group, 3M Company* ■ Robert M. Price, *President and Chief Operating Officer, Control Data Corporation* ■ Terry P. Quinn, *Vice President, ITT Europe Inc.* ■ Ing. Massimo Rizzi, *Telettra SpA* ■ Robert E. Sageman, *President and Chief Executive Officer, AT&T International* ■ Tadahiro Sakimoto, *President, NEC Corporation* ■ Dr. Dieter Von Sanden, *Member of the Board, Head of the Communications Group, Siemens AG* ■ Philip Schneider, *Vice President, Government, International and Satellite Systems, Western Union Corporation* ■ John R. Schultz, *American Telephone & Telegraph Company* ■ Shozo Shimizu, *Associate Senior Vice President and Director, NEC Corporation* ■ John Sodolski, *Vice President, United States Electronic Industries Association* ■ C. Sunmper Logan, *Vice President, GTE* ■ Nozomu Takasaki, *Vice President, Pacific Telecommunications Council, Director International Affairs, Research Institute of Telecommunications and Economics, Japan* ■ Dr. Thomas A. Vanderslice, *President and Chief Operating Officer, GTE* ■ Guido Vannucchi, *Amministratore Delegato e Direttore Generale, Telettra SpA* ■ Jean Voge, *Conseiller spécial à la Direction Générale des Télécommunications, Ministère des PTT, France* ■ Daniel P. Weadock, *Executive Vice President, ITT Corporation* ■ Stanley M. Welland, *Ph. D., Vice President, Strategic Technology Planning, Merrill Lynch & Co.* ■ Burt R. Wolder, *AT&T International* ■ Kiyomi Yukihiro, *President, Research Institute of Telecommunications and Economics, Chairman Pacific Telecommunications Council Committee, Japan.* This World Communications book was conceived and edited under the general direction of Gaston Lionel Franco, Editor and Publisher of "Le Monde Economique" International Publications series. The editorial and research work was done under the direction of Henry J. Novy.

CONTENTS

CONTENTS

NEW HORIZONS NEW POWER NEW HOPE

CONTENTS

COMMUNICATING ABOUT COMMUNICATIO

Introduction by Richard E. Butler
Secretary-General of the International Telecommunication Union

S: A TIMELY REQUIREMENT

Today's college graduates and modern telecommunications are almost the same age. Only two decades have passed since the initial merging of communications and computer technologies. Modern telecommunications, their offspring, are a fundamental factor in social, economic and cultural progress.

The harmonious development of communications has been impeded by the disparity between different countries of their technical development, financial capacity and human resources. Wide gaps remain to be bridged between the industrialized and developing or underprivileged countries still deprived of the benefits of communications infrastructure which is recognized, more and more, as vital to development. The ITU Plenipotentiaries at Nairobi, in 1982, noted that underinvestment in telecommunications can partly be attributed to « ...insufficient research, inadequate dissemination of information, and a lack of understanding within national planning ministries about the relationship between telecommunications and economic development... »

In 1965, the late Gerald C. Gross, then Secretary-General, in his introduction to G. L. Franco's book "Telecommunications in the Space Age", published on the occasion of the ITU Centenary, predicted that "thanks to space applications, telecommunication techniques will themselves know unprecedented developments". Nearly two decades later we have witnessed enormous progress and cost reductions in space and terrestrial transmission technology.

I wish to stress that low-cost communications, even to and between rural subscribers in remote areas, can now be assured and that we are on the eve of the potential application of space and terrestrial telecommunications to serve economically small traffic needs. Therefore, as a perspective of modern technology application, I have proposed "Glodom": a global approach to the major telecommunication challenge of the decade, it brings basic telephone and sound broadcasting telecommunication services to each settlement and village in rural areas of the world, through suitable mixes of space and terrestrial systems. It involves resource sharing and integration of appropriate satellite capacities, where needed, into individual countries' terrestrial systems.

It is the objective of this book to translate the complex telecommunication technology and its economics into forms that I am sure all will grasp. "World Communications" could not therefore be more timely.

It reflects the spirit of international technical cooperation between the government and private sector of countries which is the basic principle of the International Telecommunication Union since its creation back in 1865. I invite all to cooperate with us in facing the telecommunication challenge of the decade.

Les jeunes diplomés d'aujourd'hui et les télécommunications modernes sont presque du même âge. En effet, deux décennies se sont à peine écoulées depuis la fusion des technologies des télécommunications et de l'informatique, nouveau facteur, fondamental, du progrès social, économique et culturel.

Le développement harmonieux des communications a cependant été sévèrement entravé par l'inégalité subsistant entre les pays, en termes de développement technique, de capacité financière et de ressources humaines. Un grand fossé sépare les pays industrialisés et les pays en développement privés d'une infrastructure de communications, élément-clé du développement. Les plénipotentiaires de l'UIT, réunis à Nairobi en 1982, ont relevé que le sous-investissement dans les communications s'explique en partie par « ... l'insuffisance de recherche, par une diffusion inadéquate de l'information et par un manque de compréhension parmi les planificateurs nationaux, de l'interaction des communications et du développement économique et social ... ».

En 1965, le regretté Gerald C. Gross, alors Secrétaire général de l'UIT, dans son introduction à l'ouvrage de G. L. Franco « Telecommunications in the Space Age », publié à l'occasion du centenaire de l'UIT, prédisait que « grâce aux applications spatiales, les techniques des télécommunications connaîtront des développements sans précédent ». A peine 20 ans plus tard, nous sommes déjà témoins d'une prodigieuse évolution de la technologie et d'un écrasement des coûts de la télétransmission spatiale et terrestre.

Je tiens à souligner que des communications peu coûteuses peuvent maintenant être assurées même dans les régions les plus isolées, et que nous sommes à la veille d'une utilisation combinée des télécommunications spatiales et terrestres pour desservir économiquement des liaisons à faible trafic. C'est dans cette perspective que j'ai proposé le concept du système « Glodom », visant à introduire le téléphone dans les fermes et les villages les plus isolés, ce qui implique un partage des ressources de transmission spatiale et leur intégration dans les systèmes terrestres nationaux.

L'objet de cet ouvrage est de présenter la technologie des télécommunications et ses aspects économiques sous une forme accessible à tous. « World Communications » n'aurait donc pu arriver à un meilleur moment. Il reflète l'esprit de coopération technique internationale qui est le fondement même de l'UIT. Je convie tous ceux qui le peuvent à coopérer avec nous pour affronter le défi de notre temps: l'implantation universelle des télécommunications.

Los jovenes diplomados de hoy y las telecomunicaciones modernas tienen casi la misma edad. Hace sólo dos decenios que se fusionaron las tecnologías de comunicaciones y computador, cuyo producto son las telecomunicaciones modernas, factor fundamental del progreso social, económico y cultural.

La disparidad en el desarrollo técnico, la capacidad financiera y los recursos humanos de los países han impedido la armoniosa expansión de las comunicaciones. Los países en desarrollo están privados aún de los beneficios de las infraestructuras de comunicaciones tan vitales para desarrollarse. Los plenipotenciarios de la UIT señalaron en Nairobi, en 1982, que la infrainversión en telecomunicaciones puede atribuirse, en parte, « ... a la investigación insuficiente, la difusión inadecuada de información y una falta de comprensión por parte de los ministerios nacionales responsables de la planificación de la relación entre las telecomunicaciones y el desarrollo económico y social... ».

En 1965, el extinto Gerald C. Gross, a la sazón Secretario General de la UIT, en su introducción al libro publicado por G. L. Franco en el centenario de la UIT, « Telecommunications in the Space Age », predecía que « gracias a las aplicaciones espaciales, las propias técnicas de las telecomunicaciones conocerían una evolución sin precedentes ». Casi dos décadas después, presenciamos enormes avances en la tecnología espacial, y reducciones de costos y tecnología de transmisión terrenal.

Deseo subrayar que las comunicaciones económicas, incluso con abonados rurales y entre ellos en zonas remotas, pueden lograrse ya, y que estamos en vísperas de la aplicación de las telecomunicaciones espaciales para atender económicamente reducidas necesidades de tráfico. Por tanto, con miras a la aplicación de la tecnología moderna, he propuesto la noción « Glodom », para abordar el gran desafío de las telecomunicaciones del decenio, prestando servicios telefónicos y de radiodifusión a todo pueblo y aldea de las regiones rurales del mundo, mezclando los sistemas espaciales y terrenales. Glodom supone la compartición de recursos y la integración de capacidades de satélite apropiadas en los sistemas de comunicaciones terrenales de los países.

La finalidad de esta obra es traducir la compleja tecnología de las telecomunicaciones y sus aspectos económicos en formas que todo el mundo entienda. « World Communications » no podía llegar, pues, en mejor momento. Refleja el espíritu de la cooperación técnica internacional, principio básico de la Unión Internacional de Telecomunicaciones desde 1865. Invito a todos a cooperar para hacer frente al desafío de las telecomunicaciones del decenio.

NEW HORIZONS NEW POWER NEW HOPE

This figure is a striking illustration of the concept of a single all-embracing community of mankind manifesting itself in a world where information and knowledge are accessible to all in the form and shape required for practical use.

The emerging convergence of computer and communications technologies is producing information systems that match the varied needs of an exploding diversity of users, applications and regions of the world. In this perspective, communications might be viewed as the neural system of society, the means to interconnect the component parts into a dynamic, interactive, purposeful whole.

This concept of computers and communications, C&C, was elaborated by Dr. Koji Kobayashi, Chairman of the Board and Chief Executive of NEC Corporation of Japan, in a paper presented at the Massachusetts Institute of Technology, Cambridge, Ma., USA, in June 1982. The chart portrays the three segments — public systems, business systems and home systems — which make up the world of "Man and Computers & Communications", (M and C&C). The means of communications — terminals, networks and computers — are shown by vertical pillars. These represent, together with the public, business and home systems, shown in red horizontally, a matrix structure of the total M and C&C concept. The elements comprised in the three functional systems are the following:

Public systems encompass community, national or global infrastructures, and are used for social insurance, medical treatment, banking, public administration, management and a variety of control systems for space, air, sea and land transport.

Business systems include factory and office automation systems designed to take over simple, repetitive or dangerous manual tasks, support decision making, monitor and control operations, assist design, etc. and contribute not only to greater volume in business activities and increased productivity but to improved quality and creativity.

Home systems consist of machines and systems endowed with "intelligence" set up in individual homes to contribute to more convenient, healthier and safer living. They will be "user-friendly", with good man-machine interfaces and easy to use. They can also enable people to work effectively in their own homes.

The supporting computer and communications technologies and their applications are discussed further in this volume. These include: large and very large scale integrated circuits (LSI and VLSI); fiber optics and wideband transmission; satellite communications; microwave radio; speech recognition and synthesis; robotics; personal computers; man-machine interfaces and media technology, including new media such as video discs, electronic mail and interactive cable television.

Cette structure est une illustration frappante de la conception de réseaux télématiques qui vont permettre la naissance d'une communauté universelle, dans un monde où l'information et la connaissance seront accessibles à tous, de toutes les manières et sous toutes les formes utiles.

Pour répondre aux besoins les plus variés d'une diversité infinie d'utilisateurs et d'utilisations foisonnant jusque dans les régions les plus reculées du monde, l'ensemble intégré des réseaux de télécommunications et des ordinateurs jouera le rôle de système nerveux de la société, interconnectant ses innombrables systèmes informatiques en un tout dynamique, interactif et parfaitement cohérent.

Cette conception désignée sous le sigle C&C (computers and communications) a été élaborée par le Dr. Koji Kobayashi, Président-Directeur général du groupe japonais NEC Corporation. Elle a été présentée en juin 1982 au Massachusetts Institute of Technology de Cambridge, Etats-Unis. Le schéma montre la combinaison de trois secteurs : les systèmes publics, les systèmes commerciaux et les systèmes domestiques, dont l'ensemble est désigné par le sigle « M and C&C » (Man and Computers & Communications). Les moyens de communication — terminaux, réseaux et ordinateurs — sont representés par les piliers verticaux, perpendiculaires aux systèmes publics, commerciaux et privés, apparaissant horizontalement en rouge. Ces composants forment l'architecture de la conception « M and C&C ».

Les systèmes publics comprennent les infrastructures communautaires, nationales et mondiales. Ils sont utilisés dans des domaines très divers : sécurité sociale, diagnostic et traitement médicaux, opérations bancaires, administration publique, gestion et toute une variété de systèmes de contrôle pour les transports (espace, air, mer, terre), etc.

Les systèmes commerciaux trouvent leur application dans l'industrie (chaînes de production automatiques, robotique) et dans l'administration (bureautique). Ce sont des auxiliaires précieux pour la prise de décisions, la surveillance et la commande d'opérations, l'exécution de travaux conceptuels, etc. Ils contribuent non seulement à augmenter la productivité mais à améliorer la qualité et la créativité.

Les systèmes domestiques, doués d'intelligence, sont destinés à simplifier la vie au foyer et à la rendre plus sûre et plus saine. Ces systèmes conçus pour devenir familiers à tous, auront de bonnes liaisons homme-machine et seront d'une utilisation aisée. Ils permettront aussi à chacun de pouvoir exercer effectivement son travail à domicile.

Les nouvelles technologies de l'ordinateur et des télécommunications, dont il est question dans ce volume, sont aujourd'hui complémentaires et sous-tendent la nouvelle société en formation. Leurs applications concernent les circuits intégrés LSI (intégration à grande échelle) et VLSI (intégration à très grande échelle), les fibres optiques et la transmission à large bande, les télécommunications par satellite, les transmissions radioélectriques à hyperfréquences ou micro-ondes, l'analyse et la synthèse de la parole, les robots, les ordinateurs personnels, les interfaces homme-machine, les nouveaux supports d'information (vidéo-disques), le courrier électronique et la télévision interactive par câble.

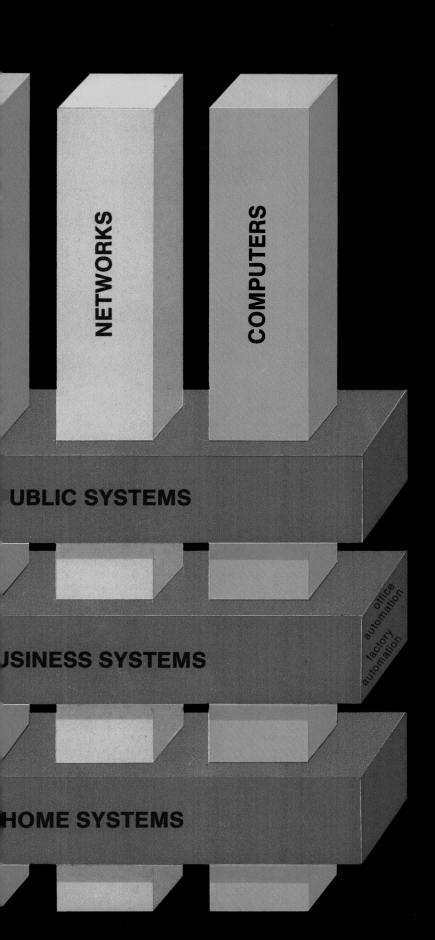

NETWORKS

COMPUTERS

UBLIC SYSTEMS

office automation

factory automation

USINESS SYSTEMS

HOME SYSTEMS

Esta gráfico ilustra claramente la noción de una sola comunidad global en la humanidad, que se manifesta en un mundo en el que la información y el conocimiento son accesibles a todos en la forma y modo que requiere su utilización práctica.

La aparición simultánea de las tecnologías de computador y de comunicaciones está produciendo sistemas de información que corresponden a las variadas necesidades de una enorme diversidad de usuarios, aplicaciones y regiones del mundo. En esta perspectiva, las comunicaciones pueden considerarse como el sistema neural de la sociedad, el medio de interconectar las partes componentes en un conjunto dinámico, interactivo y completo.

Esta noción de computadores y comunicaciones (CyC) fue concebida por el Dr. Koji Kobayashi, Presidente del Consejo y Jefe Ejecutivo de NEC Corporation de Japón, en un documento presentado en el Instituto de Tecnología de Massachusetts, Cambridge, Ma. (EE.UU.), en junio del 1982.

El gráfico muestra los tres segmentos — sistemas públicos, sistemas comerciales y sistemas domésticos — que componen el mundo de "El Hombre y los computadores y las comunicaciones" (H y CyC). Los medios de comunicación — terminales, redes y computadores — se muestran mediante columnas verticales. Estos representan, junto con los sistemas públicos, comerciales y domésticos mostrados en rojo horizontalmente, una estructura matricial de la noción total de M y CyC.

Los elementos que comprenden los tres sistemas funcionales son los siguientes:

Los sistemas públicos abarcan las infraestructuras comunitaria, nacional o global, y se emplean para la seguridad social, el tratamiento médico, la banca, la administración pública, la gestión y una variedad de sistemas de control para el transporte espacial, aéreo, marítimo y terrestre.

Los sistemas comerciales comprenden los de la automatización de fábricas y oficinas, destinados a sustituir al individuo en tareas manuales sencillas, repetitivas o peligrosas, apoyar la adopción de decisiones, verificar y controlar las operaciones, ayudar al diseño, etc., y no sólo contribuyen a aumentar el volumen de las actividades comerciales y la productividad, sino también a mejorar la calidad y la creatividad.

Los sistemas domésticos consisten en máquinas y sistemas dotados de "inteligencia", instalados en los hogares, para contribuir a una vida más agradable, más sana y más segura. Serán "familiares para el usuario", con buenos interfaces hombre-máquina y de fácil uso. También pueden permitir a la gente trabajar efectivamente en sus hogares.

Las tecnologías de computador y comunicaciones de apoyo, y de sus aplicaciones se tratan en otra parte de esta obra. Entre ellas figuran: circuitos integrados en gran y muy gran escala (LSI y VLSI); fibras ópticas y transmisión de banda ancha; comunicaciones por satélite; radiocomunicaciones por microondas; reconocimiento y síntesis de la palabra; computadores personales, interfaces hombre-máquina y tecnología de medios de información, como videodiscos, correo electrónico y televisión por cable interactiva, que son nuevos.

THE INFORMATION AGE
A WORLDWIDE REVOLUTION IN COMMUNICATIONS

AN INFORMATION BOMB is exploding in our midst, and drastically changing the way each of us perceives and acts upon our private world. How is this likely to progress, what are the consequences for us individuals, for our enterprises, what are can we, each of us, do to ensure that we benefit from the change and take the opportunities offered to us? Answers to these questions, and to others more specific, such as the problems of interfacing the new with the old, the planning requirements, the financial implications, etc. are our concern in this book. Also, more particularly, the ways in which developing countries can benefit from this technological bonanza, how it can assist them to develop their natural resources and to raise the productivity of their endeavours.

The pace of today's growth in communications outstrips all expectations; it has begun to change the world we live in and promises even greater changes. The converging technologies of telecommunications and computers, assisted by the emergence of revolutionary transmission techniques, such as digitalization, fiber optics and satellites, have made a reality of total and global instant communications. Broader potentials now exist for advances in virtually every area of knowledge and concern.

Technically it is already possible to link not only people with people but people with machines and machines with machines. This new partnership of man and machine in the handling of information, independent of time and distance, marks the emergence of a new information orientated society: the "Information Age".

▷ 16

UN VÉRITABLE RAZ DE MARÉE d'information déferle sur nous tous, affectant profondément notre perception de ce qui nous entoure ainsi que notre comportement. Où cela va-t-il nous conduire ? Quelles en seront les conséquences pour chacun de nous, pour nos entreprises, pour le développement de notre société ? Serons-nous capables d'en tirer parti et de saisir toutes les opportunités qui en découlent ?

Voici les questions fondamentales qui ont inspiré l'élaboration de cet ouvrage. Plus particulièrement les problèmes de la transition entre l'ancien et le nouveau, les exigences de la planification, les implications financières et l'adaptation de la nouvelle technologie aux besoins spécifiques du Tiers Monde, la manière dont les pays en développement peuvent bénéficier du progrès technique pour mettre en valeur leurs ressources naturelles, augmenter leur productivité et améliorer leur bien-être.

La rapidité du progrès dans ce domaine dépasse toutes les prévisions et promet de s'accélérer d'une manière encore plus spectaculaire. La symbiose entre télécommunications et ordinateurs est stimulée par l'apparition de techniques révolutionnaires, telles que la transmission numérique, les fibres optiques et les liaisons par satellite. A un horizon pas tellement distant, apparaît la possibilité de dialogue entre homme et machine (par voie de synthèse vocale) et de communication à un niveau de fréquences d'ondes entre le cerveau humain et l'ordinateur intelligent (5ème génération), une nouvelle forme de télépathie.

Déjà les machines peuvent communiquer et se comprendre entre elles, permettant l'intégration complète des installations de bureaux et d'opérations industrielles. Ces nouvelles possibilités nous font entrer de plein pied dans l'« Ère de l'Information »

▷ 16

EXPLOTA ENTRE NOSOTROS LA BOMBA de la información, que cambia radicalmente la manera en que cada uno percibe su mundo privado y actúa en consecuencia. ¿Cuál será su avance, qué consecuencias tendrá para nosotros, como individuos, y para nuestras empresas, y qué podremos hacer, todos y cada uno, para beneficiarnos del cambio y aprovechar las oportunidades que se nos ofrecen? Las respuestas a estas preguntas, y a otras más concretas, como los problemas de hermanar lo nuevo y lo antiguo, los requisitos de planificación, las consecuencias financieras, etc., es lo que nos interesa en este libro, y también, más particularmente, la manera en que los países en desarrollo podrán beneficiarse de esta fuente de riqueza tecnológica, cómo puede ayudarles a explotar sus recursos naturales y a aumentar la productividad de sus empresas.

El ritmo actual de las comunicaciones supera todas las expectativas; ha comenzado a cambiar el mundo, y promete cambios aún mayores. Las tecnologías convergentes de las telecomunicaciones y los computadores, ayudadas por nuevas técnicas de transmisión revolucionarias, como la digitalización, las fibras ópticas y los satélites, han convertido en realidad las comunicaciones totales y globales instantáneas. Hoy existen mayores posibilidades de avance en casi todas las esferas de conocimiento e interés.

Técnicamente, ya es posible vincular no sólo a las personas entre sí, sino a la persona con máquinas y a las máquinas entre ellas. Esta nueva asociación de hombre y máquina en el tratamiento de la información, independiente del tiempo y de la distancia, marca la aparición de una nueva sociedad orientada hacia la información: la "era de la información".

▷ 17

Learning to use the computer: a must for all.

Apprendre à manier l'ordinateur : une nécessité pour tous.

Saber manejar el computador: necesario para todos.

The form of communication has, of course, been changing ever since the telegraph first enabled people to communicate over distance. After the telegraph, within some 40 years, came the telephone, initially conceived as an extension of telegraphy but in fact a radical breakthrough and the basis for much of to-day's astonishing progress in the routing, transmission and processing of information. Shortly after the telephone, within one generation, came radio. By then the appetites of users had been whetted, the benefits derived from an efficient communications system had been realized and demand began to pull technology forward.

Television, adding image to voice transmission, came in the 1930s and thereafter — fuelled to some extent by the needs of war — a quick succession of inventions, many of them an enhancement of previously established technology and most of them products of major programs of telecommunications research. They included electromechanical "Strowger" type switching of telephone calls, coaxial cable and, in the wake of semiconductor technology, the termionic valve, the transistor, the computer and, since second world war, the integration of electronic circuitry into less and less space, using a novel etching process, on minute wafer-thin silicon surfaces. These trends are expected to continue as the Information Age develops during the few remaining years of the 20th Century.

Alvin Toffler, whose book "The Third Wave" (Collins 1980) introduced the reference to an information bomb, provided in his "Future Shock" (Collins) an enlightening perspective of change: "it has been observed... that if the last 50,000 years of man's existence were divided into lifetimes of approximately sixty-two years each, there have been about 800 such lifetimes. Of these 800, 650 were spent in caves.

Only during the past seventy lifetimes has it been possible to communicate effectively from one lifetime to another — as writing made it possible to do. Only during the last six lifetimes did masses of men ever see a printed word. Only during the past four has it been possible to measure time with any precision. Only during the last two has anyone anywhere used an electric motor. And the overwhelming majority of all the material goods we use in daily life today have been developed within the present, the 800th lifetime".

The speed of transmission of information has also been changing rapidly, and now almost everything can be heard or seen as it happens, in "real time". A striking illustration of the extent to which telecommunications has speeded up the passage of information from one point to another is provided by reference to three world shaking events: in 1492 Isabella of Castile, Queen of Spain, had to wait six months to learn of Christopher Columbus' discovery of the New World; four Centuries later, in 1865, the British Government learned of Abraham Lincoln's assassination 12 weeks after the event; in 1969 it took only 1.3 seconds for the world to be informed of Neil Armstrong's landing on the moon.

Falling costs are a major factor in the adoption of modern communications technology. Until the 1980s the high cost of communications equipment and of its maintenance acted as a brake on its usage, even on the development of possible applications. The technology was available and broad potential for applications existed on virtually every area of knowledge and concern. Investment and purchasing power lagged behind.

Today there is a marked tendency for costs to decrease and with it an increase in general usage. The two, of course, are linked: economies of scale as well as advances in design and manufacturing technique have contributed. For example, microelectronic technology provides capacity for information storage and for logical or intelligent manipulation of

---

dans laquelle savoir, comprendre et communiquer constituent les éléments de base de nos activités. Les portes sont grandes ouvertes à de nouvelles avances dans pratiquement tous les domaines.

La forme de communication a, bien sûr, beaucoup évolué, et vite, depuis le télégraphe de Morse dans les années 1830. Deux générations plus tard, vers la fin du siècle, le téléphone — conçu initialement comme une extension du télégraphe — fit son apparition, suivi 70 ans après par la téléphonie sans-fil (tsf) ou radio. A peine une génération passa avant que la télévision vint à ajouter la diffusion de l'image à celle du son. C'est dans cette même période que la technologie de l'ordinateur se développa pour donner naissance au premier engin pendant la deuxième guerre mondiale (1940).

Maintenant tout se mélange et s'intègre : le téléphone et l'ordinateur se marient pour nous donner accès aux sources d'information les plus diverses dans les formes voulues et, en plus, les moyens de contrôler un peu tout à distance. La radio et la télévision deviennent capables de fournir à chacun de nous les moyens d'émettre et de recevoir et s'ajoutent au téléphone et à l'ordinateur pour amplifier et embellir les fruits de la télécommunication.

Dans son livre intitulé « La Troisième Vague » (Denoël, 1980) Alvin Toffler a introduit le concept d'une « bombe nommée information » en train d'exploser, nous « mitraillant d'une avalanche d'éclats sous forme d'images et modifiant de façon inouïe notre manière de percevoir notre univers et d'agir sur lui », et, dans « Le Choc du Futur », il nous a donné une lumineuse description de l'évolution historique de l'humanité : « On a remarqué par exemple que, si les 50 000 dernières années de l'histoire de l'humanité étaient divisées en tranches d'une durée approximative de soixante-deux ans, l'équivalent de la vie d'un homme, on aboutirait à un total de 800 générations. Sur ces 800, 650 au moins ont vu le jour dans des grottes.

Ce n'est que pendant les 70 dernières générations qu'il est devenu possible d'établir une véritable communication entre deux générations successives — l'écriture a permis ce progrès. Il a fallu attendre les 6 dernières générations pour que des masses humaines soient en mesure de voir un mot imprimé.

Seules 4 générations ont pu mesurer le temps avec une certaine précision. Deux générations seulement ont eu le loisir d'utiliser un moteur électrique et la majorité écrasante des biens matériels dont nous nous servons dans notre vie quotidienne ont été inventés et produits par la génération actuelle : la 800ème ».

La rapidité de transmission de l'information s'est elle-même métamorphosée. En effet, actuellement tout peut être vu et entendu « en temps réel ». L'accélération prodigieuse de la transmission de l'information d'un point à l'autre de notre globe, grâce aux télécommunications, peut être illustrée d'une manière frappante par trois évènements historiques : en 1492, Isabelle de Castille, reine d'Espagne, a dû attendre six mois pour apprendre la découverte du Nouveau-Monde par Christophe Colomb. Quatre siècles plus tard, en 1865, le gouvernement britannique n'a appris l'assassinat du président des Etats-Unis, Abraham Lincoln, qu'au bout de douze semaines. En 1969, il n'a fallu que 1,3 seconde pour que le monde entier soit informé de l'atterrissage de Neil Armstrong sur la Lune.

L'abaissement des coûts a contribué très largement à la généralisation des techniques modernes de communication. Jusqu'en 1980, le coût élevé des équipements et de leur maintenance ont sérieusement freiné leur utilisation et même entravé la mise au point de leurs applications. En fait, la technique et les possibilités d'utilisation existaient pratiquement dans tous les domaines, mais les investissements et le pouvoir d'achat restaient insuffisants. Aujourd'hui, on observe une très nette tendance à un abaissement des prix de revient et à un accroissement parallèle des utilisations.

DEFINITION OF

The two words are inseparably linked. The meaning of communications, or telecommunications, intended here is as defined by the ITU Convention and is in general use among engineers, i. e. "any transmission, emission or reception of signs, signals, writing, images or sounds, or intelligence of any nature by wire, radio, optical or other electromagnetic systems".

The meaning of Information, states the Oxford English Dictionary, is "knowledge communicated concerning some particular fact, subject or event; that of which one is appraised or told; intelligence; news".

COMMUNICAT
OF INFORMATION

Communications as defined above include the use of telegraph, telephone and radio and all their applications such as telex, facsimile, radar and television, as well as the use of computers and allied equipment for the storage and teleprocessing of information.

The means of communication have undergone major changes in recent years and the pace of change continues to increase: analog transmission giving way to digital transmission, electromechanical crossbar switching to electronic switching, coaxial cables to fiber optic cables, the emergence of microwave two-way radio as an alternative to cable links, etc., being cost insensitive to distance through satellite transmission and heralding, inter alia, the arrival of the "wireless telephone".

The introduction of the computer in transmission systems has resulted in information systems using digital and micron technologies capable of transmitting and processing telephone calls, data, facsimile images and video signals.

INFORMATION:
USED INCREA

The meaning of information given above pre-supposes the participation of five related entities: 1) the knowledge, stored or communicated; 2) the method by which knowledge is stored or communicated; 3) the form in which it is communicated; 4) the communicator; 5) the communicatee.

Information is playing a part greater than ever before in education, in research and in decision-making whether in business or government. It is becoming available widely and cheaply and the time is fast approaching when everyone becomes able to communicate with anybody, any time, anywhere, and to access any kind of information in the form desired. The problem is how to make this possible now that the technology is available.

So far, information is transmitted — in the main — either physically i.e. transported; or by telephone or telex i.e. by means of electrical pulses over wire, or by radio wave. The telephone network is used overwhelmingly for the transmission of voice in an analog form, a method which has not changed much since telephony was introduced over 100 years ago. For its part, the computer has been used, and continues to be used, mainly for number crunching, i.e. the processing of data.

Suitably modified, however, the telephone network can transmit in digital form, i. e. in the language of the computer, at vastly increased speed and accuracy, any kind of information: numerical, textual and visual as well as voice. The computer is capable of processing and storing information, again of any kind, at the places of origin and reception. Unquestionably, the development of a global information society lies in the integration of these two technologies: telecommunications and computing.

▷ 20

▷ 20

MMUNICATIONS AND INFORMATION

mmunications et information. Ces deux mots sont insépara-
ment liés. Le terme « communications » tel qu'il est utilisé
 correspond à télécommunication dont la définition est
ntenue dans la Convention de l'Union internationale des
écommunications (UIT) à laquelle se réfèrent les techniciens
monde entier : « Télécommunication : toute transmission,
ission ou réception de signes, de signaux, d'écrits, d'images,
sons ou de renseignements de toute nature, par fil, radioé-
tricité, optique ou autres systèmes électromagnétiques ».
Selon la définition usuelle on entend par information toute
nnaissance (donnée, renseignement, nouvelle, ect.) suscep-
le d'être communiquée.

Ambas palabras están vinculadas inseparablemente. Por comunicaciones, o telecomunicaciones, se entiende aquí lo defi-
nido en el Convenio de la UIT, generalizado entre los ingenieros
del mundo entero, a saber, "Toda transmisión, emisión o recepción de signos, señales, escritos, imágenes, sonidos o informaciones de cualquier naturaleza por hilo, radioelectricidad,
medios ópticos u otros sistemas electromagnéticos".

El significado de información, según el diccionario inglés
Oxford, es "conocimiento comunicado sobre un hecho, asunto o
acontecimiento particular; aquello cuyo sentido puede ser per-
cibido o expresado; inteligencia; noticias".

La forma de comunicación viene cambiando sin cesar
desde que el primer telégrafo permitió comunicar a
distancia. Unos 40 años después del telégrafo llegó el
teléfono, concebido como una extensión de la telegrafía, pero que supuso en realidad un avance radical y la base de muchos de los asombrosos progresos
actuales en el encaminamiento, la transmisión y el
procesamiento de la información. Poco después del
teléfono, en una generación, llegó la radio. Para entonces ya se había despertado el apetito de los usuarios, se habían comprendido los beneficios de un
sistema de comunicaciones eficaz, y la demanda comenzó a impulsar la tecnología.

La televisión, que venía a sumar la imagen a la
transmisión de la voz, apareció en los años 1930, y
fue seguida — en parte como consecuencia de las
necesidades de la guerra — por una rápida sucesión
de invenciones, muchas de las cuales constituían el
mejoramiento de la tecnología ya establecida, con-
sistiendo la mayoría en productos de importantes
programas de investigación en telecomunicaciones:
la conmutación electromecánica de las llamadas telefónicas de tipo "Strowger", el cable coaxial y, después de la tecnología de semiconductores, la válvula
termoiónica, el transistor, el computador y, desde la
Segunda Guerra Mundial, la integración de circuitos
electrónicos en un espacio cada vez más pequeño,
empleando un nuevo proceso de grabado químico en
superficies de silicio del espesor de una oblea dimi-
nuta. Se espera que estas tendencias continúen a
medida que la era de la información avance en los
pocos años que quedan del siglo XX.

Alvin Toffler, cuyo libro "The Third Wave" (Collins, 1980) hace referencia a una bomba de la información, ofrece en su "Future Shock" una clara
perspectiva de cambio: « se ha observado ... que si
los últimos 50 000 años de existencia del hombre se
dividieran en vidas del orden de 62 años cada una,
habría unas 800 de esas vidas. De ellas, se habrían
pasado en las cavernas 650.

Sólo durante las setenta últimas vidas ha sido posible comunicar de una a otra, como consecuencia de
la escritura. Sólo en las últimas vidas pudieron
ver masas de hombres una palabra impresa. Sólo en
las cuatro últimas ha sido posible medir el tiempo
con precisión. Y sólo en las últimas dos se ha utilizado en alguna parte un motor eléctrico. Y la abru-
madora mayoría de los bienes materiales que usa-
mos hoy en nuestra vida diaria se han desarrollado
en la 800ª vida actual ».

La velocidad de transmisión de la información también ha
cambiado rápidamente, y ahora casi todo puede
oírse y verse en el momento que sucede, en tiempo
real. Hay tres acontecimientos mundiales extraordi-
narios que ilustran perfectamente el grado en que las
telecomunicaciones han acelerado el paso de la información de un punto a otro: en 1492, Isabel de
Castilla, Reina de España, tardó seis meses en conocer el descubrimiento del nuevo mundo por Cristó-
bal Colón; cuatro siglos después, en 1865, el Gobierno británico tuvo conocimiento del asesinato de
Abraham Lincoln con 12 semanas de retraso; en
1969, sólo se tardó 1,3 segundos en informar al
mundo de la llegada de Neil Armstrong a la Luna.

La reducción de los costos es un importante factor de la
adopción de la tecnología de comunicaciones moderna. Hasta los años 1980, el elevado costo del
equipo de comunicaciones y su mantenimiento fre-
naba su uso, e incluso el desarrollo de posibles aplicaciones. Se disponía de la tecnología, y virtualmente en todos los sectores de conocimiento e interés
existían amplias posibilidades de aplicación. La inversión y el poder adquisitivo iban a la zaga.

Hoy día hay una marcada tendencia a reducir
los costos y, por ende, al aumento del uso general.
Por supuesto, ambos aspectos están vinculados: a
ello han contribuido las economías de escala y los
progresos en el diseño y la técnica de fabricación. Por

: THE PROCESSING AND TRANSMISSION
INSTRUCTIONS OVER TIME AND DISTANCE

sens de la définition de l'UIT, les communications à distance
pliquent l'utilisation du télégraphe, du téléphone et de toutes
rs applications : télex, fac-similé, radio et télévision, ainsi
 l'utilisation d'ordinateurs et d'équipements auxiliaires pour
stockage et le télétraitement de l'information.

Les moyens de communication à distance se transforment à
rythme accéléré : la transmission analogique fait place à la
nsmission numérique, le commutateur électromécanique
rossbar » au commutateur électronique, le câble coaxial au
ole en fibre optique, les circuits radioélectriques bidirection-
s à hyperfréquences viennent compléter ou remplacer les
sons par câble, etc. Les transmissions par satellites de-
nnent un puissant stimulant de la radiotéléphonie.

L'introduction de l'ordinateur dans les communications a
nné naissance à la télématique qui, mettant en œuvre le
dage numérique et la microminiaturisation, assure à la fois
 trafic téléphonique accru et la transmission de l'information
us toutes les formes.

Las comunicaciones definidas anteriormente suponen el uso del
telégrafo, el teléfono y la radio, y todas sus aplicaciones, como
télex, facsímil, radar y televisión así como el uso de computadores y equipo conexo para el teleprocesamiento de datos.

Los medios de comunicación han sufrido importantes variaciones en los últimos años, y el ritmo del cambio sigue
en aumento: la transmisión analógica da paso a la digital, la
conmutación electromagnética de barras cruzadas a la conmutación electrónica, los cables coaxiales a los de fibras
ópticas, surge la radiocomunicación bidireccional por microondas como alternativa a los enlaces por cable, etc., sin que
la distancia influya en el costo, mediante la transmisión por
satélite, y anunciando, entre otras cosas, la llegada del "teléfono sin hilos". La introducción del computador en los sistemas
de transmisión ha dado lugar a sistemas de información que
utilizan tecnologías digitales micrónicas capaces de transmitir
y procesar llamadas telefónicas, datos, imágenes de facsímil y
señales video.

KNOWLEDGE, INTELLIGENCE AND NEWS
LY IN EDUCATION, WORK AND LEISURE

transmission de l'information implique l'interaction de cinq
ments : 1) la connaissance, mémorisée ou communiquée ; 2)
méthode utilisée pour mémoriser ou communiquer ; 3) la
ne sous laquelle la connaissance est communiquée ; 4) celui
 la communique et, 5) celui qui la reçoit.

.'information joue aujourd'hui un rôle de plus en plus grand
s l'éducation et la recherche, ainsi que dans la prise de
isions en matière de gestion et de gouvernement. Grâce à
argissement de la disponibilité, et à l'abaissement du coût de
formation, chacun sera bientôt en mesure non seulement de
mmuniquer avec n'importe qui, en tout lieu et à tout moment,
s aussi d'obtenir aisément n'importe quel genre d'informa-
n, sous la forme désirée.

Jusqu'à présent, l'information est communiquée soit physi-
ment par transport matériel, soit électriquement par télé-
ne ou télex, donc au moyen d'impulsions transmises par fil
par ondes radioélectriques. Le réseau téléphonique transmet
ore, pour une grande part, les conversations selon le
cédé analogique qui remonte à l'invention séculaire du
phone. De son côté l'ordinateur fonctionne selon la méthode
transmission numérique.

Une modification appropriée du réseau téléphonique permet,
fait, de tout transmettre sous forme numérique, soit en
gage d'ordinateur, à très grande vitesse et avec une préci-
n améliorée pour tous les types d'information : chiffres,
tes, données visuelles et sonores. De son coté, l'ordinateur
 capable de traiter et de mémoriser n'importe quel genre
formation aux lieux d'origine ou de reception. Il est donc
éniable que le développement d'une société d'information
ose sur l'intégration et la symbiose des technologies des
communications et des ordinateurs dans un système uni-
sel de télécommunications.

El significado de información indicado anteriormente presupone
la participación de cinco entidades conexas: 1) conocimiento,
almacenado o comunicado; 2) el método por el que se almacena
o comunica el conocimiento; 3) la forma en que se comunica; 4)
el comunicador; 5) el comunicado.

La información desempeña una parte mayor que nunca en la
educación, la investigación y la adopción de decisiones, ya
sean comerciales o gubernamentales. Cada vez es más fácil y
barato obtenerla, y nos acercamos rápidamente al momento en
que todo el mundo podrá comunicar con quien quiera, en
cualquier momento y en cualquier parte, y acceder a toda clase
de información en la forma deseada. El problema es cómo hacer
esto posible ahora que se dispone de la tecnología.

De momento, la información se transmite — sobre todo —
bien físicamente, es decir, transportada, o por teléfono o télex,
o sea, mediante impulsos eléctricos por hilo u ondas radioeléctricas. La red telefónica se emplea mayormente para la
transmisión de la voz, en forma analógica, método que no ha
variado mucho desde la aparición de la telefonía, hace unos
100 años. Por su parte, el computador se ha usado, y sigue
usándose, principalmente con fines de numeración, es decir, el
procesamiento de datos.

Sin embargo, debidamente modificada, la red telefónica
puede transmitir en forma digital, a saber, en el lenguaje del
computador, a una velocidad y con una precisión mucho mayor,
cualquier clase de información: numérica, textual y visual,
además de la voz. El computador puede procesar y almacenar
información, también de cualquier clase, en los lugares de
origen y recepción. Sin duda, el desarrollo de una sociedad de
información global reside en la integración de estas dos tecnologías: las telecomunicaciones y la computadorización.

▷ 21

17

THE FIVE PHASES IN MANKIND'S INFORMA

INFORMATION	STONE AGE 1	5000 BC 2	1500 AD 3	← FROM 1800 —	
AUDIBLE RECOGNITION	Language	—	—	—	Teleph
VISIBLE RECOGNITION	Picture	Characters	—	Telegraph	—
DISSEMINATION (DELIVERY)	Loud voice (Voice Amplification)	Messenger	Dissemination of Printed matter		TE
RECORDING (STORAGE)	Professional reciters; wall painting	Documents	Printed matters	Documents Characters	Mem (Magn tap
PROCESSING				DIRECT INVOLVEMENT OF MAN	

The phases of information innovation presented above, based on a paper by Yasusada Kitahara, Executive Vice President, Nippon Telegraph & Telephone Public Corporation, span the history of communications, **The first phase** was the acquisition of linguistic ability, **the second** saw the development of letters, **the third** the invention of printing. This heralded the first true spread of information and learning within nations and across frontiers. **The fourth phase** consisted of the birth and development of telecommunications; from the first code carrying telegraph to today's transmission of voice, data, text and image, incorporating the establishment of a worldwide telephone net-

work, dense in a few industrialized countries, sparse in the rest of the world. In this phase a series of telecommunication techniques, such as telegraphy, telephony, radio, facsimile, and television made their appearance. **The fifth and present phase** is being led by the computer's entry in telecommunications. It has made it possible to process and store a great deal of complex information which could not be handled by conventional means. As a result the fields of human intellectual activity have expanded remarkably and a new society has evolved based on this intellectual activity. In this new type of society production of information plays a more important role than conventional industrial production, hence it is variously called the post-industrial society, or the Information society. In the information society, computers and telecommunications will be combined to form an information system.

L'illustration des différentes phases de l'évolution de l'info mation, présentée ci-dessus, est fondée sur un exposé d Yasusada Kitahara, vice président de "Nippon Telegraph Telephone Public Corporation", sur l'histoire des communica tions. **La première phase** fut celle de l'acquisition de la maîtris du langage, **la seconde** correspond à la mise au point de l'écr ture, **la troisième** à l'invention de l'imprimerie qui fut le début d la diffusion de l'information et de la connaissance parmi le peuples et à travers les frontières. **La quatrième phase** commencé par l'établissement du premier code télégraphiqu pour aboutir à la constitution d'un réseau téléphonique mondia

ON DEVELOPMENT

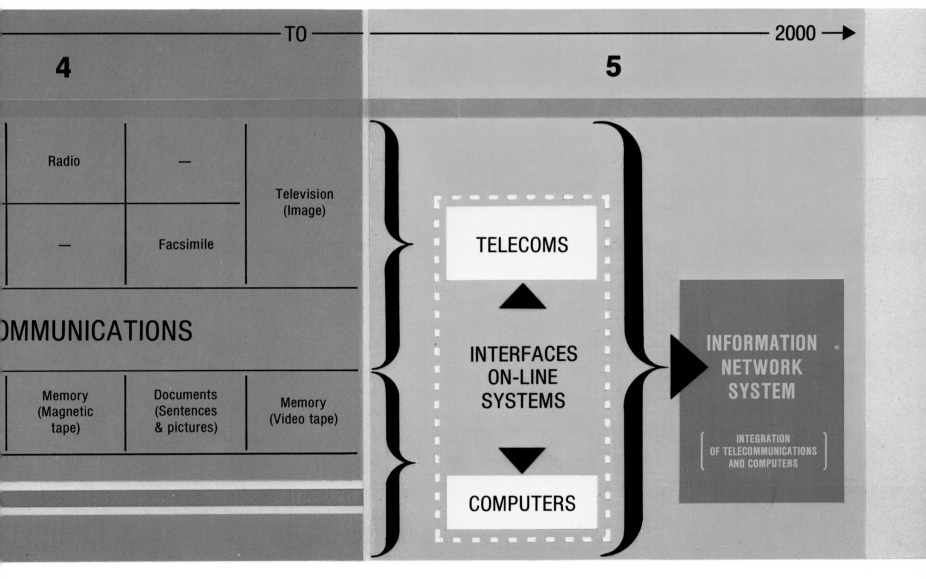

		TO		5	2000 →
		4			

Radio — Television (Image)

— Facsimile

OMMUNICATIONS

Memory (Magnetic tape) | Documents (Sentences & pictures) | Memory (Video tape)

TELECOMS

▲

INTERFACES ON-LINE SYSTEMS

▼

COMPUTERS

INFORMATION NETWORK SYSTEM

[INTEGRATION OF TELECOMMUNICATIONS AND COMPUTERS]

s dense dans quelques pays industrialisés, et relativement che dans le reste du monde. C'est durant cette phase qu'ap- raissent d'importantes techniques de télécommunication, les que la télégraphie, la téléphonie, le fac-similé, la radio et télévision. **La cinquième phase, l'actuelle,** est caractérisée par ntrée de l'ordinateur dans les télécommunications, ce qui rmet de traiter et d'emmagasiner une quantité énorme d'in- rmations complexes. De ce fait, les divers domaines de l'ac- ité intellectuelle humaine sont remarquablement étendus et production de l'information joue un rôle plus important que la oduction industrielle. Pour cette raison, la société ainsi créée appelée tantôt société post-industrielle, tantôt société nformation. Dans la société d'information, les ordinateurs et s télécommunications seront inextricablement intégrés pour rmer un système d'information.

Las fases de innovación de la información expuestas, basadas en un trabajo de Yasusada Kitahara, Vicepresidente Ejecutivo, Nippon Telegraph & Telephone Public Corporation, abarcan la historia de las comunicaciones. **La primera fase** fue la adquisi- ción de capacidad lingüística; **la segunda,** la elaboración de letras; **la tercera,** el invento de la impresión. Esto anunciaba la difusión de la información y el aprendizaje en los países y allende las fronteras. **La cuarta fase** consistió en el nacimiento y desarrollo de las telecomunicaciones; desde el primer telégrafo transmisor de código hasta la transmisión de voz, texto e imagen actual, incluido el establecimiento de una red telefónica mundial, densa en algunos países industrializados, y poco

densa en el resto del mundo. En esta fase apareció una serie de técnicas de telecomunicación, como telegrafía, telefonía, radio, facsímil y televisión. **La quinta fase, la actual,** se caracteriza por la entrada del computador en las telecomunicaciones, que permite procesar y almacenar gran cantidad de información compleja que no puede tratarse por medios convencionales. Como resultado, se han extendido notablemente las esferas de actividad intelectual humana, y se ha desarrollado una nueva sociedad basada en esa actividad intelectual. En este nuevo tipo de sociedad que se crea, la producción de información desempeña un papel más importante que la producción indus- trial clásica; de ahí que se la denomine sociedad postindustrial o sociedad de información. En la sociedad de información, los computadores y las telecomunicaciones estarán combinados para formar un sistema de información.

information streams. It is here that the trend towards lower costs has been quite extraordinary. Taking digital magnetic recording for information storage, the cost of storage for an element of information has been reduced by some 40 per cent annually over two decades. The cost of terrestrial communications has fallen likewise, by about 11 per cent per year over a similar period. Another example of reducing costs is communication satellites: the first, launched in 1965 cost US$ 23,000 per channel; within 6 years this cost had dropped to little more than $ 600, and in the early 1980s it has been reduced to about $ 60. The forthcoming use of large powerful satellites, such as the *Intelsat* series *VI* promises to reduce the per channel cost of communication satellites still further.

There is good reason to expect these trends to continue, at least until the late 1980s, at similar rates. Speed improvements and cost reductions are both made possible by microminiaturization. As the linear dimensions of silicon devices continue to be reduced, — and there is every likelihood of this — there will be associated reductions in costs and improvements in performance. In communications the use of greater bandwidths, corresponding to a rising demand for a wider range of services and made increasingly realizable by the use of optical fiber cable and satellite transmission, will undoubtedly maintain the trend in communication costs sharply downwards.

For the user, the real cost of telephoning has been falling steadily and is continuing to fall, in most countries, relative to the cost of living. This has doubtless contributed to the exponential growth of telephone stations in the world together with changes in life style, in the mobility of individuals and the desire to replace the old with the new; between 1945 and 1983 the number of telephones increased at an average rate of nearly 7 per cent per year, from 49 million to 565 million.

The advent of the computer in communications has introduced unprecedented power for the analysis and dissemination of almost any kind of data in vast quantities at speeds close to that of light. This has transformed man's access to, and use of, information and the world is now poised to achieve a synthesis of knowledge without parallel in history. The technologies of computers and communications will permit the harnessing of the tools of knowledge and their application in a manner that could release man's full creative potential. How such trends are likely to progress as the world's communication systems grow, is fully documented and illustrated in the pages that follow and in the examples of industrial achievements they contain.

The Information Age will see a fundamental change in the nature of business, industry, work, travel and life style. A striking illustration of this new life style, is given on pp. 30, 34. The ease with which ideas can be transmitted will drastically reduce the necessity of physical transmission of objects and people. The coming generation of communications facilities will make it possible to transmit pictures as well as sound in immense quantities. Documents will be produced on television screens or reproduced in facsimile — as printed, or typed, or handwritten, or photographed, thousands of miles away.

Examples of this abound: for some time now, the *Wall Street journal* has been sent facsimile from New York City to printing works in Chicago and Los Angeles; the *Pravda* from Moscow to a number of printing works in a country-wide spread through the satellite network Molnya; the *Financial Times* from London to Frankfurt; the *International Herald Tribune*, edited in Paris, to London, Zurich, Hong Kong and Singapore; and, in 1983, the *Economist* from England to Connecticut, USA. The necessity will cease to read through hundreds of pages to uncover

▷ 24

La microélectronique offre d'extraordinaires possibilités de stockage et de traitement d'information. Dans ce domaine la chute des prix a été absolument stupéfiante. Par exemple, en deux décennies le coût de mise en mémoire d'un élément d'information a diminué de 40% par an, tandis que le coût des communications terrestres s'est abaissé d'environ 11%. Le coût de lancement des satellites de communication s'est également écroulé : en 1965, lors du premier lancement, une voie de transmission revenait à US $ 23 000 ; en 6 ans, ce prix est tombé à un peu plus de $ 600 et, au début de 1980, il n'était plus que de $ 60. L'utilisation future de satellites à grande capacité (*Intelsat* series *VI*) devrait permettre de réduire encore ce prix.

De même, le prix des stations terriennes émettrices/réceptrices s'est régulièrement abaissé. Certaines stations terriennes utilisées uniquement pour la réception, par exemple les stations communautaires utilisées en Inde pour recevoir les émissions du satellite *ATS-6*, coûtaient à peine $ 70.

La baisse persistera certainement jusqu'à la fin de la décennie, grâce aux progrès de la microminiaturisation. La réduction des dimensions linéaires des organes au silicium se poursuivra également, ce qui entraînera des réductions de coût et des améliorations de rendement. L'utilisation accrue de moyens de transmission à bandes larges, telles que fibres optiques et micro-ondes, accentuera sans aucun doute cette tendance à la baisse.

Pour les utilisateurs, le coût réel du téléphone a diminué et continue de le faire. Durant ces dernières années les tarifs des conversations téléphoniques (et de location des installations) ont baissé dans la plupart des pays, par rapport au coût de la vie. Ces bas prix, alliés aux changements de style de vie, à la mobilité croissante de personnes et au désir de se moderniser, ont contribué à une augmentation exponentielle du nombre des postes téléphoniques dans le monde, lequel est passé de 49 millions à 565 millions entre 1945 et 1983, ce qui correspond à une augmentation annuelle d'environ 7%. Ce taux d'expansion se maintient.

L'avènement de l'ordinateur et son utilisation dans les communications ont eu pour conséquence la mise en œuvre d'une capacité inégalée d'analyse et de diffusion de quantités énormes de données de toutes espèces, à des vitesses proches de celle de la lumière. Ce phénomène a complètement transformé les modes d'accès à l'information et l'utilisation de celle-ci par l'homme. Ainsi, le monde s'apprête à réaliser une synthèse des connaissances universelles sans précédent dans l'histoire. L'humanité dispose en effet des moyens nécessaires pour créer à l'échelle universelle une société d'information, fondée sur la technologie des télécommunications et des ordinateurs, et régie par la volonté et l'énergie de l'esprit humain. Ces nouvelles techniques permettront de forger de nouveaux outils de connaissance, et de les utiliser d'une manière appropriée, pour mettre en valeur la créativité de l'homme dans son intégralité.

L'émergence de la société d'information apportera des modifications profondes dans le commerce et l'industrie, l'éducation, le travail, les voyages et jusque dans notre mode de vie individuel et social. On en trouvera aux pages 30 et 34 une illustration frappante. La facilité de transmission des idées se traduira par un fléchissement considérable des besoins en matière de transport physique d'objets et de déplacement de personnes. Les futurs équipements de communication permettront de transmettre des images et des sons en quantités fabuleuses. Des documents manuscrits, imprimés ou photographiés seront présentés sur des écrans de télévision ou reproduits en fac-similé, à des milliers de kilomètres de distance.

Depuis quelques temps déjà, le *Wall Street Journal* est envoyé en fac-similé de New-York à des imprimeries de Chicago et de Los Angeles. La *Pravda* de Moscou est transmise par le réseau à satellites

▷ 24

Reaching out to the world by phone.

Le monde à la portée du téléphone.

ejemplo, la tecnología microelectrónica ofrece capacidad para almacenar información y para la manipulación lógica o inteligente de mucha información. La tendencia a la reducción de los costos ha sido extraordinaria al respecto. Utilizando la grabación magnética digital para almacenar la información, el costo de un elemento de información se ha reducido en torno al 40 por ciento anual en dos decenios. El costo de las comunicaciones terrenales también ha disminuido en un 11 por ciento anual durante un período análogo. Otro ejemplo de la disminución de los costos son los satélites de comunicaciones: el primero, lanzado en 1965, costó 23 000 $ por canal; en 6 años, ese costo ha pasado a menos de 600 $, y en estos años se ha reducido a unos 60 $. El próximo uso de satélites grandes y poderosos, como los de la serie *Intelsat VI*, permitirá reducir todavía más el costo por canal de los satélites de comunicación.

Todo hace esperar que prosigan esas tendencias, al menos hasta finales del decenio, a tasas similares. La microminiaturización es lo que hace posible mejorar la velocidad y reducir los costos. A medida que disminuyan las dimensiones lineales de los dispositivos de silicio — y esto no admite duda — se reducirán también los gastos y aumentará el rendimiento. El uso de anchuras de banda mayores en las comunicaciones, de acuerdo con la creciente demanda de una gama más amplia de servicios, cada vez más factible al utilizar cables de fibras ópticas y la transmisión por satélite, mantendrá la tendencia al acusado descenso del costo de la comunicación.

El costo real del teléfono disminuye sin cesar para el usuario, y seguirá bajando en la mayoría de los países con relación al costo de la vida. No hay duda de que esto ha contribuido al crecimiento exponencial de los aparatos telefónicos en el mundo: entre 1945 y 1983, el número de teléfonos aumentó a una tasa media de cerca del 7 por ciento anual, pasando de 49 millones a 565 millones.

La aparición del computador en las comunicaciones ha introducido una potencia sin precedentes para analizar y difundir casi toda clase de datos en grandes cantidades, y a velocidades próximas a la de la luz. Esto ha transformado el acceso del hombre a la información, y el mundo puede realizar ya una síntesis de conocimientos sin paralelo en la historia. La tecnología de computadores y comunicaciones permitirá aprovechar los instrumentos del conocimiento y su aplicación de forma que puedan liberar todo el potencial creativo del hombre. En las páginas que siguen, y en sus ejemplos de las conquistas industriales, se documenta e ilustra la probabilidad del progreso de esas tendencias a medida que crecen los sistemas mundiales de comunicaciones.

En la era de la información cambiará fundamentalmente el carácter de los negocios, la industria, el trabajo, los viajes y el estilo de vida. En las págs. 30-34 figura un buen ejemplo de ese nuevo estilo de vida. La facilidad con que pueden transmitirse nuevas ideas reducirá drásticamente la necesidad de la transmisión física de objetos y personas. Las facilidades de comunicaciones de la próxima generación permitirán transmitir imágenes y sonido en inmensas cantidades. Los documentos se producirán en pantallas de televisión, o se reproducirán en facsímil, en forma impresa, mecanografiada, manuscrita o fotografiada, a miles de kilómetros.

Abundan los ejemplos: hace ya algún tiempo que el *Wall Street Journal* se envía en facsímil desde Nueva York a las imprentas de Chicago y Los Angeles; *Pravda*, desde Moscú a varias imprentas de todo el país, por la red de satélite Molnya; el *Financial Times* desde Londres a Francfort, y el *International Herald Tribune*, editado en París, a Londres, Zurich, Hong Kong y Singapur. Ya no será necesario leer centenares de páginas para descubrir una información concreta; el acceso desde la oficina o el hogar

▷ 25

El teléfono llega al mundo entero.

THE STAGES AND CHARACTERISTICS OF TH

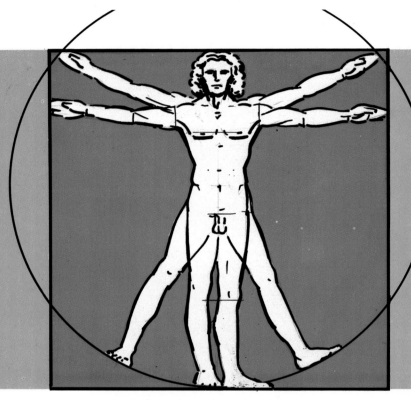

PRIMARY STAGE

☐ Information
gathering is initiated through
formation of policies designed
to strengthen agricultural
and basic industrial processes.

☐ L'information est
initialement rassemblée pour
la formulation de politiques
destinées à consolider
l'agriculture et les procédés
industriels de base.

☐ La reunión
de información se inicia
mediante la formación
de políticas destinadas
a reforzar los procesos
agrícolas e industriales básicos.

DEVELOPMENT STAGE

☐ Emphasis
is placed on accomplishing
a fundamental upgrading
of literacy levels and
on satisfying governments'
communication
and information needs.

☐ L'accent est mis
sur l'élévation du niveau
d'alphabétisation et sur la
satisfaction des besoins du
gouvernement en termes de
communications et d'information.

☐ Se insiste
en la realización de una
mejora esencial de los niveles
de alfabetización y en la
satisfacción de las necesidades
de los gobiernos en materia
de comunicación e información.

In industrialized countries the development toward the information society has been governed by the rates of technological advances in industrialization and in telecommunications; the two were broadly parallel until the advent of the semiconductor and micron technologies in the 1950s. Since then telecommunications have leapt ahead.

In developing countries progress is differently affected by the ready availability of high technology on the one hand and by an acute shortage of investment, low levels of literacy and low industrial activity on the other. The application of telecommunications technology is slowed down by social and economic factors and must therefore proceed in stages:

The primary stage sees the beginnings of information gathering. Effective communications are seen to be a fundamental prerequisite for modernization, and national integration; but telecommunication facilities are primitive, often limited to radio. Telephone density is low and computer usage virtually nil.

In the development stage takes place a fundamental upgrading of literacy levels. Information strategies are developed to support national planning activities. The build-up of a telecommunications infrastructure is begun with imported system designs,

material and technical personnel. Their use tends at first to be restricted to government, to pursue objectives such as national security, law enforcement, educational development. National leaders recognize the need to broaden the use of information and to acquire processing and distribution facilities.

The growth stage sees industry and commerce join the government as major users of communications technology. Services grow and become based increasingly on the treatment of information and its distribution. A high degree of literacy among the population is attained and demand for telephones and television increases. Imports of equipment and systems software rise sharply. Technical specialists such as telecommunications experts, computer operators and programmers, analysts and planners become established. In this third stage there exists an expanded public awareness of the need for formal systems of information and control.

The information stage, characterizing the development of the Information Society, is that of innovative information production. At this point in its existance, a nation has created a highly effective information infrastructure that is utilized as an extension of the national administrative, planning and management process.

Agriculture, industry and commerce have become equipped with monitoring, control and communication devices, thereby raising productivity to the highest level and releasing manpower for other activities. There is a switch to education, health care, the professions and the services. The country is able to determine its strategies in the full knowledge of situations. The possession of integrated interactive information processing, storage and communication systems enables the nation in this fourth stage to participate in the global system of collective intelligence and information exchange.

Dans les pays industrialisés, le développement de la sociét d'information résulte des progrès concomitants de l'industri lisation et des techniques de télécommunication dûs à la d couverte des semi-conducteurs et à la mise en œuvre de procédés de miniaturisation qui remontent aux années 195 Depuis cette époque, les télécommunications ont fait u extraordinaire bond en avant.

Dans les pays en développement, la situation a évolué sou l'influence contradictoire de la disponibilité de techniques pe fectionnées, s'accompagnant d'une insuffisance d'investiss ment, de bas niveaux d'alphabétisation et d'une faible activit industrielle. L'application de la technologie des télécommun cations, entravée par des facteurs sociaux et économiques, n peut progresser que par étapes.

La première étape correspond aux débuts du rassemblement d l'information. L'efficacité des communications est une conditio essentielle de l'intégration et de la modernisation de tout pay Or, au stade initial, les moyens de télécommunication son primitifs, la densité téléphonique est faible et l'utilisation de ordinateurs pratiquement inexistante.

L'étape du développement comporte l'élévation du nivea d'alphabétisation et l'adoption d'une stratégie adéquate d l'information. La mise en place de toute infrastructure de télé

MERGING INFORMATION SOCIETY

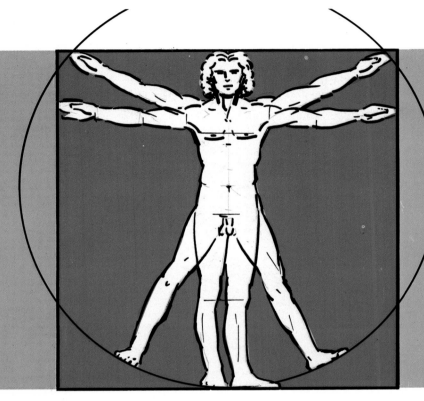

GROWTH STAGE

- ☐ Government is joined by industrial and commercial users of telecommunications and computer technologies, and service sector begins to emerge.
- ☐ Aux besoins publics s'ajoutent ceux des usagers industriels et commerciaux de télécommunications et d'informatique, et un nouveau secteur de service commence à émerger.
- ☐ Los usuarios industriales y comerciales de tecnologías de telecomunicaciones y computador se unen al gobierno, y aparece un nuevo sector de servicios.

INFORMATION STAGE

- ☐ A high degree of automated mechanization is accomplished in industrial processes, and nations become innovative *producers* of knowledge.
- ☐ Un haut niveau de mécanisation automatisée est atteint dans les procédés industriels, et les nations deviennent des *producteurs* innovateurs de savoir.
- ☐ En los procesos industriales se realiza un elevado grado de mecanización automatizada, y las naciones se convierten en *productores* innovadores de conocimiento.

---

ommunications exige l'acquisition de plans, de matériel et de ersonnel technique en provenance de l'étranger. Les pouvoirs ublics s'en réservent l'utilisation pour atteindre certains ob- ctifs : défense nationale, application des lois, instruction et nrichissement culturel de la population, acquisition d'équipe- ents de traitement et de diffusion de données, etc.

ans l'étape de la croissance, les services de l'industrie et du ommerce deviennent eux aussi de grands utilisateurs d'infor- atique. Lorsque la population atteint un degré d'alphabétisa- on suffisant, la demande augmente dans les domaines de la léphonie et de la télévision. Puis les importations de matériel t de logiciel s'accroissent brusquement. Des spécialistes en lématique viennent s'installer dans le pays. A ce troisième tade, le public et les dirigeants prennent conscience de l'utilité e l'informatique dans le contrôle et la gestion.

étape de l'information est une phase du développement de la ociété caractérisée par une production novatrice d'informa- on. Il se crée alors à l'échelle nationale une infrastructure nformatisée qui constitue un moyen très efficace d'adminis- ation, de planification et de gestion du pays.

L'agriculture, l'industrie et le commerce étant équipés de ispositifs de surveillance, de contrôle et de communication, la roductivité augmente, ce qui permet de libérer de la main- œuvre de certains secteurs au profit d'autres domaines 'activité : éducation, santé publique, professions libérales, ervices. Le pays devient alors capable de déterminer ses tratégies en pleine connaissance des situations existantes. La ossession de systèmes interactifs et intégrés d'information, de raitement, de stockage et de transmission de données, permet tout pays ayant atteint ce quatrième stade de participer au ystème global d'intelligence collective et d'échange d'infor- ation.

En los países industrializados la evolución hacia la sociedad de información se ha regido por el ritmo tecnológico en la indus- trialización y en las telecomunicaciones; en general, ambas fueron paralelas hasta la aparición de las tecnologías de se- miconductores y micrónicas en los años 1950. Desde entonces, las telecomunicaciones han registrado un gran avance.

El progreso en los países en desarrollo resulta diversamente afectado por la rápida disponibilidad de alta tecnología, por un lado, y la aguda escasez de inversiones, los bajos niveles de alfabetización y la reducida actividad industrial, por otro. Los factores sociales y económicos frenan la aplicación de la tec- nología de las telecomunicaciones, por lo que debe procederse por etapas.

La etapa inicial marca el comienzo de la recopilación de infor- mación. Las comunicaciones eficaces se consideran un requi- sito previo esencial para la modernización y la integración nacional; pero las facilidades de comunicación son primitivas, con frecuencia limitadas a la radio. La densidad telefónica es baja, y el uso de computadores prácticamente nulo.

En la etapa de desarrollo se mejoran fundamentalmente los niveles de alfabetización. Se elaboran estrategias de informa- ción para apoyar las actividades de planificación nacional. Comienza a establecerse una infraestructura de telecomunica- ciones, con diseños de sistemas, material y personal técnico

del extranjero. Su uso tiende a limitarse, primero, al gobierno, para objetivos como seguridad nacional, aplicación de leyes y fomento de la educación. Los líderes nacionales reconocen la necesidad de ampliar el uso de la información y de adquirir equipo de procesamiento y distribución.

En la etapa de crecimiento, la industria y el comercio se unen al gobierno como principales usuarios de tecnología de comuni- caciones. Crecen los servicios, y se basan cada vez más en el tratamiento de la información y en su distribución. Se alcanza un elevado grado de alfabetización y aumenta la demanda de aparatos telefónicos y de televisión. Las importaciones de equipo y de sistemas crecen fuertemente. Surgen especialistas como expertos en telecomunicaciones, operadores y progra- madores de computador, analistas y planificadores. En esta tercera etapa, el público adquiere mayor conciencia de la ne- cesidad de sistemas de información y control formales.

La etapa de información, que caracteriza el desarrollo de la sociedad de información, es la de producción de información innovadora. En este punto, una nación ha creado una infraes- tructura de información muy eficaz que se emplea como ex- pansión del proceso nacional de administración, planificación y gestión.

La agricultura, la industria y el comercio cuentan con dis- positivos de verificación, control y comunicación, aumentado así la productividad al más alto nivel y liberando mano de obra para otras actividades. Hay un desplazamiento hacia la edu- cación, la atención sanitaria, las profesiones y los servicios. El país puede determinar sus estrategias conociendo perfecta- mente las situaciones. La posesión de sistemas interactivos integrados para procesar, almacenar y comunicar información permite al país, en esta cuarta etapa, participar en el sistema global de intercambio colectivo de inteligencia e información.

specifically needed information; access from office or home to data banks will provide almost instantaneously the item requested.

Television is already becoming a true interactive communications medium. Broadband telecommunications will make it widely possible to hold conferences via satellite between people continents apart; wideband TV channels will bring to every house equipped with a receiver information of any kind, which can be stored for later reference. Cable and satellite TV channels will bring the latest cultural spectacles and sporting events into the home more and more frequently and with no time lag.

Many other most basic changes will take place as instantaneous two-way transmission of information over any distance becomes widely available. Places of work need no longer be concentrated and the need to travel to distant work places will be greatly reduced; better documentation and speedier access to advice will simplify the decision-making process and improve the quality of decisions; market requirements will be quantified and transmitted in near to real time, effective management control from a distance will increase the opportunities for work in small groups and for local production of locally needed products and services.

The implications of change brought about by the development of communication technologies are important in terms of social restructuring in both highly industrialized and basically agricultural or mining communities. A trend is emerging in which local communities are becoming viable as social units.

Culturally, small communities will no longer need to be isolated. The telephone eases the maintenance of social contact; the television and radio bring to the home, the cinema, the theatre, the concert, the sporting event, the political meeting, and much else — albeit without as yet quite catching the flavour of the live show and the excitement of the crowd. This will be extended and its reality increased. Similarly, teleshopping may reverse the process whereby the goods are concentrated into huge emporia to which people must trek in their thousands. In industry, too, the distribution system may change and even the production process itself may often be broken down into smaller units with the possibility of remote management control. The urban centre will no longer have exclusive advantages.

So far these developments have been concentrated in the industrialized countries but they are also, of course, of immense importance to the isolated communities in the Third World. As the industrialized West transforms itself into a computerized information-based society, developing countries will be able, granted adequate funding, to enter this new era with computerized communications applied and adapted to their needs. Satellite communications technology, with costs unaffected by distance, will provide an opportunity and a challenge for the raising of educational and living standards everywhere. How this challenge can be met is discussed later.

The information industries are no longer easily categorized. The fusion of the computer and telecommunication technologies has tended to blur the distinction between their various components. The historical bases for distinction among them are rapidly disappearing, as shown on the map of "Information Business" overleaf. A decade ago everyone knew what a telephone company did, or a newspaper, a broadcaster, a book publisher or a postal service. Now it is not only less clear but many questions remain unanswered. For example, is "electronic mail" something that "belongs" to the national PTT, the electronics industry, the telecommunications common carrier, or someone else? Is it regulated, and if so, by whom? Tentative answers to such questions may be gleaned from the Information Business map on the next page.

□

Molnya à des imprimeries disséminées en URSS. Il en est de même pour le *Financial Times* entre Londres et Francfort ; de l'*International Herald Tribune*, entre Paris, Londres, Zurich, Hong-Kong et Singapour, et de *L'Economist* entre l'Angleterre et les Etats-Unis.

Bientôt, il ne sera plus nécessaire de parcourir des centaines de pages pour découvrir l'information recherchée. L'accès à des banques de données, à partir du bureau et du domicile, fournira à chacun, presque instantanément, l'article ou le sujet désiré. Il suffira de disposer de références et de codes appropriés pour obtenir n'importe quel ouvrage, brochure, journal ou enregistrement sonore, en n'importe quelle langue, et pour n'importe quel besoin.

La télévision devient déjà un moyen interactif de communication, permettant la tenue de téléconférences entre des participants siégeant dans différentes parties du globe. Des circuits TV à large bande apporteront, dans chaque foyer équipé d'un récepteur approprié, toutes sortes de renseignements qui pourront être enregistrés, en vue d'une consultation ultérieure. La télévision par câble ou par satellite apportera à domicile le reflet immédiat des évènements culturels et sportifs.

La possibilité de télécommunications conversationnelles permettra la décentralisation et réduira considérablement l'obligation de se déplacer pour se rendre au travail. L'amélioration des systèmes de référence et de documentation et l'accès plus rapide à des conseils simplifieront et amélioreront la prise de décision. La demande des consommateurs sera quantifiée pratiquement en temps réel, ce qui permettra d'offrir des produits et des services mieux adaptés à leurs besoins.

Les changements engendrés par le perfectionnement des communications exerceront une influence sur la restructuration sociale, aussi bien dans les collectivités hautement industrialisées que dans les communautés agricoles ou minières. Aucune collectivité, aussi petite soit elle, ne sera désormais condamnée à vivre dans l'isolement. Le téléphone facilite les contacts sociaux ; la télévision et la radio apportent déjà à domicile le cinéma, le théâtre, le concert, les manifestations sportives, les réunions politiques et autres. Bientôt, on parviendra à renverser le système commercial des grandes surfaces vers lesquelles les gens sont conviés à se rendre par milliers pour y choisir ce dont ils ont besoin. Ils examineront, choisiront et achèteront de chez eux. A l'échelle industrielle, le système de production et de distribution va également changer. C'est ainsi que les centres urbains ne seront plus les seuls à être avantagés sur ce plan.

Jusqu'ici, cette évolution intéressait principalement les pays industrialisés, mais elle est évidemment d'une immense importance pour les communautés isolées du tiers monde. Plus l'occident industrialisé se transforme en une société d'information, plus les pays en développement disposant des moyens financiers requis seront en mesure de s'engager dans la voie de la communication programmée, appliquée et adaptée à leurs besoins.

Les industries et services de l'information sont finalement de plus en plus confondus, et la distinction qui existait historiquement entre eux s'estompe et tend à disparaître rapidement, comme on le voit sur la carte-diagramme à la page suivante. Il y a une dizaine d'années, chacun savait ce que faisaient une entreprise téléphonique, un quotidien, une institution de radiodiffusion, un éditeur ou un service postal. Aujourd'hui, non seulement tout cela est moins clair mais beaucoup de questions restent sans réponse. Par exemple, le courrier électronique est-il du ressort des services des PTT ? Est-il du domaine de l'industrie de l'électronique ? Dépend-il de services de télécommunication publics ou privés, ou de quelqu'un d'autre ? Cette activité est-elle réglementée ? et par qui ? Quelques tentatives de réponses pourraient être formulées en examinant la carte-diagramme "Information Business Map" qui suit.

□

*The microprocessor
enters man's universe.*

*Le microprocesseur
pénètre l'univers des hommes.*

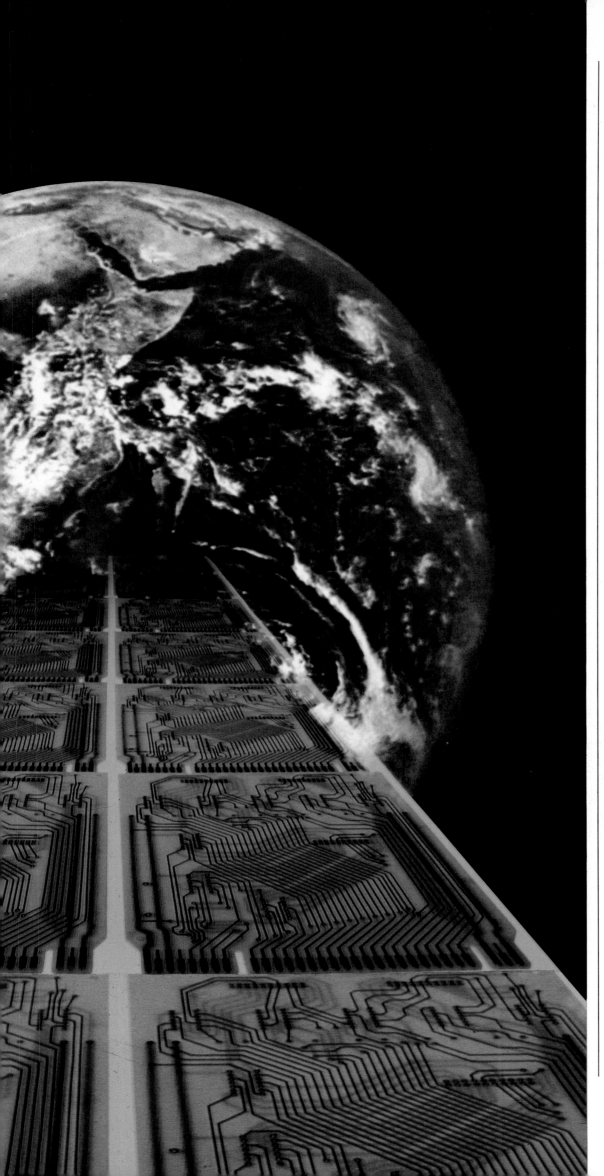

a los bancos de datos permitirá obtener casi instantáneamente el tema requerido.

La televisión se convierte en un medio interactivo de comunicaciones. La TV por circuito cerrado ofrecerá grandes posibilidades para celebrar conferencias por satélite entre personas de continentes distintos; los canales TV de banda ancha llevarán a todas las casas provistas de receptor toda clase de información, que puede almacenarse para utilizarla posteriormente. Los canales de TV por cable y satélite llevarán al hogar los espectáculos culturales y los acontecimientos deportivos más recientes.

Cuando se generalice la transmisión bidireccional de información a cualquier distancia, se producirán otros muchos cambios fundamentales. Ya no habrá que concentrar los lugares de trabajo, y se reducirá mucho la necesidad de desplazarse a lugares de trabajo distantes; al tener mejor documentación y poder obtener asesoramiento más rápidamente, se simplificará el proceso de adopción de decisiones y se mejorará su calidad; las necesidades del mercado se cuantificarán y transmitirán casi en tiempo real; el control eficaz de la gestión a distancia ofrecerá mejores oportunidades para trabajar en pequeños grupos y producir localmente productos y servicios necesarios in situ.

Las implicaciones del cambio experimentado merced al desarrollo de tecnologías de comunicación son importantes para la reestructuración social, tanto en comunidades muy industrializadas como en las fundamentalmente agrícolas o mineras. Surge la tendencia de la viabilidad de las comunidades locales como unidades sociales.

Culturalmente, las pequeñas comunidades ya no estarán aisladas. El teléfono facilita el contacto social; la televisión y la radio llevan al hogar el cine, el teatro, el concierto, el acontecimiento deportivo, la reunión política, y mucho más, aunque todavía sin captar el sabor del espectáculo en directo y el entusiasmo de la multitud. Pero se seguirá progresando y aumentará su realismo. Igualmente, la telecompra puede invertir el proceso de concentración de bienes en enormes emporios a los que la gente se desplazará a millares. También en la industria, el sistema de distribución puede cambiar, e incluso el propio proceso de producción podrá dividirse muchas veces en unidades más pequeñas, con la posibilidad de control a distancia. El centro urbano dejará de tener ventajas exclusivas.

Hasta ahora, la evolución se ha concentrado en los países industrializados, pero también reviste gran importancia para las comunidades aisladas del Tercer Mundo. A medida que el occidente industrializado se convierta en una sociedad computadorizada basada en la información, los países en desarrollo podrán entrar en esta nueva era — si disponen de la financiación adecuada — de comunicaciones por computador aplicadas y adaptadas a sus necesidades. La tecnología de comunicaciones por satélite, en que la distancia no influye en el costo, ofrecerá una oportunidad y un desafío para elevar el nivel educativo y de vida en todas partes..

Las industrias de la información ya no pueden clasificarse fácilmente. La fusión de las tecnologías de computador y telecomunicaciones hace menos clara la distinción entre los diversos componentes de las industrias de información. Las bases históricas de la distinción desaparecen rápidamente, como lo muestra el gráfico de la "Industria de la información".

Diez años antes, todos sabían lo que podía hacer una compañía telefónica o un periódico, una empresa de radiodifusión, una editorial o un servicio postal. Ahora, no sólo está menos claro, sino que muchas preguntas quedan sin respuesta. Por ejemplo, ¿"pertenece" el "correo electrónico" a los CTT nacionales, a la industria electrónica, la empresa pública de telecomunicaciones, o a quién? ¿Está reglamentado y, en caso afirmativo, por quién?

□

El microprocesador
entra en el universo del hombre.

THE "INFORMATION BUSINESS" MAP: A N

This map, a creation of John McLaughlin and his colleagues at Harvard University's Program on Information Policy Research, depicts the "Information Business" as it is today, showing the products and the services that are part of it and how they relate to each other. It shows also how the information business has evolved over the past two centuries: the "information market place" 200 years ago in ocher, 100 years ago in green, and in 1983 in blue. 80 products and services are considered to be involved in this business — to acquire, package, store, process, transmit or distribute information.

The Products-Services axis (North-South) was chosen largely because industrial activity is generally viewed in this manner. Displaying corporate activities along this axis helps highlight some facets of virtual integration and illustrates how the traditional notions of "product" and "service" are tending to blur in the middle ground of "systems". Progression along this axis from the Product extreme to the Service extreme can also be interpreted as evidence of increasing customer dependence upon supplying institutions.

The Conduit-Content axis (East-West) was chosen because it helps distinguish between companies which are producers of information, such as publishers, and those which provide means for recording and transmitting information. Progression along this axis from the Conduit to the Content extremes might best be visualized in terms of increasing "information value- added".

"Dumb products" such as typewriters, filing cabinets, copiers and paper are located in the lower left-hand corner. As information is added to these products, either in the form of "intelligence", e. g. memories of typewriters, or of an ability to communicate, they migrate rightward. A printed form is further in this direction than a piece of blank paper.

Conduit services, principally mail and parcel delivery, are located in the upper left-hand corner. Telecommunication common carriers start slightly to the right, being normally more involved in the information "content" of the message e. g. some processing in transmission and entry protocols. Further to the right are broadcasters, high on the Service Axis and midway between Content and Conduit because they provide both program material and ensure its distribution.

"Professional services" are placed in the upper right-hand corner because they generate information. They include writers, artists, scientists, and others whose products — books, records, TV and radio programs, etc. — are shown in the lower right-hand corner.

Computers are centrally situated, as they are an ubiquitous kind of tool involved in practically every aspect of information — processing, recording, storage, transmission, broadcasting, painting, designing, etc. Some idea of this spread of applications is indicated by the shaded area on the map. This is elaborated on page 148.

This graphic presentation, notwithstanding its obvious shortcomings — subjectivity in locating the products/services; inability to show overlaps between the various activities; non-inclusion of key components and materials, provides useful guidance of what constitutes the information business. Each government agency, company or individual involved can be situated in this complex setting. "Information" is the common denominator. Corporations can in this manner analyze their positions and define their strategies.

Cette carte-diagramme est une création de John McLaughlin et de ses collègues qui collaborent au « Program on Information Resources Policy » de l'Université de Harvard aux Etats-Unis. Cette carte représente l'évolution des industries et des services de l'information au cours des deux siècles écoulés. Elle montre « l'étendue du domaine des activités liées à l'information » : il y a 200 ans en ocre, il y a 100 ans en vert, et en 1983 en bleu. Cette cartographie englobe 80 produits et services intéressant l'acquisition, le conditionnement, le stockage, le traitement, la transmission et la diffusion de l'information.

L'axe Produits-Services (nord-sud) correspond à la présentation traditionnelle de l'activité industrielle. En plaçant sur le même axe les activités commerciales, on met en évidence certains aspects pratiques de leur intégration, ce qui permet de mieux comprendre comment les notions de « produit » et de « service » tendent à se confondre dans l'ensemble des « systèmes ». La progression de l'extrémité « produit » à l'extrémité « service » montre aussi la dépendance des usagers à l'égard des fournisseurs.

L'axe Conduit-Contenu (est-ouest) permet de distinguer les sociétés productrices d'information, par exemple les éditeurs, de celles qui fournissent les moyens d'enregistrer et de transmettre l'information. La progression de gauche à droite, le long de cet axe, met en évidence la plus-value que représente la « valeur ajoutée sous forme d'information ».

Les produits passifs (« muets »), tels que machines à écrire et à copier, classeurs, papier, etc. se trouvent dans la partie inférieure gauche de la carte mais ils se déplacent vers la droite, au fur et à mesure que de l'information vient s'y ajouter sous forme de renseignements, de mémoire ou de capacité de communiquer.

Les services « conduit », notamment la distribution du courrier et des colis, se trouvent en haut à gauche. Les services publics de télécommunications figurent légèrement plus à droite car ils sont directement impliqués dans la transmission du contenu du message dont ils régissent les modalités d'émission et de réception. Ensuite, plus loin à droite, on trouve les radiodiffuseurs dans la partie supérieure de l'axe nord-sud des Services, à mi-chemin entre Conduit et Contenu car ils produisent eux-mêmes le contenu des programmes dont ils assurent la diffusion.

Les « services professionnels » sont placés dans la partie supérieure droite de la carte. Il s'agit des écrivains, des artistes, des scientifiques et de tous ceux dont les « produits » : livres, enregistrements, programmes de télévision et de radio, etc. figurent en bas à droite.

Les ordinateurs sont situés au centre, car ce sont des instruments dont l'influence se fait sentir en permanence dans presque tous les secteurs de l'information : traitement, enregistrement, mémorisation, transmission, radiodiffusion, représentations conceptuelles (graphiques et picturales), etc. La partie ombragée de la carte donne une idée de l'étendue des applications de l'ordinateur. Il en sera également question à la page 148.

Cette présentation graphique, en dépit de son caractère très schématique, de la subjectivité du choix et de la position des produits et des services, et malgré d'autres insuffisances, donne une image assez fidèle du domaine de l'industrie et des services de l'information. Elle devrait permettre à toute institution publique, entreprise ou personne privée concernée de se situer dans ce complexe dont le dénominateur commun est « l'information ». Les entreprises peuvent, de cette manière, analyser leurs positions et définir leurs stratégies.

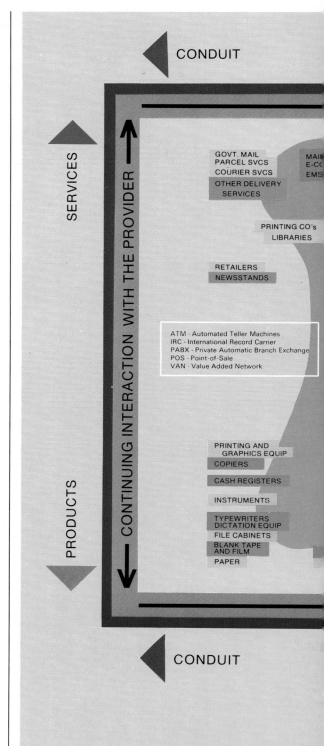

CONDUIT

SERVICES

PRODUCTS

CONTINUING INTERACTION WITH THE PROVIDER

GOVT. MAIL
PARCEL SVCS
COURIER SVCS
OTHER DELIVERY
SERVICES

MAIL
E-CO
EMS

PRINTING CO's
LIBRARIES

RETAILERS
NEWSSTANDS

ATM - Automated Teller Machines
IRC - International Record Carrier
PABX - Private Automatic Branch Exchange
POS - Point-of-Sale
VAN - Value Added Network

PRINTING AND
GRAPHICS EQUIP
COPIERS

CASH REGISTERS

INSTRUMENTS

TYPEWRITERS
DICTATION EQUIP
FILE CABINETS
BLANK TAPE
AND FILM
PAPER

CONDUIT

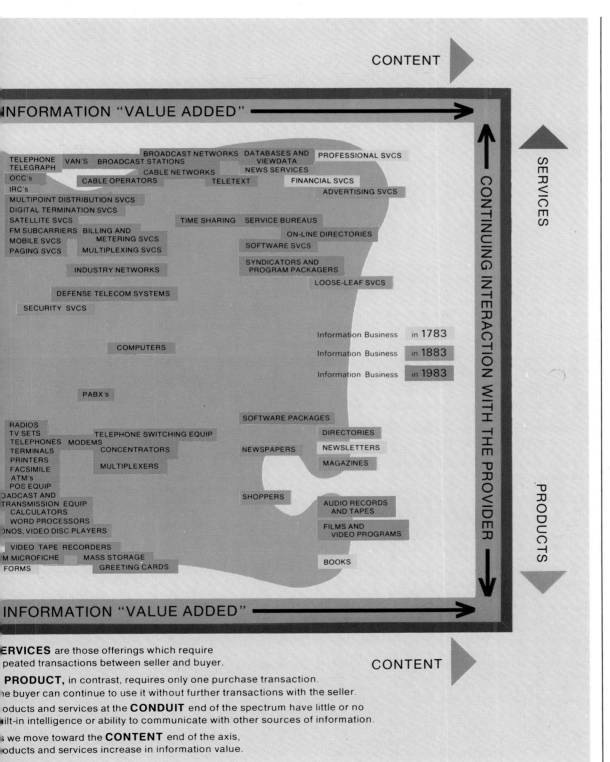

CONTENT

INFORMATION "VALUE ADDED"

TELEPHONE VAN'S BROADCAST STATIONS
TELEGRAPH
OCC's
IRC's
MULTIPOINT DISTRIBUTION SVCS
DIGITAL TERMINATION SVCS
SATELLITE SVCS
FM SUBCARRIERS BILLING AND
MOBILE SVCS METERING SVCS
PAGING SVCS MULTIPLEXING SVCS

BROADCAST NETWORKS DATABASES AND PROFESSIONAL SVCS
VIEWDATA
CABLE NETWORKS NEWS SERVICES
CABLE OPERATORS TELETEXT FINANCIAL SVCS
ADVERTISING SVCS

TIME SHARING SERVICE BUREAUS
ON-LINE DIRECTORIES
SOFTWARE SVCS

INDUSTRY NETWORKS SYNDICATORS AND
PROGRAM PACKAGERS
LOOSE-LEAF SVCS

DEFENSE TELECOM SYSTEMS

SECURITY SVCS

Information Business in 1783
Information Business in 1883
Information Business in 1983

COMPUTERS

PABX's

SOFTWARE PACKAGES
RADIOS
TV SETS DIRECTORIES
TELEPHONES MODEMS TELEPHONE SWITCHING EQUIP
TERMINALS CONCENTRATORS NEWSPAPERS NEWSLETTERS
PRINTERS MAGAZINES
FACSIMILE MULTIPLEXERS
ATM's
POS EQUIP
OADCAST AND SHOPPERS
TRANSMISSION EQUIP AUDIO RECORDS
CALCULATORS AND TAPES
WORD PROCESSORS
ONOS, VIDEO DISC PLAYERS FILMS AND
VIDEO PROGRAMS
VIDEO TAPE RECORDERS
M MICROFICHE MASS STORAGE BOOKS
FORMS GREETING CARDS

INFORMATION "VALUE ADDED"

SERVICES
PRODUCTS

CONTINUING INTERACTION WITH THE PROVIDER

CONTENT

ERVICES are those offerings which require
peated transactions between seller and buyer.

PRODUCT, in contrast, requires only one purchase transaction.
he buyer can continue to use it without further transactions with the seller.

oducts and services at the CONDUIT end of the spectrum have little or no
ilt-in intelligence or ability to communicate with other sources of information.

s we move toward the CONTENT end of the axis,
oducts and services increase in information value.

En el gráfico, creado por John McLaughlin y sus colegas del Programa sobre investigación de la política de información de la Universidad de Harvard, se describe la « Industria de la información » en su forma actual, y se muestran los productos y servicios que forman parte de ella y su relación entre sí. También se muestra la evolución de la industria de la información en los dos últimos siglos: el « mercado de la información » hace 200 años, en ocre; hace 100 años, en verde y, en 1983, en azul. Se considera que intervienen en esta industria 80 productos y servicios, para obtener, empaquetar, almacenar, procesar, transmitir o distribuir información.

El eje Productos-Servicios (norte-sur) se ha elegido en gran medida por considerarse generalmente así la actividad industrial. La presentación de las actividades empresariales a lo largo de este eje ayuda a destacar algunas facetas de integración virtual e ilustra cómo tienden a confundirse en un ámbito medio de "sistemas" las nociones tradicionales de "producto" y "servicio". La progresión a lo largo de este eje del extremo Producto al extremo Servicio puede interpretarse también como prueba de mayor dependencia del cliente de las instituciones suministradoras.

El eje Conducto-Contenido (este-oeste) se ha elegido porque ayuda a distinguir las empresas productoras de información, como editoriales, de las que proporcionan medios de registrar y transmitir información. Como mejor se aprecia la progresión a lo largo de este eje desde el extremo Conducto al extremo Contenido es en términos de creciente « valor añadido de la información ».

Los productos "mudos", como máquinas de escribir, clasificadores, copiadoras y papel, se encuentran en el extremo inferior izquierdo. Cuando se agrega información a esos productos, en forma de "inteligencia", v.g., memorias de máquinas de escribir o capacidad para comunicar, se desplazan hacia la derecha. Un formulario impreso sigue mejor esta dirección que una hoja de papel en blanco.

Los servicios de conducto, principalmente correo y entrega de paquetes, se encuentran en el extremo superior izquierdo. Las empresas de telecomunicaciones se sitúan ligeramente a la derecha, por participar normalmente más en el "contenido" de la información del mensaje; v.g., algún procesamiento en la transmisión y protocolos de entrada. Más a la derecha están las empresas de radiodifusión, en lo alto del eje de Servicios, y a medio camino entre Contenido y Conducto, porque proporcionan material de programas y aseguran su distribución.

Los "servicios profesionales" se encuentran en la parte superior derecha, porque generan información. Comprenden escritores, artistas, científicos y otros cuyos productos — libros, grabaciones, programas de TV y radio, etc. — se muestran en el extremo inferior derecho.

Los computadores están en el centro, pues son un instrumento omnipresente en casi todos los aspectos de la información: procesamiento, grabación, transmisión, radiodifusión, pintura, diseño, etc. La parte sombreada del gráfico da una idea de sus aplicaciones que se consideraran en la pág. 148.

Esta presentación grafica, a pesar de su esquematización, de la subjetividad en la situación de productos/servicios, de la incapacidad de mostrar superposiciones entre las diversas actividades y no inclusión de componentes y materiales esenciales, da una idea de lo que es la industria de la información. En este escenario pueden situarse todos los organismos públicos, empresas o individuos que intervengan. El denominador común es la "información". Así, las empresas pueden analizar sus posiciones y definir sus estrategias.

INNOVATION AND CHALLENGE
A WIDENING RANGE OF NOVEL SERVICES

WPOWERNE WHOPENEWHORIZO

A HOST OF NEW SERVICES, based on the lightning advances in semiconductor and micron technologies of the past two decades, have made their appearance in recent years and are revolutionizing management practice. The chart on p. 32 shows the sharply upward trend in their use. So far this has been primarily in office and factory where the progression has latterly been more rapid than generally expected and continues to gain momentum. There are signs, however, that it is spreading to the home and that by the end of the century we may well have the style of home life so strikingly depicted on p. 34. As our futurologist states therein, the electronic home may well symbolize life in the near future, a convenient, comfortable life that includes access to heretofore unavailable information and unimagined services.

The novel services are basically related to telecommunications and information processing: to the telephone and the computer. Their purpose is to enable managers and their staffs to work more efficiently and economically of both time and effort; to make decisions and plan their business strategy on fuller and better information than was possible before. Devices such as word processors, facsimile transducers, non-impact copiers, "intelligent" terminals, graphic display controllers, filing and retrieval systems, display writers, message distribution systems, digital PBXs (Private Branch Exchanges), intelligent telephones, etc. have been developed to provide the range of services outlined here. Plus, of course, the software needed to program and link these various devices into what is sometimes called "the comprehensive electronic office".

The telephone and its networks continue to be a basic element in the development of the new electronic services. It remains, for most people, the only "ter-

▷ 30

LES INNOVATIONS ET LES PROGRÈS prodigieux accomplis en l'espace de deux décennies dans les domaines des semi-conducteurs et de la microminiaturisation sont autant de défis lancés au monde. Ils ont donné naissance, ces dernières années, à une quantité de nouveaux services, et sont en train de révolutionner les méthodes de gestion. Le diagramme de la page 32 montre la progression rapide de leur utilisation, notamment dans les bureaux et les usines où le rythme des mises en exploitation s'est considérablement accéléré. Cette tendance se maintient et certains signes font présager que, d'ici à la fin du siècle, elle transformera même la vie familiale de la manière décrite à la page 34.

Les nouveaux services sont principalement liés aux télécommunications et au traitement de l'information : au téléphone et à l'ordinateur. La prise de décisions et l'élaboration des stratégies commerciales, sur la base d'une information plus complète et précise que jusqu'ici, sont désormais possibles grâce à l'avènement du microprocesseur, de l'ordinateur individuel et de leurs équipements électroniques périphériques.

Les dispositifs utilisés à cet effet sont les machines de traitement de texte, les transducteurs de fac-similé, les imprimantes sans percussion, les terminaux programmables, les moniteurs à affichage graphique, les systèmes d'archivage, les systèmes de distribution de messages, les centraux numériques PBX (Private Branch Exchanges), les appareils téléphoniques programmables, etc., qui ont été mis au point dans le but de rendre tous les services de la gamme décrite ici. Il faut évidemment ajouter à cela le logiciel nécessaire pour programmer et relier ces différents dispositifs, de manière à constituer ce qui est parfois appelé « le bureau électronique intégral ».

Le téléphone et ses réseaux demeurent la base essentielle du développement des nouveaux services électroniques. Le poste téléphonique reste, pour la plupart

▷ 30

EN LOS ÚLTIMOS AÑOS HAN SURGIDO muchos servicios nuevos, basados en los esclarecedores avances de las tecnologías de semiconductores y micrónicas de los dos últimos decenios, que revolucionan la práctica de la gestión. En el gráfico de la pág. 32 se muestra la marcada tendencia de su uso. Hasta ahora, esto sucedía sobre todo en las oficinas y en las fábricas, donde la progresión ha sido últimamente más rápida de lo previsto, en general, y sigue cobrando impulso. Pero hay indicios de que se extiende al hogar, y de que, para finales de siglo, el estilo de vida casero será el descrito tan sorprendente en la pág. 34. Según declara nuestro futurólogo, el hogar electrónico puede muy bien simbolizar la vida en un futuro cercano; una vida agradable y cómoda, que comprende el acceso a una información y unos servicios inimaginables hasta ahora.

Los nuevos servicios están fundamentalmente relacionados con las telecomunicaciones y el procesamiento de la información: el teléfono y el computador. Su finalidad es permitir a los directores y a su personal trabajar con mayor eficacia y economía; tomar decisiones y planear su estrategía comercial sobre la base de una información más completa y mejor que antes. Se han desarrollado procesadores de texto, transductores de facsímil, copiadores no percusivos, terminales "inteligentes", controladores de presentación gráfica, sistemas de archivo y recuperación, escritores de visualización, sistemas de distribución de mensajes, CAP digitales, teléfonos inteligentes, etc., para la gama de servicios expuesta. Y además, claro es, el soporte lógico necesario para programar y vincular esos aparatos en lo que se denomina a veces « oficina electrónica completa ».

El teléfono y sus redes siguen siendo uno de los elementos básicos de los nuevos servicios electrónicos. Para la mayoría, es aún el único « terminal » que existe en

▷ 31

Every source of information at everyone's fingertips: the interactive terminal provides universal access.

La télématique pour tous à portée du doigt : le terminal interactif ouvre toutes les portes.

La telemática para todos al alcance de la mano: el terminal interactivo abre todas las puertas.

minal" in the home and in the majority of offices. In 1983, the number of installed telephone stations in the world topped 565 million. In 1981 in the USA there were some 175 million (about one-third of them business, two-thirds private) but only 600,000 word processors and 1.25 million desk-top computers.

The contrast is even more marked in other industrialized countries and much more so in the developing world. Even if one looks ahead a decade the telephone will continue to predominate.

The International Data Corporation, estimated in 1982 that the number of electronic devices of all types in use in the USA, including electronic typewriters, would increase from 11 million in 1981 to 50.7 million in 1986, the major gains being in the computer categories. The number of telephones is most unlikely to be less than 200 million, thus remaining — probably to the end of the century — the prime method of communications.

Major programs of modernization and expansion of telephone networks are under way in most areas of the world and especially in countries where the density is already high. A new generation telephone handset is gradually making its entry, in varying degrees of sophistication. At one end of the spectrum it is a handset with push buttons and at the other an "intelligent" telephone station, incorporating microprocessor, visual display unit, in-built memory facilities, simplified call making, message storage handling and other "convenience" features. Such a telephone can communicate with word processors, facsimile machines, desk and main frame computers, monitoring and control devices and various other equipment located in the work places or the home.
The Private Branch Exchange (PBX) has undergone complete metamorphosis in recent years, from the operator controlled plug-in exchange to the present digital, fully automatic version (PABX) fully programmable and able to handle calls at many times the manual speed, to choose the least expensive route for calls to travel, and to provide a detailed record of their destination and duration. It becomes truly the neural system of the workplace.

Other advances in telephony include the development of coinless payphones and electronic push button payphones which are microprocessor-controlled and alert automatically the area telephone authority of faults and — in the case of coin payphones — when the coin box needs emptying. Modifications to payphones, including the use of prepaid cards to eliminate pilfering, will improve the quality of the service and its accessibility.
The integrated information system is gradually becoming the general practice in office and factory automation, and is being vigorously promoted by the leading suppliers of electronic equipment, to overcome the difficulty in integrating devices with varying band rates, codes and protocols into homogeneous networks. Computers must be able to converse with other computers, whatever make or model, electronic mail can only become generally usable if facsimile machines can communicate with one another, and similar considerations apply to other equipment.
Device compatibility is being achieved by ingenious software design which is basic to the development and functioning of all the new services. An example of this is the software program UNIX, developed by Bell Laboratories. This is an operating system which governs how computers manage themselves. UNIX acts as an umbrella under which ten formerly incompatible DEC and IBM computer systems can work together: "Numeric and text files are linked to UNIX and, through UNIX, to a Decmate word processing system, resulting in a complete system of electronic text searching, data manipulation, text editing, document distribution and file building".

Another example is provided by the Combustion Engineering Corporation, a US thermal engineering

des gens, l'unique « terminal » utilisable dans les maisons particulières et dans la plupart des bureaux. En 1983, le nombre des téléphones installés dans le monde atteignait 565 millions. En 1981, on comptait aux Etats-Unis 175,5 millions d'installations téléphoniques (dont un tiers environ dans l'industrie, le commerce et les affaires deux tiers chez les particuliers), mais il n'existait que 600 000 machines de traitement de texte et 1,25 million d'ordinateurs de table.

Le contraste est encore plus frappant dans d'autres pays industrialisés mais il l'est bien davantage dans les pays en développement. Même au cours de la prochaine décennie, il est à prévoir que le téléphone continuera à prédominer. International Data Corporation a estimé, en 1982, que le nombre des appareils électroniques de tous types en utilisation aux Etats-Unis, y compris les machines à écrire électroniques, passerait de 11 millions en 1981 à 50,7 millions en 1986 ; la plus grande partie de cette progression correspondra à la mise en exploitation d'appareils de la catégorie des ordinateurs. Il est probable que le nombre des postes téléphoniques dépassera 200 millions aux Etats-Unis et le téléphone demeurera, probablement jusqu'à la fin du siècle, le principal moyen de communication.

Les principaux programmes de modernisation et d'extension des réseaux téléphoniques sont en voie de réalisation dans la plupart des régions du monde et tout particulièrement dans les pays où la densité du réseau est déjà élevée. Une nouvelle génération de combinés téléphoniques fait progressivement son apparition, dans une grande diversité de types et de degrés de perfectionnement. Parmi ceux-ci, il convient de mentionner, tout d'abord, le simple combiné à touches et, à l'autre extrémité de la gamme, le poste téléphonique programmable à microprocesseur incorporé, équipé d'un écran de visualisation, d'une mémoire, d'un dispositif d'appel simplifié, d'un enregistreur de messages et d'un accès à distance, ainsi que d'autres options à choix. De tels appareils peuvent communiquer avec des unités de traitement de texte, des appareils de fac-similé, des ordinateurs, des dispositifs de surveillance et de commande, ainsi qu'avec divers autres équipements placés dans les lieux de travail ou à domicile.
L'installation d'abonné avec postes supplémentaires ou commutateur privé (PBX) a subi une métamorphose complète au cours de ces dernières années, entre l'époque du standard à fiches desservi par une opératrice et la version actuelle à fonctionnement numérique automatique. Ce central automatique (PABX) est intégralement programmable et peut traiter les appels à des vitesses plusieurs fois supérieures à la commutation manuelle ; il est capable de choisir les acheminements de transmission les moins coûteux. Il enregistre tous les renseignements utiles sur la destination et la durée des commmunications. Ainsi, le PABX devient véritablement le système nerveux d'un bureau, d'une fabrique, d'une entreprise ou d'un ministère.

Parmi les progrès accomplis, il convient de mentionner l'appareil téléphonique à prépaiement sans monnaie, les appareils à prépaiement électronique à touches, qui sont capables de signaler automatiquement à l'administration téléphonique du secteur tous les dérangements et, dans le cas des appareils à prépaiement avec monnaie, le moment où il convient de vider les caissettes. Les modifications qui seront apportées aux appareils téléphoniques à prépaiement, afin de permettre notamment l'utilisation de cartes d'abonné, constituent une amélioration appréciable de la qualité de service.
Un système d'information intégré se généralise par l'automatisation des travaux de bureau et des procédés de fabrication. Il fait l'objet d'une promotion intense de la part des grands constructeurs d'équipements électroniques, dont le principal souci est de surmonter les difficultés d'intégration des dispositifs non normalisés dans des réseaux homogènes. Chaque ordinateur doit être capable de dialoguer avec des ordinateurs de toutes provenances et de tous modèles. Le courrier électronique ne peut se généraliser que si les

A NEW ENVIRONI

Considerable efforts are currently being made by manufacturers and operators alike, to make the technology of electronics "friendly" to the people it serves.

Document creation and distribution network designs of today have been tailored by the communications specialist to meet his own requirements. Office equipment is intended for use by trained personnel. But the wind of change is blowing hard, and soon managers and other users will be able to satisfy their personal requirements for information or data without the intervention of a specialist. The intensive speech synthesis research currently in progress may soon make possible person-to-machine dialogue.

Progress in this direction is illustrated here: a householder operates a work station controlling home security and supplies;

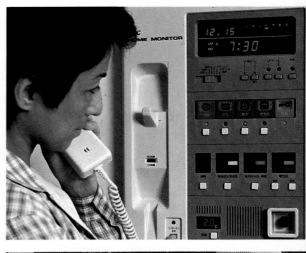

students listen to a professor with the help of a video screen; a user enters information on a personal computer for transmission by telephone; a principal accesses a data base through a computer; an "operator" watches over the automatic desk-top operation of an electronic PABX. All made "user-friendly".

The object is to have an interface between human and machine that is so "friendly" that people can act in familiar ways, rather than deal with a machine on a machine's terms.

All this began with the enhancement of the telephone handset. Extra facilities and options, either built in or attached directly, make possible new subscriber communications including data services, facsimile, telex, electronic mail and videotex. The trend to use the telephone as a terminal rather than just for speaking and listening provides the impetus for the fully integrated telecommunication service network (ISDN).

▷ 32

▷ 32

...mocratiser l'informatique et en rendre l'accès facile et fami-
r, voilà le but que poursuivent tous ceux qui lancent au-
...rd'hui des appareils électroniques, des plus simples aux plus
...mpliqués.

Jusqu'ici les réseaux étaient conçus par des spécialistes de
communication qui les ont façonnés en fonction de leurs
...pres besoins. C'est pourquoi l'utilisation du matériel de
...reau, électronique ou non, ne peut être confiée qu'à un
...rsonnel spécialement formé à cet effet. Il est maintenant fort
...bable qu'au cours de la présente décennie les usagers, les
...us divers, seront capables de se servir des équipements sans
...courir à l'assistance de spécialistes. Les recherches axées
...r la synthèse de la parole vont même rendre le dialogue
...mme/machine de plus en plus accessible.

Los fabricantes y los operadores estan haciendo considerables
esfuerzos para que la tecnología electrónica sea "familiar" para
el usuario.

El especialista en comunicaciones ha adaptado los diseños
de las redes de creación y distribución de documentos actuales
para atender sus propias necesidades. El equipo de oficina está
destinado al uso de personal capacitado. Pero el viento del
cambio sopla con fuerza, y a gran velocidad, y probablemente
en una década los directores y otros usuarios tengan que
atender sus necesidades personales de información y datos sin
intervención de un especialista. La intensiva investigación sobre síntesis vocal permitirá el diálogo hombre-máquina.

Ilustremos los progresos en ese sentido: un jefe de familia
opera una estación de trabajo que controla la seguridad del

el hogar y en la mayoría de las oficinas. En 1981, el
número de teléfonos instalados en el mundo era de
560 millones. Ese mismo año, había en EE.UU. 175,5
millones (un tercio de ellos, comerciales, y dos tercios, particulares), pero sólo 600 000 procesadores de
texto y 1,25 millones de computadores de sobremesa.

El contraste es aún mayor en otros países industrializados, y mucho más en el mundo en desarrollo.
Incluso dentro de un decenio seguirá predominando
el teléfono. La International Data Corporation esti-
maba que el número de aparatos electrónicos de
toda índole utilizados en EE.UU., incluidas las máquinas de escribir, pasará de 11 millones en 1981 a
50,7 en 1986, correspondiendo los principales aumentos a los computadores. No es nada probable
que el número de teléfonos sea inferior a 200 millones, con lo que seguirá siendo — quizá a finales de
siglo — el principal medio de comunicación.

En la mayoría de las regiones están en marcha
importantes programas de modernización y expansión de las redes telefónicas, y sobre todo en países
donde la densidad es ya alta. Gradualmente, se está
introduciendo una nueva generación de microtelé-
fonos, con diversos grados de sofisticación. En un
lado del espectro hay un microteléfono de teclado, y
en el otro una estación telefónica "inteligente", con
microprocesador, un visualizador, facilidades de
memoria incorporadas, simplificación de las llamadas, capacidad para almacenar mensajes y otras
propiedades. Tal teléfono puede comunicar con terminales de texto, máquinas facsímil, computadores
de sobremesa y centrales, dispositivos de verificación
y control en los lugares de trabajo o en el hogar.

La centralita automática privada (CAP) se ha transformado
completamente en los últimos años, pasando de la
central enchufable controlada por operadora a la
actual versión digital, plenamente automática, totalmente programable y que puede tratar una cantidad
de llamadas muchas veces superior a la velocidad
manual, elegir la ruta más económica para las llamadas, proporcionar un registro detallado de su
destino y duración. Se está convirtiendo en el sistema
neural del lugar de trabajo. Otros avances de la telefonía son los aparatos de pago sin monedas y los de
teclado electrónico, contralados por microprocesador y que alertan automáticamente al encargado de
la zona, en caso de avería o cuando hay que vaciar el
cajetín de las monedas. Las modificaciones de estos
aparatos, que comprenden el uso de tarjetas pagadas
previamente para suprimir el robo, mejorarán la calidad del servicio y su acceso.

El sistema de información integrado se está generalizando
prácticamente en la automatización de oficinas y
fábricas, y los principales proveedores de equipo
electrónico lo fomentan a fondo, para superar la
dificultad de integrar dispositivos, con una diversidad de anchuras de banda, códigos y protocolos, en
redes homogéneas. Los computadores habrán de
poder conversar con otros de cualquier marca o modelo; el correo electrónico sólo podrá emplearse generalmente si las máquinas de facsímil pueden comunicar entre sí, y a otros equipos se les aplican
consideraciones análogas.

La compatibilidad de dispositivos se logra mediante el in-
genioso diseño del soporte lógico, fundamental para
el desarrollo y funcionamiento de todos los servicios
nuevos. Un ejemplo de ello es el programa UNIX,
realizado por Bell Laboratories. Se trata de un sistema de operación que gobierna el funcionamiento de
los computadores. UNIX sirve de cobertura a 10
sistemas de computador DEC e IBM antes incompatibles, que pueden trabajar conjuntamente: « Los
archivos numéricos y de texto se vinculan a UNIX y,
a través de él, a un sistema de tratamiento de texto
Decmate, obteniendo un sistema completo de búsqueda electrónica de textos, manipulación de datos,
edición de textos, distribución de documentos y
constitución de archivos ».

Otro ejemplo lo ofrece la Combustion Engineering Corporation, empresa de ingeniería térmica es-

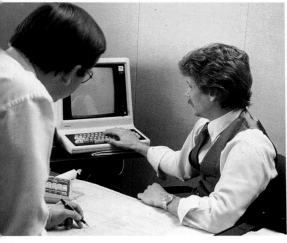

L'ambiance nouvelle créée dans les foyers, les écoles et les
...reaux est illustrée ci-contre : une japonaise utilise le dispo-
...if de surveillance, de sécurité et de consommation de sa
...ison ; des étudiants canadiens suivent un cours universitaire
...r un écran de télévision ; un usager en déplacement "note" un
...nseignement dans son ordinateur personnel pour une trans-
...se téléphonique ; un directeur commercial interroge une
...se de données au moyen de son ordinateur de bureau ; une
...pératrice » américaine observe le fonctionnement d'un au-
...commutateur téléphonique privé « PABX ». Tout cela doit se
...re de la manière la plus familière possible.

L'évolution a commencé par le perfectionnement du combiné
...éphonique. Par la suite, des options incorporées ou reliées
...rectement à l'appareil offriront à l'abonné de nouvelles pos-
...ilités : transmission de données, fac-similé, télex, courrier
...ectronique et vidéotex. Ce développement du téléphone don-
...ra l'impulsion nécessaire à la création d'un réseau de télé-
...mmunication avec intégration complète de services (RNIS).

hogar y los suministros; los alumnos escuchan a un profesor
mediante una pantalla video; un usuario introduce información
en un computador pérsonal para transmitirla por teléfono; un
profesor accede a una base de datos a través de un computador
de sobremesa; un "operador" observa el funcionamiento automático de una CAP electrónica. Todo ello de manera familiar
para el usuario. El objetivo final es disponer de un interfaz entre
el hombre y la máquina tan familiar que la gente pueda actuar
con naturalidad, en vez de tratar con el aparato en términos
propios de la máquina.

Todo ello comienza con el perfeccionamiento del microteléfono. Otras facilidades y opciones, incorporadas y directamente
vinculadas, permitirán nuevas comunicaciones de abonado,
incluidos servicios de datos, facsímil, télex, correo electrónico
y videotex. Esta tendencia al uso del teléfono como terminal, y
no sólo para hablar y escuchar, llevará a una red de servicios
de telecomunicación totalmente integrada (RDSI).

▷ 33

concern which developed a message system that allows terminals from all over the world to exchange messages through the company's central IBM computer. The system interfaces with the international telex network, and allows users not only to receive documents but also to send them.

Some suppliers are promoting devices with enhanced capabilities. For example, a new design of a facsimile transducer marketed by NEC Corporation combines the functions of a facsimile and a printer. Besides transmitting facsimile to facsimile it can receive and print data sent out from a communicating word processor, telex or computer terminal. Equipped with a suitable modem — a device used to convert digital into analog and vice-versa — the machine can transmit a standard letter-size page in 20 seconds.

Several other vendors with systems-design strength offer single products which do word processing, data processing, electronic mail, filing and sometimes graphics and voice annotation. Others supply laser printers that double as copiers and can send documents electronically for printout in distant locations. One Japanese company markets a laser printer that can also act as a copier and image processor.

Many other devices with enhanced capacities are becoming available: desk-top computers perform word processing; word processors are enhanced to process data, and so on. Unescapably, due to user pressure and to vendor effort to gain market ascendancy, the devices used to produce the new services will be integrated into homogeneous communication processing and control systems which can access data banks held in computer memories anywhere in the world, process words and data in the form desired by the user, obtain information such as credit ratings, schedule of trains or planes, weather forecasts, telephone numbers, stock and share prices, sources of supply, or simply news, however distant.

All this appears conveniently on a screen by the punching of a simple command on a keyboard. In time, which is continually being compressed, companies are expected to end up with multiple electronic "highways" as the technology is assimilated into corporate communication systems.

The market progression of information products has begun to gather momentum. A broad discussion of demand is given on p. 306. Forecasts of the value of electronic equipment shipments by the US industry in 1987 range from US$30 billion for telecommunications equipment to US$60 billion for data processing equipment and peripherals, compared to US$20 and US$40 billion in 1982 (See Box p. 308).

Over half the total sales 1987 forecast for data processing equipment and peripherals is accounted for by desk-top computers which are the vigorous leaders of the progression stakes, at a compound annual growth rate likely to exceed 50%. They are followed by non-impact printers with 25%, electronic typewriters with 28% and word processors with 26%. PABXs and facsimile machines are a long way behind with compound annual growth rates of 12% and 13% respectively.

Desk-top computers in use in the USA in 1986 are expected to top the 14 million mark, compared to 1.25 million in 1981; computer terminals to increase from 6.9 million to 19.1 million, and the number of software packages in use from 1.2 million to 10 million in the same period. The comment is that "computer technology is at a watershed. Microprocessors have opened up computer power to the masses".

The main reason for this explosive growth in desk-top computer usage is that they can be used for a wide range of tasks, from inventory control and general ledger to financial analysis and word processing. The latter is in fact the most popular application, two-thirds of the number installed in 1980 being used for this purpose, followed by financial analysis, accounting and data base access. Another finding of the same IDC survey is that about one-third of desk-top computers are used exclusively at work, only 18% exclusively at home.

machines de fac-similé peuvent communiquer les unes avec les autres. Les mêmes considérations sont valables pour n'importe quel équipement.

La compatibilité des installations est réalisée grâce à un logiciel ingénieux qui est indispensable au développement et au fonctionnement correct de tous les nouveaux services. Le programme du logiciel UNIX, mis au point par Bell Telephone Laboratories en est un bel exemple. Il s'agit d'un système régissant le comportement individuel des ordinateurs qui se comporte comme un parasol sous lequel 10 systèmes d'ordinateurs précédemment incompatibles DEC et IBM peuvent travailler ensemble : des archives alpha-numériques sont reliées à UNIX et, par son intermédiaire, au système de traitement de textes Decmate. Ce dispositif représente un système complet de recherche électronique de textes, de traitement de données, de mise au point et de distribution de documents et de constitution de dossiers.

Certains constructeurs commercialisent des dispositifs de capacité supérieure. Par exemple, une nouvelle conception de transducteurs de fac-similé commercialisés par NEC Corporation combine les fonctions d'une unité fac-similé et celles d'une imprimante. De tels dispositifs peuvent recevoir et imprimer des données provenant d'une unité de traitement de texte, d'un terminal télex ou d'un ordinateur. Equipé d'un dispositif de conversion numérique/analogique et inverse, ce système assure la transmission d'une page normale de format A4 en 20 secondes.

Il existe actuellement des systèmes capables d'accomplir les fonctions de traitement de texte et de données, de courrier électronique, d'archivage et parfois même d'établissement de diagrammes ou de notation d'indications verbales. Des imprimantes à laser sont utilisables pour la reprographie et capables de transmettre des documents à distance.

Certains ordinateurs de table peuvent déjà servir au traitement de texte, tandis que des unités de traitement de texte sont aussi capables d'assurer le traitement de données, etc. D'une manière générale les systèmes de traitement et de supervision auront accès à des banques de données contenues dans les mémoires d'ordinateur disséminées dans le monde. Ces appareils assurent le traitement de texte et des données sous la forme requise par l'utilisateur ; ils permettent également d'obtenir des renseignements concernant le contrôle de solvabilité, les horaires d'avions, les prévisions météorologiques, les numéros de téléphone, les cours de bourse, les sources d'approvisionnement ou simplement les dernières nouvelles.

L'affichage de toutes ces informations sur écran sera commandé par clavier. Dans un délai toujours plus rapproché, les grandes firmes disposeront d'artères multiples à grand trafic électronique formant de vastes réseaux de communication intégrés.

Le marché des matériels télématiques prend un essor extraordinaire. On trouvera à la p. 306 un exposé sur la demande dans cette branche. Les prévisions sur la valeur des équipements livrables par l'industrie des Etats-Unis en 1987 oscillent entre 30 milliards de dollars US pour les équipements de télécommunications et 60 milliards pour les matériels et périphéraux informatiques, par rapport à 20 et 40 milliards, respectivement, en 1982 (voir encadré p. 308).

Plus de la moitié de l'ensemble des prévisions de ventes pour 1987 se rapportent aux ordinateurs de table qui sont largement en tête dans la répartition de cette progression, avec un taux d'accroissement annuel global qui dépassera probablement 50%. Ces matériels sont suivis par les imprimantes sans percussion 25%, les machines à écrire électroniques 28%, et les processeurs de texte 26%. Les centraux PABX et les télécopieurs (fac-similé) suivent derrière avec un taux de progression annuel de 12% et 13% respectivement.

En 1986, le nombre des ordinateurs de table dépassera probablement le cap des 14 millions, contre 1,25 millions en 1981, tandis que les terminaux d'ordinateurs passeront de 6,9 millions à 19,1 millions et le nombre des unités de logiciel en usage passera de 1,2 million à 10 millions dans le même délai. Cet essor irrésistible découle du fait que les ordinateurs

▷ 36

▷ 36

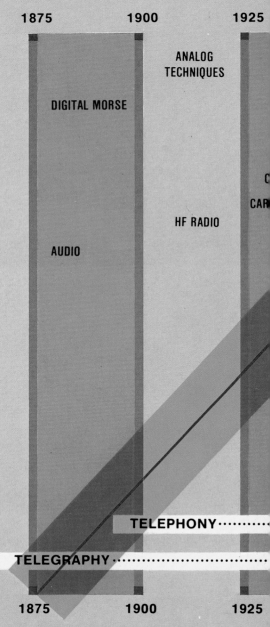

THE ACCELERATING

This graph illustrates the introduction of communication services over the past two centuries. During the first half of the 19th Century, telegraphy was the only non-physical means of communicating over distance. The second half-century saw the introduction in rapid succession of the telephone and radio. Considerable resources were allocated to the construction of a global telephone network. People were able to talk to one another from anywhere to anywhere. Broadcasting became worldwide and news could come across the globe almost as it was unfolding. This laid the foundation for to-day's proliferation of services operated via the public switched telephone network.

The past three decades saw the birth first of the semiconductor and then of integrated circuit technologies, the introduction of the computer-first, main frame, requiring air conditioned cubic space; then desk-top, usable in any office; then hand-held, of briefcase size. Digital switching, optical transmission, microwave radio and satellite transmission were developed in the same period. The number of services and their use ascended steeply, and their integration into work stations in offices and factories, and later in homes and vehicles, is proceeding rapidly. Demand for the application of all this technological achievement is developing strongly.

MAND FOR NEW SERVICES 1850-2000

graphique illustre l'introduction des services de communi-
on au cours des deux derniers siècles. Au 19ème, le télé-
phe était le seul moyen de communiquer à distance par
aux électriques. Puis le téléphone et la radio firent leur
arition. Des ressources considérables furent consacrées à
onstruction d'un réseau mondial du téléphone. Il fut possible
onverser à toute distance. La radiodiffusion globale naquit
20ème siècle. Les trois dernières décennies ont vu d'abord
ention des semiconducteurs et du circuit intégré, puis de
dinateur, le premier, l'ENIAC, étant énorme et centralisé.
uite vinrent le mini-ordinateur. l'ordinateur de table et le
atif. La commutation numérique, la transmission optique et

En este gráfico se ilustra la indroducción de los servicios de
comunicación en los dos últimos siglos. Durante la primera
mitad del siglo XIX, la telegrafía era el único medio no físico de
comunicar a distancia. En la segunda mitad se introdujeron, en
rápida sucesión, el teléfono y la radio. Se asignaron considerables recursos para la construcción de una red telefónica
global. La gente podía hablar entre sí desde cualquier parte. La
radiodifusión adquirió carácter mundial, y las noticias podían
atravesar el globo casi a medida que se producían.

En las tres últimas décadas aparecieron las tecnologías de
semiconductores, y luego de circuitos integrados, introducién-
dose el computador: primero el central, que necesitaba cente-

tadounidense, que ha desarrollado un sistema de
mensajes que permite a los terminales del mundo
entero intercambiar mensajes a través del computador central IBM de la empresa. El sistema está conectado a la red télex internacional, y permite a los
usuarios recibir y enviar documentos.

Algunos proveedores promueven dispositivos con
mayores capacidades. Por ejemplo, un nuevo diseño
de transductor de facsímil comercializado por NEC
combina las funciones de un facsímil y una impresora. Además de transmitir de facsímil a facsímil,
puede recibir e imprimir datos enviados desde un
terminal de texto, télex o computador comunican-
te. Provisto de un módem adecuado — dispositivo
usado para la conversión digital-analógica, y vice-
versa — el aparato puede transmitir una página de
tamaño carta normal en 20 segundos. Otros vendedores del sector de diseño de sistemas ofrecen productos de tratamiento de texto, procesamiento de
datos, correo electrónico, archivo y, a veces, anota-
ción gráfica y vocal. Otros suministran impresoras
láser que sirven de copiadoras y pueden enviar documentos electrónicamente para imprimirlos en
otros lugares. Una empresa japonesa comercializa
una impresora láser que puede actuar también de
copiador y procesador de imágenes.

Existen otros muchos dispositivos con capacidades
mejoradas: computadores de sobremesa que efectúan el tratamiento de texto; terminales de texto
perfeccionados para procesar datos, etc. Ineludible-
mente, debido a la presión del usuario y al esfuerzo
del vendedor por conquistar un mayor mercado, los
aparatos utilizados para producir los nuevos servicios se integrarán en sistemas de procesamiento y
control de la comunicación homogéneos que pueden
acceder a bancos de datos mantenidos en memorias
de computador de cualquier parte del mundo; obtener información sobre clasificación crediticia, horarios de trenes o aviones, previsiones meteorológicas,
números de teléfono, precios de títulos y acciones,
fuentes de suministro, o simples noticias, a distancia.

Todo esto aparece en una pantalla, simplemente
pulsando una tecla. Con el tiempo — y los plazos
disminuyen sin cesar — se espera que las compañías
dispongan de múltiples arterias electrónicas, a medida que la tecnología se inserte en los sistemas de
comunicación de las empresas.

La progresión del mercado de productos de información cobra ya impulso. En la pág. 306 se considera ampliamente la demanda. Las previsiones del valor de las
exportaciones de equipo electrónico por la industria
estadounidense en 1987 varían entre 30 000 millones
$ EE.UU. para el equipo de telecomunicaciones y
60 000 millones para el de tratamiento de datos y
equipo periférico, frente a 20 000 y 40 000 millones
en 1982 (véase el recuadro de la pag. 308).

Más de la mitad de las ventas totales de equipo de
datos y periférico previstas para 1987 está representada por los computadores de sobremesa, que van a
la cabeza de la progresión, a una tasa de crecimiento
anual tal vez superior al 50%. Siguen las impresoras
no percusivas, con el 25%, las máquinas de escribir
electrónicas, con el 28%, y los procesadores de texto,
con el 26%. Y, bastante más lejos, las CAP y las
máquinas de facsímil, con índices de crecimiento
anual del 12% y el 13%, respectivamente.

Se espera que los computadores de sobremesa
utilizados en EE.UU. en 1986 superen los 14 millones, frente a 1,25 millones en 1981; los terminales de
computador pasarán de 6,9 millones a 19,1 millones,
y el número de conjuntos de soporte lógico empleados aumentará en el mismo período de 1,2 millones a
10 millones. Se dice que la « tecnología de computador se encuentra en un momento decisivo. Los
microprocesadores permiten a las masas acceder a la
energía del computador ».

La razón de este crecimiento explosivo de los
computadores de sobremesa es que pueden usarse
para muchas tareas, desde el control de existencias y
contabilidad general hasta el análisis financiero y el
tratamiento de textos. Esta última es, en realidad, la

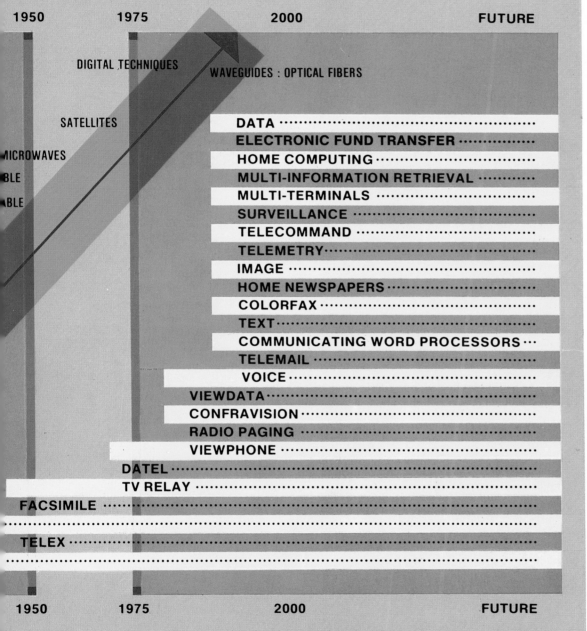

| 1950 | 1975 | 2000 | FUTURE |

DIGITAL TECHNIQUES
WAVEGUIDES : OPTICAL FIBERS

SATELLITES
DATA ·················
ELECTRONIC FUND TRANSFER ···············
ICROWAVES
HOME COMPUTING ·················
BLE
MULTI-INFORMATION RETRIEVAL ···········
ABLE
MULTI-TERMINALS ················
SURVEILLANCE ···············
TELECOMMAND ·················
TELEMETRY···············
IMAGE ················
HOME NEWSPAPERS ···············
COLORFAX ··················
TEXT ·················
COMMUNICATING WORD PROCESSORS ···
TELEMAIL ···············
VOICE ··················
VIEWDATA·················
CONFRAVISION ·············
RADIO PAGING ···············
VIEWPHONE ·············
DATEL ·················
TV RELAY ·················
FACSIMILE
TELEX ···················

| 1950 | 1975 | 2000 | FUTURE |

transmission micro-ondes par satellite ayant été dévepées en même temps, le nombre de services et leur emploi
mentera à un rythme croissant dans les bureaux, les usines,
plus récemment, dans les foyers et les véhicules.

l'intégration progressive de tous ces services issus de l'é-
ronique, finira par aboutir à un Réseau Numérique avec
gration de Services (RNIS) qui donnera à tous ceux qui
sèdent un poste interactif de télévision, un accès sélectif
informations les plus variées, aux banques de données et à
rs centres de traitement, et à une vaste gamme de matériel
r la culture et les loisirs.

nares de metros cúbicos de aire acondicionado; luego, el de
sobremesa, utilizable en cualquier oficina, y después el portátil,
del tamaño de un maletín. En el mismo período se desarrollaron
la conmutación digital, la transmisión óptica, las radiocomunicaciones por microondas y la transmisión por satélite. El número de servicios y su uso crecieron fuertemente, y su integración en lugares de trabajo de oficinas y fábricas, y después
en hogares y vehículos, se extiende rápidamente. Aumenta
mucho la demanda de todo este logro tecnológico.

▷ 37

TWO-WAY CABLE SERVICE PICTURES/DATA	**VOICE-OPERATED COMPUTERS AND TYPEWRITERS**
TELEVISION VIDEOPHONES NEWS BY WIRE	**WORD PROCESSING AUTOMATIC TRANSLATION**
TELETEXT ELECTRONIC MAIL VIDEOTEX	**BUSINESS DATA STOCK PRICES ECONOMIC TRENDS**
INFORMATION RETRIEVAL DATA BANKS	**HOME SHOPPING TELEBANKING FINANCIAL PLANNING**
TRAVEL AND WEATHER INFORMATION	**EMPLOYMENT OPPORTUNITIES WORK FROM HOME**

THE FAMILY OF TO

A TV-phone rings. Eight o'clock in the morning — the start of the day for Mr. X, a 35 year-old bank employee. Ever since he began telecommuting, he uses the hour each day he'd formerly spent commuting to and from his office as he likes. At the moment that means studying the Spanish language lessons offered by a data bank as part of a lifelong education program. The TV-phone call is from a native Spanish speaker with whom Mr. X converses twice a week.

The advent of voice-operated typewriters and automatic translating machines has overcome the language barrier in business and personal communications. Yet, perhaps because those machines have removed its necessity, more people want to be able to read foreign literature in its original language. Mr. X makes it a rule to study Spanish for an hour every morning.

As he studies, Mrs. X sits beside him at their home computer and plans her daily shopping with the help of information services provided by department stores and supermarkets. Although her shopping usually includes only local stores, today she has selected international outlets as well; a dress in this autumn's recently announced Paris collection just appeared on the computer screen. Since the computer knows her clothing sizes, she can "try on" the dress as it appears on the screen. She urgently needs to buy an anorak for her 12 year-old boy and a tie for her husband. She tunes in to the display of a mail order store, selects from a wide choice and tele-settles her account, confident that her purchases will arrive in good time.

After completing his hour of studying, Mr. X begins his workday at his computer. Today his work consists of analyzing data. Other days, as occasion demands, he holds teleconferences with various branches — sometimes including oversea ones.

Depite living in a provincial city, Mr. and Mrs. X and their children lead an international life-home computers, TV-phones, and other "21st Century" inventions bring the world, in a variety of communication forms, into their home. Twice weekly the children tune into their French class and participate in exploratory "tele-trips" to France, seeing for themselves how young people live, learn and play in a different part of the world.

The whole family can enjoy games between themselves or with friends who live elsewhere, learn about global events instantaneously, and even undergo a check-up by a world-famous physician, if need be, from the comfort of their own home. For Mr. X and his family, language and distance are no longer barriers between people.

Naturally, Mr. and Mrs. X's "electronic home" does not exist. Yet. But in the very near future, the electronic home and the life style it produces will become reality. The introduction of personal computers, calls from automobiles and airplanes, two-way cable TV service — and the increase in the sophistication of the contents to be transmitted, such as pictures and data — have already changed many facets of our lives. Only one final step remains to be taken before such an electronic home becomes reality: the introduction of computers and communications to each household as an integrated system. Its realization is only a matter of time. And as you read this page, technology moves closer and closer to achieving it.

The electronic home symbolizes life in the near future — a convenient, comfortable life that includes access to heretofore unimagined information and services. Those alone, perhaps, do not guarantee the advancement of mankind. But the electronic home promises to bring us something infinitely more valuable: the expansion of our lives beyond time and distance. To be informed immediately and to speak freely with anybody — have long been among man's fundamental desires. When these desires have been fulfilled, mankind will certainly have advanced. A new culture of electronic living is developing, with its own values, language, norms, and rules of conduct. Time is needed to adjust, but for the very young the period of adaptation is unlikely to be very long. This is how the Japanese members of NEC interpret the future.

EDUCATION COURSE PLANNING TRAINING

SAFETY/SECURITY HOME MONITORING ENERGY CONTROL

KEEP FIT PROGRAMS MEDICAL CHECK'UP HOME BABY SITTER

CULTURAL AND SPORTING EVENTS ENTERTAINMENT

I.Q. TESTS GAMES ETC. ETC. ETC.

videophone sonne. Il est huit heures du matin. La journée mmence pour M. X, employé de banque, 35 ans. Depuis qu'il pose de la télématique chez lui, il passe à sa guise l'heure il perdait précédemment pour se déplacer tous les jours de n domicile à son bureau et retour. Pour le moment, il suit un urs d'anglais fourni par une banque de données dans le cadre n programme régulier d'éducation. Un appel sur le video-one : c'est un ami anglais avec qui M. X. converse agréable-nt dans cette langue deux fois par semaine.

L'introduction des machines à écrire commandées à la voix des appareils de traduction automatique ont supprimé les stacles linguistiques dans les communications d'affaires et relations personnelles. Pourtant, en raison même de l'utili-ion de ces machines, beaucoup plus de gens ont l'ambition lire dans le texte original la littérature étrangère. C'est urquoi M. X s'est donné pour règle de « faire » une heure anglais tous les matins.

Pendant que M. X étudie, son épouse établit son plan d'em-ttes quotidiennes, en tenant compte des renseignements rnis à leur ordinateur domestique par les magasins spécia-és et les supermarchés. Aujourd'hui, elle a l'intention de ofiter des offres exceptionnelles. Une robe présentée récem-nt à Paris dans la collection d'automne fait justement son parition sur l'écran. L'ordinateur familial connaît la taille de ne X et ses mensurations ; elle peut donc demander cette e « à l'essai ». Elle veut aussi acheter un anorak pour son et une cravate pour son mari. Elle compose le numéro du gasin de vente par correspondance et fait son choix dans ssortiment qui lui est présenté. Elle règle ensuite la facture « télé-débitant » son compte bancaire, pleinement confiante e la marchandise sera livrée en temps utile.

Après sa leçon d'anglais, M. X commence sa journée de vail par une analyse de données mais parfois il tient des éconférences avec les responsables de diverses filiales de sa nque, dont certaines sont à l'étranger.

Bien qu'ils habitent une ville de province, M. et Mme X et rs enfants mènent une vie internationale ; les ordinateurs mestiques, les videophones et les autres inventions du 21ème siècle » leur apportent le monde à domicile. Deux fois r semaine les enfants « vont » en classe d'anglais et parti-ent à des « télévoyages » aux Etats-Unis où ils peuvent voir leur propres yeux comment vivent les jeunes américains.

Les membres de la famille ont la possibilité de jouer entre x ou avec des amis qui vivent dans d'autres régions, ou, si le soin s'en fait sentir, chacun d'eux peut consulter un médecin uté par videophone tout en restant comfortablement installé ns son fauteuil. Désormais, pour M. X et sa famille, la langue la distance ont cessé d'être des obstacles entre les gens.

Evidemment, la « maison électronique » de M. et Mme X existe pas encore, mais le mode de vie qu'elle peut engendrer viendra bientôt une réalité. L'introduction des ordinateurs dividuels, la généralisation des communications téléphoni-es avec des personnes circulant en automobile ou à bord avions, et bien d'autres innovations modifient déjà notre istence. Il ne nous reste en somme qu'un dernier pas à anchir pour entrer dans une vraie maison électronique : la sponibilité d'ordinateurs et de services télématiques dans aque ménage. Ce n'est en somme qu'une question de temps.

La maison informatisée promet de nous conduire hors des ntraintes du temps et de la distance. Etre informé immédia-ment et parler librement avec chacun, ce sont là des aspira-ons fondamentales de l'individu. Lorsqu'elles seront satisfai-s, l'humanité aura vraiment progressé dans la nouvelle lture de la communication électronique qui est en train de ître, avec ses propres valeurs, son langage, ses normes et s règles de conduite.

Bien sûr, il nous faudra un certain temps pour comprendre, similer et réagir mais, pour les jeunes, cette période d'adap-tion ne risque pas d'être très longue. Déjà ils trouvent dans la cture sur l'écran la façon la plus naturelle de s'informer et hésitent aucunement à former les numéros de sources d'in-rmations les plus diverses pour leurs besoins d'étude ou de straction. Cette vision est celle des collaborateurs japonais e NEC interprétant le futur, lequel, dans leur pays, est proba-ement beaucoup moins lointain que dans beaucoup d'autres.

Suena un videoteléfono. Son las ocho de la mañana: comienza el día para el Sr. X, empleado de banca de 35 años. Desde que dispone de la electrónica, utiliza a su antojo la hora diaria que paşaba antes entre su casa y la oficina. En este momento, estudia las lecciones de japonés ofrecidas por un banco de datos, como parte de un programa de formación permanente. La llamada procede de un japonés con quien conversa el Sr. X. dos veces a la semana. La aparición de teleimpresores accionados por la voz y de máquinas de traducción automáticas ha superado la barrera del idioma en las comunicaciones comer-ciales y personales. Sin embargo, quizá porque esas máquinas han suprimido su necesidad, es mayor el número de personas que desean leer literatura extranjera en el idioma original. El Sr. X se ha fijado la norma de estudiar japonés durante una hora cada mañana.

Mientras él estudia, la Sra. X se sienta a su lado en su computador doméstico y planea sus compras diarias con la ayuda de los servicios de información de los grandes almace-nes y supermercados. Aunque normalmente sus compras se limitan a los almacenes locales, hoy parece seleccionar tam-bién mercados internacionales; acaba de aparecer en la pantalla del computador un vestido de la colección parisina anunciada recientemente de este otoño. Como el computador conoce su talla puede "probarse" el vestido cuando aparece en la pantalla. Necesita comprar urgentemente un anorak para su hijo de 12 años, y una corbata para su marido. Marca y conecta con una tienda de venta por correo, elige entre un amplio surtido y lo carga en su cuenta, en la confianza de que sus compras llegarán a tiempo.

Una vez terminada su hora de estudio, el Sr. X comienza su trabajo diario con el computador. Hoy consiste en analizar datos. Otros días, según las exigencias, celebra teleconferen-cias con diversas ramas, a veces incluso con el extranjero.

A pesar de vivir en una ciudad de provincias, el Sr. y la Sra. X y sus hijos llevan una vida internacional: computadores domésticos, videoteléfonos y otras invenciones del "siglo XXI" llevan el mundo a su hogar, en una diversidad de formas de comunicación. Sus hijos sintonizan dos días por semana con su clase de japonés, y participan en "televiajes" exploratorios a Japón, viendo cómo viven, aprenden y juegan los jóvenes en una parte diferente del mundo.

Toda la familia puede jugar entre sí o con sus amigos de otras partes, conocer acontecimientos globales instantánea-mente, e incluso ser reconocidos por un famoso médico mun-dial, en caso necesario, sin perder la comodidad de su propio hogar. Para el Sr. X y su familia, el idioma y la distancia han dejado de constituir barreras entre las gentes.

Por supuesto, el "hogar electrónico" del Sr. y la Sra. X no existe. Todavia. Pero dentro de muy poco, el hogar electrónico y el estilo de vida que depara serán realidad. La introducción de computadores personales, las llamadas desde automóviles y aviones, el servicio bidireccional de televisión por cable — y la mayor sofisticación del contenido de la transmisión, como imágenes y datos — han cambiado ya muchas facetas de nuestra vida. No hay mas que dar el paso final para convertir en realidad ese hogar electrónico: la implantación de computado-res y comunicaciones en cada casa como sistema integrado. Su realización es sólo cuestión de tiempo. Mientras lee usted esta página, la tecnología se aproxima cada vez más a esa meta.

El hogar electrónico simboliza la vida del futuro próximo: una vida agradable y cómoda que comprende el acceso inimagina-ble hasta ahora a la información y a los servicios. Quizá ellos solos no garanticen el progreso de la humanidad. Pero el hogar electrónico promete aportarnos algo infinitamente más valioso: la expansión de nuestras vidas por encima del tiempo y de la distancia. La información imediata y la libre expresión con cualquiera han figurado siempre entre los viejos deseos fun-damentales del hombre. Cuando esos deseos se cumplan, la humanidad habrá avanzado. Se desarrolla una nueva cultura de vida electrónica, con sus valores, idioma, normas y reglas de conducta propios. El ajuste requiere tiempo, pero para los muy jóvenes el período de adaptación no será largo. Así es como los miembros de la firma japonesa NEC Corporation interpretan el futuro.

The new facilities of the Information Age have been alluded to in the foregoing review of the services and systems on which they rest. Several applications are described in the Box on p. 34 in the context of the electronic home of the future. There is a videophone, used for talking and laughing with friends in full sight of one another, teleconferencing with colleagues at home and abroad, consultations with doctors and specialists, taking courses in modern languages, lessons in history, physics, gardening, tennis, or any other subject of interest.

The home computer can find out what is available in the shops and how priced, place orders, pay for them; transfer funds; buy and sell shares. A two-way TV service is available. Games can be played with or through the computer. Information on transportation schedules, the weather, the availability of hotel accommodation, etc., all accessible in the home equipped with a phone, video screen and table top computer. Only funds, skilled labour and the time to do it all seem to be missing to make this a reality worldwide today.

Among the many new services initiated in recent years are several which have been grafted onto the public switched telephone or telex networks and are in fact enhancements of these automated information distribution systems. They include teletex, telefax, integrated text and data communication (IDN), videotelephony and videoconferencing, videotex and teletext (sometimes called cabletext).
— *Teletex:* is an enhanced international telex service, operating at very much higher speeds and transmitting text using upper and lower case characters.
— *Telefax:* is an "electronic mail" service used to transmit documents of DIN A4 format or smaller, from one facsimile system to another via the telephone switched network.
— *Integrated Digital Network (IDN):* is used for access to data banks, for the transfer of money and other man-machine communications. It is designed to handle digital signals using modems and packet-switching techniques.
— *Videotex:* is an interactive (two-way) computerized data retrieval service using a slightly modified television receiver in conjunction with the normal public telephone line. The heart of the system consists of a central computer with information storage and the capability of contacting other videotex centers or external computers to obtain the information requested. It is used for teleshopping, telebanking, the retrieval of specific information such as telephone numbers or train times, lodging of messages, etc.
— *Teletext or Cabletext:* is a broadcasting (one-way) system used for the transmission of a limited number of pages by television broadcasting stations together with their program emissions via two of the unused lines in an ordinary video signal. A special decoding unit in domestic receivers permits selection and display on the screen.

In addition to the above, a large number of remote monitoring and control systems have been developed. They include one- or two-way alarms, energy control, fault identification and correction in industrial processes in telephone exchanges and in other complex systems.

Enhancements of these systems are continually being worked out to make them easier to use, more compatible and more generally available worldwide. For example, a second generation teletex is being developed to transmit both alpha-numerical and pictorial material. Another is the development, under the name of Datafax, of a digital high-speed facsimile service over the public data networks, which includes error correction and automatic operation. Several other developments are in hand, all designed to broaden the use of telecommunications by making them more accessible, more reliable and easier to operate. How these services are being integrated into terminals and a global system is shown in the Box opposite.

de table peuvent servir à une multitude de tâches, allant du contrôle d'inventaire à la comptabilité générale et à l'analyse financière, aussi bien qu'au traitement de texte. Cette dernière utilisation est, en fait, la plus répandue ; ensuite viennent l'analyse financière, la comptabilité et l'accès aux bases de données.

Les nouvelles facilités de la société d'information ont été évoquées, plus haut, dans l'analyse des systèmes sur lesquels elles reposent. Plusieurs, quelques unes plutôt futuristes, sont décrites à la page 34, dans le cadre de la maison électronique de l'avenir. Il y a le vidéophone, qui nous permettra de nous retrouver face à face avec la famille ou des amis distants, des moyens — sans quitter son domicile — de participer à des téléconférences, donner ou obtenir des consultations médicales, suivre des cours de langue, d'histoire, de physique, de géographie, de jardinage, de tennis, de natation, etc. L'opération d'un clavier permet à l'ordinateur domestique de repérer dans les magasins les articles dont nous avons besoin, de les commander et de les payer. L'ordinateur peut également d'effectuer des transferts de fonds, acheter ou vendre des actions, et participer à des jeux, avec ou contre l'ordinateur.

Les mêmes facilités, adaptées aux besoins de l'industrie ou du commerce, permettent la surveillance, la commande, l'identification et la correction d'erreurs ou de dérangements — par exemple dans les centraux téléphoniques ou les chaînes de production industrielle. Seul le manque de fonds, de main-d'œuvre spécialisée et de temps empêche que tout cela devienne une réalité à l'échelle du monde entier. Parmi les nombreux services mis en exploitation au cours de ces dernières années, plusieurs ont été greffés sur le réseau commuté du téléphone ou du télex et sont en fait des développements de ces systèmes :
— *Télétex :* est un télex amélioré, beaucoup plus rapide et transmettant des textes en utilisant des caractères majuscules et minuscules.
— *Téléfax :* est un service de « courrier électronique » destiné à remplacer le courrier classique. Il peut transmettre des documents de format A4 d'un centre de fac-similé à un autre par voie du réseau téléphonique commuté.
— *Réseau Numérique Intégré (RNI) :* donne accès aux banques de données et sert pour le transfert d'argent et autres communications homme-machine, conçu pour une fonction numérique utilisant modems et commutation par paquet.
— *Vidéotex :* est un système interactif (bidirectionnel) d'accès aux centres d'informations et banques de données qui fait apparaitre les renseignements sur un écran de télévision légèrement modifié par voie du réseau commuté téléphonique, commandé par un simple clavier. La base essentielle du système est un ordinateur central avec stockage d'information, capable de contacter automatiquement d'autres ordinateurs ou des centraux de videotex pour obtenir l'information demandée.

Ce service permet d'effectuer à distance des achats des opérations bancaires, d'obtenir des numéros de téléphone, horaires de transport public, etc., ou d'envoyer des messages à d'autres abonnés.
— *Télétext ou Cablotext :* est un système de radio-diffusion (unidirectionnel) pour la transmission d'un nombre limité de pages d'information par les stations de télévision, simultanément avec leur programmes, en se servant de voies disponibles. Un décodeur permet aux abonnés de recevoir ce qu'ils ont demandé sur leurs écrans de télévision.

Des perfectionnements continuels visent à faciliter le maniement des systèmes et à améliorer leur compatibilité pour en généraliser l'utilisation à l'échelle mondiale. Une deuxième génération d'appareils Télétext servira à transmettre tout matériel alpha-numérique et d'images (viewdata). Le Datafax assurera la transmission automatique en fac-similé numérique à très grande vitesse sur les réseaux publics de données, avec correction des erreurs. D'autre variantes permettront bientôt d'élargir l'utilisation des nouveaux services de télécommunication en les rendant plus accessibles et plus fiables. On voit, ci-contre, l'état de leur intégration progressive dans les terminaux.

□

□

This chart shows the relationships, as some are and others may develop in the future, between the services of the information age and the terminals where the information appears. It presupposes a gradual conversion of the telecommunications system from all-analog to all-digital. This means that once an analog signal from a subscriber loop has been converted to a digital signal, it remains digital for its entire passage through the network unitil it is converted back to analog for application to the called party's local loop. It assumes that an increasing degree of "intelligence" will be introduced into the terminals, allowing for interactive communication.

SERVICES	EXAMP
Speech	Telephone
	Video telephone
	Mobile communication
Information transmission	Telex
	Facsimile
	Electronic mail
Information guide	Information guides
	Electronic newspapers
	Electronic magazines
Information retrieval	Calculation, memory, b
	Data banks and databa
Information processing	Editing
	Documentation
	Translation
Electronic Funds transfer	Shopping
	Pay by phone
Entertainment	Game, play
	Movie, Picture
	Music
Education	One-way system
	Two-Way (conversation
Medical care	Simple diagnosis
	Remote diagnosis syste
Other services	Questionnaire, Voting,
	Monitoring, Alarm
	Telemetering
	Telecommand
	Telecontrol

tableau montre les relations, telles qu'elles se sont déjà
blies, et telles qu'elles se développent entre les divers
vices de l'ère de la télématique, et les terminaux sur lesquels
s'afficher l'information. La conversion graduelle des trans-
ssions du type entièrement analogique au type entièrement
nérique implique que, dès l'instant où un signal analogique
nant d'une boucle d'abonné a été converti en un signal
nérique, celui-ci reste numérique pendant toute sa traversée
réseau, jusqu'au moment où il est reconverti en signal
logique et inséré dans la boucle locale de l'abonné appelé.
a suppose une augmentation du degré d'« intelligence » des
minaux et une communication interactive.

En este gráfico se muestra la relación entre los diversos servicios de la era de la información y los terminales donde
aparece la información, algunos como son, y otros como pueden desarrollarse en el futuro. Esto presupone una conversión
gradual del sistema de telecomunicaciones de todo analógico a
todo digital, lo cual significa que, una vez convertida una señal
analógica recibida de un bucle de abonado en digital, seguirá
siendo digital mientras atraviesa la red, hasta que se convierte
de nuevo en analógica para aplicarla al bucle local de la
persona llamada. Supone un mayor grado de "inteligencia" en
los terminales, permitiendo la comunicación interactiva.

aplicación más popular, habiéndose empleado con
tal fin los dos tercios de los aparatos instalados en
1980, seguida del análisis financiero, la contabilidad
y el acceso a bases de datos. Otra conclusión del
mismo estudio de la IDC es que aproximadamente
un tercio de los computadores de sobremesa se utilizan sólo en el trabajo, y el 18% en el hogar.

Las nuevas facilidades de la era de la información se basan
sobre todo en el análisis anterior de los servicios y
sistemas. En la pág. 34, recuadro, se describen varias
aplicaciones en el hogar electrónico del futuro.
Existe un videoteléfono, con el que se puede hablar y
bromear con los amigos, viéndose plenamente, tele-
conferenciar con colegas del país y del extranjero,
consultar a médicos y especialistas, seguir cursos de
lenguas modernas, de historia, física, jardinería, tenis
o cualquier otro asunto de interés.

Con el computador doméstico se puede conocer lo
que hay en los almacenes, hacer pedidos y pagarlos;
transferir fondos; comprar y vender acciones. Se
dispone de un servicio TV bidireccional. El computador permite los juegos electrónicos, directamente o
a través de el. Y obtener información sobre horarios
de transporte, el tiempo, habitaciones de hotel, etc.,
todo ello en el hogar provisto de un videoteléfono y
un computador de sobremesa con pantalla de un
tamaño similar. Para convertir esto en realidad en el
mundo entero sólo faltan, al parecer, los fondos, el
personal especializado y el tiempo para realizarlo.

Entre los servicios de los últimos años, varios se
han implantado en las redes telefónicas públicas con
conmutación o télex y mejoran esos sistemas de distribución automatizada de la información. Pueden
citarse teletex, telefax, texto integrado y comunicación de datos, videotelefonía y videoconferencia, videotex y teletexto (denominados a veces cabletexto).

— *Teletex:* es un servicio télex internacional mejorado, que funciona a grandes velocidades y transmite
texto en mayúsculas y minúsculas.

— *Telefax:* es un servicio de "correo electrónico"
para transmitir documentos de formato A4 o menor,
de un sistema facsímil a otro a través de la red telefónica con commutación.

— *La red digital integrada (RDI):* se emplea para
acceder a bancos de datos, transferir dinero y otras
comunicaciones hombre-máquina. Manipula señales digitales usando módems y técnicas de conmutación de paquetes.

— *Videotex:* es un servicio interactivo de recuperación de datos que emplea un receptor de TV ligeramente modificado y la línea telefónica normal. El
sistema se basa en un computador central que almacena información con posibilidades de vincularlo
a otros centros videotex o computadores externos
para obtener la información solicitada. Se usa para
telecompra, telebanca, obtención de información
como números telefónicos y horarios de trenes,
transmisión de mensajes, etc.

— *Teletexto o cabletexto:* es un sistema de radiodifusión (unidireccional) para la transmisión de un
limitado número de páginas por estaciones de TV,
con sus emisiones de programas a través de líneas no
usadas en una señal video normal. Una unidad de
decodificación especial en los receptores domésticos
permite la selección y presentación en pantalla.

Además, hay muchos otros sistemas de control
remoto, como las alarmas unidireccionales o bidireccionales, control de energía, identificación de
averías y corrección de procesos industriales de centrales telefónicas y otros sistemas complejos.

Estos sistemas se mejoran constantemente para
facilitar su uso, hacerlos más compatibles y genera-
lizarlos en mayor grado en el mundo entero. Por
ejemplo, se está desarrollando un teletex de segunda
generación para transmitir material alfanumérico y
pictográfico. Otro sistema, conocido como Datafax,
es un servicio de facsímil digital de gran velocidad
por redes públicas para datos, que comprende la
corrección de errores y el funcionamiento automático. Están en marcha otras novedades, todas ellas
destinadas a ampliar el uso de las telecomunicaciones, haciéndolas más accesibles y seguras y facilitando su funcionamiento. En el recuadro se muestra
la manera de integrar estos servicios en terminales y
en un sistema global.

□

TERMINALS

	TELEPHONE	VIDEO DISPLAY	FACSIMILE	PRINTER	KEYBOARD	OTHERS

THE POWER OF TELECOMMUNICATIONS FOR ECONOMIC AND SOCIAL DEVELOPMENT

PEOPLES AND GOVERNMENTS, regardless of their stage of development, have become increasingly aware of the important role played by telecommunications. They are the basic pre-requisite to social and economic progress and an essential part of the infrastructure of administration.

The power of telecommunications for economic and social development has been evaluated many times in recent years. Voluminous reports have been prepared — by companies in the communications industry, such as AT&T, ITT, Siemens and others; by international organizations concerned with development aid — the World Bank, OECD, the United Nations — and by the ITU itself. The principal studies deal with the contribution of telecommunications to broad macroeconomic development, to the specific needs of rural areas and to the needs of industries and services.

Some good correlations exist between the development of national communication systems and the wealth of nations expressed in terms of GNP (Gross National Product). Telecommunications are a major contributing factor to economic growth and industrial expansion, but are also a consequence of expansion. In the complexity of modern times they have become a means to efficient management. Most important, however, is the finding that the development of communications networks is a pre-requisite of social and economic progress.

The evidence so far accumulated from the studies undertaken confirms the intuitive perception of many planners and development experts about the vital importance of telecommunications in the development process. The most widely pursued line of micro-economic research has been correlation studies which have established that there is an orderly

▷ 40

LES PEUPLES ET LES ETATS, quelque soit le stade de développement atteint, ont progressivement pris conscience de l'importance des télécommunications dans la gestion administrative, politique et industrielle des pays. Ces moyens sont à la fois le préalable et le fondement de tout progrès économique et social en général, et une partie essentielle de l'infrastructure de l'administration.

Le pouvoir des télécommunications dans le développement économique et social a souvent été le sujet de recherches approfondies. Des rapports volumineux ont été élaborés à ce sujet par des entreprises de l'industrie des télécommunications, telles que AT&T, ITT, Siemens et d'autres, ainsi que par des organisations internationales responsables de l'aide au développement dans ce domaine : notamment la Banque mondiale, l'OCDE, les Nations Unies et l'UIT elle-même. Les principales études traitent de la contribution des télécommunications au développement économique dans son ensemble, aussi bien qu'à la satisfaction des besoins spécifiques des régions rurales, des industries et des services publics.

Il existe une assez bonne corrélation entre le développement des systèmes nationaux de télécommunications et la richesse des pays exprimée en PNB (Produit National Brut). Les télécommunications constituent un important facteur de croissance économique et industrielle mais elles sont en même temps une conséquence de cette expansion. Il importe donc de considérer que l'amélioration des réseaux existants ainsi que la planification et la mise en place de nouveaux réseaux sont des préalables indispensables au progrès social et économique.

De nombreuses études récentes, réalisées dans des pays industrialisés ainsi que dans des pays en développement, ont amplement confirmé la perception intuitive des experts en matière de planification et de développement économique, à savoir : l'existence

▷ 40

LOS PUEBLOS Y LOS GOBIERNOS, más o menos desarrollados, son cada vez más conscientes del importante papel que desempeñan las telecomunicaciones. Estas son la base del progreso social y económico en general, un requisito previo de él, y una parte esencial de la infraestructura de la administración.

La contribución aportada por las telecomunicaciones al desarrollo económico y social se ha evaluado mucho en los ultimos años. Empresas de la industria de comunicaciones, como AT&T, ITT, Siemens y otras organizaciones internacionales interesadas en la ayuda y la inversión para el desarrollo, como el Banco Mundial, la OCDE, las Naciones Unidas y la propia UIT, han preparado voluminosos informes. Los principales estudios tratan de la contribución de las telecomunicaciones a un amplio desarrollo macro-económico, y de las necesidades de las zonas rurales y de las industrias y servicios.

Existe una buena correlación entre el desarrollo de sistemas nacionales de comunicación y la riqueza de las naciones, expresada en términos de PNB (producto nacional bruto). Las telecomunicaciones son uno de los principales factores que contribuyen al crecimiento económico y a la expansión industrial, pero son también una consecuencia de la expansión. En la compleja época moderna, se han convertido en un medio indispensable para la gestión eficaz. Pero la conclusión de que el desarrollo de las redes de comunicaciones es un requisito previo del progreso social y económico es primordial. Los estudios confirman la percepción intuitiva de muchos planificadores y expertos en desarrollo sobre la vital importancia de las telecomunicaciones para el desarrollo.

La línea de investigación microeconómica más

▷ 41

Constructing the telecommunication infrastructures for the world: a must for all nations.

Construire l'infrastructure globale des télécommunications : une haute priorité pour toutes les nations.

Construcción de la infraestructura de las telecomunicaciones mundiales: una gran prioridad para todas las naciones.

relationship between economic development and telephone density. The telecommunications system grows faster than the Gross Domestic Product (GDP) in every fast-growing economy. In Brazil, for example, during a period when GDP rose in real terms at over 6% per year (1973-1977), the number of telephone exchange lines grew at the rate of 14.5%; the corresponding figure for South Korea, with a 10% annual growth in GDP, was 19.1%.

The low density of telephone networks in developing countries is due to two major causes: one is the relatively high cost of building a network in rural areas, the other is a tendency of national planners and international financial aid agencies to concentrate on other infrastructures and services. This is despite the fact that investment in telecommunications is associated with high financial rates of return. For example, World Bank telecommunications projects are expected to yield returns of between 15% and 35% on the capital invested.

Investment in telecommunications suffers because the benefits are intangible, and may even appear inappropriate where living standards are low, whereas they are capital hungry, need scarce foreign exchange and depend to a major extent on imports of equipment, skilled engineers, experienced managers, technicians and other specialists. Critics of telecommunications argue further that their concentration in urban areas accelerates migration into towns and so adds to the social and administrative problems. On the other hand, a widely dispersed, freely available, telecommunications network reduces the economic advantage of the cities relative to rural areas. This has been demonstrated in North America and the USSR.

Studies conducted in the Soviet Union in the 1970s on the developmental effect of telecommunications concluded that "the 'value' of telecommunications in an economic system greatly exceeded the sum total of revenues accruing to the national telecommunications authority". One of the researchers, B.A. Voronov: *The Consumption of Communications Output*, Vestnik Sviazi, No.8, 1969, suggested that national planners allocating investment priorities should evaluate the contribution of telecommunications to increases in GDP, industrial output and the quality of life. Otherwise underinvestment will result. Other studies deal with income generating effect and savings in various directions; a survey of 57 industrial enterprises and 21 construction units showed that the availability of trunk telephone services cut expenditure on travel by 7 to 10 per cent, and reduced the idle time of transportation equipment by 10 per cent.

A research program conducted by M.A. Gorelik of the Moscow Institute (M.A. Gorelik & I.B. Efimova: *The Economic Efficiency of Development of Long Distance Telephone Communication*, Vestnik Sviazi, No.5, 1977) established that the 'benefits' of the trunk telephone were approximately 4.3 times higher than its costs. His findings were similar to those of Andrew Hardy's studies of 15 industrialized and 37 developing countries (A.P. Hardy: *The Role of the Telephone in Economic Development*, Institute of Communication Research, Stanford University, Jan. 1980), and close to Edwin Parker's estimate in his study of rural telecommunications in the USA (E. Parker: *Economic and Social Benefit from the REA Telephone Loan Program*, Equatorial Communications, Stanford University, March 1981). Parker found that 'benefits' were 6 to 7 times higher than the cost to the government and that the REA Telephone Loan Program was a net contributor to the Federal Treasury. The conclusion of this considerable body of internationally conducted research is that the development of telecommunications has a highly positive effect on the overall process of economic and social development.

Studies of the utilization of telecommunications services by specific industries, conducted mainly in Africa, Latin America, the Middle East, the USA and the USSR, produced positive evidence of their value. In agriculture it ensured the efficient co-ordination of production and marketing. Examples of this are given in

▷ 44

d'une corrélation directe entre le développement économique et la densité téléphonique. La recherche micro-économique consiste le plus souvent en études de corrélation, lesquelles ont établi que dans la plupart des économies à croissance rapide, le réseau de télécommunications se développe plus rapidement que le PNB. Au Brésil, par exemple, pendant une période au cours de laquelle le PNB a augmenté en valeur réelle de plus de 6% par an (1973-1977), le nombre des lignes de centraux téléphoniques a augmenté annuellement de 14,5% ; pour la Corée du Sud, les chiffres correspondants ont été de plus de 10% pour l'augmentation annuelle du PNB et 19,1% pour l'augmentation de la densité téléphonique.

La faible densité des réseaux téléphoniques dans les pays en développement est due à deux causes essentielles : le coût élevé des installations dans les zones rurales et le faible revenu en provenant, ainsi que la tendance des planificateurs nationaux et des institutions internationales à donner priorité à d'autres infrastructures. Et ceci malgré le fait que les investissements dans les télécommunications ont un rendement relativement élevé. Par exemple, la Banque Mondiale compte obtenir un rendement de 15 à 35 % sur ses investissements dans ce secteur.

Les investissements dans le domaine des télécommunications pâtissent de l'impossibilité d'en percevoir les bénéfices dans les pays où le niveau de vie est très bas, non seulement en raison de la pénurie de capitaux et de devises mais aussi parce que la réalisation des projets dépend en grande partie de l'importation de matériel et de la disponibilité de services d'ingénieurs spécialisés, de gestionnaires expérimentés, de techniciens et d'experts recrutés à l'étranger. Les critiques de la télécommunication soulignent le fait que la concentration des moyens de télécommunications dans les zones urbaines favorise les mouvements de migration vers les villes et aggrave du même coup les problèmes sociaux et administratifs. Par contre, plusieurs évaluations des bénéfices, directs et indirects, qui découlent de l'utilisation du téléphone dans les zones rurales ont établi un bilan très positif.

Des études faites en Union Soviétique pendant les années 1970 ont montré que « dans tout système économique, la valeur des télécommunications dépasse largement la somme totale des recettes qui reviennent à l'autorité nationale responsable de la gestion des dites télécommunications ». Dans une étude sur la « *Consommation en produits et services de télécommunications* » (Vestnik Sviazi, No 8 1969), B.A. Voronov suggère que pour pouvoir établir des priorités en matière d'investissements, il faut évaluer dans quelle mesure les télécommunications contribuent à l'augmentation du PNB, à la production industrielle et à l'élévation du niveau de vie. Une étude portant sur 57 entreprises industrielles et 21 chantiers de construction a montré que la disponibilité de services téléphoniques interurbains permettait de réduire les frais de voyage de 7 à 10% et le temps improductif des équipements de transport de 10%.

Un programme de recherche sur l'efficacité économique des communications téléphoniques interurbaines mené par M. A. Gorelik de l'Institut de Moscou (cf. M.A. Gorelik et I.B. Efimova : « *Le rendement économique du développement des communications téléphoniques à longue distance* » dans Vestnik Sviazi, No 5, 1977) a permis d'établir que les « bénéfices » des lignes interurbaines étaient approximativement 4,3 fois plus élevés que leur coût. Andrew Hardy est parvenu aux mêmes conclusions dans son étude sur 15 pays industrialisés et 37 pays en développement (cf. A.P. Hardy : « *The Role of the Telephone in Economic Development* », Institute of Communication Research, Stanford University, janvier 1980) ; ainsi qu'Edwin Parker dans son étude des télécommunications rurales aux Etats-Unis (Cf. E. Parker : « *Economic and Social Benefit from the REA Telephone Loan Program* », Equatorial Communications, Stanford University, mars 1981), Edwin Parker a trouvé que les « bénéfices » étaient de 6 à 7 fois supérieurs au prix de revient pour le gouvernement et que le REA Telephone Loan Program rapportait de l'argent à l'Etat.

▷ 44

CORRELATIO
AND GNP PE

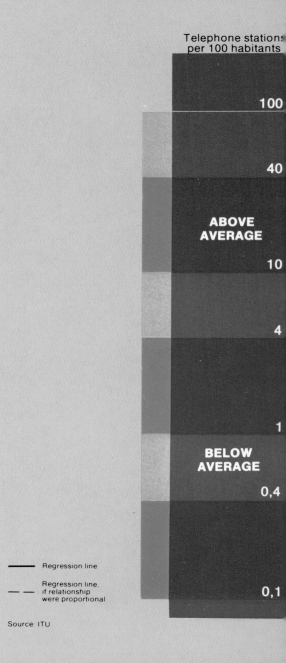

Telephone stations per 100 habitants

100
40
ABOVE AVERAGE
10
4
1
BELOW AVERAGE
0,4
0,1

—— Regression line

— — Regression line, if relationship were proportional

Source: ITU

Studies in 15 industrialized countries and 37 developing countries to relate the number of telephones and the GNP per capita over 14 years, using regression analysis with time lags and including other related variables such as number of radios and energy consumption per capita, indicate that the telephone leads development and development leads the telephone. One-way radio does not have the same effect.

This is true of all countries but the effect of telephones, especially residential telephones, is greater in developing than in industrialized countries where the marginal utility of extra telephones is small. If the greatest benefits occur in low income countries. The greatest benefits within those countries may arise in their least developed regions. It brings people closer together, however physically distant they may be, and in so doing attenuates the feeling of isolation and gives them an opportunity to consult in the pursuit of common objectives.

ETWEEN TELEPHONE DENSITIES
APITA FOR SELECTED COUNTRIES

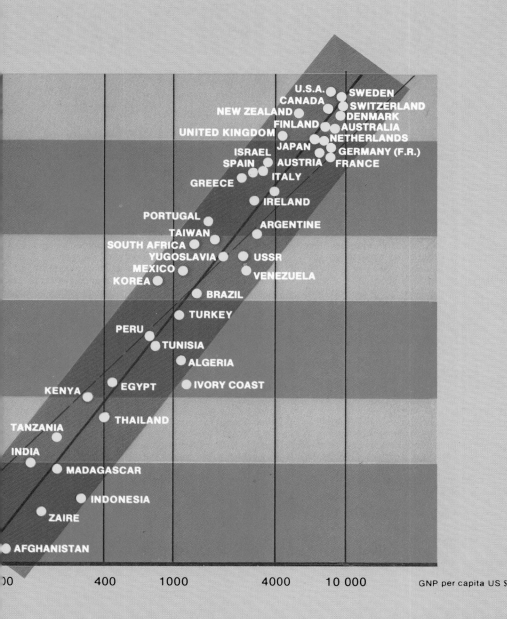

400   1000   4000   10 000   GNP per capita US $

s études ont été faites dans 15 pays industrialisés et 37 pays développement, en vue d'établir le rapport qui existe entre le mbre des appareils téléphoniques et le PNB par habitant, sur ans, à l'aide d'analyses de régression, compte tenu de erses variables. Ces études montrent que le téléphone endre le développement et que le développement provoque ssor du téléphone.

Cela est vrai pour tous les pays. Toutefois, le téléphone — rticulièrement le téléphone à domicile — a une influence plus ande dans les pays en développement que dans les pays lustrialisés. Si les pays à faibles ressources sont ceux qui ent le meilleur profit de la téléphonie, celle-ci exerce l'inence la plus bénéfique dans les régions les moins dévepées de ces pays. En effet, le téléphone rapproche les gens et ènue l'impression d'isolement et leur offre la possibilité de se nsulter dans la poursuite d'objectifs communs.

Los estudios realizados en 15 países industrializados y 37 en desarrollo para relacionar el número de teléfonos y el PNB per capita durante 14 años, utilizando análisis de regresión con diferencias de tiempo e incluyendo otras variables pertinentes, como el número de radios y el consumo de energía per capita, indican que el teléfono lleva al desarrollo, y el desarrollo al teléfono. La radio unidireccional no surte el mismo efecto.

Esto es así en todos los países, pero el efecto de los teléfonos, sobre todo los particulares, es mayor en los países en desarrollo que en los industrializados, donde la utilidad marginal de teléfonos adicionales es pequeña. Si bien los mayores beneficios se producen en países de bajos ingresos, esos mismos beneficios pueden darse en sus regiones menos desarrolladas. Acercan más a las personas, por distantes que puedan estar físicamente, atenuando así la sensación de aislamiento y ofreciéndoles la oportunidad de consultar en la persecución de objetivos comunes.

seguida son los estudios de correlación, que han establecido la existencia de una ordenada relación entre el desarrollo económico y la densidad de teléfonos. El sistema de telecomunicaciones crece con más rapidez que el producto interior bruto (PIB) en todas las economías en rápida expansión. En Brasil, por ejemplo, durante un período en el que el PIB aumentó en términos reales en más de un 6% anual (1937-1977), el número de líneas de centrales telefónicas creció en una proporción del 14,5%; la cifra correspondiente a Corea del Sur, con un crecimiento del PIB anual del 10%, fue del 19,1%.

La baja densidad de redes en los países en desarrollo se debe a dos causas principales: una, el elevado costo de construir una red en zonas rurales; la otra, la tendencia de los planificadores nacionales y de los organismos internacionales de ayuda financiera a concentrarse en otras infraestructuras y servicios. Y ello a pesar de que la inversión en telecomunicaciones se vincula a un elevado rendimiento financiero; p. e., se espera que los proyectos de telecomunicaciones del Banco Mundial produzcan entre el 15 y el 35% del capital invertido.

La inversión en telecomunicaciones padece de la intangibilidad de los beneficios, y puede incluso parecer inapropiada cuando los niveles de vida son bajos, en tanto que requiere mucho capital y divisas extranjeras, que escasean, y depende en gran medida de equipo, ingenieros especializados, directores experimentados, técnicos y otros especialistas del extranjero. Quienes critican las telecomunicaciones aducen además que su concentración en zonas urbanas acelera la migración a las ciudades, lo que agudiza los problemas sociales y administrativos. Por un lado, una red de telecomunicaciones muy dispersa y de libre disposición reduce la ventaja económica de las ciudades con relación a las zonas rurales. Así se ha demostrado en América del Norte y la URSS.

En estudios realizados en la Unión Soviética en los años 1970 sobre el efecto del desarrollo de las telecomunicaciones se concluye que «su "valor" en un sistema económico rebasa mucho la suma de los ingresos de la autoridad nacional de telecomunicaciones ». Uno de los investigadores, B. A. Voronov: *The Consumption of Communications Output*, Vestnik Sviazi, N. 8, 1969, sugirió que los planificadores nacionales, al atribuir las prioridades de inversión, deben evaluar la contribución de las telecomunicaciones al aumento del PIB, la producción industrial y el mejoramiento de la calidad de la vida. Otros estudios tratan del efecto generador de ingresos y de las variaciones en diversos sentidos; según un estudio, de 57 empresas industriales y 21 unidades de construcción, la disponibilidad de servicios telefónicos interurbanos reduce los gastos de viajes del 7 al 10%, y el tiempo desocupado del equipo de transporte en un 10%.

Un programa de investigación dirigido por M. S. Gorelik, del Instituto de Moscú (M. A. Gorelik & I. B. Efimova: *The Economic Efficiency of Development of Long Distance Telephone Communication*, Vestnik Sviazi, N° 5, 1977) establece que los "beneficios" del teléfono interurbano eran aproximadamente 4,3 veces superiores a sus costos. Sus conclusiones eran análogas a las de los estudios de Andrew Hardy sobre 15 países industrializados y 37 en desarrollo (A. P. Hardy: *The Role of the Telephone in Economic Development*, Institute of Communication Research, Stanford University, enero de 1980), y se acercaban a la estimación hecha por Edwin Parker en su estudio sobre telecomunicaciones rurales en EE.UU. (E. Parker: *Economic and Social Benefit from the REA Telephone Loan Program*, Equatorial Communications, Stanford University, marzo de 1981). Parker observó que los "beneficios" eran 6 ó 7 veces más altos que el costo para el gobierno, y que el programa de préstamo telefónico REA era un contribuyente neto a la Tesorería Federal. La conclusión es que el desarrollo de las telecomunicaciones influye muy positivamente en el proceso global de desarrollo económico y social.

▷ 45

IMMEASURABLE BENEFITS ALL AROUND

Studies carried out in recent years quantified the benefits derived from telecommunications in various economic and social sectors. A major ITU-OECD project undertaken in 1981/82 supports view that telecommunications are indeed both an extremely profitable investment and a key element in the development of trade and industry.

In the industrialized countries, increases in the stocks and transfer of knowledge, and improvements in data and information processing have played an important part in the high rates of economic growth. In developing countries, and in the rural areas of large industrialized countries the role of the telephone in economic development is even more important than in centers of high industrial activity. Taken together, all of the evidence points to a major contribution of telecommunications to national development.

Au cours de ces dernières années, plusieurs études ont été entreprises pour quantifier les avantages découlant de l'utilisation des télécommunications. Une grande étude UIT-OCDE (1981-1982) confirme péremptoirement que les télécommunications sont un investissement extrêmement profitable et un facteur essentiel de développement du commerce et de l'industrie.

Dans les pays industrialisés, l'augmentation des stocks et le transfert des connaissances, ainsi que les améliorations réalisées dans le traitement des données et de l'information ont joué un rôle important dans l'accélération de la croissance économique qui s'est produite depuis le début des années 1950. Dans les pays en développement et dans les régions rurales des grands pays industrialisés, tels que les Etats-Unis et l'URSS, le rôle du téléphone dans le développement économique est même plus important que dans les centres industrialisés.

En los últimos años se han realizado estudios para cuantificar los beneficios derivados de las telecomunicaciones en varios sectores de actividad económica y social. Un importante proyecto UIT-OCDE confirma la opinión de que las telecomunicaciones son una inversión muy rentable y un elemento fundamental del desarrollo del comercio y de la industria.

En los países industrializados, los aumentos de existencias y transferencias de conocimientos, y las mejoras en el procesamiento de datos y de información, han desempeñado un importante papel en los elevados índices de crecimiento económico registrados desde los primeros años cincuenta. En los países en desarrollo, y en las zonas rurales de grandes Estados industrializados, como EE.UU. y la URSS, el papel del teléfono en el desarrollo económico es aún más importante que en centros de fuerte actividad industrial.

OPTIMIZING THE USE OF SCARCE RESOURCES

A study from the Soviet Union reported on the benefits from the use of telephone and mobile radio to improve the shared use of agricultural machinery in 60 farms in the Rostov area. Compared to the use of machinery on single farms the communications allowed a reduction of idle machine time by a factor of two to three, an improvement in the productivity of tractors by 20 to 25 per cent, a reduction of machine time spent in transit between working locations of 30 to 40 per cent and a 5 to 10 per cent increase in overall productivity.

A similar example is found in improving livestock breeding and agricultural practices, ensuring that veterinarians are to hand when required, that timely countermeasures are taken collectively against diseases and insect pests, that the ordering and delivery of essential supplies are timed and co-ordinated.

Une étude faite en Union Soviétique fait état des avantages du téléphone et des radiocommunications mobiles pour améliorer l'utilisation en coopérative de machines agricoles dans 60 fermes de la région de Rostov. En contraste avec le taux d'emploi sur ferme unique, le temps mort des machines fut réduit par un facteur de 2 ou 3, le rendement des tracteurs amélioré de 25%, la durée des déplacements des engins entre lieux de travail diminué de 30 à 40% et la productivité générale augmentée de 5 à 10%.

L'emploi de moyens de communications modernes a également porté ses fruits dans l'élevage du bétail et les méthodes agricoles. Grâce aux systèmes d'appel par radio portative et au téléphone, des vétérinaires sont toujours disponibles et d'importants progrès ont été réalisés dans la lutte contre les épizooties et les parasites des plantes.

En un estudio de la Unión Soviética se muestran los beneficios obtenidos del uso del teléfono y de las radiocomunicaciones móviles para mejorar el empleo en común de maquinaria agrícola en 60 granjas de la zona de Rostov. En comparación con el uso individual, las telecomunicaciones permitieron reducir el tiempo ocioso de la máquinas en un factor de dos a tres, mejorar la productividad de los tractores en un 20-25%, reducir el tiempo de tránsito de las máquinas entre lugares de trabajo en un 30-40%, y aumentar la productividad global en un 5-10%.

Un ejemplo análogo es el mejoramiento de los métodos agropecuarios, disponiendo de veterinarios cuando se necesitan, adoptando oportunamente medidas colectivas para combatir las enfermedades y las plagas de insectos, y coordinando la solicitud y entrega de suministros esenciales en el momento adecuado.

PLANNING AND CONTROLLING PRODUCTION

The development of an effective telecommunications network and the advances of recent years in the technology of remote monitoring and control of machines and processes are contributing powerfully to productivity at all stages of a country's industrial development.

Good communications are not only a means of saving management travel time and enabling factories and offices to operate efficiently in apparent isolation. They are an essential basis for the automation of machinery, the control of processes, the optimization of inventory levels, the co-ordination of management functions and, increasingly, a decision-aiding tool used in defining strategies and operation modes.

On-line access in real time, audio and visual, to information on all major aspects of manufacturing, with a facility for historical recall, has become a major asset of management in the eighties and is a likely standard for the 21st Century.

Le développement d'un réseau efficace de télécommunications dans l'industrie, et en particulier des systèmes de télésurveillance et de télécommande des machines et des procédés de transformation contribue puissamment à l'amélioration de la productivité à tous les stades du développement industriel d'un pays.

Une télématique efficace est indispensable au contrôle des machines automatiques et à la surveillance des chaînes de production, à la régulation de l'approvisionnement des stocks, à la coordination des fonctions de gestion. Elle devient un auxiliaire toujours plus précieux dans la prise de décision, notamment lorsqu'elle est utilisée pour définir les stratégies et les méthodes d'exploitation.

L'accès en ligne, qui permet d'obtenir, en temps réel et sous forme audio-visuelle, tous les renseignements pertinents sur la production, deviendra un moyen de gestion industrielle indispensable au 21ème siècle.

El desarrollo de una red eficaz de telecomunicaciones y los avances tecnológicos de los últimos años en el control remoto de máquinas y procesos aumentan mucho la productividad en todas las etapas de desarrollo industrial de un país.

Las buenas comunicaciones no son sólo un medio de ahorrar tiempo de viaje para la gestión y de permitir que fábricas y oficinas operen con eficacia aparentemente aisladas. Son también una base esencial de la automatización de la maquinaria; el control de procesos, la optimación de niveles de existencias y la coordinación de funciones de gestión, y se emplean cada vez más como medios auxiliares de decisión al definir estrategias y modos de explotación.

El acceso en línea en tiempo real, audio y visual, a la información sobre todos los aspectos importantes de fabricación, con una facilidad para obtener antecedentes, se ha convertido en una gran ventaja de gestión en los años 80, y probablemente sea la norma en el siglo XXI.

AND COMMERCE

ACCESS TO MARKETS WORLDWIDE

Recent studies have demonstrated the vital contribution modern telecommunications are making to effective marketing, especially that of perishable agricultural produce.

In Mexico fruit and vegetable farmers consult by telephone to ensure that fresh tomatoes are picked and sold at the right time and that shipping is co-ordinated. In East Africa farmers have developed a telecommunications-based, highly successful, air-freighted business in flowers and soft fruit requiring a high degree of responsiveness to volatile and seasonal markets.

In the Cook Islands the opening of an airport and the adoption of an inter-island radio system led to an eightfold increase in the export of fresh fruit.

Many other instances of major contributions to agriculture by telecommunications are quoted in the studies, including co-operation in research and the sharing of experience.

De récentes études ont mis en évidence la contribution vitale des télécommunications à l'efficacité de la commercialisation, notamment celle des produits agricoles périssables.

Au Mexique, les cultivateurs se consultent par téléphone, pour que leurs tomates soient récoltées et vendues au bon moment, au meilleur prix et pour coordonner les expéditions. En Afrique orientale et centrale, les agriculteurs ont organisé un système fondé sur les télécommunications, grâce auquel l'expédition par avion des fleurs et des fruits tient compte des fluctuations de la demande.

L'ouverture d'un aéroport et la mise en service de liaisons radio dans les Iles de Cook, a eu pour résultat de multiplier par huit le volume des exportations de fruits frais. Il existe une multitude d'autres exemples de l'utilité des télécommunications dans les domaines de l'agriculture, y compris la coopération dans la recherche et le partage de l'expérience.

Estudios recientes han demostrado la vital contribución de las telecomunicaciones modernas a la comercialización eficiente, sobre todo de productos agrícolas perecederos.

En México, los agricultores de frutas y verduras consultan por teléfono para asegurarse de que los tomates frescos se recogen y venden en el momento apropiado, para coordinar los envíos. En Africa Oriental y Central, han basado sus actividades en las telecomunicaciones, para enviar por avión flores y fruta poco duradera, sumamente sensibles a mercados volubles y estacionales.

En las Islas Cook, la apertura de un aeropuerto y la adopción de un sistema de radiocomunicaciones interinsulares ha permitido multiplicar por ocho las exportaciones de fruta fresca.

Se citan muchos otros casos de importantes contribuciones de las telecomunicaciones a la agricultura, incluida la cooperación en la investigación y el intercambio de experiencia.

IMPROVING MONEY MANAGEMENT

Financial houses the world over have become the heaviest users of telecommunications services. Cash transfer, and generally the use of cash, has been greatly reduced. A range of services grouped under the label Electronic Fund Transfer (EFT) has been developed which includes not only electronic banking services but automatic credit authorization, automatic payment by telephone and electronic fund transfer across borders.

The volatility of international money markets makes the need for speed critical. EFT minimizes transfer time, thus reducing interest charges and enabling money to be put to work more quickly.

The benefits are such that no bank can now operate effectively in competition without reliable international and domestic data/text transmission services. The speed with which multinational banks have taken up electronic banking is compelling evidence of this.

Dans le monde entier, les établissements financiers sont devenus les plus gros clients des services de télécommunications. Aujourd'hui les transferts en espèces et l'utilisation de devises diminuent. Des services groupés sous la dénomination de Transfert Électronique de Fonds (TEF) ont permis d'automatiser les opérations bancaires, le contrôle des limites de crédit, le paiement par téléphone et le transfert international de fonds.

L'instabilité des marchés monétaires internationaux impose la rapidité opérationnelle. En réduisant les délais de transfert, le TEF diminue les intérêts encourus et permet un réinvestissement plus rapide des capitaux.

De nos jours, aucune banque ne peut résister efficacement à la concurrence si elle ne dispose pas de services fiables, nationaux et internationaux, de transmission de données et de textes. L'adoption de la télématique par les banques multinationales en est la preuve évidente.

Los principales usuarios de servicios de telecomunicación son ahora las instituciones financieras. La transferencia de metálico, y en general su uso, se han reducido mucho. La nueva gama de servicios Transferencia Electrónica de Fondos (TEF), no sólo abarca los servicios electrónicos bancarios, sino la concesión automática del crédito, el pago automático por teléfono y la transferencia electrónica de fondos a través de las fronteras.

Los mercados monetarios internacionales son tan volubles que la velocidad resulta mucho más crítica. La TEF minimiza el tiempo de transferencia, reduciendo así el pago de intereses y permitiendo que el dinero comience a producir antes.

Los beneficios son tales que ningún banco puede competir ahora efectivamente si no dispone de servicios internacionales y nacionales seguros de transmisión de datos y de texto. Así lo prueba el apresuramiento con que los bancos multinacionales han acogido los sistemas electrónicos.

SERVING THE PRIVATE CITIZEN AT HOME

Communications technology has only just begun to penetrate the home. It is likely that the home of the future will be equipped with a computer incorporating an interactive intelligent terminal and visual display unit, for the transmission and capture of information. On top of this will be 3 major sub-systems:
— a home control sub-system, designed to ensure security and to control a variety of equipment such as heating and air conditioning;
— a home living sub-system with game and educational functions, and facilities for medical consultation, banking, reservations and shopping;
— a home work sub-system with high-speed information and data communication and processing functions, including on-line access to files at office and factory, and facilities to participate in meetings from home.

La télématique commence seulement à pénétrer chez les particuliers. Il est probable que, dans l'avenir, chaque foyer sera équipé d'un ordinateur avec son terminal interactif programmable, à écran de visualisation. Ce système domestique comprendra trois sous-systèmes principaux :
— un sous-système conçu pour assurer la sécurité et surveiller le fonctionnement de toutes sortes d'équipements domestiques (chauffage, climatisation, etc.) ;
— un sous-système personnel pour l'étude et les loisirs, permettant d'effectuer à distance des consultations médicales, des opérations bancaires, des réservations et des achats ;
— un sous-système de travail offrant notamment les moyens d'accès à des dossiers ou fichiers se trouvant dans des bureaux et des usines, ainsi que les facilités nécessaires pour participer à des téléconférences.

La tecnología de las comunicaciones comienza a penetrar en el hogar. Probablemente el hogar del futuro estará provisto de un computador con un terminal inteligente interactivo y un visualizador, para la transmisión y captura de información. Además de este sistema doméstico, habrá 3 subsistemas principales:
— un subsistema de control, para garantizar la seguridad y controlar una variedad de equipo, como la calefacción y el acondicionamiento de aire;
— un subsistema con funciones educativas y recreativas, y facilidades para consulta médica, banca, reservas y compras;
— un subsistema de trabajo con funciones de información, comunicación y procesamiento de datos a gran velocidad, incluido el acceso en línea a ficheros de oficinas y fábricas, y facilidades para participar en reuniones desde el hogar.

the Boxes on p. 42. The use of the telephone and mobile radio improves the utilization of agricultural machinery. Other uses include the efficient sharing of scarce services such as veterinarians, timely action against epidemics, etc.

In due course farmers will be able to access information needed to optimize the selection of crops, livestock, equipment, and guidance on how to apply new methods and practices effectively, to access weather forecasts, market prices, cost of transport and insurance, availability of labour for seasonal operations, and a wide variety of reports on farming tailored to their needs.

Studies of the contribution of telecommunications in the planning and operation of transport, the scheduling and monitoring of production processes, the management of money, training and education, and in government, have produced positive and encouraging findings. There is no doubt that the greater complexity of management tasks, the more essential effective telecommunications have become.

This is a chicken-and-egg situation, but whether a cause or an effect, the development of telecommunications and especially of computerized communications is present in all situations of development and progress. They should not, however, be looked upon as a substitution for other services; better communications within a society contribute, albeit indirectly, to increases in the demand for other services, such as transportation, health, education, simply by making them more readily available and more obviously useful — just as a new highway generates additional traffic.

The social impacts of telecommunications development are difficult to measure. This becomes even more complex when one tries to look at interactions between communications and broad social phenomena such as migration from the rural areas to the cities, participation in national development or in the process of technical and political change. It is practically impossible to measure the effects on complex social phenomena of this nature, or even to identify the causal relationships that exist between them. The only certainty is that effects there are.

One of the most promising lines of research suggested by the literature is to focus on what might be called "social intelligence". Communications in general, and telecommunications in particular, are one of the major systems through which a society transfers and uses information. This system has characteristics in common with the human brain and the communications networks within the human nervous system. In this perspective, telecommunications might be viewed not simply as one technology among many others, but as the neural system of society. The "intelligence" of the individual does not depend on the "size" of the brain, but on the richness and intensity of the connections between neurons.

If we accept this analogy between the intelligence of the individual and the "intelligence" of a society, it follows that telecommunications probably deserve much more attention on the part of policy makers than they have received until now. It is demonstrably wasteful to build some elements of a total infrastructure without complementary developments in the telecommunication network.

Throughout history the expansion of knowledge has been the foundation of all progress. The rate at which knowledge has expanded, never so high as at present, is closely related to the ease and effectiveness of communications between people, both within nations and across frontiers. The dynamics of progress, whether rooted in the thought processes of engineers and scientists: "technology-push", or in the needs of users of products or services: "market-pull", are vitally affected by the effectiveness of communications.

Les études sur l'utilisation des services de télécommunications effectuées par différentes industries, principalement en Afrique, en Amérique latine, au Moyen Orient, aux Etats-Unis et en URSS, ont apporté la preuve évidente de la valeur de tels services. En agriculture, les télécommunications assurent une coordination efficace de la production et de la commercialisation : les exportateurs mexicains de fruits et de légumes utilisent le téléphone pour déterminer le moment d'expédition vers le Etats-Unis et le lieu de destination des fruits frais, et pour fixer les prix. Une coordination analogue existe au Kenya et en Zambie. En URSS, grâce à l'utilisation du téléphone et du radiotéléphone mobile, il a notamment été possible de rationaliser l'exploitation des machines agricoles, et de lutter avec succès contre les épizooties et les maladies des plantes.

Bientôt, les agriculteurs pourront avoir accès à l'information nécessaire pour choisir judicieusement leurs semences, leur bétail et leurs équipements. Par la simple manipulation d'un clavier, ils obtiendront tous les renseignements utiles sur la météorologie, les prix du marché, le coût des transports et les primes d'assurance, la disponibilité de la main-d'œuvre saisonnière et sur les méthodes agricoles adaptées à leurs besoins.

En ce qui concerne la contribution des télécommunications dans la planification et l'exploitation des transports, l'organisation et la surveillance de la production, la gestion financière, la formation professionnelle, l'éducation, aussi bien que dans l'exercice des fonctions gouvernementales, les études ont abouti à des conclusions positives et encourageantes.

Les études ont démontré qu'il y a généralement concomitance entre le développement des télécommunications et le développement économique et social. Toutefois, il ne faut jamais considérer que les télécommunications peuvent remplacer certains services. Bien au contraire, dans toute société l'amélioration des communications contribue, bien qu'indirectement, à l'augmentation de la demande d'autres services tout comme l'ouverture d'une nouvelle autoroute engendre un trafic supplémentaire.

Les répercussions sociales des télécommunications sont plus difficiles à apprécier lorsqu'on cherche à étudier les interactions entre les communications et les grands phénomènes sociaux tels que la migration des populations rurales vers les villes, la participation au développement national, ou l'évolution technique et politique. Il est pratiquement impossible de quantifier les effets des télécommunications sur les phénomènes sociaux de cette nature ou d'identifier la relation causale qui existe entre eux. La seule certitude est que ces effets existent.

L'une des options de recherche les plus prometteuses serait de se concentrer sur ce qu'on peut appeler l'« intelligence de la société ».

On peut trouver des ressemblances entre les centres de télécommunications et le cerveau humain, et faire des rapprochements entre un réseau de télécommunications et le système nerveux de la société. L'« intelligence » de l'individu ne dépend pas de la « dimension » de son cerveau mais de la richesse et de la densité des connexions entre les neurones. Si nous acceptons cette analogie entre l'intelligence de l'individu et l'« intelligence » d'une société, il nous faut également admettre que les télécommunications méritent beaucoup plus d'attention que ne leur en ont accordé jusqu'ici les gouvernements concernés. On peut en effet prouver qu'il est vain de se borner à établir seulement quelques éléments d'une infrastructure nationale, en négligeant les compléments indispensables à l'efficacité d'un réseau de télécommunication.

Dans l'histoire de la civilisation, la rapidité avec laquelle la connaissance se répand n'a jamais été aussi élevée que de nos jours. Son accélération est étroitement liée à la disponibilité et à la qualité des communications. Que la dynamique du progrès se manifeste comme une « poussée technologique » ou qu'elle résulte des besoins des usagers en produits et services, et qu'elle se traduise alors par une « demande du marché », elle dépend essentiellement de l'efficacité des communications.

□   □

APPLYING ADVAN
PROCESS: A N

The application of advanced technologies to the learning process is opening a completely new era in education and training. It is changing how the world learns. Television, audio-visual tapes and discs, cable and satellite transmission, the telephone and the computer, integrated into national and international networks of learning centers, will make education and training more readily and more widely available, at a much lower cost. This is becoming accepted as the only practical way to make significant progress in overcoming the growing constraints on the quality, accessibility and availability of curricula.

One of the currently available methods is the PLATO system of computer-based education (CBE) developed by the Control Data Corporation. PLATO is computer-controlled and the main method of delivery is computer-aided instruction with integrated terminal subsystems which include video discs, audio input and output, and touch input.

Structured computer conferences of up to 40 students can be held, or a single student can interact with another student or instructor as desired, with all the valued advantages of individualized learning. Computer-aided instruction (CAI) is beginning to supply a most vital requirement in industry, commerce and the professions. Expenditure for training in industry is vast — estimated at $100 billion annually in the USA in the late seventies — and there is therefore a considerable potential for the use of CAI. It has already reached the stage where it is cost-effective for many types of employee training.

In the USA, the Carnegie-Mellon University decided in 1982 — the first in the world — to make the computer standard equipment for its students. A network of personal computers will be installed throughout its Pittsburgh campus. When the system is fully used in 1986 students will be expected to buy their own computers, just as they now buy books. Graduating students will be able to take their computer terminals with them and plug into the Carnegie-Mellon system from anywhere.

There is little doubt that CBE and CAI will transform the approaches to education and training throughout the world, and considerably raise standards. All of this during the next two or three decades when one would expect illiteracy to fall and the technical competence of the younger generations to rise.

G TECHNOLOGIES TO THE LEARNING
ERA IN EDUCATION AND TRAINING

ruption des techniques de pointe dans la méthodologie de ude ouvre une ère absolument nouvelle pour l'enseignement a formation professionnelle. La manière d'apprendre est en n de changer dans le monde entier. La télévision, les enre- trements audio-visuels sur bande et sur disque, les trans- sions par câble et par satellite, le téléphone et l'ordinateur, s ces moyens intégrés dans des réseaux de centres péda- iques vont rendre l'enseignement et la formation profes- nnelle plus directement et plus largement accessibles, à des x très inférieurs à ceux qui se pratiquent actuellement.

La aplicación de tecnologías avanzadas al proceso de aprendi- zaje abre una era totalmente nueva en la educación y la formación, cambiando la manera de aprender. La televisión, las cintas y discos audiovisuales, la transmisión por cable y saté- lite, el teléfono y el computador, integrados en redes nacionales e internacionales de centros de aprendizaje, permitirán dispo- ner antes y mejor de la educación y de la formación, a un costo mucho menor. Esto se acepta ya como la única forma práctica de resolver los problemas para satisfacer las crecientes exi- gencias de calidad, acceso y disponibilidad de la enseñanza.

Los estudios sobre el uso de los servicios de telecomunicaciones por industrias específicas, realizados principalmente en Africa, América Latina, Oriente Medio, EE.UU. y la URSS ofrecen pruebas positivas de su valor. En los recuadros de la pág. 42 se dan ejemplos. El empleo del teléfono y las radiotelecomunicaciones móviles ha mejorado mucho la utilización de la maquinaria agrícola. Entre otros usos cabe citar la distribución eficaz de servicios escasos, como veterinarios, la ac- ción oportuna contra las epidemias, etc.

Algún día los agricultores dispondrán de la infor- mación necesaria para optimar la selección de cose- chas, ganado, equipo, y orientaciones sobre la ma- nera de aplicar eficazmente nuevos métodos y prác- ticas para acceder a previsiones meteorológicas, precios de mercado, costos de transporte y seguros, etc., y a una amplia variedad de información agrícola adaptada a sus necesidades.

Los estudios de la contribución de las telecomu- nicaciones a la planificación y explotación del transporte, la programación y verificación de los procesos de producción, la gestión monetaria, la formación y la gestión gubernamental han produci- do resultados positivos y alentadores. Cuanto más complejas son las tareas de gestión, más esenciales y eficaces resultan las telecomunicaciones.

Es el caso del huevo y la gallina, pero ya se trate de causa o efecto el desarrollo de las telecomunicacio- nes, y especialmente de las computadorizadas, se encuentra en todas las situaciones de evolución y progreso. Sin embargo, no ha de considerarse como una sustitución de otros servicios; las mejores co- municaciones en una sociedad contribuyen, aunque sea indirectamente, a aumentar la demanda de otros servicios, como transporte, salud, educación, facili- tando el acceso a ellos y haciéndolos más útiles, lo mismo que una nueva autopista genera más tráfico.

Es difícil evaluar el impacto social de las telecomunicaciones, labor aún más compleja cuando se trata de conside- rar la interacción entre las comunicaciones y amplios fenómenos sociales, como la migración de las zonas rurales a las ciudades, la participación en el desa- rrollo nacional o el proceso del cambio técnico y político. Es prácticamente imposible medir los efec- tos de las telecomunicaciones sobre fenómenos so- ciales complejos de esta índole, e incluso identificar la relación causal que existe entre ellos. Lo único seguro son los efectos.

Una de las líneas de investigación más promete- doras sugeridas por la literatura es lo que puede denominarse "inteligencia social". Las comunica- ciones en general, y las telecomunicaciones en parti- cular, son uno de los principales sistemas de que se sirve una sociedad para transferir y utilizar la infor- mación. Tal sistema tiene muchas características en común con el cerebro humano y las redes de comu- nicación del organismo. Las telecomunicaciones pueden considerarse no sólo como una tecnología más entre las muchas existentes, sino como el sistema neural de la sociedad. La "inteligencia" del indivi- duo no depende del 'tamaño' del cerebro, sino de la riqueza e intensidad de las conexiones entre neuro- nes.

Si aceptamos esta analogía entre inteligencia del individuo e "inteligencia" de una sociedad, llegare- mos a la conclusión de que las telecomunicaciones tal vez merezcan mucha más atención de las autori- dades de la que han recibido hasta ahora. Construir algunos elementos de una infraestructura global sin los desarrollos complementarios en la red de teleco- municaciones es ineficaz y antieconómico.

La expansión del conocimiento ha sido la base de todo el progreso a lo largo de la historia. La tasa de expansión del conocimiento, jamás tan alta como ahora, está íntimamente vinculada a la facilidad y eficacia de las telecomunicaciones entre los pueblos, tanto dentro de las naciones como a través de las fronteras. La dinámica del progreso, ya esté arraiga- da en los procesos de reflexión de ingenieros o científicos — "impulso de la tecnología" — o en las necesidades de los usuarios de productos o servicios — "presión del mercado" — resulta vitalmente afectada por la eficacia de las comunicaciones.

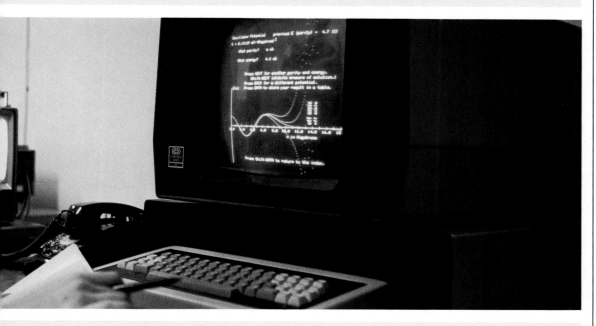

es méthodes d'enseignement sont en voie d'être acceptées me étant le seul moyen de surmonter les contraintes ssantes des coûts sur la qualité, la disponibilité des pro- mmes d'études.

.'un des systèmes utilisés pour l'enseignement par ordina- porte le nom du philosophe Platon. Le système PLATO mis point par Control Data Corporation (voir p. 324) fonctionne ordinateur programmé, et la méthode principale consiste à enser l'enseignement à l'aide d'un ordinateur comportant sous-systèmes terminaux intégrés. Ce système permet ganiser des cours par ordinateur groupant une quarantaine udiants. Il offre aussi à un étudiant isolé tous les avantages 'étude individuelle.

.'enseignement dispensé par ordinateur répond à un besoin entiel de l'industrie, du commerce et des professions libé- s. Ce type d'enseignement est déjà économiquement renta- pour la formation du personnel dans de nombreuse branches ctivités.

\ Pittsburg, aux Etats-Unis, la Carnegie-Mellon University a la première institution du monde à décider, en 1982, de tre à la disposition de ses étudiants un équipement norma- d'ordinateurs. En 1986, lorsque son système sera pleine- nt opérationnel, les étudiants feront chacun l'acquisition de propre ordinateur, tout comme aujourd'hui ils achètent rs livres. Les universitaires seront autorisés à emmener c eux leur terminal d'ordinateur et à le brancher sur le tème Carnegie-Mellon, quel que soit l'endroit ou ils se uvent.

l est certain que les systèmes CBE (Computer-Based Edu- ion) et CAI (Computer-Aided Instruction) transformeront nplètement les méthodes d'enseignement et de formation fessionnelle dans le monde entier au cours des deux ou trois chaines décennies. La compétence technique des jeunes érations atteindra alors un niveau sans précédent.

Uno de los sistemas disponibles es el de educación basada en computador (EBC) PLATO, desarrollado por la Control Data Corporation (véase pág. 324). Se controla por computador, y el principal método de entrega es la instrucción mediante com- putador con subsistemas terminales integrados, que compren- den videodiscos, entrada y salida audio, y entrada por tacto.

Pueden celebrarse conferencias estructuradas por compu- tador, para 40 alumnos, o bien un solo alumno puede actuar con otro o un instructor, según desee, disponiendo de todas las ventajas valiosas del aprendizaje individualizado. La instrucción con ayuda de computador (IAC) comienza a atender un requisito sumamente vital en la industria, el comercio y las profesiones. Los gastos de formación en la industria son grandes, estimán- dose en 100 000 millones $ anuales a finales de los años setenta, por lo que el uso de la IAC tiene grandes posibilidades. Para muchos tipos de formación de empleados es ya rentable.

En EE.UU., la Universidad de Carnegie-Mellon decidió en 1982 — por primera vez en el mundo — poner a disposición de sus alumnos equipo de computador normalizado. En su campus de Pittsburgo se está instalando una red de computadores personales. Cuando se utilice plenamente el sistema, en 1986, se espera que los alumnos adquieran sus propios computado- res, lo mismo que compran ahora libros. Los universitarios podrán llevar consigo sus terminales y conectarlos al sistema Carnegie-Mellon desde cualquier parte.

No hay duda de que la EBC y la IAC transformarán la manera de impartir la educación y la formación en el mundo entero, ni de que aumentarán considerablemente su nivel. Y todo ello en los dos o tres decenios próximos, en que se espera que dismi- nuya el analfabetismo y aumente la competencia técnica de las jóvenes generaciones.

APPLICATIONS IN GOVERNMENT, EDUCATI

ECONOMIC AND SOCIAL BENEFITS

The economic and social benefits of the telephone reviewed on p. 38 were surveyed in the context of the ITU/OECD global project. Their common message is that telecommunications in developing countries are key to dynamic growth and social profit.

A study by S.N. Kaul in the Indian State of Oudhra Pradesh revealed that when a village telephone is available it is used for long distance calls as a substitute for personal travel, and is highly prized. Another study carried out in Egypt by A.A. Kamal (1981) concluded that telecommunications are an extraordinarily important, and potentially profitable, investment from a social and economic standpoint, with benefits valued at many times their cost. The problem is no longer a question of whether to invest in telecommunications but one of deciding on what level of investment and in what services which will best serve national development goals.

Selon les conclusions des études entreprises par l'UIT et l'OCDE sur les avantages économiques et sociaux du téléphone (voir p. 38), les télécommunications sont incontestablement la clé d'une croissance dynamique et du progrès social dans les pays en développement.

Une étude conduite par S.N. Kaul dans l'Etat indien d'Oudhra Pradesh a montré que, lorsqu'un village dispose d'un téléphone, celui-ci est très apprécié et permet souvent de remplacer un voyage personnel par une conversation interurbaine. Dans une autre étude menée en Egypte, en 1981, A.A. Kamal conclut que les télécommunications représentent un investissement socialement fructueux et économiquement rentable. La question n'est donc plus de savoir s'il convient d'investir dans les télécommunications, mais de décider de l'ampleur des investissements à consentir et des services auxquels il faut les consacrer pour atteindre les objectifs de développement.

Los beneficios económicos y sociales del teléfono considerados en la pág. 38 se muestran en varios estudios realizados dentro del proyecto global UIT/OCDE. Su mensaje común es que las telecomunicaciones en los países en desarrollo son la clave del crecimiento dinámico y del progreso social.

Un estudio de S. N. Kaul, en el Estado indio de Oudhra Pradesh, reveló que cuando un pueblo dispone de teléfono no se usa para llamadas a larga distancia, en vez de desplazarse, y es muy apreciado. Otro estudio efectuado en Egipto por A. A. Kamal (1981) concluye diciendo que las telecomunicaciones son una inversión importantísima y potencialmente rentable en términos sociales y económicos, con unos beneficios muy superiores a su costo. Ya no se trata de invertir en telecomunicaciones, sino de decidir en nivel de inversión y los servicios que sirvan mejor los objetivos nacionales de desarrollo.

SCHEDULING AND OPERATING TRANSPORT

Research indicates that the potential of telecommunications as a substitute for transport is very substantial.

A study by M. Tyler (1981) estimated that improved communications could save oil importing countries some US$ 18 billion a year in transport costs. The Stanford Research Institute in the USA projected that the use of mobile radio to control movements of vehicles for pickups and deliveries could increase output per vehicle by 15 to 25%.

While it is true that good telecommunications can generate an increase in people's desire for face-to-face meetings, there is invariably a net economy, through fewer trips and better utilization of vehicles. A teleconferencing system developed by NASA and Dow Chemical led to a net reduction in travel of 25% (a diversion effect of 35% and a generation of 10%).

Il est démontré que les télécommunications peuvent se substituer au transport dans des proportions très appréciables.

Une étude de M. Tyler (1981) estimait que la rationalisation des services de télécommunications permettrait aux pays importateurs de pétrole d'économiser chaque année environ 18 milliards de dollars en frais de transport. Le Stanford Research Institute des Etats-Unis estime que, grâce à un « téléguidage » efficace, il serait possible d'augmenter de 15 à 25% la charge moyenne des véhicules de livraisons et des transports locaux.

S'il est vrai que de bonnes télécommunications peuvent inciter les gens à participer physiquement à des réunions, elles constituent néanmoins une source d'économie en réduisant le nombre des voyages personnels et en rationalisant l'utilisation des véhicules. Le système des téléconférences institué par la NASA et Dow Chemical a permis une réduction des voyages de 25% (effet dissuasif: 35% et effet contraire: 10%).

La investigación muestra que las telecomunicaciones representan un medio muy importante de sustitución del transporte.

En un estudio de M. Tyler (1981) se estima que el mejoramiento de las comunicaciones puede economizar a los países importadores de petróleo unos 18 000 millones $ EE.UU. anuales en costos de transporte. El Instituto de Investigación de Stanford (EE.UU.) prevé que el uso de las radiocomunicaciones móviles para controlar los movimientos de vehículos puede aumentar la producción por vehículo del 15 al 25%.

Si bien es cierto que las buenas telecomunicaciones pueden generar un mayor deseo de la gente a reunirse, invariablemente hay una economía neta, al viajar menos y utilizarse mejor los vehículos. Un sistema de teleconferencia desarrollado por la NASA y Dow Chemical supuso una reducción neta en los viajes del 25% (un efecto de desviación del 35% y una generación de 10%).

HEALTH AND SOCIAL SERVICES

Telecommunications are increasingly being used, in industrialized and developing countries alike, to provide essential services for the sick, the old and the needy. Experiments in Alaska and the Pacific region established that satellite-based systems, though costly, can be invaluable in remote areas by providing immediate access to doctors and a 24-hour link with medical help.

Telecommunications systems are also used to provide old people with alarms branched on computerized assistance centers, by voluntary societies to relieve distress and provide lifelines and by doctors to monitor the functioning of patients' organs at a distance. Speed of response is the keynote.

Services also exist to provide advice on how to stay healthy, by means of a structured dialogue between patient and computer, which identifies elements that need to be changed, controlled or modified for healthier and longer lives.

Dans les pays industrialisés comme dans les pays en développement, les télécommunications sont de plus en plus utilisées pour fournir des services aux malades, aux personnes âgées et aux nécessiteux. Des expériences faites dans les régions de l'Alaska et du Pacifique montrent que des systèmes à satellite, bien que très coûteux, peuvent être d'un secours inestimable.

Les télécommunications sont également utilisées pour équiper des personnes âgées de dispositifs d'alarme reliés à des centres électroniques d'assistance. Des sociétés de bienfaisance les utilisent pour venir en aide aux désespérés. C'est également par ce moyen que certains médecins surveillent à distance le fonctionnement des organes de leurs patients. Dans tous ces cas, la rapidité d'action est absolument essentielle.

Il existe aussi des services fournissant des conseils personnalisés d'hygiène et de santé, par « dialogue structuré » entre le sujet et un ordinateur.

Las telecomunicaciones se emplean cada vez más, en los países industrializados y en desarrollo, para servicios esenciales a enfermos, personas de edad y necesitadas. Experimentos realizados en Alaska y la región del Pacífico muestran que los sistemas por satélite, aunque costosos, pueden ser valiosísimos en zonas remotas, al permitir el acceso inmediato a los médicos, y un enlace permanente con servicios médicos.

También se emplean para proporcionar a las personas de edad alarmas conectadas a centros computadorizados de asistencia, por instituciones benéficas para aliviar la desesperanza y ofrecer líneas de vida, y por doctores para comprobar el funcionamiento de los órganos de los pacientes a distancia. Lo esencial es la rapidez de la respuesta.

También hay servicios para asesorar sobre la buena salud, mediante un diálogo estructurado entre paciente y computador, que identifica los elementos que se deben cambiar, controlar o modificar para una vida más larga y saludable.

AND SCIENCE

GOVERNMENT IN REAL TIME

The benefits of advanced telecommunications technology to governments span the full range of activities undertaken at the national level. National development, defence, resource allocation, financial policy, all require comprehensive up-to-date information suitably processed to provide strategic guidelines.

Interactive on-line information systems with access to multiple data banks to obtain information suitably processed for particular uses, enable quick reaction to change. Structural change is recurring worldwide on an unprecedented scale, and nations must equip themselves to cope with environmental uncertainty, i.e. define a strategy for the unexpected.

The use of techniques such as segmentation of industrial activity, multi-cycle analysis, differentiated allocation of resources, will become easier as the sophisticated telecommunications tools become available.

Pour les gouvernements, les avantages de la télématique s'étendent à une grande quantité d'activités. Le développement du pays, la défense nationale, l'attribution des crédits aux différents services publics, la politique financière et d'investissement, toutes ces activités gouvernementales exigent une information précise et complète.

Des systèmes interactifs avec accès à des banques de données constamment à jour permettent d'obtenir des renseignements spécialement traités à des fins déterminées et offrent ainsi des moyens d'adaptation rapide à tous les changements.

Dans un monde où les transformations structurelles se propagent à un rythme sans précédent, tous les pays doivent s'équiper et définir sans tarder leur stratégie de l'inattendu afin de pouvoir réagir efficacement, face à l'incertitude. Cette tâche sera facilitée par les nouveaux instruments de la télématique.

Los beneficios de la tecnología avanzada de telecomunicaciones para los gobiernos abarcan toda la gama de actividades nacionales. El desarrollo, la defensa, la asignación de recursos, la política financiera, todo necesita información completa y al día debidamente procesada.

Los sistemas de información en línea interactivos con acceso a bancos de datos múltiples, para obtener información apropiada debidamente procesada para usos especiales, permite reaccionar rápidamente al cambio. El cambio estructural no tiene precedentes, y las naciones han de sequiparse para hacer frente a la incertidumbre ambiental, es decir, definir una estrategia para lo imprevisto.

El uso de técnicas como la segmentación de la actividad industrial, los análisis de ciclos múltiples y la asignación diferenciada de recursos, resultarán más fáciles a medida que se disponga de medios de telecomunicación sofisticados.

PLANNING URBAN AND REGIONAL DEVELOPMENT

The development of integrated telecommunication system has begun to affect current practices of urban and regional plannings. In heavily industrialized countries there is a growing tendency to relocate manufacturing and space-consuming services in rural districts. Planners and industrialists in developing countries are beginning to locate new plants in rural areas.

Although many other factors affect such decisions, the availability of services — electronic mail, teleconferencing, video and mobile telephones, access to data banks — is a powerful incentive since they greatly facilitate co-operation and control over distance. Likewise the availability of home electronics, such as information guides, pay by phone, shopping from home, entertainment, games etc. will assist in reducing the population movements into urban centers and remove some of the resistance to relocating in the countryside.

Les systèmes intégrés de télécommunications commencent à avoir une influence sur les méthodes de planification urbaine et régionale. Dans les pays surindustrialisés, comme dans les pays en développement, on commence à transférer ou à installer dans les zones rurales les usines et les services dont les activités exigent de grandes superficies.

Bien que de nombreux autres facteurs influent sur ces décisions, la télématique industrielle qui favorise la coopération et la commande à distance, de même que la télématique domestique, avec tous les avantages qu'elle procure, vont contribuer à réduire considérablement le déplacement quotidien d'énormes masses de population vers des centres urbains et à affaiblir certaines résistances au relogement des gens à la campagne. Dans ces circonstances, la qualité de la vie pourra être améliorée d'une manière appréciable.

El desarrollo de sistemas integrados de telecomunicación comienza a influir en las prácticas corrientes de planificación urbana y regional. En países muy industrializados cada vez se transfieren más fábricas y servicios que requieren espacio a distritos rurales. Los planificadores y los industriales de países en desarrollo empiezan a instalar plantas en zonas rurales.

Aunque en esas decisiones influyen otros muchos factores, la disponibilidad de servicio — correo electrónico, teleconferencia, teléfonos video y móviles, acceso a bancos de datos — es un poderoso incentivo, al facilitar grandemente la cooperación y el control a distancia. Asimismo, la electrónica en el hogar, como guías informativas, pago por teléfono, compra desde casa, juegos, entretenimientos, etc., ayudará a reducir los desplazamientos de población a los centros urbanos y suprimirá parte de la resistencia a reinstalarse en el campo.

THE WORLD OF EDUCATION AND SCIENCE

Advanced computerized communications technology is being brought to bear upon education and training in business and industry, as well as in schools, universities and research establishments. The new generations have become comfortable with visual display units and computer responses. Students even use electronic mail to communicate with each other. Note taking and written tests are on the wane.

In Fiji a recent initiative taken by the University of South Pacific illustrates the considerable advantages of this approach to learning in sparsely populated territories. The ATS-1 satellite network (USA) provides facilities for formal teaching, tutorials, teleconferencing, administrative meetings and outreach programs covering a wide range of services, from agricultural courses to emergency assistance in epidemics. At a cost of US$ 112 per hour (1981) the system is a particularly cost-effective means of operating and managing regional institutions covering a wide territory.

La technologie de pointe des communications par ordinateurs va exercer une influence considérable sur l'enseignement et sur la formation professionnelle dans le commerce et l'industrie. Les nouvelles générations se sont familiarisées avec les terminaux à écran de visualisation et au dialogue avec les ordinateurs. Les étudiants utilisent le courrier électronique pour communiquer entre eux, et on enregistre un déclin de la prise de notes et des épreuves écrites.

Aux Iles Fidji, une initiative récente de l'Université du Pacifique Sud illustre les avantages considérables de la télématique pour diffuser l'enseignement sur des territoires très disséminés. Le réseau à satellites ATS-1 (Etats-Unis) est le moyen de liaison offrant des facilités pour l'enseignement officiel, pour les cours de formation pratique, pour les téléconférences et les téléréunions administratives, ainsi que pour assurer une diffusion territoriale étendue de programmes spécialisés d'étude et de gestion couvrant une large gamme de disciplines.

La tecnología avanzada de comunicaciones por computador se utiliza ya en la formación en el comercio y la industria, así como en escuelas, universidades y centros de investigación. Las nuevas generaciones se familiarizan con los visualizadores y las respuestas del computador. Los estudiantes usan incluso el correo electrónico para comunicar entre sí y galantear. Cada vez se toman menos notas y hay menos textos escritos.

En Fiji, una reciente iniciativa de la Universidad de South Pacific ilustra las ventajas de este método para el aprendizaje en territorios muy extensos. La red de satélite ATS-1 (EE.UU.) ofrece facilidades para la enseñanza oficial, reuniones pedagógicas, teleconferencias, reuniones administrativas y programas que abarcan numeresos servicios, desde los cursos agrícolas a la ayuda de emergencia en caso de epidemia. El sistema es un medio muy rentable para el funcionamiento y la dirección de instituciones regionales que abarcan un extenso territorio, pues cuesta 112 $ por hora (1981).

THE INTERNATIONAL TELECOMMUNICATION UNION AN ASSEMBLY OF ALL NATIONS

THE INTERNATIONAL TELECOMMUNICATION UNION (ITU) was founded over a century ago (1865) by a small group of nations in Europe to assist in defining a modus operandi for telegraphy across frontiers. They sought compatibility of equipment, language and method of charging for the use of facilities.

Since then it has evolved into a consortium of 158 nations joined together through a covenant, the International Telecommunication Convention, established in the Union's early years and reviewed periodically at planning meetings of member nations, the Plenipotentiary Conferences, held every 5 to 7 years in countries selected by members. The last, in 1982, was held in Nairobi, Kenya; the next, scheduled for 1989, will be held in France.

The preamble to the Convention states that: "While fully recognizing the sovereign right of each country to regulate its telecommunications, the plenipotentiaries of the Contracting Governments, with the object of facilitating relations and co-operation between the peoples by means of efficient telecommunication services, have agreed to establish this Convention which is the basic instrument of the International Telecommunication Union". At the Nairobi Plenipotentiary Conference (1982) the preamble was amended to recognize "the growing importance of telecommunications for the preservation of peace and the social and economic development of all countries".

The ITU's four basic functions are: a) regulation, b) standards, c) on-going co-ordination in conformity with Member Governments' decisions, and d) contribution to development.

These are served by *consultation* — the consideration of results of research to enable integration of new technology into telecommunications systems
▷ 50

L'UNION INTERNATIONALE DES TÉLÉCOMMUNICATIONS (UIT) a été fondée il y a plus d'un siècle (1865) par un petit groupe de pays d'Europe qui cherchaient à définir un « modus operandi » pour assurer les communications télégraphiques à travers leurs frontières nationales.

Depuis cette époque, cette institution a évolué pour devenir un ensemble de 158 pays liés par un traité : la Convention internationale des télécommunications, qui est l'instrument fondamental de l'union, lequel est revisé périodiquement lors de Conférences de plénipotentiaires qui se déroulent tous les 5 à 7 ans dans des pays choisis par les Membres. La dernière s'est tenue en 1982, à Nairobi, Kenya, et la prochaine aura lieu en 1989, en France.

Le préambule de la Convention commence ainsi : « En reconnaissant pleinement à chaque pays le droit souverain de réglementer ses télécommunications, les plénipotentiaires des gouvernements contractants, ayant en vue de faciliter les relations et la coopération entre les peuples par le bon fonctionnement des télécommunications, ont, d'un commun accord, arrêté la présente Convention, qui est l'instrument fondamental de l'Union internationale des télécommunications ». Lors de la Conférence de plénipotentiaires de Nairobi, en 1982, ce préambule a été modifié par une adjonction reconnaissant « l'importance croissante des télécommunications pour la sauvegarde de la paix et le développement social et économique de tous les pays ».

L'UIT exerce quatre fonctions fondamentales : a) réglementation, b) normalisation, c) coordination permanente conformément aux décisions des pays Membres et, d) participation au développement.

L'accomplissement de ces tâches nécessite : *des consultations* : la recherche et l'étude de ses résultats aboutissant à l'introduction de nouvelles techniques et à la mise en œuvre de recommandations visant à l'application de normes internationales ; une *coor-*
▷ 50

LA UNIÓN INTERNACIONAL DE TELECOMUNICACIONES (UIT) fue creada hace más de un siglo (1865) por un pequeño grupo de naciones en Europa, para ayudar a definir un modus operandi de la telegrafía a través de las fronteras nacionales. Trataban de lograr la compatibilidad de los equipos, la terminología y el método de tasación para usar sus facilidades.

Desde entonces, ha evolucionado hasta convertirse en realidad en un consorcio de 158 naciones, ligadas por un pacto: el Convenio Internacional de Telecomunicaciones, establecido en los primeros años de la Unión y revisado periódicamente en las reuniones plenarias de los países Miembros, la Conferencia de Plenipotenciarios, celebrada cada 5 a 7 años en países elegidos por los miembros. La última, en 1982, se celebró en Nairobi (Kenia); la próxima, prevista para 1989, se celebrará en Francia.

En el preámbulo del Convenio se estipula que: «Reconociendo en toda su plenitud el derecho soberano de cada país de reglamentar sus telecomunicaciones, los plenipotenciarios de los gobiernos contrantes, con el fin de facilitar las relaciones y la cooperación entre los pueblos por medio del buen funcionamiento de las telecomunicaciones, celebran, de común acuerdo, el siguiente convenio, que constituye el instrumento fundamental de la Unión Internacional de Telecomunicaciones». En la Conferencia de Plenipotenciarios de Nairobi se modificó el Convenio para reconocer «la importancia creciente de las telecomunicaciones para la salvaguardia de la paz y el desarrollo social y económico de todos los países».

Las cuatro funciones básicas de la UIT son: a) reglamentación, b) normas, c) coordinación de conformidad con las decisiones de los Gobiernos Miembros, y d) contribución al desarrollo.
▷ 51

ITU's headquarters in Geneva.

Le siège de l'UIT à Genève.

La sede de la UIT en Ginebra.

through the recommendation of appropriate international standards; by *co-ordination of information and data* — to permit the planning and operation of services, including the radio frequency spectrum and geostationary and other satellite orbits; and by *contribution of information and advice* — for development of the service itself and its effects on the general development of a country or area.

The contribution to sharing of the radio frequency spectrum and satellite orbit space is achieved through the International Frequency Registration Board (IFRB). The contribution to standardization and advice is through the Consultative Committees: the CCIR (International Radio Consultative Committee) and the CCITT (International Telegraph and Telephone Consultative Committee).

The convention of the Union places a great emphasis on the sharing of spectrum and orbit to insure their "rational use", since both are limited facilities and therefore scarce. Moreover, since they are the common property of mankind, it is evident that any use made of any part of them must be subject to international regulation.

In addition to the functions outlined above, the ITU has been given additional responsibilities which will absorb a growing part of its resources. These include the extension of telephone infrastructures in areas where they are deficient; the training of personnel to run and maintain the systems; and the promotion of innovative practices such as microwave transmission by satellite, the use of broadband channels and digitalization. The ITU, today a large organization with a multinational staff, is an instrument, commonly owned, used to ensure orderly and effective world communications, now and in the future.

The Plenipotentiary Conference is the policy-making organ of the Union. The Conference is held to review not only progress since the preceding conference but also the Union's Convention and the evolution of its functions in the light of prevailing circumstances and anticipated developments. This ensures that in periods of rapid technological change the Union remains in tune with the times and equipped to serve the interests of its Members. All in all, its past performance and present activities fit very well the descriptive words of a leading American industrialist: "The ITU strives to improve the effectiveness of the international network, to ensure that each nation's network works harmoniously and compatibly with others, and in pursuit of that goal promotes the broadest application of modern technology. The oldest of all international organizations, it is, in the view of many observers, the best managed and cost-effective of all; serving as the foundation for a rational telecommunications world and encouraging order, common purpose, and dedicated international co-operation".

A brief review of the changes that have been made in the ITU's convention during the past 50 years, from the Plenipotentiary Conference of 1932 in Madrid to that of 1982 in Nairobi, gives a useful picture of the Convention's evolution during periods of political as well as technological change.

The Madrid Conference (1932) defined the term telecommunication as "any telegraphic and telephonic communication of signs, signals, writing, facsimile and sounds of any kind, by wire, wireless or other systems or processes of electric signalling or visual signalling (semaphores)". The preamble of the *Madrid Convention* described it as a treaty between States, affirming that "the plenipotentiaries of the governments... being assembled in conference in Madrid, have, by common consent and subject to ratification, concluded the following Convention". *The Atlantic City Conference* (1947) expressly recognized "the sovereign right of each country to regulate its telecommunications" and specified that the purpose of the Convention was to ensure "the effectiveness of telecommunications".

▷ 54

Contemporary engraving of Samuel Morse's printing telegraph equipment, 1847.

dination d'information et de données : en vue de la planification et de l'exploitation coordonnée des différents services, et pour assurer l'utilisation en partage du spectre des fréquences et celle de l'orbite des satellites ; la *fourniture et l'échange de renseignements et de conseils* : visant à l'exploitation des services de télécommunication et du déploiement de leurs effets, afin de favoriser un développement harmonieux à l'échelle nationale ou régionale.

Les études et les travaux concernant le partage du spectre des fréquences et l'occupation des segments de l'orbite géostationnaire, incombent au Comité international d'enregistrement des fréquences (IFRB). Deux Comités consultatifs contribuent à la normalisation en fournissant des avis : le CCIR (Comité Consultatif International des Radiocommunications) et le CCITT (Comité Consultatif International Télégraphique et Téléphonique).

La Convention de l'UIT met l'accent sur l'utilisation rationnelle du spectre des fréquences radioélectriques et de l'orbite des satellites géostationnaires qui sont des ressources limitées, faisant partie du patrimoine de l'humanité, et dont l'utilisation même partielle doit par conséquent être régie par une réglementation internationale.

A part les fonctions qui viennent d'être décrites, l'UIT assume d'autres responsabilités qui absorbent une part toujours plus grande de ses ressources. Il s'agit de l'extension des infrastructures téléphoniques dans des régions où elles sont insuffisantes, la formation du personnel requis pour assurer l'exploitation et la maintenance des systèmes, de même que la mise en application de méthodes novatrices telles que les transmissions à hyperfréquences par satellite, l'utilisation de voies à large bande et l'adoption de méthodes de transmission numérique. L'UIT est aujourd'hui une grande organisation disposant d'un personnel multinational. Elle est un instrument international dont le but est d'assurer la coordination permanente et efficace des communications mondiales dans le présent et pour le futur.

La Conférence de plénipotentiaires est l'organe suprême de l'Union. Elle est organisée, non seulement pour examiner les progrès réalisés pendant les périodes qui s'écoulent entre deux conférences, mais également pour reviser la Convention, compte tenu des circonstances et de l'évolution prévisible, afin que l'Union soit toujours en mesure de servir les intérêts de ses Membres. Tout ce que représentent les activités passées et actuelles de l'Union correspond à la description qu'en fait un éminent industriel américain : « L'UIT s'efforce d'améliorer l'efficacité du réseau international, afin que le réseau de chaque pays puisse fonctionner d'une manière compatible et harmonieuse avec celui des autres pays et, en cherchant à atteindre ce but, elle contribue à mettre en valeur de la manière la plus large les innovations de la technologie moderne. Ainsi, la plus ancienne des organisations internationales est celle qui gère le mieux ses ressources, celle qui représente le fondement même de télécommunications mondiales rationnelles et celle qui fait le plus pour encourager une coopération internationale ordonnée, logique et cohérente ».

Les modifications apportées à la Convention de l'UIT au cours du demi-siècle écoulé, entre la Conférence de plénipotentiaires de 1932 à Madrid et celle de 1982 qui s'est tenue à Nairobi, reflètent bien l'évolution politique et technologique qui s'est produite durant cette période.

La Conférence de Madrid (1932) a ainsi défini le terme « télécommunication » : « Toute communication télégraphique ou téléphonique de signes, de signaux, d'écrits, d'images et de sons de toute nature, par fil, radio ou autres systèmes ou procédés de signalisation électriques ou visuels (sémaphores) ».

Le préambule de la *Convention de Madrid* décrit celle-ci comme un traité entre Etats dont « les plénipotentiaires des gouvernements ... réunis en conférence à Madrid ont, d'un commun accord et sous réserve de ratification, arrêté la Convention suivante ». Par la suite la *Conférence d'Atlantic City* (1947)

▷ 54

Gravure contemporaine du télégraphe de Samuel Morse, 1847.

The dates are of the major events of the past 146 years since the telegraph was invented, and of the ITU of the Conferences since its foundation in 1865.

It is appropriate to mention here the great names associated with the inventions of the telegraph, radio and television. Morse patented his telegraph machine in 1837. Bell launched his telephone in 1876. Soon followed the invention of radio, associated with the names of Maxwell, Hertz, Lodge, Popov, Marconi, De Forest and Branly.

Marconi's television in the 1930s, and the discovery of the

transistor by William Shockley and his Bell Laboratories colleagues in the 1950s were two subsequent milestones of great significance.

Les dates ci-contre sont celles des évènements les plus importants des 146 années écoulées depuis l'invention du télégraphe et celles des principales conférences de l'UIT depuis sa fondation en 1865.

Il convient de citer ici les noms des pionniers. Le premier fut Samuel Morse qui déposa un brevet pour sa machine télégraphique en 1837. Alexander Graham Bell fit connaître son téléphone en 1876. Ensuite, ce fut l'invention de la radio, à laquelle sont associés Maxwell, Hertz, Lodge, Popov, Marconi, De Forest et Branly.

La télévision de Marconi, dans les années 1930, puis la découverte du transistor par William Shockley et ses collègues de Bell Laboratories, dans les années 50, furent des jalons d'une grande importance.

Las fechas corresponden a los principales acontecimientos de los 146 años últimos, desde la invención del telégrafo, y a las conferencias de la UIT desde su fundación, en 1865.

Procede mencionar los grandes nombres asociados a las invenciones del telégrafo, la radio y la televisión. Morse patentó su aparato telegráfico en 1837. Bell lanzó su teléfono en 1876. Siguió pronto la invención de la radio, asociada a los nombres de Maxwell, Hertz, Lodge, Popov, Marconi, De Forest y Branly.

La televisión de Marconi en los años 1930, y el descubrimiento del transistor por William Shockley y sus colegas de Bell en los años 1950, fueron dos grandes hitos.

HE ITU: A MIRROR OF THE HISTORY
) TELECOMMUNICATIONS

Estas se realizan mediante *consultas* (la consideración de resultados de investigación para la integración de nueva tecnología en sistemas de telecomunicaciones, recomendando normas internacionales apropiadas); *coordinación de información y datos* (para planificar y explotar los servicios, incluidos el espectro de frecuencias radioeléctricas y la órbita de satélites geoestacionarios y otros), y *contribución de información y asesoramiento* (para expandir el propio servicio y sus efectos sobre el desarrollo general de un país o zona).

La contribución o la compartición del espectro de frecuencias y el espacio orbital de los satélites se logra a través de la Junta Internacional de Registro de Frecuencias (IFRB). La contribución a la normalización y el asesoramiento se hace a través de los Comités Consultivos: el CCIR (Comité Consultivo Internacional de Radiocomunicaciones) y el CCITT (Comité Consultivo Internacional Telegráfico y Telefónico).

Para compartir el espectro y la órbita se insiste en el «uso racional» y, como ambos son recursos limitados y, por tanto, escasos, y además patrimonio de la humanidad, es evidente que todo uso de cualquier parte de ellos debe reglamentarse internacionalmente.

Además de las funciones señaladas, se han conferido a la UIT otras responsabilidades que absorberán una parte cada vez mayor de sus recursos. Estas comprenden la extensión de las infraestructuras telefónicas en aquellas regiones donde son deficientes; la formación de personal para utilizar y mantener los sistemas, y la promoción de prácticas innovadoras, como la transmisión de microondas por satélite, el uso de canales de banda ancha y la digitalización. La UIT es actualmente una gran organización con un personal multinacional; un instrumento de propiedad común, empleado para asegurar el orden y la eficacia de las comunicaciones mundiales, ahora y en lo futuro.

·**La Conferencia de Plenipotenciarios** es el órgano supremo de la Unión. No sólo se celebra para examinar los progresos realizados desde la conferencia anterior, sino para revisar el Convenio de la Unión y la evolución de sus funciones, a la luz de las circunstancias y de los acontecimientos previstos. Así, en periodos de rápida evolución tecnológica, la Unión está al día y equipada para servir los intereses de sus Miembros. En general, sus realizaciones pasadas y sus actividades presentes corresponden a las palabras descriptivas de un importante industrial americano: «La UIT trata de mejorar la eficacia de la red internacional, de que la red de cada nación funcione armoniosamente y en forma compatible con las otras, y en la persecución de ese objetivo fomenta la aplicación más amplia de la tecnología moderna. La más antigua de las organizaciones internacionales es también, a juicio de muchos observadores internacionales, la mejor dirigida y la más rentable; sirve de base a un mundo racional de telecomunicaciones, y estimula el orden, el fin común y una verdadera cooperación internacional».

Un breve resumen de los cambios introducidos en el Convenio de la UIT en los últimos 50 años, desde la Conferencia de Plenipotenciarios de 1932, en Madrid, hasta la de 1982, en Nairobi, da una buena idea de la evolución del Convenio durante períodos de cambios políticos y tecnológicos.

La Conferencia de Madrid (1932) definió el término telecomunicación como «Toda comunicación telegráfica o telefónica de signos, señales, escritos, imágenes y sonidos de cualquier naturaleza por hilo, radioelectricidad u otros sistemas o procedimientos de señalización eléctricos o visuales (semáforos)». El preámbulo del *Convenio de Madrid* describe éste como un tratado entre Estados, afirmando que «los plenipotenciarios de los gobiernos... reunidos en la Conferencia de Madrid, de común acuerdo y a reserva de ratificación, celebran el siguiente Convenio».

▷ 55

*Grabado contemporáneo del
telégrafo de Samuel Morse, 1847.*

Study Group Structure of the International Radio Consultative Committee (CCIR)

Study Group

  I : Spectrum utilization and monitoring

 II : Space research and radioastronomy

III : Fixed service (point-to-point) at frequencies below about 30 MHz

IV : Fixed service (point-to-point) using communications satellites

  V : Propagation in non-ionized media

 VI : Propagation in ionized media

VII : Standard frequencies and time signals

VIII : Mobile services (as for maritime, aeronautical and land mobile communications)

 IX : Fixed services using radio relay system

  X : Broadcasting service (sound)

 XI : Broadcasting service (television)

CMV : CCIR/CCITT Joint Study Group — Vocabulary

CMTT : CCIR/CCITT Joint Study Group — Transmission of sound broadcasting and television signals over long distances

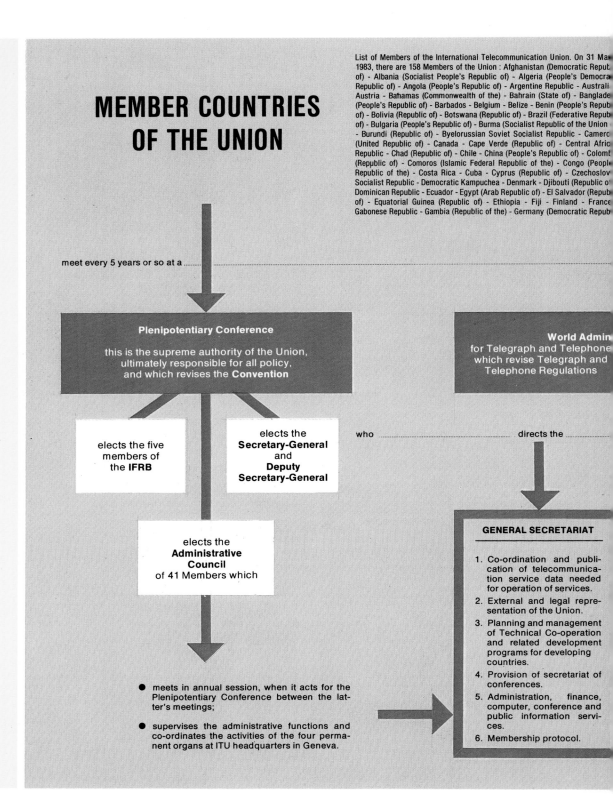

Germany (Federal Republic of) - Ghana - Greece - Grenada - Guatemala ublic of) - Guinea (Revolutionary People's Republic of) - Guinea-Bissau public of) - Guyana - Haiti (Republic of) - Honduras (Republic of) - Hungarian ple's Republic - Iceland - India (Republic of) - Indonesia (Republic of) - Iran amic Republic of) - Iraq (Republic of) - Ireland - Israel (State of) - Italy - Ivory st (Republic of) - Jamaica - Japan - Jordan (Hashemite Kingdom of) - Kenya ublic of) - Korea (Democratic People's Republic of) - Korea (Republic of) - vait (State of) - Lao People's Democratic Republic - Lebanon - Lesotho gdom of) - Liberia (Republic of) - Libya (Socialist People's Libyan Arab ahiriya) - Liechtenstein (Principality of) - Luxembourg - Madagascar mocratic Republic of) - Malawi - Malaysia - Maldives (Republic of) - i (Republic of) - Malta (Republic of) - Mauritania (Islamic Republic of) - ritius - Mexico - Monaco - Mongolian People's Republic - Morocco (King- n of) - Mozambique (People's Republic of) - Nauru (Republic of) - Nepal - herlands (Kingdom of the) - New Zealand - Nicaragua - Niger (Republic of - Nigeria (Federal Republic of) - Norway - Oman (Sultanate of) - Paki- n (Islamic Republic of) - Panama (Republic of) - Papua New Guinea - Para-

guay (Republic of) - Peru - Philippines (Republic of the) - Poland (People's Republic of) - Portugal - Qatar (State of) - Romania (Socialist Republic of) - Rwandese Republic - Saint Vincent and the Grenadines - San Marino (Republic of) - Sao Tome and Principe (Democratic Republic of) - Saudi Arabia (Kingdom of) - Senegal (Republic of) - Sierra Leone - Singapore (Repu- blic of) - Somali Democratic Republic - South Africa (Republic of) - Spain - Sri Lanka (Democratic Socialist Republic of) - Sudan (Democratic Republic of the) - Suriname (Republic of) - Swaziland (Kingdom of) - Sweden - Switzer- land (Confederation of) - Syrian Arab Republic - Tanzania (United Republic of) - Thailand - Togolese Republic - Tonga (Kingdom of) - Trinidad and To- bago - Tunisia - Turkey - Uganda (Republic of) - Ukranian Soviet Socialist Republic - Union of Soviet Socialist Republics - United Arab Emirates - Uni- ted Kingdom of Great Britain and Northern Ireland - United States of America - Upper Volta - Uruguay (Eastern Republic of) - Vatican City State - Vene- zuela (Republic of) - Viet Nam (Socialist Republic of) - Yemen (People's Demo- cratic Republic of) - Yemen Arab Republic - Yugoslavia (Socialist Federal Re- public of) - Zaire (Republic of) - Zambia (Republic of) - Zimbabwe (Republic of).

Study Group Structure of the International Telegraph and Telephone Consultative Committee (CCITT)

Study Group

    I : Telegraph operation and quality of service

   II : Telephone operation and quality of service

  III : General tariff principles

  IV : Transmission maintenance of international lines, circuits and chains of circuits, maintenance of automatic and semi-automatic networks

   V : Protection against dangers and disturbances of electromagnetic origin

  VI : Protection and specifications of cable sheaths and poles

 VII : New networks for data transmission

VIII : Telegraph and terminal equipment, local connecting lines

  IX : Telegraph transmission quality, specification of equipment and rules for the maintenance of telegraph channels

   X : Telegraph switching

  XI : Telephone switching and signalling

 XII : Telephone transmission performance and local telephone networks

XIV : Facsimile telegraph transmission and equipment

 XV : Transmission systems

XVI : Telephone circuits

XVII : Data transmission

XVIII : Digital networks

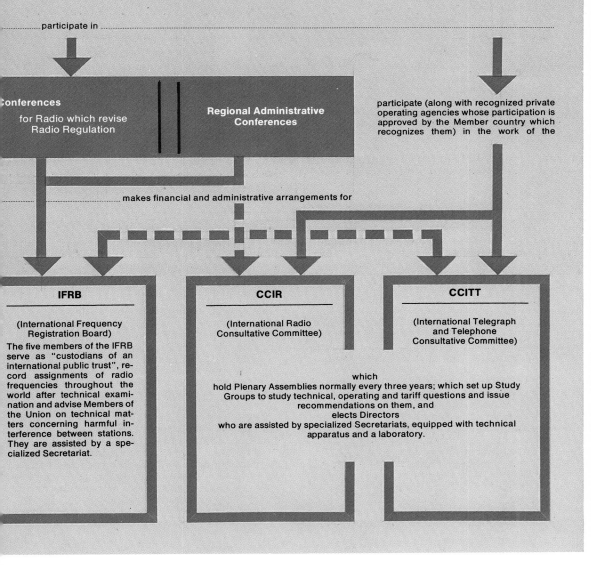

... participate in ...

Conferences for Radio which revise Radio Regulation   **Regional Administrative Conferences**

participate (along with recognized private operating agencies whose participation is approved by the Member country which recognizes them) in the work of the

makes financial and administrative arrangements for

IFRB

(International Frequency Registration Board)
The five members of the IFRB serve as "custodians of an international public trust", re- cord assignments of radio frequencies throughout the world after technical exami- nation and advise Members of the Union on technical mat- ters concerning harmful in- terference between stations. They are assisted by a spe- cialized Secretariat.

CCIR

(International Radio Consultative Committee)

CCITT

(International Telegraph and Telephone Consultative Committee)

which
hold Plenary Assemblies normally every three years; which set up Study Groups to study technical, operating and tariff questions and issue recommendations on them, and elects Directors who are assisted by specialized Secretariats, equipped with technical apparatus and a laboratory.

The Buenos Aires Conference (1952) added the objective of "facilitating relations between the peoples" by means of telecommunications. The Geneva Convention (1959) further added "to foster the creation, development and improvement of telecommunication equipment and networks in new or developing countries by every means at its disposal, especially its participation in the appropriate programs of the United Nations". The Malaga-Torremolinos Convention (1973) included an instruction "to co-ordinate efforts with a view to harmonizing the development of telecommunication facilities, notably those using space techniques". The Nairobi Convention (1982) added "to promote and to offer technical assistance to developing countries in the field of telecommunications".

At the Montreux Conference (1965), a requirement was first written into the Convention stipulating that the Plenipotentiary Conference "shall consider the reports of the Administrative Council on the activities of the Union", defined at the Nairobi Conference (1982) as "the activities of all the organs of the Union since the previous Plenipotentiary Conference". Another, most important, duty of the Conference was to establish the basis for the budget. The Buenos Aires Conference (1952) specified this function together with the need "to determine a fiscal limit for the ordinary expenditure until the next Plenipotentiary Conference". This was to be determined "after considering a program of the administrative conferences and meetings", broadened at Nairobi to include "any medium-term plan submitted by the Administrative Council".

At the Nairobi Conference (1982), emphasis was placed on the inclusion in "ordinary expenditure" of the cost of "technical co-operation and assistance provided to the developing countries". Special attention was given to this function of ITU, with recognition of the important role of telecommunications for development and the need to foster investment in it by other institutions and in co-ordination with their national planning proposals.

However, many of the major ITU-led projects are financed by the Member countries themselves, either through funds made available to the United Nations Development Program (UNDP) or other multilateral aid source and funds in trust arrangements for the development of the infrastructures, maintenance of the system, or training of personnel. The growing recognition of the importance of telecommunications throughout the world, and more particularly of the need for an integrated global system, is likely to make more rather than less funds earmarked for this purpose, and the volume of technical assistance provided by the ITU is expected, therefore, to grow rather than to recede. Another financial function of the Plenipotentiary Conference is to "examine the accounts of the Union and finally approve them if appropriate".

The Atlantic City Conference (1947) determined that the Plenipotentiary Conference "shall elect the Members of the Union who are to serve on the Administrative Council". The Geneva Conference (1959) broadened this to include the Secretary-General and the Deputy Secretary-General; further, at Malaga-Torremolinos (1973), to include members of the IFRB and, at Nairobi (1982), the directors of the International Consultative Committees. The insertion of such powers in the Convention gives the Conferences delegates considerable control over the ITU's functions, finances and senior staffing.

The Administrative Council is the ITU's controlling organ, or "supervisory board". It is composed of members of the Union elected by the Plenipotentiary Conference "with due regard to the need for equitable representation of all parts of the world". The membership, originally fixed at 18 in 1947, was gradually increased to reach 41 by 1982. The Administrative Council was established as the body which "in the intervals between the Plenipotentiary Conferences..... shall act on behalf of the Plenipotentiary

▷ 56

a expressément reconnu « à chaque pays le droit souverain de réglementer ses télécommunications », en spécifiant que la Convention a pour but d' « assurer le bon fonctionnement des télécommunications ».

La Conférence de Buenos Aires (1952) précisait que cette Convention était aussi conclue « en vue de faciliter les relations entre les peuples » grâce aux télécommunications. La Convention de Genève (1959) a ajouté, parmi les buts de l'Union, que celle-ci « encourage la création, le développement et le perfectionnement des installations et des réseaux de télécommunications dans les pays nouveaux ou en voie de développement par tous les moyens à sa disposition, en particulier par sa participation aux programmes appropriés des Nations Unies. La Convention de Malaga-Torremolinos (1973) spécifiait notamment que: « l'Union coordonne les efforts en vue de permettre le développement harmonieux des moyens de télécommunication, notamment ceux faisant appel aux techniques spatiales ». La Convention de Nairobi (1982) ajoute : « de promouvoir et d'offrir une assistance technique aux pays en développement dans le domaine des télécommunications ».

A la Conférence de Montreux (1965), on trouve stipulé pour la première fois dans la Convention que la Conférence « examine le rapport du Conseil d'administration sur l'activité de l'Union », laquelle a été définie par la suite et notamment par la Conférence de Nairobi (1982) comme « l'activité de tous les organes de l'Union depuis la dernière Conférence de plénipotentiaires ». Une autre attribution essentielle de la Conférence consiste a établir les bases du budget. La Conférence de Buenos Aires (1952) spécifiait que cette fonction consistait notamment à déterminer « le plafond des dépenses ordinaires pour la période allant jusqu'à la prochaine Conférence ».

Il s'agissait donc initialement de tenir compte du « programme des conférences administratives et des réunions », mais cette attribution a été élargie à Nairobi pour comprendre « tout autre plan à moyen terme présenté par le Conseil d'administration ».

A la Conférence de Nairobi (1982), un nouvel élément a été inclus dans la méthode d'établissement du budget. Dorénavant, les « dépenses ordinaires » de l'Union couvriront une partie des charges afférentes à la coopération technique et à l'assistance fournie aux pays en développement.

Toutefois, de nombreux projets importants mis en œuvre par l'UIT sont financés par les pays Membres eux-mêmes, soit au moyen de fonds mis à la disposition du Programme des Nations Unies pour le Développement (PNUD) ou d'autres sources d'aide multilatérale, soit au moyen de fonds mis à disposition à titre onéreux, pour la mise en place des infrastructures, de la maintenance du système ou de la formation de personnel. Du fait que l'importance des télécommunications est reconnue d'une manière de plus en plus universelle, de même que la nécessité de la mise en place d'un système intégré à l'échelle mondiale, il est probable que l'affectation de fonds à cette fin va s'intensifier et que le volume de l'assistance technique fournie par l'UIT tendra à augmenter, plutôt qu'à diminuer.

La Conférence d'Atlantic City (1947) a décidé que la Conférence de plénipotentiaires devait élire « les Membres de l'Union qui font partie du Conseil d'administration ». En 1959, la Conférence de Genève a élargi cette compétence en incluant aussi cette désignation le Secrétaire général et le Vice-secrétaire général. En 1973, à Malaga-Torremolinos, il a été décidé que la Conférence de plénipotentiaires élirait les membres de l'IFRB et, en 1982 à Nairobi, les directeurs des Comités consultatifs internationaux. La spécification de ces responsabilités supplémentaires dans la Convention permet aux délégués aux Conférences de plénipotentiaires de contrôler très rigoureusement les activités et les finances de l'UIT et de désigner eux-mêmes ses hauts fonctionnaires.

Le Conseil d'administration est l'organe de contrôle et de « supervision » de l'UIT. Il est composé de Membres de l'Union élus par la Conférence de plénipotentiaires, compte tenu de « la nécessité d'une répartition équitable des sièges entre toutes les régions du mon-

▷ 56

THE TELECOMM
ASSEMBLE TO SH

The World Telecommunication Forum is recognized as the most universal and authoritative symposium of telecommunication engineers and economists, investors and lawyers. The Forum assembles, every four years, a "brains trust" of several thousand top executives to present and discuss the planning, financing, management, legal aspects and implementation of the world telecommunication network. It is a continuing dialogue initiated at the previous World Telecommunication Forums.

The 4th World Telecommunication Forum, held during World Communications Year 1983, highlighted the telecommunication

requirements of both industrialized and developing countries, latest technical innovations and technological trends and the efforts made or to be made to finance national, regional and worldwide development plans. Forum 83 adopted the Geneva Declaration on communications infrastructure development. The list of speakers included ministers of ITU Member countries, chairmen, presidents, group executives and chief scientists from industry, common carriers, international and financial organizations.

Charles Brown, Chairman AT&T, opened the 4th World Telecommunication Forum. Key note sessions dealt with themes such as: Development of communication infrastructures; the changing scenery of worldwide communications; Technology and social responsibility; The world communications market and investment in infrastructure development; Communications policy; The impact of the electronic revolution; The wireless society; Closing the communications gap.

CATION FORUM: WORLD LEADERS
= THE FUTURE OF COMMUNICATIONS

Forum mondial des télécommunications est considéré me le symbole universel et la manifestation qui fait autorité ni les ingénieurs, les économistes, les investisseurs et les tes. Le Forum rassemble, tous les quatre ans, un «brain t» comptant plusieurs milliers de hauts dirigeants qui pré- tent la planification, le financement, la gestion et les as- s légaux de la mise en œuvre du réseau mondial des communications. C'est un continuel dialogue entamé lors précédents forum mondiaux des télécommunications.

e 4e Forum tenu pendant l'Année mondiale des communi-

El Foro Mundial de las Telecomunicaciones se considera como el simposio más universal y prestigioso de ingenieros de tele- comunicación y economistas, inversores y juristas. El Foro reúne, cada cuatro años, a varios miles de ejecutivos superio- res, que presentan y discuten la planificación, financiación, gestión, aspectos jurídicos y ejecución de la red mundial de telecomunicaciones, continuando un diálogo iniciado en los foros anteriores.

El 4° Foro Mundial de las Telecomunicaciones, celebrado en el Año Mundial de las Comunicaciones 1983, destaca las nece-

ons, en 1983, fut ouvert par Charles Brown, président de T. Le Forum '83 adopta la Déclaration de Genève sur le loppement des infrastructures de communications et mis mière la nécessité des télécommunications aussi bien pour pays industrialisés que pour les pays en développement. Le m souligna également l'importance des efforts faits ou à pour financer les plans de développement nationaux, ré- aux et mondiaux. Parmi les orateurs figuraient des minis- de pays Membres de l'UIT, des présidents et directeurs de pagnies et des directeurs de recherche, appartenant à ustrie, aux services publics et aux organismes internatio- .

es thèmes principaux furent les suivants : Le développe- t des infrastructures ; La mutation des télécommunications diales ; Technologie et responsabilités sociales ; Le marché dial des télécommunications et les investissements pour le loppement des infrastructures ; Politique des télécommu- tions ; L'impact de la révolution électronique ; La société s fils ; Combler le fossé : solutions pour le développement télécommunications.

sidades en telecomunicaciones de los países industrializados y en desarrollo, las últimas innovaciones técnicas y las tenden- cias tecnológicas y los esfuerzos realizados o futuros para financiar planes de desarrollo nacionales, regionales y mun- diales. El Foro 83 adoptó la Declaración de Ginebra sobre desarrollo de la infraestructura de las comunicaciones. Habla- ron Ministros de países Miembros de la UIT, presidentes, eje- cutivos de grupos y jefes científicos de la industria, las em- presas, y organizaciones internacionales y financieras.

Charles Brown, Presidente de AT&T, abrió el 4° Foro Mundial de las Telecomunicaciones. En las principales sesiones se trataron temas como: Desarrollo de la infraestructura de las comunicaciones; El panorama cambiante de las comunicacio- nes mundiales; Tecnología y responsabilidad social; El mercado mundial de las comunicaciones y la inversión en el desarrollo de la infraestructura; Política de las comunicaciones; Impacto de la revolución electrónica; La sociedad de la radiocomunica- ción; tender puentes.

La Conferencia de Atlantic City (1947) reconoció expresamente «el derecho soberano de cada país a reglamentar sus telecomunicaciones» y especificó que la finalidad del Convenio era asegurar el «buen funcionamiento de las telecomunicaciones».

La Conferencia de Buenos Aires (1952) agregó el objetivo de «facilitar las relaciones entre los pue- blos» por medio de las telecomunicaciones. El *Con- venio de Ginebra* (1959) incorporó que «fomentará la creación, el desarrollo y el perfeccionamiento de las instalaciones y de las redes de telecomunicaciones en los países nuevos o en vías de desarrollo, por todos los medios de que disponga, y en particular por me- dio de su participación en los programas adecuados de las Naciones Unidas». El *Convenio de Mála- ga-Torremolinos* (1973) agregó que «coordinará ... los esfuerzos en favor del desarrollo armónico de los medios de telecomunicación, especialmente los que utilizan técnicas espaciales». El *Convenio de Nairobi* (1982) agregó «promover y proporcionar asistencia técnica a los países en desarrollo en el campo de las telecomunicaciones».

En el Convenio de Montreux (1965) se estipuló por primera vez que la Conferencia de Plenipotenciarios «examinará el informe del Consejo de Administra- ción sobre las actividades de la Unión», definidas en Nairobi (1982) como «las actividades de los órganos de la Unión desde la última Conferencia de Pleni- potenciarios». Otro deber, más importante, de la Conferencia es establecer la base del presupuesto. La *Conferencia de Buenos Aires* (1952) especificaba esta función junto con la necesidad de «determinar el tope de sus gastos ordinarios hasta la siguiente Con- ferencia de Plenipotenciarios». Esto había de deter- minarse «después de considerar el programa de las conferencias administrativas y reuniones», ampliado en Nairobi para incluir «cualquier otro plan a medio plazo presentado por el Consejo de Administra- ción».

En la Conferencia de Nairobi (1982) se insistió en incluir en los «gastos ordinarios» el costo de «la cooperación y asistencia técnicas que brinde a los países en desarrollo». Ahora bien, muchos de los principales proyectos dirigidos por la UIT se finan- cian por los propios países miembros, bien con fon- dos del PNUD u otras fuentes de ayuda y fondos multilaterales de los acuerdos de fideicomiso para desarrollar las infraestructuras, mantener el sistema o formar el personal. Al reconocerse cada vez más la importancia de las telecomunicaciones en el mundo entero, y sobre todo la necesidad de un sistema glo- bal integrado, es probable que se asignen más fondos con este fin, por lo que se espera que el volumen de la asistencia técnica de la UIT aumente, en vez de dis- minuir. Otra función financiera de la Conferencia de Plenipotenciarios es «examinar las cuentas de la Unión y aprobarlas, si procede».

La Conferencia de Atlantic City (1947) determinó que la Conferencia de Plenipotenciarios «elegirá a los Miembros de la Unión que han de formar parte del Consejo de Administración». La *Conferencia de Ginebra* (1959) amplió esto para incluir al Secretario General y al Vicesecretario General; además, en *Málaga-Torremolinos* (1973), para incluir a los miembros de la IFRB, y en *Nairobi* (1982), a los directores de los Comités Consultivos Internaciona- les. La inserción de tales facultades en el Convenio confiere a los delegados en las Conferencias de Ple- nipotenciarios considerable control sobre las fun- ciones, las finanzas y el personal superior de la UIT.

El Consejo de Administración es el órgano de control o «junta supervisora» de la UIT. Se compone de miembros de la Unión elegidos por la Conferencia de Plenipotenciarios «teniendo en cuenta la necesi- dad de una distribución equitativa de los puestos entre todas las regiones del mundo». El numéro de miembros, fijado originalmente en 18, en 1947, ha pasado gradualmente a 41, en 1982. El Consejo de Administración, establecido como el órgano que «en

▷ 57

Conference within the limits delegated to it by the latter", shall ensure "the efficient co-ordination of the work of the Union..... and exercise effective financial control over its permanent organs". *The Geneva Convention* specified "the promotion of international co-operation, especially through Union participation in the appropriate programs of the United Nations" and the *Nairobi Convention* required that the Council "shall determine each year the policy of technical assistance". The Union's activities in this latter respect, and its program, are discussed in "Development of human resources and technology transfer" (p. 340).

The ITU's permanent organs and their functions (given on p. 52) have evolved over time. Essentially they consist of the General Secretariat, the International Frequency Registration Board (IFRB), and the International Consultative Committees (CCIR and CCITT).

The General Secretariat is the ITU's executive body, directed by the Secretary-General aided by a Deputy Secretary-General. The Secretary-General reports to the Administrative Council and is responsible "for all the administration and financial aspects of the Union's activities". He chairs a Co-ordination Committee which is, in fact, the Union's Management Committee, consisting of the Deputy Secretary-General, the Directors of the International Consultative committees, the chairman of the IFRB and his vice-chairman.

The International Frequency Registration Board (IFRB) exists "to effect an orderly recording of frequency assignments made by the different countries" and "to furnish advice to Members with a view to the operation of the maximum practicable number of radio channels", extended later to include the "recording of the positions assigned by countries to geostationary satellites", and to advise Members on "the equitable, effective and economical use of the geostationary satellite orbit".

The International Consultative Committees, CCIR and CCITT, were assigned jointly the role "to conduct studies and formulate recommendations" — the CCIR on "technical and operating questions relating specifically to radio communication" and the CCITT on "technical, operating and tariff questions relating to the telecommunication services", except those falling within the competence of the CCIRR. Both are organized in study groups, as shown on p. 52-53, and their activities are discussed on p. 230 (Spectrum) and in the Box on p. 240 (Standards).

The establishment of an independent "International Commission for Worldwide Telecommunications Development" was an important decision taken at Nairobi. This commission is to be composed of representatives of the highest decision-making authorities with the specific terms of reference to examine and recommend a range of methods, both tried and untried, "for stimulating telecommunications development in the developing world, using appropriate and proven technologies" leading to "progressive achievement of self-reliance... and the narrowing of the gap between the developing and developed countries".

The Commission will be composed of "15 to 20 representatives of the highest decision makers from administrations, operating agencies and industry in the developing and developed countries as well as the major financial institutions (including the development banks and the UNDP) and other appropriate entities, also seeking as good a representation of all the regions of the world as possible". This is indeed a recognition by the nations of the world that the gap in telecommunications infrastructures between industrialized and developing countries must be reduced, and that an immense co-opearative effort is required to achieve this.

de ». A l'origine, en 1947, le Conseil était composé de 18 pays Membres ; son effectif a progressivement augmenté et a été fixé à 41 en 1982. « Dans l'intervalle qui sépare les Conférences de plénipotentiaires, le Conseil d'administration agit en tant que mandataire de la Conférence de plénipotentiaires, dans les limites des pouvoirs délégués par celle-ci ». A ce titre, « il assure une coordination efficace des activités de l'Union et exerce un contrôle financier effectif sur les organismes ». La Convention spécifie encore que le Conseil favorise la coopération internationale, notamment par la participation de l'Union aux programmes appropriés des Nations Unies et le texte adopté à Nairobi stipule que le Conseil « définit chaque année la politique d'assistance technique ».

Les organes principaux de l'UIT sont : le Secrétariat général, le Comité international d'enregistrement des frequences (IFRB), et les comités consultatifs internationaux (CCIR et CCITT), voir p. 52.

Le Secrétariat général est l'organe administratif de l'UIT. Il est dirigé par un Secrétaire général assisté d'un Vice-secrétaire général. Le Secrétaire général « est responsable devant le Conseil d'administration pour la totalité des aspects administratifs et financiers des activités de l' « Union ». Il préside le Comité de coordination, qui est en fait le Comité de gestion de l'Union, composé du Secrétaire général, du Vice-secrétaire général, des Directeurs des Comités consultatifs internationaux et des président et vice-président du Comité international d'enregistrement des fréquences.

Le Comité international d'enregistrement des fréquences (IFRB) a été institué pour « effectuer l'inscription et l'enregistrement méthodique des assignations de fréquence faites par les différents pays » et pour « fournir des avis aux Membres en vue de l'exploitation d'un nombre aussi grand que possible de voies radioélectriques ». Par la suite, les tâches du Comité ont englobé, à titre supplémentaire, l'enregistrement des positions assignées par les différents pays à leurs satellite géostationnaire et la fourniture d'avis aux Membres « en vue de l'utilisation équitable, efficace et économique de l'orbite des satellites géostationnaires ».

Les deux Comités consultatifs internationaux à qui fut assigné un rôle commun qui consiste à « effectuer des études et d'émettre des recommandations », pour ce qui concerne le CCIR « sur les questions techniques et d'exploitation se rapportant spécifiquement aux radiocommunications » et pour ce qui concerne le CCITT « sur les questions techniques, d'exploitation et de tarification concernant les services de télécommunications », à l'exception de celles qui sont spécifiquement de la compétence du CCIR. Ces deux Comités permanents constituent en leur sein des commissions d'études, comme cela est indiqué aux pages 52-53. Leurs activités sont citées à la page 230 (Spectre des fréquences) et à la page 240 (Standards).

La création d'une « Commission internationale indépendante pour le développement des télécommunications mondiales » fut une importante décision prise à la Conférence de Nairobi en 1982. Cette commission aura pour tâche de recommander une série de méthodes, connues ou inédites « pour stimuler le développement des communications dans les pays en développement à l'aide de techniques appropriées... de manière à assurer progressivement l'autosuffisance des pays en développement et à réduire l'écart entre les pays en développement et les pays développés ».

La Commission sera composée de « 15 à 20 représentants des centres de décision les plus élevés des administrations, des exploitations et de l'industrie des pays en développement et des pays développés, ainsi que des grandes institutions financières (y compris les banques de développement et le PNUD) et d'autres instances appropriées, en visant la meilleure représentation possible de toutes les régions du monde ». Il s'agit là, véritablement, d'une reconnaissance par les différents pays du monde de la nécessité de réduire l'écart qui existe entre les pays industrialisés et les pays en développement, en ce qui concerne les infrastructures de télécommunications, et qu'à cet effet il est essentiel de déployer un immense effort de coopération.

□

A WORLDWIDE
AND CONSTRU(

The growing realization among people and nations of the critical role of communications in the social and economic development of all countries led, in 1981, to the proclamation of 1983 as World Communications Year by the General Assembly of the United Nations.

The UN resolution, adopted by consensus, recognized "the fundamental importance of communications infrastructures as an essential element in the economic and social development of all countries" and that "a World Communications Year" would provide the opportunity for all countries to undertake an

in-depth review and analysis of their policies on communications development and stimulate the accelerated development of communications infrastructures".

The ITU was entrusted as lead agency for the Year with responsibility for co-ordinating the inter-organizational aspects of the program of action undertaken with all the other agencies of the UN. This was endorsed by the Nairobi Plenipotentiary Conference and by the Administrative Council of the ITU. The Conference adopted a Resolution on the Year recognizing the basic objectives laid down by the United Nations General Assembly.

Agency interests range widely, from the special infrastructure aspects of telecommunications (ITU); correspondence and written message (UPU); mass communications broadcasting television, print and book media (UNESCO); to the many user interests health care (WHO); transport (IMCO, ICAO); and various other parts of this United Nations family whose functional purposes depend upon satisfactory communications facilities.

New horizons have opened wide, and new hopes created by the exciting new communications technologies. These can only be realized if the potential of technological advances are widely understood and appreciated, by those who govern and by those who determine investment strategies. To create this understanding and to stimulate the active interest and co-operation of all concerned was the prime objective of the World Communications Year.

The vast program of action generated by the ITU to assist countries to take policy decisions in matters of investment and the choice of technology, in the adoption of standards and in the sharing of facilities, has already had, and continues to have, a major impact. The Nairobi Conference devoted considerable attention to increasing the scope of the ITU's technical co-operation and assistance activities, instructing the Administrative Council and the Secretary-General to carry out the necessary studies in order to improve the effectiveness of its assistance to Member countries.

□

prise de conscience du rôle capital des communications a ussé, en 1981, l'Assemblée générale des Nations Unies à oclamer 1983 « Année mondiale des communications ». La solution, adoptée à l'unanimité, reconnaît : « l'importance ndamentale des infrastructures des communications en tant l'élément essèntiel du développement économique et social de us les pays » et qu'« une Année mondiale des communica- ns fournirait à tous les pays l'occasion d'examiner en pro- ndeur et d'analyser leur politique en matière de développe- ent des communications et encouragerait le développement

La mayor comprensión por pueblos y naciones del vital papel de las comunicaciones en el desarrollo económico y social de todos los países llevó en 1981 a la proclamación por la Asam- blea General de las Naciones Unidas de 1983 como Año Mundial de las Comunicaciones.

La resolución de las NU, adoptada por consenso, reconoce « la importancia fundamental de la infraestructuras de las co- municaciones como un elemento indispensable al desarrollo económico y social de todos los países » y que « el Año Mundial de las Comunicaciones brindará la oportunidad a todos los

el intervalo entre las Conferencias de Plenipotencia- rios..., actuará como mandatario de la Conferencia de Plenipotenciarios, dentro de los límites de las fa- cultades que ésta le delegue », asegurará « la coordi- nación eficaz de las actividades de la Unión y ejer- cerá un control financiero efectivo sobre sus órganos permanentes ». El *Convenio de Ginebra* especificaba que promoverá « la cooperación internacional, ... es- pecialmente por la participación de la Unión en los programas apropiados de las Naciones Unidas », y el *Convenio de Nairobi* requiere que el Consejo « de- terminará cada año la política de asistencia técnica ».

Los órganos permanentes de la UIT y sus funcio- nes (citadas en la pág. 52) han evolucionado con el tiempo. Esencialmente constan del Consejo de Ad- ministración, la Secretaría General, la Junta Internacional de Registro de Frecuencias (IFRB) y los Comités Consultivos Internacionales (CCIR y CCITT).

La Secretaría General es el órgano ejecutivo de la UIT, dirigido por el Secretario General, secundado por un Vicesecretario General. El Secretario General infor- ma al Consejo de Administración y es responsable « de todos los aspectos administrativos y financieros de las acitividades de la Unión ». Preside un Comité de Coordinación que es, en realidad, el Comité de Gestión de la Unión « integrado por el Vicesecretario general, los Directores de los Comités Consultivos Internacionales, el Presidente de la IFRB y su Vice- presidente ».

La Junta Internacional de Registro de Frecuencias (IFRB) tiene el cometido de « efectuar la inscripción y regis- tro metódicos de las asignaciones de frecuencias he- chas por los diferentes países » y de « asesorar a los miembros con miras a la explotación del mayor nú- mero posible de canales radioeléctricos », ampliado posteriormente para incluir la « inscripción ... de las posiciones asignadas por los países a los satélites geoestacionarios », y asesorar a los Miembros sobre « la utilización equitativa, eficaz y económica de la órbita de los satélites geoestacionarios ».

Los Comités Consultivos Internacionales han de « realizar estudios y formular recomendaciones »; el CCIR so- bre « cuestiones técnicas y de explotación relativas específicamente a las radiocomunicaciones », y el CCITT sobre « las cuestiones técnicas, de explota- ción y de tarificación que se refieren a los servicios de telecomunicación », salvo las que competen al CCIR. Ambos están organizados en comisiones de estudio, como se muestra en las páginas 52-53 y sus activida- des se analizan en la pág. 230 (Spectrum) y en el recuadro de la pág. 240 (Standards).

La creación de una « Comisión internacional independiente para el desarrollo mundial de las telecomunicaciones » fue una importante decisión tomada en Nairobi. Formarán parte de ella representantes de los principales res- ponsables de los centros de decisión más elevados, con el mandato concreto de examinar y recomendar una serie de métodos, incluso nuevos, « para estimu- lar el desarrollo de las telecomunicaciones en el mundo en desarrollo mediante la utilización de tec- nologías apropiadas y probadas » que lleve a « la progresiva autosuficiencia del mundo en desarrollo y la reducción de la diferencia entre los países en de- sarrollo y desarrollados ».

La Comisión se compondrá de « 15 a 20 represen- tantes de los principales responsables de los centros de decisión más elevados de las administraciones, de los organismos de ejecución y de la industria de los países en desarrollo y desarrollados, así como de las principales instituciones financieras (incluidos los bancos de desarrollo y el PNUD) y demás entidades competentes, procurando conseguir la mejor repre- sentación posible ». Esto demuestra que las naciones del mundo reconocen que la diferencia en las in- fraestructuras de telecomunicaciones entre países industrializados y en desarrollo debe reducirse, y que ello exige un inmenso esfuerzo de cooperación.

céléré des infrastructures des communications ». L'As- mblée générale a désigné l'UIT comme responsable de nnée et l'a chargée de coordonner les aspects inter-organi- tions du programme des activités entreprises par toutes les tres institutions des Nations Unies. Cette décision a été térinée par la Conférence de plénipotentiaires de Nairobi et r le Conseil d'administration de l'UIT. La Conférence a adopté e résolution au sujet de l'Année mondiale des communica- ns dont elle a reconnu les objectifs fondamentaux.

En ce qui concerne les intérêts des diverses institutions ecialisées des Nations Unies, il convient de mentionner les pects particuliers de l'infrastructure des télécommunications IT) et ceux de la correspondance et de la transmission de essages écrits (UPU), les moyens d'information des masses, ls que la radiodiffusion sonore et télévisuelle, aussi bien que presse et les imprimés, les livres, etc. (UNESCO) ; à cela il ut ajouter les intérêts d'une multitude d'usagers dans divers maines tels que la santé publique et les soins médicaux MS), les transports (OMI, OACI), et ceux d'autres organismes s Nations Unies dont le fonctionnement dépend de la dispo- bilité et de la qualité des moyens de communication.

De nouvelles perspectives ont été ouvertes et de nouveaux poirs ont été soulevés par les technologies des communica- ns. Leur potentiel ne sera réalisable que si elles sont bien mprises et correctement évaluées par ceux qui gouvernent et ux qui déterminent les stratégies d'investissement.

L'année mondiale des communications fut instituée, dans le ut précis de créer cette compréhension et de stimuler l'intérêt la coopération de tous ceux qui sont concernés.

Le vaste programme d'action conçu par l'UIT pour aider des ys à définir leur politique d'investissement et leur choix de chnologies, à adopter des normes internationales et à s'en- aider, a déjà donné d'excellents résultats. La Conférence de airobi s'est concentrée sur l'accroissement du rôle de coopé- tion et d'assistance technique de l'UIT et a chargé le Conseil administration et le Secrétaire général d'entreprendre les udes nécessaires pour améliorer l'efficacité de l'assistance urnie aux pays membres.

países de realizar un examen y análisis a fondo de sus políticas en materia de desarrollo de las comunicaciones y estimulará el crecimiento acelerado de la infraestructura de las comunica- ciones ». Confió a la UIT, como organismo rector del Año, la responsabilidad de coordinar los aspectos interinstitucionales del programa de acción emprendido con todos los demás or- ganismos de las NU. Esto fue respaldado por la Conferencia de Plenipotenciarios de Nairobi y por el Consejo de Administración de la UIT. La Conferencia adoptó una resolución sobre el Año, reconociendo los objetivos básicos enunciados por la Asamblea General de las Naciones Unidas.

Los intereses de los organismos abarcan una amplia gama, desde los aspectos especiales de la infraestructura de las telecomunicaciones (UIT), la correspondencia y los mensajes escritos (UPU), las comunicaciones de masas, la radiodifusión, la televisión, los medios de impresión y los libros (UNESCO) hasta múltiples intereses de los usuarios por la atención sani- taria (OMS), el transporte (OMI, OACI), y otros organismos de las NU cuyos fines funcionales dependen de facilidades de comunicación satisfactorias.

Las nuevas y apasionantes tecnologías de las comunicacio- nes han abierto otros horizontes y creado nuevas esperanzas, que sólo pueden realizarse si se comprende y aprecia general- mente el potencial de los avances tecnológicos por quienes gobiernan y determinan las estrategias de inversión. El objetivo primordial del Año Mundial de las Comunicaciones es crear esa comprensión y estimular el interés y la cooperación activos de todos los afectados.

El vasto programa de acción de la UIT para ayudar a los países a tomar decisiones políticas en materias de inversión y elección de tecnología, adopción de normas y compartición de facilidades, ha producido ya excelentes resultados. La Confe- rencia de Nairobi consagró gran atención a las actividades de cooperación y asistencia técnicas de la UIT, para darles mayor alcance y eficacia, y encargó al Consejo de Administración y al Secretario General los estudios necesarios para que su asis- tencia a los países Miembros sea más eficaz.

□

THE ORIGINS AND SCIENTIFIC FOUNDATIONS OF MODERN COMMUNICATIONS

COMMUNICATIONS over distance has always been a preoccupation of man, from time immemorial. The story goes that Noah on the Ark, after 150 days of anguish, sent out a raven to find land. Unsuccessful, the raven returned. Some days later Noah sent a dove. The dove returned with an olive branch, proof that at last the flood water had receded (*Genesis VIII-7*). Noah had sent out his signal and it came back with information from a distance. This, according to the etymology of the word, is "telecommunications".

Communications through the ages of man ranged from physical delivery of messages, by runner, horse or pigeon, to the use of signals carrying over distance such as light beams, smoke, noise or semaphore. Darius I of Persia used horses, the Egyptians megaphones (they had exceptionally strong lungs!), the Chinese carrier pigeons, the Greeks flashing light heliographs. The Romans built straight roads and used beacons for speed. In the Middle Ages watch towers were the rule, supplemented by smoke signals. The Renaissance favoured church bells and cannon booms. In the 18th and 19th centuries various methods were in use in the many wars that were waged, in Europe and elsewhere. Optics came into their own with flashing lights and semaphores, until in 1837 came the telegraph and its Morse code.

The scientific foundations of communications over distance, the telecommunications of today, were laid as early as in the 17th Century by Sir Isaac Newton and Gottfried von Leibniz who developed theories of motion, light and tools of calculus and mathematical logic. The 19th Century was highly productive of basic concepts which took many years to realize in practice. Michael Faraday's and Hans Christian Oersted's work during the 1830s and 1840s on the properties of electricity and magnetism, followed by

▷ 62

"Candlestick" phone and telegraph key in the early days of communications: the first instruments of the American Telephone and Telegraph Company (AT&T).

DEPUIS DES TEMPS IMMÉMORIAUX, les communications à distance sont une préoccupation de l'homme. Cela remonte à Noé sur son Arche qui, après cent cinquante jours d'angoisse, envoya un corbeau à la recherche d'une terre, mais en vain, car celui-ci s'en revint bientôt. Quelque temps après, Noé lâcha une colombe qui ramena dans son bec un rameau d'olivier, preuve que le niveau des eaux du déluge avait baissé. (*Gen. VIII-7*). Ainsi, la « sonde » qu'il avait lancée lui rapportait de loin l'information attendue. C'était déjà une « télécommunication », au sens étymologique du mot.

Durant l'histoire de l'humanité, les communications à distance sont passées du stade de la délivrance physique de messages par des coureurs, des chevaux ou des pigeons, à celui des signaux à distance au moyen de feux ou de faisceaux lumineux, de fumée, de bruit ou de sémaphores. Darius Ier de Perse utilisait des chevaux, les Egyptiens des mégaphones, les Chinois des pigeons voyageurs, les Grecs des « héliographes ». Sur les routes rectilignes qu'ils construisaient, les Romains se servaient de phares pour leurs communications rapides. Au moyen-âge, les tours de garde, qui étaient nombreuses, permettaient l'émission de signaux de fumée. Pendant la Renaissance, on utilisait plutôt les cloches des églises ou le bruit du canon. Au cours des 18ème et 19ème siècles, diverses méthodes furent appliquées dans les guerres qui sévissaient alors en Europe et ailleurs. Par la suite, l'optique s'imposa avec ses faisceaux lumineux intermittents et ses sémaphores jusqu'en 1837, année de l'avènement du télégraphe électrique et du code Morse.

Les bases scientifiques des communications à distance et des télécommunications modernes ont été établies dès le 17ème siècle par Sir Isaac Newton, qui découvrit la loi de la gravitation universelle, élabora une théorie de la lumière et des couleurs et fit, en même temps

▷ 62

Téléphone « bougeoir » et manipulateur télégraphique à l'aube des communications modernes : les premiers instruments de l'American Telephone and Telegraph Company (AT&T).

LAS COMUNICACIONES A DISTANCIA han preocupado siempre al hombre, desde tiempo inmemorial. Según la historia, tras 150 días en el arca, Noé envió un cuervo en busca de tierra. Y el cuervo volvió, sin éxito. Días después, Noé envió una paloma, que regresó con un ramo de olivo, prueba de que la crecida había cedido (*Gen. VIII-7*). La paloma de Noé fue una primera forma de radar. Transmitió una señal a distancia, y volvió con información. Y eso son las «telecomunicaciones».

A través de las épocas, las comunicaciones han variado desde la entrega física de mensajes, por medio de propios, caballos, como en Persia durante el reino de Darío I, o palomas, como in China, hasta la utilización de señales a larga distancia, como los haces luminosos, el humo, las campanas de las iglesias y los disparos de cañón en el Renacimiento. En los siglos XVIII y XIX se emplearon muchos medios en las numerosas guerras. La óptica logró sus fines con las luces intermitentes y los semáforos, hasta 1837, en que llegaron el telégrafo y el código morse.

Las bases científicas de las comunicaciones a distancia fueron enunciadas ya en el siglo XVII por sir Isaac Newton y Gottfried von Leibniz, quienes desarrollaron teorías de movimiento, luz e instrumentos de cálculo y lógica matemática. En el siglo XIX surgieron numerosas nociones fundamentales cuya realización práctica ha llevado muchos años. Michael Faraday y H. Christian Oersted formulaban, durante los años 1830 y 1840, las propiedades de la electricidad y el magnetismo; James Maxwell las teorías fundamentales sobre el electromagnetismo, comprendidas las microondas y las guiaondas ópticas. La máquina analítica de Charles Babbage, en los años 1830, y las teorías de programación mecánica de Lovelace, en los años 1850, constituyeron la base del desarrollo

▷ 63

El teléfono "candelero" y el manipulador telegráfico en los albores de las comunicaciones modernas: los primeros instrumentos de la American Telephone and Telegraph Company (AT&T).

1800-2000: TWO CENTURIES OF CONVERG

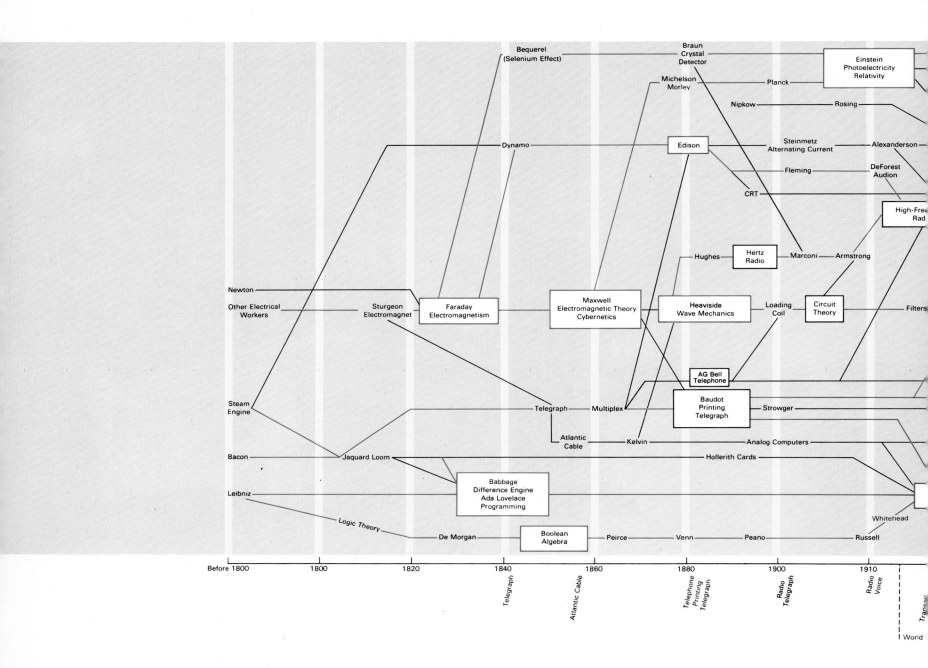

Almost all current telecommunications technology can be traced to a few major scientific theories and discoveries of the 19th and 20th Centuries, essentially those of the electron, electromagnetism, and quantum mechanics in the 19th; relativistic physics, switching logic and digital communications in the 20th. Virtually all basic innovations emanating from those theories were made during and immediately after World War II. The chart, established on the basis of research undertaken by ITT, pictures some of these major developments from the 18th Century theories of electricity and logic and shows how they

have come together to provide the basis of today's computers and telecommunications. It can also be seen how virtually all the basic commercial innovations date from the World War II era, stemming from the final acceptance of electronics as the basis of telecommunications coupled with extensive exploration into materials science which has led ultimately to the development of solid-state electronics; into number and computation techniques. These have fostered digital computers and telephone switching machines. The development and use of operational research inspired new and sophisticated management concepts.

La quasi totalité de la technologie des télécommunicatio modernes découle d'un petit nombre de théories scientifiqu établies aux 19ème et 20ème siècles : essentiellement celles l'électron, de l'électromagnétisme et de la mécanique quan que, au 19ème siècle, et de la physique relativiste, de la logiq de commutation et des transmission numériques, au 20è siècle. Pratiquement, toutes les inventions fondamentales coulent de ces théories. Le graphique, établi sur la base d recherches de ITT, montre les réalisations majeures fondées

G TECHNOLOGIES

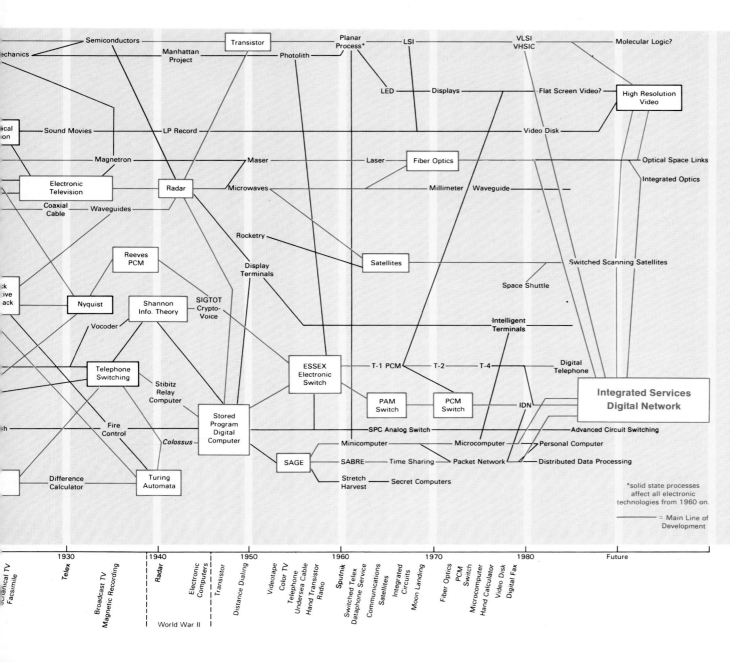

Semiconductors — Manhattan Project — Transistor — Photolith — Planar Process* — LSI — VLSI VHSIC — Molecular Logic?

echanics

LED — Displays — Flat Screen Video? — High Resolution Video

cal on — Sound Movies — LP Record — Video Disk

Magnetron — Maser — Laser — Fiber Optics — Optical Space Links

Integrated Optics

Electronic Television — Radar — Microwaves — Millimeter Waveguide

Coaxial Cable — Waveguides

Rocketry

Reeves PCM

Display Terminals — Satellites — Switched Scanning Satellites

Space Shuttle

k ive ck

Nyquist — Shannon Info. Theory — SIGTOT Crypto-Voice

Vocoder

Intelligent Terminals

Telephone Switching — ESSEX Electronic Switch — T-1 PCM — T-2 — T-4 — Digital Telephone

Stibitz Relay Computer

Integrated Services Digital Network

PAM Switch — PCM Switch — IDN

h — Fire Control

Stored Program Digital Computer — SPC Analog Switch — Advanced Circuit Switching

Colossus — Minicomputer — Microcomputer — Personal Computer

SAGE — SABRE — Time Sharing — Packet Network — Distributed Data Processing

Stretch Harvest — Secret Computers

Difference Calculator — Turing Automata

*solid state processes affect all electronic technologies from 1960 on.

= Main Line of Development

1930 | 1940 | 1950 | 1960 | 1970 | 1980 | Future

cal TV Facsimile | Telex | Broadcast TV Magnetic Recording | Radar | Electronic Computers Transistor | Distance Dialing | Videotape Color TV Telephone Undersea Cable Hand Transistor Radio | Sputnik Switched Telex Dataphone Service Communications Satellites Integrated Circuits Moon Landing | Fiber Optics PCM Switch Microcomputer Hand Calculator Video Disk Digital Fax

World War II

théories de l'électricité et de la logique qui constituent la e des ordinateurs et des télécommunications d'aujourd'hui. peut également voir que pratiquement toutes les innovations merciales fondamentales datent de la deuxième guerre ndiale et qu'elles sont fondées sur l'électronique, et aussi une exploration intensive de la science des matériaux, utissant en définitive à l'élaboration du transistor et aux niques numériques de calcul. Ceux-ci ont donné une impsion aux ordinateurs et aux dispositifs de commutation phonique et à la recherche opérationnelle qui a inspiré de veaux concepts de gestion perfectionnés.

Casi toda la tecnología de las telecomunicaciones actual se debe a unas cuantas teorías y descubrimientos científicos importantes de los siglos XIX y XX, esencialmente los electrones, el electromagnetismo y la mecánica cuántica en el siglo XIX, la física de la relatividad, la lógica de la conmutación y las comunicaciones digitales en el siglo XX. Virtualmente, todas las innovaciones básicas que emanan de esas teorías se hicieron durante la Segunda Guerra Mundial e inmediatamente después. El gráfico — establecido sobre la base de investigaciones realizadas por ITT — muestra algunos de esos grandes avances

del siglo XVIII, y su agrupación para constituir la base de los computadores y las telecomunicaciones actuales. También puede verse cómo casi todas las innovaciones comerciales básicas datan de la Segunda Guerra Mundial, fundándose en la aceptación final de la electrónica y la base de las telecomunicaciones, un amplio estudio de los materiales, que ha llevado al desarrollo de la electronica de estado sólido; de técnicas numéricas y de cálculo, que han impulsado los computadores digitales y los aparatos telefonicos con conmutación; y de la investigación operacional, que ha inspirado nuevos conceptos de gestión.

James Maxwell's theory of electromagnetism, including microwave and optical wave guides, were basic. The roots of computer development were laid by Charles Babbage's analytical engine in the 1830s, and Lovelace's theories of machine programming in the 1850s. During that period George Boole's algebra of logic established the framework for switching theory and Jean-Emile Baudot was the first to apply an efficient binary code with his printing telegraph system.

"The great domain of electricity has become a mighty kingdom" exclaimed Heinrich Hertz upon establishing that radio waves existed (1886). Indeed most physical phenomena later applied in modern telecommunications were explained by the theories of the electron. At the turn of the last century Albert Einstein's explanation of photoelectric phenomena and relativistic physics, together with Max Planck's quantum theory hypothesis, led directly to the model of the atom by Niels Bohr and to the expansion of the concept of quantum mechanics which opened the door to solid-state exploration, resulting in the development of the transistor and, ultimately, of integrated micro-circuit electronics. Once the relativistic and quantum processes were understood by engineers and electrical technicians, the technologies emerged rapidly, speeded up by the needs of the two world wars.

After quantum mechanics, only one more advance, computation theory, was needed to pull together all of the preceding physics into the computer, the keystone of modern telecommunications. Computation theory started in the mid-1930s with Alan Mathison Turing's concept of a universal imitating machine and was advanced significantly at the close of World War II by Johann Ludwig von Neumann's plans for a stored-program digital computer and by Claude Elwood Shannon's information theory in the mid 1940s. Significant advances in understanding of physical theories, particularly as they apply to telecommunications, date back to the development of the transistor in 1948.

The 19th Century had been marked by the development of a remarkable number of technological concepts. However, these — such as microwave radio, digital coding and switching techniques, have taken several generations to be realized in practice. The missing elements were generally lack of suitable materials. It was the intensive development of materials research during the two world wars, and especially during World War II, which made possible virtually all technical applications realized in the 1970s and 1980s.

Aware of the new possibilities, the telecommunications laboratories of industrialized countries contributed heavily to the new physics. A striking example of such advances is the development of digital switching and, from this, of the computer. In struggling to bring telephone networks out of the electromechanical switching mode, communications specialists used the algebra of George Boole to transform the design of telephone circuitry from a cut-and-try process into an orderly procedure which allowed switching systems to become simplified as well as modularized. In advancing the development of switching systems, engineers extended Boolean logic a step further. They reasoned that if switching circuits could route telephone calls, then it must be possible to design circuitry that could carry out routine computations. The first US computer, ENIAC, proved they were right. Essentially, the computer is a switching system.

The next major step forward, which opened the door wide for the communications explosion of today, was the invention of the transistor in 1948. The original transistor consisted of a semiconductor material — germanium — and was about the size of a pencil eraser. In a matter of months it made the bulky, undependable vacuum tube obsolete. The scene was set for today's breathtaking leap forward.

□

que Gottfried von Leibniz, la découverte du calcul différentiel et intégral, alors que ce dernier inventa lui-même une machine à calculer. Ainsi, ces deux savants apportèrent à l'humanité les instruments du calcul et de la logique mathématique. Au 19ème siècle, Michael Faraday et Hans Christian Oersted étudièrent, entre 1830 et 1840, les propriétés de l'électricité et du magnétisme. Ils furent suivis par James Maxwell qui élabora les théories fondamentales de l'électromagnétisme et celles des micro-ondes et des guides d'ondes optiques, etc. Quant aux débuts de la conception des ordinateurs, ils remontent à la décennie de 1830 au cours de laquelle Charles Babbage inventa sa machine analytique. A partir de 1850, ce furent successivement les théories de la programmation mécanique de Lovelace, l'algèbre de George Boole qui établissait le principe de la commutation et Jean-Emile Baudot qui fut le premier à appliquer un code binaire efficace à son système télégraphique imprimant.

« Le grand domaine de l'électricité est devenu un puissant royaume : » s'exclama Heinrich Hertz lorsqu'il eut prouvé l'existence des ondes radioélectriques (1866). En fait, la plupart des phénomènes physiques intéressant les télécommunications modernes ont été éclaircis par les théories sur l'électron. Au tournant du siècle, la théorie de la relativité élaborée par Albert Einstein et son interprétation de l'effet photoélectrique fondée sur l'hypothèse des quanta de Max Planck conduisait directement à la représentation électronique de l'atome qui allait être donnée par Niels Bohr. L'élargissement de la théorie et de la mécanique quantique ouvrit la porte à l'exploration de l'*état solide*, c.à.d. à l'élaboration du transistor et au développement de l'électronique et des microcircuits intégrés.

Après la mécanique quantique, il fallait faire un nouveau pas pour inventer l'ordinateur qui devait devenir la pierre angulaire de la *télématique* moderne. Cette étape fut franchie vers 1935 par Alan M. Turing qui eut l'idée d'une *machine reproductrice universelle* dont le principe fut considérablement perfectionné vers la fin de la guerre par Johann L. von Neumann qui élabora les plans d'un ordinateur numérique programmé puis, après 1945, par la théorie de l'information de Claude E. Shannon.

L'application de ces théories aux télécommunications coïncide avec la mise au point du transistor en 1948 ; il a donc fallu plusieurs générations pour le mettre en pratique, sous la forme des radiocommunications à hyperfréquences, du codage numérique et des techniques de commutation.

Les laboratoires de télécommunications des pays industrialisés ont largement contribué aux progrès de la physique moderne. Dans leurs efforts pour mettre fin à l'exploitation des réseaux téléphoniques par le procédé — jugé insuffisant — de la commutation électromécanique, les spécialistes des télécommunications ont utilisé l'algèbre de George Boole afin de coordonner la méthode de fonctionnement des circuits en simplifiant les systèmes de commutation et en les rendant « modulaires ». Au cours de leurs travaux, les ingénieurs ont estimé que si les circuits de commutation pouvaient acheminer les communications téléphoniques, il devait aussi être possible de concevoir des circuits capables d'effectuer des calculs ordinaires. Ce prolongement de la logique de Boole se révéla parfaitement justifié lors de la mise au point aux Etats-Unis du premier ordinateur ENIAC, grâce auquel il fut brillamment démontré que l'ordinateur est, essentiellement, un système de commutation.

Le grand pas en avant d'aujourd'hui fut donc l'invention du transistor en 1948, qui a déclanché l'explosion des télécommunications et de la télématique d'aujourd'hui. Le premier transistor consistait en un morceau de métal semi-conducteur : le germanium. En l'espace de quelques mois le vieux tube à vide encombrant et peu fiable fut remplacé par une pièce de la dimension d'un petit pois. Dès lors tout était prêt pour le formidable bond en avant d'aujourd'hui.

□

This is Broadway, in New York City, in the 1890s. The drawing shows the web of wires around the Western Union building.

Voici Broadway, dans la cité de New York, des années 1890. La gravure montre tous les fils aériens qui entouraient le siège de Western Union.

del computador. Durante ese período, el álgebra de
George Boole estableció el marco para la teoría de la
conmutación, y Jean-Emile Baudot fue el primero en
aplicar un código binario eficiente con su sistema
telegráfico de impresión.

**«El gran dominio de la electricidad se ha convertido en un
poderoso reino»,** exclamó Heinrich Hertz al comprobar
la existencia de las ondas radioeléctricas (1886). Las
teorías de los electrones explicaban la mayoría de los
fenómenos físicos aplicados después en las telecomunicaciones modernas. Al finalizar el siglo, las
aclaraciones de Albert Einstein sobre los fenómenos
fotoeléctricos y la física de la relatividad, junto con
las hipótesis de la teoría cuántica de Max Planck,
llevaron al modelo del átomo por Niels Bohr y a la
expansión del concepto de la mecánica cuántica, que
abrió la puerta a la exploración del estado sólido, lo
que dio lugar al desarrollo del transistor y, por último, de la electrónica de microcircuitos integrados.
Una vez comprendidos los procesos de la relatividad y cuánticos, las tecnologías surgieron rápidamente, aceleradas por las necesidades de las dos
guerras mundiales.

Después de la mecánica cuántica, sólo se necesitaba un nuevo avance, la teoría de la computadorización, para agrupar toda la física precedente en el
computador, la piedra angular de las telecomunicaciones modernas. La teoría de la computadorización
se inició a mediados de los años 1930, con la noción
de Alan Mathison Turing de una máquina teórica
universal, y avanzó considerablemente al terminar la
Segunda Guerra Mundial, merced a los planes de
Johann Ludwig von Neumann para un computador
digital de programa almacenado, y a la teoría de la
información de Claude Elwood Shannon, a mediados de los años 1940.

Los considerables avances en la comprensión de
teorías físicas, sobre todo aplicables a las telecomunicaciones, se remontan al desarrollo del transistor
en 1948. El siglo XIX se caracterizó por el desarrollo
de un notable número de conceptos tecnológicos,
pero habían de pasar varias generaciones hasta su
realización práctica, como las comunicaciones por
microondas, la codificación digital y las técnicas de
conmutación. En general, se carecía de materiales
apropiados. El intensivo desarrollo de la investigación de materiales durante las dos guerras mundiales, y sobre todo la segunda, es lo que hizo virtualmente posible todas las aplicaciones técnicas realizadas en los decenios de 1970 y 1980.

Conscientes de las nuevas posibilidades, los laboratorios de telecomunicaciones de los países industrializados contribuyeron mucho a la nueva física.
Un buen ejemplo de esos avances es la conmutación
digital y, a partir de ella, del computador. En su
lucha por sacar las redes telefónicas del modo de
conmutación electromecánico, los especialistas en
comunicaciones emplearon el álgebra de George
Boole para transformar el diseño de los circuitos
telefónicos de un proceso de tanteo en un procedimiento ordenado que permitía simplificar y modu-
larizar los sistemas de conmutación. Avanzando en
su desarrollo, los ingenieros dieron un nuevo paso en
la lógica booleana. Pensaron que si los circuitos de
conmutación podían transformar llamadas telefónicas debía ser posible diseñar circuitos que pudieran
efectuar cálculos ordinarios. El primer computador
estadounidense, ENIAC, demostró que tenían razón.
Esencialmente, el computador es un sistema de conmutación.

El siguiente paso importante, que abrió la puerta a la
actual explosión de las comunicaciones, fue la invención del transistor en 1948. El transistor original constaba de un material semiconductor — germanio — del tamaño de una goma de borrar. En cuestión de meses, dejó anticuado al voluminoso e inse-
guro tubo de vacío. Se habían establecido las condiciones para el sorprendente avance de hoy.

□

*Broadway, en la ciudad de Nueva York, en
los años 1890. El grabado muestra los hilos aéreos
que rodeaban la sede de Western Union.*

WORLD COMMUNICATIONS TODAY
SNEWPO THE HUMAN DIMENSION WERNEWHO
IN INTERNATIONAL GOALS

THE TELECOMMUNICATION SYSTEM that exists today, imperfect and imbalanced as it is, constitutes an astonishing triumph of human ingenuity over distance and delay. A census of telephone stations and television receivers, two of the most representative indicators, showed that in 1983, there were 565 million telephones and 600 million television sets. These, however, were concentrated in only 8 and 9 countries respectively. Telephone densities, expressed in numbers of stations per 100 inhabitants, tell the same story: the lowest density 0.4 per cent was in Africa, compared with 4.5 per cent in South America, 5.2 in Asia, (40.3 in Japan), 19.1 in Europe and 71.0 in North America (80% in the USA).

A survey of the telecommunications scene today reveals an enormous variation in systems, equipment and services available from one region of the world to another, so strikingly illustrated by the chart on the next page, between countries in the same region and even between areas in the same country. The most recently available statistics are given in the chart on p. 68.

Even in the USA there exist startling differences in density and usage of telephones between areas of high economic and social activity and rural areas. The Rural Electrification Administration, REA, has for the past 40 years provided funds at low interest rates for the provision and improvement of telephone services in rural areas. In all, over these four decades, REA borrowers served 6.3 million telephones, in itself a remarkable achievement. This, however, accounted for only 3.6 per cent of the total number of telephones in the country and the density of telephones per 100 of total population remains substantially less than in urban areas.

▷ 66

LE SYSTÈME ACTUEL DES TÉLÉCOMMUNICATIONS, bien qu'imparfait et déséquilibré, constitue un étonnant triomphe de l'ingéniosité de l'homme sur la distance et le temps. Un recensement des appareils téléphoniques et des récepteurs de télévision — deux des indices très représentatifs — a montré qu'en 1983 il existait 565 millions de téléphones (stations ou lignes) et 600 millions d'appareils de télévision, concentrés respectivement dans 8 et 9 pays seulement. Les densités téléphoniques exprimées en nombre d'appareils pour 100 habitants, parlent de la même manière : la densité la plus faible, 0,4%, se trouve en Afrique, tandis qu'on trouve 4,5% en Amérique du Sud, 5,2% en Asie (40,3% au Japon), 19,1% en Europe et 71,0% en Amérique du Nord (80% aux Etats-Unis).

Une étude sur la situation actuelle des télécommunications, révèle d'énormes différences dans les systèmes, les équipements et les services disponibles, d'une région à l'autre du monde, comme cela est illustré par le graphique de la page 68.

Même aux Etats-Unis, il existe de grands écarts de densité et d'utilisation des téléphones entre les zones d'intense activité économique et sociale et les zones de faible densité de population. La Rural Electrification Administration (REA) a ouvert, au cours des quarante ans écoulés, des crédits à faible intérêt, pour favoriser l'amélioration des services téléphoniques dans les zones rurales. C'est ainsi qu'au cours des quatre décennies écoulées, les emprunteurs de la REA ont acquis 6,3 millions d'appareils téléphoniques. Ce résultat est par lui-même remarquable mais il ne compte que pour 3,6% du nombre total des appareils du pays et la densité téléphonique par 100 habitants reste sensiblement inférieure à celle des zones urbaines.

▷ 66

EL ACTUAL SISTEMA DE TELECOMUNICACIONES, aunque imperfecto y desequilibrado, constituye un asombroso triunfo del ingenio humano sobre la distancia y el tiempo. Un censo de aparatos telefónicos y receptores de televisión, dos de los indicadores más representativos, muestra que en 1983 hay 565 millones de teléfonos y 600 millones de aparatos de televisión concentrados, sin embargo, tal sólo en 8 y 9 países, respectivamente. Las densidades, expresadas en número de aparatos por 1000 habitantes, presentan la misma situación: la menor densidad, 0,4%, se da en Africa, en comparación con el 4,5% en América del Sur, el 5,2% en Asia, el 40,3% en Japón, el 19,1% en Europa, y el 71,0% en América del Norte (80% en EE.UU.).

Un estudio sobre la situación de las telecomunicaciones revela una enorme variación en los sistemas, el equipo y los servicios disponibles de una región del mundo a otra, como se ilustra en el gráfico de las páginas siguientes entre países de la misma región, e incluso entre zonas del mismo país. La estadísticas más recientes figuran en los gráficos de la pág. 68.

Incluso en EE.UU. existen enormes diferencias en la densidad y uso de los teléfonos entre zonas de gran actividad económica y social y zonas rurales. La Rural Electrification Administration (REA) proporciona fondos desde hace 40 años a reducidos tipos de interés para la prestación y mejora de servicios telefónicos en zonas rurales. En total, durante estas cuatro décadas, los prestatarios de la REA han proporcionado 6,3 millones de teléfonos, lo que constituye un notable logro, pero sólo representan el 3,6% del número total de aparatos del país, y la densidad de teléfonos por 100 habitantes sigue siendo sustancialmente inferior a la de las zonas urbanas.

▷ 67

Human communications:
"raison d'être" of all technologies.

La communication entre les
hommes : raison d'être de toutes les technologies.

La comunicación entre los
hombres: razón de ser de todas las tecnologías.

Major advances in communications technology in recent years, have substantially widened the range of services carried by the network. Satellites, microwave radio, optical cable links, digital switching and transmission, offer a potential for the improvement of quality, and for the extension of access to the remotest areas. This whole gamut of rampant electronic technology is pushing hard towards the realization of fully integrated world information network. Subject to a greater geographical spread of investment, this could become the "neural system" of society, as outlined on p. 12.

Technological know-how is no longer a constraint on development. The principles are well established, the "chip"-based hardware well developed and software production is catching up with requirements. Two major hurdles, however, need to be surmounted, both economic in character: cost and investment. The first is being tackled with energy the world over. Microminiaturization has already substantially reduced the cost of switching, transmission and processing; satellites and their associated earth stations have reduced the cost of reaching the farthest outposts. Cost trends remain sharply downwards.

Geographical imbalance, however, remains a mayor problem, far from being solved. It is outlined in the pages that follow, graphically portrayed in the illustration opposite and statistically defined on the next page. The main elements within it and the factors affecting its solution have been the subject of a number of studies the ITU has instigated or carried out recently. One of these, a major global study, completed in 1980, was undertaken jointly with the Organization for Economic Cooperation and Development (OECD), to measure the benefits, direct and indirect, of investments in rural telecommunications in the developing world, and to propose technical and organizational solutions.

The ITU is the one organization striving towards a solution of this problem of imbalance, backed and assisted by other agencies of the United Nations as well as by the OECD, and by the communications industries. The Union acts, on behalf of its 158 Member nations, as co-ordinator and catalyst for the development of an integrated global telecommunication network. Since it was entrusted with the administration of a technical co-operation program in 1986, considerable progress has been made.

At the 1973 Plenipotentiary Conference in Spain, the ITU was instructed "to foster the creation, development and improvement of telecommunication equipment and networks in new or developing countries". The main features of the 1980 program were 630 field expert missions, 650 fellowships and 215 individual field projects. For 1983, Telecommunications Year, an even more comprehensive and ambitious program was approved at the Convention held in Nairobi in October 1982.

The ITU's work has resulted in the compilation of much factual information on the situation as it exists today. It has established that, in general, telecommunications have been developed primarily on the concept of financial return from the user, who has also been required to contribute capital towards investment to finance extensions of the networks. This has satisfied the large capital and provincial cities, interurban and international services. Countries' PTTs or large private operators in highly industrialized areas have been able to subsidize the extensions of the network to rural areas from the revenues obtained in urban areas where high usage rates permitted substantial profit margins. But even in these situations the temptation of operating organizations has been and continues to be to modernize and expand the existing network where it is densest and yields the highest returns on investment.

This approach to investment in telecommunications is not confined to network operators: international aid organizations and the governments of developing countries have likewise accorded a low

Les progrès importants réalisés dans la technologie des **communications** au cours de ces dernières années ont considérablement élargi la gamme des services fournis par le réseau. Les satellites, les radiocommunications à hyperfréquences, les liaisons en câble optique, la commutation et la transmission numériques offrent des possibilités d'amélioration de la qualité et de l'accès au réseau dans les zones les plus éloignées des grands centres. Tout cet arsenal technologique contribue puissamment à la réalisation d'un système mondial intégré et entièrement informatisé, un véritable « système nerveux » de la société d'information tel qu'il est décrit page 12.

Le savoir-faire technologique n'est plus une contrainte : les principes sont bien établis, le « système microprocesseur » est bien au point et la production de logiciel répond aux besoins. Cependant, deux obstacles majeurs de caractère économique doivent encore être surmontés : le prix de revient et les investissements. Le premier est en voie de solution. La microminiaturisation a déjà substantiellement réduit le coût de la commutation, de la transmission et du traitement; les satellites et les stations terriennes associées ont réduit les coûts d'accès aux régions les plus distantes des centres d'activité économique. La tendance continue à être à un abaissement considérable des prix de revient.

Le déséquilibre géographique du réseau est, néanmoins, encore loin d'être résolu. On en trouvera l'illustration graphique ci-contre et une présentation statistique à la page suivante. Il s'agit d'un phénomène que l'UIT a longuement approfondi, notamment au cours d'une étude entreprise en 1980, conjointement avec l'OCDE. Cette étude avait pour but de déterminer les avantages directs et indirects que peuvent apporter les investissements dans les télécommunications rurales dans le tiers monde.

L'UIT est l'organisation qui s'efforce de trouver une solution au problème du déséquilibre, avec l'aide et l'assistance de l'OCDE, aussi bien qu'avec celles des autres agences des Nations Unies et des industries des communications. L'UIT agit, en effet, comme coordonnateur et catalyseur d'un réseau de télécommunications mondial intégré, et c'est ainsi que, depuis qu'elle a été chargée, en 1960, d'un programme de coopération technique, des progrès considérables ont été réalisés.

Lors de la Conférence de plénipotentiaires de Malaga-Torremolinos en 1973, cette mission fut définie d'une manière plus précise, et l'UIT fut chargée de « susciter la création, le développement et le perfectionnement des installations et des réseaux de télécommunications dans les pays nouveaux et en développement ». Le programme de 1980 s'est concrétisé par 630 missions d'experts sur le terrain, 650 bourses d'études et 215 projets d'étude. Pour 1983, Année des communications, un programme encore plus ambitieux a été approuvé par la Conférence de plénipotentiaires de Nairobi.

Le travail de l'UIT a permis de rassembler beaucoup de renseignements concrets sur la situation actuelle. Il a été établi que, d'une manière générale, le développement des télécommunications dépend des recettes perçues auprès des utilisateurs qui doivent aussi assurer, en principe, le capital nécessaire pour financer l'extension du réseau. C'est ce qui a permis l'établissement de services interurbains et internationaux satisfaisants dans les capitales et les grandes villes de province. Ainsi, à l'échelon national, les services publics et les grandes entreprises privées responsables des PTT dans les régions très industrialisées ont été en mesure de subventionner les extensions de réseaux jusqu'aux zones rurales, grâce aux recettes obtenues dans les zones interurbaines où des tarifs élevés ont permis de réaliser des bénéfices substantiels. Cependant, même dans ces situations, les organismes d'exploitation ont été et continuent d'être tentés de moderniser et d'étendre le réseau aux endroits où il est le plus dense et le plus rentable.

Cette politique d'investissements dans le domaine des télécommunications n'est pas seulement celle des organismes responsables de l'exploitation du réseau : les organisations d'aide internationale et les gouvernements des pays en développement n'ont également accordé qu'une faible priorité au déve-

▷ 68

▷ 68

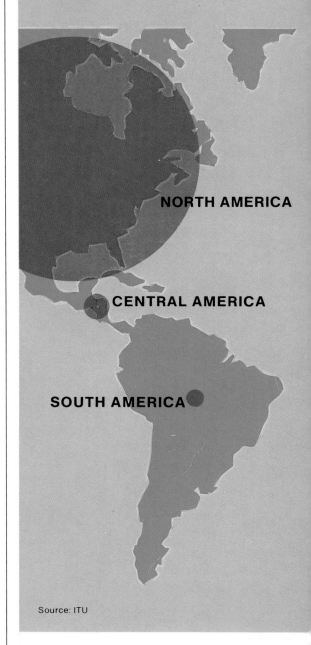

THE WORLD'S

NORTH AMERICA

CENTRAL AMERICA

SOUTH AMERICA

Source: ITU

EXISTI

DEVELOPED
25%

Strengths
Leadership
Science and Technology
Transfer capability
Investment assistance

:DS FOR BALANCE AND COHESION

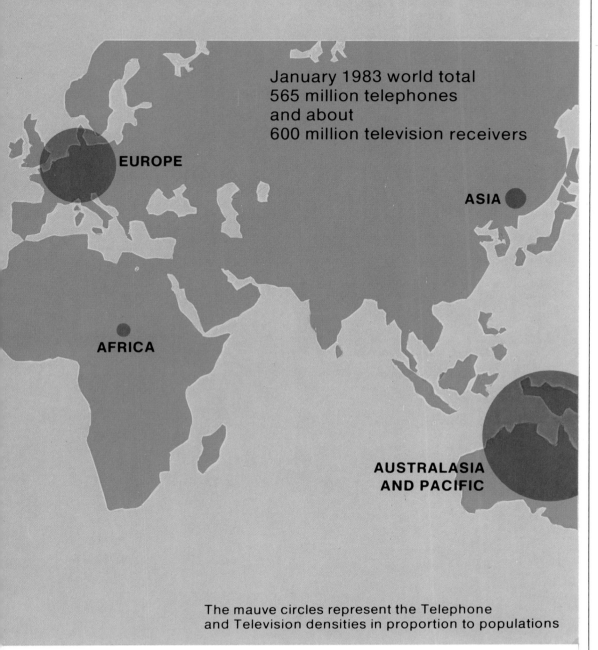

January 1983 world total
565 million telephones
and about
600 million television receivers

EUROPE

ASIA

AFRICA

AUSTRALASIA
AND PACIFIC

The mauve circles represent the Telephone
and Television densities in proportion to populations

BALANCE AMONG 158 NATIONS

15% of the Nations have

90% of the telephones
90% of the TV receivers

**DEVELOPING
75%**

Needs
Development
Identity

85% of the Nations have

10% of the telephones
10% of the TV receivers

Merced a los grandes avances de los últimos años en la tecnología de las telecomunicaciones se ha ampliado mucho la gama de servicios de la red. Satélites, radiocomunicaciones de microondas, enlaces por cables ópticos, conmutación y transmisión digitales, ofrecen un potencial para mejorar la calidad y tener mayor acceso a las zonas más remotas. Esta gama completa de creciente tecnología electrónica representa un gran impulso para la realización de la red de información mundial totalmente integrada. Si se extiende mucho más geográficamente la inversión, esto puede convertirse en el "sistema neural" de la sociedad, como se indica en la pág. 12.

Los conocimientos tecnológicos no son ya un obstáculo: los principios están bien asentados, el soporte físico basado en la "plaqueta" bien desarrollado, y la producción de soporte lógico corresponde a las necesidades. Pero hay dos grandes obstáculos, ambos económicos: el costo y la inversión. El primero se está abordando con energía en todo el mundo. La microminiaturización ha reducido ya mucho el costo de la conmutación, la transmisión y el procesamiento; los satélites y sus estaciones terrenas asociadas han disminuido el costo de alcanzar los lugares más recónditos. Las tendencias de costo siguen declinando fuertemente.

Desequilibrio geográfico. El segundo problema, el del desequilibrio geográfico, está lejos de resolverse. Se expone gráficamente en la ilustración a la izquierda, y se define estadísticamente en la página siguiente. Recientemente la UIT ha realizado varios estudios sobre los principales elementos que entraña y los factores que influyen en su solución. Uno de ellos, un importante estudio global, terminado en 1980, fue emprendido con la OCDE, para evaluar los beneficios, directos e indirectos, de las inversiones en telecomunicaciones rurales en el mundo en desarrollo, y proponer soluciones técnicas y de organización.

La UIT es la organización que trata de hallar la solución de este problema de desequilibrio, respaldada y ayudada por otros organismos de las Naciones Unidas, la OCDE y la industrias de comunicaciones. La Unión actúa, en nombre de sus 158 naciones Miembros, como coordinador y catalizador del desarrollo de una red mundial de telecomunicaciones integrada. Desde que se le confió la administración de un programa de cooperación técnica en 1960 se han hecho considerables progresos.

En la Conferencia de Plenipotenciarios de 1973, celebrada en España, se estableció que la UIT « fomentara la creación, el desarrollo y el perfeccionamiento de las instalaciones y de las redes de telecomunicación en los países nuevos o en desarrollo ». Los principales puntos del programa de 1980 fueron 630 misiones de expertos, 650 becas y 215 proyectos. Para 1983, Año de las Comunicaciones, en el Convenio celebrado en Nairobi, en octubre de 1982, se aprobó un programa todavía más completo y ambicioso.

La labor de la UIT ha permitido compilar mucha información sobre la situación actual. Se ha determinado que, en general, las telecomunicaciones se han desarrollado, ante todo, partiendo del concepto del rendimiento financiero del usuario, al que también se ha pedido que aporte capital a la inversión para financiar las ampliaciones de las redes. Esto ha permitido atender los servicios interurbanos e internacionales de las capitales y las grandes ciudades. Las CTT y las grandes empresas de explotación privadas de los países en zonas muy industrializadas han subvencionado las extensiones de la red a zonas rurales con los ingresos obtenidos en las urbanas, donde las elevadas tasas permiten conseguir sustanciales beneficios. Pero, incluso en esos casos, las organizaciones de explotación sienten la tentación de modernizar y ampliar las redes existentes donde son más densas y producen más.

Este enfoque de la inversión en telecomunicaciones no se limita a quienes explotan la red: las organizaciones internacionales de ayuda y los gobiernos

▷ 69

priority to network expansion beyond the confines of major cities. Aid given to telecommunications development by international organizations has declined during the 1970s to a very low level compared to other sectors such as transport, electric power and agriculture. Even education, traditionally the 'cinderella' of international aid, received substantially more.

The imbalance in the world telecommunication networks is not due wholly to the low priority accorded to their development in financial terms. It is also affected by their capital intensive nature, and by the need for foreign exchange. The dependence on foreign technology and on foreign skilled manpower are other factors in this imbalance necessitating massive (and expensive) manpower and management training programs. The difficulties currently experienced by operators in industrialized countries in mastering the complexities of integrated networks provide a measure of this need. However, it is the astonishing array of technological advances of the past 2 or 3 decades that provide the best hope for the extension of telecommunication networks worldwide, and a major reduction in the current imbalance.

Speaking in Bangkok in 1982 on the issues and constraints in the development of telecommunications, Richard E. Butler, Secretary-General of the ITU, stressed that the new technological options were positive elements in the current situation: "space telecommunications can enable new possibilities of investment sharing and international co-operation, arguing that satellites and their earth stations can provide domestic telecommunication facilities at a relatively low cost and especially in advance of the establishment of more conventional national network systems, expensive to build and lengthy to install.

The solution to imbalance, therefore, would appear to lie in three main directions: first to convince the decision makers in developing countries and international aid agencies that investment in telecommunications is worthwhile, potentially profitable and indirectly immensely beneficial, and therefore deserving a high priority; second, to apply the latest technologies which make the extensions of the network to rural and isolated areas more easily realizable at much reduced cost; third, to ensure that personnel in developing countries receive adequate training and technical assistance, especially in the management and maintenance of the networks.

The most promising of the advancing technologies in the context of rural areas and dispersed population generally, is broadcasting via satellites to appropriately located earth stations. Costs are rapidly diminishing and considerable progress has already been achieved since "Early Bird" was placed in geostationary orbit in 1965. The number of satellites is increasing fast and major benefits are already to hand. Satellite technology and its impact on telecommunications development is reviewed on p. 166.

There is a growing recognition of the vital role that telecommunications play and will increasingly play in support of every form of social, political and economic activity. Much research has been done, by organizations of the highest standing, to evaluate the pros and cons of an accelerated investment in telecommunication systems, nationally and internationally. The conclusions drawn from this research are that telecommunications development and overall economic development go hand in hand, that benefits far outweigh the costs, and that the more countries become developed, the greater the rate of their telephone development. While patterns differ from country to country, growth in each industrial sector's output seems to be accompanied by an increase in demand for telecommunications that is proportional, or sometimes more than proportional, to the growth in output.

loppement du réseau en dehors des grandes villes. Entre 1970 et 1980, l'aide consentie au développement des télécommunications par les organisations internationales a fort décliné par rapport aux autres secteurs d'activité, tels que les transports, la production d'électricité et l'agriculture.

Le déséquilibre des réseaux de télécommunications dans le monde n'est pas entièrement dû à l'insuffisance de la priorité accordée au financement de leur développement, ni à l'importance des capitaux et des devises étrangères nécessaires. Il découle aussi de l'obligation d'importer la technologie et la main-d'œuvre étrangère coûteuse qu'exige un tel développement et aussi des difficultés de formation du personnel de gestion requis. Les difficultés, que les entreprises d'exploitation des télécommunications des pays industrialisés éprouvent pour maîtriser l'énorme complexité des réseaux intégrés, reflètent l'importance de ce problème. Toutefois, les progrès inouïs réalisés au cours des deux ou trois décennies écoulées donnent bon espoir en ce qui concerne l'expansion des réseaux de télécommunications dans le monde entier et le redressement du déséquilibre actuel.

Parlant à Bangkok, en 1982, des problèmes du développement des télécommunications, M. Richard E. Butler, Secrétaire général de l'UIT, a insisté sur le fait que les récentes options technologiques sont des éléments positifs dans la situation actuelle : « les télécommunications spatiales offrent de nouvelles possibilités de répartition des investissements et de coopération internationale », compte tenu du fait que les satellites et les stations terriennes permettent l'établissement de liaisons de télécommunications nationales d'un coût relativement bas, notamment lorsqu'il s'agit d'éviter la mise en place de réseaux nationaux de type classique, dont la construction est coûteuse et nécessite beaucoup de temps.

La solution au déséquilibre mondial paraît se situer dans trois directions principales. La première est de convaincre les dirigeants des pays en développement et les institutions d'aide internationale que les investissements dans le domaine des télécommunications valent la peine. Ils sont potentiellement rentables et promettent de gros bénéfices indirects, c'est pourquoi ils méritent une haute priorité. Deuxièmement, il importe d'appliquer les techniques les plus récentes car elles permettent de réaliser plus facilement les extensions de réseaux en faveur des zones rurales et des régions reculées et d'en réduire considérablement le coût. Troisièmement, il faut offrir au personnel des pays en développement une formation et une assistance technique adéquates, spécialement en ce qui concerne la gestion et la maintenance des réseaux.

L'une des plus prometteuse des technologies de pointe — dans le cadre des régions rurales et, d'une manière générale, pour les populations dispersées — est la radiodiffusion par satellites. Les coûts diminuent rapidement et des progrès considérables ont déjà été accomplis depuis que « Early Bird » a été placé sur orbite géostationnaire en 1965. Le nombre des satellites augmente rapidement et ils rapportent déjà de gros bénéfices. La technologie des satellites et son influence sur le développement des télécommunications fait l'objet de l'article de la p. 166.

On commence à reconnaître le rôle vital des télécommunications dans toutes les formes d'activités culturelles, sociales et économiques. De nombreuses recherches ont été faites par des organisations de haut standing pour évaluer les avantages et les inconvénients d'une intensification des investissements dans les systèmes de télécommunications, à l'échelon national et international. Les conclusions de ces recherches indiquent invariablement que le développement des télécommunications et le développement économique marchent la main dans la main, que les bénéfices dépassent largement les coûts et que, plus un pays se développe, plus le rythme du développement de son réseau téléphonique s'accélère. Bien que les tendances ne soient pas uniformes, la croissance de la production par secteur industriel semble correspondre à une augmentation proportionnelle, et parfois plus que proportionnelle, de la demande en matière de télécommunications.

THE WOR

Telephones by World Regions -

WORLD REGIONS	TOTAL IN SERVICE	PER O WOR
Africa	5,028,177	
Asia	74,905,484	14
Europe	189,896,985	37
Central America	6,236,897	
North America	208,479,406	41
Oceania	10,182,879	
South America	13,556,038	
World (Total)	508,285,866	100

Countries with 1,000,00

(shown with the city reporting to have the
Development : Telephones per 100 popula

UNITED STATES
WASHINGTON, DC
SWEDEN
STOCKHOLM
SWITZERLAND
ZURICH
CANADA
RED DEER
DENMARK
KOEBENHAVN
NEW ZEALAND
WELLINGTON
AUSTRALIA
WOOLONGONG
NETHERLANDS
AMSTERDAM
UNITED KINGDOM
LIVERPOOL
FINLAND
HELSINKI
JAPAN
OSAKA
GERMANY, FED. REP.
FRANKFURT/OFFENBACH
FRANCE
PARIS (VILLE)
NORWAY
OSLO
AUSTRIA
BREGENZ
BELGIUM
BRUSSELS
ITALY
MILAN
HONG KONG
HONG KONG ISLAND
ISRAEL
TEL AVIV
SPAIN
BILBAO
GREECE
RHODES
CZECHOSLOVAKIA
PRAWA
GERMAN DEM. REP.
BERLIN
CHINA-TAIWAN
TAIPEI

(SCALE: 12 mm = 15 tels/100 pop.)

S TELEPHONES IN SERVICE

ata are as of January 1, 1981

PER 100 PULATION	PRIVATELY OPERATED NUMBER	PERCENT PRIVATELY OPERATED	AUTOMATIC NUMBER	PERCENT AUTOMATIC	NUMBER CONNECTING WITH THE UNITED STATES	PERCENT CONNECTING WITH THE UNITED STATES
2.5	7,105	0.1	4,380,720	87.1	4,821,544	95.9
7.1	3,697,566	4.9	73,386,347	98.0	72,074,642	96.2
24.6	35,603,208	18.7	188,044,167	99.0	187,929,173	99.0
6.9	5,206,170	83.5	6,162,706	98.8	6,143,525	98.5
81.4	206,218,044	98.9	208,132,111	99.8	208,479,406	100.0
14.7	3,019	0.0	10,032,261	98.5	10,163,714	99.8
6.3	1,998,616	14.7	12,831,057	94.7	12,864,931	94.9
19.1	252,733,728	49.7	502,969,369	99.0	502,476,935	98.9

re telephones and not less than 15 per 100 population

(hone development.) 109
uary 1, 1981

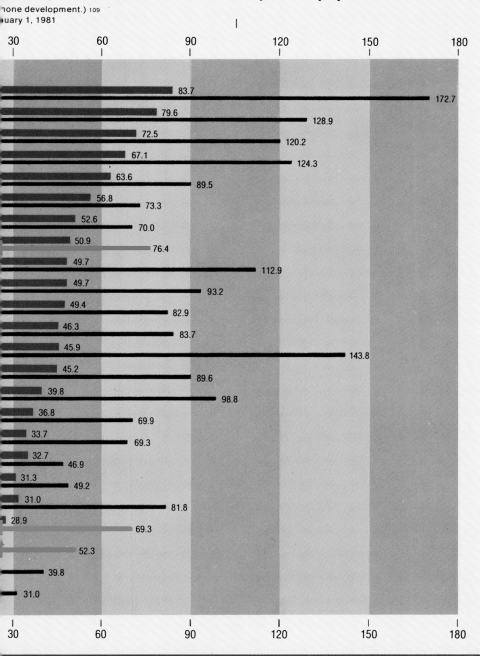

| | 30 | 60 | 90 | 120 | 150 | 180 |

83.7
172.7
79.6
128.9
72.5
120.2
67.1
124.3
63.6
89.5
56.8
73.3
52.6
70.0
50.9
76.4
49.7
112.9
49.7
93.2
49.4
82.9
46.3
83.7
45.9
143.8
45.2
89.6
39.8
98.8
36.8
69.9
33.7
69.3
32.7
46.9
31.3
49.2
31.0
81.8
28.9
69.3
52.3
39.8
31.0

Source: AT&T

de países en desarrollo también han concedido poca prioridad a la expansión de las redes allende las principales ciudades. La ayuda de esas organizaciones para el desarrollo de las telecomunicaciones ha declinado algo en los años 70, situándose en un nivel muy bajo, en comparación con otros sectores, como el transporte, la energía eléctrica y la agricultura. Hasta la educación, tradicionalmente la cenicienta de la ayuda internacional, ha recibido mucho más.

El desequilibrio de las redes mundiales no se debe totalmente a la poca prioridad concedida a su desarrollo en términos financieros, sino también a sus grandes necesidades de capital y de divisas extranjeras. La dependencia de la tecnología extranjera y del personal calificado del exterior es otro factor de este desequilibrio, pues se requiere muchísimo personal (oneroso) y muchos programas de formación de dirigentes. Las dificultades de las empresas de explotación en los países industrializados para dominar las complejidades de las redes integradas sirven para evaluar tal necesidad. Sin embargo, los increíbles avances tecnológicos de los 2 ó 3 últimos decenios permiten abrigar las mayores esperanzas en cuanto a la extensión de las redes mundiales de telecomunicaciones, y una importante reducción del desequilibrio existente.

Hablando en Bangkok, en 1982, sobre los problemas y condicionamientos del desarrollo de las telecomunicaciones, Richard E. Butler, Secretario General de la UIT, subrayó que las nuevas opciones tecnológicas son elementos positivos en la situación actual: « las telecomunicaciones espaciales pueden ofrecer nuevas posibilidades de distribución de la inversión y de cooperación internacional », aduciendo que los satélites y sus estaciones terrenas pueden proporcionar facilidades de telecomunicaciones nacionales a un costo relativamente bajo, especialmente antes de establecerse sistemas de redes nacionales más convencionales, cuya construcción es costosa y su instalación lleva mucho tiempo.

La solución del desequilibrio parece, por tanto, orientarse en tres direcciones principales: primero, convencer a las autoridades de los países en desarrollo y a los organismos de ayuda de que la inversión en telecomunicaciones vale la pena, es potencialmente rentable y proporciona inmensos beneficios indirectos, por lo que merece gran prioridad; segundo, aplicar las tecnologías más recientes que permitan ampliar más fácilmente la red a las zonas rurales aisladas y reducir mucho el costo; tercero, hacer que el personal de los países en desarrollo reciba la debida formación y asistencia técnica, sobre todo en la gestión y mantenimiento de las redes.

La más prometedora de las tecnologías avanzadas, para las zonas rurales y la población dispersa en general, es la radiodifusión por satélite a estaciones terrenas debidamente ubicadas. Los costos disminuyen rápidamente, y ya se han realizado considerables progresos desde que se puso en órbita geoestacionaria, en 1965, el « Early Bird ». El número de satélites aumenta rápidamente, y ya se obtienen importantes beneficios. La tecnología de satélites y sus repercusiones se tratan en la pág. 166.

Cada vez se reconoce más el vital papel de las telecomunicaciones en toda clase de actividad cultural, social y económica. Se han realizado grandes investigaciones para evaluar las ventajas y los inconvenientes de una inversión acelerada en sistemas de telecomunicación, tanto nacional como internacionalmente. Según las conclusiones de esa investigación, el desarrollo de las telecomunicaciones y el progreso económico global son simultáneos, los beneficios compensan con creces los costos, y cuanto más se desarrollan los países mayor es su expansión telefónica. Si bien las tendencias difieren de un país a otro, el crecimiento del producto de cada sector industrial parece ir acompañado de un aumento de la demanda de telecomunicaciones, proporcional, o más, al crecimiento de la producción.

□

FOCUS ON WORLD DEVELOPMENT OF INFRASTRUCTURES AND NETWORK INTEGRATION

NEWHOPE · NEWHORIZON

THE DEVELOPMENT OF AN INTEGRATED WORLD telecommunication network began to take shape in the 1960s and has proceed apace during the 1970s and 1980s. Major new routes have been established and links provided between all large towns in almost everyone of the 158 countries that are members of the ITU. This is shown on the world network map on p. 72. Two regional networks, Panaftel and Medarabtel, in a state of rapid evolution, are shown separately in subsequent pages as well as developments in the Pacific region and Latin America.

The imbalance between the industrialized North and the developping South is the main problem remaining in terms of network expansion. More particularly the imbalance prevailing between urban areas and the deep countryside. An imaginative proposal in partnership with the OECD is embodied in the GLODOM system (an acronym of GLObal and DOMestic) illustrated and described on p. 82

Unquestionably, the advent of powerful communications satellites of the 1990s, such as *Intelsat series V* and *VI*, has transformed the situation in rural and isolated areas and véry substantial progress can be expected in the remaining decade of this Century.

Subscriber dialling and its extension worldwide is one of the most positive advances made towards network integration in the past 2 or 3 decades. It was the first of an increasing number of international telecommunications facilities made available to millions of users. The first intercontinental telephone call dialled direct by a subscriber was from Philadelphia to Geneva in 1966. Four years later subscriber dialling was possible from 6 countries. Within 19 years the number of countries increased to 74 and is expected that it will be available for most if not all ITU Member nations by the end of this Century.

▷ 74

The keys to worldwide access: the modern telephone.

L'ORGANISATION D'UN RÉSEAU de télécommunications mondial intégré, qui a commencé à prendre forme après 1960, a progressé très rapidement au cours des deux dernières décennies. Des artères importantes ont été mises en place, et de nouvelles liaisons ont été établies entre toutes les grandes villes de la plupart des 158 pays Membres de l'UIT. (Voir la carte du réseau mondial à la page suivante).

Le déséquilibre entre le Nord industrialisé et le Sud en développement est le problème principal dans le contexte de l'expansion du réseau. Plus particulièrement le déséquilibre entre les villes et les campagnes. Ceci est un fait dans tous les pays de grande superficie géographique, même s'ils sont industrialisés.

Une proposition imaginative pour redresser le déséquilibre Nord-Sud, émanant d'une étude entreprise conjointement par l'UIT et l'OECD, le Système GLODOM (un acronyme de GLObal et DOMestic, en anglais), est décrit plus loin (voir p. 82). Le développement des satellites dans la présente décennie — de plus en plus puissants et performants, tels que les séries *Intelsat V* et *VI* — transformera la situation et on anticipe un progrès considérable avant la fin du siècle.

L'introduction du téléphone automatique sur le réseau international, pour des millions d'abonnés qui en sont aujourd'hui bénéficiaires, a été l'un des progrès les plus positifs réalisés au cours des deux ou trois décennies.

La première communication intercontinentale établie automatiquement par un abonné fut faite de Philadelphie à Genève, en 1966. Quatre ans plus tard, en 1970, il était possible de composer directement un numéro téléphonique à l'étranger à partir de 6 pays. Dix ans plus tard ce nombre de pays s'élevait à 74 et, pour la fin du siècle, on peut s'attendre à ce que cette facilité existe dans la plupart, sinon dans tous les pays Membres de l'UIT.

L'extension des réseaux et l'augmentation rapide, non seulement du nombre d'appareils téléphoniques (7% par année et plus) mais du nombre de conversations

▷ 74

Les touches d'accès au monde : le téléphone moderne.

LA ORGANIZACIÓN DE UNA RED MUNDIAL de telecomunicaciones integrada comenzó a tomar forma en los años 60, avanzando rápidamente desde entonces. Se han establecido importantes arterias y enlaces entre todas las grandes ciudades de la mayoría de los 158 países Miembros de la UIT, como se muestra en el mapa de la red mundial de la pág. 72. Más adelante se presentan dos redes regionales, Panaftel y Medarabtel, en rápida evolución.

El desequilibrio entre el norte industrializado y el sur en desarrollo es el principal problema de la expansión de redes. Y sobre todo el desequilibrio entre zonas urbanas y rurales. Así sucede en todos los países extensos, aunque sean industrializados, como Australia, Canadá, la URSS e incluso EE.UU.

Más adelante se describe una proposición conjunta de la UIT y de la OCDE incorporada en el sistema GLODÓM (acrónimo de GLObal y DOMéstico) (véase pág. 82). Sin duda, el desarrollo de poderosos satélites en los años 80, como los de la serie *Intelsat V* y *VI*, ha transformado la situación en las regiones rurales, y se prevé un gran progreso en el último decenio del siglo.

La introducción del servicio automático en la red internacional fue uno de los avances más positivos en los 2 ó 3 últimos decenios. La primera llamada telefónica intercontinental directa la realizó un abonado desde Filadelfia a Ginebra, 1966. Cuatro años después, en 1970, esto podía hacerse desde 6 países. En 10 años, el número de países pasó a 74, y para finales de siglo se espera que dispongan del servicio la mayoría de los Miembros de la UIT, si no todos.

La extensión de redes y el rápido aumento, no sólo del número de teléfonos (7% anual y más) sino del de llamadas internacionales (de 81 millones en 1970 a 313 millones en 1979) ha destacado la importancia de una gestión de red eficaz. Antes del servicio au-

▷ 75

Las teclas de acceso al mundo: el teléfono moderno.

AN OVERALL VIEW OF THE WORLD TELECOM

This map of the world shows the network of submarine cables linking continents and, on the continents, the major earth stations that ensure microwave links with the galaxy of satellites in geostationary orbit. New cables are being laid across the Atlantic and the Pacific and greater numbers of communication satellites are scheduled for lauching each year. Three of the most ambitious submarine cable projects under construction are the ANZCAN cable linking Australia to North America, the cable linking Europe (France) to SE Asia (Singapore), and the TAT-8, a laser-powered optic cable of 3,580 miles across the Atlantic, scheduled to be in service by 1988. These and other programs, designed to establish, add to or enhance intercontinental links are drawn up by the World Plan Committee and four Regional Committees prepared under the aegis of the ITU by the CCITT. The Plan Committee draws up interconnections plans on a worldwide scale, based on information supplied by the telecommunication administrations of the ITU Member countries. Meetings were held in Rome in 1967, Mexico City in 1970, Venice in 1971, Geneva in 1975 and Paris in 1980. The interregional plan is itself supplemented by a routing plan for automatic and semi-automatic telephony throughout the world.

Cette carte du monde montre le réseau des câbles sous-marins reliant les continents et, sur les continents eux-mêmes, les principales stations terriennes assurant des liaisons à hyperfréquences avec la « galaxie » des satellites géostationnaires. De nouveaux câbles sont en voie d'installation et des satellites de télécommunications, toujours plus nombreux et plus puissants, sont lancés chaque année. Trois ambitieux projets de câble sous-marin sont actuellement en voie de réalisation : le câble ANZCAN entre l'Australie et l'Amérique du Nord, celui qui reliera l'Europe à l'Asie du Sud-Est et le TAT-8, un câble optique à pulsions laser de 5700 km, qui reliera l'Amérique à l'Europe en 1988. Ces réalisations permettront l'établissement des liaisons intercontinentales tracées par la Commission du Plan mondial et par quatre Commissions régionales instituées par le CCITT, sous l'égide de l'UIT. La Commission s'est réunie a Rome en 1967, à Mexico en 1970, à Venise en 1971, à Genève en 1975, et à Paris en 1980. Le plan interrégional est complété lui-même par un plan de numérotage par zone et par un plan d'acheminement pour le trafic téléphonique automatique et semi-automatique dans le monde.

Este mapa mundi muestra la red de cables submarinos que vinculan continentes y, dentro de ellos, las principales estaciones terrenas que aseguran los enlaces de microondas con la galaxia de satélites en órbita geoestacionaria. Se tienden nuevos cables a través del Atlántico y el Pacífico.

Tres de los proyectos de cables submarinos más ambiciosos en construcción son el cable ANZCAN, que une Australia y América del Norte, el que une Europa (Francia) con Asia del Sudeste (Singapur), y el TAT-8, cable óptico impulsado por láser de 5700 km, que unirá América y Europa en 1988. Estas y otras realizaciones permitirán establecer, agregar o mejorar enlaces intercontinentales mediante la Comisión Mundial del Plan y de cuatro Comisiones Regionales auspiciadas por la UIT, a través del CCITT. La Comisión elabora planes de interconexión mundiales, basados en la información proporcionada por la administraciones de los países Miembros de la UIT. Se han celebrado reuniones en Roma (1967), Ciudad de México (1970), Venecia (1971), Ginebra (1975) y París (1980). El plan interregional está complementado por un plan de encaminamiento para la telefonía automática y semiautomática mundial.

SUBMARINE TELEPHONE CABLES
CABLES TELEPHONIQUES SOUS-MARINS
CABLES TELEFONICOS SUBMARINOS

Existing and being carried out
Existants et en cours d'installation
Existentes y en curso de instalación

Proposed or planned
Proposés ou planifiés
Previstos o proyectados

Terminals (towns or locality)
Terminaux d'aboutissement des câbles
Terminales (ciudades o localidades)

SPACE SYSTEMS
SYSTEMES SPATIAUX
SISTEMAS ESPACIALES

Satellites in geostationary orbit
Satellites en orbite géostationnaire
Satélites en órbita geoestacionaria

Earth stations
Stations terriennes
Estaciones terrenas

© I.G.D.A. S.p.A - Novara

UNITED STATES
Florida
1 West Palm Beach
2 Florida City
Puerto Rico
San Juan
Virgin Islands
Saint Thomas
BAHAMAS
Nassau
UNITED KINGDOM
1 Porthcurno, Goo...
2 Guernsey, Jerse...
3 Bournemouth
4 Eastbourne
5 St. Margaret's a...
Canterbury, Bro...
6 Aldeburgh, Cove...
Winterton
7 Scarborough
8 Holyhead, Aberg...
FINLAND
Porkkala

NICATIONS NETWORK

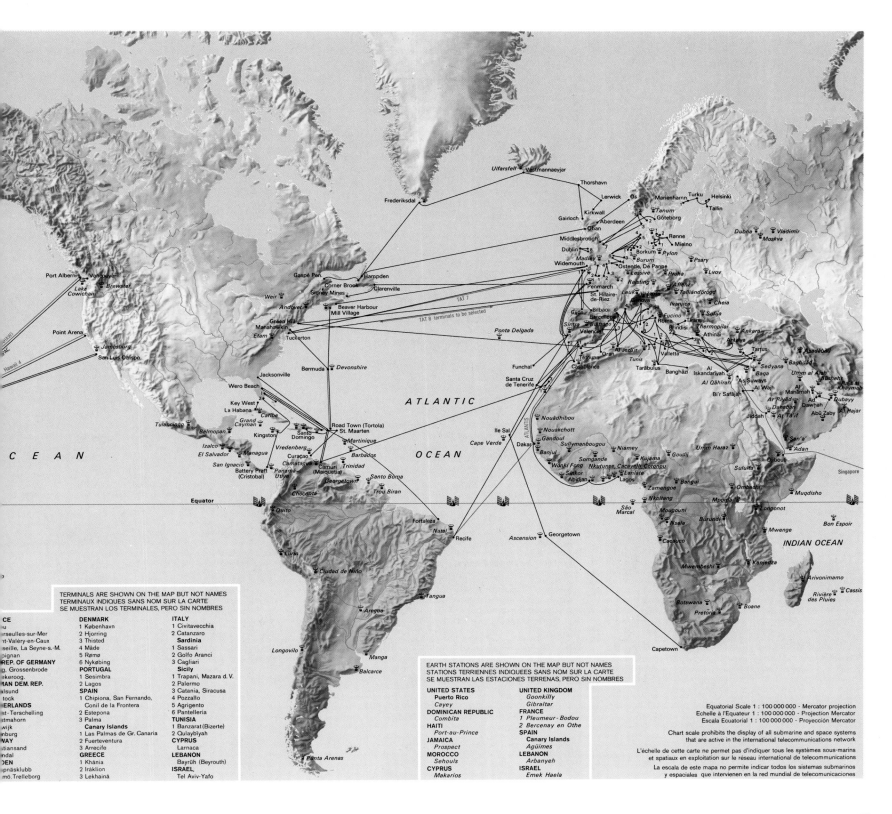

CE	DENMARK	ITALY
u	1 København	1 Civitavecchia
rseulles-sur-Mer	2 Hjørring	2 Catanzaro
nt-Valéry-en-Caux	3 Thisted	**Sardinia**
seille, La Seyne-s.-M.	4 Måde	1 Sassari
oignan	5 Rømø	2 Golfo Aranci
REP. OF GERMANY	6 Nykøbing	3 Cagliari
g, Grossenbrode	**PORTUGAL**	**Sicily**
keroog.	1 Sesimbra	1 Trapani, Mazara d.V.
MAN DEM. REP.	2 Lagos	2 Palermo
alsund	**SPAIN**	3 Catania, Siracusa
tock	1 Chipiona, San Fernando,	4 Pozzallo
ERLANDS	Conil de la Frontera	5 Agrigento
st-Terschelling	2 Estepona	6 Pantelleria
stmahorn	3 Palma	**TUNISIA**
wijk	**Canary Islands**	1 Banzarat (Bizerte)
nburg	1 Las Palmas de Gr. Canaria	2 Qulaybiyah
AY	2 Fuerteventura	**CYPRUS**
stiansand	3 Arrecife	Larnaca
ndal	**GREECE**	**LEBANON**
EN	1 Khánia	Bayrūh (Beyrouth)
spnäsklubb	2 Iráklion	**ISRAEL**
mö.Trelleborg	3 Lekhainá	Tel Aviv-Yafo

UNITED STATES	UNITED KINGDOM
Puerto Rico	Goonkilly
Cayey	Gibraltar
DOMINICAN REPUBLIC	**FRANCE**
Combita	1 Pleumeur - Bodou
HAITI	2 Bercenay en Othe
Port-au-Prince	**SPAIN**
JAMAICA	Canary Islands
Prospect	*Agüimes*
MOROCCO	**LEBANON**
Sehouls	*Arbanyeh*
CYPRUS	**ISRAEL**
Makarios	*Emek Haela*

Equatorial Scale 1 : 100 000 000 - Mercator projection
Echelle à l'Equateur 1 : 100 000 000 - Projection Mercator
Escala Ecuatorial 1 : 100 000 000 - Proyección Mercator

Chart scale prohibits the display of all submarine and space systems
that are active in the international telecommunications network

L'échelle de cette carte ne permet pas d'indiquer tous les systèmes sous-marins
et spatiaux en exploitation sur le réseau international de télécommunications

La escala de este mapa no permite indicar todos los sistemas submarinos
y espaciales que intervienen en la red mundial de telecomunicaciones

Extension of networks and the high rate of increase not only in the number of telephones (7% annually and rising) but in the number of calls made — the number of international calls rose from 81 million to 313 million between 1970 and 1979 — has highlighted the importance of efficient network management. Before subscriber dialling, telephone operators served essentially as network managers, manually recording information to route, time and bill calls, asking callers to wait if lines were busy, or routing a call via a third country and recording this routing information to enable the transitted country to be remunerated for the use of its facilities.

Subscriber dialling has changed all this. Although it brought about a better and less expensive service (the cost of international calls has actually declined in the USA and some other countries) callers became free to dial without control, causing switching and trunk line congestion. The need to introduce effective controls and appropriate records has led to major studies and trials.

Network management has been the subject of extensive research. A major study, started in 1970 by a CCITT study group, involved the USA and 13 other countries. It defined the nature of network management as "supervision of a communications network to ensure maximun utilisation under all conditions, requiring monitoring, measuring and, when necessary, action to control the flow of traffic". It involves being aware of when and where congestion exists, the use of protective controls, such as call blocking (to keep essential circuits open in an emergency) and the capability to alternate routing, which allows idle circuits to be used.

Automatic routing has already been taking place, especially in the USA and on a limited scale in some other industrialized countries, since the mid-1960s. The Nordic Pool and the Frankfurt Pool are two networks designed to allow a number of European nations to capitalize on the economics and service advantages inherent in the management of calling paths. Several Pacific countries have been using alternate routing procedures. Elsewhere also the facilities for network management exist but are not used systematically, due to political constraints.

Routing calls through third countries entails complex revenue division procedures, and tends to complicate relationships between the countries involved. Such complications might be avoided by the development of an integrated international network, utilizing to the full the controlling and recording facilities of microprocessors and computers.

Agreement on international network management is a *sine qua non* of the realization of an integrated world communications network. Several stand in the way, but the two major needs are Stored Program Control (SPC) capabilities, and compatible hardware. The work being done by CCITT in this respect is of crucial importance. It is evident that if networks can be managed to allow the maximum number of calls to be completed, telecommunication capacity will be more effectively utilized, income will be greater, and so will customer satisfaction. But even if SPC and packet switching systems are fully developed and generally available, together with the various multiplexing techniques in existence, it will be necessary to introduce a centralized system of gathering and exchanging international traffic data interactively. This will require each country to develop some kind of network control mechanism.

The CCITT international network management field trial mentioned earlier was conducted to pinpoint the criteria for making network management decisions. It produced a mass of useful data that enriched the knowledge available of what to expect in the functioning or malfunctioning of an integrated international network. An encouraging benefit of this work is the concentrated attention generated on the wider problems of network integration on a world scale, the problems of imbalance, of information and data flowing freely across national borders and generally, on the implementation of an Integrated Services Digital Network (ISDN).

▷ 78

internationales (de 81 millions en 1970 à 313 millions en 1979) a souligné l'importance d'une gestion efficace du réseau. Avant l'introduction du service automatique, les standardistes exerçaient des fonctions essentiellement administratives, en enregistrant manuellement l'acheminement et la durée des communications, en établissant des factures, en demandant aux usagers d'attendre que des lignes soient libérées ou en acheminant une communication par un pays tiers, tout en enregistrant cette information pour que le pays de transit soit rémunéré.

Le téléphone automatique a changé tout cela. Le service est devenu plus fiable et moins coûteux. Toutefois les usagers ont la possibilité de composer des numéros sans aucun contrôle, ce qui causa des encombrements.

La gestion des réseaux a été étudiée à plusieures reprises. Le CCITT a entrepris des études très approfondies sur la gestion du réseau international dont l'une commencée en 1970 comprenant les Etats-Unis et 13 autres pays. La gestion fut définie comme étant la supervision d'un réseau de communications pour en assurer l'utilisation maximale dans toutes les conditions, moyennant une surveillance, des mesures et, en cas de besoin, le contrôle de l'écoulement du trafic. A cet effet il importe de savoir quand et où se produit un encombrement et de déterminer les moyens de protection qu'il convient d'appliquer (pour maintenir ouverts les circuits essentiels en cas d'urgence) et de décider l'acheminement par voie alternative.

L'acheminement par voie alternative est utilisé aux Etats-Unis et, à un moindre degré ailleurs, depuis une vingtaine d'années. Le « pool nordique » et le « pool de Francfort » sont des réseaux conçus pour permettre à un certain nombre de pays européens de cumuler les avantages économiques et les services inhérents à la gestion des possibilités d'acheminement. Plusieurs pays du Pacifique ont également recours aux mêmes procédures.

L'acheminement des communications par des pays tiers met en jeu des procédures complexes de répartition de recettes. Le moyen d'éviter de telles complications consiste à mettre en place un réseau international intégré, en utilisant au maximum les facilités de contrôle et d'enregistrement rendues possibles par les microprocesseurs et les ordinateurs.

La gestion du réseau international est une condition essentielle de la réalisation d'un réseau mondial intégré de communications. Plusieurs obstacles doivent être surmontés mais deux exigences principales demandent à être satisfaites au préalable : la disponibilité d'une commande par programme enregistré (SPC) et d'un matériel compatible. Les travaux réalisés par le CCITT dans ce domaine sont d'une importance vitale. Il est évident que si les réseaux sont administrés de manière à permettre l'établissement d'un nombre maximum de communications, leur capacité sera utilisée plus efficacement, les recettes seront plus élevées et la satisfaction de l'usager sera plus grande. Toutefois, même si les systèmes à commande par programme enregistré et à commutation par paquets sont mis au point et disponibles, il sera nécessaire d'introduire un système centralisé de rassemblement et d'échange interactif de données relatives au trafic international.

L'essai sur le terrain de gestion de réseau international entrepris par le CCITT a fourni une grande quantité de données utiles qui ont enrichi les connaissances acquises jusque-là sur ce que l'on peut attendre du fonctionnement correct ou défectueux d'un réseau international intégré. Ces travaux ont eu l'avantage de concentrer l'attention sur les problèmes plus larges de l'intégration du réseau à l'échelle mondiale, sur les problèmes du déséquilibre, sur la libre circulation de l'information et des données à travers les frontières nationales et, d'une manière générale, sur la mise en exploitation d'un Réseau Numérique avec Intégration de Services (RNIS).

La conception du RNIS devient l'une des forces actives de l'évolution du réseau de télécommunications dans le monde. Le CCITT définit le RNIS comme étant un réseau conçu selon le modèle du Réseau Numérique Intégré (RNI) téléphonique, c'est-à-dire, un réseau capable d'assurer des transmissions numériques de

▷ 78

DEVELOPME
MAJOR TRANSOC

The three major developments in recent years are the Asian Telecom Network, the Philippine Palapa satellite system, and the ANZCAN submarine cable. The former is a trans-Asia link, essentially terrestrial and for the most part using microwave systems. Conceived in the 1960s and extending from Iran to Indonesia and the Philippines it is 7,400 km. and includes 22 links, providing an excellent base for the upgrading of national networks in Asian countries, including a major broadband microwave extension of 5,900 km in India.

A second development is the Asian satellite system launched from Indonesia (Palapa I and II) covering all Asian countries including Cambodia, Laos, Vietnam and part of Burma. The third, and the latest, is the ANZCAN (an acronym for Australia/New Zealand/Canada) submarine cable, probably the largest and most expensive telecommunications project ever undertaken. It will replace the trans-Pacific cable COMPAC, laid in the early 1960s, which no longer sufficed to handle the rapidly increasing traffic. The initial funders of the US$ 364 million project are Australia (55%), Canada (19%) and New Zealand (11%). There are 7 other part owners and more are expected to join later.

The ANZCAN cable, of the latest optical design, will have a capacity of 1,940 circuits, more than 20 times that of COMPAC and, with a life expectancy of 25 years or so, it will provide long-term reliability, meet special traffic needs such as high speed data transmission, and provide extensions to places which would otherwise require two satellite "hops".

The telecommunication network in the Pacific hemisphere, upgraded and expanded with great determination by the countries involved, is rapidly becoming one of the best in the world.

THE PACIFI

The Pacific Telecommunications Council (PTC) was set up in 1980 as a voluntary independent organization to meet a growing need for "the development, understanding, and beneficial use of telecommunications in the Pacific area". Located in Honolulu, Hawaii, where the annual conventions are held, the PTC has a large membership which includes most of the leading companies in telecommunications in the United States and Japan. The 1983 convention was attended by over 400 executives and professionals from some 24 countries with an interest in Pacific telecommunications development.

The stated objectives of PTC are:

— to provide a forum for discussion and interchange of information, views and ideas, by bringing together a multifaceted and diverse body including users, planners and providers of telecommunications services and equipment;

— to promote a general awareness of the telecommunications needs of the Pacific area;

— to organize conferences, workshops and seminars in order to promote interchange and address specific issues;

— to communicate the views and recommendations of the Council to the established national, regional and international bodies responsible for telecommunication policy.

Close links have been established with the ITU and its Secretary-General, Richard E. Butler, was the keynote speaker at the 1983 convention. Papers read included one on "The Evolution of the Digital World", by Bell Canada, another on "The Innovative Uses of Telecommunications", by the University of Hawaii, and several more on advanced technological topics such as fiber optics, satellite and undersea developments, teleconferencing, etc. that appear to hold out considerable promise for countries in the area. The Pacific region may well become the most advanced in its applications of communications technology, hence the considerable interest in PTC's activities by governments as well as by enterprises.

s trois grandes réalisations de ces dernières années sont : le
eau asiatique de télécommunications, le système à satellite
apa des Philippines et, le câble sous-marin ANZCAN. La
mière réalisation a été conçue dans la décennie de 1960. Il
git d'un réseau transasiatique à micro-ondes qui s'étend de
an à l'Indonésie et jusqu'aux Philippines sur une distance de
0 km. Il comprend 22 liaisons notamment une grande artère
micro-ondes et à large bande d'une longueur de 5900 km, en
e.

La deuxième réalisation est constituée par le système fonc-
nnant avec les deux satellites lancés à partir de l'Indonésie
lapa I et II) dont la zone de service s'étend sur tous les pays
sie, notamment le Cambodge, le Laos, le Vietnam et une
tie de la Birmanie. La troisième réalisation, la plus récente,
le câble sous-marin ANZCAN (acronyme de Australie/Nou-
le Zélande/Canada). Ce nouveau câble — appelé à remplacer
MPAC (1960) — est probablement le projet de télécommuations le plus important et le plus coûteux qui ait jamais été
repris. Cette réalisation d'une valeur de 364 millions de
lars (1982) sera prise en charge par l'Australie (55%), le
nada (19%) et la Nouvelle-Zélande (11%) et elle bénéficiera
core d'autres financements (15%).

Le câble ANZCAN, d'une conception ultra-moderne, en fibre
ique, aura une capacité de 1940 circuits, soit 20 fois plus que
MPAC (son prédécesseur). Sa fiabilité à long terme (environ
ans) permettra de satisfaire des besoins spéciaux, notam-
nt la transmission de données à grande vitesse et d'assurer
s communications qui, autrement, auraient exigé deux
onds » par satellite.

Le réseau de télécommunications de l'hémisphère du Pacifi-
e, amélioré et élargi par la volonté des pays intéressés est en
in de devenir l'un des meilleurs du monde.

Los tres principales acontecimientos de los últimos años son la
Red Asiática de Telecomunicaciones, el sistema de satélite
filipino Palapa, y el cable submarino ANZCAN. El primero es un
enlace a través de Asia, esencialmente terrenal, que usa sobre
todo sistemas de microondas. Concebido en los años 1960, se
extiende desde Irán a Indonesia y Filipinas, a lo largo de 7400
km, y comprende 22 enlaces, que permiten mejorar las redes de
los países asiáticos, incluida una extensión de microondas de
banda ancha de 5900 km en la India.

Una segunda novedad es el sistema de satélite asiático
lanzado desde Indonesia (Palapa I y II), que abarca a todos los
países de Asia, incluidos Camboya, Laos, Vietnam y parte de
Birmania. La tercera y última es el cable submarino ANZCAN
(acrónimo de Australia/Nueva Zelandia/Canadá), probablemente el proyecto de telecomunicaciones más ambicioso y
costoso emprendido hasta ahora. Sustituirá al cable trans-
Pacífico COMPAC, tendido a comienzos de los años 1960, que
ya no es suficiente. El proyecto, de 364 millones $, ha sido
financiado inicialmente por Australia (55%), Canadá (19%) y
Nueva Zelandia (11%). Hay otros 7 propietarios parciales, y se
espera que se unan más.

El cable ANZCAN, del diseño óptico más reciente, tendrá una
capacidad de 1940 circuitos, más de 20 veces el de COMPAC (su
predecesor) y, con una esperanza de vida de 25 años, ofrecerá
fiabilidad a largo plazo, atenderá necesidades especiales de
tráfico, como transmisiones de datos a gran velocidad, y podrá
extenderse a lugares que, de otro modo, requerirían dos « sal-
tos » de satélite.

La red de telecomunicaciones del hemisferio del Pacífico,
perfeccionada y ampliada por los países interesados, se está
convirtiendo en una de las mejores del mundo.

tomático, las operadoras actuaban sobre todo de
administradores de la red, registrando manualmente
información para encaminar y facturar las llamadas,
pidiendo a los usuarios que esperaran si las líneas
estaban ocupadas o encaminando una llamada a
través de un tercer país, registrando la información
para remunerar al país de tránsito.

La marcación por el abonado ha cambiado todo
esto. El servicio es mejor y menos costoso. Sin embargo, los usuarios pueden llamar sin ningún control,
lo que causa congestiones.

Gestión de las redes. Una Comisión de Estudio del
CCITT ha realizado amplios análisis sobre la gestión
de las redes internacionales; uno de ellos, iniciado en
1970, abarcó EE.UU. y otros 13 países. La gestión de
la red se definió como la «supervisión de una red de
comunicaciones para asegurar la máxima utilización
en cualesquiera condiciones, lo que requiere la verificación, medición y, en caso necesario, control del
flujo de tráfico». Para eso, hay que conocer cuándo y
dónde se produce la congestión, y determinar los
controles de protección, para mantener abiertos los
circuitos esenciales en caso de emergencia, y la capacidad de encaminamiento alternativo.

Este encaminamiento se emplea especialmente en
EE.UU. y, en menor escala, en otras partes, desde
hace dos décadas. El *pool* nórdico y el *pool* de
Francfort son dos redes concebidas para que varios
países europeos puedan capitalizar las ventajas
económicas y de servicios inherentes a la gestión de
los trayectos de llamada.

El encaminamiento de llamadas a través de terceros países entraña procedimientos de distribución de
ingresos complejos y tiende a complicar las relaciones entre los países de que se trate. Esas complica-
ciones pueden evitarse desarrollando una red
internacional integrada, utilizando al máximo las
facilidades de control y registro de microprocesadores y computadores.

El acuerdo sobre la gestión de la red internacional es una
condición sine qua non de la realización de una red
mundial de comunicaciones integrada. Subsisten
varios obstáculos, pero las dos principales necesidades son las capacidades de control por programa
almacenado (CPA) y el soporte físico compatible. La
labor realizada por el CCITT a este respecto es vital.
No hay duda de que si las redes pueden adminis-
trarse de manera que la mayoría de las llamadas
tengan éxito, la capacidad de las telecomunicaciones
se utilizará más eficazmente, aumentarán los ingresos, y la satisfacción de los abonados será mayor.
Pero incluso si se derarrollan plenamente la conmutación SPA y los sistemas de conmutación de paquetes, y se dispone de ellos con carácter general,
además de las diversas técnicas de multiplexación
existentes, será preciso introducir un sistema centralizado para reunir e intercambiar interactivamente
datos de tráfico internacional. Y para ello, cada país
habrá de desarrollar alguna clase de mecanismo de
control de la red.

La prueba práctica de gestión de la red internacional del CCITT citada se realizó para señalar los
criterios de las decisiones sobre gestión de red. Produjo una gran cantidad de datos utiles sobre los
resultados del funcionamiento de una red internacional integrada. Ese trabajo de estímulo para
centrar la atención generada en los problemas más
amplios de integración de la red a esclala mundial,
los problemas de desequilibrio, de libre transmisión
de información y datos allende las fronteras nacionales y, generalmente, sobre la aplicación de una red
digital de servicios integrados (RDSI).

El concepto de RDSI se está convirtiendo en una importante fuerza motriz de la evolución de la red de
telecomunicaciones en el mundo entero. El CCITT
define la RDSI como una «red digital integrada en la
que se utilizan los mismos conmutadores digitales y
trayectos digitales para el establecimiento de conexiones de diferentes servicios; por ejemplo, telefonía,
datos, etc. ».

ELECOMMUNICATIONS COUNCIL

Conseil des télécommunications du Pacifique (PTC) a été
titué en 1980 sous forme d'association indépendant dans le
d'assurer le développement et l'utilisation profitable des
écommunications dans la région du Pacifique. Le PTC a son
ge à Honolulu, Hawaii, où se tiennent ses réunions annuelles,
mi ses membres on trouve les plus grandes entreprises de
écommunications des Etats-Unis et du Japon. A la Conven-
n de 1983 ont participé plus de 400 dirigeants et profes-
nnels de 24 pays intéressés au développement des télé-
mmunications dans le Pacifique.

Les buts du PTC sont les suivants :

constituer un forum de discussion et d'échange d'informa-
ns, d'opinions et d'idées, rassemblant des utilisateurs, des
nificateurs et des fournisseurs de services et d'équipements
télécommunication ;

promouvoir une prise de conscience générale des besoins
matière de télécommunications dans la région du Pacifique ;

organiser des conférences, colloques et séminaires pour
oriser les échanges et pour traiter de sujets particuliers ;

communiquer les opinions et les recommandations du
nseil aux instances et institutions nationales, régionales et
ernationales responsables de la politique des télécommuni-
tions.

Le Conseil est en étroite relation avec l'UIT et son Secrétaire
néral, Richard E. Butler qui fut le conférencier principal de la
nvention de 1983. Parmi les contributions présentées il
nvient de mentionner : « The Evolution of the Digital World »
r Bell Canada, et « The Innovative Uses of Telecommunica-
ns » par l'Université de Hawaii, ainsi que d'autres sujets
atifs aux techniques de pointe. Le Pacifique pourrait bien
venir une région privilégiée en ce qui concerne les applica-
ns les plus perfectionnées et les plus poussées de la tech-
logie des communications, si l'on en juge par l'intérêt
nsidérable que les activités du PTC suscitent auprès des
uvernements et des entreprises.

El Consejo de Telecomunicaciones del Pacífico (CTP) se creó en
1980 como organización voluntaria independiente, para atender
la creciente necesidad del « desarrollo, la comprensión y el uso
benéfico de las telecomunicaciones en la región del Pacífico ».
Con sede en Honolulú (Hawaii), donde se celebran las convenciones anuales, el CTP cuenta entre sus miembros a la mayoría
de las principales empresas de telecomunicaciones de Estados
Unidos y Japón. A la convención de 1983 asistieron más de 400
ejecutivos y profesionales de unos 24 países interesados en el
desarrollo de las telecomunicaciones del Pacífico.

Los objetivos declarados del CTP son:
— ofrecer un foro para debatir e intercambiar información,
opiniones e ideas a un grupo múltiple y diverso de usuarios,
planificadores y proveedores de servicios y equipo de telecomunicaciones;
— fomentar el conocimiento general de las necesidades de la
región del Pacífico en materia de telecomunicaciones;
— organizar conferencias, coloquios y seminarios para promover el intercambio y tratar cuestiones concretas;
— comunicar las opiniones y recomendaciones del Consejo a
los organismos nacionales, regionales e internacionales responsables de la política de telecomunicaciones.

Se han establecido estrechos vínculos con la UIT y su
Secretario General, Richard E. Butler, uno de los principales
oradores de la convención de 1983. Se presentaron documentos
como « La evolución del mundo digital », de Bell Canada; « Los
usos innovadores de las telecomunicaciones », de la Universidad de Hawaii, y varios más de temas de tecnología avanzada
que parecen ofrecer grandes posibilidades a los países del
Pacífico, como fibras ópticas, satélites y fondos marinos, teleconferencias, etc. El Pacífico puede muy bien ser la zona de las
aplicaciones más avanzadas de la tecnología de las comunicaciones; de ahí el considerable interés de las actividades del CTP
para gobiernos y empresas.

▷ 79

PANAFTEL: THE PANAFRICAN TELECOMMUN

The Panafrican Telecommunication Network (PANAFTEL) is a partially implemented telephone infrastructure conceived for the continent of Africa whose telephone density is 0.4 only per 100 inhabitants the lowest in the world.

Because almost all African countries were colonies (or protectorates or dependencies) of one or other of the European powers, the facilities for international telecommunications from each country were limited almost exclusively to links with the metropolitan power. On becoming independent these African countries felt a need to communicate internationally, especially between each other, without having to follow the long, complex and expensive transit route through one or more switching centers on another continent.

This need was particularly acute between countries with close ties of trade, culture and other affinities. Technically this was also desirable, indeed necessary, to avoid double-hop satellite circuits made inevitable by extra continental transits, with unacceptable propagation time delay characteristics (CCITT Recommendation G. 114).

The project, conceived by the ITU Regional Plan Commission in 1962, began in 1965 when the United Nations Economic Commission for Africa and the ITU agreed that the Union should take the lead in planning and co-ordinating the work, and in providing technical guidance and training facilities to countries responsible for the implementation of the program.

By the end of 1982 an extensive telecommunication infrastructure had been constructed, using the most modern equipment. Some 27 automatic international telephone transit centers serving 24 countries had been built, and a further 9 were programmed; 48 automatic international telex exchanges were in service, and 4 were programmed. Over 30,000 km of high quality transmission routes, consisting mainly of radio-relay, had been completed.

A long line of PANAFTEL cable runs North-South with branches at appropriate points, providing 39 inter-capital terrestrial transmission routes (including 3 by submarine cable linking Casablanca to Dakar, Abidjan and Lagos). In addition to these terrestrial routes, 51 satellite earth stations had been installed, serving 40 countries for intercontinental and inter-African traffic. The provision of S-PAD facilities in a number of the earth stations made for maximum flexibility between countries. Altogether, in 1982, 67 routes were functioning between African countries using INTELSAT circuits.

There is now a need to develop national networks connecting international exchanges to and from subscribers. This calls for development of the urban network in the cities, towns and villages of each country together with the interurban network between them.

A PANAFTEL Co-ordinating Committee composed of the Executive Heads of the Organization of African Unity (OAU), the Economic Commission for Africa (ECA), the African Development Bank (ADB), the Pan-African Telecommunication Union (PATU) and the ITU meet regularly and provide a forum for consultation. This constitutes an effective instrument for channelling investments from bilateral and multilateral sources, and for the intensification of assistance to member States in the establishment and maintenance of their national networks.

Multinational training centres have been set up in Rufisque, Nairobi and Blantyre for the training of technical staff, and one in Dakar for the training of senior management. These are key ITU functions, as was stressed at the Nairobi Plenipotentiary Conference in October-November 1982.

L'infrastructure du réseau panafricain de télécommunications (PANAFTEL) a été conçue et partiellement mise en place dans un continent dont la densité téléphonique n'est que de 0,4 pour 100 habitants, la plus basse au monde.

Cette situation s'explique par le fait que la plupart des pays africains étaient précédemment des colonies, des protectorats ou des territoires dépendants de l'une ou l'autre des puissances européennes. A cette époque, les facilités de télécommunications internationales de chacun des pays africains se limitaient presqu'exclusivement aux liaisons avec la « puissance métropolitaine ». Lorsqu'ils devinrent indépendants, tous ces pays éprouvèrent le besoin de communiquer sur le plan international et particulièrement entre eux, sans être assujettis à un acheminement complexe et coûteux au travers d'un ou de plusieurs centres de commutation situés sur un autre continent.

Ce besoin s'est particulièrement fait sentir entre pays voisins ou entre ceux qui entretenaient des relations commerciales et culturelles ou qui étaient proches en raison d'autres affinités. Techniquement, il était indispensable d'éviter l'utilisation de circuits par satellites à double bond, rendue inévitable par le transit inter-continental qui imposait des temps de propagation inacceptables sur les circuits internationaux (Avis G.114 du CCITT).

La mise en œuvre du projet conçu par la Commission régionale du Plan de l'UIT, en 1962, a débuté en 1965, lorsque la CEA et l'UIT décidèrent que cette dernière assurerait la planification et la coordination des travaux et fournirait les directives techniques nécessaires, ainsi que la formation professionnelle requise aux pays chargés de construire les installations.

Au début de 1983, une infrastructure ultra-moderne avait été mise en place : 27 centres de transit téléphonique automatiques desservant 24 pays avaient été construits et 9 autres étaient en projet ; 48 centres télex automatiques internationaux étaient en service et 4 étaient en projet. Plus de 30 000 km d'artères de transmission de grande qualité, principalement en faisceaux hertziens, avaient été réalisés. Une longue liaison en câble PANAFTEL traverse maintenant le continent du nord au sud avec, en des points appropriés, des embranchements reliant 39 capitales (dont 3 câbles sous-marins entre Casablanca et Dakar, Abidjan et Lagos).

A part ces artères sur terre, 51 stations terriennes ont été installées pour assurer, par liaison spatiales, l'écoulement du trafic intra-africain et intercontinental dans 40 pays de ce continent. Le système SPADE (accès multiple en fonction de la demande) assurera une souplesse de fonctionnement maximale entre les pays. En 1982, 67 artères empruntant des circuits INTELSAT reliaient entre eux les pays d'Afrique.

Un comité de coordination de PANAFTEL composé des chefs responsables de l'organisation de l'Unité africaine (OUA), de la Commission économique pour l'Afrique (CEA), de la Banque africaine de développement (BAD), de l'Union panafricaine de télécommunications (PATU) et de l'UIT, se réunit régulièrement pour décider de questions importantes (répartition de l'aide financière internationale, assistance aux Etats Membres en vue de la mise en exploitation et la maintenance de leurs réseaux nationaux, etc.).

Des centres multinationaux de formation professionnelle ont été créés à Rufisque, Nairobi et Blantyre; ils contribuent activement à la formation de personnel technique de niveau moyen. Un centre a été créé à Dakar pour la formation de personnel dirigeant. La Conférence de plénipotentiaires de Nairobi (1982) a souligné le rôle essentiel de l'UIT à cet égard.

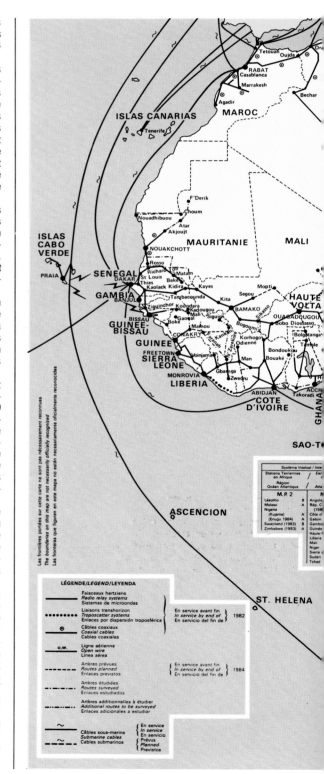

ATIONS NETWORK

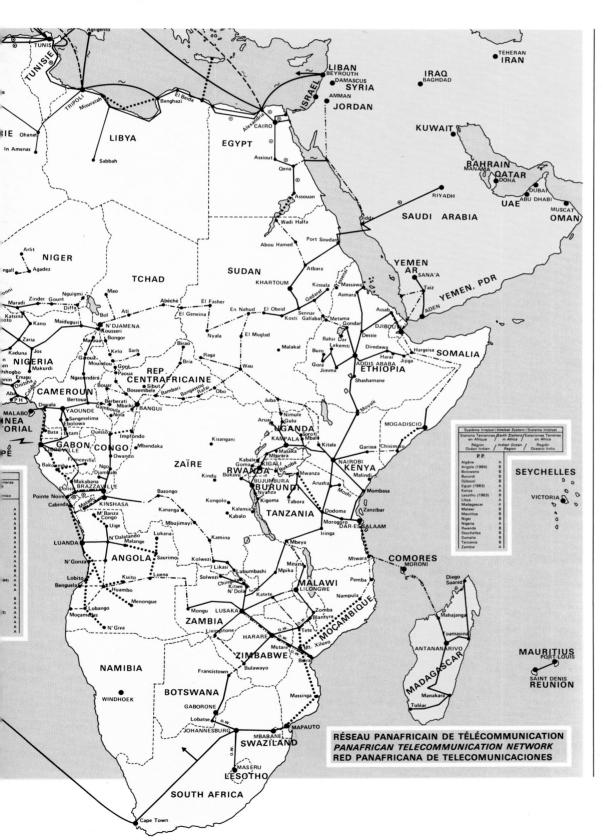

Système Intelsat / *Intelsat System* / Sistema Intelsat

Stations Terriennes / *Earth Stations* / Estaciones Terrenas		
en Afrique / *in Africa* / en Africa	Région Océan Indien	*Indian Ocean Region* / Región Océano Indio
P.P.		
Algérie	A	B
Angola (1984)	A	
Botswana	B	
Burundi	B	
Djibouti	A	
Egypt (1983)	B	
Kenya	A	B
Lesotho (1983)	A	
Libya	A	
Madagascar	A	
Malawi	B	
Mauritius	A	
Niger	B	
Nigeria	A	
Rwanda	A	
Seychelles	A	
Somalia	B	
Tanzania	A	
Zambia	A	

RÉSEAU PANAFRICAIN DE TÉLÉCOMMUNICATION
PANAFRICAN TELECOMMUNICATION NETWORK
RED PANAFRICANA DE TELECOMUNICACIONES

La Red Panafricana de Telecomunicaciones (PANAFTEL) es una infraestructura telefónica en expansión para el continente africano, cuya densidad telefónica es sólo de 0,4 por 100 habitantes, la más baja del mundo.

Como casi todos los países africanos eran colonias (o protectorados o dependencias) de alguna potencia europea, las facilidades de las telecomunicaciones internacionales de cada país se limitaban casi exclusivamente a enlaces con la potencia metropolitana. Al adquirir la independencia, esos países africanos sintieron la necesidad de comunicar internacionalmente, sobre todo entre sí, sin tener que seguir la larga, compleja y costosa ruta de tránsito a través de uno o más centros de conmutación de otro continente.

Tal necesidad era particularmente aguda entre países con estrechos vínculos comerciales, culturales y otras afinidades. Técnicamente, esto también era deseable, y en realidad necesario, para impedir circuitos de satélite de doble salto, inevitables por los tránsitos extracontinentales con características de tiempo de propagación inaceptables (Recomendación G.114 del CCITT).

El proyecto, concebido por la Comisión Regional del Plan de la UIT en 1962, se inició en 1965, al acordar la Comisión Económica para Africa de las Naciones Unidas y la UIT que la Unión debía dirigir la planificación y la coordinación de los trabajos, y proporcionar asesoramiento técnico y facilidades de formación a los países responsables del programa.

A finales de 1982 se había construido una amplia infraestructura con el equipo más moderno. Se han establecido unos 27 centros telefónicos internacionales automáticos de tránsito, que dan servicio a 24 países, y se han programado otros 9; ya están en servicio 48 centrales automáticas internacionales télex, y hay programadas 4 más. Se han terminado más de 30 000 km de rutas de transmisión de gran calidad, con muchos relevadores radioeléctricos.

Una larga línea del cable PANAFTEL atraviesa de norte a sur con ramificaciones en los puntos apropiados, ofreciendo 39 rutas de transmisión terrenal entre capitales (incluidas 3 por cable submarino que enlazan Casablanca con Dakar, Abidján y Lagos). Además de estas rutas terrenales, se han instalado 51 estaciones terrenas, que dan servicio a 40 países para tráfico intercontinental e interafricano. La provisión de facilidades SPADE en varias estaciones terrenas permite la máxima flexibilidad entre países. En total, en 1982 funcionaban 67 rutas entre países africanos que emplean circuitos INTELSAT.

Ahora hay que desarrollar redes nacionales conectadas con centrales internacionales para abonados, lo que requiere redes urbanas en las ciudades, pueblos y aldeas de cada país.

Un Comité de Coordinación de PANAFTEL, compuesto de los Jefes Ejecutivos de la Organización de la Unidad Africana (OUA), la Comisión Económica para Africa (CEPA), el Banco Africano de Desarrollo (BAD), la Unión Panafricana de Telecomunicaciones (PATU) y la UIT, se reúne regularmente y ofrece un foro y un instrumento eficaz para canalizar las inversiones de fuentes bilaterales y multilaterales, y para intensificar la asistencia a los Estados miembros en el establecimiento y mantenimiento de sus redes nacionales.

Se han creado centros multinacionales de formación en Rufisque, Nairobi y Blantyre, que contribuyen en gran medida a la formación de personal técnico de nivel medio, y otro en Dakar, para la formación de personal dirigente superior. Se trata de funciones esenciales de la UIT, cuya importancia se destacó mucho en la Conferencia de Plenipotenciarios de Nairobi, en octubre-noviembre de 1982.

The ISDN concept is becoming a major driving force behind telecommunication network evolution around the world. The CCITT defines ISDN as a "network evolved from the telephony IDN (Integrated Digital Network) that provides end-to-end digital connectivity to support a wide range of services, including voice and non-voice services, to which users have access by a limited set of standard multipurpose customer interfaces".

Considerable progress has already been made in system design as well as in the establishment of international standards and compatible interfaces. The combined impact of the system's almost limitless possibilities to provide information of every kind in the form desired, and of users' wish to avail themselves of the new services has generated a powerful momentum of advance towards the ISDN. This momentum, created essentially by the "convergence" of communications and computing, is unlikely to slow down until users' needs for interactive data, image, bulk data, audio and video services have been met. Initially, however, progress will tend to be concentrated in areas of high industrial and commercial activity.

Much of the systems design and testing done so far as been carried out independently by the major carriers and manufacturers such as AT&T, British Telecom, GTE, ITT, Siemens and Thomson-CSF, and there is now a pressing need to achieve compatibility between the various systems and designs. Research and development activities in the leading countries are gradually being directed to achieve this.

In the USA, AT&T (Bell Laboratories and the Network Architecture Planning Department) have been cooperating with other American Telephone Companies through the US Independent Telephone Association to plan and implement an ISDN which will provide "universal, ubiquitous digital capabilities", as increasingly demanded by users. Such requirements exercise a strong "market pull" on the development of compatible interfaces meeting, evolving CCITT standards.

The technical requirements of ISDN range widely. The demand for broadband facilities provided by microwave and optical cable transmission, will be substantially increased as the new services develop, e.g., high-speed data transmission, interactive terminals, video reception, but it will continue to be driven by voice needs. This calls for a high degree of compatibility between analog and digital systems.

Transmission speeds expressed in bits per second (bps) for many telemetry type applications such as meter reading, energy management and security, have very low average bit rates — less than 300 bps. Interactive data applications, generally using terminals to access data bases or communicating word processors, computers and other terminals, have much higher bit rates.

Applications include enquiry/response such as checking on airline flight status, other videotex-type services, and transactions such as service order preparations. Image applications are characterized by the transmission of fixed images (for example, a page of text on a TV frame) and include teletex, facsimile, graphics and slow-scan or freeze TV. They can be handled with a bit rate of about 64 kbps. For example, such a capability would support the transmission of a high quality facsimile image of a page in a matter of seconds. Facsimile or graphics applications, when combined with a conferencing bridge, can be used for multi-location business meetings.

Audio transmission includes signals such as music and voice, still the largest component of telecommunication traffic and likely to remain for so many years. In the USA voice has generally been encoded at a 64 kbps standard for transmission on the network. It is possible to transmit voice at lower speeds (32, 16 or even 9 kbps) with acceptable quality for some applications. Alternatively, voice could be encoded at rates exceeding 64 kbps and advanced coding techniques could be used at that speed to improve quality or service options such as encryption.

bout en bout pour une quantité de services, téléphoniques ou non, auxquels les usagers ont accès par l'intermédiaire d'un nombre limité d'interfaces normalisées à buts multiples.

Des progrès considérables ont déjà été accomplis dans la conception du système, ainsi que dans l'établissement de normes internationales et d'interfaces compatibles. L'influence combinée des capacités quasi illimitées du système a donné un puissant essor au RNIS. Cet essor, dont la source est essentiellement la convergence de la télécommunication et de l'ordinateur, ne ralentira pas avant que les besoins des usagers comme, par exemple, l'accès interactif aux banques de données, le télétraitement de l'information, les services audio et video, aient été satisfaits.

Jusqu'ici, la conception des systèmes et les essais résultent, en majeure partie, d'initiatives indépendantes provenant d'importantes entreprises de télécommunications et de grands constructeurs tels que AT&T, British Telecom, GTE, ITT, Siemens et Thomson-CSF. Maintenant il devient donc très urgent de parvenir à la compatibilité requise entre les divers systèmes et les différentes conceptions. Les activités de recherche et de développement déployées dans les pays intéressés s'orientent progressivement dans le même sens.

Aux Etats-Unis, AT&T (Bell Laboratories et le Network Architecture Planning Department) coopèrent avec d'autres firmes de téléphonie américaines par l'intermédiaire de la « US Independent Telephone Association » pour planifier et établir un RNIS qui fournira « des capacités numériques universelles et possédant le don d'ubiquité », telles que les usagers le demandent de plus en plus.

Les exigences techniques du RNIS sont très extensives. La demande pour des capacités de large bande fournies par les méthodes de transmission par micro- ondes et fibres optiques augmentera considérablement en mesure du développement des nouveaux services — par exemple, transmission ultra-rapide des données, terminaux interactifs, réception d'images —, mais la poussée principale sera le besoin de transmettre la voix. Cela demande une très grande compatibilité des systèmes analogiques et numériques.

Les vitesses de transmission, exprimées en bits par seconde (bit/s) pour de nombreuses applications de télémesure, ont un très faible débit binaire moyen, inférieur à 300 bit/s. Certaines applications de données interactives utilisent des débits binaires inférieurs à 4,8 kbit/s (kilobits par seconde). Les applications comprennent alors les opérations question/réponse, comme dans les cas de la confirmation de réservation de places sur les lignes aériennes, les transactions commerciales bancaires ou autres préparations d'ordre de service (commandes). Certaines applications se caractérisent par la transmission d'images fixes (par exemple une page de texte sur une trame TV), y compris les procédés fac-similé, graphiques et d'exploration lente ou image figée TV. Ces opérations peuvent se faire à un débit binaire de 64 kbit/s ou moins.

La transmission sonore comprend des signaux tels que la musique et la voix, cette dernière étant toujours la principale composante du trafic de télécommunications et qui le restera probablement encore pendant de nombreuses années. Aux Etats-Unis, la voix est généralement codée à 64 kbit/s pour la transmission sur le réseau. Elle peut cependant être transmise à des vitesses inférieures (32, 16 ou même 9 kbit/s) avec une qualité acceptable pour de nombreuses applications. Autrement, la voix peut être codée à des vitesses dépassant 64 kbit/s ou des méthodes de codage perfectionnées peuvent être utilisées à cette vitesse pour fournir des services de qualité améliorée avec des options comprenant le cryptage.

Le transfert massif de données comprend des applications telles que la transmission de dossiers ou de fichiers ou entre ordinateurs et notamment la transmission nocturne de données de facturation par de grandes filiales éloignées à destination de l'ordinateur central de la maison mère. Pour être pratiques, de telles applications exigent des vitesses pouvant aller jusqu'à 1544 Mbit/s.

DEVELOPMENT

While telephone densities in Latin America remain amongst the lowest of all the world regions — second in this only to Africa — and while radio and television densities are well below world averages, the implementation and expansion of intra-regional and international telecommunication links has been rapid.

The Inter-American Telecom Conference Organization (CITEL), created in 1962 and with a membership of 19 States, has been the prime promoter for this development. Its main activity has been the introduction of the Inter-American Network (ITN). Originally conceived in 1949, it was developed with technical aid from the ITU and financial assistance from the International Development Association (IDA). Principally it is a network formed from a combination of microwave, links, both across land and via satellites and cable links (including submarine). Its purpose is to interconnect all the States from Mexico to the Magellan Straits and to provide facilities for international services. A prominent aspect of the whole system has been its impact on the growth of national services of which it often forms an integral part.

A regional approach with a more 'localized' concern is that of ASETA (Asociación de Empresas Estatales de Telecomunicaciones) whose members are Bolivia, Chile, Colombia, Ecuador, Peru and Venezuela. ASETA's objective is to interlink the telecom networks of member States through a satellite system, ultimately linking up with the ITN.

The use of satellite services is a practice well established across the region, with 17 States using INTELSAT services via one or more earth stations in each State. Although these are primarily used for international connections, a number of them are also dedicated to providing domestic services. From a number of propositions introduced by the Organization of American States (OAS) those of Brazil and ASETA remain the most viable. A Brazilian national communication satellite system is a distinct possibility for the 1980s.

TOWARD A

The countries of Central America had to rely on a very rudimentary telephone service, with no connections with the outside world save through the USA (a small number of high frequency systems) until the construction of national networks utilizing the latest available technology was begun in the early 1960s. Following the launching of the national projects the Central American governments decided to pool resources in order to set up a modern network and a regional system under the control of purely Central American Organizations. The outcome was the creation of the Regional Telecom Commission (COMTELCA) which is responsible for co-ordinating the regional and international services of Guatemala, El Salvador, Honduras, Nicaragua and Costa Rica. A COMTELCA supervisory group deals with the engineering work and the Central American Telecom Institute (INCATEL) with the training of technicians, the ITU providing the required expertise. These projects were financed with funds from the Central American Bank of Economic Integration (BCIE). The Institute began operating in 1973 in Santa-Tecla, El Salvador.

Latin American public investment in telecom averages about 0.75 per cent of annual GNP. In Central American States, this is 0.5 per cent, in South American States 0.9 per cent. Between them Brazil and Mexico account for the lion's share with 73 per cent of total annual investment.

The COMTELCA microwave trunk network, part of the ITN, was inaugurated in November 1971. Central American countries either using, or planning the use of, INTELSAT linked earth stations include Nicaragua, El Salvador, Mexico, Dominican Republic, Belize, Haiti and Panama.

▷ 82

▷ 82

N CENTRAL AND SOUTH AMERICA

n qu'en Amérique latine les densités téléphoniques demeu-
t parmi les plus faibles du monde — puisque cette région
st en deuxième position seulement après l'Afrique — et bien
les densités de radiodiffusion sonore et télévisuelle soient
 inférieures aux moyennes mondiales, le développement des
communications a cependant été rapide.

'organisation de la Conférence interaméricaine des télé-
mmunications (CITEL), créée en 1962, comprend 19 Etats. Elle
à l'origine de la création du réseau interaméricain (ITN),
u en 1949 et développé avec l'assistance technique de l'UIT
aide financière de l'Association Internationale de dévelop-
ent (AID). Ce réseau est principalement formé d'une
binaison de faisceaux à hyperfréquences, de câbles (noment sous-marins) et de liaisons par satellite. Il relie entre
les Etats situés entre le Mexique et le Détroit de Magellan.
t en offrant les facilités normales du service international,
système a exercé une influence considérable sur le déve-
ement des services nationaux.

'ASETA (Asociación de Empresas Estatales de Telecom-
icaciones) a une conception plus « régionaliste » et des
ccupations plus « locales ». Ses membres sont la Bolivie le
i, la Colombie, l'Equateur, le Pérou et le Vénézuela. Elle a
r but d'interconnecter, entre eux et avec l'ITN, les réseaux
ses Etats membres, par l'intermédiaire d'un système à
llite.

'utilisation de liaisons par satellite est une pratique bien
lie dans la région, dont 17 Etats utilisent les services
telsat par l'intermédiaire d'une ou plusieurs stations ter-
nes dans chaque pays. Parmi les propositions présentées
l'Organisation des Etats Américains (OEA), celles du Brésil
le l'ASETA demeurent les plus valables. Il est d'ailleurs
able qu'au milieu de la présente décennie, le Brésil possé-
 son propre système national de télécommunications par
llite.

Si bien las densidades telefónicas de América Latina se encuentran entre las más bajas de todas las regiones del mundo
— sólo delante de Africa — y las densidades de radio y
televisión muy por debajo de las medias mundiales, la ejecución
y expansión de enlaces de telecomunicaciones intra-regionales
e internacionales han sido rápidas.

La Organización de la Conferencia Interamericana de Telecomunicaciones (CITEL), creada en 1962, con más de 19 Estados miembros, ha sido el promotor primordial de esta evolución. Su principal actividad ha consistido en introducir una Red
Inter-Americana (RIA). Concebida originalmente en 1949, se
desarrolló con la ayuda técnica de la UIT y la asistencia
financiera de la Asociación Internacional de Fomento (AIF). Es,
ante todo, una red de enlaces de microondas (incluidos
submarinos) y de satélite. Su finalidad es unir a todos los
Estados, desde México al Estrecho de Magallanes, y ofrecer
servicios internacionales. Un destacado aspecto de todo el
sistema es su impacto sobre el crecimiento de servicios nacionales de los que forma parte frecuentemente.

Un enfoque regional con un interés más 'localizado' es el de
ASETA (Asociación de Empresas Estatales de Telecomunicaciones), cuyos miembros son Bolivia, Chile, Colombia, Ecuador,
Perú y Venezuela. El objetivo de ASETA es unir las redes de
telecomunicaciones de los Estados miembros a través de un
sistema de satélite, vinculado finalmente a la RIA.

El uso de servicios de satélite es una práctica bien establecida en la región, con 17 Estados que utilizan servicios de
INTELSAT a través de una o más estaciones terrenas en cada
país. Aunque se emplean sobre todo para conexiones internacionales, varios de ellos se consagran también a servicios
nacionales. De las diversas propuestas presentadas por la
Organización de Estados Americanos (OEA), las más viables son
las de Brasil y ASETA. Una clara posibilidad para mediados del
presente decenio es un sistema brasileño de comunicaciones
nacionales por satélite.

TEGRATED REGIONAL SYSTEM

es pays de l'Amérique centrale devaient précédemment se
center d'un service téléphonique très rudimentaire sans
une connexion avec le monde extérieur, sauf par une liaison
c les Etats-Unis, établie sur un petit nombre de systèmes à
es décamétriques. Dans cette région, la construction de
aux nationaux utilisant la technologie la plus moderne a
uté il y a une vingtaine d'années.

 la suite du lancement de leurs projets nationaux, les pays
mérique centrale décidèrent de joindre leurs ressources afin
ablir un réseau moderne et un système régional soumis
usivement au contrôle des organisations de l'Amérique
rale : COMTELCA responsable de la coordination des ser-
s régionaux et internationaux du Guatémala, du Salvador,
Honduras, du Nicaragua et du Costa Rica et l'Institut
ramérican des télécommunications (INCATEL) installé à
ta-Tecla (El Salvador), qui assure depuis 1973 la formation
echniciens, tandis que l'UIT fournit l'assistance technique
ise. Ces projets ont été financés par la Banque centramé-
n d'intégration économique (BCIE).

n Amérique latine, les investissements publics dans le
aine des télécommunications représentent en moyenne
% du PNB annuel. En Amérique centrale, cette moyenne est
,5% et en Amérique du Sud de 0,9%. Parmi les pays de ces
ons le Brésil et le Mexique se taillent la part de lion avec
 du total annuel des investissements.

e réseau Comtelca a été inauguré en novembre 1971. Cer-
s pays de l'Amérique centrale utilisent ou projettent d'uti-
r les stations terriennes du réseau Intelsat, notamment le
aragua, El Salvador, le Mexique, la République Dominicaine,
ze, Haïti et Panama.

Los países de América Central dependían de un servicio
telefónico muy rudimentario, sin conexiones con el mundo
exterior, salvo a través de EE.UU. (un pequeño número de
sistemas de alta frecuencia), hasta que a comienzos del decenio
de 1960 empezó la construcción de redes nacionales que utilizan la última tecnología. Después de lanzarse los proyectos
nacionales, los gobiernos de América Central decidieron man-
comunar recursos para establecer una red moderna y un sistema regional controlado por las organizaciones de América
Central. Esto llevó a la creación de la Comisión Regional de
Telecomunicaciones (COMTELCA), responsable de coordinar los
servicios regionales e internacionales de Guatemala, El Salvador, Honduras, Nicaragua y Costa Rica. Un grupo de supervisión de COMTELCA se ocupa del aspecto técnico, y el Instituto
Centroamericano de Telecomunicaciones (INCATEL), de la formación de técnicos, proporcionando la UIT la asistencia técnica. Esos proyectos se financiaron por el Banco Centroamericano de Integración Económica (BCIE). El Instituto comenzó a
funcionar en 1973, en Santa Tecla (El Salvador).

La inversión pública latinoamericana en telecomunicaciones
es del 0,75% del PNB anual, aproximadamente. En los Estados
de América Central, es del 0,5%, y en los de América del Sur, del
0,9%. Entre ellos, Brasil y México representan la mayor parte,
con el 73% de la inversión anual total.

La red de enlaces por microondas COMTELCA, parte de la
RIA, se inauguró en noviembre de 1971. Los países de América
Central utilizan, o piensan utilizar, estaciones terrenas vinculadas a INTELSAT; entre ellos, Nicaragua, El Salvador, México,
la República Dominicana, Belize, Haití y Panamá.

Se han hecho grandes progresos en el diseño del
sistema, así como en el establecimiento de normas
internacionales e interfaces compatibles. La influencia combinada de las capacidades casi ilimitadas del sistema ha dado un poderoso impulso a la
RDSI. Ese impulso, debido esencialmente a la convergencia de la telecomunicación y del computador,
continuará hasta que se satisfagan las necesidades de
los usuarios de acceso interactivo a datos, teletratamiento de la información y de los datos y servicios
audiovisuales, por ejemplo.

Hasta ahora, la concepción de los sistemas y las
pruebas se deben, en gran parte, a iniciativas independientes de importantes empresas de telecomunicaciones y grandes constructores, como AT&T, British Telecom, GTE, ITT, Siemens y Thomson-CSF.
Es, pues, muy urgente lograr la compatibilidad requerida entre los distintos sistemas y concepciones.
Las actividades de investigación y desarrollo en los
países interesados avanzan progresivamente en ese
sentido. En EE.UU., AT&T (Bell Laboratories y el
Network Architecture Planning Department) cooperan con otras compañías telefónicas americanas
por medio de la « US Independent Telephone Aso-
ciation» para planificar y establecer una RDSI que
proporcionará «capacidades digitales universales y
poseerá el don de la ubicuidad», como solicitan cada
vez más los usuarios.

Las exigencias técnicas de la RDSI son muy grandes. La
demanda de las capacidades de banda ancha que
ofrecen los métodos de transmisión por microondas
y fibras ópticas aumentarán notablemente a medida
que evolucionan nuevos servicios — por ejemplo,
transmisión ultrarrápida de datos, terminales
interactivos, recepción de imágenes —, pero el principal avance será la necesidad de transmitir la voz.
Esto requiere una gran compatibilidad de los sistemas analógicos y digitales.

Las velocidades de transmisión (expresadas en bits
por segundo, b/s) para muchas aplicaciones norma-
lizadas de telemedida, como indicaciones, gestión de
medida y seguridad, tienen velocidades binarias muy
bajas: menos de 300 b/s. Algunas aplicaciones de
datos interactivos utilizan velocidades inferiores a
4,8 kbit/s (kilobits por segundo). Las aplicaciones
comprenden operaciones de pregunta/respuesta,
como la confirmación de reservas de plazas en las
líneas aéreas, las transacciones comerciales bancarias, preparaciones de órdenes de servicio, etc. Algunas aplicaciones se caracterizan por la transmisión
de imágenes fijas (una página de texto o una trama
TV), y comprenden facsímil, gráficos y exploración
lenta o imágenes TV. Pueden tratarse a una velocidad binaria de 64 kb/s o menos, lo que sirve de
soporte para la transmisión de una imagen facsímil
de una página, de gran calidad, en unos segundos.
Esas aplicaciones, combinadas con un puente de conexión en conferencia, deben usarse para reuniones
comerciales desde diversos lugares.

La transmisión audio comprende señales como la
música y la voz, que son aún los principales componentes del tráfico de telecomunicaciones, y probablemente lo sigan siendo durante muchos años. En
EE.UU., la voz se ha codificado en general a 64 kb/s
para la transmisión por la red. Sin embargo, puede
transmitirse a velocidades inferiores (32, 16 o incluso
9 kb/s) con una calidad aceptable para muchas
aplicaciones. En cambio, la voz puede codificarse a
velocidades superiores a 64 kb/s, o bien pueden
emplearse técnicas de codificación avanzadas a esa
velocidad para proporcionar servicios de mejor calidad, con encripción.

La transferencia masiva de datos abarca aplicaciones como la transmisión de grandes archivos de datos
entre computadores. Una de sus aplicaciones es la
transferencia nocturna de datos de facturación desde
grandes publicaciones remotas a un computador
central. Para ser realmente prácticas, tales aplicaciones requieren velocidades de hasta 1544 mb/s.

Para las imágenes animadas se necesitan también
grandes velocidades de transmisión, cuando se

▷ 83

MEDARABTEL is the acronym for the Middle East and Mediterranean Telecommunications project which was adopted by the participating members (24 Arab, 7 European and 1 African) in 1979. This followed a long period of preparation, beginning with a feasibility study and pre-investment survey in 1973 (partly financed by the Arab Fund for Economic and Social Development).

Six sub-regions have been identified and comprehensive studies of the requirements for terrestrial and satellite circuits carried out, involving ARABSAT (Arab Satellite Organisation) and INTELSAT. Much time and money have been spent, under ITU leadership and guidance, to run training courses for telecommunication engineers, including introductions to electronic switching systems, traffic engineering, signalling and tariffs.

Many of the participating countries have adopted digital switching and transmission systems, and throughout the region there is a tendency to adopt the latest electronic technology. New earth stations were put into service and plans drawn up for international switching centers. Some 40 per cent of the finance required for the implementation of the project has been pledged by the participating Arab States.

MEDARABTEL est l'acronyme qui désigne le projet de réseau de télécommunications du Moyen Orient et de la Méditerranée, établi sur la base du plan adopté par les membres participants (24 arabes, 7 européens et 1 africain). Cette réalisation a débuté en 1973 par une étude de faisabilité et de pré-investissement (financée en partie par le Fonds arabe pour le développement économique et social).

Six sous-régions ont été identifiées et les besoins en circuits de Terre et par satellite (ARABSAT et INTELSAT) ont été évalués. Il a fallu beaucoup de temps pour organiser, sous la direction de l'UIT, des cours de formation d'ingénieurs et des cours sur les systèmes de commutation électronique, l'ingénierie du trafic, la signalisation et la tarification.

La plupart des pays participants ont adopté des systèmes de communication et de transmission numériques. Dans toute la région, de nouvelles stations terrenes ont été mises en service et des plans ont été établis en vue de la construction de centres de commutation internationaux. Les Etats arabes participants ont offert de fournir 40% des fonds nécessaires pour l'exécution de ce projet.

MEDARABTEL es el acrónimo de Red de Telecomunicaciones del Oriente Medio y el Mediterráneo, creada por los países participantes (24 árabes, 7 europeos y 1 africano), tras un largo período de preparación, iniciado con un estudio de viabilidad y un estudio de preinversión en 1973 (financiado en parte por el Fondo Árabe para el Desarrollo Económico y Social).

Se han identificado seis subregiones, efectuándose estudios detallados de los circuitos terrenales y de satélite necesarios, que comprenden ARABSAT (Organización Árabe de Comunicaciones por Satélite) e INTELSAT. Bajo la dirección y guía de la UIT se ha consagrado mucho tiempo y mucho dinero a cursos de formación de ingenieros de telecomunicaciones en introducciones a sistemas de conmutación electrónicos, ingeniería de tráfico, señalización y tarifas.

Muchos de los países participantes han adoptado sistemas de conmutación y transmisión digitales, y en toda la región se tiende a adoptar la tecnología electrónica más reciente. Se pusieron en servicio nuevas estaciones terrenas y se proyectaron centros de conmutación internacionales. Los Estados árabes participantes han ofrecido aportar el 40% de los fondos necesarios para la ejecución del proyecto.

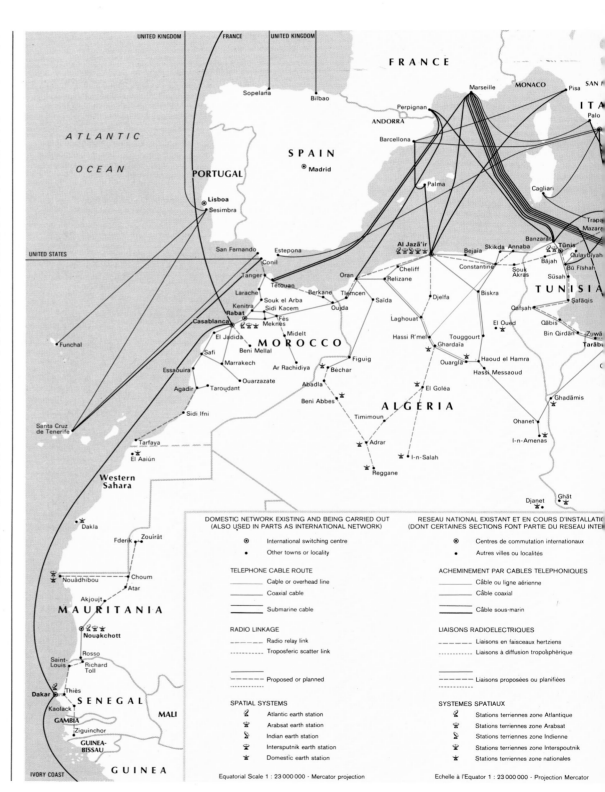

DOMESTIC NETWORK EXISTING AND BEING CARRIED OUT (ALSO USED IN PARTS AS INTERNATIONAL NETWORK)	RESEAU NATIONAL EXISTANT ET EN COURS D'INSTALLATION (DONT CERTAINES SECTIONS FONT PARTIE DU RESEAU INTER
⊚ International switching centre	⊚ Centres de commutation internationaux
• Other towns or locality	• Autres villes ou localités

TELEPHONE CABLE ROUTE / **ACHEMINEMENT PAR CABLES TELEPHONIQUES**
- Cable or overhead line / Câble ou ligne aérienne
- Coaxial cable / Câble coaxial
- Submarine cable / Câble sous-marin

RADIO LINKAGE / **LIAISONS RADIOELECTRIQUES**
- Radio relay link / Liaisons en faisceaux hertziens
- Tropospheric scatter link / Liaisons à diffusion troposphérique

- Proposed or planned / Liaisons proposées ou planifiées

SPATIAL SYSTEMS / **SYSTEMES SPATIAUX**
- Atlantic earth station / Stations terriennes zone Atlantique
- Arabsat earth station / Stations terriennes zone Arabsat
- Indian earth station / Stations terriennes zone Indienne
- Intersputnik earth station / Stations terriennes zone Intersputnik
- Domestic earth station / Stations terriennes zone nationales

Equatorial Scale 1 : 23 000 000 - Mercator projection   Echelle à l'Equator 1 : 23 000 000 - Projection Mercator

RRANEAN BASIN NETWORK

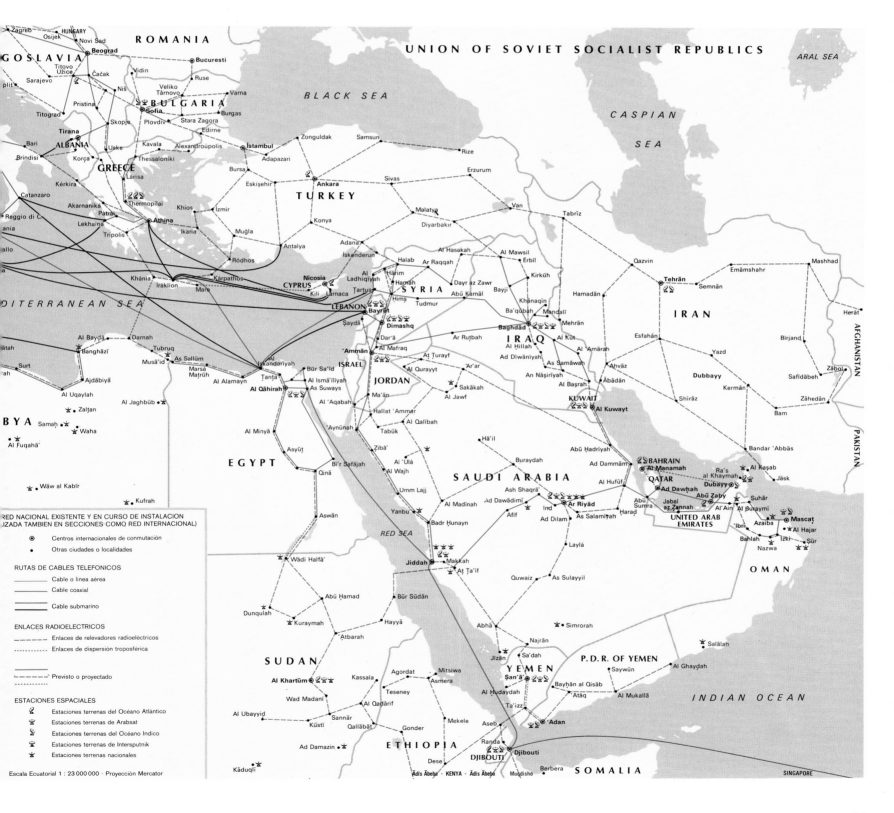

ROMANIA

UNION OF SOVIET SOCIALIST REPUBLICS

ARAL SEA

BLACK SEA

CASPIAN SEA

GOSLAVIA
Zagreb • HUNGARY
Osijek • Novi Sad
Titovo Uzice • Beograd
Sarajevo • Čačak
plit • Niš
Vidin
Veliko Târnovo
Bucuresti
Ruse
Varna

BULGARIA
Titograd • Sofia
Pristina • Skopje • Plovdiv • Stara Zagora
Burgas
Tirana
ALBANIA
Korça
Bari
Brindisi
GREECE
Kérkira • Lárisa
Catanzaro
Akarnaniká
Reggio di C
ania
Lekhainá • Pátrai
Tripolis
Thermopílai
Athína
allo

MEDITERRANEAN SEA
Al Bayda • Darnah
ãtah • Banghāzī
Surt • Tubruq
Ajdābiyā
Al Uqaylah
BYA
Samah • Zaltan
Waha
Al Fuqahā'
Wāw al Kabīr
Kufrah

Uske
Kavala
Alexandroúpolis
Thessaloníki
Khíos
Izmir
Mugla
Antalya
Khánia
Iráklion
Ródhos
Kárpathos
Kili
Maré

ZONGuldak
İstanbul
Adapazari
Bursa
Eskişehir
Ankara
Konya
Adana
İskenderun
Nicosia
CYPRUS
Lárnaca

Samsun
Sivas
Rize
Erzurum
Malatya
Diyarbakir

TURKEY

Van
Tabrīz
Erbīl
Kirkūh
Qazvin
Emāmshahr
Mashhad
Tehrān
Semnān

Al Hasakah
Al Mawsil
Ar Raqqah
Dayr az Zawr
Abū Kamāl
Bayji
Khānaqin
Mandali
Hamadān
IRAN
Herāt
Birjand
Safidābeh
Zābol
Zāhedān

Al Ladhiqīyah
Tartūs
SYRIA
Halab
Hamāh
Himş
Tudmur

Al
Hārim
LEBANON
Bayrūt
Şaydā
DIMASHQ
Dar'ā

Ba'qūbah
Baghdād
Al Hillah
IRAQ
Ar Rutbah
Al Kūt
Al 'Amārah
Mehrān
Esfahān
Yazd
Kermān
Ahvāz
Ābādān
Shīrāz
Bam

AFGHANISTAN
PAKISTAN

'Ammān
Al Mafraq
ISRAEL
Al Iskandarīyah
Būr Sa'īd
JORDAN
Al Qāhirah
Tanta
Al Ismā'īlīyah
As Suways
Al 'Aqabah

At Turayf
'Ar'ar
Ma'ān
Sakākah
Al Jawf

An Nāsirīyah
Al Basrah
KUWAIT
Al Kuwayt

Bandar 'Abbās
Dubbayy
Ra's al Khaymah
Al Kaşab
Jāsk

EGYPT
Al Minyā
Asyūṭ
Bi'r Safājah
Qinā
Aswān
Wādī Halfā'

Hallat 'Ammar
Al Qalībah
Tabūk
Ziba'
Al 'Ulā
Al Wajh
Umm Lajj
Al Madīnah
Yanbu'
Badr Hunayn

 Hā'il
Buraydah
Abū Hadrīyah
Ad Dammām
SAUDI ARABIA
Ash Shaqrā
Ar Riyād
Ad Dawādimī
Ind
Al Dilam
As Salamīyah
Afif
Al Hufūf
Abū Sumra
Harad

BAHRAIN
Al Manamah
QATAR
Ad Dawhah
Abū Zaby
Jabal az Zannah
UNITED ARAB EMIRATES
Al 'Ain
'Ibrī
Suhār
Al Buraymī
Bahlah
Azaiba
Mascaţ
Al Hajar
Izkī
Nazwa
Şūr
OMAN

RED SEA
Quwaiz
Layla
As Sulayyil

Dunqulah
Kuraymah
Hayyā
'Atbarah
SUDAN
Al Khartūm
Wad Madanī
Al Ubayyid
Kūstī
Sannār
Qallābāt
Ad Damazin
Kāduqlī

Jiddah • Makkah
Aṭ Ṭā'if
Abū Hamad
Būr Sūdān
Abhā
Simrorah
Najrān
Jizān • Sa'dah
YEMEN
Şan'ā
Al Hudaydah
Ta'izz
Aseb
Randa
Djibouti
DJIBOUTI
Dese
SOMALIA

Kassala
Agordat
Teseney
Asmera
Mitsiwa
Al Qadārif
Mekele
ETHIOPIA
Gonder
Ādīs Ābeba · KENYA · Ādīs Ābeba
Mundisho

P.D.R. OF YEMEN
Saywūn
Bayhān al Qisāb
Atāq
Al Mukallā
Al Ghaydah
Salālah
INDIAN OCEAN

Berbera
SINGAPORE

Legend

RED NACIONAL EXISTENTE Y EN CURSO DE INSTALACION
IZADA TAMBIEN EN SECCIONES·COMO RED INTERNACIONAL)

- ◉ Centros internacionales de conmutación
- • Otras ciudades o localidades

RUTAS DE CABLES TELEFONICOS
- —— Cable o línea aérea
- —— Cable coaxial
- ━━ Cable submarino

ENLACES RADIOELECTRICOS
- ----- Enlaces de relevadores radioeléctricos
- ········· Enlaces de dispersión troposférica

- —— Previsto o proyectado
- ----

ESTACIONES ESPACIALES
- ⚓ Estaciones terrenas del Océano Atlántico
- ⚓ Estaciones terrenas de Arabsat
- ⚓ Estaciones terrenas del Océano Indico
- ⚓ Estaciones terrenas de Intersputnik
- ✶ Estaciones terrenas nacionales

Escala Ecuatorial 1 : 23 000 000 · Proyección Mercator

81

Bulk data transfer encompasses applications such as the transmission of large data files between computers. One application is the nightly transfer of billing data from large remote locations such as warehouses or supermarkets to a central host location. Such applications typically are most effective at very high speed to be at all practical, up to 1,544 mbps (megabits per second).

Full motion video also requires high transmission speeds when transmitted digitally but it can be provided in a number of formats. For example, broadcast quality video requires about 4.5 MHz as an analog signal, or approximately 100 mbps as a digital signal. However, using signal compression techniques, the signal can be compressed to 6,3 or 1,5 mbps which is sufficient for some applications such as teleconferencing. Applications for full motion video include multi-location business meetings and entertainment.

The high degree of diversity in customer needs, calls for a correspondingly wide range of capabilities in the system, and creates major problems of interfacing the new with the old smoothly and economically.

Networks with different control structures will co-exist and have to interconnect effectively. Architectures for sharing the network resources will require an ingenious combination of packet and circuit switching methods to handle the great variety of applications. It will be essential for ISDN services to offer bit rates and capabilities to customers at their interfaces to the network which will accomodate a wide range of user needs. The determination of interface standards has been and continues to be a major activity of the CCITT.

The provision of universal interconnection is a necessary element in the realization of an ISDN so that messages, information and data can be passed from one system to another, from one nation to another, and between dissimilar facilities. It will be many years before national public data networks are generally integrated into a single global network that accomplishes for digital communications what has been accomplished for 565 million telephones since Alexander Graham Bell first succeeded in transmitting voice over a wire in 1876. The most likely development, currently well advanced, is for high function information systems to be developed in response to key national requirements.

An indication of the speed at which the switch over from analog to digital can take place in areas of high telephone density is given by an AT&T forecast of the progress of the Bell System in that direction. In 1982 SPC switching was operational on about 60% of the lines. In 1990 this will have increased by 90%, about 20% time division and 70% space division, a rate of change that will be hard to match. In 1982, toll tandem switches with a terminal digital capability accounted for about one-third of the total in service, by 1990 this proportion is expected to have increased by 90%. By 1990, 80% of town lines of Bell Systems will be fully digital as well as 25% of intercity circuit. Some countries where less is invested in analog circuitry will probably effect a more rapid conversion, but it obviously cannot be done overnight.

The extent and complexity of the installations and the rate of progress, will depend on the willingness of national and international business organizations to invest heavily in more productive, high performance electronic information networks. What can be achieved in the Sector of international business, and in sectors of intense economic activity, will serve as a catalyst vastly to expand mankind's capacity to manage, to coordinate enterprise on a world scale with the same speed and facility as that being enjoyed domestically by the most advanced nations.

The pages that follow describe how the world's largest telecommunications company, in network operation, equipment manufacture, system design and R&D, has turned itself outward and is beginning to apply its considerable resources to the development of global communications. A prime objective of the newly deregulated American Telephone and Telegraph Company (AT&T) is to contribute to the establishment of the ISDN of the future.

□

Les images animées demandent également l'emploi de vitesses élevées, lorsqu'on applique la technique de transmission numérique, qui peut se réaliser en un certain nombre de formats. Par exemple, pour une transmission vidéo de qualité « radiodiffusion », on utilise un signal analogique de 4,5 MHz ou un signal numérique d'environ 100 Mbit/s. Toutefois en utilisant les techniques de compression du signal, celui-ci peut être ramené à 6,3 ou 1,5 Mbit/s, vitesses suffisantes pour un certain nombre d'applications. Les utilisations en vidéo animée comprennent les « Téléréunions » d'affaires ou de loisirs.

La grande diversité des besoins des usagers exige une large gamme de variantes d'exploitation du système et suscite des problèmes ardus en ce qui concerne l'interconnexion progressive et économique du nouveau réseau avec l'ancien. Les réseaux publics analogiques existants étaient primitivement destinés au trafic téléphonique. Dans leur grande majorité, les utilisations numériques de ce réseau faisaient appel à des modems pour adapter les signaux d'entrée numériques à la largeur de bande analogique de 3 à 4 kHz, c'est-à-dire aux caractéristiques d'un réseau conçu pour la transmission analogique de la voix. Les techniques de communications pour des largeurs de bande extraordinaires (satellites et fibres optiques, par exemple) permettront de satisfaire la demande de très grandes largeurs de bande mais il est évident que les nouveaux procédés devront coexister avec les systèmes actuels à largeur de bande moyenne ou étroite, qui sont plus économiques dans leurs domaines d'application respectifs. Aux points de jonction avec le RNIS, il faudra offrir des débits binaires et des possibilités permettant de satisfaire une large gamme de besoins des usagers. La spécification des normes d'interface a été et continue d'être l'une des principales activités du CCITT.

La possibilité d'interconnexion universelle est un élément essentiel dans la réalisation du RNIS, pour que les messages, l'information et les données puissent être transposées d'un système à l'autre, d'un pays à l'autre, et entre des installations dissemblables. Il se passera encore de nombreuses années avant que les réseaux de chaque pays soient intégrés dans un réseau mondial unique capable d'assurer pour les communications numériques ce qui a été accompli pour 565 millions d'appareils téléphoniques, depuis qu'Alexandre Graham Bell a réussi, en 1876, à transmettre la voix par fil. Le degré de perfectionnement des installations et le rythme de leur mise en place dépendra de la volonté des organisations commerciales, nationales et internationales, de consentir des investissements très importants dans les réseaux informatiques les plus performants.

Une idée de la rapidité à laquelle le passage de l'analogique au numérique peut se faire dans les zones de haute densité est fournie par une prévision de AT&T sur le progrès du système Bell dans cette direction. En 1982, la commutation CEP (Concept d'Enregistrement de Programmes) était opérationnelle sur environ 60% des voies — en 1990 cette proportion se sera élevée à 90%, dont environ 20% à division temporelle et 70% à division spatiale, un taux d'évolution difficile à égaler. En 1990, 80% des voies urbaines du système Bell seront adaptées au numérique ainsi que 25% des voies interurbaines.

Ce qui peut être accompli dans les secteurs des affaires internationales ou d'intense activité économique, tels que les secteurs urbains du système Bell servira de catalyseur pour une augmentation du pouvoir de gestion de l'humanité entière à une échelle globale, avec la même rapidité et la même facilité dont font preuve chez eux les pays les plus développés.

Les pages qui suivent présentent la plus grande organisation de télécommunications du monde. American Telephone and Telegraph Company (AT&T), dont l'activité s'étend à tous les domaines de l'exploitation, de la production industrielle et de la recherche et du développement. Depuis sa récente réorganisation, AT&T s'est tournée vers l'extérieur des Etats-Unis, et commence à utiliser ses ressources considérables pour favoriser le développement des communications « globales » et l'établissement du RNIS de l'avenir.

□

TH

GLODOM is the concept designed to bring a telephone to each settlement and village of rural, isolated or under-privileged regions hence its name — an acronym of GLOBAL and DOMESTIC. It arose from the need for a global recognition, stemming from the conceptual studies of the ITU of the present availability of telecommunications, of the associated imbalances in investment policies and priorities and of an inadequate understanding of the benefits that telecommunications contribute to national social and economic development. Subsequent studies carried out jointly by the ITU and OECD pointed out that the benefits, direct and indirect, to countries development far outweigh the cost and that they were, in fact, many times greater than is generally supposed by national planners, economists and investors.

Developed Countries 25%

Moder
Techno
for
develo

Shared resources
Shared benefits
Revised telecommunication
Rural growth and developm

The essence of GLODOM is the use of the latest technology — including transmission by satellite operating to small earth stations serving domestic traffic needs for rural and remote areas and into national networks with low capacity radio and other transmission systems. GLODOM focuses on common user sharing of appropriately designed satellite transponders to contribute to the operational needs of rural areas. Satisfactory service results could be obtained through appropriate common user satellite capacity being available for developing countries and global result could evolve from an incremental regional approach.

A global solution would be to provide some 48,000 domestic earth stations located in the participating nations, functioning in unelectrified areas with solar energy. They could, as necessary, interconnect with small capacity terrestrial systems. Telecommunications could thus be installed on a vast scale before electrification and ahead of transportation and roadways.

Maintenance would be minimal. Fault identification would be computerized and provision made for major repairs at central depots. Operating the system would be simple: people could be trained quickly to align the antennas with the satellites to keep them at peak signal strength.

The investment required would not exceed 5 per cent of the total (1983) concessional aid given in one year by the OECD countries to the developing countries, and the time required to implement the system would be less than a decade.

NCEPT OF "GLODOM"

DOM est une conception des télécommunications visant à
urer des liaisons téléphoniques dans les régions les plus
avorisées. Cette notion découle des études de l'UIT qui
ent établi l'insuffisance des investissements et de la
tribution que les télécommunications peuvent apporter au
eloppement national, social et économique. D'autres études
reprises conjointement par l'UIT et l'OCDE ont permis d'é-
ir que les avantages directs et indirects que les télécom-
nications apportent au développement d'un pays dépassent
ement le coût des services fournis à l'abonné par le pres-
ire des services de télécommunications. En fait, le profit qui
résulte réellement est plusieurs fois supérieur à ce que
posent généralement les planificateurs, les économistes et
investisseurs.

GLODOM se ha ideado para llevar el teléfono a todo pueblo y
aldea de las regiones rurales, aisladas o desfavorecidas. De ahí
su nombre, acrónimo de GLObal Y DOMéstico. Nace de la
necesidad de un reconocimiento general, derivado de los estudios conceptuales de la UIT sobre las telecomunicaciones actuales, del desequilibrio de las políticas y prioridades de inversión, y de una comprensión inadecuada de los beneficios que
aportan las telecomunicaciones al desarrollo nacional, social y
económico.

Estudios conjuntos posteriores de la UIT y la OCDE muestran
que los beneficios, directos e indirectos, para el desarrollo de
los países compensan con creces el costo y que son varias
veces superiores a lo que suponen generalmente los planificadores, economistas e inversores nacionales.

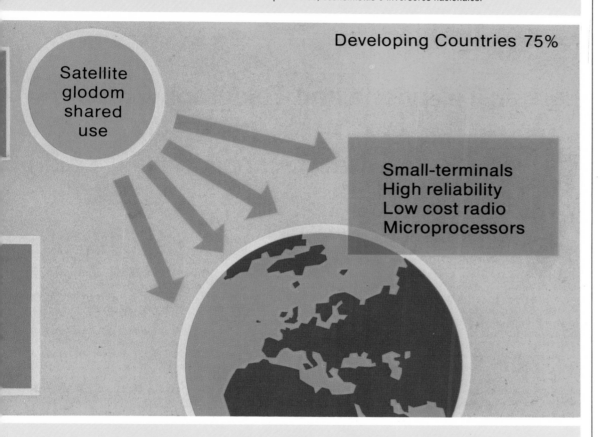

e système GLODOM est fondé sur l'utilisation des techni-
s les plus modernes notamment sur la transmission par
llite dont le coût ne dépend pas de la distance. Son fonc-
nement est assuré par de petites stations terriennes
servant des régions non électrifiées et intégrées dans des
aux nationaux de transmission. Le système GLODOM est
dé sur l'utilisation en partage de répondeurs de satellite
cialement conçus pour répondre aux besoins d'exploitation
zones rurales dans des régions ou des sous-régions déter-
es. Ainsi, la conception globale peut donner des résultats
sfaisants, à condition qu'une capacité de satellite ap-
riée soit mise à la disposition des pays en développement. En
fait, le caractère « global » du système résultera de la
me des efforts qui pourront être déployés à l'échelle « ré-
ale ». La solution globale implique la mise en service
viron 48 000 stations terriennes nationales réparties dans
pays participant au système. Ces stations pourront fonc-
ner dans des régions non électrifiées, grâce à l'énergie
ire. Ainsi, ce système de télécommunications est suscep-
completement aménagé avant même que les ré-
d'être complètement aménagé avant même que les ré-
x routiers et ferroviaires aient été aménagés.
a maintenance du système n'exigera que des efforts mini-
: les défaillances seront détectées et identifiées par des
ositifs informatisés et les réparations importantes pourront
exécutées dans des dépôts centraux. Les investissements
essaires ne dépasseront pas 5% du total de l'aide accordée
1983 par les pays de l'OCDE aux pays en développement et le
t pourrait être réalisé en moins de dix ans.

Lo esencial de GLODOM es el uso de la última tecnología,
incluida la transmisión por satélite, explotando pequeñas estaciones terrenas que atienden las necesidades del tráfico de
las zonas rurales y remotas, y redes nacionales de poca capacidad y otros sistemas de transmisión. GLODOM se centra en la
compartición por los usuarios de transpondedores de satélite
debidamente concebidos para satisfacer las necesidades de las
zonas rurales. Pueden obtenerse resultados satisfactorios po-
niendo a disposición de los países en desarrollo una capacidad
de satélite adecuada, y las realizaciones regionales pueden
producir un resultado global.

Tal solución proporcionaría unas 48 000 estaciones terrenas, ubicadas en las naciones participantes, que funcionarían
en zonas sin electrificar, con energía solar, y podrían interconectarse con sistemas terrenales de poca capacidad. Las telecomunicaciones podrían instalarse así en gran escala, antes de
la electrificación, y de las carreteras y líneas férreas.

El mantenimiento sería mínimo. Las averías se localizarían
por computador, y las reparaciones importantes se harían en
depósitos centrales. La explotación sería sencilla: podría for-
marse al personal rápidamente para alinear las antenas con los
satélites a fin de seguirlos a la intensidad de la señal de cresta.

La inversión no rebasaría el 5% del total de la ayuda anual
concedida (1983) por los países de la OCDE a los países en
desarrollo, y el sistema se realizaría en menos de un decenío.

envían digitalmente, pero puede hacerse en varios
formatos. Por ejemplo, para un video de calidad
radiodifusión se requieren unos 4,5 MHz (megahertzios) como señal analógica, o unos 100 mb/s
como señal digital. Sin embargo, utilizando técnicas
de compresión de la señal, ésta puede comprimirse
da 6,3 ó 1,5 mb/s, lo cual es suficiente para algunas
aplicaciones. El video de imágenes animadas comprende, entre otras aplicaciones, las reuniones comerciales desde diversos sitios, y las recreativas.

La gran diversidad de las necesidades del usuario exige una
amplia gama de capacidades correspondiente en el
sistema, y crea grandes problemas para conectar la
nueva red a la antigua con facilidad y economía.
También coexistirán redes con distintas estructuras
de control, que habrán de interconectarse efectivamente. Las arquitecturas para compartir los recursos
de la red requerirán una ingeniosa combinación de
métodos de conmutación de paquetes y de circuitos
para tratar la gran variedad de aplicaciones. Para los
servicios de la RDSI será esencial ofrecer velocidades binarias y capacidades a los clientes en sus
interfaces con la red, que acomodarán una amplia
gama de necesidades de usuario. La determinación
de interfaces normalizados ha sido, y sigue siendo,
una importante actividad del CCITT.

La provisión de la interconexión universal es un elemento
necesario para la realización de una RDSI, de manera que los mensajes, la información y los datos
puedan pasar de un sistema a otro, de una nación a
otra, y entre facilidades diferentes. Habrán de
transcurrir bastantes años para integrar generalmente las redes nacionales públicas de datos en una
sola red global que realice para las comunicaciones
digitales lo que se ha logrado para 565 millones de
teléfonos desde que Alexander Graham Bell logró
por primera vez transmitir la voz por hilo en 1876. El
desarrollo más probable, ya bastante avanzado, es el
de los sistemas de información de alta función que se
crearán para atender exigencias nacionales esenciales.

Una previsión de AT&T del avance del sistema
Bell en este sentido da idea de la rapidez a que puede
pasarse del sistema analógico al digital en las zonas
de gran densidad. En 1982, la conmutación CPA
(control por programa almacenado) funcionaba en
el 60% de las líneas. Para 1990, esta proporción será
del 90%, un 20% con división en el tiempo y un 70%
con división en el espacio, lo que supone una evolución difícil de igualar. En 1982, los conmutadores en
tándem con capacidad digital representaban alrededor de un tercio del total en servicio, proporción que
se espera llegue al 90% para 1990. Ese año, el 80% de
las líneas urbanas de Bell Systems serán totalmente
digitales, lo mismo que el 25% de los circuitos
interurbanos. En algunos países donde se ha invertido menos en circuitos analógicos, probablemente la
conversión sea más rápida, pero es evidente que no
puede hacerse de la noche a la mañana.

El grado y la complejidad de las instalaciones y el
ritmo de progreso dependerán de la voluntad de las
empresas nacionales e internacional con respecto a
las redes. Lo que puede realizarse en el sector de los
negocios internacionales, y en sectores de intensa
actividad económica, como los urbanos del Bell
Systems servirá de catalizador para un mayor poder
de gestión de toda la humanidad en su capacidad
para dirigir y coordinar empresas a escala mundial,
con la misma rapidez y facilidad que lo hacen ya los
países más avanzados.

En las páginas que siguen se presenta la mayor
organización de telecomunicaciones del mundo, The
American Telephone and Telegraph Company
(AT&T), cuya actividad se extiende a todos los sectores de la explotación, la producción industrial y la
concepción de sistemas, así como a la investigación y
al desarrollo. Desde su reciente reorganización,
AT&T mira hacia el exterior de EE.UU., y comienza
a utilizar sus considerables recursos para favorecer el
desarrollo de las comunicaciones globales y establecer la RDSI del futuro.

□

American Telephone and Telegraph Company

A New Outlook, a New Vision

CHANGES IN TECHNOLOGY and public policy have led to a major restructuring of the world's largest telecommunications company. Out of this, a new and significantly different enterprise is emerging.

Over the years, the United States has stood almost alone among the nations of the world in entrusting to private industry the provision of public telecommunications services — relying on government regulation to ensure that the public interest is served.

For most of this century, this private industry effort has been led by the American Telephone and Telegraph Company (AT&T) and its affiliated companies. With an integrated organizational structure incorporating research and development, manufacturing and a nationwide family of operating telephone companies, the Bell System has served about 80 per cent of the nation's telephones, managed the nationwide long distance network and provided telephone connections between the USA and other countries.

Like other privately-owned telephone companies in the United States, the Bell System historically operated as a regulated monopoly — its products, prices and profits closely scrutinized by state and federal regulatory authorities. However, in recent years, public policymakers in the USA have been looking increasingly to competition rather than to regulation to assure the development and distribution of telecommunications products and services. **The impetus for change** has come in part from pressure — including litigation — by companies desiring to enter or expand their role in segments of the communica-

▷ 86

L'ÉVOLUTION TECHNOLOGIQUE et les changements de la politique en matière de services publics aux Etats-Unis ont abouti à une restructuration fondamentale de la plus grande entreprise de télécommunications du monde. De ceci, émerge une toute nouvelle entreprise, très différente de l'ancienne.

Pendant des années, les Etats-Unis ont été pratiquement le seul pays du monde à confier à l'industrie privée la fourniture de services publics de télécommunications tout en assurant la protection de l'intérêt public par une étroite réglementation des services offerts. Pendant la plus grande partie du siècle, cet effort a été assumé principalement par l'American Telephone and Telegraph Company (AT&T) et ses filiales : le Bell System. C'est dans le cadre d'une structure intégrée, et d'activités déployées à l'échelon national par une série d'entreprises téléphoniques, que le Bell System a couvert plus de 80% de la téléphonie nationale, notamment en assumant la gestion de l'ensemble du réseau interurbain et en assurant les liaisons téléphoniques entre les Etats-Unis et les autres pays.

Comme d'autres entreprises privées des Etats-Unis, le Bell System a fonctionné comme un monopole assujetti à une réglementation, ses produits, ses prix et ses bénéfices étant étroitement surveillés par les autorités locales et fédérales. Toutefois, au cours des dernières années, les dirigeants des Etats-Unis ont jugé préférable de se fier à la concurrence plutôt qu'à la réglementation pour favoriser le développement et la distribution des produits et des services de télécommunications.

La poussée vers le changement vient en partie de la pression et de l'agressivité des entreprises qui désiraient jouer un plus grand rôle, ou s'introduire dans certains secteurs du marché des communications histo-

▷ 86

LOS CAMBIOS TECNOLÓGICOS y de la política pública en Estados Unidos han llevado a una importante reestructuración de la mayor empresa mundial de telecomunicaciones, surgiendo una nueva compañía, totalmente distinta.

A lo largo de los años, Estados Unidos ha sido casi la única nación del mundo en confiar a la industria privada los servicios públicos de telecomunicaciones, ocupándose el gobierno de la reglamentación para garantizar el servicio del interés público.

Durante la mayor parte de este siglo, ese esfuerzo de la industria privada lo han realizado The American Telephone and Telegraph Company (AT&T) y sus empresas filiales. Con una estructura orgánica integrada que abarca la investigación y el desarrollo, la fabricación y una serie de empresas telefónicas en todo el país, Bell System ha proporcionado alrededor del 80% de los teléfonos nacionales, administrado la red de larga distancia del país y realizado conexiones telefónicas entre EE.UU. y otros países.

Como otras empresas telefónicas privadas en EE.UU., Bell System ha operado históricamente como monopolio reglamentado, sometiéndose sus productos, precios y beneficios a un estrecho control de las autoridades de fiscalización estatales y federales. Sin embargo, en los últimos años, las autoridades públicas del país se han ocupado en mayor medida de la competencia que de la reglamentación, para garantizar el desarrollo y la distribución de productos y servicios de telecomunicaciones.

El impulso del cambio se ha debido en parte a la presión — incluida la litigación — de empresas que desean

▷ 86

The new 660 ft-high HQ of AT&T (model), Philip Johnson's architecture breaks with contemporary style as the restructured company breaks with a century-old operational mode.

Le nouveau siège de AT&T (maquette) s'élève 203 mètres dans la cité de New York. L'architecture de Philip Johnson rompt avec le style contemporain tout comme AT&T réstructurée rompt avec le style traditionnel de ses operations.

La nueva sede de AT&T (maqueta) de 203 metros, en la ciudad de Nueva York. El estilo arquitectónico de Philip Johnson es una ruptura con el estilo contemporáneo, lo mismo que AT&T rompe con su forma tradicional de operar desde hace un siglo.

tions market and, more significàntly perhaps, by the convergence of communications and computer technologies. This has blurred the traditional boundaries between the telecommunications and data processing industries and, in so doing, has changed the very nature of both.

The transition from regulated monopoly to a competitive telecommunications market actually began in the late 1960s with a series of federal regulatory decisions introducing competition in selected areas of the telecommunications market. It culminated in two major decisions in the early 1980s, both of which required fundamental changes in the organizational structure of the Bell System.

A landmark decision was made in 1981 by the Federal Communications Commission in its Second Computer Inquiry which, in effect, deregulated the provision of new customer equipment and of services that combine communications and data processing functions. It also mandated that, beginning in 1983, AT&T could offer these services through a separate subsidiary, totally independent of the company's regulated operations. To comply with this, AT&T created a new company called AT&T Information Systems.

The FCC's decision was followed in early 1982 by a Consent Decree agreement which ended a seven-year-old antitrust case against AT&T by the US Department of Justice. That decree required AT&T to divest its 22 local operating telephone companies by the beginning of 1984. In turn, it lifted previous restrictions that prevented AT&T from entering unregulated markets such as information processing.

These two government actions set in motion one of the most massive corporate restructuring efforts ever undertaken — the disaggregation of a company with 70 million customers, 3 million share owners, a million employees and assets of almost $150 billion.

riquement considérés comme des monopoles naturels. Un autre facteur — peut-être encore plus déterminant — est celui de la symbiose progressive des télécommunications et des ordinateurs.

La transition entre la situation de monopole réglementé et celle de l'affrontement commercial sur le marché des télécommunications a commencé, un peu avant 1970, par une série de décisions de caractère législatif, à l'échelon fédéral, introduisant la concurrence dans certaines branches des télécommunications. Cette évolution a abouti au début de la présente décennie, à un bouleversement profond de l'organisation du Bell System.

La levée de la réglementation fut, pour le Bell System, une décision historique, prise en 1981 par la FCC (Federal Communications Commission) suivant sa deuxième enquête sur les ordinateurs. Cette décision a soustrait à la réglementation en vigueur la fourniture de nouveaux équipements aux abonnés et les services dans lesquels se combinent les fonctions de communication et celles du traitement des données. La FCC a également décidé, qu'à partir de 1983, AT&T ne pourrait offrir ce type de services que par l'intermédiaire d'une filiale totalement indépendante des activités réglementées de la compagnie. Pour satisfaire à ces exigences, AT&T a créé une nouvelle société, AT&T Information Systems.

La décision de la FCC fut suivie, au début de 1982, d'un accord qui mit un terme à un procès intenté sept ans plus tôt contre AT&T, au titre de la loi anti-trust, par le Département de la justice des Etats-Unis. Aux termes de cet accord, AT&T devra se déssaisir, dès 1984, de ses 22 entreprises locales d'exploitation téléphonique, en échange de la levée de toutes les restrictions antérieures qui l'empêchaient de participer, sur les marchés non-réglementés, aux activités de traitement de l'information.

Cette restructuration — la plus vaste qui ait jamais été entreprise — implique la désagrégation d'une compagnie disposant de 70 millions d'abonnés, 3 millions d'actionnaires, un million d'employés et un actif s'élevant à environ 150 milliards de dollars US.

introducirse en el mercado de las comunicaciones, o jugar un mayor papel en algunos sectores, quizá, sobre todo, debido a la convergencia de la tecnología de comunicaciones y de computador. Esto ha hecho más confusas las demarcaciones tradicionales entre las industrias de telecomunicaciones y procesamiento de datos, cambiándose así la propia naturaleza de ambas.

La transición del monopolio reglamentado a un mercado de telecomunicaciones competitivo comenzó realmente en los últimos años 1960, con una serie de decisiones normativas federales que introducían la competencia con dos importantes decisiones a comienzos del presente decenio, que requerían cambios fundamentales en la estructura orgánica de Bell System.

Una decisión histórica la tomó, en 1981, la Federal Communications Commission, a raíz de su segunda encuesta sobre computadores, según la cual se liberalizan los servicios que combinan las funciones de comunicaciones y procesamiento de datos. También estipulaba que, a principios de 1983, AT&T podría ofrecer esos servicios sólo a través de otra filial, totalmente independiente de las operaciones reglamentadas de la empresa. Para ello, AT&T creó una nueva compañía, denominada AT&T Information Systems.

La decision de la FCC fue seguida, a comienzos de 1982, por un acuerdo de decreto por consentimiento que ponía fin a un pleito de siete años por antimonopolio contra AT&T por el Departamento de Justicia de EE.UU. Según el decreto, AT&T tiene que renunciar a sus 22 compañías telefónicas de explotación locales para principios de 1984. En cambio, se levantan las restricciones anteriores que impedían a AT&T participar en mercados no reglamentados, como el procesamiento de la información.

Esas dos acciones gubernamentales pusieron en marcha uno de los mayores esfuerzos de reestructuración empresarial emprendidos hasta ahora: la

▷ 87   ▷ 87   ▷ 87

On the left: Some half-million electronic components are packed into this silicon chip. This unit of 256K RAM designed by AT&T Bell Laboratories is produced by AT&T Western Electric. Its capacity to store over a quarter-million bits of information is four times that of previous memory devices.

Sur la gauche : Plus d'un demi-million de composants électroniques sont entassés dans cette « puce » de silicium. C'est une unité de 256K RAM conçue par AT&T Bell Laboratories et fabriquée par AT&T Western Electric. Sa capacité d'emmagasiner plus d'un quart de million de bits d'information est quatre fois plus grande que celle des dispositifs qui la précèdent.

A la izquierda: Más de medio millón de componentes electrónicos encapsulados en la minúscula plaqueta de silicio. Esta memoria de acceso selectivo (MAS) 256K fue concebida por AT&T Bell Laboratories y es fabricada por AT&T Western Electric. Su capacidad para almacenar más de un cuarto de millón de bits de información es cuatro veces mayor que la de los dispositivos precedentes.

On the right: "clean room" facilities at AT&T Western Electric's Allentown Works, Allentown, Pa., one of the world's most advanced facilities for the production of very large scale integrated circuits.

Sur la droite : « chambre propre » dans l'usine de AT&T Western Electric à Allentown, Pennsylvania, une des plus perfectionnées du monde pour la fabrication des circuits intégrés à très grande échelle.

A la derecha: Fabricación en una "sala limpia" en la planta de AT&T Western Electric de Allentown, Pensilvania, una de las más perfeccionadas del mundo para la producción de circuitos integrados en muy gran escala.

The divested Bell operating companies will be grouped into seven regional companies, each independent of AT&T and of the others. The companies will handle calling *within* newly defined local service areas which generally correspond to the government's definition of metropolitan areas. Calling *between* metropolitan centers will be provided by AT&T and competing long distance carriers who will have equal access to local telephone company facilities.

The local telephone companies will also offer customer equipment, cellular radio services and directory services, including Yellow Pages.

The seven regional companies will also jointly own a central services organization that will provide them with assistance in areas such as network planning and engineering and serve as a single point of contact for national security and emergency preparedness requirements of the US government.

The remaining AT&T organization will include:
— *AT&T Western Electric,* for manufacturing and supply;
— *AT&T Bell Laboratories,* for research and development;
— *AT&T Communications,* for nationwide and international long distance services, operating under regulation;
— *AT&T Information Systems,* an unregulated subsidiary providing enhanced communications and information services and equipment for business, government and residence customers.
— *AT&T International,* representing all of the above outside the USA. This company has been marketing AT&T products, services and expertise around the world since 1980.

A new vision for AT&T has been brought about by divestiture. The company will be smaller than it is now, but with a broader vision of its mission and

Les entreprises d'exploitation Bell seront groupées en sept compagnies régionales, indépendantes l'une de l'autre et de AT&T. Ces entreprises écouleront les communications *à l'intérieur* des zones de services locales nouvellement délimitées, qui correspondent à la définition officielle des zones métropolitaines. Les communications entre les centres métropolitains seront assurées par AT&T et par ses concurrents opérant sur le réseau interurbain.

Les exploitations téléphoniques locales offriront, outre le service téléphonique, des équipements d'abonnés, des services de radiotéléphonie cellulaire, ainsi que des services d'annuaire électronique, y compris les « Yellow Pages ». Elles disposeront d'une organisation centrale d'assistance dans divers domaines, tels que la planification et l'ingénierie. Cette organisation servira de point de contact unique pour la sécurité nationale et les mesures d'urgence du gouvernement des Etats-Unis.

La nouvelle organisation d'AT&T, restructurée, comprendra :
— *AT&T Western Electric*, pour la fabrication et l'approvisionnement d'équipements ;
— *AT&T Bell Laboratories*, pour la recherche et le développement ;
— *AT&T Communications,* pour assurer les services de télécommunications nationaux et internationaux interurbains, assujettie à la réglementation traditionnelle ;
— *AT&T Information Systems*, filiale non-réglementée, pour fournir des services améliorés de télécommunication et d'informatique, ainsi que tous les équipements requis ;
— *AT&T International*, pour représenter tous les membres d'AT&T cités ci-dessus. Cette compagnie diffuse les produits, les services et l'assistance technique de AT&T dans le monde depuis 1980.

Une grande perspective est ouverte pour AT&T par la déréglementation. En effet, si la compagnie devient plus petite, sa mission s'élargit et son marché s'agrandit. Elle ne sera plus une simple entreprise téléphonique, ni même une entreprise de télécommunications.

disgregación de una empresa con 70 millones de clientes, 3 millones de accionistas, 1 millón de empleados y un activo de cerca de 150 000 millones de $.

Las antiguas empresas de explotación Bell estarán agrupadas en siete empresas regionales, todas ellas independientes de AT&T y entre sí. Las compañías tratarán las llamadas "dentro" de zonas de servicio locales definidas de nuevo, que corresponden a la definición gubernamental de zonas metropolitanas. Las llamadas "entre" centros metropolitanos correrán a cargo de AT&T y de empresas competidoras de la red interurbana.

Estas compañías ofrecerán también equipo de abonado, servicios radiocelulares y servicios de guía, incluidas las páginas amarillas.

Las siete compañías regionales dispondrán también conjuntamente de una organización de servicios centrales que les prestará asistencia en planificación e ingeniería de redes, y servirá de único punto de contacto para la seguridad nacional y para atender las necesidades de preparación de emergencia del gobierno. La organización de AT&T subsistente comprenderá:
— *AT&T Western Electric*, para fabricación y suministro;
— *AT&T Bell Laboratories*, para investigación y desarrollo;
— *AT&T Communications*, para servicios nacionales e internacionales de larga distancia, sometidos a la reglamentación tradicional;
— *AT&T Information Systems*, filial no reglamentada que proporcionará mejores servicios y equipo de comunicaciones e información a clientes comerciales, gubernamentales y particulares;
— *AT&T International*, para representar a todos los miembros de AT&T citados. Esta compañía se ocupa de los productos, servicios y asistencia técnica de AT&T en el mundo entero desde 1980.

Este desposeimiento ofrece una "nueva visión de AT&T". La empresa será más pequeña que ahora,

▷ 90

▷ 90

▷ 90

The nerve center for the nationwide network of AT&T Communications at Bedminster, New Jersey. From here Network Operations Managers can monitor the system and redirect calling routes as traffic requirements demand. The insert shows members of the staff taking a "real time" reading on the condition of the network.

Le centre nerveux du réseau national de AT&T Communications à Bedminster, New Jersey. De là, les directeurs des opérations du réseau peuvent surveiller le système et rediriger les circuits d'appel selon les besoins du trafic. L'encadré montre le personnel qui suit en « temps réel » les conditions du réseau.

El centro neural de la red nacional de líneas largas de AT&T Communications en Bedminster, Nueva Jersey. Desde aquí, los directores de las operaciones pueden vigilar el sistema y reencaminar las llamadas de acuerdo con las necesidades del tráfico. En el recuadro puede verse el personal que sigue en "tiempo real" las condiciones de la red.

On the left: Computerized frame creation terminal designed by AT&T Bell Laboratories produces graphics for use with videotex services. These will provide an interactive communication service between home video terminals and computerized information sources as well as facilities such as shopping and banking from home.

Sur la gauche : Ce terminal informatique conçu par AT&T Bell Laboratories produit des graphiques sophistiqués utilisables avec le système Videotex. Ce système fournira un service télématique entre les terminaux domestiques et les sources d'information centralisées, ainsi que la faculté de s'approvisionner et de payer sans bouger de chez-soi.

A la izquierda: Un terminal computadorizado diseñado por AT&T Bell Laboratories produce gráficos sofisticados utilizables con los servicios videotex. Este sistema proporcionará un servicio de información electrónica entre terminales domésticos y las fuentes de información centralizadas, y permitirá realizar operaciones bancarias desde el hogar.

On the right: A mobile phone installed in a car. A new cellular radio technology developed by AT&T Bell Laboratories enables thousands of people in a city to have mobile phones instead of just a few hundred as in the past.

Sur la droite : Radio téléphone à bord d'une voiture. La technologie « alvéolaire » réalisée par AT&T Bell Laboratories permet à des milliers de personnes d'avoir des téléphones mobiles dans les zones urbaines, ce qui n'était possible que pour quelques centaines d'usagers.

A la derecha: Radioteléfono instalado en un automóvil. La tecnología radiocelular desarrollada por AT&T Bell Laboratories permite a miles de personas de una ciudad disponer de teléfonos móviles, en lugar de unos centenares, como hasta ahora.

market. It will no longer be simply a telephone company, or even a telecommunications company; it will be fully engaged in the Information Business, offering a wide range of products and services to facilitate the movement and management of information. Free from restrictions limiting AT&T to the regulated telecommunications business, the company can now develop its technologies to the fullest extent and apply them in virtually any area of the worldwide information market place.

A key to AT&T's strength in Information Age technology is the close working relationship between Bell Laboratories, its research and development organization, and Western Electric, its manufacturing arm. With a 1982 Budget of $2 billion, Bell Laboratories is widely considered the world's preeminent industrial research and development organization.

Certain innovations by Bell Laboratories have been of such moment that they resulted in the award of the Nobel Prize to seven Bell Labs scientists over the years. In 1927, Clinton Davisson demonstrated the wave nature of matter. His fundamental work, for which he shared the 1937 Nobel Prize in Physics, is part of the foundation for much of today's solid-state electronics. In 1947, John Bardeen, Walter Brattain, and William Schockley invented the transistor. For this work they received the 1956 Nobel Prize in Physics.

Philip Anderson of Bell Labs shared the 1977 Nobel Prize in Physics for developing an improved understanding of the electronic structure of glass and magnetic materials. In 1978, the Nobel Prize in Physics was awarded to Arno Penzias and Robert Wilson, for their discovery of the faint background radiation remaining from the "big bang" explosion that gave birth to the universe billions of years ago.
The technology of the Information Age has to a major extent

AT&T se voit ainsi engagée dans le « business » de l'information, prête à offrir à l'échelle universelle une gamme étendue de produits et de services destinés à faciliter la communication et la gestion de l'information.

Depuis la levée de la réglementation, qui limitait les activités de la compagnie strictement au domaine réglementé des télécommunications aux Etats-Unis, AT&T peut maintenant développer ses nouvelles technologies au maximum, et les appliquer dans tous les domaines du marché mondial de l'information.

La force d'AT&T dans la nouvelle technologie de l'informatique réside dans l'étroite collaboration entre Bell Laboratories et Western Electric. Avec un budget de 2 milliards de dollars US en 1982, Bell Laboratories est considérée comme le centre de recherche et de développement le plus important.

Certaines innovations par Bell Laboratories ont été d'une telle importance que le Prix Nobel a été attribué à sept de ses chercheurs. En 1927, Clive Davisson a démontré le caractère ondulatoire de la matière. Ses recherches fondamentales, pour lesquelles il partagea le Prix Nobel de Physique, 1937, constituent une partie des bases essentielles de l'électronique d'aujourd'hui. En 1947, John Bardeen, Walter Battrain et William Shockley ont inventé le transistor. Pour ce travail ils ont reçu le Prix Nobel de Physique, 1956.

Philip Anderson a partagé le Prix Nobel de Physique, 1977, pour avoir amélioré la compréhension de la nature électronique du verre et des matériaux magnétiques. En 1978, le Prix Nobel de Physique fut attribué à Arno Penzias et Robert Wilson pour leur découverte de la légère radiation résiduelle d'arrière-plan provenant de la violente explosion qui créa l'univers il y a quelques milliards d'années.
La technologie de la société d'information a, dans une très large mesure, été conçue et mise au point par Bell Laboratories et Western Electric, depuis l'invention du transistor, en 1948, jusqu'aux récents progrès accomplis dans les domaines de la microélectronique, des communications par fibres optiques, ainsi que

pero su visión y su mercado tendrán más alcance. Ya no será sólo una compañía telefónica, ni siquiera de telecomunicaciones; intervendrá totalmente en el comercio de la información, ofreciendo una amplia gama de productos y servicios para facilitar el movimiento y gestión de la información. Y el mercado que trata de abarcar es global. Liberada de las restricciones anteriores que limitaban sus actividades a la telecomunicaciones reglamentadas, la empresa tiene ahora libertad para desarrollar sus tecnologías al máximo y aplicarlas en todo mercado mundial de la información.

La estrecha relación entre Bell Laboratories, su organización de investigación y desarrollo, y Western Electric, la de fabricación, es la clave de la fuerza de AT&T en la era de la información.

Con un presupuesto en 1982 de 2000 millones $, Bell Laboratories es considerada como la mayor organización industrial del mundo en materia de investigación y desarrollo.

Algunas innovaciones de Bell Laboratories han sido tan trascendentales que a siete de sus investigadores se les ha concedido el Premio Nobel. En 1927, Clinton Davisson demostró el carácter ondulatorio de la materia. Su fundamental labor, por la que compartió el Premio Nobel de Física de 1937, forma parte de la base de la electrónica actual. En 1947, John Bardeen, Walter Brattain y William Schockley inventaron el transistor, lo que les valió el Premio Nobel de Física en 1956.

Philip Anderson compartió el Premio Nobel de Física en 1977 por su labor sobre la estructura electrónica del vidrio y los materiales magnéticos. En 1978 se concedió el Premio Nobel de Física a Arno Penzias y Robert Wilson, por descubrir la radiación residual ligera derivada de la violenta explosión que creó el universo hace miles de millones de años.
La tecnología de la era de la información ha sido concebida y desarrollada en gran parte por Bell Laboratories y

▷ 91

▷ 91

▷ 91

been conceived and developed by Bell Laboratories and Western Electric, from the invention of the transistor in 1948 to recent developments in microelectronics, fiber optic communications, information processing systems and software. For example, the new 256 kilobit random access memory chip (256K RAM), designed by Bell Laboratories and produced by Western Electric, is one of the most sophisticated microchips on the market. It packs more than a half-million components on a silicon chip no larger than a fingernail and can store more than a quarter-million bits of information. And the new Bellmac™ 32A microprocessor, smaller than a dime but able to process as much information as a room-sized computer just a decade ago.

The key Information Age technologies have resulted in a variety of innovations that have contributed to progress in communications, including:
— charge-coupled devices with potential applications in imaging, digital memory and signal processing;
— molecular-beam epitaxy, an ultra-high vacuum process that makes possible materials for electronic devices;
— silicon-gate technology, a major contributor to the success of very large-scale integrated circuits;
— computer-aided techniques to monitor the performance of switching and transmission equipment;
— error-correcting codes, which permit data to be stored, retrieved, and transmitted error-free;
— digital-switching and transmission systems, providing new voice, data and video services;
— other significant innovations have been made by Bell Labs in information theory, magnetic materials, microwave technology, network theory, speech synthesis, and systems engineering.

du matériel et du logiciel utilisés dans les systèmes de traitement de l'information. Par exemple, le nouveau microprocesseur 256 kilobit random access (256K RAM) doué d'une mémoire à accès sélectif, conçu par Bell Laboratories et produit par Western Electric, réunit, sur un espace de la dimension d'un ongle, plus d'un demi-million de composants capables de stocker plus de 250 000 bits d'information. Un autre exemple, le nouveau microprocesseur Bellmac™ 32A, plus petit qu'une pièce de dix centimes, est capable de traiter autant d'information qu'un ordinateur qui était grand comme une salle il y a seulement dix ans.

Ces technologies essentielles de la société d'Information ont permis diverses innovations qui ont largement contribué au progrès des communications. Cela comprend, entre autres :
— des mémoires à transfert de charges, avec un potentiel d'applications pour images, mémoire digitale et traitement des signaux ;
— une épistaxis à faisceaux moléculaires, procédé à vide ultrapoussé qui rend possible la production de certains matériaux pour la fabrication de dispositifs électroniques ;
— la technologie du circuit de silicium, une contribution majeure au succès de circuits intégrés à très grande échelle ;
— des techniques assistées par ordinateur pour surveiller le fonctionnement d'équipements de commutation et de transmission ;
— des codes de correction d'erreurs, qui permettent la mise en mémoire, l'extraction et la transmission des données essentiellement sans erreurs ;
— des systèmes de commutation et de transmission numériques qui fournissent aux usagers une gamme de nouveaux services voix, données et images ;
— les piles solaires, utilisées pour actionner les véhicules spatiaux et les satellites.

D'autres innovations significatives en science et en ingénierie ont été réalisées par Bell Laboratories dans les contextes de la théorie de l'information, des matériaux magnétiques, de la technologie des

Western Electric, desde la invención del transistor en 1948 hasta las recientes novedades en microelectrónica, comunicaciones por fibras ópticas, sistemas de tratamiento de la información y soporte lógico. Por ejemplo, la nueva plaqueta con memoria de acceso selectivo de 256 kilobit (MAS 256K), concebida por Bell Laboratories y producida por Western Electric, es una de las microplaquetas más sofisticadas del mercado. Agrupa más de medio millón de componentes en una plaqueta de silicio no mayor que una uña, y puede almacenar más de 250 000 bits de información. El nuevo microprocesador Bellmac™ 32A, más pequeño que una moneda de 10 centavos, puede tratar tanta información como un computador del tamaño de una habitación de hace 10 años.

Las tecnologías esenciales de la era de información permiten diversas innovaciones que han contribuido al progreso de las comunicaciones, y entre ellas:
— dispositivos de transferencia de carga, con posibles aplicaciones de imáges, memoria digital y tratamiento de señales;
— epitaxia de haces moleculares, proceso de vacío muy avanzado que permite emplear diversos materiales en dispositivos electrónicos;
— la tecnología del circuito de silicio, que tanto contribuye al éxito de los circuitos integrados en gran escala;
— técnicas con asistencia por computador para comprobar el rendimiento del equipo de conmutación y transmisión;
— códigos de corrección de errores, que permiten almacenar datos, recuperarlos y transmitirlos esencialmente sin errores;
— sistemas de conmutación y transmisión digitales que proporcionan una amplia gama de nuevos servicios vocales, de datos e imágenes.

Bell Laboratories ha introducido otras innovaciones científicas y de ingeniería importantes sobre teoría de la información, materiales magnéticos,

▷ 92 ▷ 92 ▷ 93

Bell Labs and Western Electric are also heavily involved in the development of software, the programmed intelligence that is the key to the flexibility and versatility of modern electronics technology. Their UNIX™ operating system, for example, is one of the most popular software systems. AT&T now markets an improved version of the UNIX, with a range of support services, including consultation with users.

The shaping of an "intelligent" network is a prime objective of the company. Many of the developments coming out of Bell Laboratories and Western Electric are being applied in AT&Ts nationwide communications network, which is rapidly being transformed into a network capable of providing a wide range of innovative new services, many of them tailored to the needs of individual customers. The key building blocks in this evolving network are electronic switching systems, interconnected by a computerized signalling system, and advanced transmission systems, including the latest in digital technology. One example is the giant 4ESS™ digital switching system, fully programmable, able to handle more than a half-million long distance calls per hour, offers enormous savings in energy and maintenance costs.

Another digital electronic switching system, the 5ESS™, used for local central offices, is one of the world's most advanced and versatile with capacities ranging from 1,000 to 100,000 lines. It has fiber optics circuitry and a central processor that can perform an almost limitless variety of functions. With their computer memories, these systems can be programmed to meet changing requirements.

Adding to the "intelligence" of the network is an advanced signalling system which uses high-speed data links to exchange information between the computer-controlled switching offices. Besides increasing the efficiency of the network and allowing calls to be set up much more rapidly, this signalling system can transmit, store and process detailed calling instructions. This information, interacting with centralized data bases, or Network Control Points, makes it possible, in effect, to program the network to provide new service options.

One example of this technology in action is an improved version of AT&T's 800 service, widely used by business and government to permit toll-free calls from their customers and constituents. Called Expanded 800 Service, this permits a business to use a single US 800 number, yet route incoming calls to various locations, depending on the time of day or where the calls originate. Ultimately, it will be possible for a business to have a single US number that would automatically connect callers with the branch office nearest them.

Another example is the Bell System's new automated Calling Card Service, which permits customers to dial their own credit-card calls without operator assistance. In the future, customers may be able to signal the network that they will take calls only from certain telephone numbers. Or, with just one number, a person could be reached as he or she travels across the country, or around the world when this technology is applied globally.

Advanced digital transmission technology is also being widely deployed in AT&T's US network. With the increasing demand for data communications services, the evolution to a public, nationwide, end-to-end digital network is accelerating. This includes the use of communications satellites, digital radio and cable systems and, one of the most promising new digital technologies, lightwave communications systems.

In the northeastern section of the United States, work is nearing completion on the world's largest

▷ 96

micro-ondes, de la théorie des réseaux, de la synthèse de la parole, de l'ingénierie des systèmes.

Bell Laboratories et Western Electric participent très activement à l'élaboration du logiciel, c'est-à-dire de l'intelligence programmée, qui est l'une des clés de la souplesse et de l'universalité de l'électronique moderne. Leur système UNIX™ par exemple, est l'un des supports de logiciel les plus connus. AT&T a récemment commencé à commercialiser une nouvelle conception de l'UNIX en offrant, à l'appui, une gamme de services étendue, y compris la consultation avec les usagers.

L'élaboration de la configuration d'un réseau « intelligent » constitue un objectif primordial de l'entreprise. De nombreuses innovations de Bell Laboratories et Western Electric sont utilisées dans l'ensemble du réseau de AT&T. Parmi les éléments essentiels, dans ce réseau en pleine évolution, il convient de mentionner le système de commutation numérique géant 4ESS™, capable d'écouler plus d'un demi-million de communications interurbaines par heure, et permettant de réaliser d'énormes économies d'énergie et de frais de maintenance.

Un autre commutateur électronique numérique, le 5ESS™ pour les centraux locaux, est un des systèmes les plus perfectionnés et les plus polyvalents du monde qui peut être utilisé dans des bureaux de n'importe quelle taille, utilisant 1000 à 100 000 lignes. Ses circuits sont en fibre optique et son processeur central est capable d'effectuer un nombre pratiquement illimité de fonctions. Equipés de mémoires d'ordinateurs, ces systèmes peuvent être programmés pour s'adapter à une grande diversité de besoins.

A l'« intelligence » du réseau vient s'ajouter un système de signalisation perfectionné utilisant des liaisons de données à grande vitesse pour échanger les informations entre les centres de commutation commandés par ordinateur. Ce système de signalisation peut transmettre, enregistrer et traiter des instructions détaillées, notamment pour programmer le réseau de manière à fournir de nouvelles options de service.

Un exemple de cette technologie en action est une version améliorée du service « 800 » de AT&T qui permet, comme son nom l'indique, à une entreprise d'indiquer dans sa publicité un préfixe unique pour tout le pays, le « 800 », qui acheminera les communications entrantes vers divers lieux, selon l'heure de la journée ou l'origine de l'appel, celui-ci ne coûtant que le prix d'une communication urbaine à l'utilisateur. Par exemple, une entreprise de transport aérien avec deux centres de réservations peut en fermer un le soir et recevoir tous les appels dans l'autre. Toute entreprise des Etats-Unis peut également disposer d'un numéro national unique qui connecte automatiquement la personne qui appelle avec sa succursale la plus proche. Les abonnés pourront demander au réseau de n'accepter que les communications en provenance de certains numéros téléphoniques, ou utiliser un numéro unique pour atteindre une personne en voyage, dans n'importe quel pays, aussitôt que cette technologie sera appliquée globalement.

Des techniques perfectionnées de transmission numérique sont mises on œuvre par AT&T sur tout son réseau des Etats-Unis avec l'utilisation de satellites de communication, de systèmes radioélectriques numériques et de câbles, ainsi que des systèmes de communication à ondes lumineuses. Les travaux d'aménagement d'une liaison optique de 1250 km entre la Virginie et le Massachusetts, la plus longue du monde, est en voie d'achèvement. Au début, ce câble à transmission entièrement numérique écoulera simultanément jusqu'à 80 000 communications. Par la suite, cette capacité sera doublée. Un autre project en voie de réalisation reliera tous les centres urbains de la Californie en 1985.

▷ 96

Shown here is the new 5ESS™, being installed as a local digital switching system, providing from 1,000 to 100,000 lines. It employs optical circuitry and a programmable central processor. It can perform an immense variety of functions.

Voici, montré en cours d'installation, le nouveau système de communication numérique privé, 5ESS™, d'une capacité de 1000 à 100 000 lignes téléphoniques. Son circuit est en fibre optique et son processeur central programmable peut exécuter une variété infinie d'opérations.

tecnología de microondas, teoría de redes, síntesis de la palabra e ingeniería de sistemas.

Bell Laboratories y Western Electric participan también mucho en el desarrollo de soporte lógico, la inteligencia programada, la clave de la flexibilidad y versatilidad de la tecnología electrónica moderna. Su sistema de explotación UNIX™, por ejemplo, es uno de los sistemas de soporte lógico más populares. AT&T ha comenzado hace poco a comercializar una versión mejorada del sistema UNIX, junto con una gama de servicios de apoyo, incluida la consulta con usuarios.

La configuración de una red "inteligente" es un objetivo primordial de la empresa. Muchas de las novedades de Bell Laboratories y Western Electric se aplican en la red nacional de comunicaciones de AT&T, que muy pronto será capaz de proporcionar una amplia serie de nuevos servicios, muchos de ellos adaptados a las necesidades de los clientes. Los bloques de construcción esenciales de esta red en evolución son sistemas de conmutación electrónica, interconectados por un sistema de señalización computadorizado, y sistemas de transmisión avanzados, incluida la tecnología digital más reciente. Un ejemplo es el sistema de conmutación digital 4ESS™, totalmente programable, que permite tratar más de medio millón de llamadas de larga distancia por hora, y ofrece enormes economías de energía y mantenimiento.

Otro sistema de conmutación electrónico digital para oficinas centrales locales, el 5ESS™, es uno de los sistemas de conmutación más avanzados y versátiles del mundo. Puede utilizarse en oficinas de qualquier tamaño: de 1000 a 100 000 líneas. Tiene circuitos de fibras ópticas y un procesador central capaz de realizar funciones casi ilimitadas. Provistos de memoria de computador, estos sistemas pueden reprogramarse para atender las nuevas necesidades de servicio.

A la "inteligencia" de la red se agrega un sistema de señalización avanzado que utiliza enlaces de datos de gran velocidad para intercambiar información entre las oficinas de conmutación controladas por computador. Además de aumentar la eficacia de la red y permitir establecer mucho antes las llamadas, este sistema transmite, almacena y procesa instrucciones de llamada detalladas. Tal información, interactiva con bases de datos centralizadas, o puntos de control de red, permite programar la red para proporcionar nuevas opciones de servicio.

Un ejemplo es la versión perfeccionada del servicio 800 de AT&T muy utilizado por las empresas comerciales y el gobierno para las llamadas gratuitas de sus clientes y de su personal. Denominado servicio 800 ampliado, permite a una empresa usar un sólo número 800 en EE.UU., que encamina las llamadas entrantes a varios lugares, según la hora del día o su origen. Por último, una empresa podrá disponer de un solo número nacional que conecte automáticamente a quien llama con la sucursal más próxima.

Otro ejemplo es el nuevo servicio de tarjeta de llamada de Bell System, que permite a los clientes efectuar sus llamadas con tarjeta de crédito sin asistencia de operadora. Los clientes podrán señalar a la red que únicamente admitirán llamadas desde ciertos números. Con un solo número podrá alcanzarse a una persona que viaje por el país o por otras naciones, pues el sistema es global.

La tecnología de transmisión digital avanzada también se intensifica mucho en la red de AT&T. Con la creciente demanda de servicios de comunicación de datos, se acelera la evolución a una red digital pública nacional de extremo a extremo. Esto comprende el uso de satélites de comunicaciones, sistemas radioeléctricos digitales y de cable y una de las nue-

▷ 97

Instalación del nuevo sistema de conmutación digital privado 5ESS™, que puede dar servicio a oficinas que utilizan de 1000 a 100 000 líneas telefónicas. Emplea circuitos de fibras ópticas, y su procesador central programable puede ejecutar una variedad de funciones casi ilimitada.

A Picturephone® meeting. This is a service using a digital network combining satellite and land-based facilities. It provides two-way full-color video, voice and data transmission between specially-equipped meeting rooms.

Une téléconférence « Picturephone® ». Ce service est fourni par un réseau numérique qui combine les liaisons spatiales et terrestres. Il transmet interactivement les images en couleur, la voix et les données dans des salles spécialement équipées.

Una teleconferencia « Picturephone® ». Se trata de un servicio proporcionado por red digital que combina enlaces espaciales y terrestres. Transmite interactivamente imágenes en color, voz y datos entre salas de reunión equipadas especialmente.

lightwave communications system — a 776-mile project from Virginia to Massachusetts. The all-digital cable will initially handle up to 80,000 simultaneous conversations. Developments are expected to at least double that capacity. Existing plans cater for several thousand miles of inter-city lightwave cable by 1985, some of which may handle as many as 150,000 simultaneous conversations; also, for using undersea lightwave cable across the Atlantic, and between the US mainland and Hawaii, Bell Labs has already successfully tested an undersea lightwave cable in the Atlantic. By the mid-1980s lightwave technology was beginning to be used in the local "loops", the lines that run from the telephone central exchange to the customer's home or office.

Digital electronics are being used to increase the capacity and capabilities of existing copper wire telephone plant. For example, Subscriber Loop Carrier systems permit a single pair of wires to carry several conversations and to transmit information in digital form. The newest such system can pack up to 96 conversations on as few as three copper pairs. In addition to providing additional network capacity economically, these systems also provide new service options. Such as simultaneous voice and data transmission over a single customer line. This would enable a customer to talk on the phone while another member of the family was using a computer terminal to interact with an information data bank.

A host of new network services have been created on the basis of widespread availability of digital facilities. For example, AT&T has recently developed a high-speed digital transmission service that will be available in the USA. It has also introduced a switched digital network that is being used in connection with its Picturephone ® Meeting Service, a video conferencing service. Using a combination of satellite and land-based facilities, this digital network permits two-way, full-color video, voice and data transmission between specially equipped meeting rooms in different cities.

Another new development is a nationwide packet-switched network service which is being used by AT&T Information Systems to provide its new Advanced Information Systems/NET 1000 service. This offers data processing as well as communications features, information storage and processing capabilities which will permit otherwise incompatible terminals and computers to communicate with each other. With packet switching, batches of data are gathered from multiple sources and delivered as "packets" by means of digital transmission and switched network.

The technology of mobile communications has made major advances in recent years. Conceived and developed by Bell Labs, cellular technology has vastly improved the quality and availability of mobile communications. By permitting the reuse of scarce radio channels, thousands of people in each city can now have mobile phones instead of just a few hundred.

Interactive electronic information services have also been pioneered by AT&T, particularly in videotex services which link home video terminals to computerized data banks. The company's Presentation Level Protocol has become the industry standard for videotex services in the United States. Its computerized Frame Creation Terminal, which produces sophisticated videotex graphics, represents the state-of-the-art in this field.

Sophisticated new customer equipment is expected to come onto the market over the next few years. With the freedom to add data processing features to its pro-

▷ 98

Des plans existent pour la mise en place de plusieurs milliers de kilomètres de liaisons à ondes lumineuses interurbaines, dont certaines pourront écouler simultanément jusqu'à 150 000 conversations ; d'autres sont prévus pour la mise en place de câbles optiques sous-marins à travers l'Atlantique et entre les Etats-Unis continentaux et les Hawaï. Bell Laboratories a déjà testé avec succès un câble optique sous-marin dans l'Atlantique. Et dès le début des années 1980, la technologie de la transmission optique commença à être employée pour établir les « boucles » locales, ces lignes qui vont des centraux téléphoniques aux domiciles ou aux bureaux des abonnés.

Afin d'augmenter la capacité et les possibilités des installations téléphoniques en fils de cuivre existantes, AT&T utilise l'électronique numérique. Par exemple, certains systèmes de boucle d'abonné à courants porteurs permettent d'acheminer simultanément, sur une seule paire de fils, plusieurs communications et de transmettre l'information sous forme numérique. Le système le plus récent peut transmettre jusqu'à 96 conversations sur trois paires en cuivre. A part l'augmentation de la capacité du réseau réalisé de manière économique, ces systèmes offrent d'autres options, telles que la transmission simultanée de données et de conversations sur une seule ligne d'abonné.

Un monde de nouveaux services basés sur le réseau téléphonique existant a été créé grâce au développement du système numérique. AT&T a récemment mis au point un service de transmission numérique à grande vitesse qui va être étendu à l'échelle nationale. Un autre service de vidéoconférence a été introduit sur réseau avec commutation numérique en liaison avec le Picturephone ® Meeting Service de AT&T. Ce réseau numérique — qui utilise une combinaison de transmission par satellite et par voie terrestre — permet d'établir des liaisons bidirectionnelles, vidéo couleur, téléphoniques et de transmission de données entre des salles de réunion spécialement équipées dans différentes agglomérations.

Un nouveau réseau de transmission avec commutation par paquets a été mis en exploitation à l'échelle nationale par AT&T Information Systems, pour alimenter son nouveau service d'informatique Advanced Information Systems/NET 1000, assurant les fonctions de traitement des données et de communication, avec des capacités de stockage et de traitement de l'information qui permettront également à des terminaux et des ordinateurs normalement incompatibles de communiquer entre eux. Avec la méthode de commutation par « paquets », des lots de données de provenances multiples sont rassemblés et livrés en « paquets » par un réseau à transmission et commutation numériques.

La technologie des communications mobiles a fait de grands progrès au cours de ces dernières années. Conçue et developpée par Bell Laboratories, la radiotéléphonie « à structure alvéolaire » a beaucoup amélioré la qualité et la disponibilité des communications mobiles. La réutilisation des voies radioélectriques permet à des milliers de gens d'une même agglomération — au lieu de quelques centaines seulement — d'avoir un téléphone dans leur voiture.

Les services d'informatique interactifs sont également une innovation d'AT&T, notamment les services vidéotex qui relient des terminaux vidéo domestiques à des banques de données numériques. Le mode de présentation d'AT&T est devenu une norme industrielle pour les services vidéotex aux Etats- Unis. Son terminal représente le dernier cri de la technique dans ce domaine.

De nouveaux équipements d'abonné perfectionnés seront lancés sur le marché au cours de ces prochaines années. Ajoutant les avantages du traitement de

▷ 98

A desk terminal of the AT&T's new Dimension ® AIS/System 85 electronic digital PBX. System 85 can handle voice and data communications simultaneously. Its new electronic document communications feature enables the transmitting of information throughout the office or country. It can also be used to manage energy usage in buildings.

Terminal de bureau du nouveau AT&T « Dimension ® AIS/System 85 ». Cet autocommutateur numérique privé peut transmettre voix et données simultanément et assurer le courrier électronique, ce qui permet la transmission de l'information dans l'entreprise ou dans l'ensemble du pays. Il peut également contrôler l'utilisation rationnelle de l'énergie dans les bâtiments.

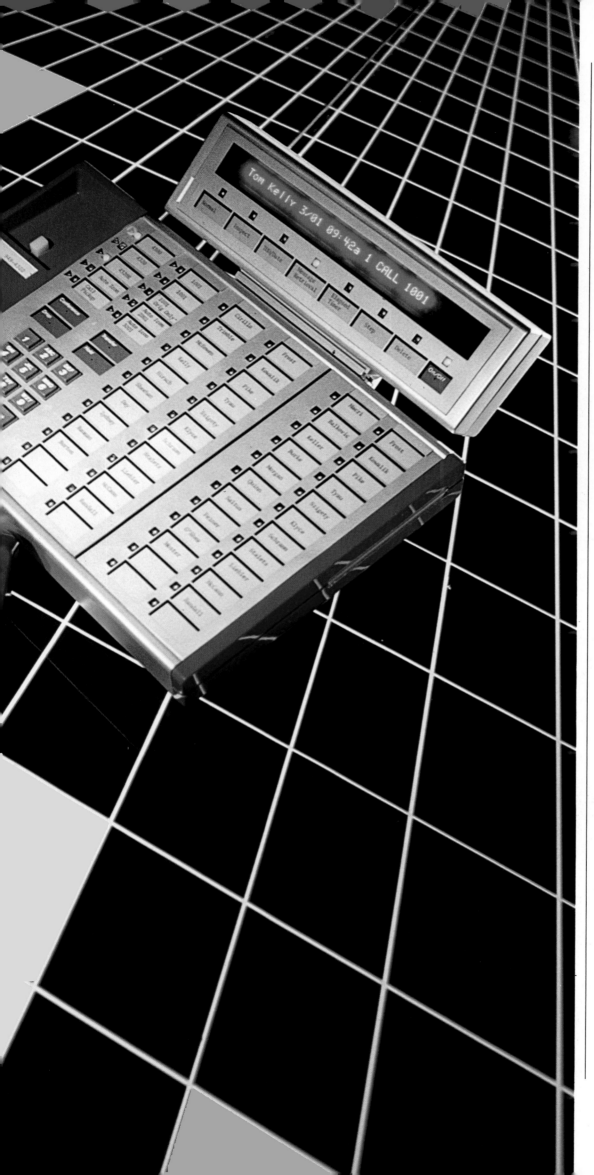

vas tecnologías digitales más prometedoras: los sistemas de comunicaciones de ondas luminosas.

En el nordeste de Estados Unidos, están casi acabados los trabajos del sistema de comunicaciones por ondas luminosas mayor del mundo: un proyecto de 1250 km, desde Virginia a Massachussets. El cable totalmente digital tratará inicialmente hasta 80 000 conversaciones simultáneas. Después, se espera duplicar como mínimo tal capacidad. Los planes prevén varios miles de km de ondas luminosas entre ciudades para 1985, algunos de los cuales pueden tratar hasta 150 000 conversaciones simultáneas; Bell Laboratories ha probado ya, con éxito, cables submarinos de ondas luminosas a través del Atlántico y entre EE.UU. continental y Hawaii. Para mediados del decenio comenzara a emplearse la tecnología de ondas luminosas en los "bucles" locales, las líneas que van desde la oficina telefónica central hasta el hogar o la oficina del abonado.

Para aumentar la capacidad y las posibilidades de la planta telefónica de hilo de cobre actual se usa la electrónica digital. Por ejemplo, sistemas de portadora de bucle de abonado que permiten cursar por un solo par de hilos varias conversaciones y transmitir información en forma digital. El más reciente de estos sistemas tiene capacidad para 96 conversaciones con tres pares de cobre nada más. Además de proporcionar mayor capacidad a la red económicamente, ofrecen otras opciones de servicio como la transmisión simultánea de voz y datos por una sola línea de abonado, con lo que éste puede hablar por teléfono mientras otro familiar utiliza un terminal de computador para interactuar con un banco de información de datos.

Se ha creado una serie de nuevos servicios de red con muchas posibilidades. Por ejemplo, AT&T ha desarrollado recientemente un servicio de transmisión digital de gran velocidad para EE.UU. También ha introducido una red digital con conmutación que se usa en conexión con su servicio Picturephone ® Meeting, servicio de videoconferencia. Utilizando una combinación de facilidades de satélite y de base en tierra, esta red digital permite transmisiones bidireccionales de imagen a todo color, voz y datos entre salas de reuniones especialmente equipadas de distintas ciudades.

Otra novedad es un servicio de red nacional con conmutación de paquetes, utilizado por AT&T Information Systems para proporcionar su nuevo servicio de sistemas de información avanzada "NET 1000", que ofrece el procesamiento de datos y posibilidades de comunicación y de almacenamiento y procesamiento de la información que hacen posible la comunicación entre sí de terminales y computadores de otro modo incompatible.

Con la conmutación de paquetes se réunen lotes de datos de distintas fuentes e se transmiten como "paquetes" mediante facilidades de transmisión y conmutación digital.

La tecnología de las comunicaciones móviles ha hecho grandes avances en los últimos años. Concebida y desarrollada por Bell Laboratories, la tecnología radiocelular ha mejorado la calidad y la disponibilidad de las comunicaciones móviles. Al permitir la reutilización de escasos canales radioeléctricos, son miles las personas de cada ciudad que pueden tener teléfonos móviles, en lugar de unos centenares.

AT&T también va a la vanguardia de los servicios de información electrónica interactivos, particularmente de videotex, que vinculan los terminales video domésticos con bancos de datos computadorizados. El protocolo de nivel de presentación de la empresa se ha convertido en la norma industrial de los servicios videotex en Estados Unidos. Su terminal de creación de trama computadorizado, que produce gráficos

▷ 98

Terminal de oficina del nuevo «AT&T Dimension® AIS/System 85» para centralitas digitales electrónicas. El sistema 85 puede transmitir simultáneamente comunicaciones vocales y de datos. Su capacidad para realizar las operaciones de correo electrónico permite transmitir información dentro de una empresa o en todo el país. También puede aplicarse para controlar el uso de la energía en los edificios.

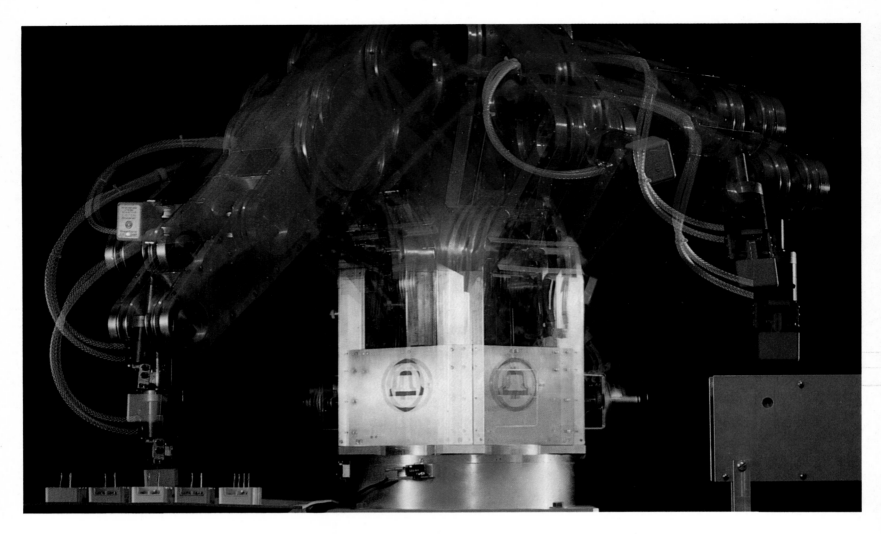

ducts and services, AT&T will seek to be a leader in the world market for communications equipment and information management systems.

During 1983, AT&T Information Systems introduced a number of new products that incorporate information processing features. For example, its new Genesis™ Telesystem, a microprocessor-based telephone system, offers a wide range such as banking by phone, electronic directory, answering, intercom and paging services. Features are selected by programming the basic console or by adding auxiliary modules or cartridges. An enhanced digitalized version of the company's popular Dimension® PBX system, known as Dimension® System 85, provides a host of information management capabilities, including electronic mail, data transmission and sensor-based security systems.

Serving the global market is a prime objective of the new deregulated company. In 1980 it consolidated its international marketing operations in a single subsidiary, AT&T International. Since then, the company has significantly enlarged its presence in major world markets, serving 23 countries to-day. It has also undertaken an extensive research and development program to create a broad line of products geared to the technical standards of the various countries it seeks to serve.

Most of AT&T's innovative new products are now designed to international standards. Among others, this includes its major electronic switching systems such as the 4ESS™ digital toll switcher and the new 5ESS™ local digital switching system; its most advanced transmission systems such as digital microwave radio and lightwave cables, and a wide

▷ 99

données à ses produits et services, AT&T cherchera à devenir le leader du marché mondial des équipements de communications et des systèmes de gestion informatique.

AT&T Information Systems a introduit en 1983 plusieurs nouveaux produits qui incorporent des facultés de traitement de l'information. Par exemple, son nouveau Genesis™ Telesystem est un système téléphonique contenant un microprocesseur qui donne un grand nombre de facilités, comprenant opérations de banque par téléphone, annuaire électronique, et services de répondeur, d'intercom et d'appel de personne par radio de poche. Les facilités sont sélectionnées en programmant la console de commande ou en ajoutant des modules auxiliaires ou des cartouches. Un modèle amélioré numérique du système PBX Dimension® baptisé Dimension® System 85, fournit une quantité de possibilités de gestion d'information, comprenant le courrier électronique, la transmission de données et des systèmes de sécurité à capteur.

Servir le marché mondial est l'objectif primordial de AT&T déréglementée. En 1980, ses activités sur le marché mondial ont été regroupées au sein d'AT&T International. Depuis lors, elle a considérablement affermi sa présence sur les principaux marchés du monde, en mettant en œuvre un programme de recherche et de développement, dans le but de créer une gamme étendue de produits adaptés aux normes techniques des pays qu'elle projette de desservir.

La plupart des nouveaux produits d'AT&T sont désormais conformes aux normes internationales, tels que le commutateur numérique interurbain 4ESS™ et le système de commutation numérique local 5ESS™, les liaisons radioélectriques à hyperfréquences numériques, les câbles optiques, et une gamme importante de matériel destiné aux lo-

▷ 99

videotex sofisticados, representa lo más avanzado en este campo.

Un nuevo equipo de abonado sofisticado podría encontrarse en el mercado los próximos años. Al agregar propiedades de procesamiento de datos a sus productos y servicios, AT&T tratará de ponerse a la cabeza del mercado mundial de equipo de comunicaciones y sistemas de gestión de la información.

En 1983, AT&T Information Systems itrodujo nuevos productos sobre propiedades de tratamiento de la información. Por ejemplo, su nuevo Genesis™ Telesystem, sistema telefónico con microprocesador, ofrece una amplia gama de facilidades, como banca por teléfono, anuario electrónico, servicios de respondedor, intercom y radiobusca. Las características se seleccionan programando la consola básica y agregando módulos auxiliares o cartuchos. Una nueva versión digitalizada del sistema popular PBX Dimension®, denominado Dimension® System 85, ofrece muchas posibilidades de gestión de información, incluidas correo electrónico, transmisión de datos y sistemas de seguridad por sensores.

Servir al mercado global es un objetivo primordial de la nueva compañia no sometida a reglamentación. En 1980 consolidó sus operaciones de comercio internacional en una sola filial: AT&T International. Desde entonces, la empresa ha ampliado mucho su presencia en importantes mercados mundiales, ha emprendido un programa de investigación y desarrollo, para crear una vasta gama de productos adaptados a las normas técnicas de los paises.

La mayoría de los productos nuevos de AT&T se han diseñado de acuerdo con las normas internacionales. Esto comprende sus principales sistemas de conmutación electrónica, como el conmutador digital de larga distancia 4ESS™ y el nuevo sistema de

▷ 99

Above: A robotic computer-controlled device, developed at AT&T Western Electric's Engineering Research Center, at work on the assembly of tiny components.

Ci-dessus : Dispositif robotique, conçu par le centre de recherche d'ingéniérie d'AT&T Western Electric, assemblant des minuscules composants électroniques.

Dispositivo de robot controlado por computador desarrollado en el centro de investigación de AT&T Western Electric, montando componentes electrónicos diminuitos.

range of customer premises equipment, including the Dimension® PBX series and new electronic telephones.

In addition to its own sales offices around the world, AT&T International is marketing Bell System technology and services through other channels, including joint ventures and in-country manufacturing.

For example, AT&T International has been working with the Lucky Goldstar Group to manufacture 1AESS™ switching equipment in the Republic of Korea since 1978. And the company has formed a joint venture with the Netherlands firm of N.V. Philips — one of the world's largest distributors of communications equipment — to manufacture and market the new 5ESS™ digital switching system and other products using technology developed by the Bell System.

AT&T also owns Telectron, Ltd., a manufacturing firm in Ireland, which now produces transmission equipment designed to international standards by its Bell Laboratories and Western Electric.
The 1980s mark a turning point in the history of this century-old business and in the American telecommunications industry as a whole. What was once a regulated monopoly is becoming one of the most competitive of businesses.

The merging of communications and computer technology is driving worldwide change as new, innovative, services are planned and introduced. The potential to increase the productivity of individuals, companies and nations has never been greater. Now free to use its technology to the fullest, the new AT&T expects to be a world leader in the provision of Information Age products and services. □

caux d'abonnés, y compris la série Dimension® PBX et les nouveaux téléphones électroniques.

En dehors de ses propres bureaux de vente installés dans le monde, AT&T International commercialise la technologie et les services du Bell System par l'intermédiaire d'entreprises conjointes et d'usines installées dans divers pays.

Par exemple, AT&T International travaille avec le Lucky Goldstar Group pour fabriquer l'équipement de Commutation 1AESS™ en République de Korée, depuis 1978. La compagnie travaille aussi avec la firme néerlandaise N.V. Philips, l'un des plus importants distributeurs de matériel de communications du monde, avec laquelle AT&T International a établi une opération conjointe de fabrication et de vente du nouveau système de commutation numérique 5ESS™, ainsi que d'autres produits utilisant la technologie mise au point par le Bell System.

D'autre part, AT&T possède Telectron Ltd., en Irlande qui produit des équipements de transmission conçus selon les normes internationales par Bell Laboratories et Western Electric.
La restructuration de Bell System marque un tournant dans l'histoire de cette entreprise centenaire et, d'une manière générale, dans l'industrie américaine des télécommunications. Ce qui était autrefois un monopole assujetti à la réglementation fédérale est devenu une affaire commerciale très compétitive.

La fusion de la technologie des communications avec celles des ordinateurs ouvre de grandes perspectives en termes d'augmentation de la productivité pour les individus, les industries et les nations. Désormais libre de mettre en application, dans son intégralité, la technologie qu'elle a créée, AT&T espère devenir aujourd'hui un leader mondial sur le marché des produits et des services de l'Ere de l'Information. □

conmutación digital local 5ESS™; sus sistemas de transmisión más avanzados, como las radiocomunicaciones digitales de microondas y los cables de ondas luminosas, y una amplia gama de equipo de abonado; incluida la serie CAP Dimension® y muchos teléfonos electrónicos nuevos.

Además de sus propias oficinas de ventas en el mundo entero, AT&T International comercializa la tecnología y los servicios de Bell System por otros canales, incluidas empresas mixtas y la fabricación nacional.

Por ejemplo, AT&T International trabaja con Lucky Goldstar Group para fabricar equipo de conmutación 1AESS™ en la República de Corea desde 1978. AT&T ha creado una empresa mixta con la firma holandesa N.V. Philips, uno de los principales distribuidores de equipo de comunicación del mundo, para la fabricación y venta del nuevo sistema de conmutación digital 5ESS™ y otros productos que emplean tecnología desarrollada por Bell System.

AT&T posee Telectron, Ltd., empresa irlandesa, que produce ahora equipo de transmisión concebido según las normas internacionales por sus Bell Laboratories y Western Electric.
El presente decenio marca un giro en la historia de esta empresa, que data de hace un siglo, y de la industria americana de telecomunicaciones en su conjunto. Lo que era una empresa reglamentada se está convirtiendo en una de las más competitivas.

La fusión de la tecnología de comunicaciones y computador ofrece mayores perspectivas para aumentar la productividad de los individuos, las empresas y las naciones. Ahora que puede utilizar su tecnología al máximo, la nueva AT&T espera ser un líder mundial en el suministro de productos y servicios en la Era de la Información. □

Above: The "Genesis™" Telesystem terminal, developed by AT&T Bell Laboratories, which can be customized by the use of plug-in modules and interchangeable cartridges.

Ci-dessus : Voici le terminal « Genesis™ » Telesystem conçu par AT&T Bell Laboratories qui peut être personnalisé par modules supplémentaires et cartouches interchangeables.

El terminal del telesistema « Genesis™ », concebido por AT&T Bell Laboratories. Puede individualizarse mediante módulos enchufables y cartuchos intercambiables.

THE NEW TECHNOLOGIES REACHING OUT BEYOND THE BOUNDS OF THE IMAGINATION

EWPOWE RNEWHOPE

THE INTRODUCTION OF ELECTRONIC "intelligence" has transformed the technology of telecommunications. This "intelligence" is the machine's ability to follow instructions, to store them, transmit them, point out errors they may contain, correct its own errors, and to find ways of implementing these instructions when encountering obstacles.

The technological feat that this represents is the outcome of the progress made in less than 50 years in the technology of semi-conductor materials, such as germanium, silicon and now gallium arsenide.

The basis of this astonishing progress has been solid-state electronics: the discovery of the transistor and the micro-processor in which it functions and their continuous enhancement at an ever increasing rate. The consequence has been an increase in the ability to store, process and transmit information of any kind or shape at speeds well beyond the bounds of imagination.

The technology of hardware is now well established and its costs are tumbling. It is reasonable to expect that in the 1980s and 1990s the telecommunications industry will concentrate on refining and applying the technological methods now available: microminiaturization, digitalization, the use of distributed intelligence for computation and control, optical wave guide and microwave transmission.

Remaining to be mastered is the technology of producing the requisite instructions that can be understood by the electronic systems and effectively acted upon by them. This is the problem of software — the programmed intelligence that is the key to the flexibility and versatility of Information Age technology. Its importance is demonstrated by the fact

▷ 102

L'AVÈNEMENT DE L'« INTELLIGENCE ÉLECTRONIQUE » a transfiguré les télécommunications. Cette « intelligence » permet à une machine d'obéir à des instructions, de les mémoriser, de les transmettre, de signaler les erreurs qu'elles peuvent contenir, de corriger ses propres erreurs et de surmonter les obstacles qui se présentent.

Le tour de force que cela représente dérive du progrès fait en moins d'un demi-siècle dans la technologie des matériaux semiconducteurs tels que le germanium, le silicium et maintenant l'arseniure de gallium. L'invention et le perfectionnement toujours plus rapide des transistors et du microprocesseur qui les contient, ont eu pour conséquence une augmentation de la capacité de mémoriser, de traiter et de transmettre l'information, sous n'importe quelle forme et à n'importe quelle vitesse, au delà des limites de l'imaginable.

La technologie de l'équipement, maintenant bien établie, il est donc raisonnable de prévoir que d'ici à la fin du siècle l'industrie se concentrera sur le raffinement des procédés, des produits et des systèmes existants : microminiaturisation, commutation numérique, transmission par ondes lumineuses, radiotéléphonie cellulaire (alvéolaire), application des lasers, communications via satellites, etc.

Mais il reste une autre technologie à maîtriser : celle du génie du logiciel qui est indispensable à la production efficace de programmes et d'instructions susceptibles d'être interprétées et exécutées par les systèmes électroniques. Le problème est celui de l'intelligence programmée, qui est la base essentielle de la flexibilité et de la versatilité de la technologie de l'information. L'importance que l'industrie attache à la résolution de ce problème est soulignée par le fait que dans la plupart des grands centres de recherche, l'activité de près de la moitié des chercheurs et des ingénieurs lui est consacrée.

▷ 102

LA INTRODUCCIÓN DE LA « INTELIGENCIA » electrónica ha transformado la tecnología de las telecomunicaciones. La inteligencia es la capacidad de la máquina para seguir instrucciones, almacenarlas, transmitirlas, señalar los errores que puedan contener, corregir los errores de la máquina y hallar la manera de aplicar esas instrucciones en caso de obstáculos.

Esta hazaña tecnológica es el resultado de los progresos realizados en menos de 50 años en la tecnología de materiales semiconductores, como germanio, silicio y arseniuro de galio.

La base de este asombroso avance es la electrónica de estado sólido: el descubrimiento del transistor y del microprocesador, que actúa con el consiguiente aumento, casi increíble, de la capacidad para almacenar, procesar y transmitir información de cualquier clase o forma a velocidades inimaginables.

La tecnología del soporte físico está ya bien arraigada, y sus costos disminuyen. Hay razones para esperar que en los decenios de 1980 y 1990 la industria de las telecomunicaciones se consagre a perfeccionar los métodos tecnológicos actuales: microminiaturización, digitalización, el uso de inteligencia distribuida para cálculo y control y transmisión por guiaondas ópticas.

Queda por dominar la tecnología de producir las instrucciones necesarias que puedan comprender y seguir efectivamente los sistemas electrónicos. Se trata del problema del soporte lógico: la inteligencia programada que es la clave de la flexibilidad y versatilidad de la tecnología de la era de la información. El hecho de que en la mayoría de las principales unidades de IyD casi la mitad de los científicos y de los ingenieros se dediquen al desarrollo del soporte lógico demuestra su importancia.

▷ 103

The far-reaching partnership of man and electronics.

L'homme, l'électronique, une toute autre perspective.

Trascendental asociación del hombre y la electrónica.

that in most of the major R&D units in the industry almost half the scientists and engineers are involved in the development of software and of its production.

The driving force behind the development of communication techniques is the spectacular advance of the past 2 to 3 decades in the technology of silicon semiconductors. More recently, photonics has revolutionized transmission by cable of voice, data and image, producing speeds and qualities inconceivable a decade ago.

Other major advances in the field of telecommunications are the advent of the computerized space station, the geostationary satellite and the enhancement of microwave broadcasting practice. These are examined on p. 146. It suffices to say in this context that satellite technology, being cost-insensitive to distance, is the key to the establishment of effective communications in the rural and sparsely populated areas of the world. Microwave transmission, in cellular or other forms, makes communications from satellites and between moving objects not only possible but highly effective. Both satellite and microwave technologies are, however, highly dependent on semiconductor technology and micronics to realize their potential.

Semiconductor technology has its roots deep in the 1930s, when research efforts were being directed to the development of cheaper and more reliable diodes (rectifiers) for logic gates, the forerunners of the computer's central processing unit (CPU). Other research effort was directed towards the development of the high frequency radio detector. When it was realized that semiconductor diodes were suitable as radar and microwave detectors, progress was rapid. A vacuum tube-driven computer, the SAGE, developed by US telephone companies and data processing firms — then only in their infancy — embodied all of today's concepts of distributed data communications, intelligent video terminals and magnetic core memories. At the time of the early SAGE development, a device called a MODEM (from *mo*dulator/*dem*odulator) was developed, enabling data digital signals to be transmitted over standard telephone voice circuits.

Solid-state technology was born out of the realization that vacuum tubes were expensive, unreliable, and that smaller components were essential to the development of speed and power in communication systems. Propagation delay of electron flow was one of the main impediments to rapid data processing and research was therefore concentrated not only on reducing the distance between components, but also their size, particularly that of the active electrical devices. In the early 1940s telephone engineers Horton and Holden devised the first fundamental solid-state logic circuits. This was followed in the late 1940s by the discovery at Bell Laboratories that a point-contact germanium wafer could be made to serve as an analog amplifier. The device was named a transistor. It was used as a replacement for valves in radio sets and thereafter as a switch or digital logic gate. Within three years, in 1951, William Shockley, working at Bell Laboratories, invented the junction transistor using silicon as the semiconductor material. This was the first major breakthrough leading to lower electronic component costs.

Computer design derived a major boost from these advances. IBM redesigned the early SAGE computer as an all solid-state machine, and marketed it as the 7090 in the 1960s. This was an outgrowth from the Project Whirlwind valve prototype of 1951-53 developed at the Lincoln Laboratories of the Massachusetts Institute of Technology (MIT). Another spin-off from Whirlwind was Jay Forrester's magnetic core memory, similar to a magnetic core memory device used for telephone call routing. This interaction between telephone call routing and the development of computer memory is a good example of the cross-fertilization that has constantly taken

Les progrès spectaculaires des 2 ou 3 dernières décennies réalisés dans la technologie des semiconducteurs constituent la force qui sous-tend le développement des techniques de communication. Plus récemment la photonique (transmission par ondes lumineuses) a révolutionné la transmission par câble du son, des images et des données, produisant des vitesses et des qualités non concevables il y a à peine dix ans.

D'autres progrès majeurs dans la technologie des communications sont l'avènement de la station spatiale informatisée, le satellite géostationnaire et le perfectionnement de transmission par ondes hertziennes ou micro-ondes. Ces aspects du progrès sont examinés à la p. 146. Il suffit de dire dans le présent contexte que le relai par satellite, dont le coût n'est pas affecté par la distance, est un élément-clé pour l'installation des télécommunications dans les régions rurales et peu peuplées. La transmission à micro-ondes est un moyen extrêmement efficace de communication par satellite et entre objets mobiles. Mais les deux méthodes dépendent étroitement des technologies des semi-conducteurs et de microminiaturisation pour réaliser leur potentiel.

La technologie des semi-conducteurs remonte aux années 1930. La recherche se concentrait alors sur la mise au point de diodes redresseuses plus fiables et meilleur marché, destinées aux dispositifs logiques, précurseurs des unités de traitement central des ordinateurs. D'autres efforts étaient orientés vers la mise au point de dispositifs de radiodétection. Dès que l'utilité des diodes semi-conducteurs pour la radiolocalisation et la radiodétection à micro-ondes fut découverte, les progrès furent rapides. L'ordinateur SAGE, développé par des compagnies téléphoniques et des firmes d'ordinateurs, alors balbutiantes, était actionné par un tube à vide et comprenait déjà tous les concepts actuels de la transmission de données, des terminaux vidéo intelligents et des mémoires à tores magnétiques. L'ordinateur Sage coïncida avec la mise au point d'un dispositif appelé MODEM (*mo*dulateur/*dém*odulateur), permettant la transmission de signaux numériques sur des circuits téléphoniques normalisés.

La technologie des circuits intégrés résulta de la nécessité de remplacer les tubes à vide, coûteux, peu fiables et trop encombrants pour assurer aux systèmes de commutation la rapidité et la capacité requises. Le temps de propagation des flux d'électrons constituait l'un des obstacles au traitement rapide des données. En conséquence, un programme de recherche fut établi pour réduire la distance entre les composants, ainsi que leurs dimensions et, au début des années 1940, Horton et Holden, ingénieurs de Bell Laboratories, mirent au point les premiers circuits logiques fondamentaux à l'état solide.

A la fin de cette décennie, on découvrit à Bell Laboratories, qu'une pastille de germanium utilisée comme point de contact pouvait servir d'amplificateur analogique. Ce dispositif, le transistor, fut utilisé pour remplacer le tube à vide dans les appareils de radio et ensuite comme commutateur ou comme « porte » de logique numérique. Trois ans plus tard, en 1951, William Shockley, aussi de chez Bell Laboratories, inventa le transistor de jonction utilisant le silicium comme matériau semi-conducteur.

La conception des ordinateurs a été profondément influencée par les progrès réalisés dans les dispositifs à semi-conducteurs. IBM remania son premier ordinateur Sage pour en faire un appareil d'état solide, qui fut commercialisé dans les années 1960 comme modèle IBM 7090. Cette réalisation découlait du projet Whirlwind mis au point pendant la période 1951-53 aux Lincoln Laboratories de l'Institut de technologie du Massachusetts (MIT). C'est encore de ce projet Whirlwind que découle la mémoire à noyau magnétique de Jay Forrester, analogue à un dispositif du même type utilisé pour l'acheminement des appels téléphoniques. Le modèle IBM 7090 devint le cœur du premier système commercial de distribution de données en 1941, le SABRE d'American Airline.

Un service de commutation/transfert de messages télégraphiques et des techniques de partage de temps

▷ 104

▷ 104

MICROELECTR

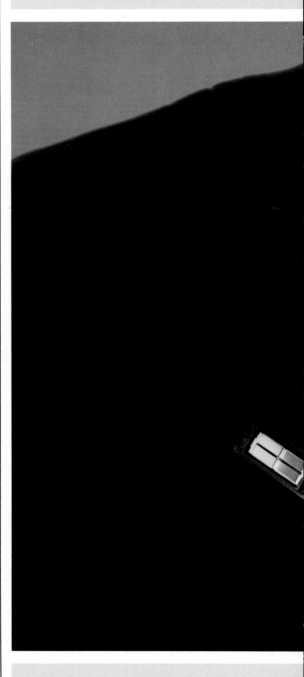

Displayed in the palm of a hand on this page is a "chip", an electronic device on which are packed more than a quarter of a million electronic components. The word "chip" means "a tiny piece of material" small and rather flat — traditionally a splinter of stone or wood but in this case a wafer-thin piece of semi-conductor material, silicon. On this silicon base is built a labyrinth of tiny transistors, or "logic gates", structured in various configurations or circuits through which flow electrical pulses routed by the opening and shutting of the gates, to achieve a specific planned function. The functions can be: to program and control (CPU), to memorize (RAM or ROM) or simply to select or categorize. The "chip" portrayed here is a device which can store information, equivalent to 10,000 telephone numbers. Retrieval takes about one hundred thousand

millionth of a second per bit, i.e. the recall of a number is instantaneous. This 256K RAM was developed by Bell Laboratories and is manufactured by Western Electric. Another, the BELLMAC 32, of about 1 cm², contains 150,000 transistors and has the power of a super minicomputer at a fraction of the price.

CS: THE "MARVEL ON A CHIP"

séntée dans le creux d'une main, voici la « puce », dispositif
tronique dans lequel sont disposés plus d'un quart de
on de composants : les transistors ou « portes logiques ».
consiste en une très mince rondelle de silicium, un matériau
iconducteur qui sert de base pour un labyrinthe de minus-
s circuits de diverses configurations structurées afin d'ob-
r la fonction voulue, que ce soit la programmation et le
trôle d'un ordinateur (CPU), la mémorisation de l'informa-
(ROM ou RAM) ou simplement la sélection et le classement.
semble forme des circuits dont les fonctions sont décrites à
age suivante. La « puce » ci-dessous est un dispositif de
noire dynamique, le 256K RAM, ou circuit intégré à très
de échelle (VLSI), qui peut enregistrer 10 000 numéros de
phone. Le rappel d'un numéro est instantané. Le 256K RAM,

En la palma de una mano se muestra una "plaqueta", dispositivo electrónico en que se empaquetan más de 250 000 componentes electrónicos. Por "plaqueta" se entiende una "fina
pieza de material" pequeña y bastante plana: tradicionalmente,
una placa de piedra o madera, pero en este caso, una fina oblea
de material semiconductor, silicio. Sobre esta base de silicio se
monta un laberinto de transistores diminutos o "puertas lógicas", estructuradas en varias configuraciones o circuitos a
través de los cuales se encaminan impulsos eléctricos,
abriendo y cerrando las puertas, para lograr una función específica. Las funciones pueden ser: programar y controlar
(UCP), memorizar (MAS o MLS) o simplemente seleccionar o
clasificar. La "plaqueta" mostrada aquí es un dispositivo que
puede almacenar información equivalente a 10 000 números

eloppé par Bell Laboratories, est fabriqué par Western
tric, deux membres du groupe AT&T. Une autre « puce », le
LMAC 32, contient sur 1 cm² 150 000 transistors et déve-
e la puissance d'un super mini-ordinateur pour une fraction
ne du prix.

telefónicos. La recuperación lleva unos 100 000 millones de
segundo por bit, con lo que la repetición de un número es
instantánea. Esta MAS 256K ha sido desarrollada por Bell
Laboratories y es fabricada por Western Electric. Otra, la
BELLMAC 32, de 1 cm², contiene 150 000 transistores y posee
la potencia de un superminicomputador, a una fracción del
precio.

Los espectaculares avances en la tecnología de semiconductores de los 2 ó 3 últimos decenios constituyen la fuerza motriz del desarrollo de las comunicaciones. Más recientemente, la fotónica ha revolucionado la transmisión por cable del sonido, imágenes y datos, produciendo velocidades y calidades
inconcebibles hace 10 años.

Otros importantes avances son la estación espacial
informatizada, el satélite geoestacionario y el mejoramiento de la transmisión por microondas. Esto se
examina en la pág. 146. Baste decir que la tecnología
de satélite, al no influir la distancia en el costo, es un
elemento clave para la instalación de telecomunicaciones en las regiones rurales y poco pobladas. La
transmisión por microondas, celulares o en otras
formas, no sólo hace posible la comunicación por
satélite y entre objetos móviles, sino sumamente eficaz. Pero la explotación de las posibilidades de ambos métodos depende mucho de la tecnología de
semiconductores y de la micrónica.

La tecnología de semiconductores se arraigó en los años
1930, en que la investigación se orientó hacia el desarrollo de diodos más baratos y seguros (rectifica-
dores) para puertas lógicas, los precursores de la
unidad de procesamiento central del computador.
Otros esfuerzos se orientaron hacia el desarrollo del
detector radioeléctrico de alta frecuencia. A com-
probarse que los diodos de semiconductores eran
apropiados como detectores de radar y microondas,
se avanzó rápidamente. El computador de tubo de
vacío, SAGE, desarrollado por compañías telefónicas y empresas de tratamiento de datos de EE.UU. —
entonces en embrión — incorporó todos los conceptos actuales de las comunicaciones de datos, terminales video inteligentes y memorias de núcleo
magnético. Coincidiendo con la aparición del SAGE
se desarrolló un dispositivo llamado MÓDEM (de
*mo*dulador/*dem*odulador), que permite transmitir
señales de datos por circuitos telefónicos normalizados.

La tecnología de estado sólido surgió al comprobar que los tubos de vacío eran demasiado caros e
inseguros, y que para desarrollar sistemas de comunicación rápidos y potentes se requerían componentes más pequeños. El tiempo de propagación del
flujo de electrones fue uno de los principales obstáculos para procesar rápidamente los datos, y la investigación no se centró sólo en reducir la distancia
entre componentes, sino también en el tamaño, sobre todo de dispositivos eléctricos activos. A comienzos de los años 1940 los ingenieros Horton y
Holden concibieron los primeros circuitos lógicos de
estado sólido. Esto fue seguido a finales del decenio
por el descubrimiento en Bell Laboratories de que
podía fabricarse una oblea de germanio como punto
de contacto para servir de amplificador analógico. El
dispositivo, denominado transistor, se aplicó para
sustituir a la válvula en los aparatos de radio y, después, como conmutador o puerta lógica digital. Tres
años más tarde, en 1951, William Shockley, que tra-
bajaba en Bell Laboratories, inventó el transistor de
unión, que utiliza el silicio como material semiconductor. Fue el principal avance en la reducción de los
costos de componentes electrónicos.

El diseño de computador. Los progresos en los dispositivos de semiconductores impulsaron fuertemente el
diseño de computador. IBM rediseñó el primer
computador SAGE como aparato de estado sólido,
comercializado en los años 1960 como computador
IBM 7090. Fue el resultado de un prototipo de válvula del proyecto Whirlwind de 1951-53, desarrollado en los Lincoln Laboratories del Instituto de Tecnología de Massachusetts (MIT). Otra derivación de
Whirlwind fue la memoria de núcleo magnético de
Jay Forrester, similar a un dispositivo del mismo
tipo, utilizado para el encaminamiento de llamadas
telefónicas. Esta interacción entre ese encaminamiento y el desarrollo de la memoria de computador
es un buen ejemplo de los fecundos resultados de la
conmutación telefónica y de los computadores de
programa almacenado. El IBM 7090 fue el centro del
SABRE, primer sistema comercial de distribución de
datos instalado en 1941, por American Airline.

▷ 105

place between telephone switching and stored-program computers. The IBM7090 became the heart of SABRE, the first commercial distributed-data system installed in 1941 by American Airline.

Computerized store-and-forward telegraphic message service and time-sharing techniques were utilized by SABRE, following SAGE technology. Minicomputers, used as front-end processors to relieve main frames of telecommunications tasks, spun off a new industry producing small computers, multiplexers, and hybrid data processing services.

Another major source of computer and software innovation and know-how came from a US Government-financed program designed to speed up data processing and develop more reliable computers, software and peripherals. The results included low-cost ferromagnetic tape, the widespread use of semiconductors in computer architecture and the prototype for IBM's 360 computer series.

From the developments outlined above, it becomes clear that much of the progress of the past few decades took place during an era of virtually unlimited spending for space and defence. The inventions were there before, but the funds needed to exploit them were not. The integrated circuit, for example, is not a product of yesterday, or even a previous decade. Photolithographic technology, which gradually led to the integrated circuit, began only a few years after the invention of the transistor. It was accelerated by the need for faster, more reliable computers, and smaller electronic controls for rocketry and space travel.

The pace of technological innovation is never easy to gauge; the market penetration of the end product or service is also difficult to time or evaluate: critical in this are the elements of mass (a volume and density of sales sufficient to generate widely based demand) and the element of unit cost. A third factor affecting the pace of the application of new technology is the market resistance based on the need to make do with existing equipment due to the heavy investment it represents. This means that developing nations are more likely to be open to the latest technologies, for example all-digital networks and microwave transmission, than countries where dense all-analog networks are in use and where the effective interfacing of the new with the old is a pre-requisite of economic progress.

Microelectronics technology is the key to almost every one of today's advances in communications. Improvements in performance and cost reductions are both made possible by microminiaturization. The cost of digital magnetic recording for information storage has fallen by 40% compounded annually over the past two decades and that of semiconductor computer memory by 28%. Dr. Lewis Branscomb, chief scientist of IBM, stated in 1979 "the scientific limits to further progress in microminiaturization are rather well understood. There is general agreement that the linear dimensions of silicon devices can continue to be reduced by another factor of a least 3 to 6. This provides the potential for an area reduction of more than a factor of ten, with associated reduction in cost, and improvement in performance".

The acceleration of progress in integrated circuit design was confirmed by Bell Laboratories. The near-magical powers of microprocessors and their widespread use, it was explained, is due simply to their immense information handling capacity, incredibly small size and low cost. The trend in these directions continues and, according to Bell Laboratories, "each year microelectronic devices grow more powerful and more economical". Several microprocessor chips produced recently are capable of processing 32 bits, or binary digits, simultaneously, reflecting the current state-of-the-art in Very Large Scale Integration (VLSI) technology. Such chips contain 150,000 transistors, incoporate a 32-bit internal data path and a full 32-bit address space, and are functionally the equivalent of the room-sized computers of the 1970s.

Another milestone was the successful production of a 256-kilobit random access memory chip (256K RAM) which quadrupled the capacity of previously

▷ 106

furent employés par SABRE en se servant de la technologie SAGE.

L'utilisation de mini-ordinateurs en tant que processeurs frontaux pour soustraire les tâches de télécommunication aux unités centrales de traitement a engendré toute une industrie de petits ordinateurs, de multiplexeurs et de services hybrides de traitement de données. Une autre source importante d'innovation fut une série de programmes de recherche financés par le gouvernement américain. Il en résulta une bande ferro-magnétique à bas prix et un emploi beaucoup plus général des semi-conducteurs dans l'architecture des ordinateurs et la mise au point d'un nouveau prototype d'ordinateur de la série IBM 360.

Les développements ébauchés ci-dessus indiquent clairement que le plus grand progrès s'est produit pendant une période de financement sans limite pour le contrôle de l'espace et la défense. Les inventions existaient, mais les fonds nécessaires pour les exploiter manquaient. Le circuit intégré, par exemple, n'est pas né d'hier. La technique photolithographique, qui mena au circuit intégré commença à être appliquée quelques années avant l'invention du transistor. Son utilisation et son raffinement furent accélérés par le besoin de contrôles électroniques plus compacts pour les fusées et les engins spatiaux.

Le rythme du progrès technique n'est guère facile à évaluer, ni la pénétration d'un produit ou d'un service sur le marché. A cet égard les éléments critiques sont le volume et la densité des ventes (l'effet de masse) suffisants pour généraliser la demande et le coût unitaire. Un troisième élément est la présence sur le marché d'équipements obsolescents qui représentent un gros investissement, ce qui est le cas en ce qui concerne les réseaux téléphoniques dans beaucoup de pays. Cela implique que les pays en développement sont généralement plus ouverts aux techniques de pointe que les pays dotés de réseaux denses.

La technologie de la microélectronique est la clé de la quasi totalité des progrès théoriques et pratiques ainsi que de la baisse des prix dans les domaines de l'informatique et des télécommunications. Le coût d'un enregistrement numérique magnétique pour le stockage de l'information a accusé une diminution annuelle de 40% au cours des deux dernières décennies, tandis que celle du prix de la mémoire d'ordinateurs à semi-conducteurs a été de 28%. Le Dr. Lewis Branscomb, directeur scientifique de IBM, a déclaré (en 1979) : « Les limites scientifiques des progrès réalisables dans le domaine de la microminiaturisation sont assez bien connues. On admet généralement que les dimensions linéaires des dispositifs au silicium pourront encore être réduites d'un facteur d'au moins 3 à 6. Cela implique des possibilités de nouvelles réductions de l'ordre d'un facteur supérieur à 10, avec une réduction parallèle des prix et une amélioration de la performance ».

L'accélération du progrès dans la conception des microprocesseurs est confirmée par Bell Laboratories, selon lesquels : les pouvoirs quasi magiques des circuits intégrés sont dûs à leur immense capacité de traitement de l'information, à leurs dimensions incroyablement petites, et à la modicité de leur prix, facteurs auquels s'ajoute le fait que chaque année les dispositifs microélectroniques deviennent plus puissants et plus économiques. Plusieurs microprocesseurs mis au point récemment contiennent 150 000 transistors, une voie de données interne de 32 bits et un format complet d'adresse, aussi de 32 bits. Ils sont équivalents fonctionnellement aux ordinateurs géants de 1970.

Une nouvelle étape a été récemment franchie avec la commercialisation d'un microprocesseur dynamique de 256 kilobits (256K RAM) qui permet de quadrupler la capacité des mémoires disponibles antérieurement. Cette minuscule « puce » de moins de 1,7×0,8 cm contient plus d'un demi-million de composants et peut stocker 262 144 bits d'informations, soit l'équivalent de 16 pages de livre. Un laser commandé par ordinateur peut être utilisé pour remplacer les éléments défectueux.

La conception et la réalisation du microprocesseur à 32 bits n'ont pu être menées à bien que par des méthodes de conception assistée par ordinateur

▷ 106

THE CIR

To carry out instructions a computer depends on its central processor unit (CPU), the control unit — the heart or nerve center of the system. In personal computers this 'brain' is often a single 'chip', integrated circuit or microprocessor. This chip, containing, for example, 450,000 transistors laced together by 20 meters of vapor-deposited tungsten 'wire', is manufactured from the semiconductor material silicon. Patterned in and on its silicon base, and joined by 'wires' etched from exquisitely thin films of metal, are thousands upon thousands of minuscule switches or transistors making up a circuitry resembling the nerves and neurons of the human brain (see photo pp. 114 and 270).

This chip, barely the size of a thumbnail, but akin to the street plan of a great metropolis seen from miles above when viewed under the microscope, combines aptitudes for memory and also for logic — the process by which incoming digital information is translated into outgoing digital information.

The microprocessor, first introduced in 1959, is capable of performing astounding feats of logic by the programmed sequences of hundreds of thousands of tiny electronic gates opening and closing against a stream of digital pulses. In eleven years the number of calculations possible per second has leaped from 50,000 to one million and shows promise of going well beyond this.

To enable a computer to function, the inputs — number, text, voice and image — must first be translated into a code of electrical pulses; a high voltage pulse representing the digit 1; the low voltage pulse the digit 0. Being binary (i.e. containing only two digits) these pulses are called "bits", an abbreviation of "binary digits". Information in the form of "bits", usually in groupings of eight, called "bytes", is sent shuffling through the circuits somewhat like trains in a railroad shunting yard.

THE

Termed an "Address", the message travels from the 'Address Unit' to the EPROM Unit (Erasable Programmable Read-Only Memory) which contains the basic program instructions for performing specific tasks. Most microprocessors also incorporate a 'RAM Unit' (Random Access Memory) where information can be independently stored on a temporary basis. This is complemented by 'ROM' chips (Read Only Memory Unit), in which large amounts of information can be stored during their manufacture or added subsequently. Storage capacities are measured in K's, each K containing 1024 bits of information (not 1,000 as 'K' usually represents).

The Address is as specific as the co-ordinates on a grid. The memory is organized on horizontal and vertical lines, each intersection being a location where data are stored (typically one "byte" on each). The "byte" is located by the numbers identifying the horizontal and vertical lines.

Program instructions are sent to the Instruction Unit which interprets the program and breaks it down into extremely detailed steps, preparing it for the 'ALU' (Arithmetic-Logic Unit) where hundreds of thousands of calculations take place per second.

All of the reading of digital instructions and the action on them has so far been the result simply of minute amounts of voltage being routed through various kinds of gates — the basic decision — making circuitry on digital switching consists of two or more binary inputs and binary outpus. This is the process, on a micro scale, designed to implement the programmer's instructions.

Two other units play important roles in this labyrinth of microscopic circuitry. The 'Interrupt Unit' allows signals of higher priority to assume control and operate new programs while the Off-Chip-Addressing Unit directs communications with outside sensors, display and other chips.

RY OF A MICROPROCESSOR

fonctionnement d'un ordinateur dépend d'un processeur
tral qui en est le centre nerveux, souvent constitué par un
l microprocesseur. Ce dispositif, moins grand qu'un ongle,
tient un très grand nombre de transistors, ou « portes »
ques, qui constituent un circuit intégré à travers lequel
ulent des impulsions électriques à la manière de trains dans
gare de triage, mais à une vitesse approchant celle de la
ière.

.es transistors, il peut y en avoir 1/2 million sur un
timètre carré, sont reliés par des mètres de « fil » de
ngstène d'une épaisseur infinitésimale, gravé à l'acide sur
base semi-conductrice de silicium.. Cela rappelle la confi-
ation des synapses qui entourent et relient les neurones du
veau humain (voir photos pp. 114 et 270).

Ce microprocesseur est capable de performances logiques
péfiantes dans les séquences programmées d'ouverture et
fermeture des minuscules « portes » électroniques
mmandant le flux des impulsions numériques. Placé sous un
roscope le microprocesseur ressemble à une grande mé-
pole vue de quelques kilomètres d'altitude, dans laquelle se
binent d'énormes capacités de mémoire et de logique, un
cessus par lequel l'entrée d'information sous forme numé-
ue est ré-arrangée et ressort, aussi sous forme numérique,
s l'ordre et la séquence voulue. Les « entrées » - chiffres,
tes, sons, images sont codées sous forme d'impulsions élec-
ues. Toute impulsion de tension élevée représente le chiffre
toute impulsion de tension basse le chiffre 0 (voir démons-
ion p. 124). Les impulsions sont dénommées « bits »
réviation de binary digits). Le débit binaire d'information
coule généralement par groupes de huit bits appelés octets
« bytes ».

Para cumplir instrucciones, un computador depende de su unidad procesadora central (UPC): corazón o centro nervioso del
sistema. En los computadores personales, este "cerebro" es
con frecuencia una sola "plaqueta" circuito integrado o microprocesador, que contiene, por ejemplo, 450 000 transistores
enlazados por 20 metros de "hilo" de tungsteno con depósito de
vapor, y se fabrica a base de silicio como material semiconductor. Ordenados en su base de silicio, y sobre ella, y unidos
por "hilos" fijados al ácido de películas de metal sumamente
finas, miles y miles de computadores o transistores diminutos
componen una serie de circuitos a veces tan minúsculos como
los nervios y neurones del cerebro humano (véase foto, págs.
114 y 270).

Esta plaqueta, apenas del tamaño de una uña, y semejante al
plano de una gran metrópoli vista a kilómetros de altitud,
cuando se observa con microscopio, combina aptitudes de
memoria y también de lógica: el proceso por el que la información digital de entrada se convierte en digital de salida.

El microprocesador, introducido en 1959, es capaz de realizar sorprendentes hazañas de lógica por las secuencias programadas de centenares de miles de puertas electrónicas diminutas que se abren y cierran ante un tren de impulsos
digitales. En once años, el número de cálculos posibles por
segundo ha pasado de 50 000 a un millón, cifra que se espera
superar en creces.

Para que funcione un computador, hay que convertir en
código de impulsos eléctricos las entradas: números, texto, voz
e imagen; un impulso de alta tensión representa el dígito 1; el de
baja tensión, el 0. Al ser binarios, esos impulsos se denominan
"bits", abreviatura de "binary digits". La información en forma
de "bits", normalmente en grupos de ocho, denominados "bytes", se envía sin orden a través de los circuitos; algo así como
los trenes en una estación de clasificación.

SABRE utilizó técnicas de servicios de mensajes
telegráficos y almacenamiento y retransmisión computadorizados y compartición en el tiempo, según la
tecnología SAGE. Los minicomputadores, empleados como procesadores de acceso para aliviar a las
unidades principales, han dado lugar a una industria
que produce pequeños computadores, multiplexa-
dores, y servicios de procesamiento de datos híbri-
dos.

Otra importante fuente de innovación en este
campo fue un programa de varios miles de millones
de dólares financiado por EE.UU. para acelerar el
procesamiento de datos y desarrollar computadores,
soporte lógico y equipo periférico más seguro. Entre
los resultados cabe citar la cinta ferromagnética de
bajo costo, el uso generalizado de semiconductores
en la arquitectura de computadores y el prototipo
para la serie de computadores IBM 360.

Dicha evolución muestra que muchos de los
progresos de los últimos decenios se produjeron en
una era de gasto virtualmente ilimitado en actividades espaciales y de defensa. Las invenciones ya
existían, pero se carecía de fondos para explotarlas.
El circuito integrado, por ejemplo, no es un producto
de ayer, ni siquiera de hace un decenio. La tecnología fotolitográfica, que llevó al circuito integrado,
comenzó hace tan sólo unos años, después de inven-
tarse el transistor, acelerándose debido a la necesidad de computadores más rápidos y seguros, y de
controles electrónicos más pequeños para cohetes y
viajes espaciales.

El ritmo de la innovación tecnológica. Nunca es fácil calcu-
lar eso ritmo; también es difícil seguir o evaluar la
penetración en el mercado del producto o servicio
final: para ello son esenciales los elementos de masa
(volumen y densidad de ventas suficientes para generar la demanda sobre una amplia base) y el elemento de costo unitario. Un tercer factor que influye
en el ritmo de la aplicación de nueva tecnología es la
resistencia del mercado, fundada en la necesidad de
hacerlo son equipo existente, debido a la fuerte inversión necesaria. Esto significa que quizá los países
en desarrollo propendan más a las últimas tecnologías — por ejemplo, redes, digitales y transmisión
por microondas — que los países donde se utilizan
densas redes analógicas y donde la conexión efectiva
de las nuevas y las antiguas es esencial para el progreso.

La tecnología microelectrónica es la clave de casi todos los
avances actuales en las comunicaciones. El costo de
grabaciones magnéticas digitales para almacenar la
información ha disminuido en un 40% anual en los
dos últimos decenios, y el de la memoria de computador por semiconductores, en un 28%. El Dr. Lewis
Branscomb, jefe científico de IBM, dijo en 1979:
« Los límites científicos del nuevo progreso en la
microminiaturización se conocen bastante bien. En
general, se coincide en que las dimensiones lineales
de los dispositivos de silicio pueden seguir reducién-
dose en otro factor de 3 a 6, por lo menos. Esto
permite una disminución del área de un factor
superior a diez, con la reducción asociada del costo, y
un mejor rendimiento ».

La aceleración del progreso en el diseño de plaquetas fue confirmada por Bell Laboratories, expli-
cando que la fuerza casi mágica de los microprocesadores y su uso generalizado se debe a su inmensa
capacidad de tratamiento de la información, a su
tamaño, pequeñísimo, y a su bajo costo, comentando
que « cada año, los dispositivos microelectrónicos
son más potentes y económicos ». Varias plaquetas
de microprocesador producidas recientemente son
capaces de procesar 32 bits, o dígitos binarios, simultáneamente, reflejando el actual estado de la
ciencia en la tecnología de integración en muy gran
escala (VLSI). Contienen 150 000 transistores, incorporan un trayecto de datos interno de 32 bits, y un
espacio completo de dirección de 32 bits, y funcionalmente equivalen al computador del tamaño de
una habitación de los años 1970.

Otro hito es la producción de una plaqueta de
memoria de acceso selectivo de 256 kilobits (256K

TING OF DIGITAL FLOWS

cheminement des flux numériques se fait à partir des
esses (entrées) qui passent de l'unité d'adresse à la mé-
re de lecture programmable EPROM (Erasable Program-
ole Read-only Memory) qui contient les instructions pour
écution des tâches. Cela est complété par des circuits ROM
ad Only Memory Unit) mémoire permanente, et des circuits
M (Random Access Memory) mémoire à accès aléatoire.
'adresse correspond aux coordonnées d'un grille. La mé-
re est structurée de manière à ce que chaque intersection
un point de stockage de données (généralement un octet
donnée). Le repérage et l'identification de chaque octet se
au moyen des numéros de référence des lignes horizontales
erticales.

.es instructions de programme sont envoyées à l'unité
struction qui interprète le programme et le divise en phases
détaillées, pour le préparer à l'ULA (Unité de logique
hmétique) où s'effectuent des centaines de milliers de cal-
s par seconde.

l est remarquable que toutes les opérations de lecture des
tructions numériques et de traitement de celles-ci résultent
n tout petit voltage électrique envoyé à travers diverses
tes de portes — le dispositif de commutation numérique —
pelé à prendre des décisions de base comportant deux
rées binaires ou plus et une seule sortie binaire. C'est cette
cédure élémentaire, réalisée à une échelle microscopique,
est destinée à mettre en œuvre les instructions du pro-
mmeur.

Deux autres unités jouent un rôle important dans ce laby-
he de circuits microscopiques. L'« unité d'interruption »
met aux signaux prioritaires de prendre le contrôle et d'en-
er de nouveaux programmes pendant que l'unité d'adres-
e achemine les communications à destination des détec-
rs extérieurs, des dispositifs de visualisation et d'autres
roprocesseurs.

Denominado "Dirección", el mensaje pasa de la "Unidad de
dirección" a la Unidad MLSPB (memoria de lectura solamente
programable y borrable), que contiene las instrucciones de
programa básicas para realizar tareas concretas. Muchos
computadores tienen también una "Unidad MAS" (memoria de
acceso selectivo), donde puede almacenarse la información
temporalmente. Esto se complementa con plaquetas "MLS"
(unidad de memoria de lectura solamente), en que puede almacenarse mucha información, o agregarse después. Las capacidades de almacenamiento se miden en K, conteniendo cada K
1024 bits de información (no 1000, como representa normalmente K).

La Dirección es tan específica como las coordenadas de una
cuadrícula. La memoria se organiza en líneas horizontales y
verticales; cada intersección es un lugar donde hay datos
almacenados (normalmente, un "byte" en cada una). El "byte"
se localiza por los números que identifican las líneas.

Las instrucciones de programa se envían a la Unidad de
instrucción, que interpreta el programa y lo divide en pasos
sumamente detallados, preparándolo para la "ULA" (unidad de
lógica aritmética), donde se realizan centenares de miles de
cálculos por segundo.

Toda la lectura de las instrucciones digitales y la acción
sobre ellas ha sido hasta ahora simplemente el resultado de
diminutas cantidades de tensión encaminadas a través de
puertas de varias clases: la decisión básica que forma circuitos
en la conmutación digital consta de dos o más entradas binarias y una salida binaria. Este es el proceso, en microescala,
para aplicar las instrucciones del programador.

Hay otras dos unidades importantes en este laberinto de
circuitos microscópicos. La "Unidad de interrupción" permite a
las señales prioritarias asumir el control y operar nuevos
programas mientras la Unidad de direccionamiento dirige comunicaciones con sensores del exterior, visualizaciones y otras
plaquetas.

▷ 107

available devices. One tiny chip, of less than 1.7×0.8 cm contains more than half a million components and has the capacity to store 262,144 bits of information, the equivalent of about 16 pages of a book. A computer controlled laser-activated technique allows spare elements on the chip to be substituted for faulty elements, giving a much enhanced yield.

The design and layout of the 32-bit microprocessor was achieved by the use of computer-aided design techniques (CAD) and most certainly could not have been done without. To give some idea of the complexity involved, if each transistor were a house and the connecting lines roads, designing the chip would correspond roughly to the layout for a 64 square-mile city of 300,000 people with 5,000 miles of roads. The software in the CAD tools used in the design contained 600,000 lines of code. Increasingly, as designs become ever larger, more complex and customized, the key to progress is CAD.

By 1985 the US Defense Department's Advanced Research Projects Agency expects to produce chips with one million logic gates. These devices will have only 0.5 micron (0.0005 mm) spacing between elements. This has been termed the very-high-speed integrated circuit (VHSIC). Such microscopic electronics will be working on the molecular level permitting electron movement at close to the speed of light.

Photonics — the use of light to carry information — has made great strides in recent years. In 1981 American Telegraph and Telephone (AT&T) announced that "lightwave systems are a clear success", and that the use of optical fibers to transmit information had passed surprisingly rapidly from research through development to deployment, "driven by the promise of higher bandwidth and lower cost".

Modern fiber optic technology has its origins in research on waveguides undertaken in the 1920s by G.C. Southworth and others. The first result of this work has the coaxial cable in 1928, followed by practical waveguides — hollow tubes which guided electromagnetic radiation. Research in solid-state physics produced designs of extremely accurate "atomic" clocks which in turn led to the construction of the first *MASER* (Microwave Amplification by Stimulated Emission of Radiation) in 1954. The maser produced coherent microwaves utilizing a quantum effect, as predicted by Soviet physicists as early as 1939. Maser research was directed in optics and the first *LASER* (Light Amplification by Stimulated Emission of Radiation) was produced in 1960, using identical theoretical underpinnings.

The significance of the development of photonics in telecommunication system was underlined by Dr. Charles K. Kao, scientist of International Telephone and Telegraph (ITT) and a pioneer in the field of fiber optics, in the following glowing terms: "The stage is set for an enrichment of life like that which followed the invention of the steam engine, the light bulb and the transistor".

Fiber optic systems' only components are the light source, the optical fiber, the light detector and the connectors and couplers needed to assemble them. The light signal is modulated or imprinted with information using electronic equipment to drive the light source. At one end of the system is the coder which converts analog voice signals to digital signals and a light source device or emitter which converts electrical pulses to pulses of light energy. The optical fiber provides a guide or "highway" which the light energy follows, even around bends. At the other end of the system is an optical detector which converts the light pulses back to electrical pulses and the decoder which converts the electrical pulses back to analog (See Box p. 124).

Light sources for optical fiber transmission are of two kinds, both based on semiconductor technology: the Light Emitting Diode (LED) and the laser. LEDs used in fiber optics are similar to those used in the visual display of pocket calculators or watches. The semiconductor diode laser consists of several layers

▷ 108

(CAD). Pour donner une idée de la complexité de l'opération, si le transistor était une maison et les circuits d'interconnexion des routes, le microprocesseur représenterait approximativement une ville de 100 km² avec 8000 km de rues et une population de 300 000 habitants, et le logiciel des appareils CAD utilisé pour la conception comprendrait 600 000 lignes de code. Plus la conception d'un microprocesseurs s'élargit, plus l'incorporation de systèmes devient complexe. Dans ces conditions, il n'y a que l'ordinateur pour la réaliser.

L'Advanced Research Projects Agency du Département de la défense des Etats-Unis compte produire dans les années 80 des microprocesseurs comportant un million de portes logiques. L'espacement entre chacun des éléments ne dépassera pas 0,5 microns (0,0005 mm), dans des circuits à très grande vitesse d'intégration (VHSIC). Les systèmes microscopiques fonctionnant à l'échelle moléculaire, permettront aux électrons de se mouvoir à des vitesses proches de celle de la lumière.

La photonique (du grec photo = lumière) est une technique utilisant la lumière pour transporter l'information qui a progressé à pas de géant en très peu de temps. En 1981, la société AT&T affirmait que les systèmes à ondes lumineuses constituaient un véritable pas en avant et que l'utilisation des fibres optiques pour transmettre l'information avait passé, avec une rapidité surprenante, du stade de la recherche à celui de l'application, compte tenu des perspectives d'utilisation de largeur de bande plus élevée et de coûts réduits.

La technologie des fibres optiques a son origine dans la recherche sur les ondes guidées entreprise vers 1920 par G.C. Southworth et d'autres, laquelle avait abouti à la réalisation du câble coaxial en 1928, puis aux guides d'ondes : tubes permettant de guider le rayonnement électromagnétique. La recherche dans le domaine de la physique de l'état solide a abouti à la mise au point d'horloges « atomiques » de grande précision qui, à leur tour, ont conduit à la construction du premier MASER (Microwave Amplification by Stimulated Emission of Radiation), en 1954. Le Maser produit des micro-ondes cohérentes utilisant un effet quantique, comme l'avaient prévu les physiciens soviétiques dès 1939. Le premier LASER (Light Amplification by Stimulated Emission of Radiation) a été réalisé en 1960, sur les mêmes bases théoriques.

L'importance du développement de la photonique dans les systèmes de télécommunications a été mis en évidence par le Dr. Charles K. Kao, l'un des responsables de la recherche chez ITT, pionnier dans le domaine des fibres optiques : « notre vie va s'enrichir — dit-il — comme après l'invention du moteur à vapeur, de l'ampoule électrique et du transistor ».

Les systèmes à fibres optiques ont pour seuls composants la source lumineuse, la fibre optique, le détecteur de lumière et les connecteurs et coupleurs nécessaires pour assembler ces composants. Le signal lumineux est modulé ou « imprimé » par l'information, à l'aide de l'équipement électronique servant à exciter la source lumineuse. A l'une des extrémités du système on trouve le codeur qui convertit les signaux analogiques vocaux en signaux numériques (voir p. 124) et une source lumineuse ou émetteur qui convertit les impulsions électriques en impulsions d'énergie lumineuse. Les fibres optiques constituent un guide ou « artère » que l'énergie lumineuse suit même dans les courbes. A l'autre extrémité du système, on trouve un détecteur optique qui reconvertit les impulsions lumineuses en impulsions électriques et un décodeur qui reconvertit les impulsions électriques en signaux analogiques.

Les sources lumineuses utilisées pour la transmission optique sont de deux types fondés sur la technologie des semi-conducteurs : la diode photoémettrice (LED) et la diode laser. Les diodes LED utilisées dans les systèmes en fibres optiques sont semblables à celles utilisées pour l'affichage dans les calculatrices de poche ou les montres ! La diode semi-conductrice de laser est formée de plusieurs couches de matériau semi-conducteur qui émettent de la lumière en déchargeant de l'énergie sous forme de photons, sous l'influence d'une petite charge électrique.

▷ 108

PHOTONICS: THE

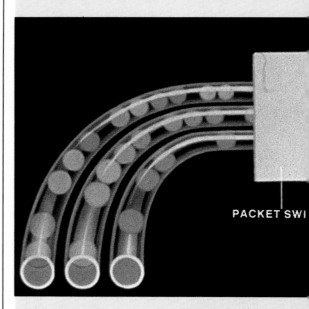

PACKET SWI

Packet switching, illustrated above, routes pre-addressed batches of digital information (represented by coloured balls) through the packet network, concentrating them in a few digital transmission channels. Messages are broken down into smaller units, "packets" which are then individually addressed and routed through the network. The process of routing and transferring data by means of addressed packets makes it possible for a channel to be occupied only during the transmission of the packet.

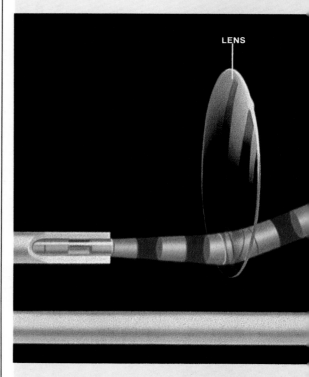

LENS

Lightwave multiplexing, illustrated above and developed by Bell Laboratories, puts two or more signals on one glass fiber by using a system of lenses and a filter. This method substantially increases the carrying capacity of glass fibers, by putting two or more wavelengths (colours) on each fiber. Techniques developed in the early 1980s enabled the carriage of some 2,600 messages or data signals simultaneously on one pair of fibers, four times the capacity of previous systems. The new systems utilize light sources (each wavelength must have its own light source and detector) operating at 90 million pulses per second, twice the standard rate previously achieved.

OF LIGHT TO CARRY INFORMATION

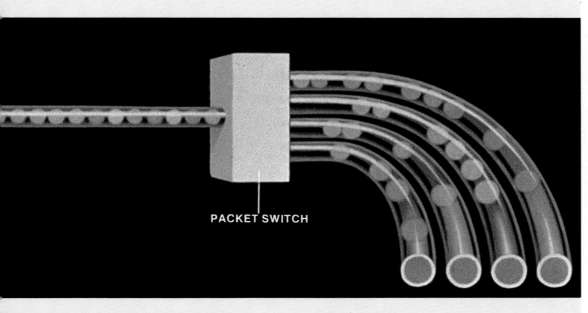

PACKET SWITCH

commutation par paquet, illustrée ci-dessus, achemine des pré-adressés d'information numérique (représentés par des es en couleur) à travers le réseau paquet, les concentrant s quelques canaux de transmission numérique. Dans ce tème les messages sont divisés en groupes de plus en plus ts, les paquets, ensuite adressés individuellement et ache-és à travers le réseau.

e procédé permet de n'occuper une voie que partiellement r la transmission d'un paquet.

La conmutación por paquetes, ilustrada aquí, encamina lotes de información digital predireccionada (representados por bolas de colores) a través de la red, concentrándolos en unos cuantos canales de transmisión digital. Los mensajes de paquetes se dividen en grupos más pequeños, que se envían y encaminan luego individualmente por la red. El proceso de encaminamiento y transferencia de datos por paquetes permite ocupar sólo un canal durante la transmisión. Esta técnica se utiliza sobre todo para transmitir grandes volúmenes de datos.

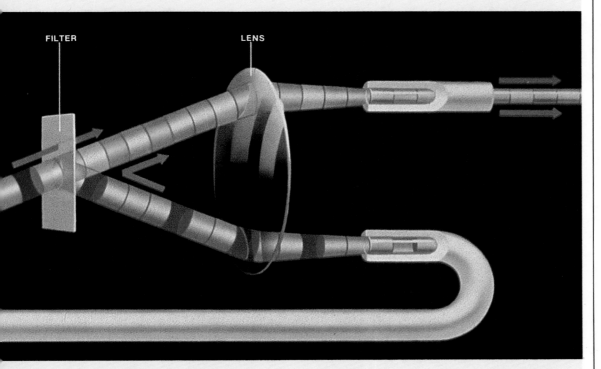

FILTER   LENS

multiplexeur optique ci-dessus développé par Bell Laborato-s, envoie deux signaux, ou plus, le long d'une seule fibre de re par un système de lentilles et de filtres. Cette méthode gmente la capacité des fibres optiques en envoyant plusieurs gueurs d'ondes (couleurs) sur chaque fibre. Des techniques fectionnées récemment rendent possible le transport de elques 2600 signaux simultanément sur une paire de fibres, atre fois plus que les systèmes antérieurs. Ces nouveaux stèmes utilisent des sources de lumière (chacune avec sa pre source et son détecteur) opérant à 90 millions d'impul-ns par seconde, deux fois plus vite qu'auparavant.

El multiplexador óptico, de Bell Laboratories, permite enviar dos o más señales por una fibra de vidrio, mediante un sistema de lentes y un filtro. Este método aumenta sustancialmente la capacidad de transmisión de fibras de vidrio, enviando varias longitudes de onda (colores) por cada fibra: las técnicas desa-rrolladas hace poco permiten transmitir unos 2600 mensajes o señales de datos simultáneamente por un par de fibras, cuatro veces más que los sistemas anteriores. Los modernos utilizan fuentes luminosas (cada longitud de onda debe tener su fuente luminosa y detector propios), operando a 90 millones de im-pulsos por segundo, duplicando así la velocidad.

MAS), que cuadruplica la capacidad de los disposi-tivos anteriores. Una fina pastilla, menor de 1,7×0,8 cm, contiene más de medio millón de componentes, con capacidad para almacenar 262 144 bits de infor-mación, equivalente a unas 16 páginas de un libro. Una técnica de activación por láser controlada por computador permite sustituir los elementos defec-tuosos por otros, mejorando mucho la producción.

El diseño y la presentación del microprocesador de 32 bits se logró técnicas de diseño asistido por computador (DAC), sin lo que seguramente no podría haberse hecho. Para dar una idea de su com-plejidad, si cada transistor fuera una casa, y las líneas de conexión carreteras, el diseño de la plaqueta co-rrespondería a la presentación de una ciudad de 100 km, con 300 000 habitantes y 8000 km de carreteras. El soporte lógico de los instrumentos DAC utilizados en el diseño contenían 600 000 líneas de código. A medida que el diseño de la plaqueta se hace más amplio, más complejo y especializado, la clave del progreso es DAC.

Para 1985, el Organismo de Proyectos de Investi-gación Avanzada del Departamento de Defensa de EE.UU. espera producir plaquetas con un millón de puertas lógicas, con una separación entre elementos de sólo 0,5 micrones (0,0005 mm). Esto se llama circuito integrado a muy gran velocidad (VHSIC). En esa electrónica se trabajará a nivel molecular, moviéndose los electrones casi a la velocidad de la luz.

La fotónica — el uso de la luz para transmitir infor-mación — ha dado grandes pasos en los últimos años. En 1981, American Telegraph and Telephone (AT&T) anunció que « los sistemas de ondas lumi-nosas son un verdadero éxito », y que el uso de fibras ópticas para transmitir información había pasado con sorpendente rapidez de la investigación al des-pliegue, a través del desarrollo, « ante la esperanza de mayor anchura de banda y menor costo ».

La moderna tecnología de fibras ópticas tiene sus orígenes en la investigación de las ondas guiadas de los años 1920 de G.C. Southworth y otros. El primer resulta-do fue el cable coaxial en 1928, seguido de guiaondas prácticos: tubos huecos que guiaban radiación elec-tromagnética. La investigación de la física de estado sólido produjo diseños de relojes "atómicos" de gran precisión, que llevaron a su vez a la construcción del primer MÁSER (Microwave Amplification by Sti-mulated Emission of Radiation), en 1954. El máser produjo microondas coherentes que utilizan un efecto cuántico, según predijeron físicos soviéticos ya en 1939. La investigación del máser se dirigió hacia la óptica, y en 1960, se obtuvo el primer LÁSER (Light Amplification by Stimulated Emission of Ra-diation), con las mismas bases teóricas.

El significado del desarrollo de la fotónica en los sistemas de telecomunicación fue subrayado por el Dr. Charles K. Kao, uno de los grandes científicos de la International Telephone and Telegraph (ITT) y pionero en fibras ópticas, en los siguientes términos: « Se han logrado las condiciones para enriquecer la vida como las que siguieron a la invención del motor de vapor, la bombilla y el transistor ».

En los sistemas de fibras ópticas, los únicos componentes son la fuente luminosa, la fibra óptica, el detector de la luz y los conectores y acopladores necesarios para agrupar esos elementos. La señal luminosa se mo-dula o imprime con información utilizando equipo electrónico para excitar la fuente de luz. En un ex-tremo del sistema está el codificador, que convierte las señales vocales analógicas en digitales, y un emi-sor de fuente luminosa que convierte los impulsos eléctricos en impulsos de energía luminosa. Las fi-bras ópticas proporcionan una guía o "arteria" que sigue la energía luminosa, incluso en los codos. En el otro extremo se encuentra un detector óptico que convierte los impulsos luminosos de nuevo en eléc-tricos y el descodificador, que convierte los impulsos eléctricos de nuevo en analógicos (véase recuadro, pág. 124).

Las fuentes luminosas para la transmisión de fi-bras ópticas son de dos clases, ambas basadas en la tecnología de semiconductores: el diodo fotoemisor

▷ 109

of semiconductor material which emit light when a small electrical charge causes the material to give off energy in the form of photons. These are amplified within the laser and emerge as a coherent beam of high intensity light of extremely narrow spectral width.

Lasers produce what scientists call *coherent light* i.e. light waves that all have the same wavelength, are in phase and can be sharply focussed to travel in the same direction over long distances with practically no loss of power. For example, a laser beam aimed at the moon almost 250,000 miles away puts a circle of light less than two miles wide on the moon's surface. Were it possible to project a searchlight beam that far, it would spread out to several times the moon's 2,160 mile diameter.

Optical communication technology's most attractive attributes are freedom from electrical interference, from ground isolation problems, lightness and, above all, low cost. The weight and space savings of glass fiber cables are considerable: for example, 200 reels of copper wire weigh 1,600 pounds; a single spool of optical fiber, having the same message-carrying potential, weighs only 4.4 pounds. The carrying capacity of optical cable can only be described as enormous: Bell Laboratories have recently developed a wavelength multiplexing technique (See Box p. 106) that could ultimately put 300,000 calls on 144 glass fibers in a cable no ticker than a finger. Wavelength multiplexing, which puts two or more wavelengths (colours) of light on a fiber, multiplies its capacity by the number of wavelengths. Advances in the technology are now very rapid. It is expected, for example, that the present standard rate of 45 million pulses per second will eventually be doubled, enabling each wavelength multiplied pair of fibers to carry some 2,600 different messages or data signals, four times the capacity of most current systems.

Today's problems relate mainly to the need to improve the consistency of performance and reliability of the ancillary devices needed to make an optical communications system — the connectors, repeaters, modulators, transmitters, receivers, and the like. The rapid progress being made and the weight of R&D resources deployed in the laboratories of the leading producers suggest, however, that any gating factors remaining today will soon be removed. The CCITT has initiated a full program of technical appraisal and review, much of which has been completed, to serve as a basis for the definition and adoption of optical fiber standards, including tolerances and test methods.

The technological trends are clearly towards integration and speed of communication through the spread of digitalization: greater bandwidths enabling the inclusion of voice, data and image in an integrated communications system; the linkage of services into systems within local installations and between them over distance; conversion from analog switching and transmission to digital in order to speed up information flow and permit distributed data processing. Associated with these trends are the reducing costs of practically all equipment and the consequent expansion of the market for what might be termed "information hardware".

Underlying these trends, and a *sine qua non* of their being attained, is the development of appropriate software. This, and the problems associated with its production and use, is the theme developed in "Deep Involvement of Man in Systems Through Software", p. 318.

Outstanding among innovators in the communications industry is Siemens AG, who ranks third in the world as manufacturer of telecommunications equipment. The company profile which follows illustrates the considerable progress that is being made in electronics engineering, especially in the application of digital switching and optical cable transmission. It also demonstrates how much can be achieved by the effective transfer of the latest technologies to the developing world.

Le laser produit ce que les savants appellent la *lumière cohérente*, c'est-à-dire des ondes lumineuses en phase ayant toutes la même longueur d'onde, très focalisées et se propageant dans la même direction sur de longues distances, pratiquement sans aucune perte d'énergie. Un faisceau de laser dirigé sur la Lune, distante de 384 000 km, se présente sur la surface de celle-ci comme un cercle lumineux de moins de trois kilomètres de diamètre, alors qu'un faisceau lumineux s'étendrait théoriquement sur une largeur égale à plusieurs fois le diamètre de la Lune qui mesure 3500 km environ.

La technologie des communications optiques présente des avantages très attrayants : son utilisation n'est pas sujette aux perturbations électriques et ne pose aucun problème d'isolation par rapport au sol et, par dessus tout, son prix de revient est modique. Les économies de poids et d'encombrement des câbles en fibre optique sont considérables. Par exemple, 200 bobines de fil de cuivre pèsent 800 kg, tandis qu'une seule bobine de fibre optique ayant la même capacité d'écoulement de messages ne pèse que 2,2 kg. Cette capacité est véritablement colossale. Les Bell Laboratories ont récemment mis au point une technique de multiplexage en longueur d'onde permettant d'écouler jusqu'à 300 000 communications par 144 fibres de verre contenues dans un câble de la grosseur d'un doigt. Le multiplexage (voir p. 106) en longueur d'onde permet de multiplier la capacité d'une fibre par le nombre de longueurs d'onde utilisées. Il est prévu que la rapidité de modulation normale, qui est actuellement de 45 millions d'impulsions par seconde pourra être doublée. Ainsi, pour chaque paire en fibre optique, la multiplication par le nombre de longueurs d'onde utilisées fera passer à 2600 le nombre des messages ou des signaux de données soit 4 fois la capacité de la plupart des systèmes actuels.

Aujourd'hui, les problèmes consistent avant tout à améliorer la cohérence en ce qui concerne la performance et la fiabilité de tous les dispositifs auxiliaires nécessaires pour fabriquer un système de communications optique : connecteurs, répéteurs, modulateurs, émetteurs, récepteurs, etc. La rapidité des progrès accomplis et l'importance des ressources consacrées à la recherche et au développement dans les laboratoires des grands constructeurs font toutefois penser que toutes les entraves subsistant aujourd'hui seront bientôt éliminées. Le CCITT a déjà entrepris un programme complet d'évaluations et d'études techniques qui permettra de définir et d'adopter les normes des fibres optiques.

L'orientation des nouvelles technologies se fait nettement vers l'intégration et la rapidité des communications, par une généralisation de la méthode numérique : extension des largeurs de bande permettant l'inclusion du son, des données et de l'image dans un système de communications intégré : interconnexion des services entre eux, à distance, et avec des systèmes d'installation locales ; conversion de la commutation et de la transmission, du mode analogique au mode numérique, afin d'accélérer le flux de l'information et de faciliter le télétraitement des données.

L'intégration qui se produit aujourd'hui au niveau des systèmes et des méthodes de communication résulte des grands bouleversements technologiques dont nous sommes les témoins. Il existe actuellement une nette tendance à inclure l'intelligence électronique dans la plupart des installations de télécommunications et à favoriser la prolifération de fonctions et de services de communication supplémentaires, toujours moins chers et plus faciles à comprendre. Cette question et les problèmes liés à la production et à l'utilisation du logiciel sont traités à la page 318.

Au premier rang des innovateurs dans l'industrie de la communication se trouve Siemens AG, troisième constructeur mondial d'équipements de télécommunications. La présentation du profil de Siemens, illustre également le progrès considérable de l'industrie électronique, particulièrement en commutation numérique et en transmission par câble optique. Elle montre, aussi, l'énorme contribution que représente un transfert de technologie efficace pour le développement des télécommunications dans le tiers monde.

SOURCE OF MODE

Research Area
Radar and Air Defense
Cybernetics and Cryptology
Nuclear Energy
Rocketry

The military requirements of the second world war gave a major impetus to the development of electronics. The technology was finally accepted as the basic infrastructure of telecommunications after a century and a half of hesitant progress. The pattern of innovation and development is shown here. Solid-state devices, micronics, digital switching, all had their source in the huge research programs financed by the war efforts.

POTENTIAL FO

Future Large-Scale Research Programs Research Area
Energy
Automotive Electronics
Defense
Health
Food Production

The potential for continued radical technological advances in the 80s and 90s remains high. Large scale research programs are in progress in most industrialized countries and some of the possible effects are listed in this figure. Energy saving, defence, and fundamental advances in microelectronics may ultimately provide a basis for a totally new concept of telecommunications.

TELECOMMUNICATIONS TECHNOLOGY

Technology

Solid-state devices Printed circuits Accurate pulse modulators Video terminals Electronic memories	Data transmission Microwave relays Information Theory Masers Lasers	Modems Stored-program computer High-speed computers Distributed data processing
Stored-program computer Real-time computation Error-correcting codes	Boolean logic gates Mass storage High-speed CPUs	Solid-state computers Data-on-voice circuits Core memory
Semiconductors	Machine computation	

Communications satellites
Data communications (high-speed data acquisition and reduction techniques).

exigences militaires de la deuxième guerre mondiale ont né une forte impulsion au développement de l'électronique, fut acceptée comme infrastructure de base par l'industrie télécommunications après un siècle et demi d'une prossion hésitante. Ci-dessus : la séquence d'innovations et de eloppements. Les transistors, la miniaturisation, la mutation numérique, sont tous sortis des immenses prommes de recherche et de développement financés par l'ef- de guerre.

Las electrónica se desarrolló enormemente debido a la exigencias militares de la Segunda Guerra Mundial. La tecnología fue aceptada como estructura básica de las telecomunicaciones, tras siglo y medio de progreso vacilante. Aquí se muestra el ritmo de innovación y el desarrollo. Los transistores, la miniaturización y la conmutación digital se derivan de los enormes programas de investigación financiados por los esfuerzos bélicos.

RADICAL TECHNOLOGICAL CHANGE

Umbrella effect

Transducers Microwave solar satellites Control systems	Logistics Mobile communications Plasma and subatomic physics	Geophysical resource management Giant computers Distributed intelligence
Low-cost, ultrareliable microelectronics Low-cost displays	Fiber optics Modular integrated optics	

High-energy physics lasers,
    particle beams
Giant array processors
Space laser communications
	Space platforms
	High-vacuum manufacturing
	Super conductive memories
	VHSIC: integrated optics
	    sensing and imaging
		Robotics; pattern recognition
		Photoelectricity

File management Data banks	Instrumentation; telemetering Robotics	

Molecular biophysics; organic computers; bionics; robotics
Inventory control - Resource management

Source: ITT

possibilités d'avances fondamentales dans la technologie communications dans les prochaines années restent sidérables. D'ambitieux programmes de recherche sont en rs dans la plupart des pays industrialisés et quelques effets sibles sont énumérés ici : économies d'énergie, besoins taires, ainsi que des avances fondamentales dans les techues microélectroniques qui pourraient éventuellement pro- re un concept de télécommunications entièrement neuf.

Sigue habiendo grandes posibilidades de avances tecnológicos radicales en los años 80 y 90. En la mayoría de los países industrializados están en marcha grandes programas de investigación, y en esta figura se enumeran algunos de sus posibles efectos: economías de energía, defensa y avances fundamentales en la microelectrónica pueden servir de base de una noción de telecomunicaciones totalmente nueva.

(LED) y el diodo láser. Los LED empleados en fibras ópticas son análogos a los usados en la visualización de calculadoras o relojes de bolsillo. El diodo láser semiconductor consiste en varias capas de material que emite luz al desprender energía en forma de fotones, debido a una pequeña carga eléctrica. Esto se amplifica en el láser y surge como un haz coherente luminoso de gran intensidad, con una anchura espectral limitadísima.

El láser produce *luz coherente*, es decir, ondas luminosas, todas de la misma longitud de onda, situadas en fase, y que pueden centralizarse para viajar en la misma dirección a larga distancia casi sin pérdida de energía. Por ejemplo, un haz láser dirigido hacia la Luna, a 384 000 km de distancia, representa un círculo luminoso de menos de tres km de anchura en la superficie de la Luna. Si fuera posible llevar hasta allí el haz de un proyector, se extendería varias veces el diámetro de la Luna: 3500 km.

A la tecnología de comunicaciones ópticas se le confieren atributos más importantes como la exención de interferencia eléctrica, de problemas de aislamiento a tierra, la ligereza y, sobre todo, su bajo costo. Las economías de peso y espacio de los cables de fibra de vidrio son considerables: por ejemplo, 200 carretes de hilo de cobre pesan 800 kg: una sola bobina de fibra óptica, con las mismas posibilidades de mensajes, pesa sólo 2,2 kg. La capacidad de transmisión del cable óptico es enorme. Bell Laboratories ha desarrollado una técnica de multiplexación de longitud de onda que puede transmitir hasta 300 000 llamadas por 144 fibras de vidrio en un cable del grosor de un dedo. La multiplexación (véase recuadro, pág. 106) de longitud de onda, con dos o más longitudes de onda (colores) de luz en una fibra, multiplica su capacidad por el número de longitudes de onda. Los avances son ahora rapidísimos. Por ejemplo, la tasa normal actual de 45 millones de impulsos por segundo acabará duplicándose, con lo que por cada par de fibras multiplicado de longitud de onda pasarán 2600 mensajes o señales de datos diferentes, cuatro veces la capacidad de los sistemas más corrientes.

Los problemas consisten ahora, sobre todo, en mejorar la coherencia de rendimiento y fiabilidad de los dispositivos auxiliares necesarios para un sistema de comunicaciones ópticas: conectores, repetidores, modulares, transmisores, receptores, etc. El rápido avance y la importancia de los recursos de IyD usados en los laboratorios de los principales productores indican, empero, que todos los factores de contención subsistentes se suprimirán en breve. El CCITT ha emprendido un programa completo de evaluacion y examen técnico, en gran parte terminado, que servirá de base para la definición y adopción de normas de fibras ópticas, incluidas las tolerancias y los métodos de prueba.

La tecnología tiende a la integración y mayor velocidad de las comunicaciones, al generalizarse la digitalización: mayores anchuras de banda que permiten incluir voz, datos e imágenes en un sistema de comunicaciones integrado; la vinculación de servicios en sistemas de instalaciones locales y entre sí a distancia; la conversión de la conmutación y transmisión analógica en digital, para acelerar los flujos de información y permitir el proceso de distribución de datos. Estan tendencias conllevan la reducción de costos de casi todo el equipo, y la expansión consiguiente del mercado para lo que puede calificarse de "soporte físico de la información".

La base de esas tendencias, y una condición sine qua non de su cristalización, es el desarrollo de soporte lógico apropiado. Esto, y los problemas asociados a su producción y empleo, constituyen el tema desarrollado en la pág. 318.

Entre los grandes innovadores de la industria de comunicaciones figura Siemens AG, el tercer fabricante de equipo del mundo. El perfil de la empresa que sigue muestra sus grandes progresos en ingeniería electrónica, sobre todo en la aplicación de conmutación digital y transmisión por cables ópticos. También muestra lo que puede lograrse con la transferencia eficaz de la última tecnología al mundo en desarrollo.

109

SIEMENS

Siemens AG Communications Group

A World Leader in Communications

THE LEADING POSITION OF SIEMENS AG is based on its ability to convert technical innovation into future-oriented projects of nation-wide importance, drawing upon a wide range of electrical and electronic products and systems of its own design and manufacture. Its artistry lies in the economical and effective interfacing of the latest technology with existing methods in line with the particular problems, resources and needs of the country or organization concerned. Such expertise, global in its spread and application, is basic to the successful development of telecommunications infrastructures and to the supply, installation and maintenance of communications equipment. Complete systems and installations are the company's strong point, which explains why more than half its total sales are outside Siemens' home country, the Federal Republic of Germany.

Five principal factors contribute to Siemens' eminence in the world of communications:
— a broad spectrum of products, ranging from telephone instruments to mainframe computers, from components to complex automatic equipment, from fractional-horsepower electric motors to complete power stations;
— a major investment in research and development, one of the largest in the world of private enterprise;
— a large home market, receptive to new ideas;
— a geographic spread involving ongoing operations in 128 countries (including manufacturing and R&D facilities in many of them);
— broadly based (both technically and geographically) project planning and advisory services; facilities for instruction and training; and financial advisory services, maintaining close contact with finance houses, banks and the world capital market.

▷ 112

Receiver module used to convert the light back into electrical signals in the optical fiber waveguide cable system developed by Siemens AG.

L'ÉMINENTE POSITION DE SIEMENS AG dans l'industrie de la communication est due à sa capacité de conversion de l'innovation technologique en projets de pointe d'importance nationale, puisant dans une vaste gamme de produits et de systèmes électriques et électroniques de sa propre conception. Sa compétence consiste à établir une interface entre la technologie de pointe et les méthodes courantes, qui correspond aux problèmes, ressources et besoins particuliers du pays ou de l'organisation concernée. Ce savoir-faire, appliqué globalement, est indispensable au bon développement des infrastructures et à la fourniture, installation et maintenance des équipements de communication. Le point fort de la compagnie est la conception et l'installation de systèmes intégrés, ce qui explique le fait que plus de la moitié de ses ventes sont réalisées hors de la République Fédérale d'Allemagne.

Cinq principaux facteurs ont contribué à faire de Siemens l'un des premiers constructeurs de matériels de communications dans le monde :
— une vaste gamme de produits, qui s'étend des appareils téléphoniques jusqu'aux ordinateurs centraux, des simples composants aux centrales électriques les plus complexes ;
— un investissement considérable en recherche et développement, parmi les plus ambitieux dans le monde de l'industrie privée ;
— un grand marché national, ouvert aux idées nouvelles ;
— un expansion géographique de ses activités qui s'étend à 128 pays (avec des usines et des laboratoires de recherche dans plusieurs d'entre eux) ;
— une gamme très étendue, aussi bien sur le plan technique que géographique, de services d'études pour la conception et la planification de projets ;
— des centres d'instruction et de formation, ainsi que des services financiers qui sont en étroites relations avec diverses sources de financement.

▷ 112

Module de récepteur pour reconvertir un rayon lumineux en signaux électriques dans un système de câbles optiques, mis au point par Siemens AG.

LA POSICIÓN DE VANGUARDIA DE SIEMENS AG se basa en su capacidad para convertir la innovación técnica en proyectos de importancia nacional orientados hacia el futuro, con una amplia gama de productos y sistemas eléctricos y electrónicos de diseño y fabricación propios. Su arte reside en vincular en forma económica y eficaz la última tecnología con métodos existentes, de acuerdo con los problemas, recursos y necesidades peculiares del país u organización de que se trate. Tal pericia, de extensión y aplicación global, es fundamental para desarrollar con éxito infraestructuras de telecomunicaciones y para el suministro, instalación y mantenimiento de equipo de comunicación. El punto fuerte de la empresa son sistemas e instalaciones completos, lo que explica por qué más de la mitad de sus ventas totales no se realizan en el país sede de Siemens, la República Federal de Alemania.

Siemens sobresale en el mundo de las comunicaciónes debido a cinco factores principales:
— una amplia gama de productos, que van de aparatos telefónicos a computadores centrales, de componentes a equipo automático complejo, y de motores eléctricos de poca potencia a estaciones de energía completas;
— importantes inversiones en investigación y desarrollo: entre las mayores de las empresas privadas del mundo;
— un vasto mercado nacional, receptivo a nuevas ideas;
— una extensión geográfica que abarca operaciones progresivas en 128 países (incluidas las instalaciones de fabricación y de IyD en muchos de ellos);
— servicios consultivos y de planificación de proyectos muy amplios (tanto técnica como geográficamente); centros de instrucción y capacitación, y servicios consultivos financieros, que mantienen es-

▷ 113

Módulo de receptor para convertir un rayo luminoso en señales eléctricas en el sistema de cables de guiaondas de fibras ópticas, desarrollado por Siemens AG.

110

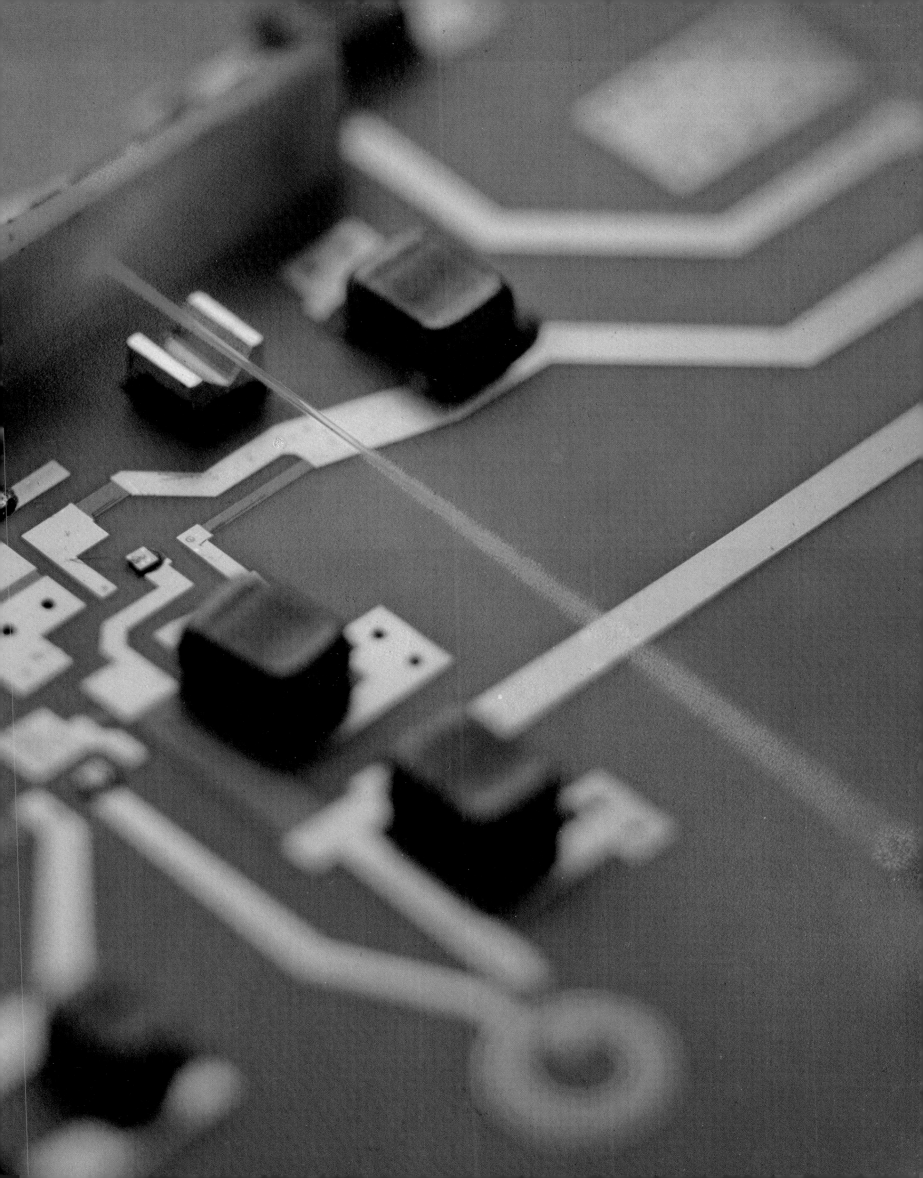

The widespread and intensive electrical and electronic engineering activities of Siemens AG — sales in 1982 totalled DM 40.1 billion (ca. US$ 16.5 billion) — spur innovation and support growth in innumerable ways.

The company is one of the world's leading manufacturers of electric and electronic equipment and systems. It maintains production facilities, subsidiaries, liaison offices, local sales offices and agencies in 128 countries and employs 324,000 people worldwide. It is structured in six Groups, each Group being responsible for the business it conducts throughout the world.

Three of the Company's six Groups — Communications, Components and Data Systems (together accounting for 36 percent of total sales in 1982) — are deeply involved in communications engineering and both their development and manufacturing activities are largely dependent on electronic technology, with special emphasis on microminiaturization and digitalization.

The Components Group (UB B) with sales of DM 1.7 billion (ca. $ 700 million) in 1982, produces integrated circuits, discrete semiconductors, passive components and electron tubes.

The Data Systems Group (UB D) which produces teleprocessing systems, mainframe computers and system and application software, had sales of DM 2 billion (ca. $ 823 million) in 1982.

In the Power Engineering and Automation (UB E), Electrical Installations (UB I) and Medical Engineering (UB Med) Groups too, electronics has become increasingly important.

The Siemens Communications Group (UB K), the largest in the company, accounted for 28% of total sales in 1982, a total of DM 11.3 billion (ca. $ 4.6 billion), the industry's third largest in the world and by far the largest in Europe. Its activities include the production and installation of public, private and special purpose communications networks, communications terminals and a range of safety/security systems.

The Group develops, designs, manufactures, installs, and provides maintenance services for a range of systems and products which extends from individual devices, such as telephone subscriber equipment, to complete networks. The Group ranks among the few manufacturers who combine the three "C" technologies (Communications, Computers, Components) under one roof — technologies which will shape the course of future developments.

Siemens' mastery of the most advanced digital technology, its ability to manufacture the components and products required and its experience in the design and engineering of the most complex systems of communications into which they all fit combine to strongly substantiate the company's claim of being a world leader in the construction of communications systems.

Siemens' comprehensive range of systems and services provides a broad base for communications projects of all types, as follows:

Public switching systems: digital telephone switching systems; analog telephone switching systems; operating and maintenance systems for telephone switching systems; text and data switching systems.

Transmission networks: analog and digital multiplex equipment; analog and digital line transmission systems; analog and digital radio relay systems; satellite earth stations; mobile radio systems; local and long-haul copper and optical waveguide cables; telecommunication cable accessories; wideband communication systems; receiving antennas.

Private and special purpose communication networks: communication system EMS for telephony, analog and digital, with unlimited scope for expansion; EMS 2000 INFO voice information system; EMS 5800 Document for communication and information processing via bus networks; EMS 3000 DATA for integration of data processing systems; EMS 1000 TEXT for text communication; special

▷ 116

Les activités d'ingénierie de Siemens dans les domaines de l'électricité et de l'électronique (un C.A. de plus de 40 milliards de DM, 16,5 milliards de dollars en 1982) stimulent l'innovation et la croissance dans d'innombrables directions.

Siemens est maintenant un des principaux constructeurs mondiaux d'équipements et de systèmes électriques et électroniques. Siemens possède des usines, des succursales, des bureaux de liaison, des bureaux de vente et des agences dans 128 pays, et emploie 324 000 personnes dans le monde entier (1983). La société est structurée en six Divisions, chacune étant entièrement responsable de ses propres activités. Trois d'entre elles, les Divisions de Communications, de Composants et d'Informatique, représentent 36 pour cent du chiffre d'affaires de Siemens AG (1982), et sont profondément impliquées dans l'ingénierie des communications. Elles englobent le développement de composants et de systèmes.

La Division Composants (UB B), (C.A. de 1,7 milliard de DM 700 millions de dollars en 1982 ou 4% du total Siemens) produit des circuits intégrés, des semiconducteurs discrets, des composants passifs et des tubes à électrons.

La Division Informatique (UB D) (C.A. de 2 milliards de DM 823 millions de dollars en 1982 ou 5% des ventes Siemens) fabrique des systèmes de télétraitement et de gros ordinateurs ainsi que des programmes de logiciel.

Pour les Divisions Energie et Automatisation (UB E), Installations Techniques (UB I), et Médicale (UB Med), l'électronique est devenue de plus en plus importante.

La Division Communication UB K (C.A. de 11,3 milliards de DM, 4,6 milliards de dollars, ou 28% des ventes Siemens en 1982), se place au troisième rang de l'industrie mondiale et est le plus grand constructeur d'Europe. Ses activités comprennent la production et l'installation de réseaux de communication de tous types ainsi que de systèmes de sécurité. Elle développe, conçoit, fabrique, installe et fournit des services de maintenance pour toute une gamme de systèmes et de produits. Depuis le combiné téléphonique jusqu'au réseau complet. Le groupe est un des rares constructeurs qui exploite les trois technologies « C » (Communications, Computers and Components) qui détermineront les futurs développements dans les communications.

Siemens propose une gamme exhaustive de produits et de services. offrant ainsi une large base à toutes les activités de communication :

Systèmes de commutation publics : systèmes de commutation téléphonique analogiques et numériques ; systèmes permettant d'automatiser l'exploitation et la maintenance des autocommutateurs ; systèmes de commutation de textes et de données pour centraux de grande, moyenne et petite capacité.

Réseaux de transmission : matériels de multiplexage analogique et numérique ; systèmes analogiques et numériques de transmission par câbles ; systèmes hertziens analogiques et numériques ; stations terriennes pour satellites ; équipements radiotéléphoniques mobiles ; câbles en cuivre et conducteurs optiques pour réseaux urbains et interurbains, publics et privés ; accessoires pour câbles de télécommunication ; réseaux en large bande ; antennes réceptrices.

Réseaux de communication privés et spécialisés : systèmes analogiques et numériques de communication EMS (téléphonie), aux possibilités d'extension illimitées ; systèmes de messageries en phonie EMS 2000 Info ; EMS 5800 Document, pour la transmission de documents et de données par des réseaux locaux ; EMS 3000 DATA, destiné à la connexion avec un système informatique ; EMS 1000 TEXT, pour la communication de textes ; réseaux spécialisés destinés aux chemins de fer, à la police, aux entreprises de production et de distribution d'énergie, et à la défense du territoire notamment.

▷ 116

Partial view of the earth station at Raisting in Upper Bavaria, the world's largest (1983), showing two of the five antenna systems. Siemens was the general contractor.

Une vue partielle de la plus grande station terrienne du monde, à Raisting en Haute Bavière, montrant deux des cinq antennes du système. Siemens était maître d'œuvre.

trecho contacto con sociedades financieras, bancos y el mercado mundial de capitales.

La difusión y las intensas actividades eléctricas y electrónicas de Siemens AG — en 1982, las ventas totalizaron 40 106 millones DM (16 505 millones $ EE.UU.) — impulsan la innovación y apoyan el crecimiento en muchas formas.

La empresa es uno de los principales fabricantes del mundo de equipo y sistemas eléctricos y electrónicos. Mantiene instalaciones de producción, filiales, oficinas de enlace y agencias de venta locales en 128 países, y emplea a 324 000 personas en el mundo entero. Está estructurada en seis grupos, cada uno de ellos responsable de sus operaciones mundiales desarrollo, producción y comercialización.

Tres de los seis grupos de la empresa — comunicaciones, componentes e informática (que representaron, juntos, el 36% de las ventas totales en 1982) — están muy arraigados en la ingeniería de las comunicaciones, y sus actividades de desarrollo e investigación dependen en gran parte de la tecnología electrónica, insistiendo especialmente en la microminiaturización y la digitalización.

El grupo Componentes (UB B). con unas ventas de 1700 millones DM (700 millones $) en 1982, produce circuitos integrados, semiconductores discretos, componentes pasivos y tubos electrónicos. Representa alrededor del 4% de las ventas totales.

El grupo Informática (UB D). que produce sistemas de teleprocesamiento y grandes computadores centrales, así como soporte lógico, vendió en 1982 por valor de 2000 millones DM (823 millones $).

En los grupos de ingeniería energética y automatización (UB E), instalaciones eléctricas (UB I) e ingeniería médica (UB Med), la electrónica tiene también cada vez más importancia.

El grupo Comunicaciones (UB K). el mayor de la empresa, representó en 1982 el 28% de las ventas totales, que ascendieron a 11 300 millones DM (4600 millones $); ocupa el tercer lugar de la industria en el mundo, y es con mucho el mayor de Europa. Sus actividades comprenden la producción e instalación de redes de comunicaciones públicas y privadas para fines especiales, terminales de comunicaciones y una gama de sistemas de seguridad.

El grupo de comunicaciones desarrolla, diseña, fabrica, instala y presta servicios de mantenimiento para una gama de sistemas y productos que se extienden desde dispositivos individuales, como equipo de abonado telefónico, hasta redes completas. Figura entre los pocos fabricantes que combinan las tres tecnologías « C » (comunicaciones, computadores y componentes), tecnologías que configurarán el curso de la futura evolución de las comunicaciones.

El amplio espectro de sistemas y servicios ofrecidos por Siemens proporciona una base firme para todo tipo de proyectos de comunicaciones:

Sistemas públicos de conmutación: sistemas telefónicos digitales y analógicos; sistemas de operación y mantenimiento para centrales telefónicas; sistemas de conmutación de textos y datos para centrales de gran capacidad y datos para centrales de capacidad pequeña a mediana.

Redes de transmisión: equipos múltiplex analógicos y digitales; sistemas de transmisión por linea analógicos y digitales; sistemas de radioenlace analógicos y digitales; estaciones terrenas; sistemas de radio móviles; cables guiaondas de cobre y de fibra óptica, locales y de larga distancia, para redes públicas y privadas; accesorios para cables de telecomunicaciones; sistemas de comunicaciones de banda ancha; antenas receptoras.

Redes privadas y especiales de comunicación: sistema de comunicación EMS para telefonía, analógico y digital, con margen ilimitado de ampliación; sistema de información vocal EMS 2000 INFO; EMS 5800 Document para procesamiento de comunicación y de información por redes comunes; EMS 3000 DATA para integración de sistemas de proceso de datos; EMS 1000 TEXT para comunicación de tex-

▷ 117

Una vista parcial de la estación terrena mayor del mundo, instalada en Raisting, Alta Baviera, en la que pueden verse dos de los cinco sistemas de antenas. El contratista general fue Siemens.

*The microchip, shown above,
—in its actual size (5 mm) — is one of the
highly-integrated components manufactured
cost-efficiently in large series production by Siemens.
These are key elements in the continuing development
of communications technology.*

*Le microprocesseur — montré ci-dessus en
grandeur réelle (5 mm) — est un des composants à
très grande intégration qui sont fabriqués
économiquement en grandes séries par Siemens.
Ce sont des éléments-clé dans le développement
de la technologie des communications.*

*El microprocesador presentado aquí en tamaño
natural (5 mm) es uno de los componentes
sumamente integrados fabricados en grandes series
por Siemens AG. Se trata de elementos
fundamentales para el desarrollo continuo
de la tecnología de las comunicaciones.*

114

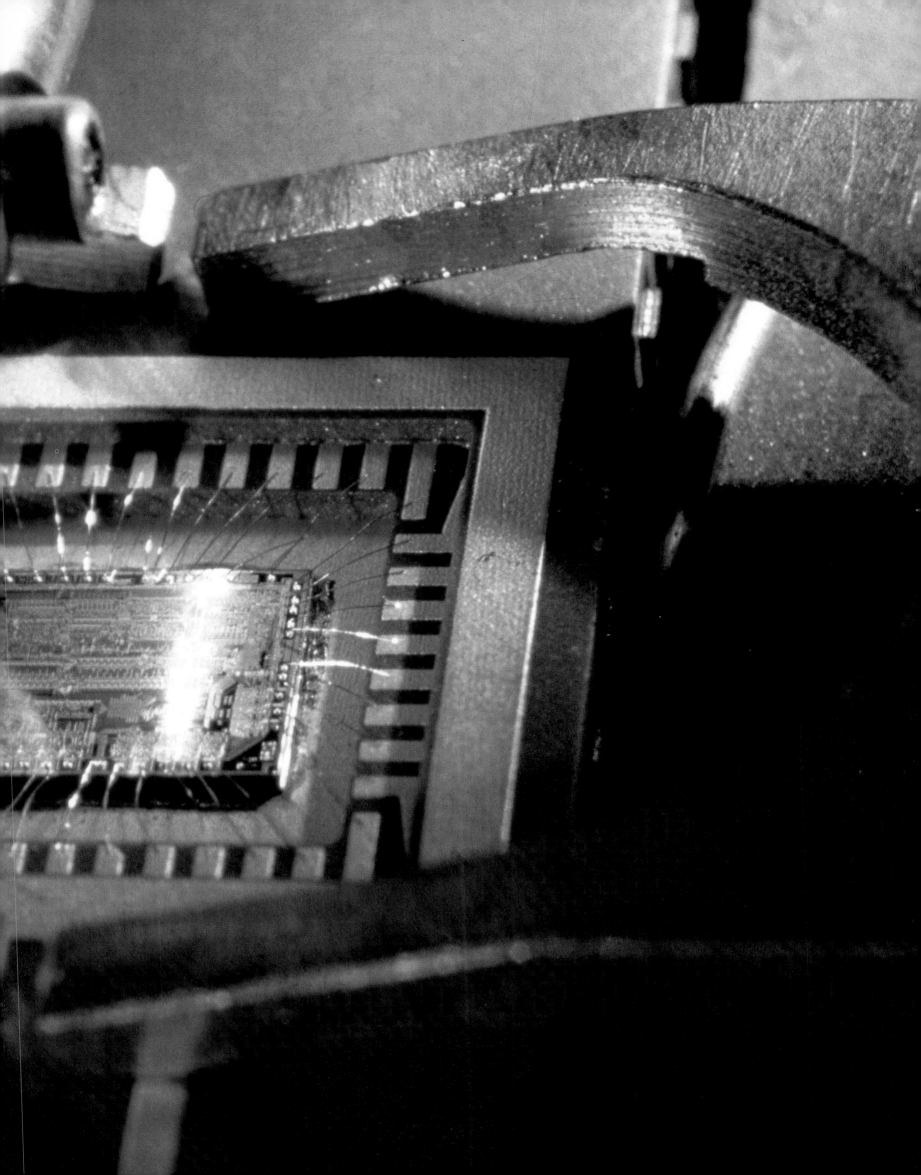

networks e.g. for railways, police, utilities, national defence.

Communication terminals: telephones in all convenient classes; facsimile equipment; interactive videotex terminals; teleprinters; teletex stations; word processing and workstation systems; printer systems.

Safety and Securing systems: operation controls; danger alarms; intrusion protection; fire protection; gas detection; railway signalling; traffic engineering; radio and radar systems.

Research and Development - powerful and innovative. Corporate management is characterized by "a positive attitude toward innovation", the declared aim of company policy being "always to keep ahead in the development of new processes and technologies in order to cope with the rapid progress in the technical world and the accompanying radical changes".

Investment in research and development is immense and compares favorably with that of any of the world's leading companies. Some 30,000 employees are engaged worldwide on R&D projects.

Expenditure on R&D increased in 1982 despite a general slowdown in industrial activity. In that year research and development expenses amounted to DM 3.4 billion (ca. $ 1.4 billion) — 8% of total sales and one-ninth of the R&D expenditures by German industry as a whole. About one-tenth is used for work on basic research and know-how. The other nine-tenths is spent on converting the results into new or improved products, systems and facilities.

In the Communications Group alone, about 8,500 Siemens employees are involved in research and development. In the last fiscal year, the Communications Group spent a total of DM 1.4 billion (ca. $ 577 million) on research and development.

An increasing proportion of the research effort is being concentrated on future-oriented targets, most of them in the broad area of computer and communications technology. With the increasing use of microcomputers in all sectors of technology and the growing complexity of computers and related systems, the development of software is assuming paramount importance.

Another key area of research is microelectronics. Here work is being concentrated on architecture concepts and circuit engineering for very-large-scale-integrated (VLSI) semiconductor circuits. Memory chips with a storage capacity of 256 Kbits were being produced by Siemens in 1983. The progress being made in further miniaturization in the 1980s suggests that one chip containing a million bits will be in production by the end of the decade.

Siemens is "at home" worldwide, being actively represented, by highly qualified people on the company payroll, in 128 countries and its products manufactured in 28 of these. In addition, numerous joint ventures with local companies promote the transfer of technology to points of application and usage. Siemens broad geographical spread and its background of over 100 years operating experience abroad are vital factors militating for the company's competence in the design and installation of complete systems and also, of course, in the provision of maintenance facilities essential to the efficient operation of modern communications facilities.

In 1982 about 50,000 people were employed by the Communications Group. Siemens manufactures communications equipment and systems in 16 plants within the FRG and West-Berlin as well as in another 23 factories in Europe and overseas.

Project management — a key strength of Siemens. The Communications Group's principal activities abroad are centered in West European countries such as Austria, Switzerland, Belgium, the Scandinavian nations and Greece, as well as in overseas countries such as the USA, Egypt, Nigeria, South Africa, the Philippines, Australia and a number of countries in South and Central America. The emphasis placed by the "World Communications Year 1983" on the

▷ 120

Terminaux de communication : postes téléphoniques répondant à tous les besoins ; télécopieurs ; terminaux de vidéotex interactifs ; téléimprimeurs ; terminaux de télétex ; systèmes de traitement de textes ; terminaux informatiques ; bureauviseurs ; imprimantes.

Systèmes de sécurité : systèmes de conduite des interventions ; systèmes d'alarme ; systèmes de protection contre les intrusions ; systèmes de protection-incendie ; équipements de signalisation ferroviaire ; systèmes de contrôle et de régulation de la circulation ; systèmes radio et radars.

La recherche et le développement sont des éléments puissants et novateurs dans le progrès de Siemens. La direction générale affiche « une attitude positive envers l'innovation » avec l'objectif de « se tenir à la pointe du développement des nouveaux procédés et des nouvelles technologies afin d'être constamment an niveau du progrès technique et de faire face aux changements fondamentaux qui l'accompagnent ». Les investissements de Siemens dans la R&D sont d'un niveau comparable à celui des plus grandes firmes du monde. Trente mille personnes sont employées globalement dans les laboratoires. Les dépenses en 1982 (un montant de 3,4 milliards de DM 1,4 milliard de dollars US ou 8% du C.A. et 1/9ème des dépenses totales R&D de l'industrie de la RFA) ont augmenté malgré le ralentissement général de l'activité industrielle. Environ 10% est attribué à la recherche fondamentale et 90% à la conversion des résultats en produits, systèmes et installations.

Dans la seule Division Communications environ 8000 personnes sont employées dans les laboratoires. En 1982 la Division a dépensé 1400 millions de DM (577 millions de dollars).

Une proportion croissante de l'effort de recherche est concentrée sur des objectifs axés sur l'avenir, la plupart dans le secteur de la télématique. L'utilisation croissante de micro-ordinateurs et la complexité de plus en plus grande des ordinateurs et des matériels périphériques donnent une importance primordiale au développement du logiciel.

Un autre secteur-clé de la recherche est la micro-électronique. Les activités de Siemens se concentrent sur des concepts d'architecture et d'étude de circuits semiconducteurs à très grande échelle (VLSI). Des microprocesseurs de 256 Kbits étaient déjà fabriqués dans les usines Siemens en 1983. Les progrès réalisés en miniaturisation dans les années 1980 laissent prévoir qu'un microprocesseur d'une capacité d'un million de bits serait réalisé avant la fin de la décennie.

Siemens est « chez elle » dans le monde entier. Ses employés, hautement qualifiés, la représentent dans 128 pays et ses produits sont fabriqués dans un pays sur cinq. De nombreuses entreprises à risques partagés avec des compagnies locales facilitent le transfert de technologie sur les lieux d'application. La répartition géographique de Siemens et son expérience de plus d'un siècle d'activité à l'étranger sont des facteurs déterminants qui militent en faveur de la compétence en matière de conception et d'installation de systèmes complets ainsi que pour la fourniture de maintenance et de service après-vente.

La Division Communication emploie (1982) environ 50 000 personnes dans 16 usines en RFA et Berlin Ouest, ainsi que dans 23 usines en Europe et Outre-mer.

La gestion des projets : un atout essentiel de Siemens. Les activités principales de la Division Communications sont concentrées en Europe (Autriche - Suisse - Belgique, pays scandinaves et Grèce) et dans certains pays d'Outre-mer tels que les Etats-Unis, l'Egypte, le Nigéria, la République d'Afrique du Sud, les Philippines, l'Australie et quelques pays d'Amérique Latine.

L'accent qu'a placé « l'Année Mondiale des communications 1983 » sur l'importance de l'expansion des réseaux de télécommunications dans le Tiers Monde — une zone d'un intérêt tout à fait spécial

▷ 120

A picture of quartz fiber, as fine as human hair, which can be made up in any kind of cable to provide a transmission path for modulated light.

Fibres de verre, aussi fines qu'un cheveu, avec lesquelles on peut fabriquer toute sorte de câbles de transmission par rayons lumineux modulés.

tos; redes especiales, p.ej., para ferrocarriles, policía, servicios públicos, defensa nacional.

Terminales de comunicación: teléfonos de todo tipo de confort; equipos de facsímil; terminales de videotexto interactivo; teleimpresores; puestos de teletexto; sistemas de procesamiento de textos; terminales de datos; sistemas de puestos de trabajo; sistemas impresores.

Sistemas de seguridad: sistemas de control de operaciones; sistemas de alarma; sistemas anti-intrusión; sistemas de protección contra incendios; sistemas de detección de gases; sistemas de señalización ferroviaria; ingiería de tráfico; sistemas de radio y radar.

La fuerza y la innovación de la investigación y el desarrollo. La gestión de la empresa se caracteriza por una «actitud positiva hacia la innovación», pues el fin declarado de su política es «mantenerse siempre al día en el desarrollo de nuevos procesos y tecnologías, con el fin de seguir el rápido progreso del mundo técnico y de los cambios radicales concomitantes».

La inversión en investigación y desarrollo es inmensa, y superior a la de cualquiera de las principales compañías mundiales. Unos 30 000 empleados se dedican en el mundo entero a proyectos de IyD.

El gasto en IyD aumentó en 1982, a pesar de una reducción general de la actividad industrial. Ese año ascendió a 3400 millones DM (1400 millones $), el 8% de las ventas totales y un noveno de los gastos en IyD de la industria alemana en su conjunto. Alrededor de un décimo se dedica a trabajos de investigación básica y conocimientos técnicos, y los otros nueve décimos a la conversión de los resultados en productos, sistemas y servicios nuevos o mejores.

Solamente en el grupo de las comunicaciones trabajan en la investigación y el desarrollo unos 8500 empleados de Siemens. En 1982, el grupo de comunicaciones destinó a IyD un total de 1400 millones DM (577 millones $).

Aumenta sin cesar la parte de la investigación aplicada a objetivos futuros, la mayoría de ellos en el amplio sector de la tecnología del computador y las comunicaciones. Al crecer el uso de los microcomputadores en todas las esferas de la tecnología y hacerse más complejos los computadores y los sistemas conexos, el desarrollo de soporte logico adquiere primordial importancia. Otro sector clave de la investigación es la microelectrónica, donde el trabajo se centra en nociones de arquitectura e ingeniería para circuitos de semiconductores integrados en muy gran escala (VLSI). En los talleres de Siemens se producen en 1983 plaquetas de memoria con una capacidad de almacenamiento de 256 Kbits. Con los progresos que se están haciendo en materia de miniaturización, para finales del decenio se producirá una plaqueta con un millón de bits.

Siemens es universal. pues está representada activamente por personal permanente calificado en 128 países, fabricándose sus productos en 28 de ellos. Además, numerosas empresas mixtas con compañías locales fomentan la transferencia de tecnología a puntos de aplicación y uso. La amplia extensión geográfica de Siemens y sus más de 100 años de experiencia de explotación en el extranjero son factores vitales en la competencia de la empresa para diseñar e instalar sistemas completos, así como para prestar servicios de mantenimiento y de postventa esenciales para el eficaz funcionamiento de las instalaciones de comunicaciones modernas.

En 1982, el grupo de comunicaciones empleaba a unas 50 000 personas. Siemens fabrica equipos y sistemas de comunicaciones en 16 plantas de la República Federal de Alemania, incluido Berlín Occidental, así como en otras 23 fábricas de Europa y de ultramar.

La gestión de proyectos: una fuerza vital de Siemens. Las principales actividades del grupo de comunicaciones en el extranjero se centran en naciones de Europa Occidental, como Austria, Suiza, Bélgica, los países escandinavos y Grecia, así como en los de otros, continentes, como EE.UU., Egipto, Nigeria, Suda-

▷ 121

Con las fibras de vidrio, tan finas como un pelo humano, se puede fabricar toda clase de cables para un trayecto de transmisión por rayos luminosos modulados.

This Siemens laser printer, used here to print Japanese text, can be programmed for different characters. It operates at an exceptional speed; only one minute is required to produce more than 200 pages of text, even if completed forms and graphics are included. It has captured 30% of the European market and large numbers have been sold in the USA and Japan.

Cette imprimante à laser, employée pour imprimer un texte japonais, peut être programmée pour différents caractères. Ce dispositif a une vitesse exceptionnelle — une minute pour imprimer plus de 200 pages — même si elles comprennent des formulaires et des graphiques. Elle représente plus de 30% du marché européen et a été commandée en grand nombre aux Etats-Unis et au Japon.

Esta impresora láser, empleada aquí para un texto japonés, puede programarse para distintos caracteres. Trabaja a una velocidad excepcional: en un minuto puede producir más de 200 páginas de texto, incluso con formularios y gráficos. Ha conquistado el 30% del mercado europeo, y en EE.UU. y Japón se venden grandes cantidades.

最大16K字までの文字を自由に取扱うことができ

⑨超高速ラインプリンタ
N7370高速漢字プリンタシステム

他に超高速のラインプリンタとして

システム・アウトプット・ファ

プを入力して超高速で印字

して用

ことができま

イジカルオーバ

て作成しフロッピ

社を用意し

increased expansion of telecommunications networks in the Third World acquires a special significance.

In the field of foreign ventures, the planning and implementation of major projects place especially heavy demands on a company's engineering, project management and financial resources as well as on its cooperative capability. Siemens has acquired global experience and universal technical know-how in this sector. Numerous major projects have been carried out in close partnership with customers and have become the pacemakers of national economies.

Recent examples of Siemens projects abroad include orders from Egypt for electronic exchanges and cable networks; from Oman for communications networks using exchange, transmission and cable technology; from Indonesia for a digital telephone-network based on EWSD technology; from the USA for the supply of systems for text and data communications and for optical fiber transmission.

Siemens has received orders for its EWSD digital telephone exchanges from many countries, totalling considerably more than 1 million line units. Up to now, over 700,000 line units of the electronic Telex and Teletex services as well as of the EDS and EDX data exchange systems have been sold in about 40 countries. No less than a million teleprinters had been supplied up to the end of 1982. EMS technology, i.e. PABX systems, has been sold to some 40 countries, to the tune of almost 2 million line units, including the world's largest stored-program microprocessor-controlled installation in Brussels.

The following are examples of major projects undertaken by Siemens in recent years:

Africa: in Egypt, turnkey projects to expand the national communication network and the construction of radio relay routes with solar generation; in Nigeria, radio relay routes, exchanges and local cable networks for a long-haul route.

America: in Argentina, the trebling of transmission capacity on a long-haul route; in Colombia, the supply and engineering of a centralized road traffic control for Bogota; in Paraguay, construction of local cable networks for Asunción and other localities; in the United States the beginning of Teletex sales and installations.

Asia: in the Philippines, the setting-up of a national network in conjunction with the national telecommunications industry.

Australasia: in Australia, the construction of a private telephone network for a power supply organization.

Europe: in Belgium, the supply of the world's largest PABX for the EC Commission; in Norway, a radio relay system using digital technology for radio and TV.

Principal growth areas for Siemens communications technology are expected to lie in digital transmission and in subscriber equipment. More specifically significant growth will take place in:
— communications networks based on digital transmission equipments, which make increasing use of optical fibers as line elements. The company's competitive position is especially good as a result of its long experience — stretching over decades — in establishing networks;
— new communications technologies for the office. In this sector Siemens will further expand its standing in the world market on the basis of its strong position in telephone and text communication.

In conclusion, the company's innovative potential, competitive technology and wide experience with complex systems, allied to a worldwide organization geared to overseas requirements, means that Siemens is well able to enter the field wherever opportunities may present themselves.

□

pour la Division Communications — acquiert une importance toute particulière.

Siemens possède une expérience mondiale et un savoir-faire technique universel dans la planification et la réalisation de grands projets à l'étranger. De nombreux grands projets ont été réalisés en étroite coopération avec le client et sont devenus l'élément moteur du développement économique des pays concernés.

Les récents contrats obtenus par Siemens à l'étranger comportent des commandes de centraux électroniques et de réseaux câblés pour l'Egypte ; de réseaux de communication utilisant la technologie la plus moderne, de transmission et de câblage pour l'Oman ; d'un réseau numérique basé sur la technique EWSD de Siemens pour l'Indonésie ; et la fourniture de systèmes de communication de textes et de données et de transmission par fibres optiques pour les Etats-Unis.

Siemens a reçu d'importantes commandes pour son système de commutation numérique EWSD en provenance de plusieurs pays pour plus de 1 million de lignes. En 1983 plus de 700 000 lignes des services électroniques Télex et Télétex et de systèmes de communication de données EDS et EDX ont été vendus dans 40 pays. Un million de téléimprimeurs, qui ont acquis une réputation mondiale, avaient été livrés à fin 1982. La technologie EMS — systèmes PABX — a été vendue à plus de 40 pays (env. 2 millions de lignes), y compris le plus grand système de commutation à commande par programme enregistré du monde entier, qui a été installé à Bruxelles.

Voici quelques exemples d'importants projets réalisés par Siemens ces dernières années :

Afrique : en Egypte, projets clés en main pour l'expansion du réseau national et pour la construction de relais hertziens avec générateurs d'énergie solaire ; au Nigéria, relais hertziens, centraux téléphoniques et réseau câblé local pour une liaison à grande distance.

Amérique : en Argentine, triple expansion de la capacité de transmission sur une voie d'acheminement à longue distance ; en Colombie, fourniture et conception d'un contrôle central de trafic routier à Bogota ; au Paraguay, construction d'un réseau local de câbles pour Asunción et d'autres localités ; aux Etats-Unis, commencement des ventes et installation du Télétex.

Asie : aux Philippines, construction d'un réseau national conjointement avec l'industrie nationale des télécommunications.

Australasie : en Australie, construction d'un réseau téléphonique privé pour une société de distribution d'énergie électrique.

Europe : en Belgique, fourniture de la plus grande installation de commutation téléphonique privée du monde pour la CEE ; en Norvège, un relais de radiodiffusion utilisant la technologie numérique pour radio et télévision.

Les principaux secteurs de croissance pour la technologie des télécommunications de Siemens sont prévus dans la transmission numérique et dans l'équipement des abonnés. Plus précisément, la croissance sera la plus forte dans :
— les réseaux de communication numériques avec l'utilisation progressive de fibres optiques, secteur particulièrement favorable à Siemens ;
— la bureautique, secteur où Siemens développera sa présence dans le monde en fonction de sa forte position sur le marché du téléphone et de la transmission de texte.

Pour conclure, son potentiel d'innovation, sa puissance technologique et sa grande expérience de systèmes complexes, plus une organisation mondiale adaptée aux besoins d'outre-mer, font que Siemens est particulièrement apte pour satisfaire toutes les demandes, dans n'importe quel pays, comme dans n'importe quel secteur de la technologie des communications.

□

This is the Siemens' video telephone which combines the telephone service with interactive videotex. Introduced by Deutsche Bundespost in 1983, it provides access to data banks, timetables, or telephone directories, and can be used to check inventories or transfer money.

Ce vidéo téléphone de Siemens combine le service du téléphone avec celui de vidéotex interactif. Introduit par le Deutsche Bundespost en 1983, il permet d'accéder aux banques de données, de consulter les horaires ou l'annuaire du téléphone, de contrôler les stocks, ou de transférer de l'argent.

frica, Filipinas, Australia y varios países de América del Sur y Central. El hincapié del « Año Mundial de las Comunicaciones 1983 » en la mayor extensión de redes de telecomunicaciones en el Tercer Mundo — sector de particular interés para el grupo de comunicaciones — adquiere un significado especial.

En cuanto a las empresas extranjeras, la planificación y ejecución de importantes proyectos impone grandes exigencias a la empresa en materia de ingeniería, gestión de proyectos y recursos financieros, así como en lo relativo a su capacidad de cooperación. Siemens ha adquirido experiencia global y conocimientos técnicos universales en este sector. Se han realizado muchos proyectos importantes en íntima asociación con los clientes, que marcan la pauta de las economías nacionales involucradas.

Entre los ejemplos recientes de proyectos de Siemens en el extranjero figuran pedidos de Egipto: centrales electrónicas y redes de cable; de Omán: redes de comunicaciones con tecnología de centrales, transmisión y cables; de Indonesia: una red telefónica digital basada en la tecnología EWSD de Siemens, y de EE.UU.: suministro de sistemas de comunicaciones de texto y datos y de transmisión por fibras ópticas.

Siemens ha recibido ya pedidos de sus centrales telefónicas digitales EWSD de muchos países, que totalizan bastante más de 1 millón de unidades de líneas. Hasta ahora, se han vendido ya, en unos 40 países, más de 700 000 unidades de líneas de los servicios electrónicos télex y teletex, así como de sistemas de centrales de datos EDS y EDX. Y ya se han suministrado al menos un millón de teleimpresores, que han adquirido fama mundial. Se ha vendido tecnología EMS, es decir, sistemas CAP, a unos 40 países, por un total de casi 2 millones de unidades de líneas, incluida la mayor instalación controlada por microprocesadores con programa almacenado del mundo, en Bruselas.

He aquí algunos ejemplos de importantes proyectos emprendidos por Siemens en los últimos años:

Africa: en Egipto, proyectos llave en mano para ampliar la red nacional de comunicaciones; en Nigeria, arterias de radioenlaces, centrales y redes de cables locales para una ruta de larga distancia.

América: en Argentina, triplicación de la capacidad de transmisión de una ruta de larga distancia; centralizado en Colombia, suministro y realización de un control de tráfico rodado para Bogotá; en Paraguay, construcción de redes de cable locales para Asunción y otras localidades; en Estados Unidos, comienzo de ventas e instalaciones de teletex.

Asia: en Filipinas, establecimiento de una red nacional con la industria nacional de telecomunicaciones.

Australasia: en Australia, construcción de una red telefónica privada para una empresa de suministro de energía.

Europa: en Bélgica, suministro de la mayor CAP del mundo a la Comisión Económica Europea; en Noruega, un radioenlace con tecnología digital para radio y TV.

Se espera que los principales sectores de crecimiento en la tecnología de comunicaciones de Siemens sean la transmisión digital y el equipo de abonado. Más concretamente, registrarán un gran crecimiento:
— las redes de comunicaciones basadas en equipos de transmisión digital, que utilizan cada vez más como elementos de línea las fibras ópticas;
— las nuevas tecnologías de comunicaciones para oficinas. Aquí, Siemens se extenderá aún más en el mercado mundial, basándose en su fuerte posición en el sector telefónico y de comunicación de textos.

En conclusión, en razón de las posibilidades innovadoras de la empresa, de su tecnología competitiva y de su gran experiencia en sistemas complejos, unido a una organización mundial capaz de atender las necesidades de los países, Siemens puede introducirse en todo campo que ofrezca oportunidades.

□

El videoteléfono de Siemens, que combina el servicio telefónico con el videotex interactivo. Introducido por la Deutsche Bundespost en 1983, permite a los abonados al teléfono acceder a bancos de datos, consultar horarios o la guía telefónica, controlar existencias o transferir dinero automáticamente.

THE SPREAD OF DIGITALIZATION IN TRANSMISSION TECHNIQUES

THE PRESENT WORLDWIDE network of terrestrial transmission systems of cables and radio relay links, space communication links and a hierarchy of switching systems is — with few exceptions — based on analog techniques. These may be obsolescent but still serve well the essential needs of communication by voice in real time over any distance, and remain the basis of the world's 565 million telephones. It should be realized, therefore, that due to the size of the present network, the investments made in it, the applied depreciation method and related replacement policy, and the continued growth of the system, the process of change from analog to digital can only be evolutionary.

Another important factor is that the process of change is driven mainly by technological and economic considerations, not to any marked extent so far by the demand of users. This balance of influences may, and probably will, change over the next few years in view of the very attractive features of digitalization, cost-wise and as a means of improving the quality and reliability of the service. There are also the boundless possibilities of integrating into the system a wealth of non-voice services.

The birth of the digital era occurred some 20 years ago with the introduction of Pulse Code Modulation (PCM) systems in the lower levels of telephone networks, followed in the past decade by digital switching systems and their installation in some of the national public networks. Private digital data networks are also being installed for business customers, using the packet switching technique illustrated on p. 106. These developments were triggered primarily by advances in semiconductor technology resulting not only in important cost savings, but also in technical and operational network advantages.

▷ 124

LE RESEAU MONDIAL des télécommunications utilise actuellement des systèmes de transmission terrestres par câbles et par relais de faisceaux hertziens, des liaisons spatiales et toute une hiérarchie de systèmes de commutation, tous fondés sur les techniques analogiques. Bien que celles-ci soient dépassées, elles répondent encore convenablement aux besoins essentiels des communications téléphoniques, en temps réel, sur n'importe quelle distance, et demeurent à la base du fonctionnement des 565 millions de téléphones existant dans le monde. En conséquence, il convient d'admettre qu'en raison même de la dimension du réseau, des investissements qu'il a nécessités de la méthode d'amortissement appliquée et de la politique de remplacement, que le passage du système analogique au système numérique devra être évolutif.

Le besoin de changement d'un système analogique à un système numérique découle principalement de considérations économiques et techniques mais, jusqu'ici, très peu de la demande des usagers. Toutefois, cette situation pourrait se modifier au cours de ces prochaines années, en raison des caractéristiques attrayantes de la numérisation, des facteurs de coût, d'amélioration de la qualité et de la fiabilité du service, et des possibilités quasi illimitées d'intégration dans une multitude de services télématiques.

L'ère numérique a commencé il y a une vingtaine d'années avec l'introduction de la modulation par impulsions et codage (MIC) aux niveaux inférieurs des réseaux téléphoniques et, au cours de la dernière décennie, avec la mise au point de systèmes de commutation numérique, et leur installation dans certains réseaux nationaux. Des réseaux de données numériques distincts ont également été installés pour des entreprises commerciales, utilisant la technique de commutation par paquets (voir illustration : p. 106). Cette évolution a été principalement stimulée par les progrès réalisés dans le domaine des semi-conducteurs dont l'utilisation permet de réaliser

▷ 124

LA ACTUAL RED MUNDIAL de sistemas de transmisiones terrenales por cable y relevadores radioeléctricos, enlaces de comunicaciones espaciales y una jerarquía de sistemas de conmutación se basa — con algunas excepciones — en técnicas analógicas. Aunque estén anticuadas, todavía atienden perfectamente las necesidades esenciales de comunicación por voz en tiempo real a cualquier distancia, y siguen siendo la base de los 565 millones de teléfonos del mundo. Por tanto, debido al tamaño de la red existente, las inversiones realizadas en ella, el método de amortización aplicado y la política de sustitución conexa, así como el constante crecimiento del sistema, el proceso de cambio de analógico a digital ha de ser revolucionario.

Otro importante factor que ha de tenerse en cuenta es que ese proceso se debe principalmente a consideraciones tecnológicas y económicas, y en modo alguno a la demanda de los usuarios, hasta ahora. Este equilibrio de influencias puede cambiar, y probablemente lo haga los próximos años, en vista de las atractivas propiedades de la digitalización, de los factores de costo y de que es un medio de mejorar la calidad y fiabilidad del servicio, mas, naturalmente, las posibilidades casi ilimitadas de integrar en el sistema muchos servicios no vocales.

La era digital nació hace 20 años, con la introducción de sistemas de modulación por impulsos codificados (MIC) en los niveles más bajos de redes telefónicas, y fue seguida, el pasado decenio, por la concepción de sistemas de conmutación digital y sus instalaciones en algunas redes públicas nacionales. También se están instalado redes digitales de datos separadas para clientes comerciales, utilizando la técnica de conmutación de paquetes que se ilustra en la pág. 106. Esta evolución fue impulsada, ante todo, por los avances tecnológicos de semiconductores, que no sólo han supuesto una importante reducción de los

▷ 125

The digits of digitalization.

Les chiffres binaires du numérique.

Las cifras de la digitalización.

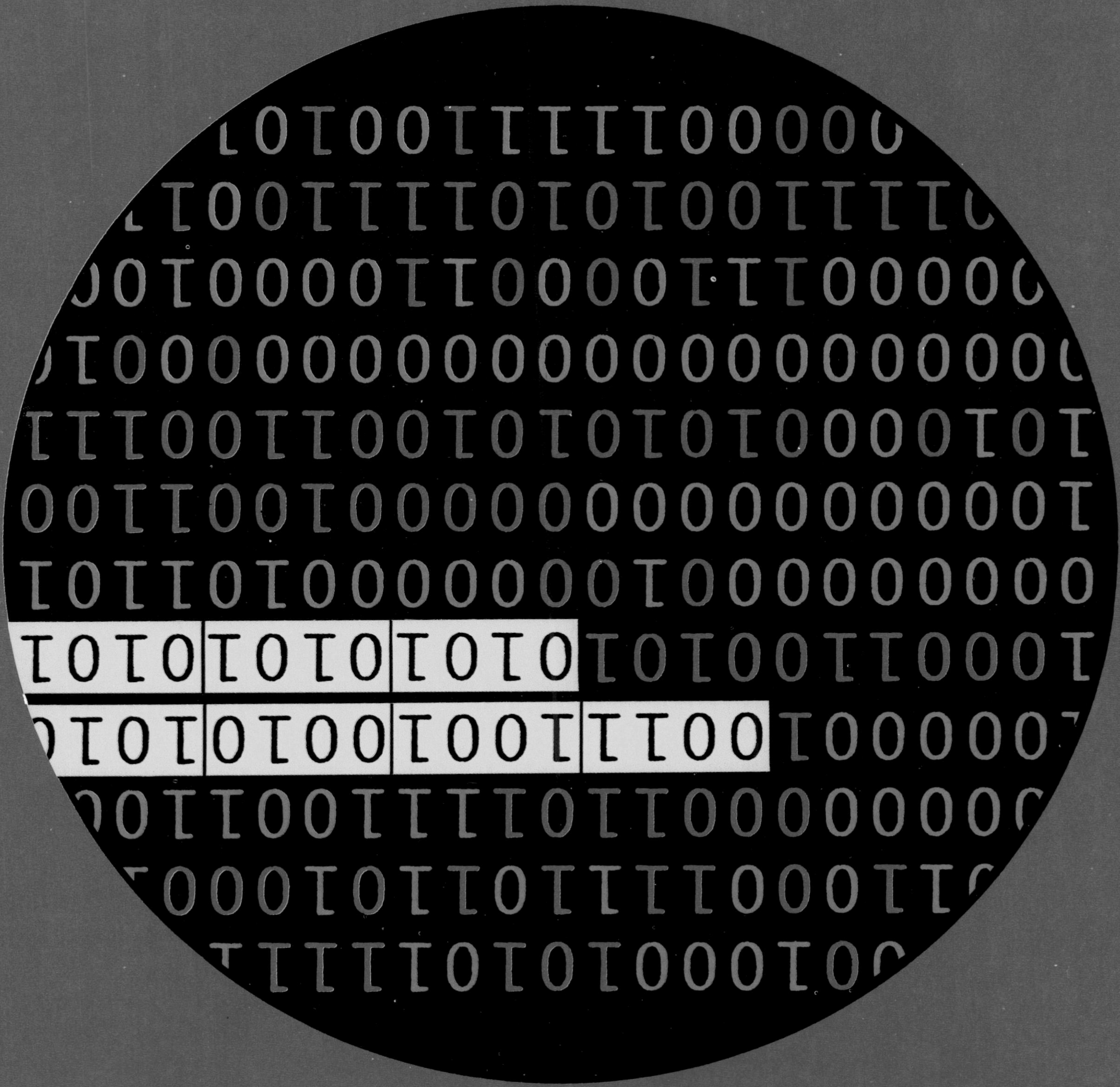

The entry of the computer in telecommunications, which began in the 1960s, introduced the concept of digitalization, which is the computer's essential modus operandi, and made possible the use of new and more efficient call-handling techniques in analog network by what is known as Stored Program Control (SPC). Dialled numbers are stored in the computer's memory while it searches for the most convenient line route to a called party. On finding that route, the computer automatically instructs the electromechanical equipment, relays and cross-bar switches, to make the connection by closing metallic contacts. The use of SPC considerably improved the effectiveness of electromechanical analog systems, not only in the routing of calls but in network maintenance and service administration. It became a common control center at the exchange level for maintenance personnel who use it to diagnose equipment problems within the network and perform maintenance work in a programmed manner.

Administrative overloads can be similarly handled, and the computer itself can be programmed to handle duties once performed exclusively by operators, including the automatic calculation of time and the billing of calls. In general, the use of computers in telephone exchanges has optimized the use of network facilities and diminished the urgency of the changeover to digital switching and transmission.

This limited, *first generation*, computerization of telephone switching practice by the use of SPC was based on "space division switching", i.e. telephone units such as junctors, trunk relay sets, senders, receivers, etc., were controlled via computer bus systems and scanners, drivers and market units by simple control commands.

The architecture of *the second generation* of digital exchange systems, conceived in the second half of the 1970s, was mainly influenced by the progress made in the field of minicomputers. It became economically feasible to decentralize certain control functions. This resulted in system architectures in which mini- or microcomputers were used to perform a number of routine functions in the exchange periphery. The peripheral control complexes, or regional processors, were connected to a central control complex via special bus systems. The switching networks of these second generation systems are still mostly based on analog space division subscriber concentration networks.

Digital switching systems, of which the third generation, currently being introduced, is mostly based on dispersed and distributed control principles made possible by the development in quick succession of Integrated Circuits (ICs), Large Scale Integrated Circuits (LSI), Very Large Scale Integrated Circuits (VLSI) and Very High Speed Integrated Circuits (VHSIC). Microprocessors in the peripherals perform the routine functions of signalling conversion. The central processing unit performs call co-ordination, man-machine interfacing, etc. The information exchange (control) between these peripheral units themselves and between the peripheral units and the central control units, is message-based and appropriate message protocols govern the information flow via the fully transparent switching network.

In this way the switching network not only connects subscriber and trunk inlets and outlets to each other, but also provides the switched or semi-permanent data channels between the various control units in a system. These data channels are integrated in the normal switching and multiplexing scheme used in the switching network. The subscriber concentration stage is also fully digital. The analog subscriber lines are terminated on highly integrated subscriber line interface circuits, which perform all essential functions of the interface between an automatic exchange and each subscriber line connected to it. These types of exchanges will be capable of evolving into ISDN exchanges and may form the basis of ISDN implementation in national networks.

The spread of digitalization and the integration of telecommunication services are taking place partly be-

d'importantes économies et offre d'énormes avantages techniques et opérationnels dans l'exploitation des réseaux.

L'entrée de l'ordinateur dans les télécommunications se fit à partir de 1960 en y introduisant la numérisation qui est à la base même de son fonctionnement. Il devenait possible de traiter plus efficacement les communications dans le réseau analogique, en mettant en œuvre une méthode de commande par programme enregistré « SPC » (Stored Program Control), selon laquelle les numéros qui ont été composés sont stockés dans la mémoire de l'ordinateur, tandis que celui-ci cherche le trajet d'acheminement le mieux approprié pour atteindre la personne appelée. Dès qu'il a déterminé l'itinéraire, l'ordinateur donne automatiquement à l'équipement électromécanique (relais et commutateurs) l'ordre d'établir la communication, par connexion des contacts métalliques.

La méthode SPC a considérablement amélioré l'efficacité des systèmes analogiques, non seulement pour l'acheminement des communications mais également pour la maintenance et la gestion administrative du réseau. L'ordinateur est devenu ainsi un centre de contrôle général, au niveau du central, tant pour le personnel de maintenance qui l'utilise pour faire ses diagnostics que pour la programmation de ce travail.

Les surcharges administratives peuvent ainsi être allégées et l'ordinateur peut être programmé pour accomplir des tâches qui, auparavant, nécessitaient obligatoirement l'intervention humaine : calculs de durée et facturation des communications. Les ordinateurs ont permis de rationaliser l'utilisation des facilités de réseau et, dans un certain sens, leur utilisation a rendu moins urgente la numérisation de la commutation et de la transmission.

Dans la *première génération* d'équipements numérisés, l'utilisation de la méthode SPC était fondée sur la commutation par répartition dans l'espace. A ce stade, tous les dispositifs obéissaient aux instructions de systèmes d'ordinateur omnibus.

Dans l'architecture de la *deuxième génération* de centraux numériques, conçue après 1975, on constate l'influence des progrès accomplis dans le domaine des mini-ordinateurs. Dès cette époque, il devenait économiquement intéressant de décentraliser certaines fonctions de contrôle. A cet effet, des architectures de systèmes ont été mises au point dans lesquelles des mini ou des micro-ordinateurs étaient utilisés pour accomplir un certain nombre de fonctions de routine à la périphérie de l'unité centrale de contrôle. Les organes de contrôle périphériques où les processeurs sectoriels étaient reliés par des circuits omnibus à une unité de contrôle spécialisée. Les réseaux de commutation de ces systèmes de la deuxième génération sont encore basés principalement sur le principe de la concentration des abonnés par répartition dans l'espace.

Les systèmes à commutation numérique de la troisième génération sont principalement fondés sur des principes de répartition et de décentralisation du contrôle. L'application de tels principes a été rendue possible par la mise au point successive et accélérée de plusieurs types de circuits intégrés, notamment des types LSI (intégration à grande échelle) et VLSI (intégration à très grande échelle). Placés dans les organes périphériques de l'équipement téléphonique, les microprocesseurs exercent des fonctions de routine pour la conversion de la signalisation. L'unité de traitement central assure la coordination des appels, la jonction homme-machine, etc. L'échange d'information (contrôle) entre ces unités périphériques et entre celles-ci et les unités de contrôle central est fondée sur les messages. Les protocoles de messages appropriés régissent le flux d'information de commutation (entièrement transparent).

Ainsi, le réseau de commutation ne se borne pas à assurer les jonctions appropriées entre l'abonné et les entrées et les sorties du réseau, et également entre celles-ci, mais il assure aussi, en commutation ou d'une manière semi-permanente, l'établissement des voies de données entre les diverses unités de contrôle du système. Ces voies sont intégrées dans le plan normal de commutation et de multiplexage. Les

▷ 126

▷ 126

ELEMENTS C

The upper half of this chart illustrates the method of transmitting information digitally; the lower half describes the conversion of analog signals, i.e. electrical pulses analogous to sound waves, into pulses corresponding to numerical values.

Digital transmission involves the use of the binary notation, digits 1 and 0, to express any value, which is accomplished by positioning the digits and adding the results. In binary notation displacement to the left multiplies by a factor of 2 (instead of × 10 by the decimal system). The binary number 1101 thus represent, from left to right, 1 unit + (0 × 2) + (1 × 4) + (1 × 8) = 13. A more detailed illustration is given in the chart.

In an electronic switching device, such as the microprocessor described on p. 104, the digit 1 is received as a positive signal or electrical pulse; 0 as a negative signal or no pulse.

In pure binary notation, the digits indicate whether the corresponding power of 2 is absent or present in each position, as indicated below:

Binary Digits	0010	0110	0101	0100	1101
Place Value of Binary Digits	8421	8421	8421	8421	8421
Decimal Value	2	6	5	4	13

In a computer, all arithmetic calculations are performed as a series of additions and subtractions. For instance, multiplication of 25 by 4 in binary arithmetic is performed as a series of additions:

```
  11001   (= 25)
  11001   (add 2
 110010   (= 2×
  11001   (add 2
1001011   (= 3×
  11001   (add 2
1100100   (= 4×
```

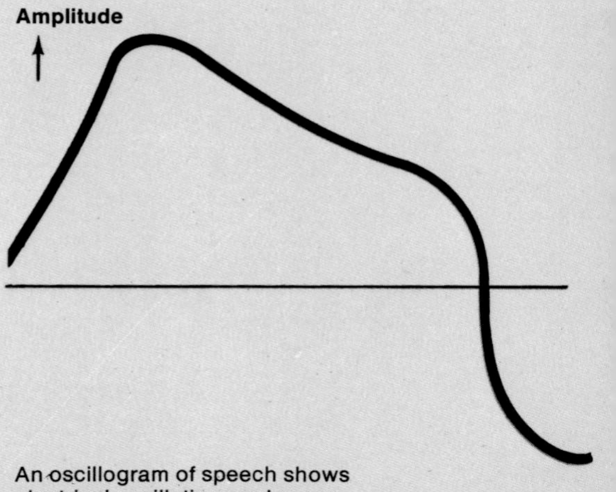

Amplitude

An oscillogram of speech shows electrical oscillation analogous to the sound waves, ...

Time

Programmed opening or shutting of circuit gates, known as logic gates, positions the digits in their desired values at speeds so great that they are expressed in nanoseconds, or one thousand millionth of a second (a nanosecond is to a second as a minute is to 2,000 years).

Everything that can be given a value, and this includes voice, data, music or image, can be represented and transmitted digitally, faster than any other means known to man and in the most accurate and faithful manner.

The lower half of the chart shows how analog signals can be converted to digital. The reverse is equally possible, with the use of modems which operate in both directions. This enables computers to communicate via the predominantly analog switched telephone circuit.

LECTRONIC DIGITAL SWITCHING

diagramme ci-dessous illustre, en haut, la méthode numéri-
de transmission de l'information, et, en bas, la conversion
scillations électriques « analogues » aux ondes sonores, en
me numérique. La transmission numérique est basée sur la
ation binaire. Tandis que dans la notation décimale, tout
lacement d'un chiffre vers la gauche le multiplie par 10,
s la notation binaire, ce déplacement le multiplie par 2, et
ls les chiffres 0 et 1 sont utilisés. Par exemple, le nombre 13
crit en binaire 1101, soit de droite à gauche : 1 unité +
×2)+(1×4)+(1×8) = 13. Une démonstration plus détaillée
araît, sur la gauche, dans l'illustration ci-dessous.
Dans un dispositif de commutation électronique, tel que le
roprocesseur présenté à la p. 104, des commutateurs re-
naissent dans le flux de courant deux états possibles :

La mitad superior del gráfico ilustra el método de transmitir
información digital, y la inferior la conversión de señales
analógicas, o sea, impulsos eléctricos análogos a ondas sonoras en impulsos correspondientes a valores numéricos.

La transmisión digital supone el uso de la notación binaria,
dígitos 1 y 0, para expresar cualquier valor, lo que se logra
posicionando los dígitos y agregando los resultados.

En la notación binaria, todo desplazamiento hacia la izquierda multiplica por un factor de 2 (en lugar de ×10 en el
sistema decimal). Por ejemplo, el número 13 se escribe en
binario 1101: de derecha a izquierda, 1 unidad+(0×2) +
(1×4) + (1×8) = 13. En el gráfico se ilustra con más detalle.

En un dispositivo de conmutación electrónica, como el procesador de la pág. 104, el dígito 1 se recibe como señal positiva

costos, sino támbién ventajas técnicas y operacionales de la red.

La entrada del computador en las telecomunicaciones, iniciada
en los años 1960, introdujo la noción de digitalización, el modus operandi esencial del computador, y
permite utilizar técnicas de tratamiento de llamadas
nuevas y más eficaces en la red analógica, mediante
lo que se conoce como control por programa almacenado (CPA). Los números marcados se almacenan
en la memoria del computador, mientras éste busca
la ruta más conveniente con la persona llamada. Al
hallar esa ruta, el computador da instrucciones automáticamente al equipo electromecánico, como los
conmutadores de relés y barras cruzadas, para efectuar la conexión cerrando contactos metálicos.

El uso del CPA ha hecho mucho más eficaz los
sistemas analógicos electromecánicos, no sólo en el
encaminamiento de las llamadas sino en el mantenimiento de la red y la administración de servicios.
Se ha convertido en un centro de control común a
nivel de la central para el personal de mantenimiento, que lo emplea para diagnosticar problemas de
equipo en la red y para realizar trabajos de mantenimiento en forma programada.

Las sobrecargas administrativas pueden tratarse
en forma análoga, y el propio computador puede
programarse para efectuar tareas realizadas antes
exclusivamente por operadores humanos, incluido el
cálculo automático del tiempo y la facturación de
llamadas. En general, el uso de computadores en
centrales telefónicas ha optimado el empleo de facilidades de red y ha reducido la urgencia del paso a la
conmutación y la transmisión digital.

Esta limitada computadorización de *primera generación* de la práctica de conmutación telefónica
utilizando CPA se basaba en la "conmutación por
división de espacio", es decir, instalaciones telefónicas
como conjuntores, grupos de relés de líneas interurbanas, transmisores, receptores, etc., controlados a
través de sistemas bus de computador y de explora-
dores, excitadores y unidades de mercado, mediante
instrucciones de control sencillas.

En la arquitectura de la *segunda generación* de
sistemas de centrales digitales, concebidos después
de 1975, influyó sobre todo el progreso realizado en
materia de minicomputadores. Resultó económicamente factible descentralizar ciertas funciones de
control. Esto entrañó arquitecturas de sistemas en
que se utilizaban mini o microcomputadores para
ejecutar diversas funciones de rutina en la periferia
de la central. Los complejos de control periféricos, o
procesadores regionales, se conectaban a una unidad
de control de la central a través de sistemas bus
especiales. Las redes de conmutación de estos sistemas de la segunda generación se basan todavía
principalmente en redes analógicas de concentración
de abonados por división en el espacio.

Los sistemas de conmutación digitales de tercera generación,
introducidos actualmente, se basan ante todo en
principios de control disperso y distribuido, posibles
gracias al desarrollo en rápida sucesión de circuitos
integrados (CI), circuitos integrados en gran escala
(LSI) y circuitos integrados en muy gran escala
(VLSI). Los microprocesadores en el equipo periférico telefónico realizan las funciones de rutina de la
conversión de señalización. La unidad de procesamiento central efectúa la coordinación de llamadas
interfaz hombre-máquina, etc. El intercambio de
información (control) entre esas unidades periféricas
y entre ellas y las unidades de control central se basa
en los mensajes, y los protocolos apropiados de
mensaje rigen el flujo de información a través de la
red de conmutación totalmente transparente.

De esta manera, la red de conmutación no sólo
conecta al abonado y las entradas y salidas principales entre sí, sino que proporciona también los canales de datos conmutados o semipermanentes entre
las diversas unidades de control de un sistema. Esos
canales de datos están integrados en el esquema
normal de conmutación y multiplexación usado en la
red de conmutación. La etapa de concentración del
abonado es también totalmente digital. Las líneas de
abonado analógicas terminan en circuitos de interfaz
de la línea de abonado muy integrados, que realizan

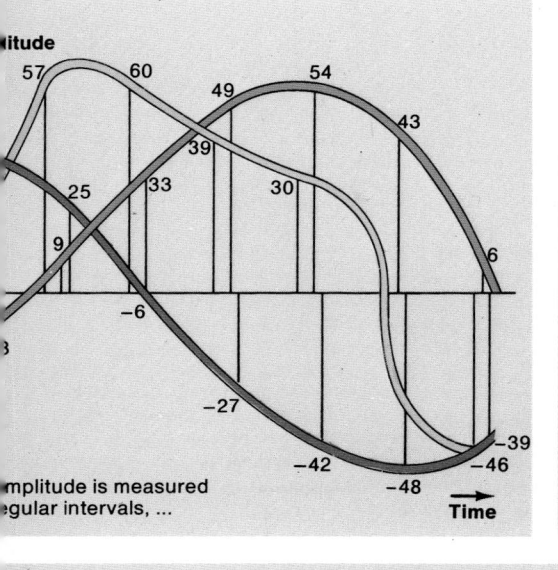

Number of Bits Required for Typical Messages

Type of Message	No. of Bits Rec'd
Brief telephone voice message	1 Million
"Vocoder" telephone voice message	100,000
Page of text in facsimile form	200,000
Page of text in computer code (1,200 characters)	10,000
Typical inter-office memo (600 letters)	3,000
Typical telegram (15 words)	400
Newspaper photograph	100,000
High-quality color photograph	2 Million
A color television frame	1 Million
Picturephone frame	100,000

Sources : AT&T, ITT

litude

57 60 49 54
43
25 33 39 30
9
6
−6
−27
−39
−42 −48 −46

mplitude is measured
gular intervals, ...   Time

10	1	0	0	0	1	0	1	0
−13	0	0	0	0	1	1	0	1
37	1	0	1	0	0	1	0	1
57	1	0	1	1	1	0	0	1
9	1	0	0	0	1	0	0	1
25	1	0	0	1	1	0	0	1
60	1	0	1	1	1	1	0	0
33	1	0	1	0	0	0	0	1
−6	0	0	0	0	0	1	1	0
39	1	0	1	0	0	1	1	1
49	1	0	1	1	0	0	0	1

1 1 0 1 1 0 0 0 0 0 1 0 1 0 0 0 1 →

and the results are transferred in digital form together
with the values from other voice channels

Source: Siemens

vert » ou « fermé ». En présence d'une impulsion électrique,
commutateur marque « 1 », en l'absence d'impulsion, il
rque « 0 ». Les ouvertures et fermetures programmées des
rées en circuit, appelées « portes logiques », positionnent
« 0 » et les « 1 » à leur valeur désirée, le tout à des vitesses
tablement fantastiques, mesurées en milli-millionièmes de
onde ou nanoseconde (une nanoseconde représente ce
ne minute dure par rapport à deux mille ans).
Tout ce qui peut être interprété par une valeur chiffrée :
sique, images données, peut être transcrit et transmis
nériquement, en temps réel, avec la plus grande exactitude.
La partie inférieure du diagramme montre le mode de
version de signaux « analogues » en signaux numériques, et
e versa, grâce à des modems (modulateurs-démodulateurs).
te technique permet à l'information sous forme numérique
iliser les circuits téléphoniques existants.

o impulso eléctrico; el 0 como señal negativa y sin impulso. La
aberturas o cierres programados de entradas en circuitos, o
puertas logicas, posicionan los dígitos en sus valores desea-
dos, a velocidades tan grandes que pueden expresarse en
nanosegundos, o milmillonésimas de segundo (un nanosegundo
es al segundo lo que un minuto a 2000 años).

Todo lo que puede recibir un valor, y esto comprende voz,
datos, música o imagen, puede representarse y transmitirse
digitalmente, a la mayor velocidad conocida y con la máxima
exactitud.

La parte inferior del gráfico muestra la conversión de las
señales analógicas en digitales. También puede hacerse lo
inverso, usando módems que operan en ambas direcciones.
Esto permite a los computadores utilizar los circuitos telefónicos.

▷ 127

TOWARDS CHEAPE

The development of integrated circuit design

The development of integrated circuit design, both actual and anticipated, is shown here for a period spanning three decades, from 1970 to 2000.

This diagram, included in a paper presented to the Massachusetts Institute of Technology in 1982 by Dr. Koji Kobayashi, Chairman of the Board and Chief Executive Officer of NEC Corporation, relates performance and reliability to costs. The basic capacities of both the memory and the logic gate functions have expanded manifold whilst costs have plummeted. The expected continuation — indeed acceleration — of these trends should enable designers to incorporate intelligence in their circuitry and thus build systems that are functionally closer to humans.

The startling reduction in the weight of computer systems achieved during this period is also shown on the chart. The changes that have taken place since the first electronic computer, ENIAC, using vacuum tubes, to microprocessors using VLSI, have reduced the weight of a CPU to one millionth of what it was. Yet the tiny VLSI chip has more than 100 times the computing power of ENIAC.

Integration/Chips

Relative Failure Rate/Logic Gate

Relative Cost/Logic Gate

---

lignes d'abonné analogiques aboutissent à des interfaces à forte intégration qui accomplissent toutes les fonctions essentielles de l'interface classique entre un central automatique et chacune des lignes d'abonné qui en dépendent. Ces types de centraux formeront l'infrastructure du RNIS dans les réseaux nationaux.

La généralisation de la numérisation et l'intégration des services de télécommunications sont dues à la fois à la disponibilité de nouvelles techniques, à l'action puissante et persuasive des protagonistes intéressés, et au fait que c'est une méthode plus efficiente de communiquer. La poussée technologique d'aujourd'hui pourrait se voir demain entièrement résorbée, du fait de l'expansion du marché. Les réseaux numériques mettent à la disposition de l'usager des fonctions et des applications pratiquement illimitées, grâce à la décentralisation du contrôle et aux possibilités d'accès rapide à toutes les catégories d'informations possibles.

La supériorité des réseaux numériques s'explique de la façon suivante :

Meilleure qualité de transmission. L'information transmise numériquement est moins sujette à la dégradation que les signaux analogiques, parce que les impulsions peuvent être régénérées autant de fois que nécessaire, sans perte de qualité, indépendamment de la distance.

Vitesse de transmission supérieure, avec un faible taux d'erreur. Le codage de l'information sous forme numérique permet d'assurer des transmissions à la vitesse de la lumière et un contrôle intégral des erreurs.

Secret mieux gardé. La transmission numérique se prête au cryptage de l'information, garantie du secret des communications.

Meilleure fiabilité, coût moins élevé, moindre poids et dimensions réduites. Des pas de géant ont été faits en direction de l'abaissement des coûts et la fiabilité a été améliorée, grâce au développement de la technique des circuits intégrés.

Économie et compatibilité entre la transmission numérique et la communication numérique. La commutation numérique peut être réalisée directement sur les flux binaires numériques.

Compatibilité avec les nouvelles liaisons de transmission. Les liaisons à large bande sont mieux adaptées à la transmission numérique.

Compatibilité entre phonie et données. Les sons vocaux numérisés peuvent être facilement injectés dans le trafic de données, ce qui supprime la nécessité de dispositifs de conversion et de réseaux spécialisés.

Future intégration des services. Un « bit » est toujours un « bit », quelle que soit son origine. En conséquence, tout circuit numérique peut transmettre indifféremment la voix, les données, les informations visuelles, les messages télex, etc. On peut ainsi réaliser économiquement l'intégration d'une multitude de services.

La transition du mode analogique au mode numérique et de l'électromécanique à l'électronique est une opération très complexe, exigeant une planification minutieuse et une connaissance approfondie des besoins, en ce qui concerne la compatibilité du matériel et du logiciel utilisés. La conversion se fera à l'échelle mondiale et il est donc essentiel que les équipements et les méthodes de gestion du réseau soient normalisés.

Bien que la situation se présente d'une manière différente selon les pays, des organismes internationaux, tels que le Comité consultatif international télégraphique et téléphonique (CCITT) de l'UIT et la Conférence européenne des administrations des postes et des télécommunications (CEPT) élaborent des recommandations en matière de normes et d'interfaces.

D'importants progrès ont déjà été accomplis, notamment au cours de la dernière période d'études du CCITT, mais il reste encore beaucoup à faire en matière de normalisation. Le monde est confronté à une situation absolument nouvelle mais il ne dispose se, pour le moment, que d'instruments encore imparfaitement adaptés aux tâches qui s'imposent.

Le profil d'ITT Corporation, qui suit, illustre parfaitement la manière dont la technologie de la numérisation se répand à travers le monde. Le succès d'ITT est fondé sur le transfert de technologie et de savoir-faire aux pays clients.

□

---

cause the technology is available and its protagonists are powerful and persuasive, and partly because it is an immeasurably more efficient way to communicate. The "technology-push" of today may become absorbed by the "market-pull" of tomorrow.

Digital networks provide the user with the benefits of almost unlimited functions and applications and to distributed control plus ready access to all possible kinds of information from the most distant places. Few telecommunications administrations can afford to ignore this development or demand or to avoid making provision for it when extending or modernizing their networks.

The superiority of digital over analog networks can be explained as follows:

Better transmission quality. Information transmitted digitally suffers less degradation than analog signals because the digital pulses can be regenerated as often as necessary without loss of quality, regardless of distance.

Higher transmission rates with lower error content. Encoding information in digital form enables speed of light transmission and tight error control.

Greater privacy. Digital transmission lends itself to digital encryption of information, guaranteeing communications privacy.

Greater reliability, lower cost, smaller weight and size. Quantum leaps in the direction of lower costs and improved reliability have been made through the development of integrated circuit technology, culminating in the VLSI chip.

Economy and compatibility between digital transmission and digital switching. Digital switching can be performed directly on digital bit streams, thereby eliminating costly analog digital conversion and other interface devices.

Compatibility with new transmission links. Broadband links, such as satellites, waveguides and optical fibers, are more suitable for digital than analog transmission.

Compatibility of voice and data. Digitized voice can be freely intermixed with data traffic, eliminating the need for conversion devices and dedicated networks.

Future integration of services. Since a "bit" is a "bit", regardless of source, a digital channel can transmit digitized voice, computer data, encoded visual information, telex, and many other digital signals. This will make "intelligent", distributed and integrated multiservice network economically feasible.

The transition from analog to digital, from electromechanical to electronics, is a highly complex operation, needing careful planning, and a keen and constant awareness of the need for compatibility of both the hardware and the software employed. Also great care will be needed to make the systems of the future "user friendly", very much as the telephone has become — to toddlers as well as centenarians — after five generations of usage.

National and international standards, a good implementation strategy, are therefore the strategic issues in this field. Although the situation is different in various countries, international bodies such as the International Telegraph and Telephone Consultative Committee (CCITT) of the ITU, and the European Conference of Postal and Telecommunication Administrations (CEPT) are working on recommendations for standards and interfaces.

Much progress has already been made, notably in the last CCITT study period, but much remains to be done. The world is grappling with a totally novel situation, with tools still imperfectly adapted to the task in hand. But the opportunity is great, as are the challenges to engineers and administrations.

The company profile that follows, of the ITT Corporation, illustrates the way in which digital technology is spreading through the world. ITT is among leaders in the development and application, internationally, of digital products and systems. Of particular interest is its success in transferring technology to client countries, both in product know-how and in people skills.

□

SMALLER, MORE POWERFUL "CHIPS"

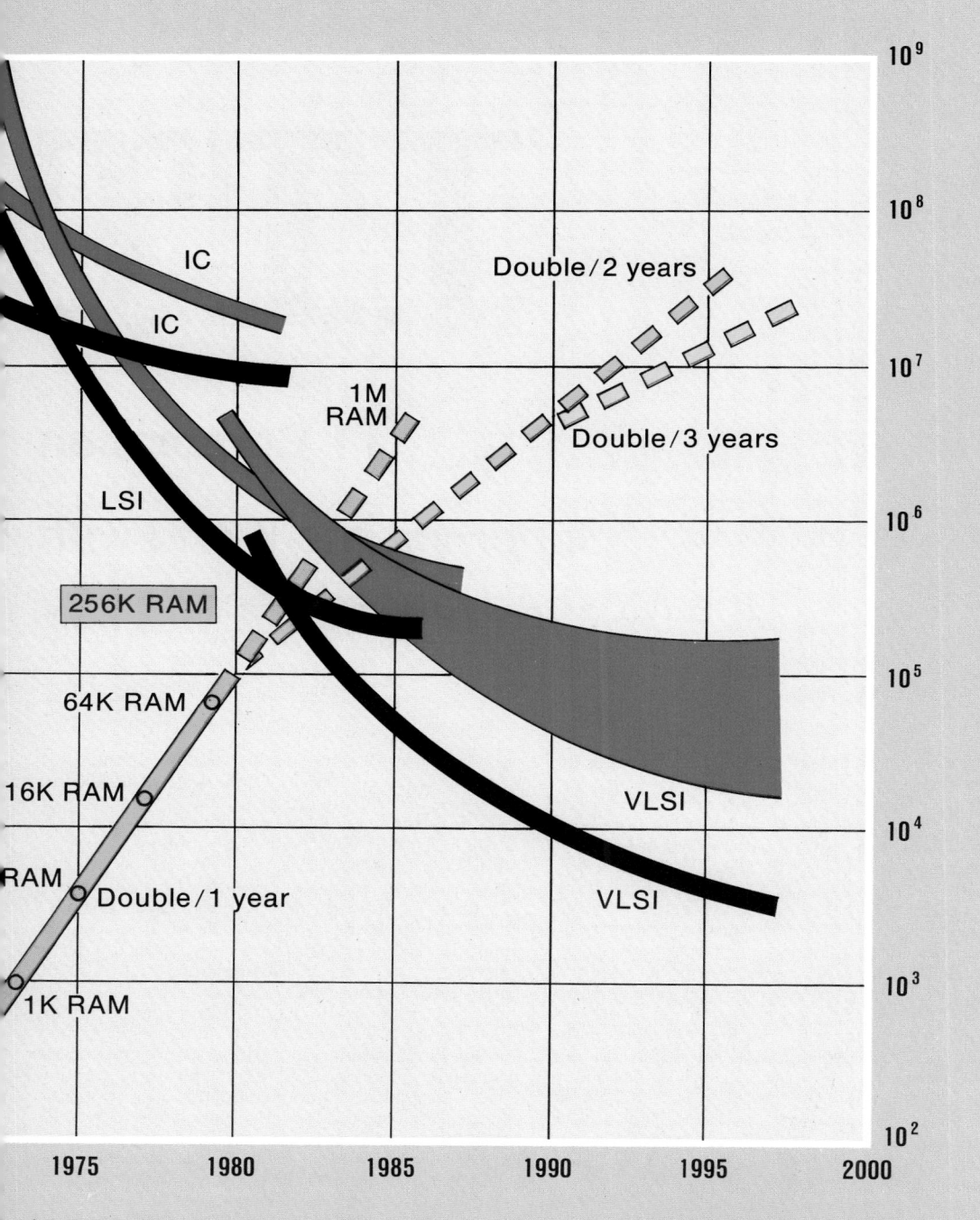

todas las funciones esenciales del interfaz entre una central automática y cada línea de abonado conectada a ella. Esas centrales podrán convertirse en centrales de RDSI y constituir la base de la aplicación de la RDSI en redes nacionales.

La expansión de la digitalización y la integración de servicios de telecomunicaciones se deben, en parte, a que se dispone de la tecnología y al poder y la persuasión de sus protagonistas y, en parte, a que es una manera de comunicar mucho más eficaz. El "empuje de la tecnología" de hoy puede quedar absorbido por el "impulso del mercado" de mañana.

Las redes digitales ofrecen al usuario los beneficios de funciones y aplicaciones casi ilimitadas, debido a la distribución del control y al rápido acceso a toda clase de información posible desde los lugares más lejanos. Pocas administraciones pueden ignorar esta evolución de la demanda o no tomar disposiciones al respecto, ampliando o modernizando sus redes.

La superioridad de las redes digitales sobre las analógicas puede explicarse como sigue:

Mejor calidad de transmisión. La información transmitida digitalmente se degrada menos que las señales analógicas, porque los impulsos digitales pueden regenerarse con la frecuencia necesaria sin pérdida de calidad y con independencia de la distancia.

Velocidades de transmisión más altas con menos errores. La información codificada en forma digital permite la transmisión a la velocidad de la luz y controla totalmente los errores.

Mayor privacidad. La transmisión digital tiende al cifrado digital de la información, garantizando el secreto de las comunicaciones.

Mayor fiabilidad, menor costo, menor peso y tamaño. Mediante el desarrollo de la tecnología de circuitos integrados se han dado grandes pasos para reducir los costos y mejorar la fiabilidad.

Economía y compatibilidad entre transmisión digital y conmutación digital. La conmutación digital puede realizarse directamente en trenes de bits digitales, eliminando así la costosa conversión analógico/digital y otros dipositivos de interfaz.

Compatibilidad con nuevos enlaces de transmisión. Los enlaces de banda ancha, como satélites, guiaondas y fibras ópticas son más apropiados para la transmisión digital que para la analógica.

Compatibilidad de voz y datos. La voz digitalizada puede mezclarse con tráfico de datos, sin necesidad de dispositivos de conversión ni de redes exclusivos.

Futura integración de servicios. Como un "bit" es un "bit", con independencia de su origen, un canal digital puede transmitir voz digitalizada, datos de computador, información visual codificada, télex y muchas otras señales digitales. Esto puede hacer económicamente factible la red de múltiples servicios inteligentes, distribuidos e integrados.

El paso de analógico a digital, de electromecánico a electrónico, es una operación muy compleja, que requiere minuciosa planificación y un profundo y constante conocimiento de la necesidad de compatibilizar el soporte físico y el soporte lógico empleados. También habrá que tener gran cuidado para que los sistemas del futuro sean "familiares para el usuario".

Por tanto, las cuestiones estratégicas en la materia son las normas nacionales e internacionales, y una buena política de aplicación. Aunque la situación difiere en varios países, organismos internacionales como el Comité Consultivo Internacional Telegráfico y Telefónico (CCITT) de la UIT, y la Conferencia Europea de Correos y Telecomunicaciones (CEPT) recomiendan normas e interfaces.

Ya se han realizado muchos progresos, sobre todo en el último período de estudios del CCITT, pero queda mucho por hacer. El mundo se encuentra ante una situación totalmente nueva, con instrumentos que todavía no se adaptan perfectamente a la tarea en curso. Pero se vislumbran amplios horizontes.

El perfil que sigue de la ITT Corporation ilustra perfectamente cómo se difunde en el mundo entero la tecnología digital. ITT figura entre los líderes del desarrollo y aplicación internacional de productos y sistemas digitales. Su éxito en la transferencia de tecnología a los países clientes y la formación de personal reviste particular interés.

□

...eprésenté ici une période de trois décennies, de 1970 à ... correspondant à l'évolution des circuits intégrés exis-... futurs.

...iagramme, figurant dans un document présenté en 1982 ... (Massachusetts Institue of Technology) par Koji Ko-...ai, PDG de la NEC Corporation, représente les rapports ...mances et fiabilité/coût. Les capacités fondamentales de ...noire et des fonctions logiques se sont multipliées alors ... coûts se sont effondrés.

...oursuite de ces tendances et leur accélération probable ...ent permettre aux concepteurs d'introduire « l'intelligen-...ans leurs circuits et de construire ainsi des systèmes ... un comportement fonctionnel plus proche de celui de ...me.

...iagramme fait apparaître une réduction surprenante du ...des ordinateurs au cours de cette période. Depuis le ... ordinateur électronique ENIAC, qui utilisait des tubes à ...usqu'aux microprocesseurs utilisant l'intégration à très ... échelle (VLSI), la réduction du poids de l'unité centrale ...ateur a été d'un millionième du poids initial et la puis-...de calcul est devenue 100 fois supérieure.

Aquí se muestra para tres decenios, de 1970 a 2000, el desarrollo del diseño de circuitos integrados, reales y previstos.

Este diagrama, incluido en un documento presentado al Instituto de Tecnología de Massachusetts por el Dr. Koji Kobayashi, Presidente del Consejo y Jefe Ejecutivo de NEC Corporation, en 1982, relaciona el rendimiento y la fiabilidad con los costos. Las capacidades básicas de la memoria y de las funciones de puerta lógica se han multiplicado, mientras los costos han caído en vertical. La continuación prevista — en realidad, aceleración — de esas tendencias debe permitir a los proyectistas incorporar inteligencia en sus circuitos y constituir así sistemas que se aproximan más funcionalmente al ser humano.

En el gráfico se muestra también la sorprendente reducción del peso de los sistemas de computador lograda en este período. Los cambios que se han producido desde el primer computador electrónico, ENIAC, utilizando tubos de vacío, hasta los microprocesadores que usan VLSI, han reducido el peso de una UCP a una millonésima de lo que era. Y la fina plaqueta VLSI tiene una potencia superior más de 100 veces a la del ENIAC.

ITT Corporation

Supplying the World with the Most Advanced Technology

FROM ITS MODEST BEGINNINGS as the operator of two small telephone companies in the Caribbean, ITT has grown to become the leading supplier of tele-communications equipment and service outside the U.S. Today the company is a $ 23 billion complex of operations, with more than 300,000 people operating in 96 countries on all continents. It has been active in the telecommunications industry for more than 60 years, and through its subsidiaries for more than 100 years. Its products, both traditional and innovative, are in use by telephone administrations in more than 100 nations.

But there is challenge in the air. The pace of tech-nological change is increasing and new markets are emerging. As proud as it is of its past successes, ITT is well aware of the magnitude of the demands the future will make upon its creativity and capacity to adapt. Transmitting voice in analog form is no longer sufficient. Technological progress has made it possi-ble to transmit and receive, in large quantities and faster than ever before, a wide variety of informa-tion. Distinctions between switching and transmis-sion are becoming less sharply defined. Digitaliza-tion and transmission by microwave and optic cable have transformed world communications and open-ed up undreamt-of opportunities.

Telecommunication network products have always been, from the earliest days of telephony, a key element in ITT's range of manufactures. The company is one of the leading producers of switching and transmission equipment, from the familiar traditional to the latest, most sophisticated. This includes all types of elec-tromechanical switches, fully digital switches, and mi-crowave, coaxial cable, satellite and fiber optics transmission systems.

◁ 130

The ITT concept of distributed control.

APRÈS DES DÉBUTS MODESTES dans l'exploitation de deux petites entreprises téléphoniques des Caraïbes, ITT est devenue le principal fournisseur de services et d'équipements de télécommunications en dehors des États-Unis. Aujourd'hui cette société représente un ensemble d'opérations qui s'élèvent à 23 milliards de dollars et emploie plus de 300 000 personnes dans 96 pays du monde. Elle a exercé une action positive sur toute l'industrie des télécommunications pen-dant plus de 60 ans et même, par l'intermédiaire de ses succursales, pendant plus de 100 ans. Ses produits sont utilisés par les administrations téléphoniques de plus de 100 pays. Mais il y a un défi dans l'air. La rapidité de l'évolution technologique augmente et de nouveaux marchés apparaissent. Aussi fière qu'elle soit de son passé, ITT connaît la magnitude de l'ampleur des exigences que le futur fera peser sur sa capacité d'adaptation et de créativité. La numérisation et la transmission par micro-ondes et câbles optiques ont transformé le monde des communications et offrent des opportunités jusqu'alors inimaginables.

Les composants de réseaux de télécommunications ont tou-jours été — dès les premiers jours de la téléphonie — un élément-clé des fabrications d'ITT. Cette société est l'un des principaux producteurs d'équipements de communication et de transmission, depuis le tradi-tionnel, familier à tous, jusqu'au plus moderne et perfectionné. Sa gamme de produits comprend les commutateurs électroniques à commande par pro-gramme enregistré, les commutateurs numériques et les systèmes de transmission en hyperfréquences, à câble coaxial, à fibres optiques et à satellite.

ITT a fabriqué et installé dans le monde quelque soixante millions de lignes d'équipement téléphoni-que local et plus de trois millions de lignes interur-baines. Pour de nombreux centraux téléphoniques, sa commutation est devenue la norme.

◁ 130

Le concept ITT de répartition de contrôle.

DESDE SUS MODESTOS COMIENZOS como operador de dos pequeñas compañías telefónicas en el Caribe, ITT se ha convertido en el principal proveedor de equipo y servicios de telecomunicaciones fuera de EE.UU. Hoy, la empresa es un complejo de opera-ciones de 23 000 millones $, con más de 300 000 empleados en 96 países de todos los continentes. Actúa en la industria de telecomunicaciones desde hace más de 60 años, y a través de sus filiales desde más de 100 años. Sus productos, tradicionales y nuevos, los usan las administraciones telefónicas de más de 100 países.

Pero hay un desafío. El ritmo del cambio tecnoló-gico aumenta, y surgen nuevos mercados. En razón de sus éxitos pasados, ITT conoce la magnitud de la demanda, que exigirá la adaptación de su creativi-dad y capacidad. Ya no basta con transmitir voz en forma analógica. El avance tecnológico permite transmitir y recibir en grandes cantidades y a mayor velocidad una amplia variedad de información. Ca-da vez es más difícil distinguir la comunicación de la transmisión. La digitalización y la transmisión por microondas y cables ópticos han transformado el mundo de las comunicaciones y abierto horizontes increíbles.

Los productos de la red de telecomunicaciones han sido siempre, desde los primeros días de la telefonía, un elemento clave en la gama de fabricación de ITT. La empresa es uno de los principales productores de equipo de comunicación y transmisión, desde el fa-miliar tradicional hasta el más moderno y sofistica-do. Esto comprende toda clase de conmutadores electromecánicos, electrónicos de control por pro-grama almacenado, totalmente digitales, y sistemas de transmisión por microondas, cable coaxial, saté-lites y fibras ópticas.

◁ 131

La noción ITT de control distribuido.

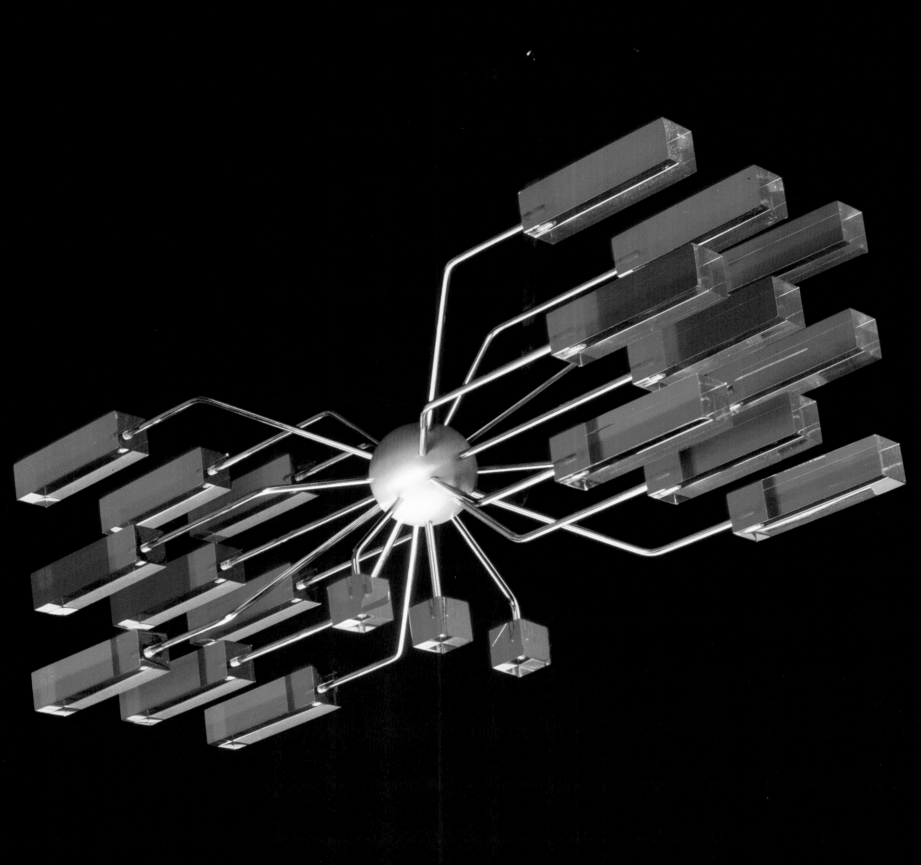

Worldwide, ITT have manufactured and installed some sixty million lines of local telephone switching equipment and more than three million trunk or toll lines. For many of the world's telephone exchanges its switching has become the standard.

Fully digital electronic switching has been successfully developed by ITT. The System 12 telephone exchange places the company at the leading edge of switching technology. It represents a major breakthrough in the application of advanced technology and systems design and provides a full range of exchange solutions consistent with the realities of today's analog network and the all-digital information delivery network of tomorrow.

System 12 is designed to meet the growing demands of telephone administrations and their customers for higher quality service, lower costs and increased revenue opportunities as the long-term transition is made to an integrated services digital network, and is unique in its planned ability to handle both voice and data simultaneously.

The fully digital structure is the ITT 1240's direct response to the upward trend in the demand for data communications. Digitalization eventually will extend from the exchange out to the individual subscriber, whose conventional telephone will be replaced with a multifunctional terminal. Full digitalization of the network will permit the highest possible degree of voice/data integration and improve transmission quality and reliability. Thus, while the ITT 1240 functions perfectly in today's largely analog environment, it has been designed and constructed for the digital environment of tomorrow.

The equipment covers the entire range of local, tandem and toll exchange applications from the smallest remote subscriber unit to the largest local or toll exchange of more than 100,000 lines or 60,000 trunks using standard modules of hardware and software. Thus the smallest exchange can be expanded easily and economically to the largest size, and the ITT 1240 can be applied in various configurations for independent or dependent exchanges, including supervised or remote operation, to fit every network planning requirement.

Fully distributed control is a concept unique to the ITT 1240. Instead of control at the center, control logic resides in discrete, easily handled units throughout the system. Thus, there is no longer any single point in the system where most of the memory is stored or most of the logical functions are executed. The distributed control architecture represents an advance in technology on a par with the invention of Pulse Code Modulation (PCM) by ITT scientist Alec Reeves.

In a centralised control configuration, if the control function goes down, the entire system goes down with it. When control is distributed over a large number of modules, a malfunction in any one module will have only a marginal effect on the total system, without reducing service below the acceptable limit. Before the 1240 became available, the necessity of centralizing most or all control logic compelled telephone administrations either to start with a small processor, which was difficult to replace when the exchange expanded, or with a large processor, which was uneconomical for small capacity requirements at the beginning. Distributed control eliminates this constraint on network planning.

Moreover, fully distributed control means that processing power can be added at the same time as other modules of the system are being added. As a result, only the requisite amount of control is provided at any given stage of growth, and new processing power is added only in proportion to increased size or traffic capacity requirements. In the future, control can easily evolve to the level of one microprocessor for each subscriber's terminal.

▷ 134

A section of ITT System 12 digital exchange. These systems function in an analog environment but have been designed for tomorrow's digital world. They handle both voice and data simultaneously with fail-safe reliability.

La commutation électronique numérique a été mise au point avec succès par ITT. Le central téléphonique Système 12 est un produit de pointe dans la commutation. Il représente une percée importante dans l'application des techniques les plus avancées et dans la conception de système. Il permet un passage économique et opportun du réseau analogique d'aujourd'hui au réseau entièrement numérique de demain.

Le Système 12 a été conçu pour répondre aux besoins croissants des administrations téléphoniques et de leurs abonnés désirant un service de meilleure qualité, moins coûteux et d'un meilleur rendement, pendant la longue période d'adaptation des réseaux au système numérique intégré. Il est le seul capable d'acheminer simultanément la téléphonie et les données. La structure entièrement numérique du Système 1240 est la solution adoptée par ITT pour faire face à l'augmentation de la demande de transmission de données. La numérisation s'étendra en définitive du central à l'abonné qui aura remplacé son téléphone par un terminal polyvalent. Cette numérisation permettra un très haut degré d'intégration téléphonie/données et améliorera la qualité et la fiabilité de la transmission. Par conséquent, bien que le Système 1240 d'ITT fonctionne parfaitement dans la situation largement analogique d'aujourd'hui, il a été conçu et construit pour l'environnement numérique de demain.

L'équipement recouvre la gamme entière des centraux locaux, en tandem et interurbains, desservant toutes catégories d'abonnés de la petite installation lointaine d'abonné jusqu'aux plus grands centraux urbains de 100 000 lignes ou interurbaines de 60 000 circuits. Ainsi le plus petit central peut être facilement et économiquement agrandi car le système est utilisable dans les configurations les plus diverses, de manière à satisfaire toutes les exigences de planification du réseau.

Une commande complètement répartie est l'une des caractéristiques majeures du Système ITT 1240. Au lieu d'être centralisé, le mode de commande logique réside dans des unités discrètes, faciles à manipuler, qui sont réparties dans tout le réseau. Ce n'est donc plus en un seul point que la mémoire est principalement enregistrée et que la plupart des fonctions logiques sont exécutées. L'architecture de la commande répartie de l'ITT 1240 va de pair avec la modulation par impulsions et codage (MIC) inventée par le chercheur d'ITT, Alec Reeves.

Dans toute structure à commande centralisée, si le système de commande ne fonctionne plus, l'ensemble du système en fait de même. En revanche, lorsque la commande est répartie sur un grand nombre de modules, le mauvais fonctionnement de l'un d'eux n'exerce qu'une influence marginale sur l'ensemble du système. Avant la mise au point du Système 1240, la nécessité de centraliser la plus grande partie de l'ensemble du logiciel de commande contraignait les administrations téléphoniques à commencer soit par un petit ordinateur difficilement remplaçable en cas d'extension du central, soit par un grand ordinateur assez peu économique dans la période initiale de l'exploitation. La commande répartie élimine cet inconvénient.

Le Système 1240 ne peut avoir de défaillances grâce à sa commande décentralisée, seuls de petits groupes de lignes ou de circuits peuvent se trouver hors service à un moment donné. De nombreux dispositifs de contrôle étant dédoublés, le risque de sérieuse perturbation de l'ensemble du système est éliminé. Une autre caractéristique qui va dans le même sens est l'incorporation dans le Système 1240 d'un tout nouveau réseau de commutation numérique basé sur un unique microprocesseur breveté LSI (intégration à grande échelle). Chaque microprocesseur contient son propre logiciel et sa propre mémoire et est capable d'accomplir trois tâches essentielles : transmission de la voix et/ou de données.

▷ 134

Une partie du central numérique ITT Système 12. Ce système fonctionne dans un environnement analogique quoique conçu pour le monde numérique de demain. Il transmet simultanément voix et données avec fiabilité totale.

ITT ha fabricado e instalado en el mundo entero unos 60 millones de líneas de equipo de conmutación telefónica local, y más de tres millones de líneas interurbanas. La conmutación de ITT es ahora la norma para muchas centrales telefónicas mundiales. **La conmutación electrónica totalmente digital** ha sido desarrollada con éxito por ITT. La central telefónica Sistema 12 sitúa a la compañía a la cabeza de la tecnología de conmutación. Representa un importante avance en la aplicación de tecnología y diseño de sistemas avanzados, y ofrece una amplia gama de soluciones compatible con las realidades de la red analógica actual y la red de suministro de información totalmente digital de mañana.

El Sistema 12 se ha concebido para atender la creciente demanda de las administraciones telefónicas y sus clientes de un servicio de mejor calidad, menor costo y mayores oportunidades de ingresos, pues a largo plazo se tiende a una red digital de servicios integrados, y su capacidad planificada es única para tratar simultáneamente voz y datos.

La estructura plenamente digital es la respuesta directa del sistema ITT 1240 a la creciente tendencia a solicitar comunicaciones de datos. La digitalización pasará finalmente de la central al abonado individual, cuyo teléfono clásico se sustituirá por un terminal de información multifuncional. La digitalización completa de la red permitirá el mayor grado posible de integración voz/datos y mejorará la calidad de transmisión y la fiabilidad. Así, aunque el sistema ITT 1240 funciona perfectamente en el medio en gran medida analógico de hoy, se ha diseñado y construido para el medio digital de mañana.

Abarca toda la gama de aplicaciones de centrales locales, en tándem e interurbanas, desde la unidad de abonado distante más pequeña hasta la mayor central local o interurbana de más de 10 000 líneas o 60 000 enlaces que utilizan módulos normalizados de soporte físico y lógico. Así, la central más pequeña puede ampliarse con facilidad y economía hasta el mayor tamaño, y el ITT 1240 puede aplicarse en varias configuraciones de centrales independientes o dependientes, incluida la operación supervisada o remota, ajustándose a todo requisito de planificación de la red.

El control totalmente distribuido es una noción única del sistema ITT 1240. En lugar del control en el centro, la lógica de control reside en unidades discretas, fácilmente manejables, a lo largo del sistema. Ya no hay, pues, ningún punto del sistema donde se almacene la mayor parte de la memoria o se ejecute la mayor parte de las funciones lógicas. La arquitectura de control distribuido del ITT 1240 representa un avance tecnológico paralelo a la modulación por impulsos codificados (MIC) por el científico de ITT Alec Reeves.

En una configuración de control centralizado, si la función de control disminuye, lo hace todo el sistema. Cuando el control se distribuye en un gran número de módulos, el mal funcionamiento de uno solo tendrá un efecto marginal sobre el sistema, sin reducir el servicio por debajo del límite aceptable. Antes de disponerse del 1240, la necesidad de centralizar la mayor parte o toda la lógica de control obligó a las administraciones a comenzar con un pequeño procesador, de difícil sustitución al ampliarse la central, o con un gran procesador, antieconómico para las necesidades iniciales, de pequeña capacidad. El control distribuido suprime este condicionamiento.

El sistema 1240 es totalmente seguro porque, a través del control distribuido, sólo pueden quedar fuera de servicio al mismo tiempo pequeños grupos de líneas o enlaces. Hay una duplicación de muchas unidades funcionales, que eliminan el riesgo de fallo

▷ 135

Una parte de la central digital de ITT Sistema 12. El sistema funciona en un medio analógico, pero se ha concebido para el mundo digital de mañana. Transmite simultáneamente voz y datos con una seguridad absoluta.

The architecture of the ITT 1240 depicted here uses the unique concept of fully distributed control to overcome the limitations of central control systems. It is remarkably simple, consisting of a number of autonomous terminal modules, each with its own microprocessor, connected to a digital switching network. Control logic resides in discrete units distributed is the system. A malfunction in any one module would have only a marginal effect on the total system.

L'architecture du système ITT 1240, que l'on voit ici, utilise la répartition de contrôle afin de surmonter les limitations des systèmes à contrôle central. La conception générale est simple : un nombre de modules terminaux indépendants, chacun avec son microprocesseur, sont reliés à un réseau de commutation numérique.Le contrôle logique est contenu dans des unités discrètes distribuées dans le système. Une défaillance dans un des modules n'aurait qu'un effet marginal sur l'ensemble.

La arquitectura del sistema 1240 de ITT, que utiliza el concepto único de control totalmente distribuido para superar las limitaciones de los sistemas de control central. La concepción general es muy sencilla: consta de cierto número de módulos terminales independientes, con sendos microprocesadores, conectados a una red de conmutación digital. El control lógico reside en unidades discretas, fácilmente manejables, en todo el sistema. A diferencia de un sistema de control central, el fallo en uno de los módulos sólo tiene un efecto marginal sobre el conjunto.

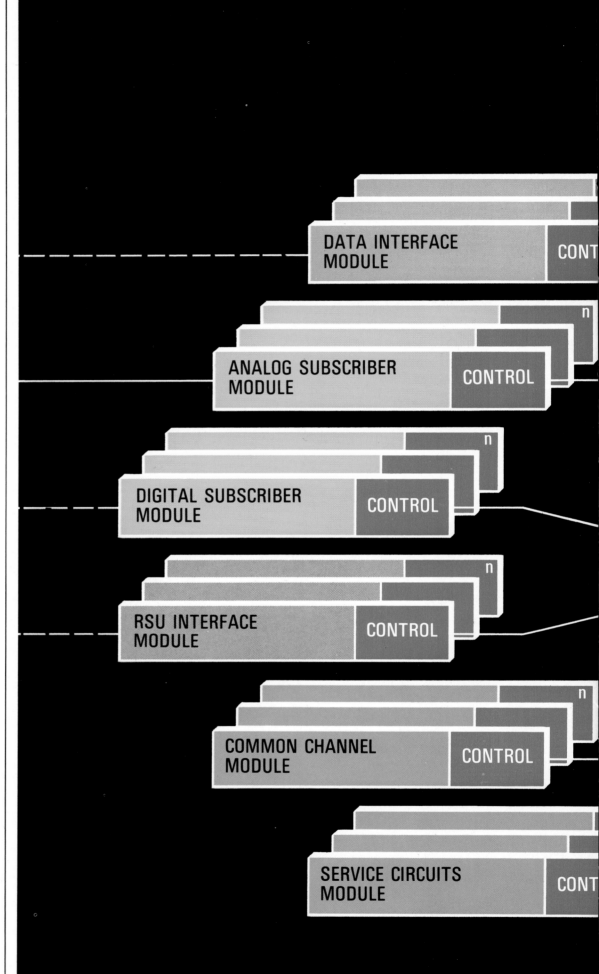

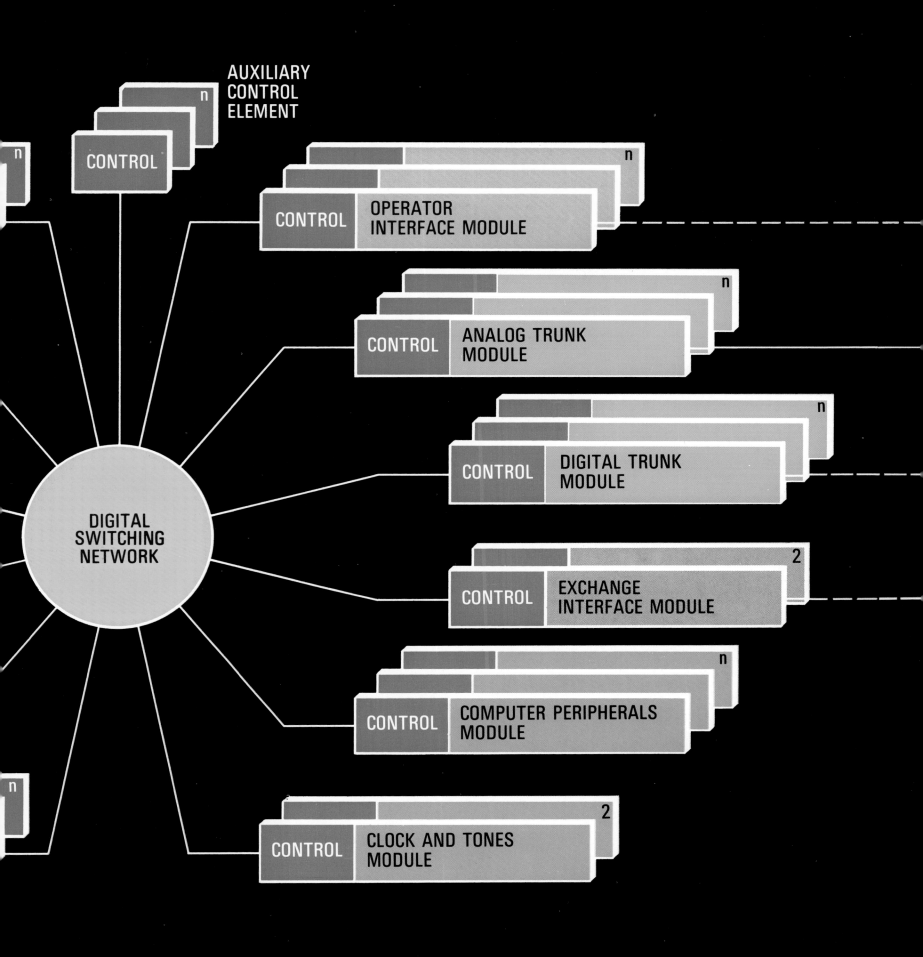

The 1240 system is fail-safe because, through distributed control, only small groups of lines or trunks can go out of service at any given time. Many functional units are duplicated, essentially eliminating the risk of disrupting the entire system. Moreover, the system incorporates a revolutionary new Digital Switching Network based on a single, patented, custom LSI chip. Each chip contains its own logic and memory so that it can carry out three essential tasks: speech and/or data transmission, path selection, and communication between distributed microprocessors. Since each chip is fully self-contained, failure of any one chip in the network simply means the path is rerouted through another. The system is therefore virtually nonblocking and the momentary loss of any one chip, or several chips, has negligible effect.

The design of the 1240 ensures that it will function equally well in the largely analog environment of today and in the largely digital environment of tomorrow. Each hardware module has its own software module with a fixed interface to the rest of the system. Therefore, to introduce a new hardware module it is necessary only to change its associated software module. And the software is structured so that additions do not require extensive retesting of the software already in place.

Given this versatility, a telephone administration can introduce new hardware and software to provide new service at any time it is convenient and cost-effective to do so, without major changes to the existing system. There is no need to wait, perhaps several years, for gradual incorporation. Further, with the rapid proliferation of data networks, great flexibility will be needed to meet adequately the wide variety of interfaces. Also, as the demand for data services grows, the structure of the system will permit the introduction of these services without major changes and/or replacement of existing equipment, thereby utilizing the existing facilities more effectively, rather than requiring additional capital investments. The system is thus obsolescence-resistant.

The concept of fully distributed control is a marked departure from conventional exchanges and deserves a close look. It provides a massive amount of processing power to overcome capacity limitations found in centralized systems, and at the same time allows isolation between functions, which is necessary to assure high-quality performance and easy introduction of new capabilities.

Implementation of distributed control involves a number of imaginative new engineering concepts. The most important are a switching network which can be controlled from its end-points without requiring a central control to establish and maintain paths, and a software structure which allows a number of autonomous microprocessors to cooperate in handling all of the exchange functions. This software structure requires each microprocessor to establish paths through the switching network both for terminal-to-terminal connections and for passing control information to other microprocessors.

No separate data communication is provided for the microprocessors. They communicate with each other along the same paths that are used for speech. The simplicity of the resulting structure permits a broad number of different types of terminals to use the same switching network. Thus, not only can data terminals be readily integrated into existing ITT 1240 exchanges, but many as yet undefined terminal devices can also readily be accommodated. The only requirements are that the new devices be able to communicate digitally and that they respect the hardware interface format for communicating with other terminals.

▷ 138

sélection de trajet et communication entre microprocesseurs disséminés. Puisque chaque microprocesseur est entièrement autonome, la défaillance de l'un d'eux dans le réseau n'entraîne que le réacheminement sur un autre. Le système n'est donc pas bloqué et la perte momentanée d'un ou même de plusieurs microprocesseurs n'a qu'un effet mineur.

La conception du Système 1240 fait que chaque module d'équipement a son propre logiciel et un dispositif d'interconnexion avec le reste du système. Ainsi, pour introduire un nouveau module, il suffit de changer son logiciel qui est structuré de telle façon que les adjonctions n'exigent pas d'importantes vérifications du logiciel existant.

Compte tenu de cette polyvalence, une administration téléphonique peut introduire un nouvel équipement et un nouveau logiciel pour suppléer à de nouveaux services, sans que cela entraîne une modification profonde du système existant. Dès l'instant où la demande de services de données augmente, la structure du système permet d'introduire ces services sans modification importante, ni remplacement de l'équipement existant. Par conséquent il est possible d'utiliser plus efficacement ce qui existe sans qu'il soit nécessaire d'augmenter les investissements. Le système est donc résistant à l'obsolescence.

La notion de commande répartie s'écarte beaucoup de l'idée classique des centraux téléphoniques et mérite d'être examinée de plus près. Sa mise en œuvre donne une grande puissance de traitement qui permet de surmonter les limites de capacité inhérentes aux systèmes centralisés. Il devient possible d'isoler les fonctions, ce qui est indispensable pour obtenir un haut niveau de performance et pour mettre aisément en œuvre de nouvelles dispositions.

La réalisation de la commande répartie fait intervenir l'emploi de plusieurs nouveaux concepts de technique électronique. Le plus important étant la création d'un réseau de commutation pouvant être commandé à partir de ses extrémités, sans commande centrale pour établir et maintenir les voies de communication et une structure de logiciel permettant à plusieurs microprocesseurs de coopérer à toutes les fonctions du central. Dans une telle structure chaque microprocesseur doit pouvoir établir des acheminements à travers le réseau de commutation, aussi bien pour les communications entre terminaux, que pour transmettre des informations de commande à d'autres microprocesseurs.

Il n'y a pas de liaisons séparées pour la transmission de la parole et celle des données. La simplicité de cette structure permet à un grand nombre de terminaux de types différents d'utiliser le même réseau de commutation. Ainsi, non seulement divers terminaux de données peuvent être intégrés facilement dans des centraux ITT 1240 existants mais de nombreux autres dispositifs d'une conception encore indéterminée pourront aussi être aisément adaptés.

Le logiciel du Système ITT 1240 est également révélateur d'une conception révolutionnaire de l'ensemble du central. Ses fonctions sont réparties entre les nombreux microprocesseurs du système. Une erreur de logiciel ne risque donc d'affecter qu'une partie relativement petite du système. Aussi l'adjonction de nouveau matériel ou la modernisation des services n'exige que la modification du logiciel correspondant, et non pas de l'ensemble du système.

Des équipements de transmission de conception avancée viennent compléter les progrès d'ITT en matière de technologie de la commutation. La grande gamme d'équipements ITT comprend des systèmes de transmission par faisceaux hertziens, par câble coaxial, satellite, et plus récemment par fibres optiques.

En 1966, deux chercheurs de chez ITT ont proposé de transmettre l'information au moyen de fibres de

▷ 138

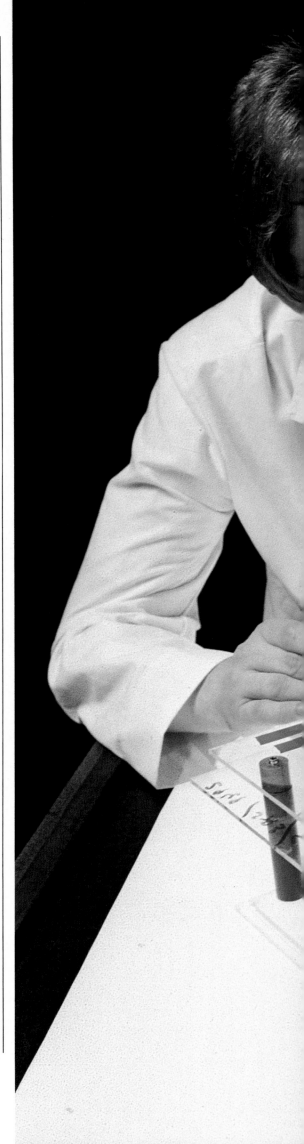

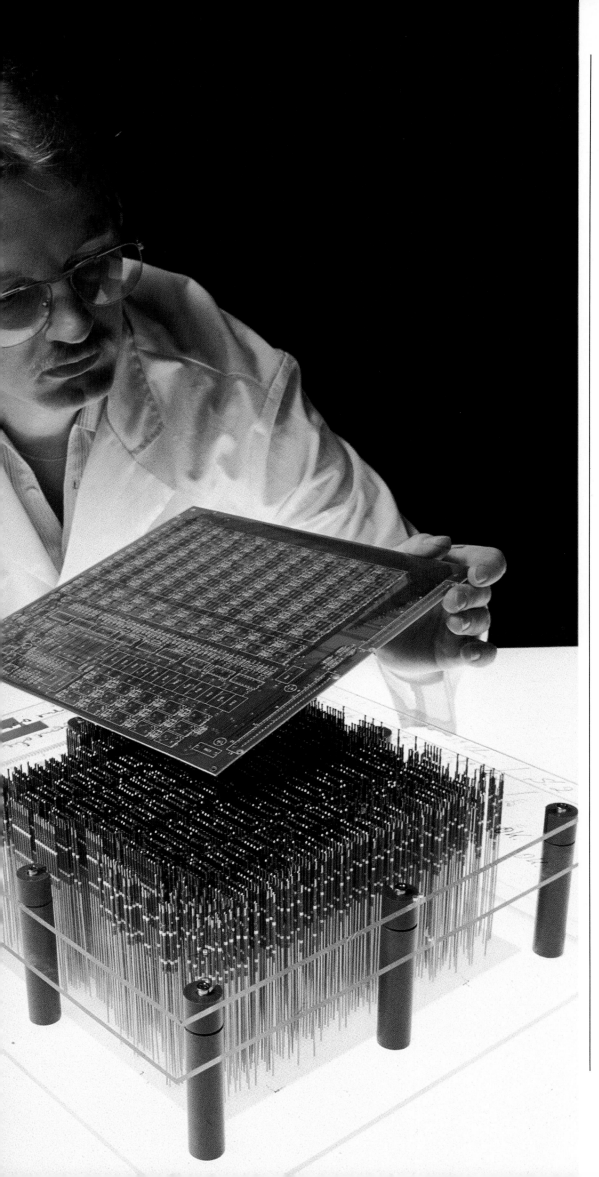

de todo el sistema. Además, el 1240 incorpora una nueva red de conmutación digital revolucionaria, basada en una plaqueta LSI adaptable y patentada. Cada plaqueta contiene su propia lógica y memoria, por lo que puede realizar tres tareas esenciales: transmisión de palabra y/o datos, selección de trayecto, y comunicación entre microprocesadores distribuidos. Como cada plaqueta es independiente, el fallo de una en la red sólo significa que hay que encaminar el trayecto por otra. Por eso, el sistema prácticamente no puede bloquearse, y el efecto de la pérdida momentánea de una o varias plaquetas es mínimo.

El diseño del 1240 garantiza que funcionará igual en el medio en gran medida analógico de hoy que en el considerablemente digital de mañana. Cada módulo de soporte físico tiene su propio módulo de soporte lógico, con un interfaz fijo con el resto del sistema. Por tanto, para introducir un nuevo módulo de soporte físico sólo hay que cambiar su módulo de soporte lógico asociado. Y el soporte lógico se ha estructurado de manera que las adiciones no supongan grandes pruebas del soporte lógico ya instalado.

Debido a esta versatilidad, una administración telefónica puede introducir nuevo soporte físico y lógico para proporcionar otros servicios en cualquier momento que convenga y sea rentable hacerlo, sin muchos cambios del sistema existente. No hay que esperar años para la incorporación gradual. Además, la rápida expansión de redes de datos impondrá una gran flexibilidad para atender la amplia gama de interfaces. También, cuando aumenta la demanda de servicios de datos, la estructura del 1240 permitirá introducirlo sin grandes modificaciones, ni sustituir el equipo, utilizando así las facilidades existentes con mayor eficacia, en vez de hacer nuevas inversiones de capital. Por tanto, el sistema no cae en desuso.

La noción de control plenamente distribuido se aparta mucho de las centrales clásicas y merece atento examen. Ofrece una gran cantidad de energía de procesamiento para superar las limitaciones de capacidad de los sistemas centralizados, y permite al mismo tiempo aislar las funciones, lo cual es necesario para un rendimiento de gran calidad y la fácil introducción de nuevas capacidades.

La aplicación del control distribuido entraña varios conceptos técnicos nuevos e imaginativos. Los más importantes son una red con conmutación que pueda controlarse desde sus extremos, sin requerir un control central para establecer y mantener trayectos, y una estructura de soporte lógico que permita a varios procesadores autónomos cooperar en la realización de todas las funciones de la central. En esa estructura de soporte lógico, cada microprocesador ha de establecer trayectos a través de la red de conmutación, tanto para las conexiones de terminal a terminal como para pasar información de control a otros microprocesadores.

Para los microprocesadores no se prevé ninguna comunicación de datos independiente. Comunican entre sí a través de los mismos trayectos usados para la palabra. La sencillez de la estructura resultante permite a un gran número de terminales distintos emplear la misma red de conmutación. Así, no sólo pueden integrarse rápidamente los terminales de datos en las centrales 1240 existentes, sino también acomodar rápidamente muchos dispositivos terminales no definidos aún.

El soporte lógico ITT 1240 es otro reflejo de los criterios de diseño revolucionarios que caracterizan a toda la central. Las funciones de soporte lógico se distribuyen en varias formas entre los numerosos microprocesadores del sistema. Por tanto, un error de soporte lógico sólo afecta a una pequeña parte del sistema. Además, para agregar nuevo soporte lógico

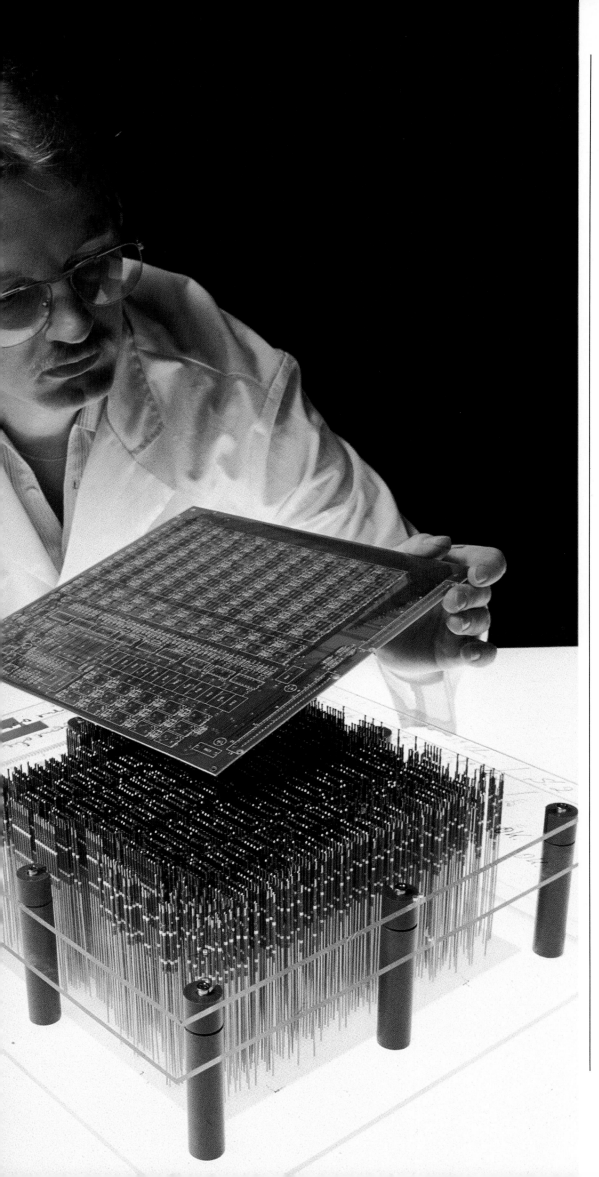

▷ 139

Un aspecto de las actividades de investigación y desarrollo de ITT, que abarcan todas las facetas de la tecnología de las comunicaciones, y comprenden sectores esenciales como microelectrónica, programación, materiales y productividad.

A view of ITT's System 1240, which has been
operating at customer locations since 1981. The
system covers the entire range of local, tandem and
toll exchange applications and is one of the most
advanced telecommunications switching systems in
the world. It is modular in conception: the smallest
can be expanded easily and economically to more
than 100,000 lines or 60,000 trunks.

Un aperçu du système ITT 1240 qui fonctionne
depuis 1981. Ce système qui recouvre la gamme
entière des applications dans les centraux
locaux, « tandem » et interurbains, est l'un des
systèmes de commutation numérique les plus
perfectionnés du monde. Il est modulaire : le plus
petit peut être facilement et économiquement
agrandi en central de plus de 100 000 lignes
locales ou de 60 000 circuits interurbains.

El sistema ITT 1240 que funciona en
los locales del cliente desde 1981. El sistema abarca
toda la gama de aplicación de centrales locales, en
tándem e interurbanas, y es uno de los procedimientos
de conmutación de telecomunicaciones más
avanzados del mundo. Es modular: el más pequeño
puede ampliarse fácil y económicamente, y
convertirse en la mayor central local o interurbana,
con más de 100 000 circuitos o 60 000 enlaces.

The ITT 1240 software is a further reflection of the revolutionary design criteria which characterize the entire exchange. Software functions are distributed in various ways over the numerous system microprocessors. A software error can therefore affect only a relatively small portion of the system. Also the addition of new hardware or the enhancement of services requires modification of only the relevant software, not of the entire system.

Transmission products of advanced design complement the company's advances in switching technology. The company's wide variety of equipment includes microwave, coaxial cable, satellite, and, most recently, fiber optic transmission systems.

In 1966 two ITT scientists proposed information transmission over hair-thin fibers of glass. At the time neither fibers nor semiconductor laser sources were available to demonstrate the practical advantages of this form of transmission. Eleven years later, technology progressed to an extent that the company was able to take optical cables out of the laboratory and begin manufacture. ITT installed the world's first optical fiber system equipped with repeaters, through six miles of normal underground ducts.

Since 1977 optical communications has undergone considerable development. Telephone companies can now consider optical fiber systems for current use as well as for the foundation of future information transfer systems. ITT is one of the few fully integrated suppliers of such systems, including cables, terminal and repeater equipment, and connectors.

In addition to fiber-optic transmission systems, the company's factories in many countries manufacture metallic cable transmission systems using a variety of multiplexing techniques that carry thousands of telephone conversations over each transmission path. Similar multiplexing techniques have been employed on the more-than-90,000 nautical miles of submarine cable installed or being manufactured as part of the international telephone network. Nearly 50 million circuit miles of conversation paths have been supplied, representing half of the world's submarine cable capacity.

Complementing this same worldwide network, ITT has designed, manufactured and installed (1982) some 100 satellite earth stations, including huge 100-foot-diameter Intelsat-type installations which provide thousands of international circuits. It also manufactures smaller ground stations, used as communications links to telephone exchanges in remote locations and for private business communications. Advanced microwave radio systems are designed and manufactured in several of the company's factories. They are used to provide multiple channels for telephony or television over radio links on line-of-sight paths between dish-like antennae mounted on towers or buildings.

ITT produces the widest range of terminal equipment available from any single supplier. From telephone sets to computer terminals, from power supplies to modems to teleprinters (its subsidiaries are among the world's oldest and largest manufacturers of teleprinters). This is because the company serves the largest of customer bases and has developed the flexibility needed to adapt to the requirements of different customers in different locations.

ITT manufactures a complete line of modern telephones — some nine million a year — and a broad range of data and text terminal equipment. The emphasis in data terminals is on data communications software, the use of LSI technology and, more recently, color displays. The company had, in 1983, the widest range of daisy wheel printers available.

In the business communications field ITT units have put more than five million lines of PABX equipment in service and have an annual production of 400,000 lines. The Unimat range of stored-pro-

▷ 142

verre de l'épaisseur d'un cheveu. Ni fibres, ni lasers n'existaient pour prouver les avantages de cette forme de transmission. Onze ans plus tard, la technique avait progressé suffisamment pour permettre le transfert du laboratoire à l'atelier de fabrication. ITT a installé le premier système de câble optique, long de 10 km dans des canalisations souterraines existantes.

Depuis 1977, les communications optiques ont connu un développement considérable. Les services téléphoniques peuvent maintenant les utiliser pour des réseaux de types courants, aussi bien que pour établir les fondations de futurs systèmes de transfert d'informations. ITT est l'un des rares fournisseurs de systèmes optiques complets, comprenant les câbles, l'équipement du terminal, les répéteurs et les connecteurs.

Le système de transmission par fibres optiques n'est qu'un élément dans la large gamme de produits ITT. Les usines de la société fabriquent dans de nombreux pays, des systèmes de transmission à câbles métalliques qui utilisent diverses techniques de multiplexage pour acheminer des milliers de conversations téléphoniques sur chaque voie. Des techniques de multiplexage ont été utilisées sur plus de 165 000 km de câbles sous-marins existants ou en cours de fabrication pour le réseau téléphonique international qui relient entre eux la plupart des pays du monde. ITT a fourni près de 80 millions de km de circuits téléphoniques en câbles sous-marins, ce qui représente la moitié de la capacité mondiale.

Pour compléter ce même réseau global, ITT avait conçu, construit et installé, jusqu'en 1982, une centaine de stations terriennes, notamment de grandes antennes du type Intelsat d'un diamètre de 30 mètres, fournissant des milliers de circuits internationaux. La gamme comprend également des stations terriennes plus petites, utilisées pour assurer les communications avec des centres téléphoniques situées dans des régions isolées et pour les réseaux de communications privées. Des systèmes perfectionnés à hyperfréquences sont conçus et fabriqués dans plusieurs usines de la société. Ils fournissent des voies multiples de téléphonie ou de télévision par faisceaux hertziens à visibilité directe entre antennes paraboliques montées sur pylônes ou bâtiments.

ITT offre une très large gamme de terminaux, à partir du simple appareil téléphonique jusqu'au terminal d'ordinateur, du système d'alimentation électrique au modem et au téléimprimeur.

Ses filiales sont parmi les plus anciens fabricants de téléimprimeurs du monde. Une grande souplesse a été requise pour satisfaire aux exigences très diversifiées de sa vaste clientèle et pour répondre aux besoins de tous les usagers, en quelque lieu qu'ils se trouvent dans le monde.

ITT fabrique une gamme complète de téléphones — environ neuf millions d'appareils par an et des équipements de terminaux pour la transmission de textes et de données. Dans ses terminaux de données, ITT a mis l'accent sur le logiciel de communications, l'utilisation de la technologie LSI et plus récemment, sur les systèmes de visualisation en couleurs. La société disposait en 1983 de la plus large gamme d'imprimantes à marguerite.

Dans le domaine des communications d'affaires, les sociétés du groupe ont mis plus de 5 millions de lignes d'autocommutateurs privés en service (PABX) et en produisent 400 000 annuellement. La gamme de PABX, entièrement électronique, Unimat, à commande par programme enregistré, est utilisée dans tous les grands pays européens et dans plus de vingt pays d'Amérique Latine, de la région Asie-Pacifique et du Moyen-Orient. ITT a ensuite mis au point un système numérique PABX hybride à clavier, avec commande par microprocesseur d'une capacité de 288 lignes ou postes.

Les services téléphoniques et les services d'informatiques d'ITT sont à l'échelle du monde entier. Ses activités

▷ 142

A cross section of an optical fiber cable. Laser light flows through a 1/8 millimeter diameter fiber within a cable with an outside diameter of only 3 millimeters o.d. gained wide acceptance.

Section d'un câble optique. Le rayon laser est transmis le long d'une fibre de 1/8 mm de diamètre contenue dans un câble optique de 3 mm de diamètre extérieur, de grande capacité opérationelle.

o mejorar los servicios sólo hay que modificar el soporte correspondiente, y no todo el sistema.

Los productos de transmisión de diseño avanzado complementan los progresos de ITT en tecnología de conmutación. La amplia variedad de su equipo comprende sistemas de transmisión por microondas, cable coaxial, satélite y fibras ópticas.

En 1966, dos científicos de ITT propusieron transmitir información por fibras de vidrio del grosor de un pelo. Entonces no se disponía de fibras ni de fuentes láser de semiconductores para demostrar las ventajas prácticas de esta forma de transmisión. Once años después, la tecnología había progresado tanto que la empresa podía comenzar la fabricación de cables ópticos. ITT instaló el primer sistema de fibras ópticas del mundo con repetidores, a lo largo de 10 km de conductos subterráneos normales.

Desde 1977, las comunicaciones ópticas se han desarrollado considerablemente. Las compañías telefónicas pueden considerar ahora sistemas de fibras ópticas para uso corriente, así como base de los futuros sistemas de transferencia de información. ITT es uno de los pocos proveedores plenamente integrados de sistemas de fibras ópticas, incluidos cables, equipo terminal y de repetidores, y conectores.

Además de los sistemas de transmisión por fibras ópticas, las fábricas de la empresa producen en muchos países sistemas de transmisión por cable metálico utilizando diversas técnicas de multiplicación que transmiten miles de conversaciones telefónicas por cada trayecto. En las más de 90 000 millas marinas de cables submarinos instalados o fabricados como parte de la red telefónica internacional se han empleado técnicas de multiplicación análogas. Se han suministrado cerca de 80 millones de km de circuitos de trayectos de conversación, que representan la mitad de la capacidad de los cables submarinos mundiales.

Complementando esa misma red mundial, ITT ha diseñado, fabricado e instalado (1982) unas 100 estaciones terrenas, incluidas enormes instalaciones de tipo Intelsat de 30 metros de diámetro, que proporcionan miles de circuitos internacionales. También fabrica estaciones terrenas más pequeñas, usadas como enlaces con centrales telefónicas de lugares remotos y para comunicaciones comerciales privadas. Los sistemas radioeléctricos de microondas se conciben y producen en varias fábricas de la empresa, empleándose para proporcionar canales múltiples de telefonía o televisión por enlaces radioeléctricos en trayectos de visibilidad directa entre antenas parabólicas montadas en torres o edificios.

ITT ofrece la más amplia gama de equipo terminal de telecomunicación de un solo proveedor: desde aparatos telefónicos hasta terminales de computador, y desde suministros de energía a módems y teleimpresores. Esto se debe a que la empresa sirve a más clientes que cualquier otro proveedor y a que ha logrado la flexibilidad necesaria para adaptarse a las necesidades de distintos clientes en diversos lugares.

ITT fabrica una serie completa de teléfonos modernos — unos 9 millones anuales — y una amplia gama de equipo terminal de datos y de texto. En los terminales de datos se insiste en soporte lógico de comunicaciones, la tecnología LSI y, últimamente, la visualización en color. La empresa dispone de la más amplia gama de impresores de margarita.

En el sector de las comunicaciones comerciales, las unidades de ITT han puesto en servicio más de cinco millones de líneas de equipo CAP, y su producción anual es de 400 000 líneas. La gama de control por programa almacenado Unimat, CAP totalmente electrónicas, se usa en los principales países europeos y en más de 20 países de América Latina, Asia y el Pacífico, Africa y el Oriente Medio. Esto ha ido se-

▷ 142

Corte transversal de un cable de fibras ópticas. La luz láser se transmite a través de una fibra de 1/8 mm de diámetro, en un cable cuyo diámetro exterior es sólo de 3 mm. Este tipo de transmisión ha demostrado su capacidad operacional y ha tenido gran aceptación.

The programmers of ITT. The company employs more than 8,000 programmers worldwide, whose goal is to improve the interface between man and machine and to assure excellence in product performance while controlling costs. Programming is fundamental to the future of digital telecommunications systems and networks.

Les programmeurs d'ITT. La compagnie emploie plus de 8000 programmeurs dans le monde, dont les objectifs visent à améliorer l'interface entre l'homme et la machine et à assurer une excellente performance des produits tout en contrôlant les coûts. La programmation est la base essentielle de l'avenir des systèmes de télécommunications numériques et des réseaux.

Los programadores de ITT. La empresa emplea a más de 8000 programadores en el mundo, con el fin de mejorar el interfaz entre hombre y máquina y de garantizar un excelente rendimiento de los productos, controlando los costos. La programación es fundamental para los futuros sistemas y redes de telecomunicaciones digitales.

gram-control, fully electronic PABXs are in use in all major European countries and in more than 20 countries in Latin America, the Asia Pacific area, Africa and the Middle East. This has been followed by the development of a digital hybrid PABX/key system incorporating microprocessor control covering a range of up to 288 lines or stations.

The provision of operations/informations services by ITT is world-wide and on a very large scale. The wide variety of communications activities include long distance telephone service in the US and the Caribbean, and value-added services that permit virtually all data and record terminals to interface with one another for telex, electronic mail and other record services. Information activities include directories, on-line data bases, a wide variety of printed business and technical material, as well as productivity improvement, training and consulting services. These services are offered within the US, and in cooperation with more than 200 administrations, to countries all over the world. ITT's Directory Operations continue to be the largest "yellow pages" producer outside the United States.

Research and development constitute a major commitment, some 25,000 scientists, engineers and technical staff being employed in ITT's laboratories. A flow of new and improved products and services results from investment in research, development and engineering (RD&E). This investment is on a massive scale: in 1982 it approached $ 1,200 million, increasing in proportion to the corporation's growth at a rate averaging some 10 per cent a year.

The company's programming capabilities are also essential to its continuing competitiveness. Currently, some 7,000 individuals are involved in one of the widest ranges of programming activities in the world.

Organizing the RD&E efforts of more than 200 units plus a dozen major laboratories around the world is a corporate function. The results, including some 30,000 patents, are made available to all other ITT companies for their respective products or systems.

Because of its international makeup and broad product range, ITT is uniquely positioned to direct and control the transfer of technology across both geographical and product line boundaries. Advances in one industrial area are applied to other product lines that will benefit from this development fallout.

Today, there are telecommunications laboratories in Belgium, Italy, Norway, Spain, the United Kingdom, the US and the Federal Republic of Germany. In addition, there are advanced technology centers in Europe and the US which complement RD&E efforts taking place throughout the world.

The transfer of technology to client countries has been an operating philosophy of ITT since its earliest days. The company also provides factory construction, technical instruction and operation and maintenance programs for telecommunications administrations of various countries. Telecommunications training centers are operating in numerous countries. Over the past five years the company provided formal training to some 367,000 non-ITT engineers and technicians in more than 100 locations.

Transfer of technology, through product know-how and people skills, has increased in importance with the accelerating demand for complex communications systems around the globe. The company has met this requirement very fully wherever its products or services have been supplied.

ITT has grown to its present size in the worldwide telecommunications industry by being responsive to change, by being flexible and by being able to meet the different needs of many customers. As a company, it is committed to new development, investing more than $ 1,000 million a year in research, development and engineering programs.

□

très diversifiées comprennent les communications téléphoniques interurbaines aux Etats-Unis et aux Caraïbes, ainsi que des réseaux à valeur ajoutée permettant l'interconnexion de n'importe quel terminal avec un autre terminal pour les services de messagerie, de courrier électronique et de fac-similé. Les activités de télématique englobent les annuaires, les banques de données en ligne, une grande variété d'imprimés commerciaux et techniques, ainsi que des services de conseils et de formation professionnelle. Ces services sont proposés non seulement aux Etats-Unis mais dans tous les pays du monde, en coopération avec plus de 200 administrations.

ITT continue d'être le plus grand éditeur de « pages jaunes » d'annuaire, en dehors des Etats-Unis.

La recherche et le développement constituent une activité essentielle du groupe qui emploie quelque 25 000 chercheurs, ingénieurs et techniciens, dans ses laboratoires. La création de nouveaux produits et la mise en exploitation de services améliorés résulte des investissements consentis en recherche, développement et ingénierie (RD&I). En 1982, ils atteignaient 1,2 milliards de dollars environ et ils augmentent, en fonction de la croissance de la société, à un rythme moyen de 10% par an.

Les capacités de programmation d'ITT sont également essentielles pour assurer sa compétitivité. Actuellement, quelque 8000 personnes collaborent à l'une des plus vastes entreprises de programmation, pour le compte du groupe.

Organiser, à l'échelle mondiale, les activités de RD&I de plus de 200 filiales et d'une douzaine de laboratoires est une fonction de la direction générale d'ITT. Les résultats acquis — notamment 30 000 brevets — sont à la disposition de toutes les sociétés du groupe ITT pour favoriser la mise en valeur de leurs produits et de leurs systèmes.

Compte tenu de son caractère international et de la gamme très étendue de ses produits, ITT est exceptionnellement bien placée pour favoriser les transferts technologiques aussi bien à travers les frontières qu'entre les différents secteurs d'activité. Les progrès accomplis dans une branche industrielle profitent généralement aux autres.

Aujourd'hui, des laboratoires de télécommunications d'ITT ou de ses sociétés affiliées fonctionnent en Belgique, Italie, Espagne, Etats-Unis, Norvège, République fédérale d'Allemagne et Royaume-Uni et il existe d'autre part, aux Etats-Unis et en Europe, des centres de technologies de pointe qui contribuent aux efforts de RD&I déployés dans le monde entier.

Les transferts de technologie ont toujours été favorisés, surtout vers les pays qui étaient ses clients ou qui le sont devenus par la suite. Le groupe offre aux administrations de télécommunications des programmes de construction d'usines, de formation technique, d'exploitation et de maintenance. Au cours des cinq dernières années, les établissements créés par ITT dans de nombreux pays ont assuré — en plus de 100 lieux géographiques — la formation de 367 000 ingénieurs et techniciens des télécommunications n'appartenant pas à ITT ou sociétés du groupe.

Le transfert de techniques, de savoir-faire et de personnel spécialisé, s'est intensifié avec l'accélération de la demande de systèmes de communications perfectionnés. ITT a répondu positivement et sans réserve à cette demande, partout où cela était possible, en fournissant ses produits et ses services.

ITT a atteint son niveau actuel dans l'industrie mondiale des télécommunications en réagissant positivement au changement et en faisant preuve de souplesse et de disponibilité face aux besoins très diversifiés de ses nombreux clients. Pour pouvoir réaliser ses objectifs elle investit chaque année plus de un milliard de dollars dans des programmes de recherche, de développement et d'ingénierie.

□

Top: The ITT communications control center. Data, record and voice communications services are provided on a worldwide basis in cooperation with more than 200 administrations. Below: A modern telephone, one of a complete line manufactured by ITT, which includes the first fully digital instrument.

En haut : Le centre de contrôle de communications d'ITT. Des services de communication téléphonique et de messages différés sont assurés dans le monde entier en coopération avec plus de 200 administrations. En bas : Un récent combiné téléphonique d'ITT, partie d'une gamme complète qui comprend le premier appareil entièrement numérique.

ONS CONTROL CENTER

New York   London   Rome   Moscow

guido del desarrollo de un sistema digital híbrido CAP/teclado con control por microprocesador que abarca hasta 288 líneas o estaciones.

ITT proporciona operaciones/servicios de información en gran escala en el mundo entero. La amplia variedad de actividades de comunicación abarca el servicio telefónico de larga distancia en EE.UU. y el Caribe, y servicios de valor añadido que permiten conectar virtualmente todos los terminales de datos y registro con otros para servicios télex, correo electrónico y otros servicios de registro. Las actividades de telemática comprenden guías, bases de datos en línea, una amplia variedad de material impreso comercial y técnico, y servicios para mejorar la productividad, la información y la consulta. Esos servicios se ofrecen en EE.UU. y, en cooperación con más de 200 administraciones, a los países del mundo entero. ITT sigue siendo el mayor productor de «páginas amarillas» de las guías fuera de EE.UU.

La investigación y el desarrollo constituyen un gran empeño; ITT cuenta en su laboratorio con unos 25 000 científicos, ingenieros y técnicos. La inversión en investigación, desarrollo e ingeniería (IDeI) ha permitido lograr un gran número de servicios nuevos y mejores. Esta inversión es enorme: en 1982 se aproximó a 1200 millones $, aumentando en proporción con el crecimiento de la empresa a un ritmo que era recientemente del 10% anual por término medio.

Para mantener la competitividad, también son esenciales las capacidades de programación de ITT. En la actualidad, unas 7.000 personas participan en una de las series de actividades de programación más amplias del mundo.

Organizar las actividades de IDeI de mas de 200 unidades, más una docena de grandes laboratorios en el mundo entero, es una función empresarial. Los resultados, incluidas unas 30 000 patentes, se ponen a disposición de todas las empresas de ITT.

En razón de su composición internacional y de su amplia gama de productos, ITT ocupa una posición privilegiada para dirigir y controlar la transferencia de tecnología a través de las fronteras geográficas y de las gamas de productos. Los avances en un sector industrial se aplican a otros que se beneficiarán de esa evolución generalizada.

Existen laboratorios de telecomunicaciones en Bélgica, Italia, Noruega, España, Reino Unido, EE.UU. y Alemania Occidental. Además, hay centros de tecnología avanzada en Europa y EE.UU., que complementan los esfuerzos mundiales de IDeI.

La transferencia de tecnología a países clientes es uno de los principios de la empresa en materia de explotación desde su creación. ITT ofrece también programas de construcción de fábricas, instrucción técnica y explotación y mantenimiento a las administraciones de varios países. En muchos funcionan centros de capacitación en telecomunicaciones. En los últimos cinco años, la empresa dispensó formación oficial en más de 100 lugares a unos 367 000 ingenieros. Mediante el conocimiento de los productos y la formación de personal, la transferencia de tecnología ha cobrado mayor importancia, al acelerarse la demanda de sistemas de comunicación complejos en todo el mundo. La empresa ha atendido plenamente tal necesidad dondequiera que ha proporcionado productos o servicios.

ITT ha logrado su actual dimensión en la industria mundial de telecomunicaciones por ser sensible al cambio, flexible y capaz de atender las distintas necesidades de muchos clientes. Está consagrada al nuevo desarrollo, invirtiendo más de 1000 millones $ anuales en programas de investigación, desarrollo e ingeniería.

□

Arriba: El centro de control de comunicaciones de ITT. La empresa presta servicios de comunicaciones de datos, mensajes y vocales al mundo entero, en cooperación con más de 200 administraciones.
Abajo: Un teléfono moderno, de la serie completa que fabrica ITT, que comprende el primer aparato totalmente digital para uso normal.

COMPUTERS
NEW AND COMMUNICATIONS POWERNEWHOP
BIRTH OF A NEW ERA

THE COMPUTER AND THE TECHNOLOGIES which have emerged to make it a practicable, low-cost tool, have brought profound change and advances in telecommunications over the past two decades. With its ability to handle vast amounts of information at lightning speeds, the computer is now impacting virtually every segment of the communications industry, and nowhere are its benefits being applied with greater effectiveness than in telephony.

The integration of the computer and communications disciplines is occuring so quickly and creating so many novel services that the International Telegraph and Telephone Consultative Committee (CCITT) of the ITU felt impelled to coin a name under which these new services could be grouped, selecting "telematics" as the most descriptive. During the next few years a diverse range of business and consumer products and services are likely to transform the telephone line and other transmission links into a multifunctional tool which will serve a multitude of communication requirements.

Leo Cherne, an American economist, once summed up the significance of the computer in a statement that now seems prophetic: "The computer is extremely fast, accurate and stupid. Man is incredibly slow, inaccurate and brilliant. The marriage of the two is a force beyond calculation".

Computers are now an integral part of communication systems. They have become both essential components in the operation of communications networks and a major user of existing transmission facilities for the movement of processed data. In fact this function, teleprocessing, has emerged as the fastest growing area of the world's computer industry.

To appreciate the development of the computer's role in telecommunications it is helpful to recall that its basic characteristics are digital in nature, and that
▷ 146

One of the world's largest fully digital communications networks put into service in Buenos Aires, Argentina, in 1982.

L'ORDINATEUR ET L'INFORMATIQUE ont bouleversé la situation dans le domaine des télécommunications, en ouvrant à celles-ci des voies inédites, particulièrement commodes et économiques. Grâce à sa capacité de traiter d'énormes masses de données, à des vitesses électroniques, l'ordinateur pénètre maintenant dans tous les secteurs de l'industrie des communications et se révèle d'une efficacité remarquable dans les réseaux téléphoniques.

L'intégration des disciplines de l'informatique et des communications s'opère à un rythme si rapide, et engendre un si grand nombre de services, que le Comité consultatif international télégraphique et téléphonique (CCITT) de l'UIT s'est trouvé dans l'obligation d'adopter un nouveau terme couvrant l'ensemble de ces nouveaux services : la « télématique ». Au cours de ces prochaines années, une nouvelle variété de produits et de services commerciaux et de consommation viendront transformer les lignes téléphoniques et autres liaisons de transmission en instruments polyvalents capables de satisfaire une multitude de besoins de communication.

Leo Cherne, économiste américain, a évalué l'importance de l'ordinateur en des termes qui paraissent aujourd'hui prophétiques : « L'ordinateur est extrêmement rapide, précis et stupide. L'homme est incroyablement lent, imprécis et intelligent. De leur union peut naître une force incommensurable ».

Les ordinateurs font désormais partie intégrante des systèmes de communication. Ils sont devenus un élément essentiel dans le fonctionnement des réseaux de communication et de grands utilisateurs des facilités de transmission existantes pour le transfert des données. En fait, leur fonctionnement à distance, appelée « télétraitement », s'est affirmé comme le secteur caractérisé par la croissance la plus rapide dans l'industrie mondiale de l'informatique.

Pour apprécier le rôle de l'ordinateur dans les télé-
▷ 146

Un des plus grands réseaux de commutation numérique du monde, mis en service à Buenos Aires, Argentine, en 1982.

EL COMPUTADOR Y LAS TECNOLOGÍAS que han surgido para hacer de él un instrumento práctico y económico han entrañado profundos cambios en las telecomunicaciones las dos últimas décadas. Con su capacidad para tratar grandes cantidades de información a velocidades electrónicas, el computador repercute ahora en todos los sectores de la industria de las comunicaciones, y en ninguna parte se aplican con más eficacia sus beneficios que en telefonía.

La integración de las disciplinas del computador y de las comunicaciones se produce a tal rapidez y crea tantos servicios nuevos pue el Comité Consultivo Internacional Telegráfico y Telefónico (CCITT) de la UIT se sintió obligado a acuñar un nombre para agrupar estos nuevos servicios, eligiendo como el más descriptivo "telemática". En los próximos años, una diversa gama de productos y servicios comerciales y de consumo probablemente conviertan la línea telefónica y otros enlaces de transmisión en instrumentos multifuncionales que atenderán muchísimas necesidades de comunicación.

Leo Cherne, economista americano, resumió en cierta ocasión el significado del computador en unos términos que parecen ahora proféticos: « El computador es sumamente rápido, preciso y estúpido. El hombre es increíblemente lento, impreciso y brillante. La unión de ambos constituye una fuerza incalculable ».

Los computadores forman ahora parte de los sistemas de comunicación. Se han convertido en un componente esencial de las redes de comunicaciones y en principal usuario de las facilidades de transmisión existentes para el movimiento de datos. En realidad, esta función, conocida como teleprocesamiento, ha surgido como el sector de más rápido crecimiento de la industria mundial del computador.
▷ 147

Una de las redes de comunicaciones totalmente digitales mayores del mundo, puesta en servicio en Buenos Aires (Argentina), en 1982.

the telecommunications of today are almost totally analog. The difference between the two methods of communications — analog is waveform and digital is "bit" or numeric form — is described in the Box on p. 124. In this lies the problem facing the nations' PTTs: that of heavy existing investment in obsolescent technology. This is made all the more galling by the fact that this obsolescent technology works perfectly for the purpose it was designed and developed i.e. to carry voice to any selected point through routes determined by an electromechanical switching apparatus known as the telephone exchange.

To interface the new with the old, it is helpful at this stage to spell out what is meant by analog and what is meant by digital, to indicate why the one is obsolescent and the other desirable, and to speculate how and when the emerging digital technology will replace the analog. Also, to determine how far the new can interface with the old and how economically and how effectively this can be done.

Traditional telephone, telegraph and telex systems, developed and refined since the 1890s, depend on banks of electrically operated switches for routing calls and transmitting the sound entering the system to the receiving end. The telephone copper wire transports electric oscillations analogous to the sound wave, i.e. the exact mirror of the varying air pressures made by the speakers' vocal chords. After being routed through the system, these electric currents wobble a diaphragm in the telephone receiver which reproduces the sound waves, and therefore the voice of the speaker. Such a system is perfectly adequate for the transmission of voice over distance, at the pace of the spoken word, but unequal to the rapid transmission of large volumes of data, and unsuitable for the transmission of image.

The new digitalized communications system is electronic in essence, relying on semiconductor technology, i.e. on the computer which executes sequential tasks according to certain rules of logic. Through pre-arranged programs it selects and transmits instructions which are despatched as high and low voltage signals travelling at near the speed of light. These are represented in the binary system, already described, in which only two numbers, 0 and 1, convey information. The computer adds, and multiples, by successive additions; it subtracts, and divides, by successive subtractions. Hundreds of thousands of calculations per second, and much more, are possible by using such simple methods. (See Box on p. 124: Elements in Electronic Switching).

This manner of communicating is much the same as that developed by Samuel Morse over 100 years ago: the transmission of dots and dashes, short and long signals, over copper wire still used in our telegraph system. But whereas the telegraph of the 1860s transmitted at the rate of 15 signals per second, the new digital systems can transmit their signals known as "bits" at rates of 4,800 per second over existing telephone lines and at twice that rate over especially conditioned telephone lines. But this method of transmission remains pedestrian in the extreme when compared to direct digital transmission over microwave radio or optical fiber cables at an astonishing several billion bits per second.

The explosive growth in computer usage in telecommunications during the past two or three decades has been the revolutionary advances in semiconductor technology and microelectronics. The computer was born out of research into telephone switching techniques. Electronic connections were essential to the computer's success, but the most basic indispensable knowledge involved the logic of circuit switching provided by telephone engineers. Switching devices progressed from the vacuum tube in the early 1940s, to the germanium-based transistor in the same decade, and to the silicon chip in the 1960s. By then electronic engineers had learned to compact many active and passive components on a square centimeter of silicon wafer. These devices, known as integrated circuits (ICs) represented the third generation of semiconductors in a decade. Progress thereafter advanced in quantum leaps.

▷ 148

communications, il convient de rappeler tout d'abord qu'il est de nature fondamentalement numérique, alors que les télécommunications d'aujourd'hui sont, dans leur quasi totalité, analogiques, (voir technique de conversion p. 124). C'est précisément là que réside le problème des administrations des PTT dans de nombreux pays : l'importance des capitaux investis dans une technologie dépassée. Celle-ci satisfait pleinement aux exigences pour lesquelles elle a été conçue et développée : transporter la voix à destination de n'importe quel point préalablement choisi, selon des acheminements déterminés par un équipement de commutation électromécanique bien connue et d'un fonctionnement sûr. Il est donc difficile de justifier un gros budget de remplacement.

Pour relier le nouveau à l'ancien, il convient de dire, à ce stade, ce qu'on entend par « analogique » et par « numérique ». Il faut se demander pourquoi l'un est caduc et l'autre valable, et aussi comment et quand la technologie numérique viendra remplacer l'analogique. Il importe encore de déterminer dans quelle mesure il sera possible de relier la nouvelle à l'ancienne et, le cas échéant, si cette opération sera réalisable économiquement et efficacement.

Les systèmes téléphoniques, télégraphiques et télex traditionnels, progressivement perfectionnés depuis 1890, dépendent de séries de commutateurs fonctionnant électriquement, pour assurer l'acheminement des communications et la transmission du son entre l'entrée du système et l'extrémité de réception. Les oscillations électriques « analogiques », qui sont la réplique exacte de la variations de pression d'air produite par les cordes vocales de celui qui parle, font vibrer un diaphragme dans le récepteur téléphonique, lequel reproduit ainsi les ondes acoustiques émises. Un tel système est parfaitement adapté pour la transmission de la voix à distance, alors qu'il est totalement inadéquat pour la transmission rapide de grandes quantités de données ou d'images.

Le nouveau système de communication numérique, essentiellement électronique, fonctionne à l'aide d'un ordinateur qui exécute des tâches séquentielles selon certaines règles logiques. Selon des programmes préalablement élaborés, il choisit et transmet des instructions sous forme de signaux à tension élevée ou basse, se propageant à des vitesses proches de celles de la lumière (voir encadré p. 124).

Ces tensions se traduisent dans le système binaire, déjà décrit, exclusivement par deux chiffres porteurs d'information : 0 et 1. Quant à l'ordinateur, il additionne et multiplie par additions successives ; il soustrait et divise par soustractions successives et effectue ainsi des milliers de calculs par seconde.

Cette manière de communiquer est très semblable à celle inventée par Samuel Morse il y a plus de 100 ans : la transmission de points et de traits, sous forme de signaux courts et longs, par un fil de cuivre, encore en usage dans nos systèmes télégraphiques. Toutefois, alors que le télégraphe de 1860 effectuait des transmissions à la vitesse de 15 signaux par seconde, les nouveaux systèmes numériques transmettent leurs signaux, les « bits », à des vitesses pouvant atteindre 4800 par seconde par les lignes téléphoniques existantes et au double de cette vitesse sur des lignes spécialement adaptées. Cependant cette méthode de transmission demeure excessivement lente et archaïque comparée à la transmission numérique directe par micro-ondes ou par câbles en fibres optiques à des vitesses pouvant atteindre plusieurs milliards de bits par seconde.

La progression fulgurante de l'utilisation des ordinateurs dans les télécommunications, au cours des trois dernières décennies, résulte des innovations révolutionnaires dans la technologie des semi-conducteurs et de la microélectronique. L'ordinateur est issu de la recherche dans le domaine des techniques de commutation téléphonique. Les dispositifs de commutation sont passés du stade du tube à vide (1940) au transistor à germanium, puis, dès 1960, au transistor au silicium. Depuis cette époque, les électroniciens ont appris à grouper une multitude de composants actifs ou passifs sur des plaques de silicium d'un centimètre carré. Ces dispositifs, appelés circuits intégrés, représentent la troisième génération des semi-con-

▷ 148

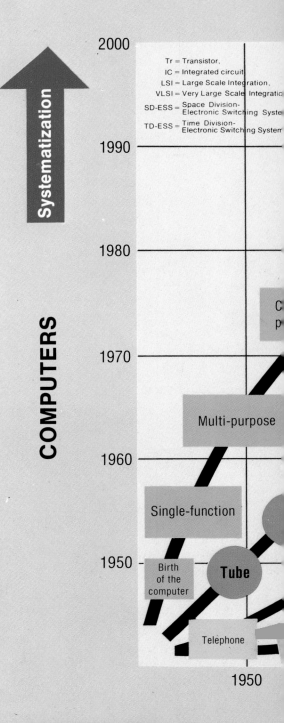

GROWING UNIFICATI

This figure, included in a presentation, "The Future Role of 'C&C' in the Home" given by Dr. Koji Kobayashi, Chairman and CEO of NEC Corporation, to the Massachusetts Institute of Technology (1982), depicts how computers and communications will be integrated toward the year 2000 into a single "C&C" system.

The vertical axis represents systemization, showing how computers are progressing from single-function to multi-purpose units and then, with the incorporation of communications technology, from centralized to distributed operation.

The horizontal axis represents the progress from the digitalization of communications, time-sharing in program control, optical transmission and eventually to fully integrated communications networks.

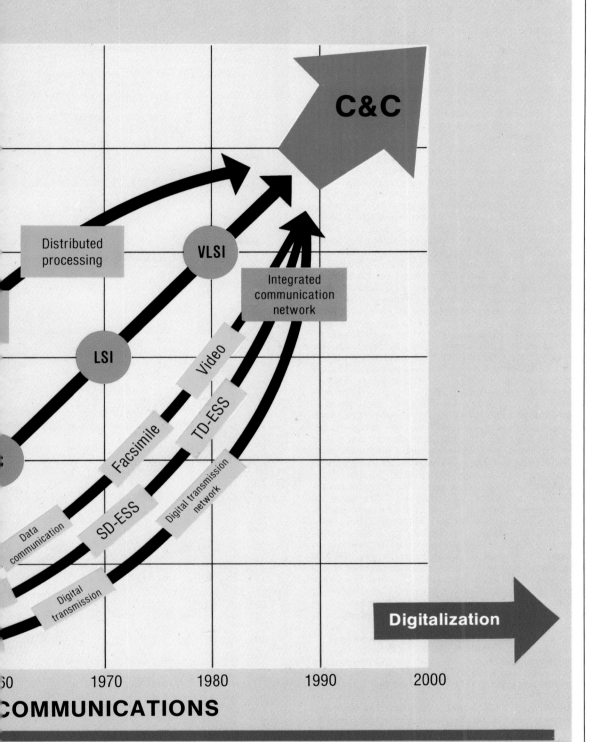

COMMUNICATIONS

Para apreciar el desarrollo del papel del computador en las telecomunicaciones, conviene recordar que sus características básicas son de índole digital, y que las telecomunicaciones actuales son casi totalmente analógicas (véase recuadro pág. 124). En esto reside el problema que se plantea a CTT nacionales: las grandes inversiones en tecnología que queda anticuada. Esto es tanto más irritante cuanto que esa tecnología anticuada cumple perfectamente el fin para el que fue concebida: llevar la voz a cualquier punto elegido y por rutas determinadas mediante un aparato de conmutación electromecánico conocido como central telefónica.

Para vincular lo nuevo con lo antiguo conviene señalar lo que se entiende por analógico y lo que significa digital, a fin de indicar por qué uno cae en desuso y el otro es deseable, y especular cómo y cuándo sustituirá la nueva tecnología digital a la analógica. Y, también, en qué medida puede combinarse lo nuevo con lo antiguo y cómo puede hacerse económica y eficazmente.

Los sistemas teléfonico, telegráfico y télex tradicionales, desarrollados y perfeccionados desde los años 1890, dependen de bancos de conmutadores operados eléctricamente para encaminar llamadas y transmitir el sonido que entra en el sistema hasta el extremo receptor. El hilo de cobre telefónico origina corrientes eléctricas "analógicas" que son el exacto reflejo de las variables presiones de aire que hacen las cuerdan vocales al hablar. Una vez encaminadas por el sistema, esas corrientes eléctricas excitan un diafragma en el receptor telefónico que reproduce las ondas sonoras y, por ende, la voz de quien habla. Tal sistema es adecuado para la transmisión de la voz a distancia, al ritmo de la palabra hablada, pero desigual a la rápida transmisión de grandes cantidades de datos, o para la transmisión de imágenes.

El nuevo sistema de comunicación digitalizado es esencialmente electrónico, y se basa en tecnología de semiconductores, es decir, en el computador que ejecuta tareas secuenciales según ciertas normas lógicas. Mediante programas organizados previamente, selecciona y transmite instrucciones que se envían como señales de alta y baja tensión, más o menos a la velocidad de la luz. Están representadas en el sistema binario, en el que sólo dos números, 0 y 1, llevan información. El computador suma, y multiplica, por adiciones sucesivas; resta, y divide, por sustracciones sucesivas. Utilizando esos sencillos métodos, se efectúan centenares de miles de cálculos por segundo, y mucho más. (Véase el recuadro de la pág. 124).

Esta manera de comunicar es muy similar a la desarrollada por Samuel Morse hace más de 100 años: la transmisión de puntos y rayas, señales breves y largas por hilo de cobre, empleada aún en nuestro sistema telegráfico. Pero, en tanto que el telégrafo de los años 1860 transmitía a la velocidad de 15 señales por segundo, los nuevos sistemas digitales pueden transmitir sus señales, conocidas como "bits" a la velocidad de 4800 por las líneas telefónicas existentes, y al doble por las líneas acondicionadas. Pero, incluso cuando se adapta expresamente, este método de transmisión sigue siendo muy rudimentario, si se compara con la transmisión digital directa por radiocomunicaciones de microondas o cables de fibras ópticas, a la increíble velocidad de varios millones de bits por segundo.

El crecimiento explosivo del uso del computador en las telecomunicaciones durante las dos o tres últimas décadas fue el resultado de avances revolucionarios en semiconductores y microelectrónica. El computador surgió de la investigación de técnicas de conmutación telefónica. Las conexiones electrónicas eran esenciales para el éxito del computador, pero el conocimiento básico indispensable era la lógica de conmutación de circuitos. Los dispositivos de conmutación pasaron del tubo de vacío a comienzos de los años 1940 al transistor basado en el germanio, en la misma década, y a la plaqueta de silicio, en los años 1960. Para entonces, los ingenieros electrónicos habían aprendido a compactar muchos componentes activos o pasivos en una oblea de silicio de un centímetro cuadrado. Esos dispositivos, conocidos como circuitos integrados (CI) representaban la tercera

▷ 149

gure ci-contre est une représentation du « rôle futur du me C&C » au foyer, tel qu'il a été présenté par le Dr. Koji /ashi, PDG du NEC Corporation, en 1982, au « Massachu-Institute of Technology ». Ce diagramme montre comment rdinateurs et les communications finiront par s'intégrer, environs de l'an 2000, en un système unique « C&C », nputers and Communications ».

axe vertical représente schématiquement comment les oreurs passent de la fonction unique à la fonction multiple en s'intégrant alors à la technologie des communications, ode d'exploitation décentralisé.

axe horizontal représente les progrès accomplis à partir de mérisation des communications : partage du temps en ere de commande par programme, transmission optique la réalisation de réseaux de communications complète-intégrés.

Esta figura, incluida en una presentación, «El futuro papel de CyC» en el hogar, del Dr. Koji Kobayashi, Presidente de NEC Corporation, al Instituto de Tecnología de Massachusetts (1982), describe cómo se integrarán los computadores y las comunicaciones para el año 2000 en un solo sistema «CyC».

El eje vertical representa la sistematización, mostrando cómo progresan los computadores de una sola función a unidades de fines múltiples, y luego con la incorporación de tecnología de comunicaciones de operación centralizada a distribuida.

El eje horizontal representa el progreso de la digitalización de las comunicaciones, compartición en el tiempo en control de programas, y la transmisión óptica a redes de comunicaciones integradas.

Integrated circuits are complex, carrying first hundreds of transistors, then thousands, and now hundreds of thousands, on the same cm^2 of silicon on which circuits are lithographically traced, needing no wires and no soldering. This lowered costs and increased reliability manifold. The growth in the complexity of integrated circuits led to Medium Scale Integration (MSI), then to Large Scale Integration (LSI) and now to Very Large Scale Integration (VLSI) which was followed by the successful design of a Central Processing Unit (CPU) on a miniature silicon chip containing the equivalent of 2,250 transistors.

The problems of computer language have become a major preoccupation of leading manufacturers and their solution has become the objective of major research projects in universities as well as in telecommunication laboratories.

Early computers functioned according to instructions that had to be laboriously hand-wired onto circuit boards, while today instructions or programs can be coded into appropriate languages and stored in the computer's Central Processing Unit. This software technique has enormously extended the computer's versatility and performance, increasing the spread of hardware applications, which in turn has further increased the demands made upon software. In many instances programming costs can exceed the cost of the computer hardware itself. Large computers require hundreds of programs, which could each require thousands of instructions.

The basis of computer software is the programming language in which mathematical symbols and shorthand become standardized. These languages at present are neither uniform worldwide nor suitable for combining into a common language, and this lack of standardization has led to considerable problems of compatibility. Assisted by important groundwork on interface conditions and communication procedures carried out by the CCITT and the ISO (the International Organization for Standardization), major advances have been made. Computer languages are now inter-translatable but there is, however, still a long way to go before computer to computer dialogues become universally possible, enabling any terminal user to communicate with any computer over a variety of systems.

Voice-image recognition is another pressing problem for computer manufacturers. The growth in man-computer dialogue is leading to a demand for a combination of speech and text/data, where, for example, one conducts a telephone conversation and exchanges written or printed text at the same time. People have been endeavouring for many years to provide computers with the ability to recognize and process spoken words. Progress has been slow but encouraging. Machines that can distinguish human speech are already on the market. These devices are able to recognize single syllables or individual vocabulary and will probably soon be able to recognize continuous speech spoken by anyone, not only the voice prints of given individuals.

Image recognition, processing and storage play fundamental roles in the activities of the human brain. Computers that read characters began slowly with printed letters and can now decipher handwritten script. The future ability of computers to read, understand, process and store images is the ultimate technology that will allow computer communication systems to approach man's own abilities and to overcome the barriers presented by the great variety of spoken languages in international communications.

The pages that follow present the NEC Corporation of Japan. This profile is a spirited interpretation of the computer's role in the communications of tomorrow. The company has led in the development of the chip — it was one of the first with the 256K RAM — and in the integration of the computer in telecommunications. Its ultimate objective is the realization of a fully integrated digitalized world network in which man and machine can converse and act in harmony.

ducteurs en une décennie. Depuis lors, les progrès ont été prodigieux.

Les circuits intégrés étaient complexes mais, à l'origine, ils ne comportaient que quelques centaines de transistors. Par la suite, on parvint à placer des milliers et même, actuellement, des centaines de milliers d'éléments semi-conducteurs sur un seul centimètre carré de silicium, avec des circuits lithographiés, ne nécessitant ni fils ni soudure. Cela a permis de réduire les coûts et d'améliorer considérablement la fiabilité. La complexité croissante des circuits intégrés a conduit successivement à l'intégration à moyenne échelle (MSI), à grande échelle (LSI) et à très grande échelle (VLSI).

Les problèmes du langage des ordinateurs préoccupent beaucoup les constructeurs. Leur solution est devenue l'objectif primordial des projets de recherche, dans les universités et dans les laboratoires de télécommunications.

Les premiers ordinateurs fonctionnaient selon des instructions qu'il fallait au préalable préparer laborieusement dans des circuits logiques, alors qu'aujourd'hui les instructions ou programmes peuvent être codés dans des langages appropriés et stockés dans le « cerveau » de l'ordinateur CPU. La technique du logiciel a considérablement étendu la polyvalence et la performance de l'ordinateur. Cette évolution a conduit à une généralisation des applications du matériel, laquelle a, à son tour, accentué la demande de logiciel. En bien des cas, le coût du logiciel peut dépasser celui du matériel. En effet, les grands ordinateurs nécessitent des centaines de programmes contenant des milliers d'instructions.

Les symboles mathématiques et les abréviations utilisables dans le logiciel sont en voie de normalisation mais, pour le moment, ils ne sont pas universels et ne se prêtent pas à des combinaisons. Ce défaut de normalisation a posé d'énormes problèmes de compatibilité. Grâce aux études entreprises dans ce domaine par le CCITT et l'Organisation internationale de normalisation (ISO), des progrès importants ont été faits : les langages sont devenus convertibles, mais il y a encore beaucoup à faire pour rendre possible le dialogue universel entre ordinateurs et pour que tout utilisateur de terminal puisse communiquer avec n'importe quel ordinateur.

L'identification de la voix et de l'image est un autre problème urgent pour les constructeurs d'ordinateurs. L'élargissement du dialogue entre l'être humain et l'ordinateur engendre, en effet, une demande de combinaison entre la parole et les textes/données. C'est notamment le cas lors de conversations téléphoniques pendant lesquelles les interlocuteurs échangent simultanément des textes manuscrits ou imprimés. Depuis de nombreuses années, les spécialistes se sont efforcés de mettre au point des ordinateurs capables de reconnaître et traiter le langage parlé. Dans ce domaine, les progrès ont été lents mais encourageants. On trouve actuellement sur le marché des machines capables de « distinguer » la parole humaine.

La reconnaissance, le traitement et le stockage de l'image jouent un rôle fondamental dans les activités du cerveau humain. Les ordinateurs qui peuvent lire des caractères ont commencé par les lettres imprimées, mais ils sont maintenant capables de déchiffrer les textes manuscrits. La capacité de lire, de comprendre, de traiter et d'emmagasiner électroniquement des images serait le stade suprême de l'informatique : l'ordinateur aurait alors acquis des facultés intellectuelles proches de celles de l'homme et surmonté les obstacles que représente la multiplicité des langues utilisées dans les communications internationales.

Les pages qui suivent sont consacrées à la firme japonaise NEC Corporation. Cette entreprise a été un pionnier de la mise au point du microprocesseur — elle fut l'une des premières à produire le modèle 256K RAM — et de l'intégration de l'ordinateur dans les télécommunications. L'ambition ultime de NEC Corporation est la réalisation d'un réseau numérique mondial entièrement intégré, dans lequel l'homme et la machine pourront converser et agir en pleine harmonie.

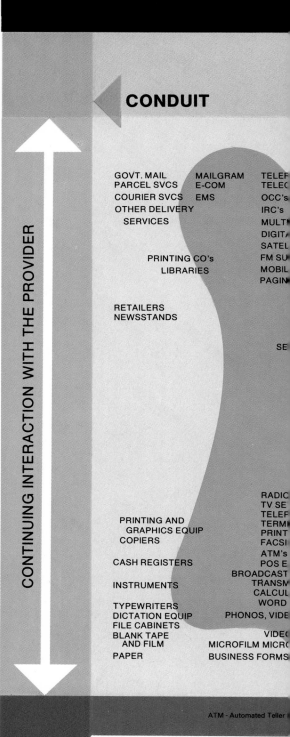

THE SPREAD OF COM

The shaded area on this "map" shows the extent to which computers have entered the information business in recent years. Whether mainframe, mini or micro, the computer has a role in practically every device or service involved in the production, transmission or processing of information. Anthony Oettinger, who heads the Program on Information Resources Policy at Harvard University, described computers in the context of merging technologies and merging markets as "the key ingredient of the change... the solvent that has leached out the glue from the traditional institutions" or, in another context, "transmission and switching facilities are a social infrastructure, like roads and electrical power facilities".

CONDUIT

CONTINUING INTERACTION WITH THE PROVIDER

GOVT. MAIL
PARCEL SVCS
COURIER SVCS
OTHER DELIVERY
SERVICES

MAILGRAM
E-COM
EMS

TELEP
TELEC
OCC's
IRC's
MULTI
DIGITA
SATEL
FM SU
MOBIL
PAGIN

PRINTING CO's
LIBRARIES

RETAILERS
NEWSSTANDS

SE

PRINTING AND
GRAPHICS EQUIP
COPIERS

CASH REGISTERS

INSTRUMENTS

TYPEWRITERS
DICTATION EQUIP
FILE CABINETS
BLANK TAPE
AND FILM
PAPER

RADIO
TV SE
TELEF
TERMI
PRINT
FACSI
ATM's
POS E
BROADCAST
TRANSM
CALCUL
WORD
PHONOS, VIDE

VIDEO
MICROFILM MICR
BUSINESS FORMS

ATM - Automated Teller

"carte" montre l'étendue de la diffusion de la technologie
rdinateur qui s'est effectuée dans le vaste domaine de
rmation. L'ordinateur, principal, mini ou micro, joue un rôle
presque tous les produits et services. Anthony G. Oettin-
responsable du « Program on Information Resources Poli-
à l'Université de Harvard a décrit les ordinateurs dans le
exte de la fusion des technologies et des marchés, comme
grédient de changement... le dissolvant de la glu des
utions traditionnelles » ou encore, dans un autre contex-
les facilités de transmission et de commutation sont une
structure sociale, au même titre que les routes et les
ux de distribution de l'énergie électrique ». En vérité, un
nombre de nouveaux domaines d'activités compétitives
ndent de cette infrastructure.

La parte sombreada de este «mapa» muestra la medida en que
los computadores se han introducido en los últimos años en la
industria de la información. Ya sea central, mini o micro, el
computador juega un papel prácticamente en todo producto o
servicio que interviene en la producción, transmisión o procesamiento de información.

Anthony Oettinger, que dirige el Programa sobre política de
recursos de la información en la Universidad de Harvard describe los computadores en el contexto de tecnologías y mercados en fusión como «el elemento clave del cambio... el
disolvente que ha lixiviado la cola de las instituciones tradicionales» o, en otro contexto, «las facilidades de transmisión y
conmutación son una infraestructura social, como las carreteras y las instalaciones de energía eléctrica».

generación de semiconductores en un decenio. Los
avances fueron después enormes.

Los circuitos integrados eran complejos, primero
con centenares de transistores, luego miles y ahora
centenares de miles, en el mismo cm^2 de silicio en
que se trazan litográficamente los circuitos, sin necesidad de hilos ni de soldadura. Esto redujo los
costos y mejoró muchísimo la fiabilidad. La mayor
complejidad de circuitos integrados llevó a la integración en escala media (MSI), luego a la integración
en gran escala (LSI) y ahora a la integración en muy
gran escala (VLSI), seguido del diseño con éxito de
una unidad central de procesamiento (UCP) en una
plaqueta de silicio minúscula que contiene el equivalente de 2250 transistores.

Los problemas de lenguaje computadorizado preocupan
grandemente a los principales fabricantes y los importantes proyectos de investigación de las universidades y de los laboratorios industriales persiguen el
objetivo de resolverlos.

Los primeros computadores funcionaban según
instrucciones de lógica cableada mediante conexiones a tableros de circuitos, mientras hoy las instrucciones o programas pueden codificarse en lenguajes
apropiados y almacenarse en la unidad central de
procesamiento del computador. Esta técnica de soporte lógico ha extendido enormemente la versatilidad y el rendimiento del computador, aumentando
el número de aplicaciones del equipo, lo que origina
a su vez una mayor demanda de soporte lógico. En
muchos casos, los costos de programación pueden
rebasar el del propio computador; los grandes necesitan centenares de programas, cada uno de los cuales puede requerir miles de instrucciones.

La base del soporte lógico de computador es el
lenguaje de programación en el que se normalizan
símbolos matemáticos y abreviados. Esos lenguajes
no son todavía uniformes en el mundo entero, ni
apropiados para combinarlos en un lenguaje común,
y esa falta de normalización supone grandes problemas de compatibilidad. Merced a un importante
trabajo básico sobre condiciones de interfaz y procedimientos de comunicación realizado por el
CCITT y la ISO (Organización Internacional de
Normalización) se han hecho grandes progresos. Los
lenguajes de computador pueden traducirse ahora
entre sí, pero todavía queda mucho para lograr diá-
logos generales de computador a computador, y
cualquier usuario terminal pueda comunicar con
cualquier computador, mediante varios sistemas.

El reconocimiento voz-imagen es otro problema apre-
miante. El crecimiento del diálogo hombre- computador lleva a la demanda de una combinación de
palabra y texto/datos donde, por ejemplo, se realiza
una conversación telefónica e intercambia texto escrito o impreso al mismo tiempo. La gente ha tratado
durante muchos años de dotar a los computadores de
la capacidad de reconocer y procesar palabras ha-
bladas, y los avances han sido lentos, pero alentadores. Ya existen en el mercado máquinas capaces de
distinguir la palabra humana. Esos dispositivos pueden reconocer sílabas sencillas o determinado voca-
bulario, y probablemente puedan reconocer pronto
el habla de cualquiera, y no sólo la voz impresa de
determinadas personas.

El reconocimiento, procesamiento y almacenamiento de imágenes juegan un papel esencial en las
actividades del cerebro humano. Los computadores
que leen caracteres comenzaron lentamente con letras impresas, y ahora pueden descifrar manuscritos.
La futura capacidad de los computadores para leer,
comprender, procesar y almacenar imágenes es la
última tecnología que permitirá aproximarse a las
propias capacidades del hombre, y superar las barreras que presentan los numerosos idiomas habla-
dos en las comunicaciones internacionales.

En las páginas que siguen se presenta la NEC
Corporation y se imagina el papel del computador
en las comunicaciones de mañana. La empresa ha
ido a la vanguardia del desarrollo de la plaqueta —
fue una de las primeras con la MAS de 256K — y de
la integración del computador en las telecomunicaciones. Su objetivo final es una red mundial digitalizada totalmente integrada en que hombre y máquina puedan conversar y actuar en armonía.

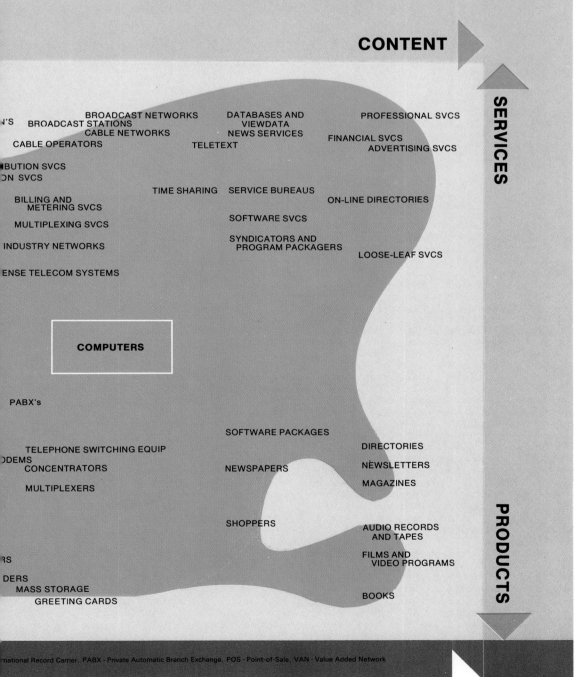

CONTENT

SERVICES

N'S
BROADCAST NETWORKS
BROADCAST STATIONS
CABLE NETWORKS
CABLE OPERATORS

DATABASES AND
VIEWDATA
NEWS SERVICES
TELETEXT

PROFESSIONAL SVCS

FINANCIAL SVCS
ADVERTISING SVCS

IBUTION SVCS
ON SVCS

BILLING AND
METERING SVCS

TIME SHARING

SERVICE BUREAUS

ON-LINE DIRECTORIES

MULTIPLEXING SVCS

SOFTWARE SVCS

INDUSTRY NETWORKS

SYNDICATORS AND
PROGRAM PACKAGERS

LOOSE-LEAF SVCS

ENSE TELECOM SYSTEMS

COMPUTERS

PABX's

SOFTWARE PACKAGES

TELEPHONE SWITCHING EQUIP
DEMS
CONCENTRATORS

DIRECTORIES

NEWSPAPERS

NEWSLETTERS

MULTIPLEXERS

MAGAZINES

SHOPPERS

AUDIO RECORDS
AND TAPES

FILMS AND
VIDEO PROGRAMS

RS

DERS
MASS STORAGE
GREETING CARDS

BOOKS

PRODUCTS

national Record Carrier, PABX - Private Automatic Branch Exchange, POS - Point-of-Sale, VAN - Value Added Network

ORMATION "VALUE ADDED"

NEC Corporation

The Computers & Communications Company C&C

NEC'S BROAD STRATEGY is to contribute powerfully to the unification of the world through the integration of computers and communications, "C&C", utilizing to the full their capacity for systems development and product innovation.

The development of communications technology has been encouraged by Man's aspiration for more versatile communications. But drastic changes in the world have changed this individual "want" to a societal "need". The world is becoming increasingly multipolarized, and many problems — such as diminishing resources, environmental pollution, and overpopulation — can no longer be solved by individual countries acting alone.

Nations need — indeed, *must* — cooperate with each other to deal with these problems. The most vital tools are "information" and the means to disseminate and process it. The communications system needed is one that contributes to the development of the infrastructure of the international society by being capable of disseminating information for processing worldwide. The key to this is "C&C" — the integration of computers and communications.

Against this backdrop, NEC took the initiative by advocating "C&C", summarizing it as follows:
— as digital technology finds its rightful place in communications, communications technology will become the same in nature as computer technology;
— with distributed-processing systems linked through communications networks, computers will become highly systematized;
— with digital communications technology, communications networks will become capable of transmitting and processing efficiently both voice and
▷ 152

LA STRATÉGIE GLOBALE DE NEC est d'apporter une puissante contribution' à l'unification du monde, grâce à l'intégration des ordinateurs et des communications, baptisée « C&C » (Computers and Communications), en utilisant au maximum sa capacité de développement et d'innovation des systèmes et des produits.

Le développement des techniques de communication a toujours bénéficié de l'aspiration humaine de communiquer par des moyens toujours plus variés. Mais les changements drastiques survenus dans les monde ont transformé le « désir » individuel en « besoin » social. Le monde devient de plus en plus multipolaire, et beaucoup de problèmes — diminution des ressources, pollution de l'environnement et surpopulation — ne peuvent plus être résolus par des pays agissant seuls.

En fait, ce n'est même plus un besoin, mais un « devoir », pour les nations de coopérer entre elles afin de résoudre ces problèmes. Pour ce faire, les outils les plus précieux sont « l'information » et les moyens de la diffuser et de la traiter. Le système de communication désiré doit contribuer à renforcer l'infrastructure de la société internationale en permettant de diffuser l'information et de traiter celle-ci dans le monde entier. La clé d'un tel système est « C&C » — l'intégration des ordinateurs et des communications.

Cela étant, NEC a pris l'initiative de préconiser cette intégration, en résumant ainsi ses vues :
— à mesure que les techniques numériques trouveront dans les communications la place qui leur revient, la technologie des communications deviendra, de même nature que celle de l'informatique ;
— avec des systèmes de traitement reliés par des réseaux de communications, la conception des ordinateurs deviendra très systématisée ;
▷ 152

LA ESTRATEGIA GLOBAL DE NEC es contribuir poderosamente a la unificación del mundo mediante la integración de computadores · y comunicaciones, « CyC », utilizando plenamente su capacidad para el desarrollo de sistemas y la innovación de productos.

La aspiración del hombre a comunicaciones más versátiles ha alentado el desarrollo de la tecnología de comunicaciones. Pero los drásticos cambios mundiales han convertido ese « deseo » individual en « necesidad » de la sociedad. Los acontecimientos recientes no corresponden a las estructuras anteriores; el mundo se multipolariza cada vez más, y los países ya no pueden resolver independientemente · muchos problemas, como la disminución de recursos, la polución del medio y la superpoblación.

Las naciones necesitan — en realidad, *precisan* — cooperar entre sí para tratar estos problemas. Los instrumentos más vitales son la « información » y los medios de difundirla y procesarla. El sistema de comunicaciones requerido contribuye a desarrollar la infraestructura de la sociedad internacional, para difundir información y procesarla en el mundo entero. La clave de tal red es « CyC », la integración de computadores y comunicaciones.

Con este transfondo, NEC tomó la iniciativa de propugnar « CyC », resumiéndolo como sigue:
— a medida que la tecnología digital ocupe su lugar en las comunicaciones, la tecnología de las comunicaciones adquirirá esencialmente la misma naturaleza que la del computador;
— con sistemas de procesamiento distribuido vinculados por redes de comunicaciones, los computadores serán sumamente sistematizados;
— con la tecnología de comunicaciones digitales, las redes podrán transmitir y procesar eficazmente se-
▷ 152

256Kbit dynamic RAM unit. The world's first was announced by NEC in 1981. A few mm², it houses some 650,000 separate elements.

Un dispositif 256Kbit RAM, dont la première au monde fut annoncée par NEC in 1981. Cette plaquette de quelques mm² contient plus de 650 000 éléments distincts.

Un dispositivo MAS dinámico de 256Kbits. El primero del mundo fue anunciado por NEC en 1981. Se trata de una plaqueta de pocos mm² que contiene más de 650 000 elementos distintos.

NEC TREE

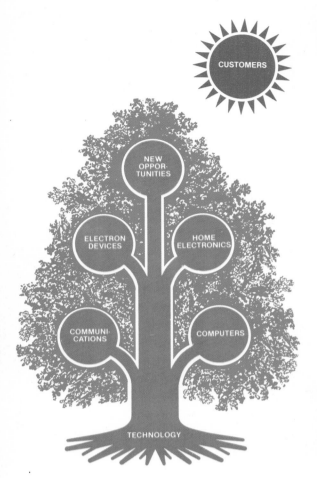

non-voice signals such as telephone calls, data, facsimile images, and video signals;
— as computers become more and more intelligent and their man-machine interfaces advance, they will approach human abilities and thought levels;
— the integration of computers and communications will contribute to the advancement of mutual understanding among the peoples of the world and will eventually create a society in which people will realize their full potentials as individuals, as members of organizations, as citizens of nations, and as members of the human race.

The origins of NEC are rooted in telecommunications. It was established in 1899 and provided a wide variety of necessary equipment in keeping with the Japanese Government's plan for expanding the nation's telephone network. In 1927, it produced the first domestically-manufactured automatic telephone switching system, and in 1930 began manufacturing radio broadcasting equipment. As early as 1939, NEC completed a 3,000-kilometer non-loaded cable carrier transmission system, linking Tokyo with Shenyan in northeastern China. After World War II, the company contributed to the restoration and expansion of telecommunication services in Japan.

Following the invention of the transistor in 1948 by scientists of Bell Laboratories, NEC started semiconductor research and built its first transistor plant in 1958. This led to the development of ICs (Integrated Circuits) such as the high-speed n-channel MOS (Metal Oxide Semiconductor) IC memories in 1968 and the MOS LSI (Large-Scale Integration) circuits for electronic calculators in 1969.

NEC began research into computers in 1954, taking the first step for Japan's computer industry. As early as 1958, it developed the parametron-type NEAC 1101 and 1102 computers. The NEAC 2201, a transistor computer exhibited at the Auto-

— avec les techniques numériques de communication, les réseaux pourront transmettre et traiter efficacement les divers signaux, qu'il s'agisse de communications téléphoniques, de données, d'images, de fac-similé ou de signaux vidéo ;
— à mesure que croîtra l'« intelligence » des ordinateurs, et que progresseront les interfaces homme/machine, ils se rapprocheront des capacités humaines et des niveaux humains de pensée ;
— l'intégration des ordinateurs et des communications facilitera la compréhension mutuelle entre les peuples du monde entier ; elle créera finalement une société où les hommes pourront déployer tout leur potentiel, en tant qu'individus, membres d'organisations, citoyens et membres de la race humaine.

Les origines de NEC se trouvent dans les télécommunications. Fondée en 1899, elle a construit une grande variété d'équipements, en rapport avec le plan du gouvernement japonais, désireux d'étendre le réseau téléphonique du Japon. En 1927, elle a produit le premier système téléphonique à commutation automatique de fabrication japonaise ; en 1930, elle a commencé à fabriquer des équipements de radiodiffusion. Dès 1939, elle a réalisé un système de transmission par câble non-chargé, long de 3000 km, entre Tokyo et Shenyan dans la Chine du nord-est. Après la deuxième guerre mondiale, elle a contribué à la restauration et à l'expansion des services de télécommunications au Japon.

En 1948, après l'invention du transistor par les chercheurs de Bell Laboratories, NEC s'est lancée dans l'étude des semi-conducteurs et a construit, en 1958, sa première usine de dispositifs transistorisés, ce qui a conduit en 1968 au développement des circuits intégrés, tels que le circuit très rapide à canaux MOS (semi-conducteur à oxyde métallique), la mémoire CI puis, en 1969, le circuit MOS avec intégration à grande échelle pour calculatrices électroniques.

En 1954 NEC s'est intéressée aux ordinateurs, la première firme japonaise à le faire. Dès 1958, elle a mis au point le prototype NEAC 1101 et les calcula-

ñales vocales y no vocales, como llamadas telefónicas, datos, imágenes facsímil y señales video;
— a medida que los computadores sean más inteligentes y avance su interfaz hombre-máquina, se aproximarán a las capacidades y niveles de pensamiento humanos;
— la integración de computadores y comunicaciones contribuirá a una mayor comprensión mutua entre los pueblos y creará finalmente una sociedad en que las personas aprovecharán todas sus posibilidades como individuos, miembros de organizaciones, ciudadanos y miembros de la raza humana.

NEC tiene sus orígenes en las telecomunicaciones. Se estableció en 1899 y proporcionó una amplia variedad de equipo necesario para el plan del gobierno japonés de ampliar la red telefónica nacional. En 1927 produjo el primer sistema automático de comunicación telefónica fabricado en el país, y en 1930 comenzó a fabricar equipo de radiodifusión. Ya en 1939, NEC completó un sistema de transmisión por corrientes portadoras de cable no cargado de 3000 km, que unió Tokio con Shenyan, en el nordeste de China. Después de la Segunda Guerra Mundial, la empresa contribuyó a restablecer y ampliar los servicios de telecomunicaciones en Japón.

Tras la invención del transistor en 1948 por científicos de Bell Laboratories, NEC inició la investigación de semiconductores y construyó su primera planta de transistores en 1958. Esto llevó al desarrollo de CI (circuitos integrados), como las memorias SMO (semiconductor de metal óxido) de canal de gran velocidad en 1968, y los circuitos LSI (integración en gran escala), SMO para calculadoras electrónicas en 1969.

NEC comenzó la investigación de computadores en 1954, dando el primer paso de la industria de computadores de Japón. Ya en 1958 había desarrollado dos computadores de tipo parametrón NEAC 1101 y 1102. El NEAC 2201, computador de transistores presentado en la Feria Automath de París, en 1959, atrajo la atención mundial.

▷ 153

▷ 153

▷ 153

The NEC "tree" on the left illustrates the company's growth on its solid technology base. Nourished by customer support, each branch promotes further growth and diversification. Shown are Dr. Koji Kobayashi, Chairman of the Board and chief executive officer of NEC Corporation, and Tadahiro Sakimoto, President of the Company.

« L'arbre » NEC, à gauche, illustre la croissance de la compagnie à partir d'une solide fondation technologique. Alimentée par l'appui de sa clientèle, chaque branche se développe et se diversifie. Sur la photo, Dr. Koji Kobayashi, Président du conseil d'administration et directeur général de NEC Corporation et Tadahiro Sakimoto, Président de la compagnie.

El «árbol» de NEC ilustra el crecimiento de la empresa, con una sólida base tecnológica. Con el apoyo de los clientes, cada rama crece y se diversifica constantemente. En la fotografía, el Dr. Koji Kobayashi, Presidente del Consejo de Administración y Director General de NEC Corporation, y Tadahiro Sakimoto, Presidente de la empresa.

The chart shows the steady continuous growth of NEC's four main product groups. The excellent balance of "C&C" technologies that is being maintained: communications, computers, electron devices and home electronics, enables the company to move people closer to a global "C&C" society.

Le graphique sur la droite montre la croissance régulière des quatre grands groupes de produits de NEC. L'excellent équilibre qui est maintenu entre les technologies C&C — communications, ordinateurs, dispositifs électroniques et électronique domestique — permet à NEC de continuer à promouvoir la réalisation d'une société globale C&C.

El gráfico muestra el constante crecimiento de los cuatro grandes grupos de productos de NEC. El excelente equilibrio mantenido entre las tecnologías "CyC" — comunicaciones, computadores, dispositivos electrónicos y electrónica doméstica — permite a la empresa avanzar hacia una sociedad "CyC" global.

SALES BY PRODUCT CLASSIFICATION

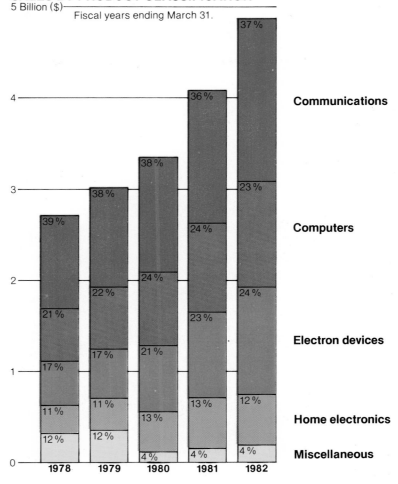

5 Billion ($)
Fiscal years ending March 31.

Communications — **Computers** — **Electron devices** — **Home electronics** — **Miscellaneous**

	1978	1979	1980	1981	1982
Communications	39%	38%	38%	36%	37%
Computers	21%	22%	24%	24%	23%
Electron devices	17%	17%	21%	23%	24%
Home electronics	11%	11%	13%	13%	12%
Miscellaneous	12%	12%	4%	4%	4%

math Show in Paris in 1959, attracted worldwide attention.

With the advent of satellite communications, NEC made an impact worldwide with satellite hookups of the Tokyo and Mexico City Olympic Games in 1964 and 1968, respectively.

But while each of these advances paved the way for today's microelectronics age and the "C&C" society built on it, technology cannot and does not exist in a vacuum.

The man-machine relationship is ideally one in which Man operates them at will but, so far, Man has tried to approach machines as much as possible by learning their "languages" and methods. Now, however, machines must move closer to humans to enable us to handle them as we like, ideally by natural voice commands. To improve man-machine relations, NEC incorporates human factors in its systems to bridge the gap between men and machines. To reach the age when Man and machine coexist on friendly terms — the age of "Man and C&C" — the improvement of both man-machine interfaces and systems intelligence is essential.

Semiconductor devices like the LSI have greatly improved the intelligence of "C&C" systems. But the pressing need for more-versatile man-machine interfaces requires as-yet-unperfected technologies such as speech recognition and synthesis, and increased emphasis must be placed on further research in software and systems engineering to create truly human-oriented "C&C" systems. The development of a global "C&C" society depends upon the integration of the core technologies of "C&C" — digital technology, computer technology, and semiconductor technology — and the development of the man-machine interface potentials of, among others, speech technology and video image technology.

Digital technology's entry in telecommunications has revolutionized both switching and transmission. Since computers are digital systems, the increasing

trices 1102. En 1959, le NEAC 2201, ordinateur transistorisé, fut exposé et remarqué a l'exposition Automath à Paris.

Avec l'avènement des communications par satellite NEC obtint une notoriété mondiale en transmettant les Jeux olympiques de Tokyo, en 1964, et de Mexico, en 1968.

La relation homme/machine est, théoriquement, une relation dans laquelle l'homme exploite la machine à son gré mais, en fait, l'homme a jusqu'ici tenté de se rapprocher des machines en apprenant leurs « langages » et leurs méthodes. Maintenant, les machines doivent se rapprocher de l'homme pour qu'il s'en serve-comme il l'entend, idéalement par commande orale. Pour y arriver NEC incorpore à ses systèmes des facteurs humains. Le perfectionnement des interfaces homme/machine et l'intelligence des systèmes sont indispensable si l'on souhaite voir le jour où l'homme et la machine coexisteront familièrement : « Man and C&C ».

Les dispositifs à semi-conducteurs, tels que les circuits avec intégration à grande échelle, ont déjà amélioré l'intelligence des systèmes « C&C ». Pourtant, pour réaliser des interfaces homme/machine plus souples, il faut recourir à des techniques encore peu explorées, par exemple la reconnaissance et la synthèse de la parole ; par ailleurs, il faut continuer la recherche dans les domaines du logiciel et des systèmes intégrés afin de créer des ensembles « C&C » qui répondent vraiment aux besoins de l'homme. Le développement d'une société mondiale « C&C » dépend de l'intégration des techniques numériques, techniques de l'informatique, technique des semi-conducteurs, ainsi que du développement d'interfaces homme/machine que permettent la technologie de la parole et de l'image.

L'arrivée de la technologie numérique dans les télécommunications a profondément transformé la commutation et la transmission. L'ordinateur étant lui-même un système numérique, la conversion progressive en numérique de la communication accélérera l'unifi-

Al llegar las comunicaciones por satélite, los enlaces por satélite de NEC en los Juegos Olímpicos de Tokio y Ciudad de México, en 1964 y 1968, respectivamente, tuvieron impacto en el mundo entero.

Pero, si bien estos avances preparaban el camino para la era microelectrónica de hoy y la sociedad « CyC » basada en ella, la tecnología no puede ni debe existir en un vacío.

La relación hombre-máquina ideal es aquella en que el hombre las maneja a su voluntad, pero hasta ahora ha tratado de acercarse más a ellas aprendiendo sus « lenguajes » y métodos. Sin embargo, las máquinas han de aproximarse más a los humanos para poder manejarlas como deseemos, idealmente mediante instrucciones vocales naturales. Para mejorar las relaciones hombre-máquina, NEC incorpora en sus sistemas factores humanos, a fin de salvar la diferencia entre hombres y máquinas. Para lograr que el hombre y la máquina coexistan en términos familiares — la era del « Hombre y CyC » — es esencial mejorar los interfaces hombre-máquina y la inteligencia de los sistemas.

Los dispositivos de semiconductores como LSI han mejorado mucho la inteligencia de los sistemas « CyC ». Pero la imperiosa necesidad de interfaces hombre-máquina más versátiles requiere tecnologías todavía imperfectas, como reconocimiento y síntesis de la palabra, y habrá que insistir más en la nueva investigación de soporte lógico e ingeniería de sistemas para crear sistemas « CyC » verdaderamente orientados al hombre. El desarrollo de una sociedad global « CyC » depende de la integración de las tecnologías básicas de « CyC » — tecnología digital, de computadores y de semiconductores — y el desarrollo de las posibilidades de interfaz hombre-máquina de tecnología vocal y tecnología video, entre otras.

La entrada de la tecnología digital en las telecomunicaciones ha revolucionado la conmutación y la transmisión. Como los computadores son sistemas digitales,

▷ 154

▷ 154

▷ 154

digitalization of communications will expedite the unification of the two. In other words, "C&C".

NEC is one of the world's leaders in digital technology, and its NEAX 61 central office digital switching system is highly acclaimed. The first NEAX system was installed in 1979, and by April 1983, the company had received orders for them from 25 countries to accommodate 5.3 million telephone lines. This achievement places NEC among the world's leading digital switching system suppliers. NEC currently produces the NEAX 61 in Japan, the United States and Malaysia. NEC also manufactures digital PBX (Private Branch Exchange) systems such as the NEAX 22 Series.

Technologies such as digital microwave and satellite communications are moving us closer to a global "C&C" society. Among the company's many recent achievements are digital microwave systems which have achieved effective use of the radio spectrum as well as higher transmission speeds. Its satellite communications applications include more than 100 earth station systems supplied to Satellite Business Systems of the USA. Many of the world's satellite communications systems use SPADE (single channel per carrier PCM multiple access demand assignment equipment) systems which are examples of digital technology applications.

Another key to digital technology is fiber optic communications. In 1982, Japan's Nippon Telegraph and Telephone Public Corporation (NTT), a government enterprise responsible for public telecommunications service in Japan, began commercial service of medium-capacity systems that allow

▷ 155

cation des deux, en d'autres termes, la société « C&C ».

NEC est un leader mondial en technologie numérique et son système NEAX 61 pour bureau central, dont le premier fut installé en 1979, a été acheté par 25 pays, ce qui représente un total de 5,3 millions de lignes téléphoniques. NEC fabrique actuellement le NEAX 61 au Japon, aux Etats-Unis et en Malaisie. NEC fabrique également des systèmes d'installation téléphonique privée (PBX), tels que NEAX 22.

Des techniques telles que les communications numériques micro-ondes par satellite font avancer vers une société mondiale « C&C ». Parmi des plus récentes innovations de la compagnie, figurent des systèmes numériques à micro-ondes qui permettent d'utiliser de façon particulièrement efficace une partie du spectre des fréquences radioélectriques et d'atteindre des vitesses de transmission jamais égalées ; ainsi que des systèmes de stations terrestres, dont plus d'une centaine ont été fournies à « Satellite Business Systems » aux Etats-Unis.

Dans le monde entier, la plupart des systèmes de télécommunications par satellite sont fondés sur la formule numérique SPADE (1 seule voie par porteuse, MIC, accès multiple par assignation en fonction de la demande) exemples d'application de la technologie numériques.

Cette technique ouvre une autre porte : les câbles à fibres optiques. En 1982, Nippon Telegraph and Telephone Public Corporation (NTT), entreprise gouvernementale responsable des services publics de télécommunication japonais, a commencé à commercialiser des systèmes de moyenne capacité permettant la transmission par câble à fibres opti-

▷ 155

la mayor digitalización de las comunicaciones acelerará la unificación de ambos. En otras palabras, « CyC ».

NEC es un líder mundial en tecnología digital, y su sistema de conmutación digital de oficina central NEAX 61 ha tenido gran éxito. El primer sistema NEAX se instaló en 1979, y en abril de 1983, la empresa había recibido pedidos de 25 países para acomodar 5,3 millones de líneas telefónicas. NEC produce actualmente el NEAX 61 en Japón, EE.UU. y Malasia. Además de sistemas digitales de oficina central, la empresa produce asimismo sistemas digitales de CP (centralitas privadas) como el de la serie NEAX 22.

Las tecnologías de comunicaciones digitales por microondas y satélites nos acercan más a una sociedad global « CyC ». Entre los muchos logros recientes de la empresa figuran los sistemas digitales de microondas que utilizan eficazmente el espectro radioeléctrico y elevadas velocidades de transmisión. Sus aplicaciones en las comunicaciones por satélite comprenden sistemas de estaciones terrenas, como las más de 100 estaciones suministradas a Satellite Business Systems de EE.UU. Muchos de los sistemas de comunicaciones por satélite mundiales emplean SPADE (un solo canal por portadora MIC con equipo de acceso múltiple asignado a petición).

Otro aspecto esencial de la tecnología digital son las comunicaciones por fibras ópticas. En 1982, la Nippon Telegraph and Telephone Public Corporation (NTT) de Japón, empresa estatal responsable del servicio público de telecomunicaciones en Japón, inició el servicio comercial de sistemas de media

▷ 155

Left: The NEC System 1000, one of the largest and fastest general purpose computers for commercial use.
Center: The central office digital switching system, the NEAX 61, a key element in ultimate ISDN (Integrated Services Digital Network).

A gauche : Le NEC système 1000 est un des ordinateurs polyvalents les plus puissants et les plus rapides à usage commercial.
Au centre : Le système de commutation numérique pour bureau central, le NEAX 61, un élément-clé dans la réalisation du RNIS (Réseau Numérique avec Intégration de Services).

A la izquierda: El sistema 1000 de NEC figura entre los computadores comerciales polivalentes más poderosos y rápidos.
En el centro: el sistema de conmutación digital de oficina central, NEAX 61, es un elemento decisivo de la RDSI (Red Digital de Servicios Integrados).

transmissions by fiber optic cables without the use of intermediate repeaters between stations. NEC systems are currently in service near Tokyo, and more elaborate, single-mode, long-wavelength, 400-megabit systems have also been supplied to NTT.

Since 1978, NEC has installed fiber optic communications systems in some 20 countries including Australia, Brazil, Ireland, Sweden and the United States. NEC is also responsible for an 8,000 fiber km-long fiber optic communications network — the world's largest — including digital switching systems, now in operation in metropolitan Buenos Aires, Argentina.

The worldwide trend toward digitalization is an unstoppable process, and digital technology is taking root in the world's communication networks.

Computer technology is progressing in two seemingly opposite directions: towards immensely powerful, ultra-high-speed machines equipped for large scale information processing, and towards distributed use of smaller systems. In 1980, the company's solid background in computers enabled it to introduce the NEC System 1000 — the top-end mainframe in the ACOS series of computers and among the largest and fastest computers currently in operation. In April 1983, NEC displayed the world's most powerful supercomputers, the SX-1 and the SX-2, capable of complicated, large-scale simulations and structural analyses at super high speed. In addition, general purpose computers are produced in a variety of sizes and a distributed information-processing network architecture (DINA) available to link them.

The "intelligent" terminal — a key component of

▷ 158

ques sans répéteurs intermédiaires entre les stations. De tels systèmes sont actuellement en service aux alentours de Tokyo ; NEC a en outre fourni à NTT des systèmes plus élaborés, à un seul mode et à plus grande longueur d'onde, d'un débit de 400 Mbits/s.

Depuis 1978, NEC a installé des systèmes de communication par fibres optiques dans un vingtaine de pays dont l'Australie, le Brésil, l'Irlande, la Suède et les Etats-Unis. NEC est en outre responsable d'un immense réseau de câbles optiques (8000 km) ainsi que des systèmes numériques de commutation, dans la zone métropolitaine de Buenos Aires (Argentine). La tendance mondiale à la numérisation est irréversible, et la technologie numérique commence à s'implanter dans les réseaux mondiaux.

La technologie des ordinateurs progresse dans deux directions, à première vue opposées : d'un côté, des machines d'une puissance et d'une rapidité extrêmes, capables de traiter d'énormes quantités de données, de l'autre côté une tendance à l'usage réparti de petits systèmes. En 1980, la solide expérience acquise par NEC lui a permis de lancer l'ordinateur NEC 1000 — haut de gamme de la série ACOS — l'une des plus puissantes et des plus rapides machines du moment. En avril 1983, NEC a présenté le plus puissant super ordinateur du monde, le NEC Supercomputer SX-1/SX-2, capable de calculer des grandes simulations très complexes et faire des analyses structurelles ultra rapides. De plus, NEC produit tout un éventail d'ordinateurs polyvalents, ainsi qu'un dispositif DINA (structure de réseau pour traitement réparti des données qui sont disponibles) pour les relier.

Le terminal « intelligent » — élément-clé du

▷ 158

capacidad que permiten transmisiones por cable de fibras ópticas sin usar repetidores intermedios entre estaciones. Los sistemas NEC están ahora en servicio cerca de Tokio, y también se han suministrado a NTT sistemas más elaborados, unimodo, de gran longitud de onda de 400 megabits.

Desde 1978, NEC ha instalado sistemas de comunicaciones por fibras ópticas en unos 20 países, incluidos Australia, Brasil, Irlanda, Suecia y EE.UU. También es responsable de una red de comunicaciones por fibras ópticas de 8000 km que comprende sistemas de conmutación digital, y funciona ya en Buenos Aires. La tendencia mundial a la digitalización es un proceso incontenible, y la tecnología digital se arraiga en las redes de comunicaciones mundiales.

La tecnología del computador progresa en dos direcciones aparentemente opuestas: hacia máquinas ultrarrápidas, sumamente poderosas, equipadas para procesar información en gran escala, y para el uso distribuido de sistemas más pequeños. En 1980, la sólida base de la empresa en computadores le permitió introducir el sistema NEC 1000 — el computador central más importante de la serie ACOS — que figura entre los mayores y más rápidos utilizados actualmente. En abril de 1983, NEC presentó el computador más poderoso del mundo, los supercomputadores SX-1 y SX-2, que pueden realizar simulaciones complicadas en gran escala y análisis estructurales a supervelocidad. Además se producen computadores de uso general en diversos tamaños, y una ARDI (arquitectura de red distribuida para procesar la información) que los vincula.

▷ 158

Two NEC satellite communications earth stations, perched high on an alpine slope above the small town of Lenk in southwestern Switzerland. They are expanding the country's global communications capacity via Intelsat satellites in orbit over the Atlantic. A third station, making possible communications with satellites in the Indian Ocean region, was added in 1983.

Deux stations terriennes de communications par satellite de NEC situées dans les Alpes, au dessus de la petite ville de Lenk dans le sud-ouest de la Suisse. Ces stations contribuent à l'expansion des communications internationales de la Suisse via les satellites Intelsat en orbite au dessus de l'Atlantique. Une troisième a été ajoutée en 1983, permettant la communication avec des satellites dans la région de l'océan Indien.

Dos estaciones terrenas de comunicaciones por satélite de NEC situadas en los Alpes, sobre la pequeña ciudad de Lenk, al sudoeste de Suiza, que participan en la expansión de las comunicaciones internacionales del país a través de satélites Intelsat, en órbita sobre el Atlántico. En 1983 se ha agregado otra estación, que permite comunicar con satélites en la región del Océano Indico.

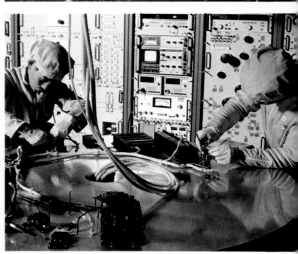

distributed processing developed by NEC in 1973 — has evolved into a variety of forms, including the popular N6300 Model 50N, which has expanded processing capabilities for graphs and words. Because the personal computer is an especially versatile component in the "C&C" network, the company introduced the PC-8000 series in 1979 — which became the sales leader in Japan's personal computer market. A wide range of other personal computer models, including the much acclaimed 16-bit systems for business use, have since been introduced.

Advances in semiconductor technology determine the rate of progress of integrated computer and communications systems. The company's R&D activities in semiconductor technologies include work to develop higher levels of product functions, performance, and quality. Citing one example, NEC's 256 Kbit dynamic RAM (Random Access Memory) chip, announced in 1981, contains more than 650,000 elements on a tiny silicon chip of only several millimeters square.

In addition to its recent achievements with silicon VLSIs, NEC is continuing its research to develop new-generation solid-state devices. These include GaAs (gallium arsenide) ICs and indium phosphide

▷ 162

système de traitement réparti mis au point par NEC en 1973 — a pris aujourd'hui de multiples formes, y compris celle du modèle N6300 50N, qui élargissent les possibilités de traitement des graphiques et des mots. Comme l'ordinateur individuel est un élément particulièrement souple employé dans le réseau « C&C », NEC a introduit, en 1979, la série PC-8000, le premier ordinateur personnel sur le marché japonais. Une grande variété d'autres modèles d'ordinateurs de table, ont été introduits depuis y compris les systèmes à 16 bit/s, utilisés dans les bureaux.

Les progrès de la technique des semi-conducteurs déterminent le rythme auquel avancent les systèmes intégrés « C&C ». Dans ce domaine, les travaux de recherche et de développement de NEC visent à atteindre de plus hauts niveaux en ce qui concerne les fonctions, la performance et la qualité des produits. Par exemple, le microprocesseur RAM (mémoire à accès aléatoire) dynamique à 256 Kbits/s de NEC, annoncé en 1981, a une capacité de plus de 650 000 éléments, bien que cette minuscule plaquette de silicium ne mesure que quelques millimètres carrés. Suivant ses récents succès en matière d'intégration à très grande échelle, NEC poursuit ses recherches afin de mettre au point une nouvelle génération de dispositifs transistorisés, parmi lesquels les transistors AsGa (arséniure de gallium), ICs et phosphure d'in-

▷ 162

El terminal « inteligente » — un componente clave del procesamiento distribuido desarrollado por NEC en 1973; reviste ahora varias formas, incluido el modelo popular N6300 50N, que ha ampliado las capacidades de procesamiento para gráficos y palabras. Como el computador personal es un componente especialmente versátil de la red « CyC », la empresa introdujo la serie PC-8000 en 1979, convirtiéndose en el principal vendedor del mercado de computadores personales de Japón. Desde entonces, ha introducido una amplia gama de otros modelos de computadores personales, incluidos los sistemas de 16 bits, muy solicitados.

Los avances en la tecnología de semiconductores determinan el ritmo de progreso de los sistemas integrados de computadores y comunicaciones. Las actividades de IyD de la empresa en tecnologías de semiconductores comprenden el desarrollo de mayores niveles de funciones de productos, rendimiento y calidad. Para citar un ejemplo, la plaqueta MAS (memoria de acceso selectivo) dinámica de 256 Kbit de NEC anunciada en 1981, contiene más de 650 000 elementos en una fina plaqueta de silicio de varios milímetros cuadrados. Además de sus recientes logros con VLSI de silicio, NEC prosigue sus investigaciones para desarrollar dispositivos de estado sólido de nueva

▷ 162

Above, left: A teleconference at NEC's Virginia office, USA, which linked several branch offices scattered throughout the country. Simultaneous transmission of high-quality video and audio signals was assured by the NETEC digital TV coder/decoder. Above, right: NEC transponders manufactured in Yokohama which are mounted on Intelsat satellites play a crucial role in global communications. Opposite: Small business computers, NEC ASTRA series, contribute to the upgrading of efficiency in a wide range of office practices. This series has been specially engineered for overseas markets.

En haut à gauche : Une téléconférence dans les bureaux de NEC en Virginie, Etats-Unis, qui a relié plusieurs agences de la compagnie éparpillées dans le pays. La transmission simultanée des signaux son et image de la plus haute qualité était assurée par le codeur/décodeur de télévision numérique NETEC. En haut à droite : Les répéteurs NEC, fabriqués à Yokohama, au Japon, sont montés à bord de satellites Intelsat où ils jouent un rôle crucial dans les communications globales. Ci-contre : Les petits ordinateurs commerciaux NEC de la série ASTRA permettent d'accroître l'efficacité d'une gamme considérable de travaux de bureau. Ils sont spécialement conçus pour les marchés étrangers.

Arriba, a la izquierda: Teleconferencia en las oficinas de NEC en Virginia (EE.UU.), que vinculó varias agencias de la empresa dispersas por el país. El codificador/decodificador de TV digital NETEC aseguró la transmisión simultánea de señales de imagen y sonido de gran calidad. Arriba, a la derecha: Transpondedores NEC fabricados en Yokohama (Japón), montados en satélites Intelsat, donde desempeñan un papel vital para las comunicaciones globales. A la derecha: Pequeños computadores comerciales de la serie ASTRA de NEC, que permiten aumentar la eficacia en una amplia gama de trabajos de oficina y concebidos especialmente para mercados extranjeros.

*Breaking new ground in the personal
computer field is NEC's 16-bit Advanced
Personal Computer (APC). By using a specially
designed LSI, this versatile personal computer
features three-dimensional graphics capability.*

*Ayant effectué une percée technologique
importante dans le secteur des ordinateurs
individuels, NEC a produit le 16-bit Advanced
Personal Computer (APC). Ce petit ordinateur,
d'une grande souplesse d'emploi, peut
fournir des graphiques tri-dimensionnels.*

*Con una importante penetración
tecnológica en el sector de computadores
individuales, NEC ha introducido el Advanced
Personal Computer (APC) de 16 bits.
Este pequeño computador, sumamente
versátil, proporciona gráficos tridimensionales.*

*Above: The NEC speech recognizer replaces the
keyboard input system. It reduces work loads and
boosts efficiency in a variety of business applications.*

*En haut : Le dispositif NEC de reconnaissance de
la parole remplace le système d'entrée à clavier ;
il facilite les travaux et rend plud efficace
toute une gamme d'opérations commerciales.*

*Arriba: El dispositivo de reconocimiento de la
palabra NEC que sustituye al sistema de
entrada de teclado: facilita los trabajos y aumenta
la eficacia de diversas aplicaciones comerciales.*

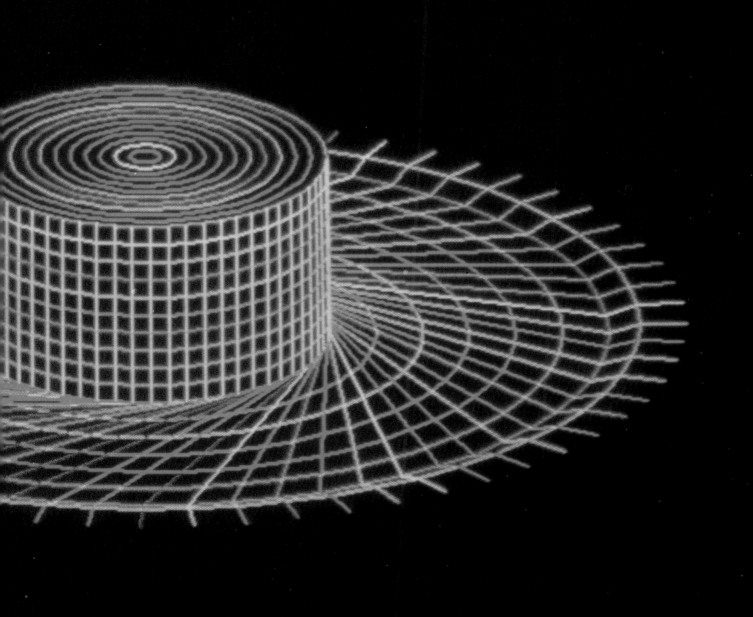

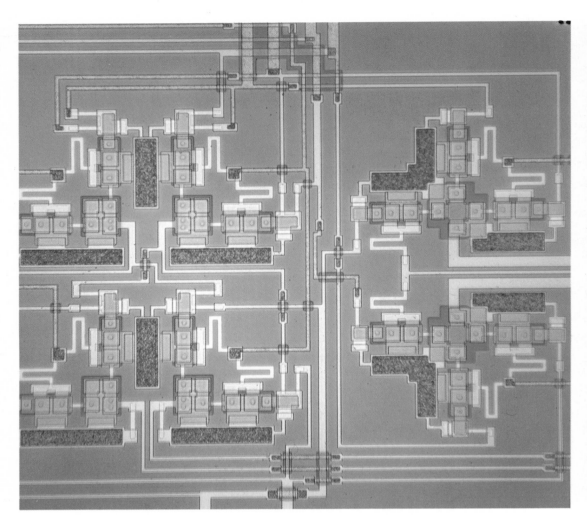
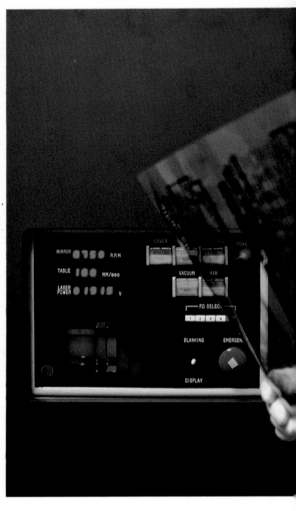

transistors for super high speed functioning, and Josephson junction logic circuits with a switching speed per gate of nearly 10 picoseconds. Each of these devices has great potential for use in "C&C" systems. **Speech recognition and synthesis technology** enjoys a high priority in the company's research and development program. The ideal machine is one that can hear and understand a human voice and operate as instructed, and the key to this is speech technology.

NEC's capabilities led to the implementation of a telephone banking system in Japan in 1980 which allows customers to inquire about their accounts, to transfer funds, and to receive other pertinent information over the phone with the help of unattended "C&C"-based equipment that recognizes and synthesises speech automatically. The contributing expertise is speaker-independent speech recognition technology — technology which has produced the SR1000, a speaker-independent speech recognizer, and which remained unmatched in 1983.

The DP-100 continuous speech recognition system was developed by NEC in 1978, and several speech recognition systems have followed in its wake. In the course of these developments, the company's speech recognition technology has advanced from speaker-dependent machines that could recognize pre-registered words spoken by one operator to speaker-independent machines that can understand words spoken by a variety of persons. Another evolution has been from isolated word recognition to more user-friendly monosyllable recognition machi-
▷ 163

dium pour le fonctionnement à vitesse accélérée, ainsi que les circuits logiques de jonction Josephson, avec une vitesse de commutation par porte ne dépassant guère 10 picosecondes. Chacun de ces dispositifs ouvre de vastes perspectives d'emploi dans les systèmes « C&C ».

La technologie de la reconnaissance et de la synthèse de la parole bénéficie d'une haute priorité dans le programme de recherche et de développement de NEC. La machine idéale devrait percevoir et comprendre la voix humaine et fonctionner selon des instructions verbales. La technologie de la parole détient la clé du succès.

En 1980, les performances techniques de NEC ont permis la mise en œuvre au Japon d'un système téléphonique bancaire qui permet à l'usager de transférer des fonds, de connaître l'état de son compte et de recevoir d'autres renseignements du même ordre, grâce à un équipement « C&C » fonctionnant sans surveillance, qui reconnaît et synthétise automatiquement la parole. Cet équipement est fondé sur la reconnaissance des mots, indépendamment de la personne qui parle ; c'est cette technique qui a produit le SR 1000, insurpassé jusqu'à ce jour.

En 1978, NEC a développé le DP-100, système de reconnaissance ininterrompue de la parole auquel plusieurs autres systèmes similaires ont fait suite. Au cours des travaux, la technologie de NEC est passée des machines dépendantes de la personne qui parle (reconnaissance de quelques mots préalablement prononcés par une personne, puis enregistrés) aux machines indépendantes de la personne qui parle
▷ 163

generación. Entre ellos figuran los CI de AsGa (arseniuro de galio) y los transistores de fosfuro de indio para el funcionamiento a supervelocidad, y los circuitos lógicos de conexión Josephson, con una velocidad de conmutación por puerta de casi 10 picosegundos. Cada uno de esos dispositivos encierra un gran potencial para usarlos en sistemas « CyC ».

La tecnología de reconocimiento y síntesis de la palabra goza de gran prioridad en el programa de investigación y desarrollo de la empresa. La máquina ideal es la que puede escuchar y comprender una voz humana y seguir sus instrucciones, y la clave de esos aparatos es la tecnología de la palabra.

Las capacidades de NEC llevaron a la aplicación de un sistema bancario telefónico en Japón, en 1980, que permite a los usuarios consultar sus cuentas, transferir fondos y recibir otra información pertinente por teléfono, con la ayuda de un equipo basado en « CyC », sin operador, que reconoce y sintetiza automáticamente la palabra. La aportación técnica es la tecnología de reconocimiento de la palabra, con independencia de quien hable, que ha producido el SR1000, reconocedor de la palabra independiente de quien hable, sin parangón hasta la fecha.

NEC desarrolló en 1978 el sistema de reconocimiento continuo de la palabra DP-100, seguido de varios sistemas del mismo tipo. En esa evolución, la tecnología de reconocimiento de la palabra de la empresa ha pasado de las máquinas dependientes de quien habla, que pueden reconocer palabras registradas dichas por un operador, a máquinas inde-
▷ 163

Left: A magnified photo of an NEC Josephson integrated circuit with the world's fastest resistor-coupled logic gates. Its potential includes utilization in future generations of super-fast scientific computers.
Center: NEC's high-speed laser pattern generator produces printed circuit board master artwork at 20 times the speed of conventional photo-plotters.

A gauche : Agrandissement d'un circuit intégré NEC du type Josephson avec les portes logiques couplage/résistance les plus rapides du monde. La capacité de ce circuit **permet d'envisager de futures générations d'ordinateurs scientifiques à vitesse accélérée.**
Au centre : Le nouveau traceur à laser ultra-rapide NEC produit des tracés de circuits imprimés vingt fois plus vite que les phototraceurs classiques.

A la izquierda: Ampliación de un circuito integrado NEC de tipo Josephson, con las puertas lógicas de acoplamiento para resistencia más rápidas del mundo. Puede utilizarse en futuras generaciones de computadores científicos de gran velocidad.
En el centro: El nuevo trazador de láser ultrarrápido de NEC, que produce matrices de circuitos impresos a una velocidad 20 veces superior a la de los fototrazadores clásicos.

nes. A single-chip speech synthesizing LSI was recently developed for a variety of applications including personal computers, and will soon become a familiar man-machine interface.

Such are the individual states of present and future "C&C" technologies which NEC foresees will bring about even greater interdependence and convergence to satisfy social needs.

NEC is on the move worldwide to increase the number of "C&C" applications. The company's aim is for "C&C" systems to take various forms, meet various needs, and allow everyone to enjoy the system's benefits. In order to accomplish this, the company has been extending its business operations to cover worldwide markets, and is prepared to contribute to the development of the global communications network. Before anything approaching a global-level communications network has been created — a necessary basis of the "C&C" world — much remains to be completed and many questions, such as what should be done about the international imbalance in telecommunications infrastructures, remain unanswered.

To these problems, NEC has developed a response from within its own resources — technology. The company first made efforts to popularize its advanced technology through direct product export or licensing partner agreements. These efforts earned the company a reputation for providing high-quality products to more than 140 countries, and steps have been taken to promote technological co-operation as a part of an effective corporate "C&C" strategy.

The foundation of technological co-operation has been set to bring the benefits of "C&C" systems to

▷ 164

(compréhension de mots prononcés par telle ou telle personne). De même, elle est passée de la reconnaissance d'un mot isolé à la reconnaissance de monosyllabes plus familières à l'usager. Une microplaquette de synthèse de la parole, avec intégration à grande échelle, a récemment été développée pour une variété d'applications, y compris les ordinateurs individuels, et deviendra bientôt une interface courante de la relation homme/machine.

Voilà où en sont, pour le présent et l'avenir les techniques « C&C », qui, selon la NEC, auront une interdépendance et une conséquence toujours plus grandes en vue de répondre aux besoins de la société.

NEC est à l'œuvre dans le monde entier. Son objectif est de faire en sorte que la disponibilité des systèmes « C&C » augmente le nombre de leurs applications, sous diverses formes, pour répondre à des besoins variés au bénéfice de chacun. Pour le réaliser NEC a étendu ses activités au monde entier et est prête à contribuer au développement du réseau global. Avant même qu'un tel réseau mondial, base nécessaire du monde « C&C », puisse être créé, il reste beaucoup à faire et à répondre à bien des questions : par exemple, comment procéder face au déséquilibre international des densités informatiques et téléphoniques ?

A ces problèmes, NEC répond en tirant parti de ses propres ressources — en premier lieu : la technologie. NEC s'est tout d'abord efforcée de populariser ses techniques de pointe par exportation directe ou par octroi de licences à des partenaires. Elle a ainsi acquis dans plus de 140 pays une réputation de haute qualité. Par ailleurs, elle s'efforce aussi de promouvoir la coopération technique, comme élément efficace d'une stratégie « C&C » de groupe.

Le principe de la coopération technique a été

▷ 164

pendientes de quien habla que pueden comprender palabras dichas por diversas personas. Otra evolución ha sido la del reconocimiento aislado de la palabra a máquinas de reconocimiento monosilábico más familiares para el usuario. Recientemente se ha desarrollado un LSI sintetizador de la palabra de una sola plaqueta con diversas aplicaciones, incluidos los computadores personales, que se convertirá pronto en un interfaz hombre-máquina familiar.

Estos son los distintos estados de las tecnologías presentes y futuras « CyC » que NEC piensa lograr con una interdependencia y una convergencia todavía mayores para atender necesidades sociales.

NEC opera en el mundo entero. La finalidad de la empresa es que los sistemas « CyC » aumenten el número de aplicaciones, revistan varias formas, atiendan diversas necesidades y hagan extensivos a todos los beneficios del sistema. Para lograrlo, la empresa ha ampliado sus operaciones comerciales para abarcar mercados mundiales, y NEC está dispuesta a contribuir al desarrollo de la red global de comunicaciones. Antes de crear nada que nos acerque a una red global de comunicaciones — base necesaria del mundo « CyC » — hay todavía mucho que hacer y bastantes preguntas — como la solución del desequilibrio internacional de la infraestructura de telecomunicaciones — siguen sin contestar.

Ante estos problemas, NEC ha elaborado una respuesta con sus propios recursos: la tecnología. La compañía trató primero de popularizar su tecnología avanzada mediante acuerdos de exportación directa de productos o de licencias. Esas actividades dieron a la empresa tal reputación que suministra productos de gran calidad a más de 140 países, y se han tomado medidas para fomentar la cooperación tecnológica

▷ 165

Right: NEC's Model-A precision assembly robot is equipped with arms, hands and optic sensors to perform tasks such as the precise assembly, adjustment, and inspection of tiny solid-state devices.

A droite : Le robot de précision NEC Modèle A. Ce robot est équipé de bras, de mains et de détecteurs optiques pour effectuer des travaux d'une grande finesse : assemblage, ajustement et inspection de minuscules dispositifs transistorisés.

A la derecha: El robot de montaje de precisión de NEC Modelo A, provisto de brazos, manos y sensores ópticos para realizar tareas como montaje de precisión, ajuste e inspección de dispositivos minúsculos de estado sólido.

● Affiliates
○ Offices

This map shows the location of NEC's 20 plants in 12 countries and of its 38 affiliates in 20 countries. In addition the company has more than 200 sales offices located in major cities throughout the world. It employs some 69,000 people worldwide and markets more than 15,000 products.

Cette carte indique la disposition des 20 usines de NEC dans 12 pays, et de ses 38 associés dans 20 pays. Outre ces usines, la compagnie possède plus de 200 points de vente situés dans les grandes villes du monde entier. Elle emploie 69 000 personnes et vend plus de 15 000 produits.

El mapa muestra la ubicación de 20 plantas de NEC en 12 países, y de sus 38 filiales en 20 países. Además, la empresa tiene más de 200 oficinas de venta radicadas en las principales ciudades del mundo. Emplea a unas 69 000 personas en el mundo entero, y vende más de 15 000 productos.

every nation and help its people use the technology by themselves. It has taken the form of local production, making it possible to manufacture "C&C" products in local markets as close to customers as possible. The more participation in this program, the more opportunities nations will have to capitalize on new, advanced "C&C" technologies. In full awareness of this move, NEC has already been engaged in local production of its products at 20 plants in 12 countries as part of its extensive technology collaboration program. The most recent example is the company's VLSI manufacturing plant in Scotland, which started production in October 1982, a fine example of what technological cooperation can and should be.

With all the technologies it has available to it, communications, computers, electron devices, and home electronics, NEC will continue, as a dependable supplier, to promote the worldwide implementation of "C&C" in the firm belief that, one day, it will foster world unity and the harmony of nations.

There is now a clear possibility of overcoming, in time, the language differences which hinder mutual awareness and understanding. An automatic translating machine is now being developed and is expected to remove barriers in communications among nations and people. And when that day comes, when everyone becomes able to communicate with anybody, anytime and anywhere in their own language, NEC will take pride in the fact that its technology contributed to Mankind's advancement.

☐

adopté pour que tous les pays puissent bénéficier des systèmes « C&C » et que les particuliers apprennent à les utiliser par eux-mêmes. Elle a pris la forme de la production locale en rendant possible la fabrication de produits « C&C» dans des marchés aussi proches que possible des usagers potentiels. Plus grande sera la participation à ce programme, plus grand sera le nombre d'occasions pour les nations de tirer profit des nouvelles techniques « C&C ». Consciente de cette évolution et conformément à son programme de collaboration technique, NEC s'est déjà engagée dans la production locale de ses produits dans 20 usines implantées dans 12 pays. Le plus récent exemple est l'usine de microprocesseurs à intégration à très grande échelle que NEC a établie en Ecosse et, qui est devenue opérationnelle en octobre 1982.

Avec les techniques dont elle dispose, communications, ordinateurs, dispositifs électroniques et électronique domestique, NEC continuera, à titre de fournisseur fiable, à promouvoir la mise en œuvre mondiale des systèmes « C&C », dans le ferme espoir qu'ordinateurs et communications conduiront un jour à l'unité et à l'harmonie universelle.

On voit aujourd'hui clairement la possibilité d'éliminer les barrières linguistiques qui freinent la compréhension mutuelle. Une machine à traduire, en cours d'élaboration, devrait faire disparaître les problèmes de langues qui s'opposent à l'établissement de communications entre les nations et les peuples. Quand viendra le temps où les hommes, où qu'ils se trouvent, pourront à tout moment communiquer entre eux en parlant chacun sa propre langue, NEC sera fière que ses techniques aient pu contribuer au progrès de l'humanité.

☐

On the left, above: Overseas trainees acquiring on-the-job experience at NEC's Yokohama plant. The company takes in many trainees from client countries the world over. On the right, below: At NEC Semiconductors UK, Livingston, Scotland, local employees manufacture VLSIs.

En haut, à gauche : La NEC reçoit de nombreux stagiaires envoyés par ses clients du monde entier. On les voit ici visitant l'usine de Yokohama. En bas, à droite : En Ecosse, à Livingston, du personnel local travaillant dans une usine de la NEC d'où sortent des semiconducteurs VLSI.

Head Office
Tokyo, Japan

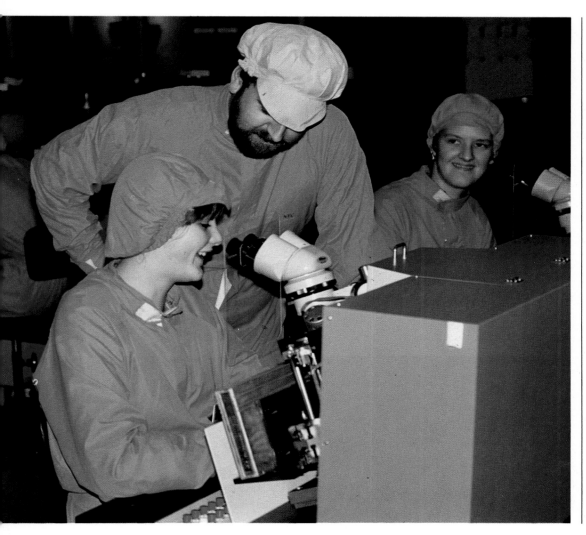

como parte de una estrategia « CyC » efectiva de la empresa.

Se han sentado las bases de la cooperación tecnológica para aportar los beneficios de sistemas « CyC » a todos los países y ayudar a su población a usar independientemente la tecnología. Ha revestido la forma de producción local, permitiendo fabricar productos « CyC » en los mercados más próximos de los usuarios. Cuanto más se participe en este programa, más oportunidades tendrán las naciones de capitalizar tecnologías nuevas y avanzadas « CyC ». Conociendo plenamente la situación, NEC interviene ya en la producción local de sus productos en 20 plantas de 12 países, como parte de su amplio programa de colaboración tecnológica. El ejemplo más reciente es la planta de fabricación de VLSI de Escocia, que inició la producción en octubre de 1982,lo cual muestra perfectamente lo que puede y debe ser la cooperación tecnológica.

Con todas sus tecnologías — comunicaciones, computadores, dispositivos electrónicos y electrónica del hogar — NEC seguira fomentando, como proveedor seguro, la aplicación mundial de « CyC » en la firme creencia de que, un día, promoverá la unidad mundial y la armonía de las naciones.

Existe ahora una clara posibilidad de superar, con el tiempo, las diferencias idiomáticas que obstaculizan el conocimiento y la comprensión mutuos. Se está desarrollando una máquina de traducción automática, y se espera suprimir las barreras de las comunicaciones entre naciones y pueblos. Y, cuando llegue ese día, cuando todos puedan comunicar entre sí, en todo momento y lugar, mediante su propio idioma, NEC estará orgullosa de haber contribuido con su tecnología al progreso de la humanidad. □

Arriba, a la izquierda: NEC recibe a muchos cursillistas enviados por sus clientes del mundo entero. Aquí, visitando la fábrica de Yokohama, donde amplían sus conocimientos.
Abajo, a la izquierda: Empleados locales fabricando VLSI en la fábrica de semiconductores de NEC en Livingston (Escocia).

QUANTUM LEAP FORWARD
EWH OF COMMUNICATION SATELLITES ORIZON
AND EARTH STATIONS

THE TREMENDOUS ADVANCE in the development and use of satellites of the past few years, an advance which is still gathering momentum, is likely to be the major factor in the realization of an integrated network of communications covering the whole world. **The geostationary satellite's** entry in telecommunications is heralding a period of profound change in the provision of communication infrastructures in the remote, sparsely populated areas of the globe. This change is driven by rapid advancements in the technology of computers and communications. The key elements in the advance of the satellite are the same as in other areas of communications technology: the ability, through progress in micronics, to pack more and more power and versatility in less and less space; improved reliability and performance of the equipment (hardware), the readier availability of sophisticated programs (software), and the effective operation of the system. Dominant in all this is the considerable reduction in costs, plus the fact that the cost of transmission by satellite is insensitive to distance.

Although the satellite communications industry is still less than 20 years old — the first commercial satellite, 'Early Bird', was launched in 1969 — it has developed into powerful competition for other systems and a key component in the build-up of communications infrastructures. It is a fact that with a satellite investment of a few hundred million US dollars, all important elements of the long line capacity of the terrestrial network, costing many times that figure, can be duplicated and that a time span of only 2 or 3 years is required for the system to be operational.

Dr. Albert D. Wheelon, Vice President of Hughes Aircraft Company and the head of its Space and Communications Group, expressed his confident belief that the next hundred years would be "the

▷ 168

LE PRODIGIEUX DÉVELOPPEMENT des satellites et de leur utilisation qui ne cesse de s'accélérer sera certainement l'élément essentiel de la réalisation du futur réseau intégré universel des télécommunications. **La mise en œuvre de satellites géostationnaires** de télécommunications annonce une évolution profonde des infrastructures dans les régions lointaines et faiblement peuplées du monde. Les facteurs de cette évolution, qui prend l'allure d'un véritable bond en avant, sont dans ce domaine : la microélectronique qui améliore sans cesse la souplesse d'équipements toujours moins volumineux, la plus grande fiabilité et les meilleures performances du matériel, la disponibilité de programmes complexes (logiciel). Il faut relever surtout la diminution considérable des prix de revient et le fait que le coût des communications par satellite est indépendant de la distance.

Si les télécommunications par satellite n'ont pas encore 20 ans (Early Bird, le premier satellite commercial, a été lancé en 1969), elles font déjà une âpre concurrence aux autres systèmes. Il est aujourd'hui universellement admis qu'en investissant quelques centaines de millions de dollars dans des satellites, il est possible de doubler en deux ou trois ans la capacité de tous les éléments essentiels du réseau de surface.

Dr. Albert D. Wheelon, Vice-Président de la Hughes Aircraft Co. et chef du Space and Communications Group de cette compagnie, affirmait à Genève, dès 1979, sa certitude que les cent prochaines années seraient « le siècle du satellite ». L'étonnant développement de l'industrie en ce domaine confirme ce point de vue.

La même année, James Martin (IBM Corp.) estimait « que l'état actuel de la technique permettrait de donner à *un seul* satellite une capacité de transmission suffisante pour que chacun, homme, femme et enfant, aux Etats-Unis et au Canada puisse utiliser son propre terminal informatique *en heure de pointe*.

▷ 168

EL ENORME AVANCE de los últimos años en el desarrollo y uso de satélites, que todavía cobra impulso, probablemente sea el principal factor de la realización de una red integrada de comunicaciones que abarque el mundo entero. **La incorporación del satélite geoestacionario** a las telecomunicaciones anuncia un período de profundos cambios en la provisión de infraestructuras de comunicación en zonas remotas y poco pobladas del globo. Este cambio se debe a la rápida evolución de la tecnología de computadores y comunicaciones. Los elementos esenciales del avance del satélite son los mismos que en otros sectores de la tecnología de comunicaciones: la capacidad, mediante el progreso de la micrónica, para agrupar cada vez más potencia y versatilidad en menos espacio; la mejor fiabilidad y rendimiento del equipo (soporte físico) y la más rápida disponiblidad de programas (soporte lógico) para la explotación efectiva del sistema. En todo ello predominan las considerables reducciones de costos, mas el hecho de que el costo de las comunicaciones por satélite es insensible a la distancia.

Aunque la industria de comunicaciones por satélite data de menos de 20 años — el primer satélite comercial, "Early Bird", se lanzó en 1969 — compite ya fuertemente con otros sistemas, y es esencial para el establecimiento de infraestructuras de comunicaciones. Con una inversión en satélites de unos centenares de millones de dólares pueden duplicarse todos los elementos importantes de la capacidad de larga distancia de la red terrenal, que cuestan varias veces esa cifra, y para que el sistema sea totalmente operacional sólo se requieren de 2 a 3 años.

El Dr. Albert D. Wheelon, Vicepresidente de Hughes Aircraft Company y jefe de su Grupo espacial y de comunicaciones, expresó la firme creencia de que los cien años próximos serán « el siglo del

▷ 169

An artist's representation of all types of "Intelsat" satellites, up to Series V.

Illustration représentant chaque série de satellites « Intelsat », de I à V.

Illustración gráfica de todos los satélites de Intelsat, series I a V.

century of the satellite". In the same year, James Martin of the IBM Corporation estimated that "*one satellite*, using today's state of the art, could have enough transmission capacity to provide every man, woman and child in the United States and Canada with a computer terminal *during peak hours*".

Worldwide satellite communication is expected to become a ten billion dollar (US$, 1982) industry by 1990, carrying millions of telephone calls, hundreds of TV programs and computer-to-computer data flows each day. Dr. Lewis Branscomb, chief scientist of IBM, labelled the satellite as "the dramatic productivity story in telecommunications", answering the rising demand for communication bandwidth "by providing capacity at a channel cost falling by about 40% annually, rivalling the productivity demonstrated in magnetic recording for data storage".

The Communications Satellite Corporation (Comsat), formed in 1962, the International Telecommunications Satellite Organization (Intelsat), formed in 1964, and the Soviet system Intersputnik formed in 1958, are the three specialist bodies set up do develop, launch and operate communications satellites.

Intelsat is an organization which provides a global television and telephone satellite system. In 1982 its membership totalled more than 100 countries and it provided communication services to 135 countries served by 250 earth stations. Since Early Bird (*Intelsat I*) it has launched four series of satellites — *II, III, IV* and *IVa* — and is in the process of launching 9 series *V* satellites, to be followed by 3 higher capacity series *Va* in the late 1980s, and series *VI* in the 1990s.

The success of Comsat, Intelsat and Intersputnik has encouraged the development of other regional satellite systems, such as the Soviet Union's Stationer series, which includes *Raduga, Loutek* and *Gorizont*; the Japanese NASDA and ISAS programs; the Arabsat complex; the South East Asia Palapa; and the European Eutelsat (also called EC3). In spite of the rapid development of these regional satellite systems, Intelsat continues to grow at more than 20% per year compounded.

Japan's space program began to move ahead following the launch of its second meteorological satellite, the *GSM-2*, in 1981. The national budget has increased steadily (US$ 481 million in 1982) and a full program of satellite launchings is being carried out by the National Space Development Agency (NASDA) and the Institute of Space and Astronomical Science (ISAS). It includes five series of satellites: *ET3* for engineering test purposes; *GMS* for meteorological forecasting; *BS* for broadcasting; *MOS* for maritime survey and earth observation technology, and *CS* for telecommunications. The latest communication satellite, *CS3*, is scheduled for launching in the late 1980s.

The US satellite program is mainly in private hands. Ten independent commercial satellite operators are involved: American Satellite, a joint venture of Fairchild Industries and Continental Telephone; AT&T; Comsat, a private company set up by act of Congress in 1962; GTE; Hughes Aircraft, the leading satellite builder turned operator; RCA American, the first integrated manufacturer of satellites and carrier; Satellite Business Systems (SBS), a joint endeavour of IBM with satellite carriers Comsat General and Insurers Aetna Life & Casualty; Southern Pacific Communications; and Western Union. Also in the business in a big way are the Port of New York and New Jersey in partnership with stockbrokers Merrill Lynch & Co, Inc. and Western Union, with a huge satellite reception centre and office area being built (1983) on Staten Island to escape the radio frequency congestion of Manhattan (See p. 188).

A major worldwide program to develop maritime communications is in progress. The International Maritime Satellite Organisation (Inmarsat), with 37 member nations, was set up in 1982 with headquarters in London. It took over three spacecraft from the US *Marisat*

▷ 170

Les **télécommunications par satellite** devraient constituer, selon certaines prévisions d'origine américaine, une industrie d'un chiffre d'affaires de dix milliards de dollars US constants au début des années 1990. Dr. Lewis Branscomb, directeur scientifique d'IBM, considère que le satellite est devenu le facteur-clé de la productivité dans les télécommunications : « il permet de faire face à la demande de largeur de bande, en offrant une capacité de communication dont le coût diminue régulièrement de 40% par an et par voie », rivalisant ainsi avec le taux de productivité réalisé dans l'enregistrement des données sur bandes magnétiques.

Trois grandes organisations internationales se spécialisent dans le lancement et l'exploitation des satellites de communications : Comsat (Communications Satellite Corporation), constituée en 1962, Intelsat (International Telecommunications Satellite Corporation) fondée en 1964 et Interspoutnik, constituée en 1958.

Intelsat une organisation qui fournit un réseau mondial de télévision et de téléphone par satellites. En 1982, elle comptait plus de 100 Etats Membres et desservait 135 pays grâce à 250 stations terriennes. Depuis Early Bird (*Intelsat I*), elle a lancé quatre séries de satellites (*Intelsat II, III, IV* et *IVa*). Aujourd'hui, elle s'apprête à lancer 9 satellites de la série *V* qui seront suivis avant 1990 de 3 satellites *Va* de plus grande capacité et, plus tard, d'une nouvelle série *Intelsat VI*. Ce programme vise à répondre à la demande croissante de télécommunications dans le monde entier, à laquelle s'ajoute celle de canaux de Télévision directe par satellite.

Le succès de Comsat, Intelsat et Interspoutnik a suscité la naissance d'autres systèmes régionaux tels que la série Stationer en URSS, avec *Radouga, Loutek* et *Gorizont*, les programmes NASDA et ISAS au Japon, le complexe Arabsat, le système Palapa en Asie du Sud-Est et le système européen Eutelsat (EC3). Malgré le progrès rapide de ces projets, Intelsat se développe toujours à un rythme annuel supérieur à 20%.

Le programme spatial du Japon a commencé à se développer à partir du lancement de son deuxième satellite météorologique *GSM-2*, en 1981. Le budget national a régulièrement augmenté (481 millions de dollars pour 1982) et la NASDA (National Space Development Agency) et l'ISAS (Institute of Space and Astronomical Science) ont établi un important programme de lancements comportant cinq séries de satellites : *ET3* (essais d'ingénierie), *GMS* (météorologie), *CS* (télécommunications), *BS* (radiodiffusion) et *MOS* (recherches maritimes et observation de la Terre).

Le programme spatial des Etats-Unis relève avant tout de l'initiative privée : American Satellite (entreprise commune de Fairchild Industries et Continental Telephone), AT&T, Comsat (créée en 1982 par le Congrès), GTE, Hughes Aircraft (constructeur devenant exploitant de satellites), RCA American (constructeur de satellites et radiodiffuseur), Satellite Business Systems (entreprise commune groupant IBM, Comsat General et les assureurs Aetna Life & Casualty), Southern Pacific Communications et Western Union. De plus, pour éviter l'encombrement des fréquences radioélectriques à Manhattan, l'Autorité du port de New York et du New Jersey, ainsi que Merrill Lynch & Co, Inc. (courtiers en bourse) se sont associés à Western Union pour installer sur Staten Island (1983) un centre de communications appelé « Téléport », offrant aux entreprises new-yorkaises un accès direct aux satellites de télécommunications pour leur trafic téléphonique, les transmissions de données et de signaux video (voir p. 188).

La croissance rapide de l'emploi des satellites en tant que relais de signaux micro-ondes a fortement stimulé, partout dans le monde, la liaison par câbles optiques des abonnés aux stations terriennes ou aux antennes situées sur les toits des grands immeubles, en raison de leur largeur de bande exceptionnelle.

Un système de câblage « en tronc » a été mis au point récemment en Angleterre par des chercheurs de l'Université de Cambridge qui consiste en une série de boucles de câbles optiques, qui desservent

▷ 170

NEW SATELL
IN SPACE FC

This 5000-pound tracking and data relay satellite is the first of two launched by the US Challenger space shuttle in 1983 which provide extremely high capacity communication links between satellite facilities. They constitute a critical element in the management of large structures in space, such as the European-built Spacelab, capable of providing a multitude of communication and information facilities simultaneously to a great number of users.

These new satellites, owned by NASA and built by the Californian constructor TRW, can maintain near-continuous

contact with 26 spacecraft at a time and thus replace most of the ground stations used in the USA to track and relay space vehicles of all types. This is a major advance on the present system, under which spacecraft are out of contact with ground controllers 80% of the time. It heralds a radically new, fully computerized, system of control, from space, of activities in space.

SERVING AS A COMMAND POST
TURE EARTH-ORBITING TRAFFIC

atellite de surveillance et de relais de données, de 2500 kg, 'un des « jumeaux » lancés par la navette spatiale améri- e Challenger en 1983.

es satellites de liaison inter-satellite de très grande capa- constituent un élément de base dans la gestion de grandes tures dans l'espace, telles que le laboratoire spatial eu- « Spacelab », en ayant la capacité de relayer un très d volume de communications susceptibles de satisfaire un d nombre d'utilisateurs.

es deux satellites, qui appartiennent à la NASA, et qui

Este satélite de vigilancia y datos de 2500 kg es el primero de los dos lanzados por el transbordador espacial estadounidense Challenger en 1983, y proporciona enlaces de comunicaciones de grandísima capacidad entre satélites. Constituye un elemento crítico en la gestión de grandes estructuras espaciales, como el Spacelab europeo, capaz de ofrecer múltiples recursos de comunicación e información simultánea a un gran número de usuarios.

Los satélites, pertenecientes a la NASA y construidos por el fabricante californiano TRW, pueden mantener contacto casi

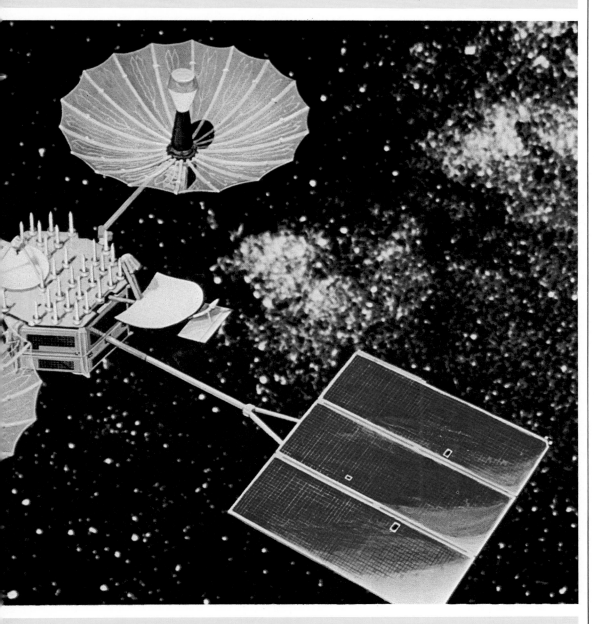

nt construits par la firme californienne TRW, peuvent tenir une liaison presque ininterrompue avec 26 satellites fois, et donc, remplacer la plupart des stations terriennes ées aux Etats-Unis pour suivre et communiquer avec de ns spatiaux de tout genre. Cela représente une avance idérable par rapport au système actuel qui laisse les en- spatiaux hors de contact avec les contrôleurs pendant 80% emps. En fait, ces nouveaux types de satellites constituent remier système entièrement informatisé de contrôle des ités dans l'espace, lui-même en orbite.

permanente con 26 vehículos espaciales al mismo tiempo, y sustituir así a la mayoría de las estaciones terrenas utilizadas en EE.UU. con los vehículos espaciales de todo tipo. Se trata de un importante avance con respecto al sistema actual, en el que el vehículo no tiene contacto con los controladores de tierra durante el 80% del tiempo. Es el presagio de un sistema de control de las actividades espaciales totalmente nuevo y computadorizado.

satélite ». El mismo año, James Martin, de IBM Corporation, estimó que « un satélite, utilizando la tecnología más avanzada, puede disponer de suficiente capacidad de transmisión para proporcionar a todo hombre, mujer y niño de Estados Unidos y Canadá un computador durante las horas punta ».

Se espera que la comunicación mundial por satélite se convierta en una industria de 10 000 millones $ (de 1982) para 1990, cursando diariamente millones de llamadas telefónicas, centenares de programas TV y flujo de datos de computador a computador. El Dr. Lewis Branscomb, jefe científico de IBM, dijo que el satélite es « la espectacular historia de la productividad en telecomunicaciones », atendiendo la creciente demanda de anchura de banda « proporcionando capacidad a un costo por canal que disminuye en torno al 40% anual, rivalizando con la productividad demostrada en la grabación magnética para almacenar datos ».

La Communication Satellite Corporation (Comsat), creada en 1962, la Organización Internacional de Telecomunicaciones por Satélite (Intelsat), en 1964, y el sistema soviético Intersputnik, en 1958 son los tres principales organismos para desarrollar, lanzar y explotar satélites de comunicaciones.

Intelsat es una de las organizaciones que proporcionan el sistema global de televisión y telefonía por satélite. En 1982 tenía más de 100 países miembros, y proporcionaba servicios de comunicación a 135 países, mediante 250 estaciones terrenas. Desde Early Bird (*Intelsat I*), ha lanzado cuatro series de satélites: *II, III, IV* y *IV*a, y va a lanzar 9 satélites de la serie *V*, seguidos de 3 de la serie *V*a, de mayor capacidad, a finales del decenio, y de la serie *VI* en los años 1990.

El éxito de Comsat, Intelsat e Intersputnik ha estimulado el desarrollo de otros sistemas regionales, como la serie Stationer de la Unión Soviética, que comprende *Raduga, Loutek* y *Gorizont*; los programas japoneses NASDA e ISAS; el complejo Arabsat; el Palapa del Sudeste Asiático; y el europeo Eutelsat (denominado también EC3). A pesar del rápido desarrollo de esos sistemas regionales de satélite, Intelsat sigue creciendo a un ritmo superior al 20% anual.

El programa espacial japonés comenzó a avanzar tras el lanzamiento de su segundo satélite meteorológico, el *GSM-2*, en 1981. El presupuesto nacional ha aumentado constantemente (481 millones $ en 1982) y el Organismo Nacional para el Desarrollo Espacial (ONDE) y el Instituto de Ciencias Espaciales y Astronómicas (ICEA) están realizando un programa completo de lanzamiento de satélites, que comprende cinco series: *ET3* para pruebas de ingeniería; *GMS* para previsiones meteorológicas; *BS* para radiodifusión, *MOS* para tecnología de vigilancia marítima y observación de la Tierra, y *CS* para telecomunicaciones. El *CS3*, se prevé lanzarlo en los últimos años 1980.

El programa de satélites de EE.UU. está principalmente en manos privadas, participando en él 10 operadores de satélites comerciales independientes: American Satellite, empresa mixta de Fairchild Industries y Continental Telephone; AT&T; Comsat, empresa privada creada por una ley del Congreso en 1962; GTE; Hughes Aircraft, el principal operador de satélites, convertido en constructor; RCA American, el primer fabricante integrado de satélites y portadores; Satellite Business System (SBS), empresa mixta de IBM con la de portadores de satélite Comsat General e Insurers Aetna Life and Casualty; Southern Pacific Communications, y Western Union. También intervienen mucho el Port of New York and New Jersey, en asociación con los agentes de bolsa Merrill Lynch y Western Union, que construyen un enorme centro de recepción por satélite en Staten Island para evitar la congestión de frecuencias radioeléctricas de Manhattan (véase pág. 188).

Está en marcha un importante programa de comunicaciones marítimas. La Organización Internacional de Telecomunicaciones Marítimas por Satélite (Inmarsat), con 37 Estados miembros, se creó en 1982, con sede en Londres. Se hizo cargo de tres vehículos espacia-

▷ 171

consortium, in which Comsat General have a controlling interest, and leased another from the European Space Agency (ESA) to handle the Atlantic Region traffic. Plans to use maritime transponders on two Intelsat V satellites will further increase capacity during the 1980s.

Satellite facilities exist also for radio amateurs, thanks to a team of British enthusiasts who built a small but highly effective spacecraft, *UOSAT*, launched in 1982, relaying programs to several countries.

World demand for satellite circuits is expected to increase exponentially (a doubling every three years). By 1990 the Intelsat system of communication satellites ringing the earth is expected to have a capacity of 110,000 circuits, almost double today's capacity, rising to half a million circuits by the end of this century.

This expansion in demand is being paralleled by an equally rapid development in satellite technology. 'Early Bird' measured 23 inches in height and 28 inches in diameter, and had a capacity for 240 circuits (two-way voice channels) and for one TV channel. Intelsat V has a capacity for 12,000 circuits plus two colour TV channels. The bigger Intelsat Vas to be launched in 1984-86 will each have a capacity for about 15,000 circuits. Beyond that, Intelsat is planning a giant series VI satellites each 468 inches in height, weighing some 4,000 pounds, and 144 inches in diameter, able to generate 2,200 watts of electrical power and to handle 110,000 circuits, nearly 500 times more than 'Early Bird'.

Size and capacity however, are not the only directions of satellite development. Longevity is another, with a vital bearing on the cost of network operation. When placed in geosynchronous earth orbit (GEO) 22,200 miles above the equator, they do not remain exactly where they are put. Perturbations by the gravity of other planets and slight inaccuracies in guidance and navigation mean that a satellite must be kept "on station" by small thrusters on board. The amount of fuel that can be carried usually determines the usable lifetime of the satellite. Already, in less than 2 decades, there are dozens of spent, unused satellites in GEO, posing something of a debris problem to future spacecraft. Intelsat VI will be equipped to provide 10 years of communications service, several times longer than the earlier series.

The growth of satellite population in GEO is beginning to create problems of overcrowding in what is a strictly limited availability of suitable orbital slots. GEO is divided into the 360 degrees of a circle and it has been deemed advisable so far to place commercial satellites a few degrees apart (each degree corresponds to a span of about 700 km in that orbit), but all slots are not equally useful, for example those in the middle of the Pacific Ocean are out of sight of most major users. Closer spanning will therefore become necessary. The allocation of orbital slots and of the different frequency bands, and generally the regulation of satellite communications, is by the International Consultative Committees of the ITU (CCIR and the CCITT).

The cost of earth stations is declining in inverse ratio to the increase in satellite capacity and performance. The more powerful and the more direct the signals emitted by the satellites in orbit, the smaller earth station antennae need be. Very large, multipurpose satellites, such as the Intelsat V series, can be received satisfactorily by small inexpensive earth stations. The cost of earth stations is therefore expected to fall from ca. US$ 10 million or more per station (1983), to a fraction of that figure, and their number sharply increased from the 250 units spread over 135 countries to several thousands by the end of the century, taking the global satellite network to a point of integration and density at which the despatch and receipt of information, data and video programs from anywhere to anywhere is restricted only by
▷ 172

un ou plusieurs immeubles, ou même un ou plusieurs blocs d'immeubles, reliés entre eux, et les câbles des stations terriennes, à partir desquelles un nombre illimité de connexions peuvent être captées, assurant à chaque abonné un apport complet de services.

Un vaste programme de communications maritimes a été mis en œuvre en dehors d'Intelsat et des divers systèmes nationaux et régionaux. Inmarsat (Organisation internationale de communications maritimes par satellite), dont le siège est à Londres, a été créée en 1982 et compte 37 Etats Membres. Elle utilise trois satellites *Marisat* (Etats-Unis) et un autre loué à l'Agence spatiale européenne (ESA) pour assurer le trafic de la région Atlantique. Il est prévu de louer des répéteurs sur deux satellites Intelsat V pour améliorer la capacité disponible au cours de la présente décennie.

Les radioamateurs ont aussi leur satellite *UOSAT*, petit mais très performant, lancé en 1982 et construit par une petite équipe anglaise enthousiaste.

La demande de circuits par satellite continuera à augmenter de façon exponentielle (et doublera, pense-t-on, tous les trois ans). Dès 1990, le réseau mondial des satellites Intelsat devrait avoir une capacité totale de 110 000 circuits (presque deux fois la capacité actuelle) pour atteindre 500 000 circuits avant la fin du siècle. Il faut noter que la technique des satellites progresse parallèlement: « Early Bird » mesurait à peu près 58 cm de haut sur 70 cm de diamètre et offrait une capacité de 240 circuits téléphoniques bidirectionnels et d'une voie de télévision. Intelsat V offre 12 000 circuits téléphoniques et deux voies de télévision en couleur (le double de la capacité des satellites Intelsat IVa qui l'ont précédé). Entre 1984 et 1986 seront lancés les nouveaux satellites Intelsat Va d'une capacité de 15 000 circuits environ. Ensuite viendront les satellites géants Intelsat VI, qui pèseront plus de 1800 kg, mesureront de 12 m de haut sur 3,65 m de diamètre, disposeront d'une puissance électrique de 2,2 kW et, avec 110 000 circuits et auront une capacité près de 500 fois supérieure à celle d'« Early Bird ».

Toutefois, les progrès ne se limitent pas là: la longévité des satellites influe aussi sur leur coût d'exploitation. En orbite géosynchrone, ils subissent de légères dérives et des moteurs d'appoint doivent périodiquement les replacer en position correcte : la durée utile du satellite dépend du volume de combustible qu'il peut emporter pour faire fonctionner ces moteurs. Intelsat VI devrait pouvoir travailler pendant 10 ans, c'est-à-dire plusieurs fois la durée utile des premiers satellites.

L'augmentation du nombre des satellites en orbite géostationnaire commence déjà à créer des problèmes, la capacité de l'orbite étant limitée : une séparation d'un degré correspond à une distance de 700 km sur l'orbite, mais tous les secteurs ne sont pas également utiles, des satellites placés au milieu de l'Océan Pacifique, par exemple, ne seraient pas visibles pour la plupart de leurs principaux utilisateurs. L'attribution des emplacements et celle des bandes de fréquences et, plus généralement, la réglementation des communications par satellite incombe à l'Union internationale des télécommunications et à ses organismes permanents.

Le coût des stations terriennes diminue en fonction de l'amélioration de la capacité et de la performance des satellites. En effet, plus les signaux provenant des satellites sont puissants et directs, plus les antennes des stations terriennes peuvent être petites. Le prix des stations terriennes (10 millions de dollars environ aujourd'hui) devrait donc considérablement diminuer et leur nombre passer de 250 pour 135 pays à plusieurs milliers avant la fin du siècle, l'émission et la réception d'information sous toutes ses formes n'étant plus alors limitées que par les réglementations nationales.

L'unification du réseau mondial sera grandement facilitée par la possibilité, déjà techniquement réalisable, qu'auront les satellites en orbite de communiquer entre eux par des liaisons à forte capacité. Ce-
▷ 172

The NASA shuttle and the rocket Arianne on their launching pads.

La navette de la NASA et la fusée Arianne sur leurs plates-formes de lancement.

les del consorcio *Marisat* de EE.UU., en que Comsat General tiene mayoría, y arrendó otro de la Agencia Espacial Europea (ESA), para cursar tráfico de la región del Atlántico. Hay planes para usar transpondedores marítimos en dos satélites Intelsat *V*, que aumentarán aún más la capacidad en los años 1980.

También existen facilidades de satélite para radioaficionados, gracias a un equipo de entusiastas británicos que construyeron un satélite reducido, pero muy eficaz, *UOSAT*, lanzado en 1982.

Se espera que la demanda mundial de circuitos de satélite aumente exponencialmente (duplicándose cada tres años). Para 1990, se prevé que los satélites de comunicaciones del sistema Intelsat que girarán en torno a la Tierra tendrán capacidad para 110 000 circuitos, casi el doble de la actual, y que aumentará a medio millón de circuitos para mediados de siglo. Esta expansión de la demanda es paralela al desarrollo, igualmente rápido, de la tecnología de satélites. "Early Bird" medía 58 cm de altura y 70 de diámetro, con capacidad para 240 circuitos (canales vocales bidireccionales) y para un canal TV. Intelsat *V* tiene capacidad para 12 000 circuitos, mas dos canales TV de color. El Intelsat *V*a, más grande, que se lanzará en 1984-86, tendrá capacidad para unos 15 000 circuitos. Además Intelsat proyecta dos gigantescos satélites de la serie *VI*, de 2000 kg cada uno, con 1190 cm de altura y 365 cm de diámetro, que pueden generar 2200 vatios de energía eléctrica, con una capacidad de 110 000 circuitos, casi 500 veces más que Early Bird.

Sin embargo, el tamaño y la capacidad no son los únicos aspectos. Otro es la longevidad, con una influencia vital en el costo de explotación de la red. Una vez colocados en órbita terrestre geosíncrona (GEO), a 35 500 km sobre el ecuador, no permanecen exactamente en la misma posición. Las perturbaciones, debidas a la gravedad de otros planetas y las ligeras imprecisiones de orientación y navegación, obligan a mantener "en posición" el satélite merced a propulsores a bordo. La cantidad de combustible transportable determina normalmente el tiempo de vida útil del satélite. En menos de dos décadas, ya hay docenas de satélites inutilizados en GEO, lo que plantea un problema para colocar nuevos vehículos espaciales. Intelsat *VI* estará equipado para 10 años de servicio de comunicaciones, varias veces más que las series anteriores.

El crecimiento de la población de satélites en GEO comienza a crear problemas de saturación, al ser muy limitadas las posiciones orbitales apropiadas. GEO se divide en los 360 grados de un círculo, y hasta ahora se ha estimado aconsejable situar satélites comerciales con unos grados de separación (correspondiendo cada grado a una separación de unos 700 km en esa órbita), pero todos los segmentos no tienen la misma utilidad; por ejemplo, los que se encuentran en medio del Océano Pacífico no están al alcance de la mayoría de los principales usuarios. Por tanto, se necesitará una separación menor. La atribución de posiciones orbitales y de las distintas bandas de frecuencia, y generalmente la reglamentación de las comunicaciones por satélite, corren a cargo de los Comités Consultivos Internacionales de la UIT (el CCIR y el CCITT).

El costo de las estaciones terrenas disminuye en proporción inversa al aumento de la capacidad y rendimiento de los satélites. Cuanto más potentes y directas son las señales emitidas por los satélites en órbita, menores tienen que ser las antenas de las estaciones terrenas. Las emisiones de satélites grandes y versátiles, como los de Intelsat *V*, pueden recibirse satisfactoriamente por pequeñas estaciones terrenas económicas. Se espera, pues, que el costo de las estaciones terrenas se reduzca de los 10 millones $EE.UU. actuales por estación, a una fracción de esa cifra, y que su número aumente mucho, pasando de las 250 dispersas en 135 países a varios miles para finales de siglo; así, la red universal de satélites lle-

▷ 173

El transbordador de la NASA y el cohete Arianne en sus plataformas de lanzamiento.

regulations imposed by the governments of the countries involved.

Another important advance in the direction of integration is the ability, now technologically established, of satellites in orbit to communicate with each other through very high capacity radio links. Such an inter-satellite service, pioneered by the US Federal Communications Commission, would obviate the need to transmit satellite communications to users through cable links between countries or retransmission through Intelsat. However, the implementation of such a service raises questions of policy that may take many years to resolve, although the allocation of frequencies for this use has already been made by the ITU.

In developing countries ITU studies have shown that reliable two-way communications using combinations of a specially dedicated satellite service with low capacity terrestrial systems can be provided economically for rural and isolated areas. Small countries can share facilities and quite a few already lease transponders for domestic traffic purposes from the big international networks, to expand or improve their communications satellite infrastructures.

The company chairman and Chief Executive officer of GTE Corporation, Theodore F. Brophy, stressed this in the following words: "already satellites have done more than any previous technology to unite all the world's telecommunications, including the most remote and inaccessible areas. Yet, the potential of satellites has only begun to be tapped".

Looking forward, in a review of the impact of new technology on satellite radio communication carried out in 1983 at the request of the US Federal Communications Commission's public advisory Committee for the 1985 Space WARC, a member of the FCC's Office of Science and Technology, A. M. Rutkowski, summarized future trends as follows:

"Over the next decade, a coalescence of technological developments can be expected to alter significantly the nature of satellite facilities. These developments include new transportation facilities such as the space shuttle, the construction of large structures in space; the use of advanced antenna and amplifier technology capable of dynamically forming arrays of spot beams to earth; the establishment of extremely high-capacity communication links between satellite facilities; and the use of digital techniques for switching, processing, storing and transmitting information, as well as managing the use of the entire facility.

"In simple terms, each space facility may be envisioned as a large computer capable of providing a multitude of communication and information resources simultaneously to a great number of users, and of modifying the use of those resources from microsecond to microsecond."

Opportunities abound and progress towards a global satellite system is not only technically possible but socially and politically inevitable. As outlined elsewhere in this volume (p. 192 especially) there will be constraints imposed by the desire of nations and private users to preserve some control of the information flow through their networks. The potential use of space and satellite technology has led to the definition of regulatory frameworks for some 20 satellite radiocommunication services, ranging from aeronautical, maritime, and space research to earth exploration services. However, satellites are bringing so much diversity in international communications that the very concept of national borders cannot fail to undergo a major change.

The company profile of Western Union Corporation that follows illustrates the growing role of satellites in the "Information Age", as a key element in an integrated communications network spanning the whole world.

□

pendant, la mise en exploitation d'un tel service, encouragée par la FCC des Etats-Unis, se heurte à des problèmes politiques dont la solution demandera peut-être des années, bien que l'UIT ait déjà réservé des fréquences à cet usage.

Dans les pays en développement, les études entreprises par l'UIT montrent qu'il est possible d'assurer aux zones rurales isolées des communications bidirectionnelles fiables, en associant un service par satellite spécialement conçu à des systèmes de Terre de faible capacité. Les petits pays peuvent utiliser en partage des facilités. Certains d'entre eux louent déjà des répéteurs d'Intelsat, d'Interspoutnik, d'Inmarsat et d'autres organisations, pour les besoins de leur trafic national, et passent ainsi, d'un seul coup, des moyens les plus primitifs aux plus modernes.

« Les satellites ont déjà contribué, plus que toute autre technologie existante, à l'unification des télécommunications dans le monde, jusque dans les régions les plus reculées et les plus inaccessibles. Pourtant nous ne faisons que commencer à exploiter leurs possibilités... Des expériences faites avec de petites antennes montrent que cette nouvelle technologie est capable de révolutionner, bientôt, aussi bien les télécommunications dans les zones urbaines que dans les zones les plus lointaines. » C'est ce qu'a déclaré M. Theodore F. Brophy, PDG de GTE. Nulle prévision ne pouvait paraître plus vraisemblable, aucune constatation ne pouvait sembler plus véridique.

Une étude de l'impact du progrès technologique sur le développement de la communication par satellite réalisée en 1983 par A.M. Rutkowski, membre de l'« Office of Science and Technology » de la Commission Fédérale des Communications des Etats-Unis (FCC), à la demande du « Public Advisory Committee for the 1985 Space WARC, » résume ainsi l'évolution probable de la technologie :

« On peut s'attendre au cours des dix prochaines années à ce qu'une coalescence de développements technologiques modifie la nature même des systèmes à satellite. Les développements probables comprennent une amélioration des techniques de lancement et une réduction de leurs coûts, comme la navette spatiale ; la construction de grandes stations dans l'espace ; l'utilisation d'une technologie avancée d'antennes et d'amplification capables de former et de projeter des rayons étroits sur des endroits précis de la terre ; la création de liaisons de très fortes capacités entre satellites et l'emploi de techniques numériques pour la commutation, le traitement, le stockage et la transmission de l'information, susceptibles de gérer au même temps la totalité d'un système ».

« Très simplement, chaque système de communication spatiale peut être considéré comme étant un ordinateur de très grande capacité capable de communiquer une multitude d'informations et de données à un très grand nombre d'utilisateurs, et d'adapter l'utilisation de telles resources de microseconde à microseconde. »

La réalisation d'un réseau mondial à satellites est non seulement possible techniquement mais socialement et politiquement inévitable. Comme nous l'avons déjà vu (notamment à la page 192), la volonté des pays et des utilisateurs de garder un certain contrôle sur l'information, qui transitera par leurs réseaux, imposera certaines restrictions. L'utilisation possible des techniques spatiales a suscité l'élaboration d'une réglementation applicable à une vingtaine de services de radiocommunication par satellite. Toutefois, les satellites apportent une telle diversité dans le domaine des communications internationales que la notion même de frontières nationales ne saurait manquer d'en être profondément modifiée.

La présentation de Western Union, qui suit, illustre parfaitement le rôle grandissant des satellites, élément-clé d'un réseau mondial intégré de communications, dans la nouvelle « Ere de l'Information ».

□

The USSR satellite "Gorizont" which was used to relay the Olympic Games of 1980 (top) and the layout of the earth station "Moskva" presented at Telecom 1979 in Geneva.

Le satellite soviétique « Gorizont » qui fut utilisé pour les Olympiades en 1980, en haut, et la maquette de la station terrestre « Moskva » présentée à Telecom 1979 à Genève.

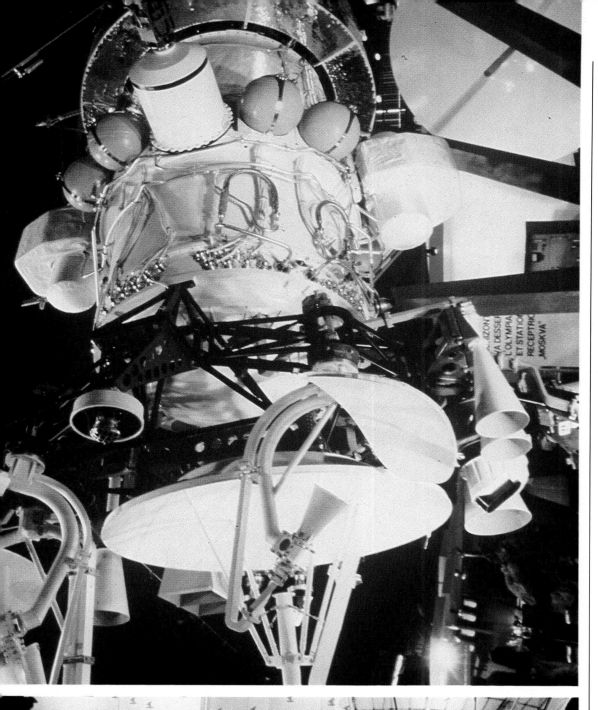

gará a tal integración y densidad que la transmisión
y recepción de programas de información, datos y
vídeo entre dos partes sólo estará limitada por las
reglamentaciones de los gobiernos de los países
interesados.

Otro importante avance hacia la integración es la
capacidad de satélites en órbita para comunicar entre sí a través de radioenlaces de gran capacidad. Con
ese servicio, encabezado por la Comisión Federal de
Comunicaciones de EE.UU., no será necesario
transmitir a usuarios por enlaces de cable entre países, ni retransmitirlos a través de Intelsat. Sin embargo, la implantación de tal servicio plantea cuestiones políticas cuya solución puede llevar años,
aunque la UIT ya haya atribuido frecuencias para tal
uso.

Los estudios de la UIT sobre países en desarrollo han mostrado que pueden proporcionarse económicamente,
para zonas rurales y aisladas, comunicaciones bidireccionales seguras, combinando un servicio de
satélite exclusivo con sistemas terrenales de poca
capacidad. Los países pequeños pueden compartir
facilidades, y muchos alquilan ya transpondedores,
para fines de tráfico nacional, a las grandes redes
internacionales, a fin de ampliar y mejorar sus infraestructuras de comunicaciones por satélite.

El Presidente de la empresa y Jefe Ejecutivo de
GTE Corporation, Theodore F. Brophy, subrayó
esto en los siguientes términos: « Los satélites han
hecho ya más que cualquier tecnología anterior para
unir todas las telecomunicaciones mundiales, incluidas las zonas más remotas e inaccesibles. Y, sin embargo, la explotación de sus posibilidades está em-
pezando... ».

En un estudio sobre el impacto del progreso tecnológico en el desarrollo de las comunicaciones por
satélite, realizado en 1983 por A.M. Rutkowski,
miembro de la "Office of Science and Technology"
de la FÇC de EE.UU., a petición del "Public Advisory Committee" para la CAMR espacial de 1985, se
resumía así la evolución probable de la tecnología:

« En el próximo decenio, la coalescencia de la
evolución tecnológica puede alterar muchísimo la
naturaleza de los sistemas de satélite. Esos cambios
comprenden nuevos servicios de transporte como el
transbordador espacial, la construcción de grandes
estaciones espaciales, el uso de antenas y de amplificadores capaces de formar redes de haces estrechos
en puntos de la Tierra, enlaces de gran capacidad
entre satélites, y el uso de técnicas digitales de conmutación, procesamiento, almacenamiento y
transmisión de información. Cada sistema espacial
puede verse como un gran computador capaz de
proporcionar enormes recursos de comunicación e
información a un gran número de usuarios, y de
adaptar el uso de esos recursos de microsegundo a
microsegundo ».

Las oportunidades abundan, y el progreso hacia un sistema
global de satélites no sólo es técnicamente posible,
sino social y políticamente inevitable. Como se dice
en otra parte de esta obra (véase a la pág. 192), habrá
condicionamientos debidos al deseo de las naciones
y de los usuarios privados de preservar algún control
del flujo de información a través de sus redes. El uso
potencial de la tecnología espacial y de satélites ha
llevado a la definición de marcos reglamentarios
para unos 20 servicios de radiocomunicaciones por
satélite, desde el marítimo aeronáutico o de investigación espacial hasta los servicios de exploración de
la Tierra por satélite. Ahora bien, los satélites aportan tal diversidad de comunicaciones internacionales
que hasta la propia noción de las fronteras nacionales habrá de sufrir un importante cambio.

El perfil de Western Union Corporation que sigue
ilustra el creciente papel de los satélites en la « Era de
la información », como elemento clave de una red
integrada que abarque el mundo entero.

□

*El satélite soviético « Gorizont » utilizado en los
Juegos Olímpicos de 1980 (arriba), y la maqueta
de la estación terrena « Moskva »,
presentada en Telecom 79, en Ginebra.*

Western Union Corporation

From Wire to Westar

ESTABLISHED IN 1851, WESTERN UNION is the senior telecommunications company in the United States and a pioneer in the employment of advanced communications technologies. It was the first company to utilize multiplex telegraphy, microwave transmission, message-switching computers and domestic communications satellites.

As a result of its continuing programs to provide a broad range of services for millions of customers, the Company has developed one of the most advanced communications systems in the world. Today, it is a leading US carrier of record message and data traffic. No longer confined to operating in the USA, since 1982 the Company has been extending these services worldwide.

Western Union operates a nationwide communications network that includes multiple satellites in orbit, a 10,000-mile transcontinental microwave system, electronic switching centers, and local transmission lines in major metropolitan areas. Its Info Master ® computer centers complement this network with message-switching and processing capabilities; and three central telephone bureaus provide convenient nationwide access to the Company's consumer services.

These modern facilities, an extensive customer base and an established reputation for dependable service place Western Union in an unique position within the telecommunications industry.

The Company's principal service offerings include:
— teletypewriter and other office message services, basically Telex I and Telex II (TWX®), which form the core network for rapid written communications among business firms in the United States and throughout the world;
— communications systems and services tailored to

▷ 176

ETABLIE EN 1851, WESTERN UNION est aux Etats-Unis la doyenne des compagnies de télécommunications, ainsi que la première à avoir employé les techniques de communication les plus avancées ; télégraphie multiplex, transmission micro-ondes, commutation de messages par ordinateur et satellites de télécommunications.

En réalisant des plans successifs visant à fournir une grande variété de services à des millions d'usagers, Western Union a mis au point l'un des systèmes de communication les plus perfectionnés du monde. Elle est aujourd'hui le principal « transporteur » de messages enregistrés et de données aux Etats-Unis. Son activité n'étant plus limitée au territoire national, la compagnie étend, depuis 1982, ses services au monde entier.

Western Union exploite un réseau de communications qui recouvre entièrement les Etats-Unis et qui comprend de multiples satellites sur orbite, un système transcontinental de transmission micro-ondes, des centres électroniques de commutation et des lignes de transmission locales dans les grandes zones métropolitaines. Des centres informatiques Info-Master ® ajoutent à ce réseau des possibilités complémentaires de commutation et de traitement de messages. De plus, trois centraux téléphoniques donnent un accès facile aux services publics de la compagnie dans tous les Etats-Unis.

Ces moyens ultra modernes, une clientèle très étendue, et une réputation de fiabilité de service, donnent à Western Union une place exceptionnelle dans l'industrie des télécommunications.

Les principaux services offerts incluent :
— des téléimprimeurs et autres services de message, fondamentalement Telex I et Telex II (TWX®), qui sont au cœur du réseau pour l'échange rapide de communications écrites entre les firmes commerciales du monde entier ;

▷ 176

CREADA EN 1851, WESTERN UNION es la principal empresa de telecomunicaciones de EE.UU., y va a la vanguardia en el empleo de tecnologías de comunicaciones avanzadas. Fue la primera en utilizar telegrafía múltiplex, transmisión por microondas, computadores con conmutación de mensajes y satélites de comunicaciones nacionales.

Debido a sus continuos programas para ofrecer una amplia gama de servicios a millones de usuarios, ha desarrollado uno de los sistemas de comunicaciones más avanzados del mundo. Hoy es la principal empresa de registro de mensajes y tráfico de datos. La empresa no se limita ya a EE.UU.; desde 1982 extiende sus servicios al mundo entero.

Western Union explota una red nacional de comunicaciones que comprende muchos satélites en órbita, un sistema de microondas transcontinental de 16 000 km, centros de conmutación electrónicos, y líneas de transmisión locales en las principales zonas metropolitanas. Sus centros de computador Info-Master ® complementan esta red con capacidades de conmutación y tratamiento de mensajes; y tres oficinas telefónicas centrales proporcionan acceso en todo el país a los servicios públicos de la empresa.

Estas modernas facilidades, su amplia base de clientes y su consagrada reputación de prestar servicios seguros, sitúan a la empresa en una posición privilegiada en la industria de telecomunicaciones. Entre los principales servicios que ofrece figuran:
— servicios de teleimpresor y otros de mensajes de oficina, fundamentalmente Telex I y Telex II (TWX®), que forman la red central de rápidas comunicaciones escritas entre compañías comerciales de EE.UU. y del mundo entero;
— sistemas y servicios de comunicaciones adapta-

▷ 177

A photo of a scaled cutaway of a powerful satellite of Western Union with its 24 transponders used for data, video and voice transmission.

Modèle transparent d'un puissant satellite de Western Union, avec ses 24 répéteurs pour la transmission de données, de son et d'images.

Fotografía a escala en transparencia de un poderoso satélite de Western Union, con sus 24 transpondedores para la transmisión de datos, imágenes y sonido.

the special needs of business and government users, including leased and shared systems that carry both data and voice traffic. Some of the services, such as the transmission of television and radio broadcasts, are provided mainly through Western Union's Westar ® satellite system;
— consumer message services, such as Money Transfer service and individual Mailgram® , Telegram and Cablegram messages;
— priority mail services, including volume handling of computer-originated Mailgram messages and a Computer Letter service;
— MetroFone℠, a long-distance telephone service.
— other services that utilize the Company's service capability, most notably contract maintenance of communications-related equipment.

Satellite communications were initiated by Western Union when, in 1974, it launched the first domestic communications satellites-*Westar I* and *Westar II*. With the launch of *Westar V* in 1982, it became the first US company to have five domestic satellites in orbit. These satellites carry data, video, voice and facsimile communications traffic.

The Westar system involves more than satellites, however. A controlling earth station in the Westar system, located at Glenwood, New Jersey, performs tracking and telemetry functions, making periodic "station-keeping" adjustments so that the satellites maintain a constant position relative to earth. In all, Western Union has seven major earth stations located near New York, Chicago, Atlanta, Dallas, Los Angeles, San Francisco and Seattle. In addition, more than 2,000 small, customer-owned earth stations now communicate through Westar. Much of the Westar capacity is committed to television and radio broadcast services, and there are television operation centers in each of the seven earth-station cities to provide separate control centers for routing high-quality video and audio signals for television and radio broadcasters.

The Westar system has had a revolutionary impact on the US television and radio broadcasting industry by providing an economic alternative to the high cost of either traditional landline transmission or the physical distribution of video-taped programs. The Public Broadcasting Service in the USA currently broadcasts via Westar to an array of satellite earth stations in Alaska, Hawaii, Puerto Rico and the Virgin Islands. The National Public Radio system and its 273 member stations nationwide are also interconnected via Westar; and major commercial television networks all use Western Union's satellite system especially for sports programs.

The print media also uses satellite transmission. Dow Jones uses Westar to transmit complete editions of *The Wall Street Journal*. Text and pictures for *U.S. News & World Report* and facsimile color pictures and text of regional editions of *Time, People* and *Sports Illustrated* magazines are also transmitted via the Company's Westar satellite system.

In addition, Westar is providing long-distance voice/data communications services at substantially reduced costs to the business community. It is possible to lease a single voice-grade satellite channel, alternate voice/data channels or data-only channels. The Company provides wideband point-to-point data transmission via Westar (at 56 Kbps and higher) to either Western Union-provided or customer-owned stations at customer locations for direct interconnection of high-speed data equipment.

Western Union's long-distance telephone service — MetroFone — also uses Westar circuits, in addition to the Company's extensive microwave network, for carrying customers' calls. Available in more than 100 US cities as an alternative to Bell's MTS and

▷ 180

— des systèmes et services de communications conçus spécialement pour les secteurs commerciaux et gouvernementaux, comprenant des systèmes loués et utilisés en partage pour la transmission de données et pour le trafic téléphonique. Certains services, tels que la transmission de programmes de radio et de télévision, sont assurés par le système à satellites Westar ® de Western Union ;
— des services publics de messages, tels que transfert électronique de fonds et messages individuels Mailgram ®, télégrammes et câbles ;
— des services de courrier prioritaire, comprenant la transmission en grand volume de messages Mailgram provenant d'ordinateur, et un service de courrier électronique ;
— un service téléphonique pour longue distance MetroFone℠;
— d'autres services utilisant les ressources de la compagnie, en particulier la maintenance sous contrat des installations de télécommunications.

Les communications par satellite furent initiées en 1974, quand Western Union mis en orbite les premiers satellites américains de communications, *Westar I* et *Westar II*. Avec *Westar V*, lancé en 1982, Western Union est devenue la première compagnie des Etats-Unis à exploiter 5 satellites en orbite. Ces satellites acheminent un trafic de données, d'images, de voix et de facsimilé.

D'autre part, le système Westar n'est pas seulement constitué de satellites. A Glenwood (New Jersey) une station terrienne de commande s'acquitte des fonctions de poursuite et de télémesure et ajuste périodiquement la position des engins spatiaux pour les maintenir sur un point fixe par rapport à la Terre. Western Union exploite en tout sept grandes stations terriennes respectivement situées près de New York, Chicago, Atlanta, Dallas, Los Angelès, San Francisco et Seattle. A cela s'ajoutent plus de 2000 petites stations terriennes appartenant à des particuliers qui peuvent maintenant communiquer grâce aux satellites Westar. Une grande partie du système Westar est réservée aux services de télévision et de radiodiffusion. Chacune des sept grandes stations terriennes mentionnées ci-dessus est équipée d'un centre de télévision pour acheminer des signaux audio-visuels de haute qualité à la demande des organismes de télévision et de radiodiffusion.

Le système Westar a eu de profondes répercussions sur l'industrie de la télévision et de la radiodiffusion aux Etats-Unis ; il permet de remplacer, de façon économique, la transmission classique par ligne terrestre ou la distribution de programmes enregistrés sur cassettes.

Le « Public Broadcasting Service » des Etats-Unis a recours au système Westar pour atteindre tout un nombre de stations terriennes dont certaines sont situées en Alaska, à Hawaii, à Puerto Rico et aux iles Vierges. Le « National Public Radio » et ses stations affiliées sont également reliées par Westar : et les grands réseaux de télévision commerciale utilisent tous le système de satellites Westar de Western Union, surtout pour les programmes de sport.

La presse fait également appel aux services de satellites ; le groupe Dow Jones utilise Westar pour transmettre des éditions complètes du *Wall Street Journal, U.S. News and World Report*. D'autre part, des textes et des images en fac-similé couleur destinés à des éditions régionales des revues *Time, People et Sports Illustrated* sont également transmis par Westar.

Le système Westar fournit par ailleurs au monde des affaires des services de téléphone à longue distance et de transmission de données à des prix très économiques. Les utilisateurs peuvent choisir entre la location d'une seule voie purement téléphonique, des voies alternatives téléphonie/données ou des voies uniquement utilisables pour la transmission de données. La compagnie assure la transmission de données à large bande via Westar (56 kbit/s ou plus)

▷ 180

From Los Angeles (CA.) to New York City, Western Union's microwave towers dot the landscape, forming a 10,000-mile terrestrial network integrated with the company's Westar satellite system.

De Los Angeles, Californie, à la cité de New York, les tours micro-ondes de Western Union jalonnent le paysage, constituant un réseau de 16 000 km intégré au système de satellites Westar.

dos a necesidades especiales de usuarios comerciales y estatales, incluidos sistemas arrendados y compartidos para cursar tráfico de datos y vocal. Algunos de los servicios, como la transmisión de señales de televisión y radiodifusión, se prestan sobre todo a través del sistema de satélite Westar® de Western Union;
— servicios públicos de mensajes, como transferencia electrónica de fondos (servicio de giro) y distintos mensajes Mailgram® , telegramas y cablegramas;
— servicios postales prioritarios, incluido un gran volumen de mensajes Mailgram originados en computador y un servicio de cartas por computador;
— servicio de larga distancia Metro Fone℠;
— otros servicios que utilizan las capacidades de la empresa, sobre todo de mantenimiento contractual de equipo relacionado con las comunicaciones.

Western Union inició las comunicaciones por satélite en 1974, lanzando hos primeros satélites de comunicaciones nacionales: *Westar I* y *Westar II*. Al lanzar el *Westar V* en 1982, se convirtió en la primera empresa estadounidense con cinco satélites nacionales en órbita. Esos satélites cursan tráfico de datos, video, vocal y comunicaciones facsímil.

Sin embargo, el sistema Westar no sólo tiene satélites. Una estación terrena de control del sistema Westar, situada en Glenwood (Nueva Jersey) cumple funciones de seguimiento y telemedida, efectuando ajustes periódicos para mantener a los satélites en una posición constante con relación a la Tierra. En total, Western Union dispone de siete estaciones terrenas situadas cerca de Nueva York, Chicago, Atlanta, Dallas, Los Angeles, San Francisco y Seattle. Y más de 2000 estaciones pequeñas de usuario comunican ahora a través de Westar. Mucha de la capacidad de Westar se dedica a servicios de radiodifusión y televisión, y en cada una de las siete ciudades con estaciones terrenas hay centros de operación de televisión para que las empresas de radiodifusión y televisión puedan disponer de centros de control separados para encaminar señales video y audio de gran calidad.

El sistema Westar ha tenido un impacto revolucionario en la industria de televisión y radiodifusión de EE.UU., al ofrecer una alternativa económica al elevado costo de la transmisión tradicional por circuitos terrestres o la distribución física de programas grabados. El servicio público de radiodifusión transmite a través de Westar a una red de estaciones terrenas de Alaska, Hawaii, Puerto Rico y las Islas Vírgenes. También están interconectados por satélite el sistema nacional público de radiocomunicación y sus 273 estaciones miembros de todo el país. Todas las redes de TV comerciales importantes emplean el sistema de satélite de Western Union, Westar.

Los medios de impresión también usan la transmisión por satélite. Dow Jones emplea Westar para transmitir ediciones completas de *The Wall Street Journal.* Igualmente se transmiten a través del sistema de satélite Westar de la empresa textos e imágenes para *U.S. News & World Report,* e imágenes y textos de color facsímil de ediciones regionales de las revistas *Time, People* y *Sports Illustrated.*

Además, Westar ofrece a la comunidad comercial servicios de comunicaciones de voz/datos a larga distancia a un costo menor. Se puede arrendar un solo canal de satélite de calidad telefónica, canales alternos voz/datos o canales de datos solamente. La empresa proporciona transmisiones de datos punto a punto de banda ancha a través de Westar (a 56 kb/s o más) a estaciones exclusivas aportadas por Western Union o a estaciones de los usuarios, en sus localidades, para la interconexión directa de equipo de datos de gran velocidad.

El servicio telefónico de larga distancia de Western Union — MetroFone — usa también circuitos Westar, además de la amplia red de microondas de la empresa, para cursar llamadas de los clientes. MetroFone, que existe en más de 100 ciudades como alternativa al servicio MTS y WATS de Bell, permite

▷ 180

Desde Los Angeles (California) a Nueva York, las torres de microondas de Western Union jalonan Estados Unidos, formando una red de 16 000 km integrada con el sistema de satélite Westar.

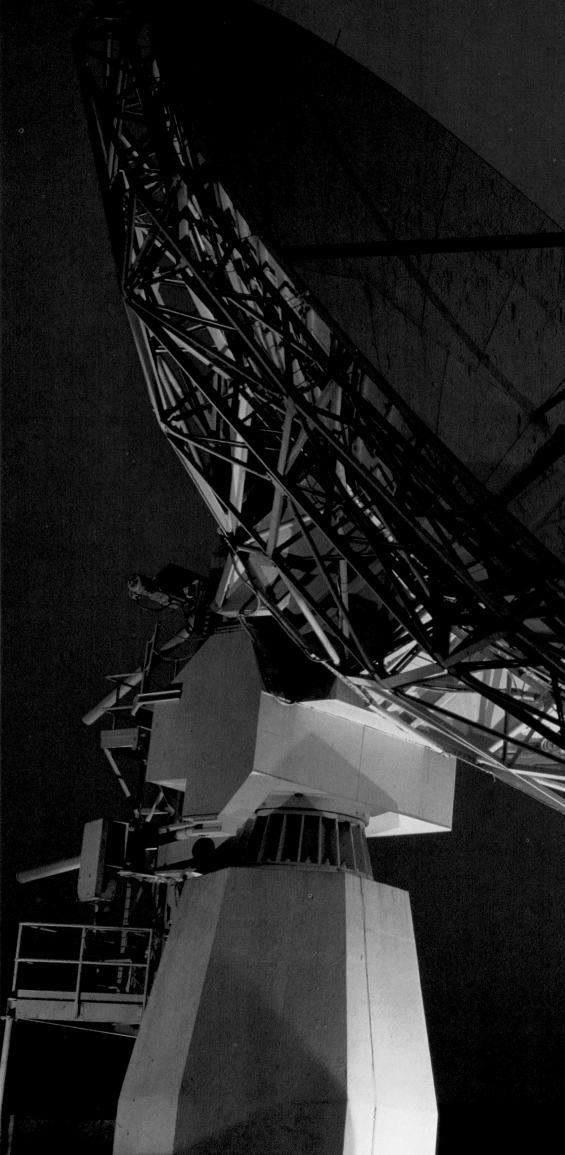

The Western Union earth station (above) in
Glenwood, New Jersey, serves as the tracking and
telemetry command center for the Westar satellite
system. Technicians (below) monitor the status and
attitude of the new satellites, as illustrated by the
oscillating signal superimposed on one of the
station's antennas (opposite).

La station terrienne de Western Union (en haut) à
Glenwood, New Jersey, qui sert de centre de dépistage
et de télémesure pour le système de satellites Westar.
Des techniciens (en bas) surveillent la situation
et la performance des nouveaux satellites, au moyen
d'un signal oscillant, montré en superimposition sur
une des antennes de la station (ci-contre).

La estación terrena de Western Union (arriba) en
Glenwood, Nueva Jersey, que sirve de centro de
seguimiento, telemedida y telemando para el sistema
de satélite Westar. Técnicos (abajo) verificando la
situación y la actitud de nuevos satélites, según ilustra
la señal oscilante supuerpuesta en una de las antenas
de la estación (a la derecha).

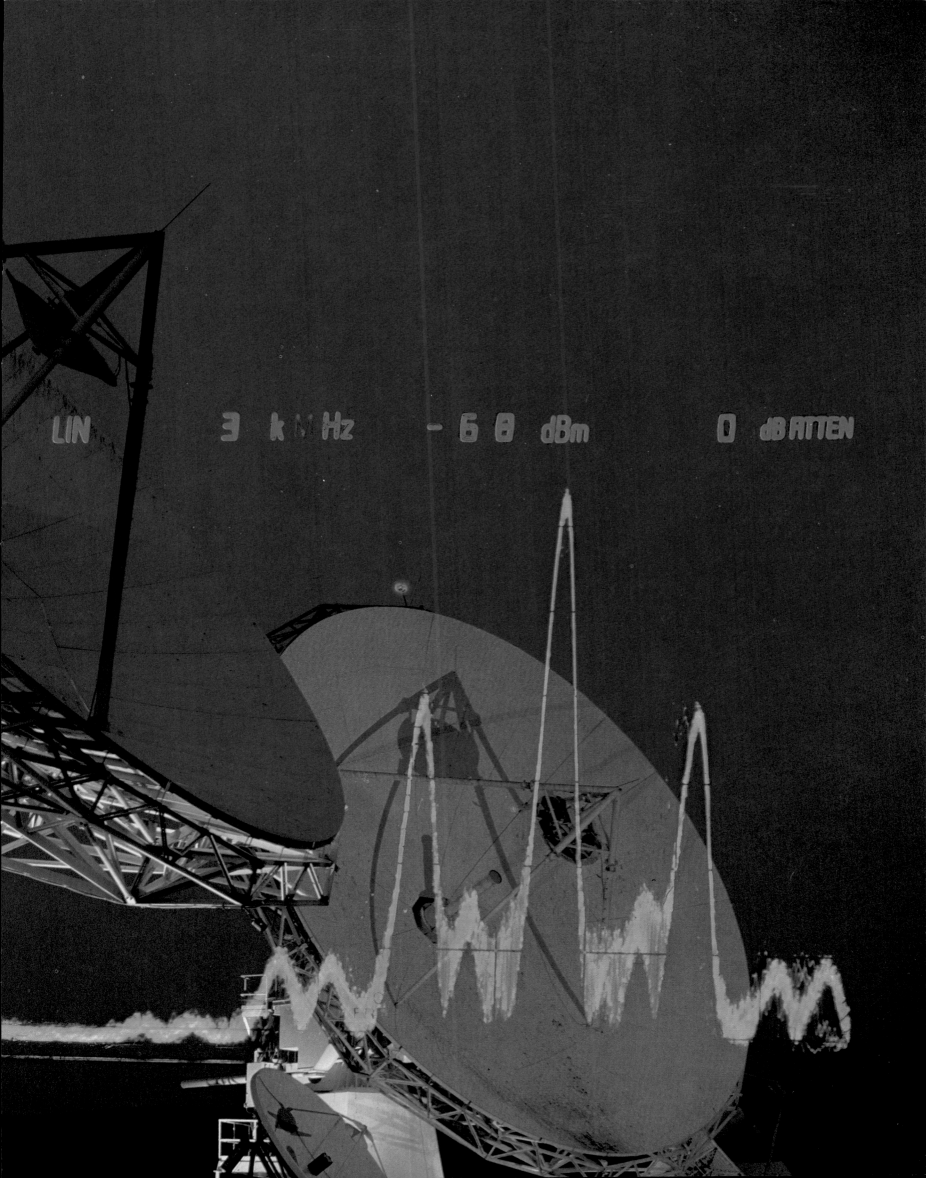

WATS service, MetroFone can save users an average of 40 per cent as compared with Bell System rates.

Much of the Westar capacity is used for the transmission of television programs, both for broadcast and for cable. This video service typically involves the leasing of complete transponders; but Western Union also has pioneered the sale of transponders, with resulting advantages to both the Company and its customers. The economic return for such a sale is approximately the same as that from a lease; but it allows Western Union to share some of the risk, to ensure a full load at launch, and to exploit its satellite program fully without diverting capital resources.

The Company also markets throughout the world the satellite facilities, skills and experience it has obtained in developing and operating its Westar system. As the demand for satellite systems by emerging nations grows, Western Union is drawing upon the expertise it has gained from planning and operating its own Westar system to provide guidance to others. For example, it counselled the Republic of Indonesia when its first communications satellite was launched, and provided technical assistance to the Mexican government in establishing a satellite system to reach remote areas of that country.

A microwave transmission network of some 10,000 miles, integrated with Western Union's domestic satellite system, spans the American continent, replacing the poles and wires with which the Company linked the nation more than a century ago (see illustration on p. 62). This high-frequency radio transmission network reaches directly into 26 major metropolitan areas to carry long-distance communications traffic for business, government and the general public.

After buying TWX from AT&T in 1971, Western Union completed on schedule its three-year program to transfer its teletypewriter subscriber lines — now called Telex II — from the Bell system to the Company's digital exchange system. To do this, Western Union connected 1,600 cities through four major

entre des points fixes qui peuvent être ses propres stations ou celles de ses clients, pour assurer à ceux-ci une liaison directe pour les équipements à grand débit.

Le service de téléphone à longue distance de Western Union — MetroFone — utilise aussi les circuits Westar ainsi que son propre réseau national de transmission micro-ondes. MetroFone est disponible dans plus de 100 villes américaines, côte à côte avec les services MTS et WATS de Bell, coûtant en moyenne 40% de moins que le Bell System.

Une grande partie de la capacité du système Westar est employée à transmettre des programmes de télévision (classique ou par câble). Ce service suppose habituellement la location de répéteurs spatiaux mais Western Union en a inauguré leur vente, à la fois à son propre bénéfice et a celui de sa clientèle. La vente rapporte à peu près autant que la location, mais la vente fait partager une certaine proportion des risques, assure à Western Union une pleine utilisation du satellite dès le lancement, et la pleine exploitation de son programme de satellite sans investissement excessif de capital.

Western Union met sur le marché mondial la compétence et l'expérience qu'elle a acquises en développant et en exploitant le système Westar. Au fur et à mesure que les pays en développement demandent des systèmes à satellites, la compagnie les conseille en se fondant sur les connaissances accumulées au cours de la planification et de la mise en œuvre de son propre système. Par exemple, elle a assisté la République d'Indonésie à lancer son satellite de communication et le gouvernement mexicain à établir un système de communications par satellite destiné à desservir les régions isolées du pays.

Un réseau de transmission par micro-ondes d'environ 16 000 km, intégré dans le système national à satellites de Western Union recouvre le territoire entier des Etats-Unis ; il remplace les poteaux et les fils employés il y a plus d'un siècle (voir illustration p. 62). Ce réseau dessert 26 zones métropolitaines à travers les

a los usuarios ahorrar una media del 40% con respecto a las tarifas de Bell System.

Mucha de la capacidad de Westar se emplea en la transmisión de programas de televisión, por radio y por cable. Este servicio video entraña el arriendo de transpondedores completos; pero Western Union va también a la cabeza en la venta de transpondedores, lo que beneficia a la empresa y a sus clientes. El rendimiento económico de esa venta es más o menos el de un arriendo, pero permite a la empresa compartir parte del riesgo, asegurar plena carga en el lanzamiento y, por ultimo, explotar totalmente su programa de satélites sin distraer recursos de capital.

La empresa comercializa también en el mundo entero las facilidades, los conocimientos y la experiencia de satélites obtenidos en el desarrollo y explotación de su sistema Westar. Como la demanda de sistemas de satélite por nuevas naciones aumenta, Western Union está aprovechando la experiencia adquirida con su propio sistema Westar para orientar a otros. Por ejemplo, Western Union asesoró a la República de Indonesia cuando lanzó su sistema de comunicaciones por satélite, y está ayudando al gobierno mexicano a establecer un sistema de ese tipo para llegar a las zonas remotas del país.

Una red de transmisión por microondas del orden de 16 000 km, integrada con el sistema nacional por satélite de Western Union, abarca el continente americano, y sustituye los polos y conductores con que vinculó la empresa al país hace más de un siglo (véase la ilustración en la pág. 62). Desde lo alto de los tejados hasta la cumbre de las montañas, en una línea a través de América, esta red de transmisión de radiocomunicaciones de alta frecuencia llega directamente a 26 zonas metropolitanas importantes, para transmitir tráfico de larga distancia a instituciones comerciales, estatales y al público en general.

Después de adquirir TWX de AT&T en 1971, Western Union completó en el plazo previsto su

▷ 181

▷ 181

▷ 181

On the left: Operators at Central Telephone Bureaus in New Jersey, Missouri and Nevada respond round-the-clock to thousands of requests daily for Western Union message and Money Transfer services.

A gauche : Des opérateurs dans les centraux téléphoniques de New Jersey, Missouri et Nevada, répondent 24 heures sur 24 aux milliers de demandes qui arrivent chaque jour aux services de messages et de transferts financiers de Western Union.

A la izquierda: Operadores de las centrales telefónicas de Nueva Jersey, Missouri y Nevada atienden permanentemente miles de solicitudes diarias de los servicios de transferencia de mensajes y de dinero de Western Union.

On the right: One of the largest computerized message switching complexes, Western Union's InfoMaster computer centers form an integral part of the company's communications network, providing electronic switching facilities for Mailgram, Telegram, and Cablegram traffic and interconnecting Telex I and Telex II subscribers.

A droite : Un des plus grands centres informatisés de commutation de messages, le centre d'ordinateurs de Western Union InfoMaster fait partie intégrale du réseau de communication de la compagnie. Cette installation de commutation électronique pour le trafic du courrier, des télégrammes et des câbles, relie également les abonnés de Telex I et II.

A la derecha: Uno de los mayores complejos de conmutación de mensajes computadorizados en servicio comercial. Los centros de computadores InfoMaster de Western Union forman parte de la red de comunicaciones de la empresa. InfoMaster es una instalación de conmutación electrónica para el tráfico de correo, telegramas y cables. Conecta también a los abonados de Télex I y Télex II.

electronic data switching centers in New York, Chicago, Atlanta and San Francisco. These centers have the capacity to provide for continued growth.

To meet more of its local communications requirements from its own resources, Western Union extended its local digital transmission cable facilities in 56 metropolitan areas. It now has in place extensive aerial and underground cable, and this has enabled the Company to improve service to its customers and to reduce expenses for leased facilities.

Of growing importance to Western Union's local distribution in metropolitan areas will be the use of optical cables. The company established one of the first experimental fiber optic lines in New York City in 1979. Early in 1983 it completed its first fiber optic installation on the West Coast, running 2 km of cable through the center of San Francisco.

At the heart of the transmission system of satellites, microwave relays and electronic switches is Info Master, one of the world's largest computer-communications installations. Two major InfoMaster centers, one in Bridgeton, Missouri, and the other in Middletown, Virginia, provide automatic message switching and storage for 75 million messages a year. All Mailgram messages pass through InfoMaster, and the special store-and-forward capabilities of the computer enable the Company to deliver Telex messages addressed to busy stations and to send multiple-address messages. With a consistent record of better than 99% reliability, the InfoMaster system assures automatic switching and computer storage for 250,000 messages each business day.

Government systems, made possible by Western Union's extensive facilities and high rate of reliability, provide federal and state agencies with dependable private communications networks. For the Department of Defense, Western Union supplies the United States portion of Autodin (Automatic Digital Network), a high-speed data communications network. The advanced Record system is a Western Union net-

Etats-Unis, et transmet un trafic considérable de communications publiques et privées.

En 1971, après avoir acheté à AT&T l'équipement TWX, Western Union a mené à terme en trois ans son programme de transfert du service de téléimprimeur — maintenant appelé Telex II — du système Bell à son propre système de centraux numériques. A cette fin, Western Union a connecté 1600 villes au moyen de 4 grands centres électroniques de commutation de données dont la capacité permet une expansion du service.

D'autre part, l'utilisation des câbles optiques sera d'une importance croissante pour le système de distribution locale dans les grandes villes. Western Union fut à l'origine de la première installation expérimentale de câble optique sur la côte ouest, dont environ 2 km. traversent le centre de San Francisco.

Au cœur du système de transmission par satellite, réseaux micro-ondes et de commutateurs électroniques se trouve le système InfoMaster un des plus vastes complexes de communications par ordinateur du monde. Deux centres à Bridgeton (Missouri) et Middletown (Virginie) assurent automatiquement la commutation et l'enregistrement de plus de 75 millions de messages par an. Tout le courrier électronique passe par InfoMaster, et la capacité de mise en mémoire/transmission de l'ordinateur permet de remettre en différé des messages Telex à des stations occupées au moment initial ou en dérangement, ainsi que l'acheminement à leurs destinataires des messages à adresses multiples. Avec une fiabilité dépassant 99%, le système InfoMaster assure automatiquement la commutation et l'enregistrement en mémoire de 250 000 messages par jour ouvrable.

Les organisations gouvernementales ont souvent recours aux services de Western Union pour satisfaire leurs besoins de communications. Le ministère de la défense des Etats-Unis dispose de la partie américaine d'un réseau perfectionné de transmission rapide de données, l'Autodin (Automatic Digital Network). Un autre système, « Advanced Record System »,

programa trienal para transferir sus líneas de abonado de teleimpresor — denominado ahora Telex II — del sistema Bell al sistema de centrales digitales de la empresa. Para ello, conectó 1600 ciudades a través de cuatro importantes centros de conmutación electrónica de datos: Nueva York, Chicago, Atlanta y San Francisco. Los centros tienen capacidad para hacer frente al constante crecimiento.

A fin de atender otras necesidades de comunicaciones locales con sus propios recursos, Western Union amplió sus facilidades locales de cable de transmisión digital en 56 zonas metropolitanas. Ya ha instalado una gran cantidad de cable aéreo y subterráneo, lo que le ha permitido mejorar los servicios a sus clientes y reducir los gastos de arriendo.

Los cables de fibras ópticas tendrán gran importancia para la distribución local de Western Union en zonas metropolitanas. La empresa estableció una de las primeras líneas experimentales en Nueva York, en 1979. A comienzos de 1983 terminó su primera instalación de fibras ópticas en la costa occidental, con unos 2 km de cable en el centro de San Francisco.

En el núcleo del sistema de transmisión por satélite, relevadores de microondas y conmutadores electrónicos se encuentra InfoMaster, una de las mayores instalaciones de comunicaciones por computador del mundo. Dos grandes centros InfoMaster, uno en Bridgeton (Missouri) y el otro en Middletown (Virginia), ofrecen conmutación y almacenamiento automáticos de 75 millones de mensajes anuales. Todos los mensajes Mailgram pasan a través de InfoMaster, y las capacidades especiales de almacenamiento y retransmisión del computador permiten a la empresa entregar mensajes télex dirigidos a estaciones ocupadas o inoperables y transmitir mensajes a direcciones múltiples. Con un récord constante de fiabilidad superior al 99%, el sistema InfoMaster asegura el tratamiento por computador de 250 000 mensajes diarios.

▷ 182   ▷ 182   ▷ 183

181

work that provides teletypewriter and medium-speed data communications to thousands of offices of the civilian agencies of the Federal government. The Federal Reserve Bank uses a Western Union information network to connect member banks to a central computer center, and another Western Union information network helps law enforcement agencies exchange data through the National Crime Information Center. Western Union also transmits weather and flight information to pilots from the Federal Aviation Administration's Weather Message Center in Kansas City.

Central telephone bureaus operated by Western Union are linked with the InfoMaster computer system. Strategically located across the United States — in New Jersey, Missouri and Nevada — these message processing centers form a national telephone grid that is one of the largest privately-owned telephone exchange complexes outside the Bell system. Each central telephone bureau has up to 10 recording rooms where hundreds of operators receive a constant stream of messages from the public 24 hours a day, seven days a week, routing each message through InfoMaster to its proper destination. Western Union operators handle about 21 million calls per year, and their average speed of answer time is about 12 seconds — or about two rings. Western Union also maintains more than 9,000 public offices and agencies where individual customers can send and receive Money Orders, as well as Mailgram, Telegram and Cablegram messages.

The Field Service Division of Western Union is another extensive network — although not an electronic one — which provides a nationwide maintenance capability backed by 1,600 field technicians at more than 400 service locations.

In addition to maintaining subscriber terminals in the Company's domestic Telex system, the Field Division services approximately 80,000 customer-owned terminals nationwide under third-party maintenance contracts. The Division services more than 400 different identifiable products, including mini- and microcomputers, word processing equipment, transcontinental microwave systems, cellular mobile radios, air-to-ground radio telephones, and satellite earth station antenna systems. It is responsible for over 400,000 pieces of equipment, which represents the widest range of customer-provided terminals or computer interfaces of any company in the communications service business.

In 1982, Western Union signed an agreement with Bell Canada to provide maintenance service in the United States to customers of Dataforce, Bell Canada's third-party maintenance division. Similarly, Dataforce provides coverage for Western Union customers having terminals in Canada. The agreement marks the first mutual service arrangement of this kind and offers potential customers, many of whom will be multinationals, service coverage in Canada by an acknowledged leader in data communications.

Telecommunications services to the nation — and the world — are provided through the interaction of Western Union's facilities. Multiple satellites, a microwave network, electronic switching centers and local transmission lines, three central telephone bureaus, and an expert technical service division — all work together to enable Western Union to offer a wide spectrum of communications services.

Teletypewriters combine the speed of the telephone with the accuracy of a written message, and Telex — a teletypewriter exchange service — is the largest single part of Western Union's business. The Company offers a nationwide direct-dial Telex capability among 140,000 subscribers in 1,600 cities throughout the United States.

▷ 186

fournit un service téléimprimeur et de transmission de données à moyenne vitesse à des milliers de bureaux des services civils du gouvernement.

La Federal Reserve Bank utilise un réseau informatique pour relier ses filiales à une unité centrale d'ordinateurs, tandis qu'un autre réseau d'information facilite l'échange des données entre le National Crime Information Center et les différents centres de police. Western Union diffuse à partir du centre météorologique de l'administration fédérale de l'aviation, à Kansas City, des messages concernant les vols et les conditions météorologiques.

Les bureaux téléphoniques centraux exploités par Western Union sont reliés au système InfoMaster. Ces bureaux — situés en des points stratégiques (New Jersey, Missouri et Nevada) — constituent des centres de traitement des messages et forment à l'échelon national, l'un des plus grands complexes de centraux téléphoniques privés outre le système Bell. Chaque bureau central compte jusqu'à dix salles d'enregistrement où des centaines d'opératrices reçoivent d'innombrables messages 24 heures par jour et 7 jours par semaine, acheminant, par l'intermédiaire du système InfoMaster, chaque message à son destinataire. Ces opératrices traitent et acheminent environ 21 millions de communications par an, 12 secondes s'écoulant en moyenne entre l'appel et la réponse de l'opératrice. Western Union maintient également plus de 9000 bureaux publics où les usagers peuvent envoyer ou recevoir des mandats et du courrier électronique.

La Division de maintenance de Western Union dispose de 1600 techniciens situés dans plus de 400 agences locales. La Division assure la maintenance des terminaux d'abonnés du système Telex national de Western Union, ainsi que celle de 80 000 terminaux appartenant à leurs utilisateurs (sur base de contrats de maintenance). Plus de 400 types d'équipement identifiables sont inclus: mini- et micro-processeurs, dispositifs de traitement de texte, systèmes de transmission micro-ondes transcontinentaux, systèmes de téléphonie mobile alvéolaire, radiotéléphones en vol, et systèmes d'antenne de stations terriennes. Elle assure l'entretien de plus de 400 000 unités d'équipement appartenant à des tiers, qui représentent le plus large catalogue de terminaux ou d'interfaces d'ordinateur que puisse posséder une compagnie de services dans les communications.

En 1982, Western Union a signé avec Bell Canada un accord de réciprocité pour servir la clientèle de Dataforce, la division maintenance de Bell Canada, aux Etats-Unis. En retour, Dataforce s'occupe des clients de Western Union qui utilisent des terminaux au Canada. C'est là le premier accord de ce genre, qui offre aux clients éventuels — dont la plupart seront des firmes multinationales — un service de maintenance au Canada assuré par une compagnie de tout premier rang en matière de transmission de données.

Le large éventail de services de télécommunications fournis par Western Union aux Etats-Unis et dans le monde est le résultat d'un amalgame de plusieurs ressources et de leur interaction. Cela comprend de multiples satellites, un réseau micro-ondes, des centraux de commutation électronique, des réseaux urbains ou régionaux de transmission par câble, trois centraux téléphoniques et, en plus, une division d'experts techniques qui s'occupent du maintien et du bon fonctionnement des systèmes.

Les téléimprimeurs joignent à la vitesse du téléphone la précision du message écrit et le service d'échange télex-téléimprimeurs, le plus grand secteur des activités de Western Union. La compagnie donne à ses 140 000 abonnés dans 1600 villes des Etats-Unis la possibilité d'utiliser ce service en automatique. Les abonnés au service Telex de Western Union ont, en outre, accès à toute une gamme d'autres services qui incluent Mailgram, Telegram, Ca-

▷ 186

Top: AirFone, the first air-to-ground telephone service, 50% owned by Western Union, subscribed by eleven US commercial airlines. Bottom: The cellular radio system automatically switches telephone calls from cell to cell as vehicles move in the area.

En haut : L'AirFone, premier des services de téléphone en vol air-sol, dont Western Union possède 50% des parts. Onze compagnies aériennes l'utilisent. En bas : Le système cellulaire micro-ondes transfère automatiquement les appels téléphoniques d'alvéole en alvéole suivant le mouvement des véhicules.

Los organismos del gobierno utilizan mucho las facilidades de Western Union para sistemas de comunicaciones privadas. Western Union suministra para el Departamento de Defensa la porción de Estados Unidos de Autodin (Automatic Digital Network), una red de comunicación de datos a gran velocidad.

El sistema de registro avanzado « Advanced Record System » es una red de Western Union que ofrece comunicaciones de teleimpresor y datos a media velocidad a miles de oficinas de organismos civiles del Gobierno Federal. El Federal Reserve Bank utiliza una red de información de Western Union para conectar los bancos de los miembros con un centro de computador central, y otra red de información de Western Union ayuda al intercambio de datos de los organismos encargados del cumplimiento de la ley a través del National Crime Information Center. Western Union transmite también información meteorológica y de vuelo a los pilotos desde el Centro de Mensajes Meteorológicos de la Federal Aviation Administration de Kansas City.

Las oficinas telefónicas centrales operadas por Western Union están conectadas al sistema de computador InfoMaster. Distribuidas estratégicamente por todo EE.UU. — Nueva Jersey, Missouri y Nevada — constituyen centros de procesamiento de mensajes y forman una red telefónica nacional que figura entre los complejos de centrales telefónicas privados más importantes fuera del sistema Bell. Cada oficina telefónica central cuenta hasta 10 salas de grabación, donde centenares de operadores reciben mensajes del público, las 24 horas del día, durante toda la semana, y encaminan cada mensaje a su propio destino, a través de InfoMaster. Los operadores de Western Union tratan unos 21 millones de llamadas anuales, y su velocidad media de respuesta es del orden de 12 segundos (unos dos toques de campanilla). Western Union mantiene también más de 9000 oficinas y agencias públicas, donde los clientes pueden enviar y recibir giros, así como mensajes Mailgram, telegramas y cablegramas.

La División de servicios descentralizados de Western Union es otra amplia red que proporciona una capacidad nacional de mantenimiento por 1600 técnicos y más de 400 oficinas de servicio. Además de mantener los terminales de abonado en el sistema nacional télex de la empresa, la división de servicios descentralizados se ocupa de unos 80 000 terminales de clientes de todo el país, mediante contratos de mantenimiento de terceros. Los servicios de la división, con más de 400 productos, comprenden mini y microcomputadores, equipo de tratamiento de texto, sistemas de microondas transcontinentales, radios móviles celulares, teléfonos aire-tierra, y sistemas de antenas de estaciones terrenas. Se ocupa de más de 400 000 piezas de equipo, la más amplia gama de terminales de usuario o interfaces de computador de todas las empresas de servicios de comunicaciones.

En 1982, Western Union firmó un acuerdo con Bell Canada para prestar servicios de mantenimientos en EE.UU. a clientes de Dataforce, la división de mantenimiento de terceros de Bell Canada. Dataforce se encarga también de clientes de Western Union con terminales en Canadá. El acuerdo es el primer arreglo de servicio mutuo de esta índole y ofrece a los posibles clientes, muchos de ellos multinacionales, la cobertura del servicio en Canadá por un reconocido líder en comunicaciones de datos.

Entre las facilidades de servicio prestadas por Western Union figuran satélites múltiples, una red de microondas, centros de conmutación electrónica y líneas de transmisión local, tres oficinas telefónicas centrales y una división de asesoramiento técnico. Todas ellas trabajan conjuntamente para prestar servicios de telecomunicaciones al país, y al mundo.

Los teleimpresores combinan la velocidad del teléfono con la precisión de un mensaje escrito, y el

▷ 187

Arriba: El nuevo sistema AirFone, el primer servicio telefónico aire-tierra, perteneciente a Western Union en un 50%, y solicitado ya por 11 líneas aéreas comerciales de EE.UU.
Abajo: El sistema radiocelular conmuta automáticamente las llamadas de una célula a otra, a medida que se desplazan los vehículos.

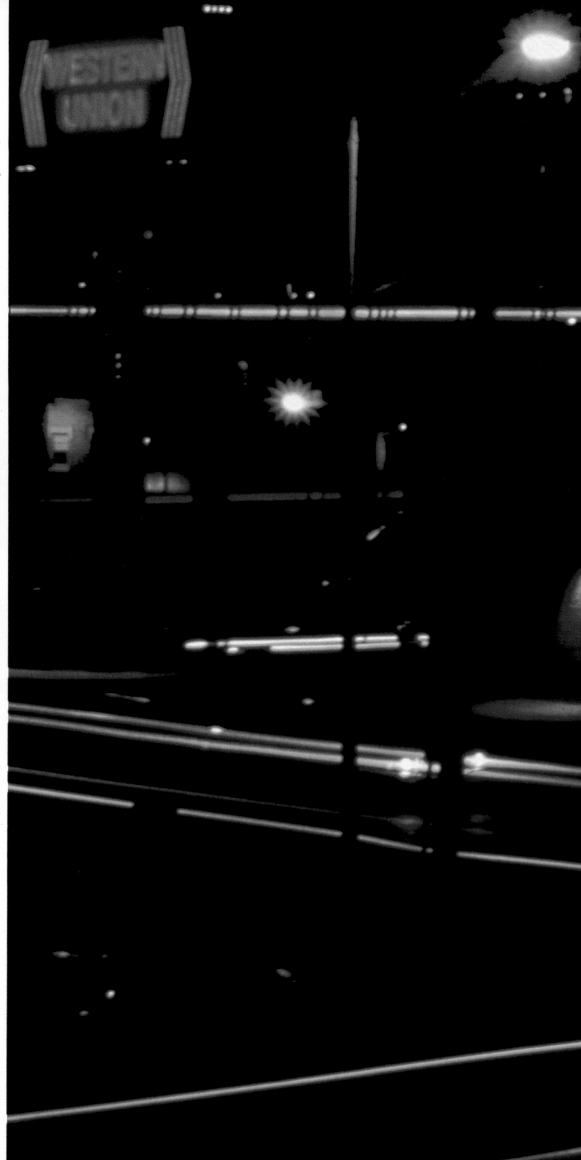

Money Orders, Mailgram, Telegram and Cablegram
messages can be sent or received at nearly 9,000
Western Union offices such as those in Houston,
Texas (top) and in Omaha, Nebraska (bottom).
Opposite: Signs at the new Houston location signal
courteous, attentive service to passing motorists.

Les mandats, lettres, télégrammes et messages câblés
sont envoyés et reçus dans les 9000 bureaux de
Western Union comme ceux de Houston, Texas (en
haut) et de Omaha, Nebraska (en bas).
Ci-contre : L'installation nouvelle de Western
Union á Houston signale un service
attentif et courtois aux automobilistes.

Los clientes de Western Union pueden enviar
y recibir giros, cartas, telegramas y cables
en las 9000 oficinas públicas y de la empresa,
como las de Houston, Texas (arriba) y Omaha,
Nebraska (abajo). La nueva instalación de
Western Union en Houston (a la derecha) señala un
servicio atento y cortés a los automovilistas.

184

In addition to the basic message exchange service, Western Union Telex subscribers have access to a variety of other services, including Mailgram, Telegram, Cablegram and Money Order. Other customer conveniences include FYI News Service, which provides stock market information, commodity reports, weather reports, news, and many other kinds of information.

Western Union has moved in the direction of becoming the basic message carrier for the entire business community with the introduction of a new service called Easy Link. Until recently only Telex subscribers could use Telex service, and they were unable to interact with the growing number of small businesses and individuals who have home computers, word processors or other terminals. With Easy Link, Western Union is filling that need.

Easy Link subscribers can communicate with Telex terminals, send Mailgram, Telegram and Cablegram messages and also reach other Easy Link subscribers. Using an "electronic mailbox", they can let incoming messages accumulate and call in to retrieve them when convenient.

In August 1982, Western Union extended its Telex service into the international marketplace. The Company had long been barred by a 1943 amendment to the Communications Act from extending its record communications service overseas, but with the passage of the Record Carrier Competition Act of 1981, it was freed from that restraint.

Many of Western Union's traditional services are now entering the worldwide market. For example, another major step into global communications has been the introduction of Teletex. First introduced in the Federal Republic of Germany (FRG) in 1981, Teletex combines text typing and processing with automatic memory communications. Sometimes referred to as "super Telex", it operates at 2,400 bits per second, almost 45 times the speed at which standard Telex messages are transmitted.

Teletex is already established in several European countries. Western Union was the carrier to bring it to the United States in 1983, having concluded an operating agreement in 1982 with the Ministry of Posts and Telecommunications of the Federal Republic of Germany to provide United States-Germany Teletex service. This was the first step toward Western Union's establishment of a worldwide Teletex network.

For fast, convenient electronic transfer of funds, Western Union operates telegraphic Money Order service. A new aspect of this is Worldwide Funds Transfer service, which enables US businesses to send funds to virtually any foreign bank account in the world at a guaranteed rate of exchange.

Western Union has just completed modernization of its domestic Money Tranfer system. Through terminals that have been installed at all public offices and most agencies, counter clerks and agents may quickly access to the InfoMaster computer to verify that a customer has been sent a Money Order and that funds should be paid. The payout may be made within minutes at any Western Union office or agency — a great convenience for travelers.

Mailgram messages — America's first mail by satellite — are sent electronically to post offices anywhere in the United States and Canada for delivery with the next business day's mail.

Western Union and British Telecom International have begun to provide a public message service that links the Western Union Mailgram message service in the United States with the Telemessage service provided by British Telecom in the UK, giving users of either service access to both.

▷ 188

blegram, Money Order. Le service d'information « FYI News Service » procure les cours de la Bourse, les rapports sur les matières premières, la météo, les nouvelles et bien d'autres informations.

Western Union est en voie de devenir le transporteur-type de messages pour le monde des affaires avec l'introduction du nouveau service Easy Link. Jusqu'à ces derniers temps, seuls les abonnés du service Télex pouvaient se servir du service Télex, et ils ne pouvaient pas communiquer avec le nombre croissant de petites firmes et d'individus munis d'ordinateurs de table, de machines de traitement de texte ou d'autres terminaux rapides. Avec Easy Link, Western Union leur permet de le faire. Les abonnés d'Easy Link peuvent communiquer avec les terminaux Télex, envoyer des lettres télégraphiques, des télégrammes, des câbles, et joindre les autres abonnés d'Easy Link. En se servant d'une « boite à lettres électronique » ils peuvent laisser les messages s'accumuler et venir les chercher quand ils le veulent.

En août 1982, Western Union a élargi son service Télex au marché mondial, ce que lui était interdit par un amendement de 1943 au « Communications Act ». Une nouvelle loi, « the Record Carrier Competition Act », passée en 1981, a éliminé cet empêchement.

Beaucoup des services traditionnels de Western Union entrent ainsi sur le marché mondial. Un autre pas d'importance majeure pour les communications mondiales a été l'introduction du Télétex. Inauguré en RFA en 1981, le Télétex combine la dactylographie et le traitement de texte avec les communications automatiques à mémoire. Ce « Super Telex » transmet les messages a 2400 bits/seconde, soit à peu près 45 fois plus vite que le service Télex.

Le service Télétex est bien établi dans plusieurs pays d'Europe : Western Union fut la compagnie qui l'introduisit, en 1983, aux Etats-Unis, en ayant conclu, en 1982, un accord d'exploitation avec le « Bundespost » de la RFA afin d'établir un service Télétex Etats-Unis-RFA. Ce fut là, pour Western Union, la première étape vers la création d'un réseau Télétex mondial.

Pour assurer un transfert rapide et facile de fonds, Western Union opère télégraphiquement un « Money Order Service ». Un nouveau service, le « Worldwide Funds Order Transfer Service » permet aux firmes américaines d'envoyer des fonds à pratiquement n'importe quelle banque au monde à un taux de change garanti.

Western Union vient de moderniser son système national de mandats « Money Transfer ». Grâce à des terminaux installés dans tous les bureaux publics et dans la plupart de ses agences, les caissiers peuvent consulter rapidement l'ordinateur InfoMaster afin de vérifier qu'un mandat a bien été envoyé et qu'il y a lieu de payer. Toute l'opération peut être effectuée en quelques minutes — une grande commodité pour les voyageurs.

Les messages « Mailgram » — premier service postal américain par satellite — sont envoyés électroniquement aux bureaux de poste de la partie continentale des Etats-Unis et du Canada, pour remise le jour suivant.

Western Union et British Telecom International ont conclu un accord visant à établir un service public de messages qui reliera le service électronique que Western Union exploite aux Etats-Unis au service Telemessage que British Telecom exploite au Royaume-Uni, les utilisateurs de l'un ou de l'autre service ayant ainsi accès aux deux.

Une autre innovation récente de Western Union a été la « lettre par ordinateur ». Il s'agit d'un service qui permet à la clientèle commerciale, lorsqu'elle ne demande pas la remise du message dans un délai de

▷ 188

Top: Western Union's computer center at Mahwah, N.J., is the hub of its service restoral network, which covers the entire USA and provides maintenance of some 400,000 pieces of communicational equipment.
Bottom: Technicians monitor the MetroFone long-distance telephone service which operates over Western Union's microwave and satellite transmission network and achieves substantial savings over traditional rates.

En haut : Centre informatisé de Western Union à Mahwah, N.J., base d'un réseau de maintenance de quelque 400 000 unités d'équipement de communications. Ce réseau couvre complètement l'ensemble des Etats-Unis.
En bas : Des techniciens surveillent le service téléphonique à longue distance MetroFone de Western Union qui fonctionne avec un réseau combiné satellite/micro-ondes, à des prix nettement inférieurs aux prix traditionnels.

télex — servicio entre teleimpresores — constituye la mayor actividad de Western Union. La empresa ofrece la posibilidad de llamada directa por télex en todo el país a más de 140 000 abonados de 1600 ciudades de EE.UU.

Además del servicio básico de intercambio de mensajes, los abonados al télex de Western Union tienen acceso a servicios Mailgram, telegramas, cablegramas y giros. Otras facilidades a los clientes comprenden el servicio de noticias FYI, que facilita información sobre la bolsa y productos básicos, información meteorológica, noticias y mucha más.

Western Union trata de imponerse en el sector de mensajes en toda la comunidad comercial con la introducción del nuevo servicio Easy Link. Hasta hace poco, el servicio télex sólo podían utilizarlo sus abonados, y sin interactuar con el creciente número de pequeñas empresas o individuos que disponen de computadores domésticos, procesadores de palabra u otros terminales de mayor velocidad. Con Easy Link, Western Union atiende esta necesidad, pues los abonados pueden comunicar con terminales télex, enviar Mailgram, telegramas y cablegramas, y conectar con otros abonados a Easy Link. Mediante un "buzón electrónico", pueden acumular los mensajes y transmitirlos cuando lo deseen.

En agosto de 1982, Western Union amplió su servicio télex al mercado internacional. La empresa tenía prohibida por una modificación de 1943 de la Ley sobre Comunicaciones la extensión de sus servicios de comunicaciones registradas al extranjero, pero, al promulgarse la Record Carrier Competition Act de 1981, se levantó esa restricción.

Ahora entran en el mercado mundial muchos servicios tradicionales de Western Union. Por ejemplo, otro importante paso en las comunicaciones globales es la introducción de teletex. Implantado primero en la República Federal de Alemania (RFA) en 1981, teletex combina el mecanografiado y procesamiento de texto con comunicaciones de memoria automáticas. A veces, se denomina "supertélex"; opera a 2400 bits por segundo, casi 45 veces la velocidad a que se transmiten los mensajes télex normales.

El teletex funciona ya en varios países europeos; Western Union lo ha implantado en 1983 en EE.UU., después de concertar en 1982 un acuerdo de explotación con el Ministerio de Correos y Telecomunicaciones de la RFA para prestar el servicio alemán teletex en EE.UU. Se trata del primer paso hacia el establecimiento por Western Union de una red teletex mundial.

Para una transferencia electrónica de fondos rápida y adecuada, Western Union opera el servicio de giro telegráfico. Las empresas comerciales estadounidenses pueden enviar ahora fondos, mediante una llamada gratuita, a cualquier cuenta bancaria extranjera, a un tipo de cambio garantizado.

Western Union ha modernizado su sistema de transferencia nacional. A través de terminales instalados en todas las oficinas públicas y la mayoría de las agencias, los empleados y los agentes pueden acceder rápidamente al computador InfoMaster, para comprobar que un cliente ha enviado un giro y que deben pagarse los fondos. El pago puede hacerse en unos minutos en cualquier oficina o agencia de Western Union: una facilidad para el viajero.

Los mensajes Mailgram — primer servicio americano de correo por satélite — se envían electrónicamente a todas las oficinas de correos de EE.UU. y Canadá para entregarlos con el correo del día siguiente.

Western Union y British Telecom International prestan un servicio público de mensajes que vinculará el servicio de mensajes Mailgram de Western

▷ 188

Arriba: El centro de computadores de Western Union en Mahwah, N.J., es la cabeza de línea de una red de servicios de restablecimiento que abarca todo el país y se ocupa del mantenimiento de unas 400 000 unidades de equipo de comunicaciones.
Abajo: Técnicos comprobando el servicio telefónico de larga distancia MetroFone de Western Union, que funciona por la red de transmisión de microondas y satélite de la empresa a precios considerablemente inferiores a las tarifas tradicionales.

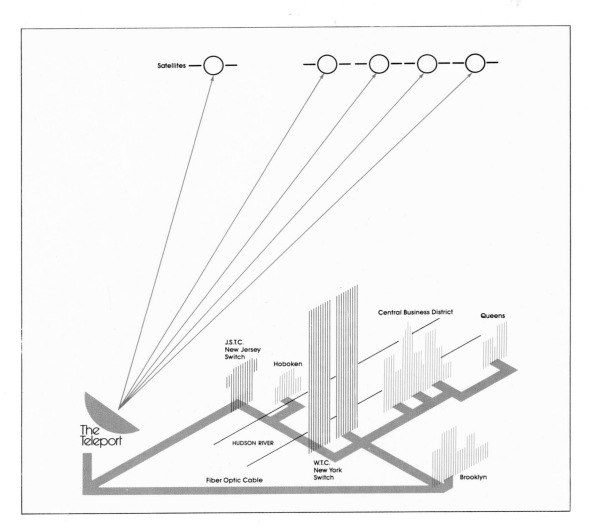

Satellites

Central Business District   Queens

J.S.T.C.
New Jersey
Switch

Hoboken

The
Teleport

HUDSON RIVER

Fiber Optic Cable

W.T.C.
New York
Switch

Brooklyn

Another initiative Western Union took was the introduction of the Computer Letter. This is a service that makes available a high-impact, low-cost message for commercial customers who do not require the next-day delivery a Mailgram message provides.

In the United Kingdom, Western Union has inaugurated a similar service through a joint venture organization with a British firm, English China Clays. The United Kingdom operation is known as Western Union Global Information Services Ltd., and its first activity, in 1982, was Priority Letter service. It uses the latest computer and laser techniques to offer communications services to industry, commerce and government within the United Kingdom.

New ventures in the telecommunications industry are being developed by Western Union in response to increased demands for advanced communications services. Three projects that are especially promising for the Company are the first air-to-ground public telephone system, cellular mobile radio service, and a new satellite/cable communications system that will serve the New York Metropolitan area.

With the Port Authority of New York and Merrill Lynch & Co., Inc., Western Union is constructing The Teleport, the world's first satellite communications center and office park (ground area for the building of offices) in Staten Island in New York Harbor. When completed, The Teleport will have 17 earth stations offering direct access to all domestic and some international communications satellites. Western Union will connect this "antenna farm" with Manhattan, Brooklyn, Queens and nearby New Jersey through a network of fiber optic cable. The Teleport will enable many New York area businesses that require rapid transmission of data or video signals to gain access to satellites without having to establish a private network.

Western Union has acquired a 50 percent ownership interest in AirFone, a new air-to-ground telephone system. Beginning in 1983, AirFone will en-

24 heures, de transmettre économiquement des messages « Mailgram ».

Western Union a inauguré un service analogue au Royaume-Uni, en s'associant à la firme britannique English China Clays, sous le nom de Western Union Global Information Service Ltd., dont la première activité, en 1982, a été le service des lettres prioritaires « Priority Letter Service ». Elle met en œuvre les applications les plus avancées du laser et de l'informatique pour offrir, au Royaume-Uni, ce service à l'industrie, au commerce et au gouvernement.

Des projets innovateurs, ou « new ventures », sont entrepris par Western Union pour satisfaire une demande croissante pour des services de pointe dans les télécommunications. Les trois projets qui promettent le plus pour la compagnie sont le système de téléphone public air-terre à bord des avions, le service de radio-téléphone mobile alvéolaire et un nouveau système de communications combinées satellite/câble pour servir la Ville de New York.

En association avec la Port Authority of New York, et avec la grande firme d'agents de change, Merrill Lynch & Co., Inc., Western Union construit « Le Téléport », premier centre combiné de communications par satellite avec lotissement de bureaux, sur Staten Island, île située dans le port de New York. Le Téléport regroupera 17 stations terriennes qui auront directement accès à tous les satellites nationaux de communication et à plusieurs satellites internationaux. Un réseau de câbles à fibres optiques reliera ce « parc d'antennes » aux « boroughs » de Manhattan, Brooklyn, Queens et au New Jersey. Le Téléport permettra à beaucoup d'entreprises de New York, qui réclament une transmission rapide de signaux de données ou de vidéo, d'accéder à des satellites sans avoir à établir leur propre système spatial privé.

Western Union a acquis 50% des parts de AirFone, le nouveau système téléphonique en vol grâce auquel les passagers d'avion peuvent communiquer, depuis 1983, avec les abonnés dans toute l'étendue

Union en EE.UU. con el servicio Telemessage prestado por British Telecom en el RU, permitiendo a los usuarios de cada servicio el acceso a ambos.

Otra iniciativa de Western Union es la introducción de la carta por computador. Es un servicio que permite a los clientes comerciales disponer de un mensaje de gran impacto y bajo costo que no necesita la entrega al día siguiente que ofrece el mensaje Mailgram. Western Union ha inaugurado también un servicio análogo en el Reino Unido, a través de una empresa mixta con una firma británica, English China Clays. La operación del Reino Unido se conoce como Western Union Global Information Services Ltd., y su primera actividad, en 1982, fue el servicio de carta con prioridad. Emplea las últimas técnicas de computador y láser, para ofrecer servicios de comunicaciones a la industria, el comercio y el gobierno, en el Reino Unido.

Western Union crea nuevas empresas de telecomunicaciones para atender la creciente demanda de servicios avanzados. Estos progresos consisten en el primer sistema telefónico público aire-tierra, el servicio radio-celular y un nuevo sistema de comunicación cable/satélite para la zona metropolitana de Nueva York.

Con la Port Authority of New York y Merrill Lynch & Co., Inc., Western Union ha iniciado conversaciones para construir Teleport, el primer parque centro/oficina de comunicaciones por satélite, en Staten Island, en el Puerto de Nueva York. Una vez terminado, Teleport dispondrá de 17 estaciones terrenas, con acceso directo a todos los satélites nacionales de comunicaciones. Western Union conectará esta "finca de antenas" con Manhattan, Brooklyn, Queens y Nueva Jersey, a través de una red de cables de fibras ópticas. Teleport permitirá a muchas empresas comerciales que necesitan transmitir rápidamente señales de datos o video acceder a satélites sin tener que establecer una red privada.

Western Union ha adquirido una participación del 50% en AirFone, nuevo sistema telefónico aire-tie-

▷ 189   ▷ 189   ▷ 189

able passengers on commercial airliners to place telephone calls to locations within the continental US. AirFone's coast-to-coast telephone connections are made possible by a series of ground stations placed at intervals across the country. Each station is equipped with radio antennas capable of handling up to 31 simultaneous calls through interconnection with local telephone companies. Eleven commercial airlines have signed up for the service, including most of the major US trunk carriers.

A series of joint ventures will take Western Union into the fast-growing area of cellular mobile radio telephone service. Previously, it was all but impossible to obtain car telephone service in most large US metropolitan areas. But the recent FCC authorization of cellular mobile radio service has opened up a major new communications market.

Anticipating the dramatic growth in mobile telephone service and equipment, in 1982 Western Union acquired E. F. Johnson & Co., a Minnesota-based maker of two-way radios and one of the leading US suppliers of mobile communications products. The merger of the common carrier activities of Western Union and the equipment design and manufacturing capabilities of E. F. Johnson is expected to strengthen the product range of the combined companies. In separate alliances with other companies, Western Union has applied for licenses to deliver cellular service in most of the larger US cities.

More than ever, the United States of America — and the world — depend on telecommunications; and the people at Western Union are ready to meet the challenge of providing new communications services to business, government and the public.

In the midst of technological growth and worldwide expansion, the major goal of Western Union has changed little from that of the Company's founders. It continues to provide affordable, efficient, superior telecommunications services to the United States — and now to the world.

des Etats-Unis. Des stations équipées d'antennes de radio capables de transmettre 31 communications simultanées par interconnexion avec des compagnies téléphoniques locales ont permis la création d'Air-Fone. Onze compagnies aériennes, la plupart des grands exploitants de liaisons interurbaines aux États-Unis, ont adopté ce service.

Une série d'entreprises conjointes, ou « joint ventures », fera entrer Western Union dans le domaine en pleine évolution du service téléphonique mobile du type alvéolaire. Récemment il était presque impossible d'obtenir de nouveaux radiotéléphones mobiles dans la plupart des grandes zones métropolitaines américaines. Le feu vert donné par la FCC à l'établissement d'un service alvéolaire a maintenant ouvert un important nouveau marché. En anticipant une fulgurante expansion de la radiotéléphonie mobile, Western Union a acquis E.F. Johnson & Co., dans le Minnesota. Cette firme fabrique des équipements radio bidirectionnels, et est le principal constructeur de matériel de radiotéléphonie mobile aux Etats-Unis. La combinaison des capacités d'exploitation de Western Union et des capacités de conception et de fabrication de E.F. Johnson devrait renforcer la gamme de produits et services offerts. En association séparée avec 2 autres compagnies, Western Union a déjà déposé des demandes de licences pour téléphonie mobile alvéolaire dans la majorité des grandes villes des Etats-Unis.

Plus que jamais, les Etats-Unis — et le monde entier — dépendent des télécommunications ; et les gens de Western Union se déclarent prêts a relever le défi de pourvoir de nouveaux services de communication aux entreprises, aux organismes gouvernementaux et au public. L'objectif principal de Western Union, qui se trouve aujourd'hui au sein d'une rapide mutation technologique, tout en assurant sa propre expansion internationale, diffère très peu de celui qu'avaient adopté les fondateurs de la compagnie. Elle continue à fournir à un prix abordable des services efficaces et de haute qualité aux Etats-Unis et, maintenant, dans le monde entier.

rra. Desde 1983, AirFone permite a los pasajeros de aviones comerciales hacer llamadas telefónicas a localidades de EE.UU. continental. Una serie de estaciones terrenas instaladas en el país permiten las conexiones telefónicas costa a costa de AirFone. Cada estación tiene antenas capaces de cursar hasta 31 llamadas simultáneas mediante la interconexión con compañías locales. Once líneas aéreas comerciales han contratado ya el servicio, incluidas las principales empresas de transporte aéreo de EE.UU.

Con una serie de empresas mixtas, Western Union se incorporará al sector de servicios telefónicos móviles celulares, en rápido crecimiento. Antes era casi imposible obtener un servicio telefónico de automóvil en la mayoría de las grandes zonas metropolitanas. Pero la reciente autorización por FCC del servicio de radio móvil celular ha abierto un nuevo e importante mercado de comunicaciones.

Previendo el espectacular crecimiento del servicio y del equipo telefónico móvil, Western Union adquirió en 1982 E. F. Johnson & Co., fabricante de radios bidireccionales radicado en Minnesota, y uno de los principales proveedores de productos de comunicaciones móviles de EE.UU. Se espera que la fusión de las actividades de Western Union y de E. F. Johnson refuerce la gama de productos de las empresas combinadas. En alianzas separadas con otras compañías, Western Union ha solicitado licencias para prestar el servicio celular en la mayoría de las grandes ciudades de EE.UU.

América, y el mundo, dependen más que nunca de las telecomunicaciones, y el personal de Western Union está dispuesto a hacer frente al desafío de proporcionar nuevos servicios a las empresas, al gobierno y al público. En medio del crecimiento tecnológico y de la expansión mundial, el principal objetivo de Western Union ha cambiado poco del perseguido por los fundadores de la empresa. Sigue prestando servicios de telecomunicaciones abordables, eficaces a Estados Unidos y, ahora, al mundo.

DIRECT BROADCAST SATELLITE TELEVISION
AN UP-AND-COMING MEDIUM

A SPECIAL USE FOR GEOSTATIONARY SATELLITES is in the provision of direct broadcast television. The world's capital expenditure on direct broadcast satellite television (DBS TV) in 1982 was estimated at US$ 50 million, not quite 10 per cent of total investment in commercial satellite systems. By 1985 this expenditure is expected to reach $200 million.

DBS involves the transmission of programs from satellite to large numbers of earth stations in the form of dish-shaped antennas which may be on individual houses, on office or apartment buildings or at earth stations from which distribution to house and office is by cable or earth-based microwave relays. As a means of transmission of TV, DBS has all the technical advantages of satellite transmission and can provide a wide choice of channels. The advantage of DBS over long cable links for this purpose centers on the fact that the cost of satellite transmission is not distance-related, so that service can be provided economically in rural and other areas of low density demand. On the other hand DBS has initial investment cost and there may be reception problems in areas of high density.'

DBS has two specific disadvantages which have political implications:
— the limitations of both orbit "parking space" for satellites, and of frequencies, which call for international agreement on the use of these facilities;
— the fact that the reception of satellite broadcasts cannot be restricted precisely to specific areas or countries, which creates political and legal problems associated with overspill, advertising and copyright.

Problems arising from these two disadvantages will be considered here. The international arrangements for dealing with them are examined on page 230.

▷ 192

L'UTILISATION DES SATELLITES GÉOSTATIONNAIRES a donné naissance à un nouveau médium dynamique et prometteur : la télévision directe par satellite (TV DS). Bien que les capitaux investis en 1982 dans cette utilisation se soient élevés au total à US $ 50 millions, à peine 10% de l'ensemble des investissements dans les systèmes commerciaux de télécommunication par satellite, le montant prévu en 1985 est de $ 200 millions, et laisse présager une expansion rapide.

La TV DS comprend la transmission de programmes relayés par des satellites à destination d'un grand nombre d'antennes paraboliques installées soit sur des maisons particulières, des immeubles d'habitation ou de bureaux soit sur le site de stations terriennes à partir desquelles la distribution aux abonnés se fait par câble. Les transmissions télévisuelles par satellite ont, sur les liaisons par câbles, l'avantage d'être insensibles à la distance en ce qui concerne le coût de la transmission. Un tel service peut donc être assuré d'une manière économique à destination des zones rurales ou autres dans lesquelles la densité d'abonnés est faible. En revanche, la TVDS exige de gros investissements initiaux et elle est sujette à des difficultés de réception dans les zones où la demande est forte.

La TV DS présente deux inconvénients particuliers qui ont des répercussions politiques :
— la limitation de l'espace orbital pour les satellites géostationnaires et du nombre de fréquences disponibles, qui constitue des problèmes de répartition à résoudre par accord international ;
— le fait que la réception des émissions par satellite ne peut être limitée à des zones ou à des pays déterminés, ce qui pose des problèmes politiques et juridiques liés au débordement des frontières, à la publicité commerciale et au droit d'auteur.

▷ 192

UN USO ESPECIAL DE LOS SATÉLITES GEOESTACIONARIOS es la provisión directa de televisión. Los gastos mundiales de capital en televisión directa por satélite (TV DS) en 1982 se estimaron en 50 millones $ EE.UU., ni siquiera un 10% de la inversión total en sistemas comerciales de satélite. Para 1985, se espera que el gasto alcance los 200 millones $.

La TV DS comprende la transmisión de programas desde satélites a un gran número de estaciones terrenas en forma de antenas parabólicas instaladas en edificios de oficinas o apartamentos o en estaciones terrenas desde las que se realiza la distribución a casas y oficinas por cable. Como medio de transmisión de TV, la DS tiene todas las ventajas técnicas de la transmisión por satélite y ofrece una amplia elección de canales. La ventaja de la TV DS sobre los largos enlaces de cable para tal fin consiste en que el costo de la transmisión por satélite no guarda relación con la distancia, por lo que el servicio puede proporcionarse económicamente en zonas rurales y otras de poca demanda. Por otra parte, la TV DS requiere una fuerte inversión inicial, y puede haber problemas de recepción en zonas de gran densidad.

La TV DS tiene dos inconvenientes concretos de implicaciones políticas: 1. Las limitaciones del "espacio de parking" de satélites en órbita, y de frecuencias, que requieren el acuerdo internacional; 2. Al no poderse limitar la recepción de programas de satélite a zonas o países específicos, se crean problemas políticos y legales de divulgación, publicidad y derechos de autor.

Consideraremos los problemas derivados de estos dos inconvenientes. Los acuerdos internacionales para resolverlos se examinan en la pág. 230.

▷ 193

Artist's representation of signals from a satellite homing in onto the antennae of public buildings, factories, offices, hotels, hospitals, and even homes, in a metropolitan area.

Illustration schématique des signaux émis par un satellite et directement captés par les antennes installées sur des édifices publics, des bureaux, des hotels, des usines, des hôpitaux et des maisons.

Ilustración gráfica de señales emitidas por un satélite y captadas por las antenas de edificios públicos, fábricas, oficinas, hoteles, hospitales e incluso hogares, en una zona metropolitana.

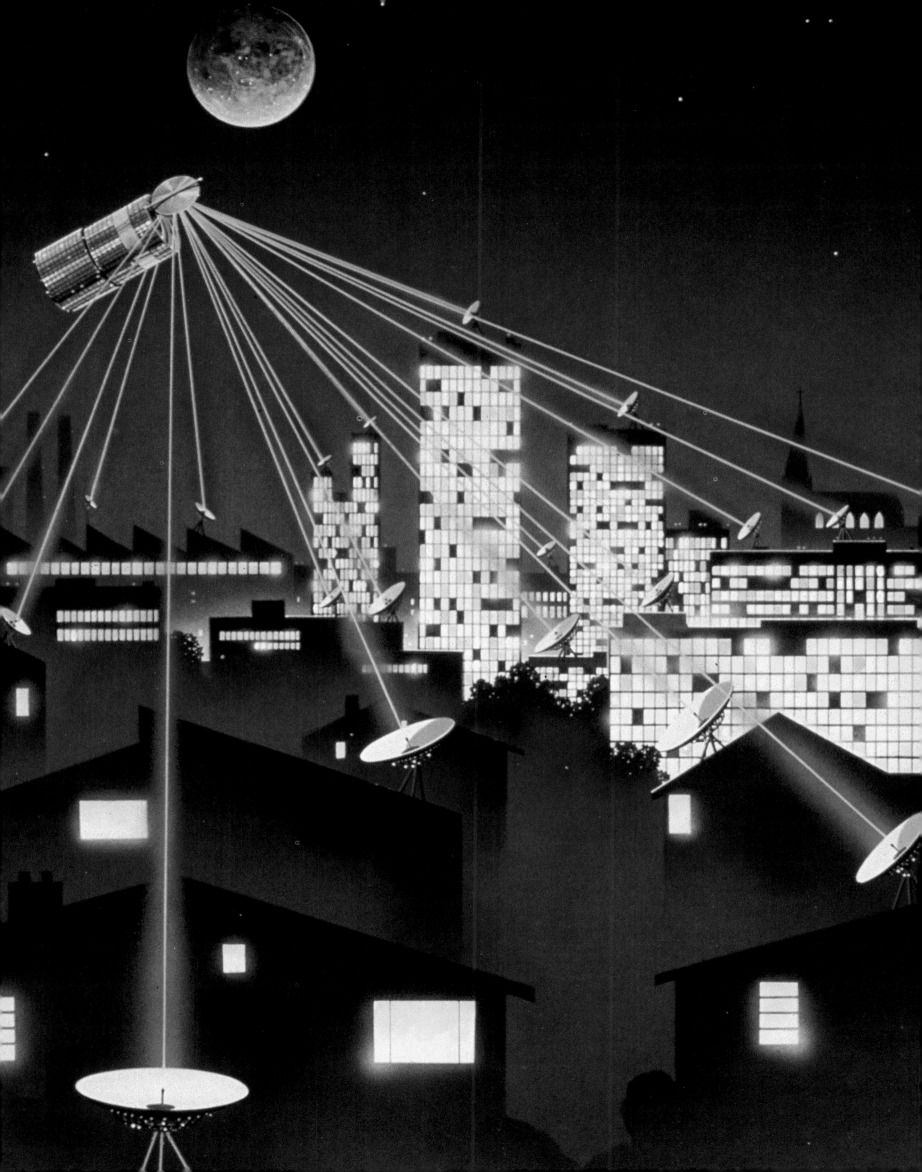

The sharing of geosynchronous orbit (GEO) and of available frequencies for a growing diversity of satellite and terrestrial applications by a growing number of countries has become extremely difficult to manage. Advanced countries' uses of satellites require increasingly precise operations, not only on the part of their own system operators but also on that of "neighbours" in GEO. Developing countries have pressing needs to extend basic telephone, telex and broadcast services nationwide. They may therefore select simpler, cheaper technology as being most cost-effective though more spectrum-hungry and more interference-prone.

Possessing technological expertise and more advanced economies, the industrial nations' priority is upon maintaining the flexibility needed to introduce technology and services at a pace determined by economic considerations. Possessing numerical strength in the UN system, and fearing that technology and market-driven development may ill-serve their interests, developing countries tend to focus upon control and regulation.

The UN Outer Space Committee began to consider this problem in the late 1960s. The issue took on a symbolic significance, reflecting developing countries' feelings about the global influence of Western news and entertainment media. The USA favoured minimal governmental control over international satellite broadcasting. Developing and Eastern countries favoured a strict regime disallowing all international DBS transmissions except with the "prior consent" of the receiving State.

A detailed, long-term plan covering all the world except the Americas was approved at the World Administrative Radio Conference (WARC) on satellite broadcasting (Geneva, 1977). The plan specified orbital positions, frequencies and coverage areas. Only in the case of Nordic European countries, which had agreed in advance, was coverage to extend beyond national boundaries. This caused much concern among Western advocates of the "free flow of information". The plan also upset technical experts, who considered it would freeze technology. It accomplished, however, the primary goal of its European and developing country proponents: the protection of future orbital access by each country for national broadcasting, and the guarantee of an orderly introduction of DBS services in relation to other competing services.

The development of DBS services in North America has been most rapid.

In the USA, in 1982, there were 10 domestic communications satellites in GEO, about one-third of their capacity being used for video distribution, the remainder taken up by telephone and telex. By 1985 the USA will have 26 domestic satellites containing some 500 transponders and the companies involved are all prepared for demand to soar even higher.

In 1982 earth stations in the USA were already in use by 4,000 television cable systems serving 23 million homes. Several hundred thousand private homes had their own dish-shaped antennas which were available from mail order catalogues. It is expected that by the 1990s every major building — office, hotel, apartment block and factory — will have an antenna to receive DBS services, which will doubtless have been extended to include home banking and shopping, access to data banks and information sources as well as television.

In preparation for the 1983 broadcasting satellite planning conference in Geneva the US Federal Communications Commitee (FCC) called for public comment on the general categories of basic service requirements, including allocation of bandwidth, type of broadcasting, size and shape of service areas, number of channels and satellite creations; on technical issues including satellite power, signal characteristics and sharing between services, and on planning principles and procedures. The responses should provide a useful outline of the shape of DBS at the end of the century in the USA and should also ensure that it is developed in the public interest.

In Canada, a country vaster than the USA with less

▷ 194

Le partage de l'orbite géosynchrone et la répartition des fréquences disponibles (voir p. 230) pour les utilisations toujours plus diversifiées de communications par satellite, posent des problèmes différents. Les pays industrialisés exigent une précision de fonctionnement des satellites toujours plus grande, non seulement de la part de leurs propres systèmes respectifs mais également de ceux de leurs « voisins » sur l'orbite. Les pays en développement éprouvent le besoin urgent d'étendre leurs services nationaux téléphoniques, télex et de radiodiffusion. Ils peuvent a priori se satisfaire d'une technologie plus simple et moins coûteuse, mais vorace en fréquences et sensible au brouillage.

Les pays industrialisés, qui possèdent des connaissances techniques plus avancées et dont les économies sont plus développées, se préoccupent principalement de maintenir la souplesse nécessaire pour assurer la mise en œuvre de techniques et de services nouveaux à un rythme déterminé par des considérations économiques. Les pays en développement qui craignent que l'évolution de la technologie et du marché ne soit contraire à leurs intérêts, se montrent prudents et se préoccupent principalement de sauvegarder leurs besoins futurs. :

Le Comité des utilisateurs pacifiques de l'espace extra-atmosphérique des Nations Unies a commencé à examiner cette question vers la fin des années 1960 sur l'ensemble du globe. Les Etats-Unis étaient en faveur d'un contrôle étatique minimal sur la radiodiffusion internationale par sàtellite. En revanche, les pays en développement et ceux du bloc de l'Est étaient partisans d'un régime strict interdisant toute transmission de radiodiffusion directe sauf par « consentement préalable » du pays de réception.

Un plan détaillé à long terme couvrant le monde entier à l'exception des Amériques a été approuvé lors de la Conférence administrative mondiale des radiocommunications (CAMR) à Genève, en 1977. Ce plan spécifiait les positions orbitales, les fréquences et les zones de couverture. Seuls les pays du Nord de l'Europe avaient admis que la couverture des transmissions pourrait s'étendre au-delà des frontières nationales, ce qui préoccupa énormément les apôtres de « la libre circulation de l'information ». Les experts techniques appréhendaient que le plan exerce une action paralysante sur la technologie. Néanmoins, le plan satisfaisait l'objectif des pays européens et ceux des pays en développement qui l'avaient proposé : la protection pour l'avenir de l'accès à l'orbite géosynchrone en faveur de tout pays.

En Amérique du Nord, le développement de la RDS (service de radiodiffusion directe par satellite) a été très rapide.

En 1982, les Etats-Unis disposaient de 10 satellites nationaux de radiocommunications, dont le tiers de la capacité était utilisé pour les transmissions vidéo, et les deux tiers pour les transmissions téléphoniques et télex. Il est prévu que les Etats-Unis auront, en 1985, 26 satellites nationaux dont l'ensemble sera équipé de 500 émetteurs/récepteurs.

En 1982, les stations terriennes aux Etats-Unis étaient déjà utilisées par 4000 systèmes de télévision par câble desservant 23 millions de familles, tandis que plusieurs centaines de milliers de maisons particulières étaient déjà équipées de leur propre antenne parabolique. On s'attend aux Etats-Unis à ce que, dans les années 1990, tous les bâtiments importants, hôtels, appartements, bureaux, usines, soient pourvus d'une antenne appropriée donnant accès direct à tous les services télématiques assurés par satellite.

C'était d'ailleurs dans cette perspective, et en vue de la conférence de 1983 à Genève sur la planification de la radiodiffusion par satellite, que la FCC des Etats-Unis avait lancé une enquête publique afin d'évaluer les besoins des diverses catégories de services de base, notamment en ce qui concerne l'attribution de largeurs de bande, les types de radiodiffusion, l'étendue et la forme des zones de services, ainsi que le nombre de canaux et de satellites nécessaires. Cette enquête porte sur les problèmes techniques: puissance des satellites, caractéristiques des signaux et partage entre les services et procédures de planification. Les réponses ont fourni beaucoup d'éléments utiles au sujet de la structure qu'aura la radiodiffusion directe par satellite, compte tenu de l'intérêt public à la fin du siècle.

▷ 194

DATA FLO
SECURITY,

The world of business is increasingly dependent on data networks and traffic between computers. Data processing can be carried out at any one of many centres, operated by a bureau or company, which can be thousands of miles apart, the main criteria being availability and suitability. For example, the analysis of daily sales and stock levels of a large retailer located in Paris can be done in Minneapolis, London, Tokyo or Frankfurt, wherever capacity is available. Large multinational companies have computers in their offices talking to each other. Many smaller companies are dependent on foreign data

bases. Data flow speeds are so great along digital routes via satellites or optic cables that distance is no longer a factor.

However, the uncontrolled flow of information and data across national borders is causing concern among many governments. Problems of security loom large, as do questions of ownership and rights of entry. Only the USA considers that free data flow is essential to wellbeing and wise conduct of business throughout the world. Other countries take a different view: there is a growing convinction that free and balanced international data flow must be regulated to safeguard the legitimate interests of nations if it is to remain balanced and free. The OECD for Europe, and the IBI for developing countries, initiated major studies of the whole problem area in 1982.

An earlier OECD investigation, conducted in 1971, revealed that there were 150 data networks in Europe at that time, and found that the use of international data transmission resulted in significant economies for multinationals. But the mood in recent years in many countries is protectionist and insular. Brazil, for example, has led in the imposition of severe restrictions which are strangulating the flow. Market dislocation, deleterious effect on local employment, unrecognised ownership, encroachments on national sovereignty, were arguments levelled at unregulated data flow. Problems of security and ownership rights exist equally within nations. A regulatory framework is obviously needed to find the right balance of freedom and protectionism. The problem has been referred to the GATT with a request to report in 1984 on whether an international agreement on services is desirable and, if so, how to proceed.

CROSS NATIONAL BORDERS
NERSHIP AND RIGHT OF ENTRY

onde des affaires dépend de plus en plus du trafic de ées numériques entre ordinateurs. Le traitement des ées se déroule dans de nombreux centres exploités par des prises spécialisées, souvent situées à des milliers de km de l'autre, le critère de choix étant la disponibilité.
r exemple, l'analyse des ventes quotidiennes et du niveau stocks d'une grande surface ayant son siège à Paris, peut ectuer à Minneapolis, à Londres, à Tokyo ou à Francfort, le lieu où le service est disponible. Les grandes sociétés nationales ont dans tous leurs bureaux des ordinateurs qui

El mundo de los negocios depende cada vez más de las redes y del tráfico de datos entre computadores. El procesamiento de datos se realiza en uno cualquiera de muchos centros, operados por una oficina o empresa, que pueden estar separados por miles de km; el principal criterio es la disponibilidad y la conformidad. Por ejemplo, el análisis de ventas y el nivel de existencias de un importante minorista radicado en París pueden hacerse en Minneapolis, Londres, Tokio o Francfort, según la capacidad. Las grandes empresas multinacionales disponen de computadores en todas sus oficinas, que comunican entre sí.

La compartición de la órbita geosíncrona (GEO) y las frecuencias disponibles constituyen administrativamente un obstaculo, para la creciente diversidad de aplicaciones de satélite y terrenales en un número de países cada vez mayor. El uso de satélites por los países avanzados requiere operaciones más y más precisas, no sólo por parte de sus propios operadores del sistema, sino también por la de los "vecinos" en GEO. Las necesidades de los países en desarrollo para ampliar sus servicios telefónicos, télex y de radiodifusión básicos a toda la nación son apremiantes. Por tanto, pueden elegir tecnología más sencilla y económica, por ser la más rentable, aunque necesite más espectro y sea más propensa a la interferencia.

La prioridad de las naciones industriales consiste en mantener la flexibilidad para introducir tecnología y servicios a un ritmo determinado por consideraciones económicas. Los países en desarrollo, que poseen la fuerza numérica en el sistema de NU, y temen que la evolución de la tecnología y del mercado pueda ser contraria a sus intereses, tienden a centrarse en el control y la reglamentación.

La Comisión del Espacio Ultraterrestre de las NU comenzó a examinar este problema a finales de los años 1960. La cuestión revistió un significado simbólico, reflejando los sentimientos de los países en desarrollo sobre la influencia global de la información y las actividades recreativas de occidente. EE.UU. favoreció el control gubernamental mínimo de la radiodifusión internacional por satélite. Los países en desarrollo y del bloque oriental se mostraron partidarios de un régimen estricto, rechazando todas las transmisiones TV DS, salvo con el "consentimiento previo" del Estado receptor.

Ginebra, 1977. La Conferencia Administrativa Mundial de Radiocomunicaciones (CAMR) de Radiodifusión por Satélite aprobó un plan detallado a largo plazo para todo el mundo, salvo las Américas. En el plan se especifican las posiciones orbitales, las frecuencias y las zonas de cobertura. Sólo en el caso de los países nórdicos europeos, que lo habían convenido previamente, se extendió la cobertura allende las fronteras nacionales. Esto causó mucha preocupación entre los partidarios occidentales de la «libre corriente de la información». El plan inquietó también a los expertos, por estimar que bloquearía la tecnología. Empero, logró el principal objetivo de sus proponentes europeos y de los países en desarrollo: proteger el futuro acceso orbital de cada país para la radiodifusión nacional, y garantizar una introducción ordenada del servicio TV DS.

El desarrollo de servicios TV DS en América del Norte ha sido rapidísimo.

En 1982 había *en EE.UU.* 10 satélites de comunicaciones en GEO, utilizándose un tercio de su capacidad para distribución video, y el resto para telefonía y télex. EE.UU. dispondría en 1985 de 26 satélites nacionales, con unos 500 transpondedores, y las empresas están preparadas para un aumento aún mayor de la demanda.

En 1982 usaban ya las estaciones terrenas 4000 sistemas de televisión por cable, al servicio de 23 millones de hogares. Varios centenares de miles de hogares privados disponían de sus propias antenas parabólicas. Se espera que, para los años 1990, todo edificio importante disponga de una antena para recibir servicios DS, que habrán de ampliarse para abarcar las operaciones de banca y compra desde el hogar, el acceso a bancos de datos y fuentes de información, así como la televisión.

Preparándose para la conferencia de planificación de radiodifusión por satélite de 1983, en Ginebra, la Federal Communications Commission (FCC) de EE.UU. hizo una encuesta pública para conocer las necesidades de servicios básicos, incluidos la atribución de anchura de banda, el tipo de radiodifusión, el tamaño y la forma de las zonas de servicio, y el número de canales y creaciones de satélite: entre las cuestiones técnicas figuraban la potencia del satélite, las características de las señales y la compartición entre servicios, así como los principios y procedimientos de planificación. Las respuestas deben dar una idea útil de la forma de la TV DS para finales de siglo en el país y confirmar que se desarrolla en interés del público.

uniquent entre eux. Beaucoup d'autres, moins grandes, dent de bases de données situées à distance, souvent à nger. La vitesse des courants de données circulant le long rtères de transmission numérique est si grande que la ce ne compte plus.
urtant, ce flux incontrôlé d'information et de données à rs les frontières nationales pose de sérieux problèmes de raineté nationale, de sécurité, de propriété ou de droit ée. Plusieurs pays ont entrepris l'étude de ces problèmes, ême que diverses organisations internationales, notaml'ONU, l'UIT, l'UNESCO, l'OCDE, la CEE, l'OII, le Conseil de pe et, plus récemment, le GATT. Seuls les Etats-Unis dèrent que la libre circulation des données est essentielle bonne marche et à la bonne conduite rationnelle des es dans le monde. L'Europe et le reste du monde dèrent que le flux international des données doit être nenté pour sauvergarder les intérêts nationaux légitimes ur préserver une mesure d'équilibre et de liberté. En 1982, E, pour l'Europe et l'IBI pour les pays en développement, trepris des études approfondies sur ces problèmes. Toutee enquête conduite par l'OCDE avait révélé l'existence en de 150 réseaux de données en Europe et conclue, que la mission internationale de données permettait aux sociétés nationales de réaliser des économies importantes. Toutel existe dans beaucoup de pays des tendances protecstes qui entravent sérieusement la circulation des es. Le cadre d'une réglementation appropriée est une sité évidente. Toute cette question a été soumise au GATT evra formuler, en 1984, ses conclusions sur le bien-fondé accord international concernant les services et, dans l'aftive, sur la procédure à suivre.

Muchas empresas más pequeñas dependen de bases de datos extranjeras. Las corrientes de datos se extienden tanto por las rutas digitales por satélite o cables ópticos que la distancia no cuenta.

Sin embargo, el flujo incontrolado de información y datos a través de las fronteras nacionales preocupa a muchos gobiernos. Los problemas de seguridad se estiman importantes, lo mismo que las cuestiones de propiedad y derechos de entrada. Sólo EE.UU. considera que la libre circulación de datos es esencial para la buena y acertada dirección de los negocios en el mundo entero. Otros países mantienen una opinión distinta: cada vez están más convencidos de la necesidad de reglamentar la libre y equilibrada circulación de datos para proteger los legítimos intereses nacionales. La OCDE para Europa, y la OII para los países en desarrollo, iniciaron importantes estudios de todo el problema en 1982.

Una investigación realizada en 1971 por la OCDE reveló que entonces había en Europa 150 redes de datos, y mostró que el uso de la transmisión internacional de datos supone considerables economías para las multinacionales. Pero la actitud de muchos países en los últimos años es proteccionista y estrecha de miras. Brasil, por ejemplo, ha impuesto restricciones que obstaculizan la circulación. Ante el flujo de datos no reglamentando se adujeron poderosos argumentos. También existen dentro de las naciones problemas de seguridad y derechos de propiedad. Es claro que se necesita un marco reglamentario para el debido equilibrio de la libre circulación de datos y el proteccionismo. El problema se ha sometido al GATT, solicitando un informe para 1984 acerca de la conveniencia de un acuerdo internacional sobre servicios y, en tal caso, la manera de realizarlo.

▷ 195

than one-tenth of its population and in which rural and remote areas predominate, DBS has progressed very well but with a different purpose and in a different manner. In 1976 a *Hermes* satellite was launched as a joint Canadian-US research project and later another satellite, *Anik B*, was launched to undertake a field trial program. Owned and operated by Telesat Canada, *Anik B* is a hybrid satellite providing 12 transponders at 6/4 GHz and four for experimental service at 14/12 GHz. The objective was to determine how DBS technology could improve the quality of service to scattered rural populations who cannot be adequately served economically by terrestrial techniques.

The experimental approach is having a significant impact on the planning for future systems in Canada and other countries with low population densities.

At the same time, improvements in earth station performance are being made without materially affecting costs, permitting a reduction in the transmission power of satellites. It has been established that satisfactory service can be achieved with a satellite providing an EIRP (Equivalent Isotropically Radiated Power) per channel much below that specified at the 1977 WARC, with related reduction in cost per space segment.

The development of DBS in Europe has been gathering momentum ever since the 1977 WARC and is expected to leap ahead during the 1990s. Each European country was allocated a number of channels, with specified frequencies, orbital locations, polarization, etc. The WARC plan provides for the utilization of the 11.7 to 12.5 GHz frequency for direct broadcasting and permits the transmission of sufficiently high power per channel for people in any country to receive programs either directly, by mounting small dish antennas (about 90 cm in diameter) on their houses and adding small "converters" to their television sets, or individually by cable from community receiving systems. The high bandwidth of satellite systems is a powerful attraction to countries where a high standard of TV picture is demanded, and where large volumes of data have to be transferred at very high speeds.

DBS broadcasts are set to begin in France and in the Federal Republic of Germany in 1984-85 (two satellites jointly financed, *TDF 1* for France and *TV-SAT* for the FRG, are scheduled for launching about then), in the UK and in Italy in 1986. Some of the most spectacular projects are being launched by the smaller countries.

The Compagnie Luxembourgeoise de Telediffusion, Europe's biggest commercial broadcasting service, plan to start broadcasts from its own satellite in 1985, over an area stretching from central France to Northern Denmark. In The Netherlands, Kabal Televisie Amsterdam (KTA) is acquiring a dish antenna to receive Moscow 1 via the Soviet *Horizon* satellite. These are only two of several such projects in Europe, which are attracting strong support from business interests. In Britain a private company, Satellite Television Ltd., transmits two hours of programs a day in the English language via British Telecom's Satellite *OTS 2*. The programs are coded and redistributed by the receiving countries' cable TV companies (in Finland and Norway in 1982). An extension of this service, which is entirely financed by multinational advertisers, is envisioned to Switzerland, Belgium and The Netherlands, where cable TV penetration is densest.

Some of the problems involved in this rush for DBS service now taking place in Europe and elsewhere are discussed in the Boxes on pp. 192 and 194.

Central to the Franco-German satellite program mentioned above is Thomson-CSF Communications, a French company which is the leading European supplier of satellite equipment and earth stations as well as a major participant in the *Intelsat VI* program. The company profile that follows contains descriptions of the *TDF1/TV-SAT* programs, designed to provide direct broadcasting facilities for French and German television, and a broad-brush outline of Thomson's other facilities and achievements.

□

Au Canada, plus vaste que les Etats-Unis, mais avec moins d'un dixième de leur population, et où les régions rurales et isolées prédominent, la RDS s'est considérablement développée d'une autre manière et à des fins différentes. En 1976, le satellite *Hermès* a été lancé dans le cadre d'un projet de recherche mixte: Canada/Etats-Unis, suivi de plusieurs autres dont le plus récent, *Anik B*, est un satellite hybride équipé de 12 répéteurs-émetteurs à 6/4 GHz et de 4 répéteurs-émetteurs pour le service expérimental à 14/12 GHz. Il s'agissait de déterminer dans quelle mesure la technique de la RDS pouvait améliorer la qualité des communications pour les populations rurales qui ne peuvent pas être desservies d'une manière adéquate et économique par les techniques de transmission terrestre.

D'autre part, des améliorations sont apportées actuellement aux stations terriennes, sans que cela influe sur les coûts, tout en permettant une réduction de la puissance d'émission des satellites. Il a été prouvé qu'un service satisfaisant peut être fourni au moyen d'un satellite dont la PIRE (puissance isotrope rayonnée équivalente) par voie est très inférieure à celle spécifiée lors de la CAMR de 1977.

Le développement de la RDS en Europe est à l'ordre du jour depuis la CAMR de 1977, et on peut s'attendre à ce qu'elle prenne un grand essor. La CAMR a attribué à chaque pays d'Europe un certain nombre de canaux, de fréquences, de positions orbitales, de polarisations, etc. Le plan de cette conférence prévoit l'utilisation de la bande de fréquences 11,7 à 12,5 GHz pour la RDS et un rayonnement d'une puissance suffisante dans chaque canal pour que la population des pays intéressés soit en mesure de recevoir les programmes soit directement, en équipant les maisons particulières d'antennes paraboliques d'un diamètre d'environ 90 cm, et en ajoutant un « convertisseur » au récepteur de télévision, soit en aménageant des capteurs collectifs avec distribution.

Il est prévu que les émissions de RDS commenceront en France et en République fédérale d'Allemagne en 1984-85, à partir de deux satellites financés conjointement : *TDF 1* pour la France et *TV-SAT* pour la RFA. Au Royaume Uni et en Italie, la RDS débutera en 1986. Des projets de très grande envergure vont être mis en œuvre par de petits pays tels que la Suisse, le Luxembourg et les Pays nordiques.

La Compagnie Luxembourgeoise de Télédiffusion, qui est l'entreprise de télédiffusion commerciale la plus importante d'Europe, projette de commencer ses émissions en utilisant son propre satellite qui couvrira, dès 1985, une zone comprise entre le centre de la France et le Nord du Danemark. Aux Pays-Bas, Kabel Televisie Amsterdam (KTA) a décidé de faire l'acquisition d'une antenne parabolique qui lui permettra de recevoir Moscou I par le satellite soviétique *Gorizont* (Horizon).

Ce ne sont là que deux des divers projets européens qui suscitent un intérêt considérable et un ferme appui des milieux commerciaux. En Grande-Bretagne, Satellite Television Ltd., transmet déjà deux heures de programmes par jour en langue anglaise par le satellite britannique *OTS 2* de British Telecom. Les émissions sont codées et redistribuées par les compagnies de télévision par câble des pays de réception (en Finlande et en Norvège, depuis 1982). Une extension de ce service, qui est entièrement financé par des annonceurs multinationaux, est envisagée à destination de la Suisse, de la Belgique et des Pays-Bas où le réseau est le plus dense.

Les problèmes posés par cette ruée sur le service de RDS et par la radiodiffusion privée en Europe et ailleurs sont traités dans les encadrés des pp. 192 et 194.

Le pilier du programme franco-allemand de télécommunications et de radiodiffusion par satellite est Thomson-CSF Communications, une société française considérée comme un des premiers fournisseurs d'équipement de satellite et de stations terriennes, et un des principaux participants au programme *Intelsat VI*. Le profil de cette société, qui suit, contient des descriptions des programmes *TDF 1* et *TV-SAT* destinés à assurer la diffusion directe de programmes par satellite à destination de la France et de l'Allemagne, et une présentation du large éventail des activités de Thomson.

□

A CHANGING
ADVERTISERS CO

As broadcasters look ahead into the next decade they confront a new mix of media, a changing market-place for their services and shifts in the lifestyles and tastes of their audiences. To meet these challenges broadcasters have a wide variety of new tools to choose from and new opportunities to re-align their methods and appeal. The 1980s and the 1990s will be a period of adaptation to new technologies already well defined, a period of evolutionary change.

An exciting new range of distribution systems for broadcast products has emerged. But these are, in the strictest sense

"narrowcast"; they will bring a host of new services to audiences, but not services predicated on large simultaneous viewing. They will be in addition to broadcasting, not in place of it. Increasingly programs will have specialized appeal, to narrower sectors of communities. Some will be exclusively sport or exclusively news, some pop music, some classical theatre, others old films, soap operas, etc. Many radio broadcasters have already adopted this "narrowcast" strategy.

The new media will have an insatiable appetite for program production and at the outset only the broadcast industry will have the resources, capacity, technology and know-how to meet this demand. Much of the program material will be re-runs, already a dominant element in many national TV programs. To the broadcast industry videodiscs, pay TV, home VCR, and, eventually, cable TV, constitute additional after-market outlets to be tapped. Forecasts indicate that the transfer of audience time from the established broadcasting networks (a daily 6½ hours watching TV and 3½ hours listening to radio for the average US citizen in 1980) may reach 50% by the 1990s.

One major impact of the new technologies of satellite TV during the coming years will be on advertising practice and product branding. Satellite "footprints" cover wide areas and reach therefore international audiences. For example, the Federal Republic of Germany (FRG) has about 20 million television homes, but its maximum footprint could include over 100 million homes. Advertisers' appeal will therefore have to be internationalized: brand names, made equally meaningful, for example, in Belgium, the FRG, France and The Netherlands; packaging harmonized; new common denominators of audience appeal defined and other steps taken by advertisers to prepare for a future in which marketing conditions will become more homogeneous but local preferences more distinct.

A new world of opportunities for advertisers is unfolding, but the problems are complex and considerable. Solutions will require a great deal of research and the employment of new techniques of marketing. As a leading advertiser exclaimed: "For the first time, technology is way ahead of the ability of creative people to exploit it".

ournant vers le futur, les spécialistes de la radio et de la ision se voient confrontés à une nouvelle combinaison de , et une mutation profonde des goûts et du style de vie de audiences. Pour répondre à ces défis, ils s'apprêtent à se r de tout un arsenal de nouveaux outils et à saisir toutes pportunités possibles d'améliorer leurs méthodes et l'at- de leurs présentations. Les années 1980 et 1990 seront une de d'adaptation aux nouvelles technologies, déjà nette- définies un période d'évolution.

e nouvelle tendance à la spécialisation se manifeste déjà

Al pensar en el próximo decenio, las empresas de radiodifusión se encuentran ante una nueva mezcla de medios, una variación del mercado de sus servicios, y cambios en los estilos de vida y gustos de sus audiencias. Han de elegir, pues, entre una amplia variedad de nuevos instrumentos y oportunidades. Los años 1980 y 1990 serán un período de ajuste a nuevas tecnologías ya bien definidas; un periodo de evolución.

Ha surgido una apasionante y nueva gama de sistemas de distribución para difundir productos. Pero, en realidad, se trata de una "difusión limitada"; aportarán una serie de servicios

En Canadá, país más vasto que EE.UU., con me- nos de la décima parte de su población, y en el que predominan las zonas rurales y remotas, la TV DS ha progresado mucho, pero con otra finalidad y en for- ma distinta. En 1976 se lanzó un satelite *Hermes* como proyecto de investigación conjunto Ca- nadá-EE.UU., y después el satélite experimental *Anik B*. El Anik B, perteneciente a Telesat Canada y explotado por ella, es un satélite híbrido que pro- porciona 12 transpondedores a 6/4 GHz y 4 para servicio experimental a 14/12 GHz. El fin persegui- do era determinar cómo la tecnología DS puede mejorar la calidad de servicio a poblaciones rurales dispersas a las que no puede atenderse debidamente con técnicas terrenales en forma económica.

El enfoque experimental tiene un importante im- pacto en la planificación de futuros sistemas en Ca- nadá y otros países poco poblados. Al mismo tiempo, mejora el rendimiento de las estaciones terrenas sin influir en los costos, lo que permite reducir la po- tencia de transmisión de los satélites; y se ha deter- minado que puede lograrse un servicio satisfactorio con un satélite cuya p.i.r.e. (potencia isótropa radia- da equivalente) por canal sea muy inferior a la es- pecificada en la CAMR de 1977, con una reducción del costo por segmento espacial.

La evolución de la TV DS en Europa viene ganando impulso desde la CAMR de 1977, y se espera que avance mucho en los años 1990. Esa conferencia atribuyó a cada país europeo cierto número de canales, fre- cuencias, posiciones orbitales, polarizaciones, etc., específicas. El plan de la CAMR prevé la utilización de la frecuencia 11,7 a 12,5 GHz para la radiodifu- sión directa, y permite la transmisión de una poten- cia suficientemente alta por canal para recibir en cualquier país programas directamente, montando pequeñas antenas parabólicas (de unos 90 cm de diámetro) en las casas, e incorporando pequeños "convertidores" en los aparatos de TV, o indivi- dualmente, por cable, de los sistemas de recepción comunal. La gran anchura de banda de sistemas de satélite es un poderoso atractivo para los países donde se solicita una imagen TV de norma elevada, y donde deben transmitirse considerables volúmenes de datos a gran velocidad.

la diffusion des programmes. On s'achemine, en effet, vers centrage » de la cible plutôt qu'à un élargissement de ience. Les nouveaux services vont probablement se spé- er et sans chercher à se substituer à la diffusion destinée and public, ils joueront plutôt un rôle complémentaire.

s nouveaux médias sont de grands dévoreurs de pro- mes et les grands organismes de télévision sont, en défi- , les seuls à disposer des ressources, des compétences, technique et du savoir-faire indispensables pour répondre te demande. Pourtant, les programmes seront constitués ande partie de rediffusions. C'est d'ailleurs là, une situa- qui est très courante dans beaucoup de TV nationales.

ur des producteurs, les vidéodisques, la TV à péage, les étoscopes et enfin la TV par câble sont des débouchés lémentaires et additionnels. On prévoit aux Etats-Unis que mps moyen d'audience quotidienne des stations publiques tait en 1980, de 6 h 30 par personne pour la télévision, et h 30 pour la radio, sera réduit de 50% vers 1990.

phénomène le plus important sera, dans ce nouveau xte, l'influence que la télévision par satellite exercera sur éthodes publicitaires et sur la promotion des produits. Al- sions par satellite atteignant d'immences audiences inter- nales. Par exemple, la RFA a environ 20 millions de foyers és de télévision, mais la couverture des émissions du lite allemand englobe plus de 100 millions de foyers. Les nceurs devront, en conséquence, internationaliser leur : les marques et les noms commerciaux devront avoir la e efficacité et la même signification, par exemple, en que, en RFA, en France et aux Pays-Bas ; les conditionne- s devront être harmonisés. De nouveaux dénominateurs nuns devront être trouvés, et les annonceurs devront faire à des conditions de commercialisation nouvelles sur des hés devenant de plus en plus homogènes, compte tenu des rences plus marquées qui se manifesteront périodique- sur le plan local.

nouvel univers s'ouvre à la publicité, mais les problèmes ont se poser sont considérables, et la recherche de solu- exigera d'importantes études. Comme le constatait ironi- ent un grand spécialiste de la publicité : « c'est bien la ière fois que la technique est en avance sur la capacité ive de ceux qui l'exploitent ».

nuevos a los auditores, pero no estarán destinados simultá- neamente a mucho público. Vendrán a sumarse a la radiodifu- sión, y no a sustituirla. Los programas serán cada vez más especializados, para sectores comunitarios más reducidos. Al- gunos serán deportivos o informativos; otros de música pop, presentando a los últimos grupos: otros de teatro clásico, y otros de películas antiguas, románticas, violentas, seriales, etc. Muchas empresas de radiodifusión han adoptado ya esta "di- fusión limitada".

Los nuevos medios tendrán un ansia insaciable de produc- ción de programas y, al principio, sólo la industria de radiodi- fusión dispone de los recursos, la capacidad, la tecnología y los conocimientos para atender esa demanda. Gran parte del ma- terial de programas consistirá en reposiciones, lo cual es ya un elemento dominante en muchos programas nacionales de TV.

Para la industria de radiodifusión, los videodiscos, la TV de pago, los magnetoscopios y, finalmente, la TV por cable, cons- tituyen otras salidas adicionales del mercado. Se prevé que el tiempo medio de audiencia diaria en EE.UU., que era en 1980 de 6.30 horas en la TV, y de 3.30 en la radio se reducirá en un 50% para 1990.

El principal impacto de las nuevas tecnologías los próximos años será el de la TV por satélite sobre la práctica publicitaria y las marcas de productos. Las "proyecciones" de satélite abarcan amplias zonas y alcanzan, por tanto, audiencias internacionales. Por ejemplo, la RFA tiene unos 20 millones de hogares con televisión, pero su proyección máxima puede abarcar más de 100 millones. Habrá, pues, que internacionali- zar la actuación de los anunciantes: por ejemplo, dando el mismo significado a los nombres comerciales en Bélgica, la RFA, Francia y Países Bajos; armonizando los envases; defi- niendo nuevos denominadores comunes para atraer al público y otras medidas para preparar un futuro en el que las condiciones de comercialización serán más homogéneas, y más claras las preferencias locales.

A los anunciantes se les ofrece un nuevo mundo de oportu- nidades, pero los problemas son considerables y habrá que estudiar mucho las soluciones. Como constataba ironicamente un gran especialista en publicidad: "Por primera vez, la tecno- logía va por delante de la capacidad de los creadores para explotarla".

Se prevé que las transmisiónes DS comiencen en Francia y en la RFA en 1984-85 (el lanzamiento de dos satélites financiados conjuntamente, *TDF1* para Francia, y *TV-SAT* para Alemania, está proyectado para entonces); en el RU para 1986, y en Italia el mismo año. Algunos de los proyectos más especta- culares corren a cargo de los países más pequeños, como Suiza, Luxemburgo y los países nórdicos.

La Compagnie Luxembourgeoise de Télédiffu- sion, el servicio de radiodifusión comercial mayor de Europa, proyecta iniciar la difusión desde su propio satélite en 1985, en una zona que abarcará desde Francia central hasta el norte de Dinamarca. En Países Bajos, Kabal Televisie Amsterdam (KTA) está adquiriendo una antena parabólica para recibir Moscú 1 a través del satélite soviético *Horizon*. En Gran Bretaña, Satellite Television Ltd. transmite dos horas de programas al día en inglés vía el satélite *OTS 2* de British Telecom. Los programas son codi- ficados y redistribuidos por las compañías de TV por cable de los países receptores (en Finlandia y No- ruega en 1982). Se prevé ampliar este servicio, fi- nanciado totalmente por anunciantes multinaciona- les, a Suiza, Bélgica y Países Bajos.

En el recuadro de las páginas 192 y 194 se exami- nan algunos de los problemas que entraña este apresuramiento por el servicio TV DS y la radiodi- fusión privada en Europa y otras partes.

La base del programa de satélite franco-alemán es Thomson-CSF Communications, empresa francesa a la cabeza de los proveedores europeos de equipo de satélite y estaciones terrenas, y uno de los principales participantes en el programa *Intelsat VI*. El perfil de la empresa que sigue contiene descripciones de los programas *TDF1/TV-SAT*, destinados a la radiodi- fusión directa para la televisión francesa y alemana, y una amplia reseña de Thomson.

□

195

Thomson-CSF Communications

All Communications Worldwide

"The human mind knows no bounds,
reaching out as the universe unfolds".

THESE WORDS of the French naturalist Buffon (1707-1788) could serve as the motto of Thomson, the French group founded in 1893 and today ranking 5th in the world telecommunications field.

For nearly a century, the Thomson Group has fostered development in the application of electricity and of electronics mobilizing all the resources of the mind, its inventiveness and its creativity, to enable the transmission, broadcast or exchange of information to be quicker, more reliable and more effective over greater distances.

The Group employs 129,000 people (1983), 81,000 of them are employed by Thomson-CSF, its subsidiary responsible for the design, manufacture and installation of the communication equipments and systems. In 1982 the Company, one of the European leaders in business electronics, achieved a turnover of 27,2 billion francs, 47% of which in the export trade.

At a time when the rapid development of digital techniques has breached the frontiers between telecommunications and computing, Thomson-CSF "Communications" Division has developed a global and very comprehensive approach to the transport, storage and processing of information. These activities fall into four distinct categories :
— *Public Telecommunications*: networks and systems of information transport between public users.
— *Radiocommunications*: transmission and broadcasting of information by means of radioelectric links, filming and processing of images.

▷ 198

*Thomson-CSF: the whole
world of telecommunications.*

« L'esprit humain n'a pas de bornes,
il s'étend à mesure que l'Univers se déploie ».

TELLE POURRAIT ÊTRE LA DEVISE du groupe français Thomson, né en 1893, et qui occupe aujourd'hui, dans le domaine des télécommunications, le 5ème rang mondial. Ces lignes écrites par le savant français Buffon (1707-1788) correspondent bien à l'optique de cette grande compagnie qui, depuis bientôt un siècle, mobilise toutes les ressources de l'esprit humain pour que l'information soit transmise, diffusée, échangée, toujours plus vite, plus sûrement et plus loin.

Le Groupe rassemble 129 000 personnes dont plus de 81 000 travaillent pour Thomson-CSF, sa filiale responsable de la conception, fabrication et installation des équipements et des systèmes de communication. En 1982, la société, une des premières d'Europe en électronique professionnelle, a réalisé un chiffre d'affaires de 27,2 milliards de francs dont 12,9 milliards ou 47% à l'exportation.

A notre époque où le développement rapide des techniques numériques fait éclater les frontières entre télécommunications et informatique, la Branche Communications de Thomson-CSF répond à une approche globale et complète du transport, du stockage et du traitement de l'information.
Ses activités sont réparties en quatre domaines :
— *Télécommunications Publiques :* réseaux et systèmes publics de transport de l'information.
— *Radiocommunications:* transmission et diffusion de l'information par le moyen de liaisons radioélectriques, prise de vues et traitement d'images.
— *Communications d'Entreprise :* matériels et systèmes de collecte, stockage, traitement et acheminement d'information pour les besoins de l'entreprise.

▷ 198

*Thomson-CSF : tout
l'univers des télécommunications.*

« El espíritu humano no tiene límites.
Se extiende a medida que se despliega el universo ».

TAL PODRIA SER LA DIVISA del grupo francés Thomson, creado en 1893, que ocupa hoy el quinto puesto mundial en el campo de la telecomunicaciones. Estas palabras del erudito francés Buffon (1707-1788) corresponden a la óptica de esta gran compañía que desde cerca de un siglo moviliza todos los recursos del espíritu humano para transmitir, difundir e intercambiar la información con mayor eficacia y rapidez, y más lejos.

El Grupo tiene 129 000 empleados, de los que más de 81 000 trabajan para la Thomson-CSF, su filial responsable de la concepción, fabricación e instalación de equipos y sistemas de comunicación.

En 1982, la cifra de negocios de esta empresa, una de las primeras de Europa en electrónica profesional, fue de 27 200 millones de francos; de ellos, 19 200 millones, o un 47%, de la exportación.

En nuestra época, en que el rápido desarrollo de las técnicas digitales suprime las fronteras entre telecomunicaciones e informática, Thomson-CSF, Departamento "Comunicaciones", responde a un procedimiento global y completo del transporte, del almacenamiento y del tratamiento de la información.

Sus actividades se dividen en cuatro campos:
— *Telecomunicaciones Públicas:* redes y sistemas públicos de transporte de la información.
— *Radiocomunicaciones:* transmisión y difusión de la información mediante enlaces radioeléctricos, tomas de fotografías y tratamiento de imágenes.
— *Comunicaciones de empresa:* materiales y sistemas de captura, almacenamiento, tratamiento y en-

▷ 199

*Thomson-CSF: el universo
completo de las telecomunicaciones.*

— *Business Communications*: equipment and systems of capture, storage, processing and transmission of information for the Business requirements.
— *Systems of data processing and software.*

These four complementary activities provide Thomson-CSF "Communications" with the mastery of the main components of the complex units which now constitute communication systems. It is also one of the few companies in the world to dispose of all the necessary attributes for the building of major communication systems.

In addition, this Group's competence rests on three elements:
— technical know-how arising from a major investment in research and development and on an integrated activity of electronic components;
— experience acquired in the conception and realization of such systems handed over as turnkey projects;
— a worldwide sales and technical assistance network covering 100 countries and a policy of international development in close collaboration with customer countries.

The technical competence of Thomson is rooted primarily and fundamentally on a major research commitment: in 1982 Thomson spent 5 billion French francs on R&D or 10 per cent of total sales. 13,000 people are employed in its laboratories.

Basic research is undertaken in the corporate laboratory near Paris at Corbeville. Among its more recent projects are those on the synthesis and control of new materials with characteristics promising much for the future of electronics: semiconductor materials III-V, such as gallium arsenide, and organic compounds such as liquid crystals, hyperfrequency ceramics.

In line with a policy fitting with the decentralized structure of the Thomson Group, most of the development earmarked for the creation of new products is handled at Divisional level. Accordingly, the Communications Division is currently carrying out research and development work on optical fibers, lasers, components for microwaves, VLSI and digital optic discs. The technical capacity of Thomson and its technological independence rests also on the integrated production of electronic tubes and components, with 31 factories worldwide and an extensive range of products.

In all its activities, Thomson sets and monitors high quality standards which put its products at the highest level of reliability attained anywhere.

The public telecommunication sector supplied by Thomson-CSF "Communications" comprises the full range of products and facilities required by members of the public to communicate with each other and to receive information in conversational code: switched telephone networks, specialized networks for the transmission of data, of still images and of moving images. New services such as videotex, teletex, facsimile, teleconferencing, all use these infrastructures.

The development of these networks over the next two or three decades is likely to result in the creation of a public network providing subscribers in a single integrated infrastructure with all the facilities needed to secure all or any of these services.

Public telephone exchanges and networks constitute a major group of products and systems designed, manufactured, installed and maintained by Thomson worldwide.

The company's temporal exchanges — the MT range — employ the most advanced technologies, both in the hardware and the software supplied.

▷ 202

— *Systèmes Informatiques et Logiciel.*

Complémentaires, ces quatre domaines donnent à Thomson-CSF "Communications" la maîtrise des principaux constituants des ensembles complexes que sont désormais les systèmes de communication.

C'est ainsi l'une des rares sociétés au monde à disposer de l'ensemble des compétences nécessaires à l'élaboration des grands systèmes de télécommunications.

Cette aptitude se fonde en outre sur trois atouts :
— une capacité technique fondée notamment sur un important effort de recherche et de développement et sur une activité intégrée de composants électroniques ;
— l'expérience acquise par la conception et la réalisation de tels systèmes livrés « clés en main » ;
— un réseau mondial de vente et d'assistance technique qui couvre 100 pays, et une politique de déploiement qui s'appuie sur une coopération avec le pays client.

La capacité technique de Thomson-CSF "Communications" se fonde d'abord et avant tout sur un effort de recherche considérable : en 1982, Thomson a consacré 5 milliards de francs à la recherche et au développement, soit 10 % de son chiffre d'affaires : 13 000 personnes travaillent dans ses laboratoires.

Les recherches de base sont conduites par le Laboratoire Central de Corbeville près de Paris. Parmi ses travaux les plus récents, il convient de citer ceux qui portent sur la synthèse et la maîtrise de nouveaux matériaux aux propriétés pleines de promesses pour l'avenir de l'électronique : les matériaux semi-conducteurs III-V, tel l'arséniure de gallium, les composés organiques tels les cristaux liquides, les céramiques pour hyperfréquences...

Suivant un schéma qui répond à la structure décentralisée du Groupe Thomson, la plupart des développements directement orientés vers la réalisation de produits nouveaux sont traités par les Branches. Ainsi la Branche Communications conduit les études avancées sur les fibres optiques, les lasers, les composants pour les ondes millimétriques, les VLSI, le disque optique numérique.

La capacité technique de Thomson et son indépendance technologique s'appuient sur une activité intégrée de tubes et composants électroniques, avec 31 usines dans le monde et une gamme étendue.

Dans l'ensemble de ses activités, Thomson s'emploie à créer et à maintenir de hauts standards de qualité qui ont placé ses productions en matière de fiabilité au meilleur niveau mondial.

Le domaine des télécommunications publiques recouvre pour Thomson-CSF "Communications" l'ensemble des moyens permettant aux usagers publics de communiquer entre eux et de recevoir des informations sous forme conversationnelle : réseaux téléphoniques commutés, réseaux spécialisés de transmission de données, réseaux spécialisés de transmission d'images fixes et réseaux de télédistribution d'images animées.

Des services nouveaux comme le vidéotex, le télétex, la télécopie et la téléconférence utilisent l'infrastructure constituée par ces réseaux.

L'évolution de ces réseaux dans les deux ou trois prochaines décennies conduira probablement à un réseau public offrant à ses abonnés, de manière intégrée, les fonctions nécessaires à l'ensemble des services utilisés.

La commutation téléphonique publique et les réseaux constituent un premier groupe de produits et de systèmes dont Thomson assure la conception, la fabrication, l'installation et la maintenance dans le monde entier.

Les centraux temporels de Thomson — la gamme

▷ 202

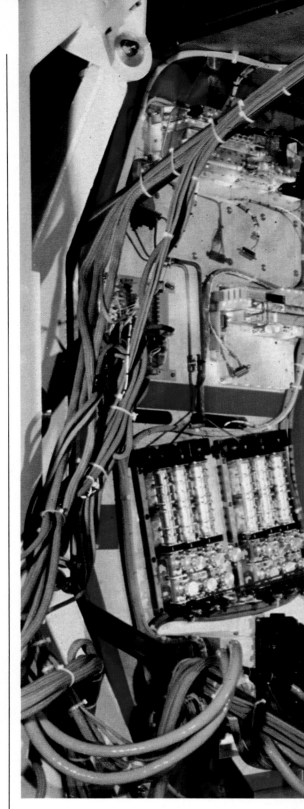

Above: On board equipment of Telecom 1, the first French program of telecommunications by satellite. Below, left to right: Mobile microwave relay in Mexico, a radio link tower at Knino Java, in Indonesia, and the Rezatelsat national satellite telecommunications network of the Zaire Republic; all designed, manufactured and installed by Thomson-CSF.

En haut : Plate-forme de la charge utile de Télécom 1, premier programme français de télécommunications par satellite. En bas, de g. à d. : Relais hertzien mobile au Mexique, station hertzienne à Knino Java, en Indonésie, et Rezatelsat, réseau national de télécommunications par satellite, tous conçus, réalisés et installés par Thomson-CSF.

caminamiento de la información para las necesidades de la empresa.
— *Sistemas informáticos y programación.*

Estos cuatro campos complementarios permiten a Thomson-CSF "Comunicaciones" dominar los principales componentes de los conjuntos complejos que son ahora los sistemas de comunicación.

También es una de las pocas compañías del mundo que dispone de un conjunto de competencias necesarias a la elaboración de los grandes sistemas de telecomunicaciones.

Además esa competencia se funda en tres elementos:
— una capacidad técnica basada en un esfuerzo importante de investigación y de desarrollo en una actividad integrada de componentes electrónicos;
— la experiencia adquirida en la concepción y la realización de esos sistemas entegrados "llave en mano";
— una red mundial de venta y asesoramiento técnico que abarca 100 países y una política de participación con el país cliente.

La capacidad de Thomson-CSF "Communications" se basa sobre todo y fundamentalmente en un esfuerzo importantísimo de investigación: en 1982, Thomson gastó 5 000 millones de francos en investigación y desarrollo, o sea, un 10% de su cifra de negocios: en sus laboratorios trabajan 13 000 personas.

La investigación básica se realiza en el laboratorio central de Corbeville, cera de París. Entre sus proyectos más recientes figuran los de síntesis y control de nuevos materiales con características prometedoras para el futuro de la electrónica: materiales semiconductores III-V como arseniuro de galio, y compuestos orgánicos como cristales líquidos, cerámicas para hiperfrecuencias, conmutación óptica, etc.

Siguiendo un esquema que responde a la estructura descentralizada del Grupo, la mayoría de los trabajos orientados a la creación de productos nuevos se tratan a nivel de las divisiones. Así, la división de comunicaciones efectúa sobre todo estudios avanzados en fibras ópticas, láseres, componentes de ondas milimétricas, VSLI y disco óptico digital.

La capacidad técnica de Thomson y su independencia tecnológica se basan también en la actividad integrada de tubos y componentes electrónicos, con 31 fábricas en el mundo y una amplía gama de productos.

En todas sus actividades, Thomson crea y mantiene normas de calidad elevadas, que han situado sus productos al mayor nivel de fiabilidad en el mundo.

El sector de comunicaciones públicas de Thomson-CSF "Communications" abarca el conjunto de los medios que permiten a los usuarios públicos comunicar entre sí y recibir informaciones en forma de conversación: redes telefónicas conmutadas, redes especializadas de transmisión de datos, redes especializadas de transmisión de imágenes fijas y redes de teledistribución de imágenes móviles.

Los nuevos servicios como videotex, teletex, facsímil, teleconferenciá utilizan la infraestructura constituida por esas redes.

La evolución de estas redes en los dos o tres decenios próximos probablemente conduzca a una red pública que ofrezca a sus usuarios, en forma integrada, las funciones que requiere el conjunto de los servicios utilizados.

La conmutación telefónica pública y las redes constituyen un primer grupo de productos y de sistemas para los cuales Thomson se ocupa de la concepción, fabrica-

▷ 203

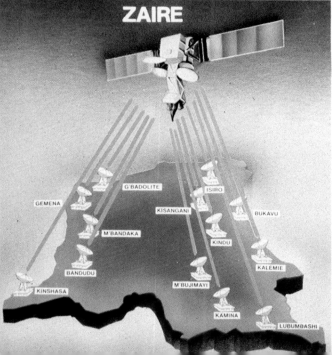

Arriba: Equipo a bordo de « Telecom 1 », el primer programa francés de telecomunicación por satélite. Abajo, de izquierda a derecha: Enlace hertziano móvil en México, la estación hertziana de Knino Java, en Indonesia, y la Rezatelsat, red nacional de comunicaciones por satélite de la República del Zaire, todas concebidas, fabricadas e instaladas por Thomson-CSF.

199

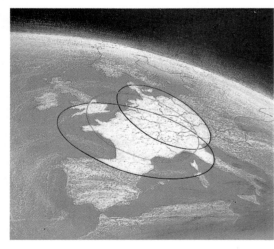

Footprint of the three geostationary satellites of the European program: Telecom 1 (red), TDF 1 (blue), TV-SAT (green). A magnification of the footprint is shown on the left. Thomson-CSF has participated in almost every European program and in many international ones, involving some 50 satellites placed in orbit.

Couverture des trois satellites géostationnaires du programme européen : Telecom 1 (rouge), TDF 1 (bleu), TV-SAT (vert). Un agrandissement de la couverture est montré à gauche. Thomson-CSF a participé à la quasi totalité des programmes européens et à de nombreux programmes internationaux, soit près de 50 satellites mis en orbite.

Cobertura de tres satélites geoestacionarios del programa europeo: Telecom 1 (rojo), TDF 1 (azul) y TV-SAT (verde). A la izquierda, una ampliación de la cobertura. Thomson-CSF ha participado en casi todos los programas europeos y en muchos internacionales, con unos 50 satélites en órbita.

The R&D activities of the company in the area of network design are concentrated on the development of a family of products needed for the effective setting up of data networks, such as :
— transmission networks employing packet switching or circuit switching techniques;
— value added networks, designed for message handling, electronic mail and facsimile;
— connecting paths, to enable the various networks to communicate with each other.

In order to conceive and design coherent systems fulfilling specific requirements, Thomson-CSF "Communications" has teams specialized in the architecture and engineering of communication networks.

Transmission by cable, microwave earth links and satellites constitute the second major group of products and systems supplied by Thomson-CSF. These include optical fiber cables and associated equipment, several of these installations having been completed in France and abroad. Among them are links of very high capacity (several tens of thousands of telephone lines) between telephone exchanges. The first link of this type was commissioned in Paris as early as 1980.

The Company ranks second in the world among suppliers of microwave installations, whether earth links or satellites. The latter constitute a major growth sector both for on-board equipment and earth stations.

The company's experience in satellite-borne equipment began over 20 years ago with the construction of the system of telecontrol and telemeasurement installed in French and European satellites. Since then Thomson-CSF has participated in practically all European and in several international programs. This includes some 50 satellites placed in geostationary orbit, among which were the Canadian *CTS* communications satellite, the European *OTS* satellite, the international satellites *Intelsat II, Intelsat IV, Intelsat IVA, Intelsat V,* and the Franco-German telecommunications satellites *Symphonie.* In the near future the satellites *TDRS, ECS, Marecs, Telecom 1, TDF 1, TV-SAT, SPOT* and *Intelsat VI* will have on-board equipment supplied by Thomson-CSF.

Its experience and proven competence led to its selection as main contractor for complete on-board equipments in particular for the Telecom 1 program.

"Telecom I" is the first French program of telecommunications by satellite. It will supply business and public services with all the new services: data transmission, transmission of image, fast telecopying, teleconferencing and teletex.

Thomson-CSF "Communications" is a main contractor for on-board equipment for the 3 satellites and for development, construction and installation, through Telspace, of the corresponding earth stations. Each satellite will carry 6 transponders 14/12 GHz (TOP of 20 W), 4 transponders 6/4 GHz (TOP of 8.5 W) plus 2 transponders 8/7 GHz earmarked for defense use.

TDF1/TV-SAT is a French-German program designed to provide direct broadcast facilities simultaneously for 3 TV programs beamed on France via TDF1) and 3 TV programs beamed on West Germany (via TV-SAT). These programs will be received by means of individual antennae of 60 to 90 cm diameter. Thomson-CSF is the main contractor for on-board equipment of the pre-operational French satellite — transponders and antennae — and for the supply of equipment for the German satellite. TDF1 and TV-SAT will be launched by *Ariane* in 1985.

▷ 206

MT — mettent en œuvre des technologies très avancées tant au niveau des matériels que des logiciels.

Par ailleurs, la compagnie développe la famille des produits nécessaires à la constitution des réseaux de données, tels que les réseaux de transports à commutation de paquets ou à commutation de circuits ; les réseaux à valeur ajoutée, destinés à la messagerie, au courrier électronique et au fac-similé ; et les passerelles permettant aux différents réseaux de communiquer entre eux.

Pour être en mesure de concevoir des systèmes cohérents répondant à des besoins spécifiques, Thomson-CSF "Communications" dispose d'équipes spécialisées dans l'architecture et l'ingénierie des réseaux de communication.

Les transmissions par câbles, par faisceaux hertziens et par satellite sont le deuxième grand groupe de produits et de systèmes de télécommunications de Thomson-CSF : fibres optiques et équipements associés avec de nombreuses installations en France et à l'étranger dont les liaisons à grande capacité (plusieurs dizaines de milliers de voies téléphoniques) entre centraux téléphoniques. La première liaison de ce type a été mise en service à Paris dès 1980 ; pour les faisceaux hertziens, Thomson-CSF se classe au 2ème rang mondial ; les liaisons par satellite constituent un secteur d'activités en plein essor, qu'il s'agisse des équipements embarqués ou des stations terriennes.

L'expérience de Thomson-CSF dans le domaine des équipements embarqués a débuté il y a près de 20 ans avec la réalisation des premiers systèmes de télécommande et de télémesure destinés aux satellites scientifiques français et européens.

Thomson-CSF a participé depuis, à la quasi totalité des programmes européens et à de nombreux programmes internationaux : près de 50 satellites mis en orbite, parmi lesquels le satellite de télécommunications canadien *CTS,* le satellite européen *OTS,* les satellites internationaux *Intelsat II, Intelsat IV, Intelsat IV A, Intelsat V,* le satellite de télécommunications franco-allemand *Symphonie.* Les satellites *TDRS, ECS, Marecs, Telecom 1, TDF 1, TV-SAT, SPOT* et *Intelsat VI* auront à leur bord des équipements Thomson-CSF.

La compagnie a été choisie comme maître d'œuvre de charges utiles complètes, en particulier pour le programme "Telecom 1".

Telecom 1 est le premier programme français de télécommunications par satellite, il offrira aux entreprises et aux administrations les nouveaux services de la télématique : transmission de données, d'images, télécopie rapide, téléconférence, télétexte. Thomson-CSF "Communications" est le maître d'œuvre des charges utiles des 3 satellites et développe à travers Telspace les stations terriennes correspondantes. Chaque satellite comprendrà 6 répéteurs 14/12 GHz (TOP de 20 W), 4 répéteurs 6/4 GHz (TOP de 8,5 W) et 2 répéteurs 8/7 GHz destinés à des besoins militaires.

TDF 1/TV-SAT est un programme franco-allemand qui a pour mission la diffusion directe simultanée de trois programmes de télévision sur la France — via TDF 1 — et de trois programmes sur la République Fédérale d'Allemagne — via TV-SAT —; ces programmes seront reçus à l'aide d'antennes individuelles de 60 à 90 cm de diamètre. Thomson-CSF est responsable de la charge utile du satellite pré-opérationnel français — répéteurs et antennes — et de la fourniture d'équipements pour le satellite allemand. TDF 1 et TV-SAT seront lancés par *Ariane* en 1985.

Thomson-CSF "Communications", premier fournisseur européen et second fournisseur mondial de stations terriennes, a livré à travers Telspace, sur les cinq continents, 92

▷ 206

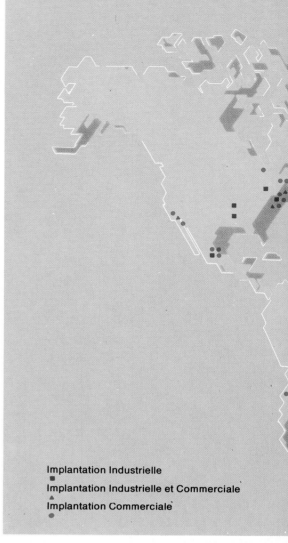

Implantation Industrielle
Implantation Industrielle et Commerciale
Implantation Commerciale

Above: World map showing the factories and offices of Thomson-CSF. Below: The electronic PABX developed by Thomson-CSF, the microcomputer Micromega 32 and the Central digital exchange MT 20 designed for city, intercity and international usage.

En haut : Les implantations industrielles et commerciales de Thomson-CSF dans le monde. En bas : Les PABX électroniques développés par Thomson-CSF, le micro-ordinateur Microméga 32 et le Central temporel MT 20, destinés à des centres de transit urbains, interurbains et internationaux.

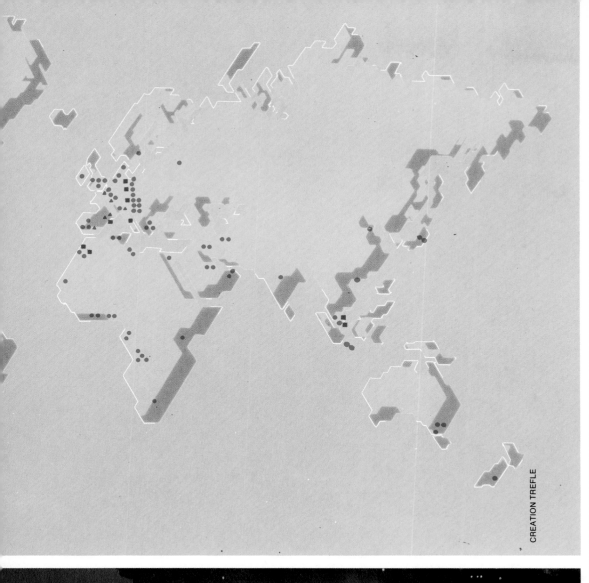

CREATION TREFLE

ción, instalación y mantenimiento en el mundo entero.

Las centrales temporales de Thomson — la gama MT — aplican tecnologías muy avanzadas tanto al nivel de los materiales como al del soporte lógico.

Por otra parte, la empresa desarrolla productos necesarios para la constitución de redes de datos, tales como las redes de trasporte de conmutación de paquetes o de conmutación de circuitos; las redes de "valor añadido" destinadas al tratamiento de mensajes, al correo electrónico y facsímil, con trayectos que permiten a las redes comunicar entre sí.

Para concebir sistemas coherentes que responden a necesidades específicas, Thomson-CSF "Communications" dispone de equipos especializados en la arquitectura e ingeniería de redes de comunicación.

Las transmisiones por cables, haces hertzianos y por satélites de telecomunicaciones Thomson-CSF son el segundo gran grupo de productos y sistemas; fibras ópticas y equipos asociados con numerosas instalaciones en Francia y en el extranjero, entre ellos los enlaces de gran capacidad (varias decenas de miles de vías telefónicas) entre centrales telefónicas. El primer enlace de este tipo fue instalado en París ya en 1980; en lo que se refiere a los haces hertzianos, Thomson-CSF ocupa el segundo lugar mundial; los enlaces por satélite constituyen un sector de actividades en auge, tanto en lo relativo a los equipos a bordo como a las estaciones terrenas.

La experiencia de Thomson-CSF en equipo a bordo de satélites comenzó hace 20 años, con la construcción de los primeros sistemas de telemando y telemedida instalados en satélites científicos franceses y europeos.

Desde entonces, Thomson-CSF ha participado prácticamente en todos los programas europeos y en varios internacionales, colocando en órbita geoestacionaria más de 50 satélites, entre ellos el de comunicaciones canadiense *CTS*, el europeo *OTS*, los satélites internacionales *Intelsat II, IV, IVA* y *V*, y el satélite de comunicaciones franco-alemán *Symphonie*. Los satélites *TDRS, ECS, Marecs, Telecom 1, TDF 1, TV-SAT, SPOT* e *Intelsat VI* llevarán pronto a bordo equipo de Thomson-CSF.

La compañía ha sido elegida principal contratista de equipo completo a bordo, en particular para el programa "Telecom 1".

Telecom 1 es el primer programa francés de telecomunicaciones por satélite. Ofrecerá a las empresas y a las admiraciones todos los servicios nuevos: transmisión y teleprocesamiento de datos, transmisión de imágenes, telecopia rápida, teleconferencia y teletexto.

Thomson-CSF "Communications" es el principal contratista para el equipo a bordo de los 3 satélites y el desarrollo, construcción e instalación, a través de Telspace, de las estaciones terrenas correspondientes. Cada satélite comprenderá 6 repetidores, 14/12 GHz (TOP de 20 W), 4 repetidores 6/4 GHz (TOP de 8,5 W) mas dos repetidores 8/7 GHz destinados a fines militares. TDF 1/TV-SAT es un programa franco-alémán para la difusión directa y simultánea de 3 programas TV en Francia (vía TDF 1) y 3 programas TV en la RFA (vía TV-SAT). Estos programas se recibrán mediante antenas individuales de 60 a 90 cm de diametro. Thomson-CSF "Communications" es el primer contratista del equipo a bordo del satélite preoperacional francés — transpondedores y antenas — y del suministro de equipo para el satélite alemán. Los satélites serán lanzados por el cohete *Ariane* en 1985.

▷ 207

Mapa mundi en el que pueden verse las fábricas y oficinas de Thomson-CSF. Abajo: Las CAP electrónicas desarrolladas por Thomson-CSF; el microcomputador Micromega 32 y la central digital MT 20, concebida para centros de tránsito urbanos, interurbanos e internacionales.

*Schematized network
of teledistribution by optical fiber.*

*Réseau schématisé
de télédistribution par fibres optiques.*

*Red esquematizada
de teledistribución por fibras ópticas.*

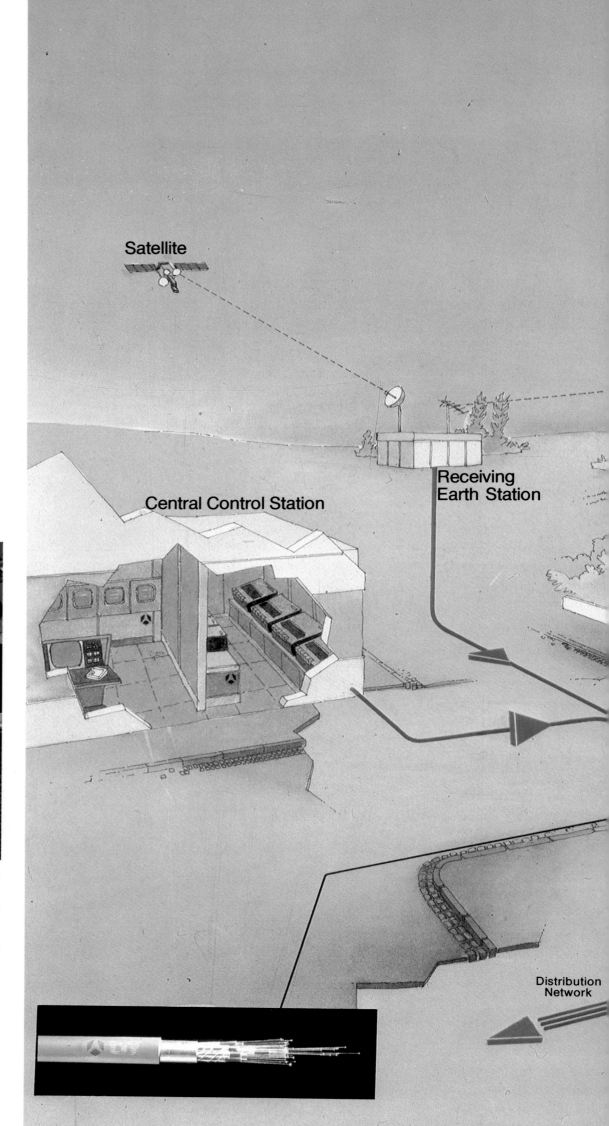

Satellite

Receiving
Earth Station

Central Control Station

Distribution
Network

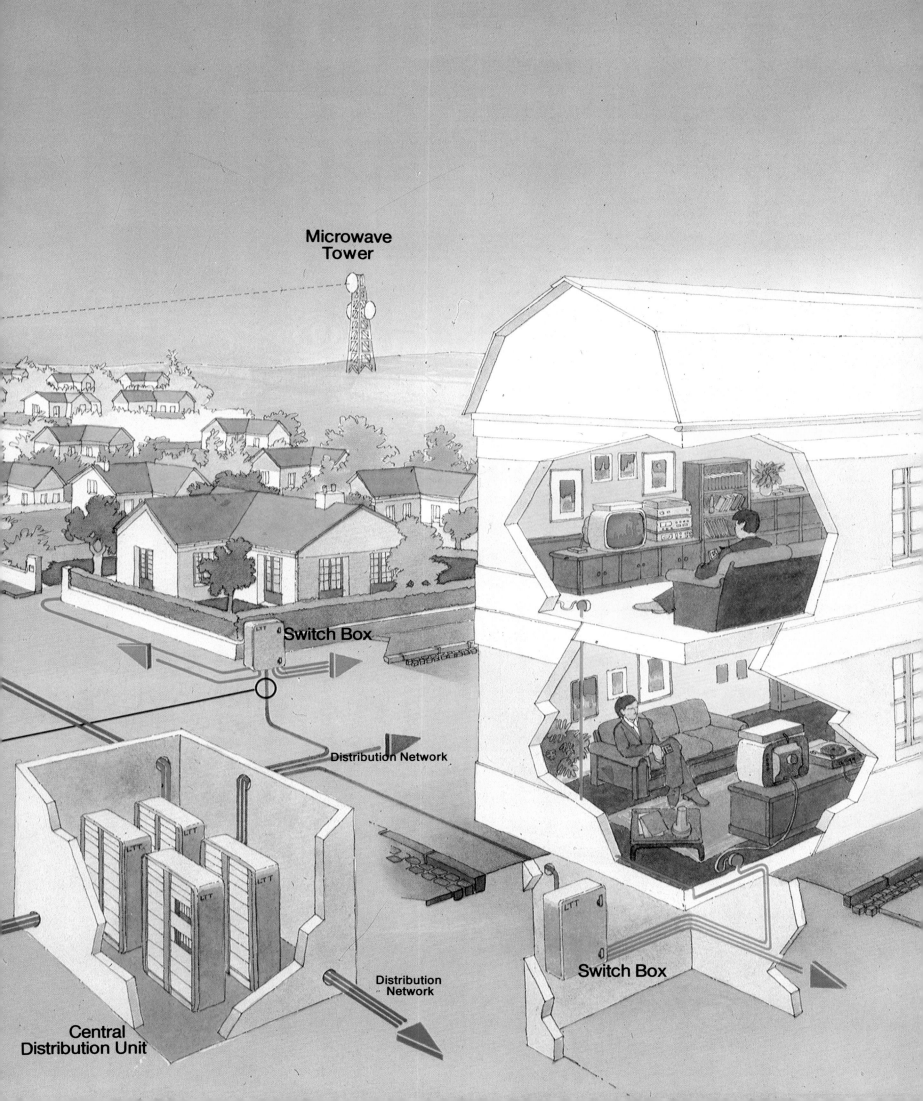

Microwave
Tower

Switch Box

Distribution Network

Central
Distribution Unit

Distribution
Network

Switch Box

As No 1 European builder of earth stations and No 2 in the world, Thomson-CSF "Communications" has supplied, through Telspace, 92 earth stations of different types for use in the 5 continents in liaison with the satellites *Intelsat, Symphonie* or *OTS*. This double capability, on earth and space, enables Thomson-CSF to set up complete telecommunications and television satellite networks.

In the professional radio communications sector, Thomson-CSF provides complete families of high technology products: tactical radio communication equipment for land use designed to operate at short or medium distances in the HF and VHF bands; radio infrastructure equipment for administrations, both civil and military; electronic defence equipment (number and countermeasures), large advanced systems of radio communications, etc.

In radio telephony, the company's activities include the supply of all types of mobile telephone equipment and systems whether operating through public or private networks.

Thomson-CSF "Communications" is also a world leader in the field of radio and television recording and broadcasting equipment. This includes a complete range of products from film making to broadcasting, through to processing of images and their transmission: radio transmitters, broadcasting transmitters and transposers; cameras and studio equipment.

The company is also a leading supplier of communication equipment and products to businesses and private users: PBXs, mini- and microcomputers, telephone and telematics terminals, message handling and recording equipment (telecopiers, digital optic discs).

The experience of Thomson-CSF Communications, as a main contractor for large systems, is considerable. The Company assumes responsibility for project design, conception and installation of "turnkey" systems. This division has also experience acquired in the field which enables it always to meet the specific customer requirements.

An example of such an undertaking is the design and construction of one of the very first national satellite communications networks, in Zaire. This network provides the whole country with facilities for every means of telecommunications in current use: telephony, telegraphy, television and radio. The vast area of the territory, its topography and the wide spread of its 25 million inhabitants, imposed the use of a customer-built network: the Rezatelsat system. This system, designed and installed by Thomson, utilizes a complex of earth stations for communication by satellite, radio links, and microwave TV broadcast stations.

Finally the international character of Thomson-CSF must be highlighted. It has a network of sales and manufacturing subsidiaries, local representatives and agencies which ensure adequate representation in more than 100 countries and enable it to be a true international partner providing all its customers worldwide the installation, maintenance, equipment and technical training services they require.

This training of users and future maintenance engineers is one of the several forms of client co-operation devised by Thomson-CSF Communications. In its most advanced state, this co-operation can include comprehensive and direct transfers of technology to serve as a base for the establishment of a national electronic industry.

☐

stations de différents types en liaison avec les satellites *Intelsat, Symphonie* ou *OTS*.

Cette double compétence, au sol et dans l'espace, permet à Thomson-CSF de réaliser des réseaux complets de télécommunications et de télévision par satellites.

Les radiocommunications professionnelles constituent un secteur dans lequel Thomson-CSF a des familles de produits à la pointe de la technologie : équipements de radiocommunications tactiques terrestres à courte et moyenne distance en gamme HF et VHF ; équipements radio d'infrastructure destinés aux administrations, tant civiles que militaires ; équipements électroniques de défense (chiffre et contremesures) ; grands systèmes avancés de radiocommunications.

En radiotéléphonie, ses activités portent sur tous les services civils de liaisons individuelles avec des personnes en déplacement, à travers les services publics ou au moyen de réseaux privés.

Thomson-CSF "Communications" est aussi l'un des grands constructeurs mondiaux en radiodiffusion et télévision professionnelles, de la prise de vue à la diffusion, en passant par le traitement des images et leur transmission : émetteurs de radio, de radiodiffusion dans toutes les gammes de puissance ; émetteurs et réémetteurs de télévision ; caméras professionnelles et équipements de studio.

Thomson est également présente dans le domaine des systèmes de communications d'entreprise et produit les équipements de base de ces systèmes : autocommutateurs téléphoniques privés, micro-ordinateurs, terminaux téléphoniques et télématiques, équipements de messagerie et d'archivage (télécopieurs, disque optique numérique).

L'expérience de Thomson-CSF "Communications" en tant que maître d'œuvre de grands systèmes est considérable. La compagnie prend en charge l'établissement des projets, la conception et la réalisation de systèmes "clés en main". Elle dispose d'une expérience acquise sur le terrain, dans le souci permanent de répondre aux besoins spécifiques de ses clients. Elle a, par exemple, étudié et réalisé l'un des tout premiers réseaux nationaux de télécommunications par satellite : celui de la République du Zaïre. Ce réseau permet à l'ensemble du pays de bénéficier de tous les types de communications actuels : téléphonie, télégraphie, télévision et radiodiffusion.

L'étendue du territoire, sa topographie et la répartition de ses 25 millions d'habitants ont nécessité l'installation d'un réseau de communication adapté : le réseau Rézatelsat. Conçu, réalisé et installé par Thomson, il met en œuvre à la fois des stations terriennes de télécommunications par satellite, des faisceaux hertziens et des émetteurs de radiodiffusion télévision.

En conclusion, il faut souligner le caractère international de Thomson-CSF. Elle dispose d'un réseau de filiales commerciales et industrielles, de délégations et de représentations locales qui assurent sa présence dans plus de 100 pays, ce qui en fait un vrai partenaire international qui assure à tous ses clients, à travers le monde, les services d'installation, de maintenance des équipements et de formation technique.

Cette formation des utilisateurs et des futurs responsables de la maintenance est l'une des multiples formes de coopération développées par Thomson-CSF Communications. Dans sa version la plus poussée, cette coopération peut aller jusqu'à des transferts directs et complets de technologie qui préludent à la création d'une véritable industrie électronique nationale.

☐

Result of the technological advance realized in the techniques of optical recording with laser, the Thomson-CSF digital optic disc, the "GIGADISC", is able to store 1 billion characters with an access time between 100 and 300 milliseconds. The new high-capacity recording system allows the processing of information of any type: texts, voice, images, data.

Fruit de l'avance technologique acquise dans les techniques d'enregistrement optique par laser, le disque optique numérique de Thomson-CSF, le « GIGADISC », est capable de stocker 1 milliard de caractères avec un temps d'accès entre 100 et 300 millisecondes. Ce nouveau système d'archivage de haute capacité permet de traiter les informations de tous types : textes, voix, images, données.

Como primer proveedor europeo y segundo del mundo, Thomson-CSF ha suministrado, a través de Telspace, 92 estaciones terrenas de diversos tipos, para utilizarlas en 5 continentes, en conexión con los satélites *Intelsat, Symphonie* y *OTS*.

Esta doble capacidad, en tierra y en el espacio, permite a la empresa realizar redes completas de telecomunicaciones y de televisión por satélite.

Las radiocomunicaciones profesionales, esencialmente para uso militar, constituyen un sector en el que Thomson-CSF tiene series de productos con las tecnologías más avanzadas: equipo de radiocomunicaciones tácticas terrestres para corta y media distancia en las bandas HF y VHF; equipo radioeléctrico de infraestructura destinado a las administraciones, civiles y militares; equipo militar electrónico (cifra y contramedida); grandes sistemas avanzados de radiocomunicaciones.

Los productos y sistemas de radiotelefonía tienen aplicación en todos los servicios civiles de enlace con personas que se desplazan, a través del sistema público o de redes privadas.

Thomson-CSF "Communications", es también uno de los grandes constructores mundiales de radiodifusión y televisión profesionales, desde la filmación a la difusión pasando por el tratamiento de las imágenes y su transmisión: emisores de radio, de radiodifusión para todas las gamas de potencia; emisores y transmisores de televisión; cámaras profesionales y equipos de estudio.

Thomson está presente también en el campo de los sistemas de comunicación de empresas, y produce equipo básico de estos sistemas: conmutadores automáticos telefónicos privados, microcomputadores, terminales telefónicos y telemáticos, equipo de transmisión de mensajes y archivo (telecopiadores, disco optico digital).

La experiencia de Thomson-CSF "Communications" como instalador es considerable. La Compañía asume la responsabilidad de sistemas completos, incluidos el diseño y la instalación de proyectos «llave en mano». Dispone de una experiencia adquirida sobre el terreno, con la preocupación permanente de atender las necesidades específicas de sus clientes. Como ejemplo, puede citarse el diseño y la construcción de una de las primeras redes nacionales de comunicaciones por satélite, en Zaire. Esta red proporciona a todo el país facilidades para cada uno de los medios de comunicación actuales: telefonía, telegrafía, televisión y radiodifusión.

La vasta extensión del territorio del Zaire, su topografía y la distribución de sus 25 millones de habitantes han exigido el uso de una red de comunicaciones adaptada a esas condiciones. El sistema Rezatelsat, concebido e instalado por Thomson, utiliza un complejo de estaciones terrenas para comunicaciones por satélite, radioenlaces y transmisores de TV por microondas.

Para concluir, debe señalarse el carácter internacional de la empresa. Thomson-CSF dispone de una red de filiales comerciales e industriales, de delegaciones y representaciones locales en más de 100 países. Esta vasta red internacional garantiza la prestación en el mundo entero de un servicio de formación de técnicos.

Esta formación de operadores y técnicos de mantenimiento es una de las diversas formas de cooperación con el cliente ideada por Thomson-CSF Communications. En su estado más avanzado, puede comprender la transferencia directa y completa de tecnología que sirva de base al establecimiento de una industria electrónica nacional.

☐

Fruto del avance tecnológico obtenido con técnicas de registro óptico por láser, el disco óptico digital de Thomson-CSF, el "GIGADISC", es capaz de almacenar mil millones de carácteres con un tiempo de acceso incluido entre 100 y 300 milisegundos. Este nuevo sistema de archivo de alta capacidad permite el tratamiento de datos de toda clase: textos, voz, imágenes y datos.

EXPLOSIVE INCREASE
ORIZONSNEW OF CABLE POWERNEWHOPENE
AND RADIO COMMUNICATIONS

AN EXPLOSIVE INCREASE is taking place in the development of both cable and radio communications. This is due to a number of influences somewhat diverse in their origin. Briefly they include:
— *a widespread belief in the intrinsic value of information* as something 'good for the people' and as a means of providing education and training; of improving social behaviour or increasing political awareness and so adding to the fullness of life;
— *the value of home access* as a vehicle for advertising, with the advantage of being able to focus on special interest groups;
— *the public appetite* for better, more varied, more conveniently accessed information on matters of their personal concern; the possibility of two-way, interactive use is an important attribute of this;
— *the attraction of profitable investment,* which has resulted in a scramble for licences to equip and operate cable television or microwave radio networks;
— *the availability of new technologies* to provide reliably and efficiently integrated interactive communications infrastructures at rapidly decreasing costs. Foremost among these are optical cables and microwave cellular radio.

These influences are powerful and likely to become even more powerful in the 1980s and 1990s. They will be tempered, however, by the need to guard against infringements of the individual's right to privacy and the risk of adding to the privileged status of those who can afford to pay.
Cable communication links include wired pairs, coaxial and optical fiber. Radio links are all in the microwave band.

Wired pairs are usually grouped in hundreds in a sheath cable running along roadsides or under ground. The wires are twisted to minimize magnetic interference. Signal losses are offset by the use of amplifiers (repeaters) every few kilometers. Wired

▷ 210

*Communications spreading
out to the four corners of the earth.*

ON ASSISTE ACTUELLEMENT à un développement spectaculaire des télécommunications par câble et des radiocommunications. Cela tient à divers facteurs :
— *le sentiment, très répandu, que l'information a une valeur intrinsèque,* qu'elle est « utile aux gens » et qu'elle permet d'assurer l'enseignement et la formation professionnelle, d'améliorer les comportements sociaux et de mieux prendre conscience des réalités politiques, bref qu'elle contribue à la plénitude de la vie ;
— *l'intérêt que présente l'accès aux foyers* pour acheminer la publicité et l'avantage de pouvoir sélectionner son audience ;
— *l'appétit du public* pour des informations meilleures, plus variées, d'accès plus facile, pour des questions qui les concernent personnellement ;
— *l'attrait d'un investissement rentable,* qui s'est traduit dans divers pays par de multiples demandes de licences d'exploitation de réseaux de télévision câblée et de communications micro-ondes ;
— *la disponibilité de nouvelles technologies* qui permettent d'établir des infrastructures de télécommunications intégrées, fiables et efficaces à un coût décroissant — surtout les fibres optiques et la technique « alvéolaire » pour radiotéléphones mobiles.

Ces facteurs sont déterminants et d'influence croissante. Celle-ci sera quelque peu contrebalancée par certains impératifs, notamment par celui du respect de la vie privée, et par la nécessité d'éviter de favoriser indûment les privilégiés.
Les liaisons de télécommunications par câble, utilisent des câbles à paires symétriques, des câbles coaxiaux et des câbles à fibres optiques. Les liaisons radioélectriques s'effectuent toujours par micro-ondes.

Les paires symétriques sont en général groupées par centaines dans l'enveloppe d'un câble à fil torsadé posé le long des routes ou enterré. L'affaiblissement du signal est compensé par l'installation

▷ 210

*Les communications
s'étendent aux quatres coins du monde.*

SE ESTÁ PRODUCIENDO UN EXPLOSIVO aumento en el desarrollo de las comunicaciones por cable y por radio, debido a varias influencias de diverso origen: en resumen, comprenden:
— *una fe general en el valor intrínseco de la información,* como algo "bueno para la gente" y como medio de dispensar educación y formación cultural, social y política, dando así mayor plenitud a la vida.
— *el valor del acceso al hogar* como vehículo de propaganda, con la ventaja de poder centrarse en grupos de especial interés.
— *el apetito del público* por un acceso mejor, más variado y apropiado a la información sobre materias de interés personal; la posibilidad del uso bidireccional e interactivo es un importante atributo.
— *la atracción de inversiones rentables,* que ha dado lugar a la lucha por licencias para equipar y explotar redes de televisión por cable o de radiocomunicaciones por microondas.
— *la disponibilidad de nuevas tecnologías* para comunicaciones integradas interactivas, seguras y eficaces, a un costo que disminuye rápidamente. Las radiocomunicaciones celulares por cables ópticos y microondas ocupan un lugar preferente.

Se trata de fuertes influencias, que probablemente se acentúen en los años 80 y 90. Sin embargo, se mitigarán por la necesidad de proteger el derecho del individuo al secreto y por el riesgo de hacer más privilegiada la situación de quienes pueden pagar.
Los enlaces de comunicación por cable comprenden los pares, los coaxiales y las fibras ópticas. Todos los radioenlaces se encuentran en la banda de microondas.

Los pares de conductores están normalmente agrupados por centenares en un cable revestido tendido a lo largo de las carreteras o bajo el suelo. Los cables están trenzados para minimizar la interferen-

▷ 211

*Las comunicaciones se
extienden a los cuatro rincones del globo.*

pairs on a trunk route normally carry 12 voice channels simultaneously, or 24-30 digital pulse code modulated (PCM) voice channels. They can be adapted for digital transmission by the use of a modem at each end. Voice grade lines can transmit data at the rate of 1,200 bits per second (bps) in each direction. Distortion reducing devices can increase this to 9,600 bps.

Coaxial cables are available ranging in bandwidth from about 10 MHz up to several hundred MHz. This makes possible more than 10,000 voice channels on a single cable with two coaxial lines, or multiples of this. They minimize distortion and have negligible crosstalk. Compared to twisted pairs coaxial cables have every advantage except cost.

Optical cables are made up of fine strands of glass of high transparency, which act as waveguides for the transmission of single frequency (monochromatic) light beams. Recent developments have produced optical fibers with transmission losses as low as or lower than conventional cables. More than 100 fibers can be bundled together in a flexible cable about 1 cm diameter.

Optical fibers have almost unlimited bandwidth potential and are therefore excellent carriers of large signal volumes over long distances or of wide band signals for local distribution. They are immune to many of the problems encountered with other communication channels, such as signal leakage, crosstalk, electrical interference or other noises and therefore highly suitable for the transmission of data.

Wavelength multiplexing greatly increases the capacity of optical cable, for example a technique developed by Bell Laboratories enables 300,000 calls to be made on 144 glass fibers grouped in a cable no thicker than a finger. It is now possible to produce very strong, pure fibers 8 miles long which can then be spliced, without loss of light signal, into lengths of 15 miles.

Radio microwave links can only be transmitted by line-of-sight but require fewer amplifiers than coaxial cables over the same distance. Interference from weather, terrain undulations, buildings and other man-made objects is minimal when beamed to and from satellites, although atmospheric interference, flying objects or birds, and echo effects, remain impediments to error-free transmission. These defects are expected to be overcome before very long.

The intensive development of coaxial and optical cable networks, and of microwave transmission, has been sustained by the insistent and growing demand for bandwidth so essential for the development of integrated digital networks and for the establishment of audio-visual communications.

Cable TV owes its origins in the late 1940s to an appliance dealer in Pennsylvania who discovered that by erecting a mountain-top antenna and linking it to his television receiver by a coaxial cable he immeasurably improved his reception and could bring in stations from distant cities. It remained little used, however, until the late 1970s.

In 1975 RCA Corporation placed its first domestic communications satellite in geostationary orbit. By bouncing signals off the satellite into dish-shaped antennae, operators found that they could deliver programs nationwide at a fraction of the cost borne by the broadcasting networks. At about the same time the US Federal Communications Commission (FCC) began to relax legal restrictions on the use of cable for broadcasting purposes. These two events of the 1970s heralded a period of tremendous growth in the use of cable for television broadcasting in the USA, soon followed by a similar surge forward in Europe and now elsewhere.

Competition in audio-visual transmission has taken various forms. Major contenders for geographic cable franchises and for satellite facilities tend to be confined to large corporations or governments, since the cost of cabling remains extremely high (over US$100 million to cable a medium size US city in 1982) and the investment required in producing programs is even higher. Most operators of cable TV networks, therefore, are either national agencies or

▷ 212

d'amplificateurs à intervalles de quelques kilomètres. Sur une artère interurbaine, les paires symétriques acheminent normalement 12 voies téléphoniques simultanément, ou 24 à 30 voies numériques par impulsions et codage (MIC) après adaptation, en utilisant un modem à 1200 bits par seconde (bit/s) dans chaque sens, et sont équipées de dispositifs de réduction de distorsion, à 9600 bit/s.

Les câbles à paires coaxiales acheminent les signaux dans des bandes de fréquences variables, depuis environ 10 MHz jusqu'à plusieurs centaines de MHz, ce qui permet de disposer de plus de 100 000 voies téléphoniques sur un même câble avec deux lignes coaxiales. Ces câbles réduisent la distorsion au minimum et, par rapport aux paires torsadées, les câbles à paires coaxiales sont plus avantageux à tous égards, sauf en matière de coût.

Les câbles à fibres optiques sont constitués de fibres de verre très fines, de grande transparence, qui guident des faisceaux lumineux à fréquence unique.

Les fibres optiques offrent des possibilités quasi illimitées en matière de largeur de bande ; elles fournissent ainsi d'excellents supports pour la transmission de forts volumes de signaux sur de grandes distances ou de signaux à large bande destinés à une distribution locale. De plus, elles sont insensibles aux interférences et conviennent donc parfaitement à la transmission de données.

Le multiplexage des longueurs d'onde accroît considérablement la capacité des fibres optiques ; c'est ainsi qu'un procédé mis au point par les Bell Laboratories permet d'établir 300 000 communications sur 144 fibres de verre groupées dans un câble de l'épaisseur d'un doigt.

Les liaisons par micro-ondes ne peuvent s'effectuer qu'en visibilité directe, mais elles exigent moins de répéteurs que les câbles à paires coaxiales pour une même distance. Les perturbations dues aux conditions météorologiques, au relief, aux bâtiments ou à d'autres constructions sont réduites à un minimum quand les émissions passent par des satellites.

Le développement des réseaux en câble à paires coaxiales et à fibres optiques, comme celui des transmissions à micro-ondes, comme celui des transmissions à micro-ondes, répond à un besoin croissant de fréquences à large bande, indispensables pour l'exploitation de réseaux numériques intégrés et pour l'établissement de communications audio-visuelles interactives au bureau ou chez soi.

La transmission par câble n'a commencé à être utilisée pour la télévision qu'à la fin des années 1970. En 1975, la RCA Corporation a placé sur orbite géostationnaire son premier satellite national de communications. En faisant transmettre les signaux par satellite à des antennes paraboliques, les exploitants ont constaté qu'ils pouvaient diffuser des programmes dans tous les États-Unis moyennant un prix de revient inférieur à celui des réseaux de radiodiffususion. Simultanément, la « Federal Communications Commission » (FCC) a commencé à assouplir les restrictions légales imposées aux Etats-Unis pour l'usage du câble pour la radiodiffusion. Ces deux évènements de la décennie 1970 ont ouvert la voie à un développement considérable du câble pour la radiodiffusion télévisuelle.

Dans le domaine de la transmission audio-visuelle, la concurrence s'est manifestée sous plusieurs formes. Les principaux candidats à l'obtention de concessions géographiques pour les réseaux câblés et les services par satellite sont en général de grandes sociétés ou des Etats, le coût du câblage étant très élevé (plus de US $ 100 millions pour une ville américaine d'importance moyenne, avec, en plus, des investissements encore supérieurs pour la réalisation de programmes.

Les systèmes utilisant la transmission micro-ondes par satellite peuvent concurrencer le câble dans la mesure où ils fonctionnent avec un minimum ou pas de câblage du tout. Ces systèmes commencent d'ailleurs à s'imposer dans les zones rurales. D'autre part, ils complètent le câble dans les régions très peuplées où la réception individuelle des émissions relayées par satellite est impraticable ou trop coûteuse.

En 1982, la FCC a répondu aux demandes croissantes de « téléphones mobiles » en approuvant le concept alvéolaire d'une « radio cellulaire mobile » (voir illustration à la page suivante). Des zones géo-

▷ 212

THE BROAD "EL[...]
WIDESPREAD A[...]

"We have an application to build a 500-mile fiber optic system [...] This seems only to be the beginning of the multi-purpose electronic highway of the future". These words were spoken by Charles D. Ferris in 1980, when he was chairman of the US Federal Communications Commission (FCC). At that time fiber optic systems had been used in the USA for telephone traffic and video transmission over short distances.

Conceptually "electronic highways" had existed since the development of the laser — light amplification by stimulated emission of radiation — in the early 1960s. The technique of

transmitting light beams through glass or plastic tubes wa[...] also known — for example as surgical probes to permit pho[...] tographs of the stomach and heart. However it was not until the late 1960s that a framework was developed, by K.C. Kao an[...] G.A. Hocklam of ITT's Standard Telephone Laboratories in the UK, for the design of optical fibers that would permit practica[...] transmission of information using laser light beams as carriers

The optical fiber waveguide was finally produced by 1970 bu[...] it took another decade before solid-state laser emitters an[...] light emitting diodes (LEDs) made field application of suc[...] fibers a practical proposition. In the year that followed Charle[...] Ferris' statement quoted above, AT&T alone built more tha[...] 15,000 miles of lightwave fiber cable, 25 times more than the year before. Since then many times that mileage has alread[...] been laid, not only by the many suppliers in North America bu[...] also in Japan, the UK, France, the Middle East and Asia. A mos[...] ambitious project is the TAT-8, a laser-powered optic cable o[...] 3,580 miles across the Atlantic, scheduled to be in service b[...] 1988.

Optical cable, necessarily broadband, is making possible no[...] only additional television programs to the home but also acces[...] from the home (or office, or factory) to almost any conceivabl[...] source of information or data processing facility. What this ca[...] mean to the household is described on p. 34.

Cable networks face economic problems: competition fro[...] DBS and other satellite-based programs, inadequate audience [...] to sustain the requisite advertising revenues, a consequent lo[...] return on investment, and the near impossibility to find suffi[...] cient program material. On the other hand, the availability o[...] two-way cable (videotex) allows cable companies to offer [...] wide range of services, including a telephone service, t[...] increase their revenue sources.

A possible drawback to two-way hook-ups is the disclosur[...] of information of a personal nature requested by the cabl[...] companies to enable them to provide services. This may ye[...] prove to be the most serious impediment to the concept of th[...] wired city. To quote Charles Ferris again "as we move into th[...] information age, we may, through inattention, create intolerabl[...] by-products of progress. The choice is stark: will these tec[...] nologies be exploited to dehumanize mankind or to advance ou[...] common humanity?". No clear answer is yet to hand.

vient de nous demander l'autorisation de construire un
me de transmission de 8000 km en fibres optiques. J'ai
ression que ce n'est que le premier tronçon d'un réseau de
tes électroniques » à utilisations multiples du futur »,
: déclaré Charles D. Ferris quand il était président de la
al Communications Commission des Etats-Unis, en 1980.
» principe des « routes électroniques » est né avec l'in-
on du laser au début des années 1960. Le procédé qui,
istait à transmettre des faisceaux lumineux à l'intérieur
tubes de verre ou de plastique, était également connu et

« Se nos ha pedido la construcción de un sistema de fibras
ópticas de 8000 kilómetros. Esto parece ser sólo el comienzo de
la arteria electrónica con fines múltiples del futuro ». Estas
palabras las pronunció Charles D. Ferris en 1980, cuando pre-
sidía la Federal Communications Commission (FCC) de EE.UU.
Los sistemas de fibras ópticas se usaban entonces en EE.UU.
para tráfico telefónico y transmisiones video a corta distancia.

Conceptualmente, las "arterias electrónicas" existían desde
el desarrollo del láser — Light Amplification by Stimulated
Emission of Radiation — a comienzos de los años 1960. Tam-

cia magnética. Las pérdidas de las señales se compensan usando amplificadores (repetidores) cada
pocos kilómetros. Los pares de conductores de una
ruta entre centrales tienen capacidad para 12 canales
vocales, o 24-30 canales vocales digitales de modulación por impulsos codificados (MIC). Pueden
adaptarse para la transmisión digital utilizando un
módem en cada extremo. Las líneas de calidad telefónica pueden transmitir datos a la velocidad de
1200 bits por segundo (b/s) en cada sentido. Mediante dispositivos para reducir la distorsión, puede
aumentarse hasta 9600 b/s.

Los cables coaxiales se encuentran en una anchura
de banda de unos 10 megahertzios (MHz) a varios
centenares MHz. Esto permite más de 10 000 canales
vocales en un solo cable con dos líneas coaxiales, o
sus múltiplos. Minimizan la distorsión, y su diafonía
es insignificante. Los pares coaxiales son más venta-
josos que los trenzados en todo, salvo en el costo.

Los cables ópticos se componen de fibras de vidrio
finas, muy transparentes, que actúan como guiaondas para la transmisión de haces luminosos de una
sola frecuencia (monocromática). Ultimamente se
han producido fibras ópticas con pérdidas de
transmisión muy bajas. En un cable de 1 cm de
diámetro aproximadamente, tan flexible como los
cables telefónicos de cobre, pueden agruparse más
de 100 fibras.

Las fibras ópticas tienen un potencial de anchura
de banda casi ilimitado, por lo que son excelentes
portadores de grandes cantidades de señales a larga
distancia o de señales de banda ancha para la distribución local. También son inmunes a muchos de los
problemas de otros canales de comunicación, como
fuga, diafonía, interferencia eléctrica, etc. Por eso,
son muy adecuados para la transmisión de datos.

La multiplexación de longitud de onda aumenta
grandemente la capacidad del cable óptico; por
ejemplo, una técnica desarrollada por Bell Laboratories permite hacer 300 000 llamadas por 144 fibras
de vidrio agrupadas en un cable de un espesor no
superior a un dedo. Ya es posible producir fibras
puras, muy fuertes, de 13 km de largo, que pueden
empalmarse, sin pérdida de señal luminosa, para
convertilas en largos de 24 km.

Los enlaces de microondas sólo pueden transmitirse por visibilidad directa, pero requieren menos amplificadores que los cables coaxiales en la misma
distancia. La interferencia de las condiciones meteorológicas, las ondulaciones del terreno, los edificios y otros objetos artificiales es mínima cuando los
haces apuntan al satelite, y viceversa, aunque la
interferencia atmosférica, los objetos volantes o los
pájaros, y los efectos de eco, siguen constituyendo un
obstáculo para la transmisión sin errores. Se espera
superar estos defectos bastante pronto.

En el desarrollo intensivo de las redes de cables
coaxiales y ópticos, y de la transmisión por microondas, ha influido la insistente y creciente demanda de anchura de banda, tan esencial para el
desarrollo de redes digitales integradas y el establecimiento de comunicaciones audiovisuales.

La TV por cable data de los años 1940, en que un
vendedor de aparatos de Pensilvania descubrió que
erigiendo una antena en la cumbre de una montaña y
vinculándola a su receptor de televisión mediante un
cable coaxial mejoraba incommensurablemente su
recepción y podía captar estaciones de ciudades le-
janas. Sin embargo, siguió usándose poco para
transmisiones de televisión hasta finales de 1970.

En 1975, RCA Corporation colocó en órbita
geoestacionaria su primer satélite nacional de comunicaciones. Transmitiendo señales a operadores
con antenas parabólicas, se observó que podían difundir programas a todo el país a una fracción del
costo soportado por las redes de radiodifusión. Casi
al mismo tiempo, la Federal Communication Commission (FCC) de EE.UU. comenzó a suavizar las
restricciones legales sobre el uso del cable con fines
de radiodifusión. Estos dos acontecimientos anun-
ciaban un período de enorme crecimiento en el uso
del cable para difundir la televisión en EE.UU., seguido pronto de un impulso análogo en Europa, y
ahora en todas partes.

La competencia en la transmisión audiovisual reviste varias formas. Los principales competidores

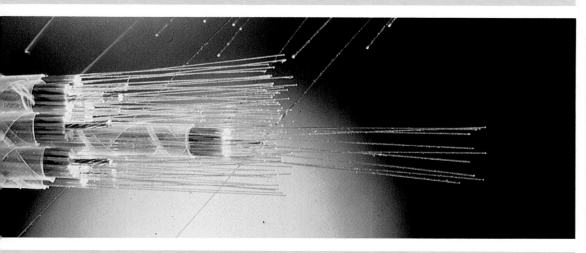

é pour fabriquer, par exemple, les sondes médicales. Mais
fut que vers la fin des années 1960 que K.C. Kao et G.A.
kam, Standard Telephone Laboratories (ITT), au Royau-
ni, réussirent à concevoir un système de fibres optiques
la transmission d'information utilisant le laser.

guide d'ondes en fibre optique fut développé en 1970 mais
ut encore dix ans pour que des émetteurs transistorisés de
ou des diodes électro-luminescentes (LED), fassent l'objet
proposition commerciale. En 1981, un an après la re-
ue de Charles D. Ferris, AT&T, avait déjà posé plus de
0 km de câble optique, 25 fois plus qu'en 1980. Depuis, des
rs de kilomètres de câbles optiques ont été utilisés au
, en Europe, au Moyen-Orient et en Asie de Sud-Est, et on
noncé, en 1983, la construction du câble transatlantique
T-8 », de 5728 km, qui entrera en service en 1988. Il sera le
ier câble sous-marin à transmission laser dans le monde.

s câbles à fibres optiques offrent bien des avantages pour
r des liaisons inter-villes et inter-continentales : large
e, aptitude aux transmissions numériques à très grande
se, insensibilité aux brouillages, affaiblissement réduit, et,
ntraste avec les satellites, aucune exigence en matière de
ences radio ou de « parking » en orbite géostationnaire.

câblage optique, obligatoirement à large bande porteuse,
non seulement à recevoir d'autres programmes TV,
permet aussi l'accès sélectif (à partir du foyer, du bureau
l'usine) à toute source d'information et à tous les ser-
télématiques rendus possibles par un équipement inte-
. Ce que cela peut signifier pour l'usage familial est
page 34.

existe un avantage pour les diffuseurs, dans la disponibilité
câble interactif (vidéotex), qui permet d'offrir toute une
ne de services, y compris le téléphone, pour augmenter
revenus. Il y a, néanmoins, un inconvénient sérieux dans
stème interactif qui exige, à chaque demande initiale, des
onnées et des informations personnelles. Pour citer à
eau Charles D. Ferris : « à mesure que nous progressons
la société d'information, nous risquons de créer par
ertance des sous-produits intolérables du progrès. Le
devant nous est catégorique : ces nouvelles technologies
t-elles exploitées pour rendre l'humanité inhumaine ou
la faire progresser ? » Il n'y a pas encore de réponse claire
te question.

bién se conocía la técnica de transmitir haces luminosos por
tubos de vidrio o plástico; por ejemplo, como sondas quirúrgi-
cas para fotografiar el estómago y el corazón. Sin embargo,
hasta finales de los años 1960 no se estableció el marco, por
K.C. Kao y G.A. Hocklam, de Standard Telephone Laboratories
de ITT en el RU, para diseñar fibras ópticas que permitirían la
transmisión con haces láser como portadores.

Finalmente se produjo, en 1970, la guiaonda de fibras ópticas, pero había de transcurrir otro decenio hasta que los
emisores láser de estado sólido y los diodos fotoemisores (LED)
aplicaran en la práctica esas fibras. Al año siguiente de pro-
nunciar Charles Ferris dichas palabras, AT&T construyó más de
24 000 km de cables de fibras de ondas luminosas, 25 veces
más que el año anterior. Desde entonces, el tendido se ha
multiplicado, no sólo por los muchos suministradores de América del Norte, sino también en Japón, el RU, Francia, el Oriente
Medio y Asia del Sudeste. Un proyecto más ambicioso, en el año
1983, es el cable óptico TAT-8, de 5700 km, impulsado por
láser, que unirá América y Europa en 1988.

El cable óptico, necesariamente de banda ancha, no sólo
permite recibir en el hogar otros programas de televisión, sino
acceder desde la casa (oficina o fábrica) a casi toda fuente de
información o facilidad de procesamiento de datos concebible.
En la pág. 34 se describe lo que puede significar esto para el
hogar.

Las redes de cable tropiezan con problemas económicos; la
competencia de TV DS y otros programas a base de satélites y
la inadecuada cobertura de la mayoría de los programas para
justificar la publicidad suponen un rendimiento insuficiente.

Además, el cable interactivo (videotex) permite a las empresas ofrecer muchos servicios, incluido el telefónico, para
aumentar sus fuentes de ingresos.

Un posible inconveniente es que, al hacer la petición, hay que
facilitar información personal. Esto puede ser el obstáculo más
serio para la noción de ciudad cableada. Citando de nuevo a
Charles Ferris, « a medida que avanzamos en la era de la
información podemos crear, por falta de atención, subproductos
de progreso intolerables. La elección es clara: ¿se explotarán
esas tecnologías para deshumanizar a la humanidad o para su
progreso común? » Todavía no se dispone de una respuesta
clara.

▷ 213

companies with major interests in communications technology or entertainment.

Systems using microwave transmission from satellites are competitive with cable insofar as they operate without, or with very little, wire and are beginning to have an impact in rural areas. In areas of high density population where microwave frequency bands are overcrowded, such systems are used to transmit to high central reception stations to which users are linked by cable.

A strong and growing demand for mobile telephones led to the approval by the FCC of the concept of "cellular mobile radio", (see opposite) a service based on the splitting up of regions into "cells", each containing one low-power transmitter communicating with the mobile telephones and with each other. The cell sites are controlled by a network switching office (NSO) through telephone wires. An average cell covers 1 to 8 square miles and adjacent cells use different channels so that there is no interference with a conversation in a neighbouring cell. FM is used for voice transmission with a channel spacing of 30 kHz.

Each market area is assigned two blocks of 333 duplex channels each, in the 825-890 MHz band, with duplex operation, the cell site and the mobile telephone use different frequencies, allowing simultaneous operation. Each area's 666 channels are usually divided equally among the cells but channels can be reused in another cell in the same area as long as cells are far enough apart to prevent interference.

As a subscriber travels round the system, he is tracked automatically by a central computer. If he moves from one cell to another during a telephone conversation, the exchange switches him to a free channel and establishes a telephone connection to the appropriate transmitter. The changeover, known as "hand-off", is almost imperceptible to the user.

As the number of customers grows, the cell can be split, a kind of electronic mitosis. The same channels are available again for "celling" and there is no limit to how many times a cell can be divided. The system can therefore expand with the traffic, to accomodate anyone who wants a portable telephone.

Several systems have been developed, none compatible with any other. The need to standardize on compatible equipment in areas densely populated and criss-crossed with national borders is self-evident, and is as difficult as any of the tasks facing the ITU's CCIR in the years ahead.

The birth of the New York "Teleport" is an example of the uses to which microwave transmission can be put, coupled with optical cable linkage. The teleport constructed in Staten Island — a borough of New York City — will transmit, and receive, information and data via satellites from anywhere to anywhere, very much as airports or seaports receive and despatch passengers and cargo. The nature and modus operandi of this striking new approach to information handling is described and illustrated on p. 188.

As we approach the new century, it is becoming more and more apparent that the concept of a port with all its implications — exchange of goods, commercial transactions, etc. — must be expanded to include telecommunications access as the critical ingredient in large business centers.

Cellular radio's advantages are not limited to moving vehicles. With almost limitless capacity available, prospective system operators foresee a demand for cordless portable telephones small enough to fit into a coat pocket. Major operators who have conducted extended trials (AT&T in Chicago and Motorola in Washington DC) expect that the use of cellular radio will extend well beyond vehicle phones to cordless portable phones, payphones, two-way business radios, paging systems, and even replace traditional wired phones in many rural areas.

Telettra SpA, a member of the Italian FIAT group, whose profile follows this section, is a successful supplier of transmission equipment and one of the most dynamic in the use and development of modern radio and cable technology.

graphiques, principalement les grandes agglomérations, sont ainsi divisées en « nids-d'abeilles ». Chaque alvéole, d'une superficie variable en fonction de la topographie (2,5 à 20 km²), est équipée d'un transmetteur de faible puissance qui communique avec les téléphones mobiles situés dans son rayon de transmission. Chaque transmetteur est relié par câble téléphonique à un centre de commutation et de contrôle, et utilise un canal différent pour éviter les interférences avec ses voisins.

Chaque zone radiotéléphonique se voit allouer deux blocs de 333 voies duplex dans la bande 825-890 MHz. En exploitation duplex, le relais alvéolaire et la station radiotéléphonique mobile utilisent respectivement des fréquences différentes, ce qui permet le fonctionnement bidirectionnel. Les fréquences allouées à chaque zone sont normalement réparties également entre les alvéoles mais elles peuvent cependant être réutilisées dans deux alvéoles de la même zone, pour autant que les deux alvéoles, utilisant une même fréquence, soient suffisamment éloignées l'une de l'autre.

A mesure que l'abonné se déplace à travers le système, il est suivi automatiquement par l'ordinateur central. S'il passe d'une alvéole à une autre au cours d'une conversation téléphonique, le central commute cette conversation sur une voie libre pour établir la liaison téléphonique avec le relais alvéolaire approprié. Cette commutation de « transfert » n'est pratiquement pas perçue par l'usager.

Quand le nombre des usagers augmente, on peut « hacher » systématiquement la communication en provoquant une sorte de « mitose électronique ». Par ce procédé, on rend à nouveau disponibles les voies nécessaires. L'opération peut se répéter dans la mesure des besoins. Le système peut ainsi se développer parallèlement à l'accroissement du trafic. Dans ces conditions, il devient alors possible de satisfaire tous ceux qui souhaitent disposer d'un radiotéléphone mobile.

Il existe plusieurs systèmes, qui ne sont pas compatibles. Pour qu'ils le deviennent, les techniques et les équipements devront être normalisés, tout particulièrement dans les zones très peuplées chevauchant les frontières nationales. Il s'agit là d'une tâche ardue et délicate qui incombera au CCIR et à l'UIT.

La naissance du « Téléport » de New York est un bel exemple de l'utilisation combinée de liaisons par satellite et fibres optiques. Construit à Staten Island, dans le port de New York, ce téléport assurera la transmission d'informations audio-visuelles et de données à destination et en provenance de n'importe quel point du globe, comme un port maritime ou un aéroport écoulent le trafic des personnes et des marchandises. La nature et le *modus operandi* de cette nouvelle conception sont illustrés à la p. 188.

Pour en revenir à la radiotéléphonie, il faut noter que les véhicules ne seront pas les seuls bénéficiaires des avantages des systèmes alvéolaires. Leur capacité effective étant pratiquement illimitée, les intéressés à l'exploitation de tels systèmes prévoient déjà une demande considérable. Les grandes firmes qui ont fait, dans ce domaine, des essais approfondis (AT&T à Chicago et Motorola à Washington, DC) prévoient que les systèmes alvéolaires desserviront non seulement les postes téléphoniques installés à bord des véhicules mais également les radiotéléphones de poche, les publiphones, les émetteurs-récepteurs d'entreprises et les systèmes d'appel unilatéral, et même que, dans de nombreuses zones rurales, leur utilisation viendra se substituer à celle des appareils « câblés » traditionnels. En fait, le « téléphone mobile » pourrait devenir le téléphone universel de demain.

L'un des protagonistes en vue dans ce domaine des transmissions est Telettra SpA, membre du groupe italien FIAT. Parmi les grandes réalisations de ce constructeur on peut citer le réseau à micro-ondes reliant l'Arabie saoudite et le Soudan, et la liaison qui dessert le trajet du nouveau chemin de fer transsibérien. Telettra, dont le profil suit, est l'une des firmes les plus dynamiques en matière de mise au point et d'utilisation des nouvelles technologies de transmission.

ADVANCED CELL

Cellular technology is based on a grid of hexagons, or cells cover specific geographic areas. Each cell contains a low wered radio transmitter and control equipment located building called a "cell site".

The cell site is connected by wireline facilities to a M Telephone Switching Office (MTSO), which is connected t regular landline network through the telephone central o With its electronic switching capability, the MTSO monito mobile units and automatically switches or "hands-off" versations in progress as the mobile unit moves from one c another.

Each cell has a set of radio frequencies, allowing reu every channel for many different simultaneous conversatio the given service area.

As demand for the service grows, dividing cells into sr cells can meet customer needs even in the most densel pulated areas.

TECHNOLOGY FOR MOBILE PHONES

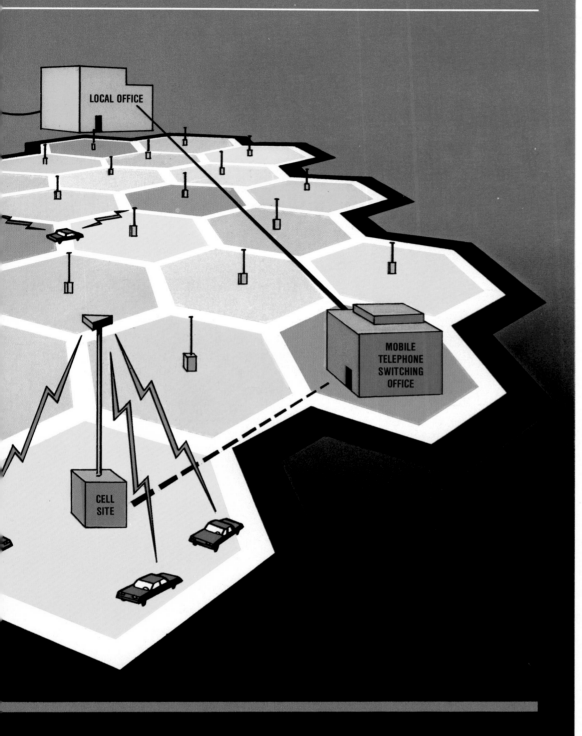

LOCAL OFFICE

MOBILE TELEPHONE SWITCHING OFFICE

CELL SITE

por la concesión geográfica de cables y servicios de satélite tienden a limitarse a grandes empresas o gobiernos, puesto que el costo del cableado sigue siendo muy alto (más de 100 millones $ para cablear una ciudad de tamaño medio en 1982), y la inversión para producir programas, todavía mayor.

Los sistemas que utilizan transmisión de microondas desde satélites compiten con el cable, puesto que operan con muy pocos conductores o sin ellos, y comienzan a tener impacto en las zonas rurales. Son complementarios del cable en regiones de gran densidad de población donde la recepción individual de transmisiones por satélite no es factible o es antieconómica.

En 1982, la FCC reaccionó ante la creciente demanda de teléfonos móviles y aprobó la noción de "radio móvil celular" (veáse ilustración a la izquierda). Las ubicaciones de las células se controlan por una oficina de conmutación de la red (OCR) a través de hilos telefónicos. Una célula media abarca de 2,50 a 20 km cuadrados, y las células adyacentes usan distintos canales para que no haya interferencia con una conversación en una célula vecina. La MF se emplea para la transmisión de la voz con una separación de canales de 30 kHz.

Cada zona de mercado tiene asignados dos bloques, de 333 canales dúplex cada uno, en la banda 825-890 MHz. Con la explotación dúplex, el relé de la célula y el teléfono móvil emplean frecuencias distintas, lo que permite la explotación simultánea. Los 666 canales de cada zona están divididos por igual entre las células, pero los canales pueden reutilizarse en otra célula de la misma zona, simpre y cuando no haya interferencia.

Cuando un abonado viaja dentro del sistema, es seguido automáticamente por un computador central. Si pasa de una célula a otra durante una conversación telefónica, la central le conmuta con un canal libre y establece una conexión telefónica con el transmisor apropiado. La transferencia es casi imperceptible para el usuario. A medida que crece el número de clientes, la célula puede dividirse: una especie de mitosis electrónica. Se dispone de los mismos canales para la distribución de las células, y la división de cada una de ellas es ilimitada. Por tanto, el sistema puede ampliarse con el tráfico.

Se han desarrollado varios sistemas, todos incompatibles entre sí. La necesidad de normalizar un equipo compatible en zonas densamente pobladas y que cruzan las fronteras nacionales es evidente, y constituye una de las difíciles tareas que esperan al CCIR de la UIT los años próximos.

El Telepuerto de Nueva York, construido en Staten Island, es un ejemplo de los usos de la transmisión por microondas, junto a la vinculación por cable óptico. Transmitirá, y recibirá, información y datos de una parte cualquiera a otra, lo mismo que un aeropuerto o un puerto recibe y despacha pasajeros y carga. En la pág. 188 se ilustra la naturaleza y el modus operandi del nuevo y sorprendente enfoque del tratamiento de la información. A medida que nos acercamos al siglo próximo, cada vez es más clara la necesidad de ampliar el concepto de un puerto con todas sus implicaciones — intercambio de productos, transacciones comerciales, etc. — para incluir el acceso a las telecomunicaciones como elemento crítico de los grandes centros comerciales.

Las ventajas de la radio celular no se limitan a los vehículos móviles. Los presuntos operadores del sistema, que disponen de una capacidad casi ilimitada, prevén una demanda de teléfonos portátiles sin hilo tan pequeños que caben en un bolsillo. Importantes operadores que han realizado extensas pruebas (AT&T en Chicago y Motorola en Washington DC) esperan que su uso sea muy superior al teléfono de los vehículos, abarcando los teléfono portátiles sin hilo, los aparatos de previo pago, los sistemas de radiobusca, etc., y sustituyendo incluso a los teléfonos de hilo tradicionales en muchas zonas rurales.

Telettra SpA, miembro del grupo italiano FIAT, cuyo perfil sigue a esta sección, es un proveedor de equipo de transmisión y uno de los más dinámicos en el uso y desarrollo de tecnología moderna de radio y cable.

—stème « cellulaire » de la radiotéléphonie mobile est fondé —un schéma en « nids-d'abeilles » constitué par des alvéoles —rme hexagonale. Chaque alvéole est dotée d'une station, —entre, comportant notamment un émetteur de faible puis- —e et un équipement de contrôle.

—e centre est relié par câble à un central de commutation —téléphonique de zone, lui-même relié normalement au ré- —téléphonique public. Un système électronique permet au —al de zone de surveiller la circulation des véhicules —és de téléphones et de transférer toute conversation en —s au centre alvéolaire approprié, dès qu'un véhicule passe —e alvéole à une autre.

—aque alvéole dispose d'une série de fréquences permettant —utilisation de chaque canal pour différentes conversations —ltanées dans une zone de service donnée.

—a demande augmente, une subdivision des alvéoles per- —de répondre aux besoins, même dans des zones à très forte —ité de population.

La tecnología celular se basa en una retícula de hexágonos, o células, que abarca zonas geográficas concretas. Cada célula contiene un transmisor radioeléctrico de baja potencia y equipo de control situado en un edificio denominado ubicación.

La ubicación de célula está conectada por instalaciones de línea alámbrica a una oficina de conmutación telefónica móvil (OCTM) vinculada a la red de línea terrestre regular, a través de la oficina telefónica central. Con su capacidad de conmutación electrónica, la OCTM controla las unidades móviles y conmuta automáticamente o transfiere conversaciones en curso a medida que la unidad móvil pasa de una célula a otra.

Cada célula tiene una serie de frecuencias radioeléctricas que permiten reutilizar cada canal para muchas conversaciones simultáneas distintas en una zona de servicio dada.

Cuando aumenta la demanda del servicio, la división de las células en otras más pequeñas permite atender las necesidades del usuario incluso en la zonas más pobladas.

□

Telettra Società per Azioni

Evolution beyond the Theory

THROUGHOUT THE WORLD, telecommunications requirements today are for complex systems which, by using state-of-the-art technology, are capable of keeping up with rapid economic changes and, at the same time, of cutting overall operating costs.

Set up in 1946, in the immediate aftermath of World War II, and being born, therefore, in the electronics era, Telettra has always known how to apply new technology. Specifically, its business is the application of electronics to telecommunications, on a worldwide basis. The name and the τ logo indicate an organization of several national companies, including Italy's largest privately-owned telecom manufacturer, — a company with eight thousand employees throughout the world and a turnover of over US $ 1 million a day.

The member companies can collectively count on a comprehensive network of branch offices and agencies. Several well-established foreign licensees boost the number of factories using Telettra technology to twenty. Where appropriate, the Company promotes or participates in joint ventures with the best operators in complementary and neighbouring industrial sectors.

Telecommunication systems consist of parts, complex in themselves, associated with other parts via linkage systems which may extend over very long distances. They are entities, but except as an intellectual challenge to their makers, they are not wanted in vacuo; they need to have a useful and economic function as part of a greater system that is alive and functions.

This means that the demands for telecommunication installations will arise from consumers who are already operating in the wider system which the new installation must fit and support. Such consumers

▷ 216

DANS LE MONDE ENTIER, les télécommunications exigent la mise en œuvre de systèmes complexes qui, bien que se trouvant en amont de l'évolution technologique, doivent maintenir le niveau de la progression économique et minimiser en même temps les coûts d'exploitation.

Créée en 1946, immédiatement après la deuxième guerre mondiale, donc née dans l'ère de l'électronique, Telettra a toujours su comment appliquer cette technologie. Elle s'est développée dans un contexte de grand progrès technologiques et s'est spécialisée dans l'application de l'électronique aux télécommunications, à l'échelle mondiale.

Son nom et son label τ désignent un groupement de plusieurs entreprises nationales — dont Telettra SpA, le plus grand constructeur italien privé de matériel de télécommunication — avec un effectif de 8000 employés répartis dans différents pays, et un chiffre d'affaires de plus d'un million de dollars US par jour.

Tous les membres du groupe Telettra bénéficient collectivement d'un réseau mondial de succursales et d'agences. Plusieurs firmes bien établies à l'étranger exploitant les licences Telettra, les équipements du groupe sont donc fabriqués dans 20 usines dans le monde. Chaque fois qu'elle le juge approprié, la société s'associe avec les exploitants les plus qualifiés dans des secteurs industriels complémentaires, soit en y participant directement, soit en les soutenant activement.

Les systèmes de télécommunication se composent généralement de différentes parties complexes, liées les unes aux autres par des réseaux qui peuvent s'étendre sur de très grandes distances, nécessairement conçues comme ayant une fonction économique et une utilité immédiate dans le contexte le plus vaste de la vie des communautés qu'elles desservent.

▷ 216

LAS TELECOMUNICACIONES REQUIEREN en el mundo entero complejos sistemas capaces de seguir, gracias a la tecnología, los rápidos cambios económicos, y de reducir, al mismo tiempo, los gastos globales de explotación.

Creada en 1946, inmediatamente después de la Segunda Guerra Mundial, y nacida, pues, en la era de la electrónica, Telettra sabe cómo aplicar la nueva tecnología. Concretamente, se dedica a la electrónica de las telecomunicaciones, a escala mundial. El nombre y el logotipo τ indican una organización de varias empresas nacionales, incluido el principal fabricante privado de telecomunicaciones de Italia, con 8000 empleados en el mundo entero y una cifra de negocios de un millon de dolares al día.

Las empresas miembros pueden representar una red completa de sucursales y agentes; con los concesionarios extranjeros debidamente establecidos, hay 20 fábricas que utilizan tecnología de Telettra. Cuando procede, la compañía fomenta empresas mixtas con los mejores explotadores en sectores industriales complementarios y similares, o participa en ellas.

Los sistemas de telecomunicaciones constan de partes, complejas en sí, unidas a otras mediante sistemas de vinculación que pueden extenderse a distancias muy grandes. Se trata de entidades, pero, salvo como desafío intelectual a sus fabricantes, no se quiere que existan en un vacío; tienen que cumplir una función útil y económica, como parte de un sistema mayor que es la vida.

Eso significa que las demandas de instalaciones de telecomunicación procederán de consumidores que operan ya en el sistema más amplio que la nueva instalación ha de equipar y apoyar. Esos consumidores habrán de saber, antes de hacer un pedido, que

▷ 216

Transmission systems encircling the whole world.   *Systèmes de transmission dans le monde entier.*   *Los sistemas de transmisión en el mundo entero.*

will require to know, before placing an order, that the new installation will in fact provide them with the service they need, matching their requirements most efficiently, and using the most advanced and tested technology. In short, feasibility and design studies, often extensive and in-depth, linking consumer requirements with possible available installations, are an essential preliminary to any decision on implementation.

Some consumers may be equipped with suitable staff and experience to undertake the task of specifying their requirements and buying the telecommunication system off the shelf. Others may be ill-equipped even to carry out their own analysis of needs. In either case, the supplier must be equipped to undertake the feasibility and design studies jointly with the consumer. He will have to be able to do this in any part of the world; at the same time he must satisfy normal commercial considerations such as quality and reliability in supply, implementation, and future maintenance; financial and industrial stability; advanced technological development.
Telettra is structured and organized to operate on turnkey basis worldwide. From preliminary feasibility studies, network design and implementation, and on to maintenance — assistance is available at every stage of the operation. In developing countries this imposes the presence on the spot or the availability on a regular cycle or at short notice, of skilled experienced engineers ready to assist and train clients' staff. Here, as elsewhere, company policy is to transfer know-how to the customer wherever conditions are suitable.

Installations completely designed and imple-
▷ 217

Cela signifie que la demande d'installations de télécommunications provient d'utilisateurs qui sont déjà reliés à un large système auquel la nouvelle installation doit s'adapter et qu'elle doit compléter. Ces utilisateurs voudront être certains, avant de passer une commande, que la nouvelle installation pourra satisfaire efficacement à leurs besoins en leur apportant la technologie fiable la plus avancée. Des études de faisabilité et de conception, permettant d'établir la relation entre les besoins de l'utilisateur et les installations disponibles, sont un préalable essentiel à toute décision de mise en œuvre.

Certains utilisateurs possèdent l'expérience nécessaire et peuvent spécifier leurs propres besoins, d'autres ne le peuvent pas. Dans les deux cas, le constructeur doit être en mesure de réaliser des études de faisabilité et de conception avec son client. Il doit pouvoir le faire n'importe où dans le monde, tout en répondant à des exigences normales comme la qualité des équipements, la fiabilité des livraisons, la mise en œuvre, la maintenance, la stabilité financière et industrielle et une technique avancée.
La structure de Telettra est telle qu'elle peut offrir des contrats « clés en mains » dans le monde entier, depuis l'étude de faisabilité et de conception jusqu'à la mise en œuvre de réseaux et leur maintenance. Dans les pays en développement, la présence du personnel hautement qualifié de Telettra assure la formation professionnelle nécessaire. Là, comme ailleurs, la politique de la société est de transférer à ses clients les connaissances techniques et le savoir-faire nécessaire au bon fonctionnement des installations.

Parmi les grandes installations conçues et mises en œuvre par Telettra, il y a le réseau micro-ondes qui relie l'Arabie saoudite et le Soudan (la plus grande enjambée du monde en visibilité directe, au dessus
▷ 217

la nueva instalación les proporcionará realmente el servicio que necesitan, atendiendo sus necesidades con mayor eficacia y utilizando la tecnología más avanzada y experimentada. En resumen, los estudios de viabilidad y diseño, con frecuencia amplios y profundos, que vinculan las necesidades del consumidor a las posibles instalaciones disponibles, son un requisito previo esencial de toda decisión en materia de aplicación.

El proveedor debe poder emprender con el consumidor los estudios de viabilidad y diseño en cualquier parte del mundo. Al mismo tiempo, ha de atender consideraciones comerciales normales, como calidad y seguridad de suministro, aplicación y futuro mantenimiento; estabilidad financiera e industrial, y desarrollo tecnológico avanzado.
La estructura de Telettra le permite operar llave en mano en el mundo entero. Desde los estudios preliminares de viabilidad hasta el diseño y ejecución de la red, y el mantenimiento, se dispone de asistencia en todas las etapas de la explotación. En los países en desarrollo, esto tiene el importante beneficio secundario de una presencia permanente de ingenieros especializados, para asistir y formar al personal del cliente. Aquí, como en otras partes, la política de la empresa consiste en transferir los conocimientos al cliente siempre que las condiciones sean apropiadas.

Entre las instalaciones totalmente diseñadas y realizadas figuran el sistema de microondas que une Arabia Saudita y Sudán, con el salto de visibilidad directa sobre el mar más alto del mundo, y el radioenlace para el servicio del nuevo ferrocarril transiberiano, que funciona en las condiciones más extremas de clima y terreno. Debido a la fiabilidad del servicio de mantenimiento de Telettra y a la
▷ 217

Transmission systems: on the left, microwave transceivers being installed in Saudi-Arabia; in the center, a low consumption backbone in Papua-New Guinea; on the right, the coaxial cable system in Lybia.

Des systèmes de transmission : à gauche, des émetteurs/répéteurs micro-ondes en cours d'installation en Arabie saoudite ; au centre, une structure de basse consommation à Papua-Nouvelle Guinée ; à droite, le système de câble coaxial en Lybie.

Sistemas de transmisión: a la izquierda, transmisores/repetidores de microondas instalados en Arabia Saudita; en el centro, una estructura de bajo consumo en Papua-Nueva Guinea; a la derecha, el sistema de cable coaxial, en Libia.

mented include the microwave system linking Saudi Arabia and Sudan, involving the world's longest line-of-sight hop over sea, and the radio link serving the New Transiberian Railway route, operating in the most extreme conditions of climate and terrain. The reliability of Telettra's maintenance service and the quality of its products has not made it necessary to provide routine inspection visits of its installations at intervals more frequent than six-monthly. This post-installation service can be guaranteed, including both maintenance and modernization, to keep up with future advances in technology.

The necessary continuing financial strength is assured, for Telettra is a subsidiary of FIAT — a Group with a turnover of over US$ 15.3 billion (1982) — with all this implies in terms of financial solidity and permanence. It also means having access, as an extension and backup to its own R&D resources to the Fiat Research Center, where work is being done in numerous areas crucial to Telettra's extensive activities.

Telettra's R&D teams, aware right from the start that electronics were of front-line importance in communications, have built up, in-house, a know-how capability which enables the company to supply the right products, at the right price, and to ensure that they interface effectively with existing equipment and systems.

Commercial success over its first three-and-a-half decades has given the Company the financial strength to tackle large-scale overseas projects without hesitation, and Telettra installations are to be found in over fifty countries — throughout the five continents.

The Company's production and marketing philosophy entails setting up sister companies abroad, with local interests being encouraged to take a majority shareholding. Since different parts of the world have different telecom requirements, it is clear that a variety

de la mer), et la liaison micro-ondes qui dessert le trajet du nouveau chemin de fer transsibérien dans les conditions climatiques et orographiques les plus rudes. La qualité et fiabilité du matériel Telettra permet des intervalles de six mois, ou plus, entre les opérations courantes de maintenance et de réapprovisionnement. Ce service après vente, qui peut faire l'objet d'une garantie, comprend la modernisation des systèmes, tenant compte de la progression technologique.

L'assise financière des opérations est assurée par l'appartenance de Telettra au groupe FIAT dont la taille (CA de US $ 15,3 milliards en 1982) et le statut international guarantissent l'accès au marché financier et assurent, en cas de besoin, un appui des plus solides. Cette même appartenance donne également accès au Centre de Recherche de FIAT, lequel œuvre dans plusieurs secteurs qui sont d'une importance capitale pour Telettra.

Les équipes de recherche et de développement de Telettra, conscientes, dès le début, du rôle vital de l'électronique dans le domaine des communications, ont un savoir-faire qui permet à la compagnie de travailler indépendamment dans n'importe quel secteur des communications. Les succès commerciaux de ces trente-cinq premières années ont donné à Telettra une assise financière qui lui permet d'entreprendre, sans hésitation et à son propre compte, des projets de la plus grande envergure n'importe où au monde. Il existe maintenant des installations de Telettra dans plus de cinquante pays sur les cinq continents.

La philosophie de Telettra en matière de production et de vente à l'étranger consiste à créer des « sociétés-sœurs » dans lesquelles la majorité des actions est réservée aux intérêts locaux. La forme de ces initiatives varie de pays en pays, tenant compte des différentes conditions qui existent, notamment celles affectant le développement des télécommunications. L'objectif de Telettra est de combiner la souplesse d'approche nécessaire pour bien comprendre les be-

calidad de sus productos, no es necesario efectuar inspecciones ni visitas periódicas de sus instalaciones con mayor frecuencia de seis mes. El servicio de postinstalación puede asegurarse, incluidos el mantenimiento y la modernización, para seguir el ritmo de la tecnología.

La fuerza financiera está asegurada, pues Telettra es filial de Fiat — grupo con una cifra de negocios superior a US $ 15,3 mil/millones, con la actividad y continuidad financiera que esto supone. También significa el acceso, como ampliación y apoyo de sus recursos de IyD, al Centro de Investigación de Fiat, que trabaja en numerosas esferas esenciales para las amplias actividades de Telettra.

Los equipos de IyD de Telettra, conscientes desde el principio de que la electrónica es primordial en las comunicaciones, han establecido una capacidad de conocimientos técnicos que permite a la empresa suministrar los mejores productos, al precio adecuado, adaptándolos al equipo y los sistemas existentes. Los éxitos comerciales de sus tres y media primeras décadas han dado a la empresa la fuerza financiera para abordar grandes proyectos en el extranjero, sin dudarlo, y las instalaciones de Telettra se encuentran en más de 50 países de los cinco continentes.

La política de producción y comercialización de la empresa entraña la creación de empresas hermanas en el extranjero, estimulando a los intereses locales a adquirir una participación mayoritaria. Como las necesidades de telecomunicaciones difieren en las diversas partes del mundo, es evidente que existen diversas situaciones operacionales. El objetivo de Telettra es combinar la flexibilidad del método requerido para atender las necesidades de cada mercado con un conocimiento global de las prácticas de telecomunicaciones y el dominio de la tecnología más recientes. La experiencia adquirida con el desarrollo de distintos sistemas telefónicos para especificaciones de

▷ 220

▷ 220

▷ 221

The child and the robot: the child punches out his instructions, the robot receives them and executes. Children of to-day are in instinctive harmony with electronics. They are the future of the world: they will know how to make the robots work for them. Experience and to-day's trends point to a bright future of automation. Taking into account that systems are born of the symbiosis of hardware and software, Telettra has committed important resources to the development of software which makes its products live.

L'enfant et le robot : l'enfant transmet ses instructions, le robot les reçoit et les exécute. Les enfants d'aujourd'hui sont en harmonie instinctive avec l'électronique. Ils sont l'avenir de ce monde : ils sauront comment faire travailler les robots. L'expérience et les tendances d'aujourd'hui augurent d'un brillant avenir pour l'automation. Les systèmes naissant d'une symbiose du matériel et du logiciel, Telettra, a engagé des ressources considérables pour le développement du logiciel qui donne vie à ses produits.

El niño y el robot: el niño transmite las instrucciones; el robot las recibe y las ejecuta. Los niños de hoy tienen una armonía instintiva con la electrónica. Son el futuro de la humanidad: sabrán hacer trabajar a los robots. La experiencia y las tendencias actuales presagian un brillante futuro de la automatización. Teniendo en cuenta que los sistemas se han derivado de la simbiosis del soporte físico y lógico, Telettra ha consagrado importantes recursos al desarrollo del soporte lógico que anima sus productos.

218

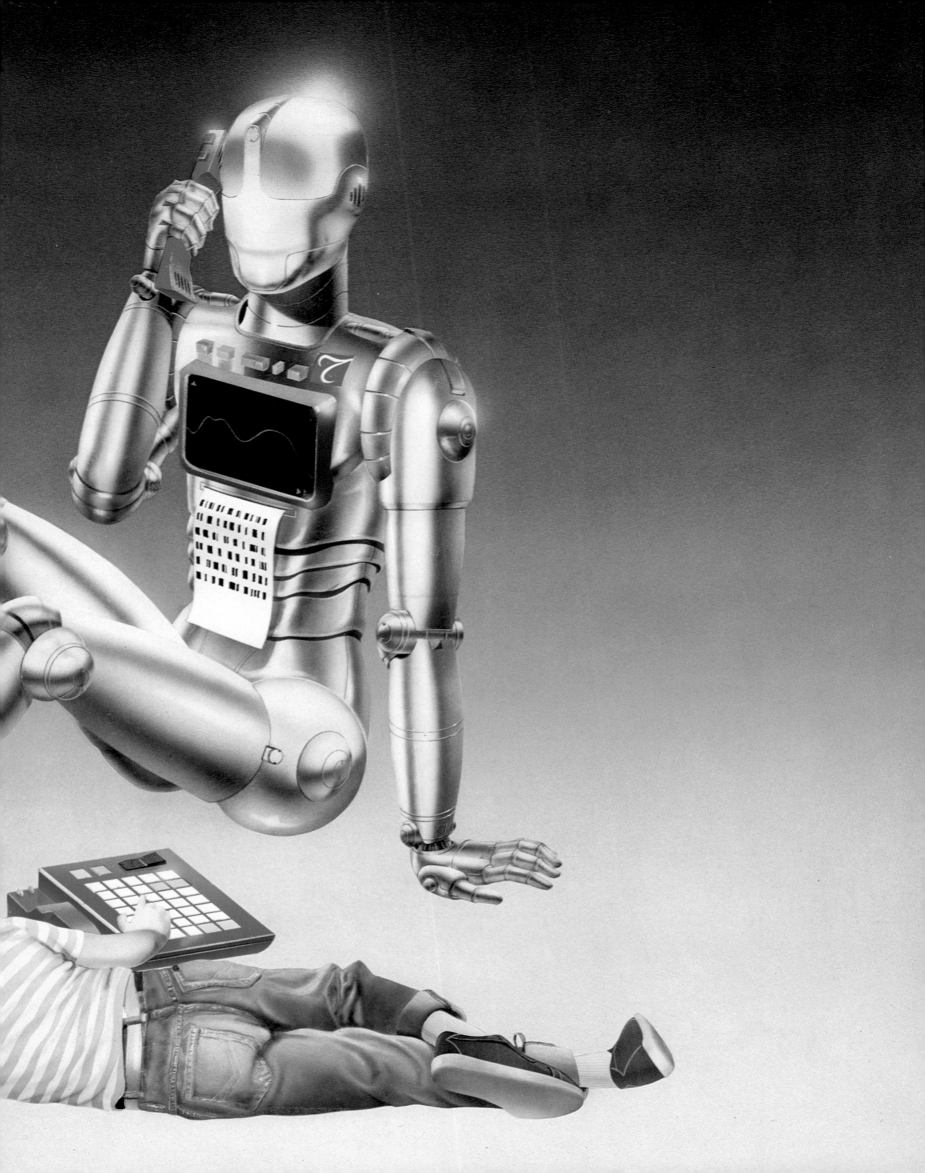

of operational situations exists. Telettra's objective is to combine the flexibility of approach required to provide what each market needs with a global awareness of telecommunications practice and a mastery of front-end technologies. The experience it has amassed through the development of different telephone systems to widely varying PTT specifications constitutes a technological stock which is readily available to new users.

Telettra itself is the prime supplier of transmission equipment to the Italian market. In Spain, where 51% of Telettra Española shares are held by the National Telephone Operating Agency, CTNE, the Company has undisputed leadership in many local applications. This is in accordance with Spanish policy, favourable to the integration of local resources, including manufacturing, into one national unit.

Similarly, in Brazil, where Telettra do Brasil had been set up with Italian capital in 1974, the majority shareholding passed in 1981 to Agropecuaria do Brasil Central. Here, as elsewhere, it was recognized that the company's progress-oriented and purely electronics-based approach was the key to development.

Planning is given a high priority. Telettra spends time and energy to ensure that what it sets out to supply will be effective and timely having regard to technological changes in the market, both in supply and demand. This calls for competent market intelligence to provide knowledge of what is going on not only within the Company but also outside, so that the company can put its development effort into lines which are likely to prove right and yield products and systems fully competitive in the years to come.

Two years, or ten. Year two thousand. Making the planning decisions — for research and investment — for a technologically front-line company in a fast-burgeoning sector like telecommunications is a daunting task. Telettra's approach is to base its strategic planning and long term decision-making on a systematic study of technological evolution and tendencies.

So, current product characteristics and production volume are seen within a two-year market spectrum, whereas new product lines are set against a ten-year span. These represent very long plan time commitments in the context of modern electronics. Current technological trends which are receiving a lot of Telettra's attention are fiber optics and VLSI. The company is also involved in the development and production of high precision electronic and mechanical components, using the most up-to-date techniques.

Research and development was the starting point of this young company's progress. Its history brings this to light and also its extraordinary capacity for good design. Known for many years as "Laboratori di *Te*lefonia *Elett*ronica e *Ra*dio", hence Telettra, the company has kept to its tradition of putting technology first. A consequence of starting out with the laboratory as a central function is that it has never been conceived as a world separate from the actual concerns of the market. The research lab was an entity, a business had to sell its ideas, its products, its innovative capacity to survive. But there may also be a purely national aspect to this: a technician's capacity to trouble shoot, modify, innovate, as a result of a direct dialogue with the user of his products, recalls the characteristics of the omnicompetent Renaissance artisan, whose descendants are perhaps more at home in Italy than in any other industrialized country. In effect, a modern design tool such as CAD (computer-aided-design) and a manufacturing aid such as CAM (computer-aided-manufacturing) allow the inventive brain an almost immediate check

▷ 222

soins de chaque marché avec une profonde connaissance des techniques les plus modernes des télécommunications. Telettra s'efforce de maintenir le maximum de flexibilité tout en appliquant les technologies de pointe et en les adaptant aux besoins locaux. Par exemple, les différents systèmes téléphoniques qui ont été élaborés au fur et à mesure et conformément aux spécifications les plus variées des diverses administrations de PTT, constituent une partie du « stock technologique » immédiatement disponible pour de nouveaux usagers.

Telettra SpA est elle-même le premier fournisseur d'équipements de transmission sur le marché italien. En Espagne, où l'exploitation nationale des téléphones, CTNE, détient — conformément à la politique espagnole — 51% des actions de Telettra Española, l'entreprise a un rôle directeur incontesté dans de nombreuses applications locales. De même, au Brésil, Telettra do Brasil, créée avec un capital italien en 1974, est passée en 1981 sous le contrôle d'Agropecuaria do Brasil Central. Là comme ailleurs, il a été reconnu que la philosophie de Telettra, tournée vers la technologie de pointe, et la nature de ses solutións basées uniquement sur l'électronique, constituaient la clé du développement.

La planification reçoit une très haute priorité. Elle ne doit pas seulement donner l'assurance qu'une compagnie est efficace et qu'elle fournira en temps voulu tous les équipements ou services offerts. Il faut aussi que ce qu'elle offre soit également efficace et tienne compte de l'évolution technologique sur le marché. Telettra est équipée pour prévoir le sens de l'évolution technique et donne en conséquence à ses efforts de recherche l'orientation qui sera vraisemblablement la plus pratique et la plus concurrentielle dans les années à venir — dans deux ans, six ans, ou à l'an 2000. Telettra élabore sa stratégie et planifie ses décisions à long terme sur la base d'une étude systématique de ces évolutions.

C'est ainsi que les caractéristiques des produits, et le volume de la production en cours sont envisagés deux ans à l'avance, mais les nouveaux produits le sont dans une perspective de dix ans. Dans le contexte de l'électronique, ce sont là des engagements à très long terme. Les nouveautés technologiques auxquelles Telettra s'intéresse le plus sont les fibres optiques et les circuits intégrés sur une très grande échelle (VLSI). La compagnie s'intéresse aussi au développement et à la production de composants électroniques et mécaniques de très haute précision, appliquant les techniques les plus modernes.

En tenant compte de la nature d'un système qui naît de la symbiose des matériels et des logiciels, Telettra a engagé des ressources importantes dans la mise au point des logiciels qui animent ses systèmes. Elle produit maintenant des systèmes complets pour centraux téléphoniques publics à commutation électronique et réseaux privés.

La demande probable sur le marché ayant été identifiée, l'étape suivante consiste à décider quelle est la meilleure manière de fournir le produit ou le service ainsi définis — soit l'appel aux fournisseurs, soit la fabrication dans le cadre de la société. Dans un cas comme dans l'autre, une recherche et une mise au point sont nécessaires.

L'activité de recherche et développement fut le point de départ de cette jeune entreprise. Son histoire le révèle et explique également son aptitude extraordinaire à bien concevoir produits et systèmes en temps utile. Comme elle l'avait fait pendant de nombreuses années, sous le nom de « Laboratori di *Te*lefonia, *Elett*ronica e *Ra*dio », Telettra a maintenu sa politique de primauté accordée à la technologie. De ce point de vue, les laboratoires de recherche et de développement n'ont jamais été conçus comme un monde dissocié du marché. Le laboratoire, considéré

▷ 222

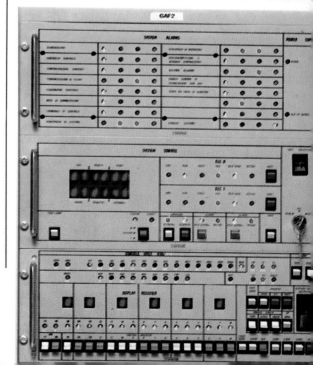

Switching is entering Telettra's domain because the latest mode is electronic and because Telettra was born initially as an electronic company. Opposite: Switching exchanges in Italy and abroad: the Italian way of doing things well.

La commutation est entrée dans le domaine de Telettra parce que les systèmes les plus récents étant électroniques, sont naturellement du ressort de Telettra, compagnie à vocation électronique. Ci-contre : les centraux de commutation en Italie et à l'étranger : la manière italienne de bien faire les choses.

CTT tan diversas constituye un venero tecnológico inmediato para los nuevos usuarios.

La propia Telettra es el principal proveedor del mercado italiano de equipo de transmisión. En España, donde el 51% de las acciones de Telettra Española pertenecen a la Compañía Telefónica Nacional de España (CTNE), la empresa es un líder indiscutible de muchas aplicaciones locales. Esto se conforma a la política española, favorable a la integración de recursos locales, incluida la fabricación, en una unidad nacional.

Del mismo modo, en Brasil, donde se estableció en 1974, con capital italiano, Telettra do Brasil, la mayoría de las acciones pasaron en 1981 a Agropecuaria do Brasil Central. También aquí se reconoció que la clave del desarrollo es el enfoque basado meramente en la electrónica y orientado hacia el progreso de la empresa.

Se concede gran prioridad a la planificación. Telettra consagra tiempo y energía para que sus suministros sean eficaces, eficientes y oportunos, habida cuenta de los cambios tecnológicos del mercado, tanto en la oferta como en la demanda. Para esto hay que conocer debidamente no sólo lo que se hace en la empresa, sino también fuera, lo que le permitirá orientar su esfuerzo de desarrollo hacia líneas que probablemente resulten acertadas, y fabricar productos y sistemas competitivos en los años próximos.

Dos años, o diez. Año 2000. Proyectar las decisiones — de investigación e inversión — de una empresa técnicamente a la vanguardia en un sector que cambia con tanta rapidez como las telecomunicaciones es una enorme tarea. El enfoque de Telettra consiste en basar su planificación estratégica y sus decisiones a largo plazo en un estudio sistemático de la evolución y las tendencias tecnológicas.

Por tanto, las características del producto corriente y el volumen de producción se prevén con un margen de mercado de dos años; las nuevas series de productos se establecen para un período decenal. Se trata de compromisos a muy largo plazo en el contexto de la electrónica moderna. Telettra presta gran atención a las fibras ópticas y los circuitos VLSI así como a la evolución y producción de componentes electrónicos y mecánicos de la mayor precisión que utilizan las tecnologías más avanzadas.

La investigación y el desarrollo fue el punto de partida del progreso de esta joven empresa. Así lo muestran su historia y su extraordinaria capacidad para diseñar productos. Conocida durante muchos años como "Laboratori di *T*elefonia *Elett*ronica e *Ra*dio" — de ahí Telettra — la empresa antepone la tecnología. Como el laboratorio cumple una función esencial, nunca se ha concebido como un mundo separado de las preocupaciones reales del mercado. Un laboratorio de investigación, como unidad comercial, ha de vender sus ideas, productos y capacidad innovadora para sobrevivir. Pero esto puede ser también un asunto puramente nacional: la capacidad del técnico para investigar averías, modificar e innovar, como resultado del diálogo directo con el usuario final, recuerda en cierto modo las características del artesano omnicompetente del Renacimiento, figura cuyos últimos descendientes quizá se encuentren más en Italia que en cualquier otro país industrializado. En efecto, un instrumento de diseño moderno como DAC (diseño asistido por computador) y un medio auxiliar de fabricación como FAC (fabricación asistida por computador) permiten al cerebro inventivo verificar casi inmediatamente la viabilidad de nuevas ideas, de soluciones de concepción lateral, sin romper el hilo de la intuición. Un redescubrimiento de la mejor tradición de creatividad.

La experiencia, y la observación de las tendencias, indican claramente que el futuro de las telecomuni-

▷ 223

La conmutación ha entrado en la esfera de Telettra, porque los sistemas más recientes son electrónicos, y tal es la vocación de Telettra. Aquí se muestran las centrales de conmutación de Italia y de otras partes: la manera italiana de hacer bien las cosas.

on the feasibility of new ideas, of laterally-thought solutions, without breaking the thread of intuition. A rediscovery of the best tradition of creativity.

Telettra's R&D effort can be described as an activity involving practically all sectors of the Company itself, which is therefore of particularly ready access to the customer. This advantage is a result of the Company's strongly market-oriented philosophy. Constant contact with the market-place sharpens the vision of the laboratory staff, who pride themselves on always being ahead of their time-often busy developing new generation product lines even as the previous ones are just entering production.

Satisfying changing market demand is one of Telettra's most successful accomplishments. During the company's lifetime it has been affected, like any other manufacturer of capital goods, by the vagaries of its various national and international markets. Rapid changes in the supply and demand cycles, and financial overstretching, have forced some painful readjustments even in such a key sector as telecommunications. The company was always able to benefit from its particular structure and especially from technological agility, as a thoroughbred electronics-based manufacturer, to adapt fast to changed market requirements. Like electronics itself, the Company is fast-developing, many-faceted, always ready to apply itself to new tasks. Its identity lies in its ideas and its mobility.

Catering as it does for a multiplicity of markets has benefited Telettra — firstly by spreading commercial risks widely, secondly, by providing a cross-fertilization of ideas between one market and another, which can be a great source of strength especially when conceived with rapidly changing technologies.

Telettra's market orientation is evidenced by the presence in its product range of systems for the public, private, and the military sectors. For all three, each with its own particular characteristics and problems, the Company's policy is to make available to its customers a wide range of state-of-the-art products and services.

For the public telecom sector, where millions of subscribers are involved, the Company offers FDM multiplex and line systems with up to 3,600 and 10,800 channels, respectively; pulse code modulation (PCM) multiplex and line systems up to 7,680 channels (565 mb/s); optical fiber transmission systems up to 140 mb/s (1,920 channels); analogue and digital radio-link systems (up to 2,700 and 1,920 channels respectively); and space-division and PCM stored program controlled exchanges, including speech-and-data nodal exchanges. The new electronic switching exchanges for Italy's national telephone network use Telettra products.

For the extremely various private sector, where requirements may range from monitoring a factory's functions to supervisory control of a gas pipeline network covering thousands of kilometers, Telettra's products include hardware and software developed in-house, electronic private exchanges, power line carrier systems, supervisory control systems with semi-intelligent peripherals, line management, data processor and interface equipment.

And in the defence field products from both public and private sectors reinforce the specific list of transportable high-power HF radio stations, vehicular medium-power stations, telephone multiplex and radio-link systems, mobile low-capacity telegraph multiplex equipment, and FSK modems. Being market-oriented, having a progress-pitched company structure, a broad state-of-the-art product base, and a flexible R&D effort ready to synchronize

▷ 224

comme une entreprise, devait vendre ses idées, ses produits, sa capacité d'innover, pour survivre. C'est une originalité unique dans l'industrie des télécommunications, qui ne peut être que bénéfique pour Telettra dans le contexte de la haute technologie de nos jours.

Mais ceci a peut-être un aspect purement national: en effet, la capacité d'un technicien de résoudre les problèmes, de modifier et d'innover, grâce au dialogue direct avec l'utilisateur final, rappelle en quelque sorte les caractéristiques de l'artisan omnicompétent de la Renaissance, figure qui se retrouve plus naturellement en Italie que dans tout autre pays industrialisé. Dans ce sens, la conception assistée par ordinateur (CAO) et la fabrication assistée par ordinateur (FAO) permettent aujourd'hui à des cerveaux inventifs de contrôler immédiatement les possibilités de réalisation d'idées nouvelles, de solutions « latérales », sans rompre le fil de l'intuition.

L'activité de recherche et de développement de Telettra fait entrer en jeu pratiquement tous les secteurs actifs de la société et devient de ce fait d'un accès facile aux clients. Le contact constant avec les différents marchés qui en résulte donne une vision plus nette au personnel du laboratoire, qui est fier d'être à la pointe du progrès et qui s'efforce de mettre au point les lignes de production d'une nouvelle génération de produits, alors que la précédente aborde à peine la chaîne de production.

Satisfaire les marchés internationaux est, pour Telettra, un objectif prioritaire. Au cours de son existence, Telettra a subi les effets, comme tout autre fabricant de biens d'équipement, des fluctuations de marché sur le plan national et international qui ont imposé des réajustements pénibles, même dans un secteur-clé comme les télécommunications. Telettra a toujours su mettre à profit sa structure particulière, et notamment son pouvoir d'innovation, pour s'adapter rapidement aux nouvelles conditions. Comme l'électronique elle-même, la société évolue rapidement, et elle est toujours prête à innover. Idées originales et mobilité caractérisent généralement Telettra.

L'orientation de Telettra sur le marché se manifeste par l'étendue de la production de systèmes destinés aux secteurs publics, privés,et défense. Dans ces secteurs, qui ont tous leurs propres caractéristiques et problèmes, Telettra tient à mettre à la disposition de ses clients une vaste gamme de produits et de services.

Pour le secteur des télécommunications publiques dans lequel les clients se comptent par millions, Telettra offre des systèmes multiplex et en ligne (MRF) ayant jusqu'à 3600 et 10800 voies respectivement, des systèmes multiplex et en ligne MIC (modulation par impulsions et codage) ayant jusqu'à 7680 voies (565 mbit/s), des systèmes de transmission en fibres optiques jusqu'à 140 mbit/s (1920 voies), des systèmes analogiques et numériques à micro-ondes (jusqu'à 2700 et 1920 voies respectivement), et des centraux à commutation spatiale et à commande par programme enregistré, notamment des centres nodaux pour téléphonie et données. Les nouveaux centraux à commutation électronique du réseau téléphonique public italien utilisent des équipements Telettra.

Pour le secteur privé, dont les besoins sont très diversifiés allant du contrôle des fonctions d'une fabrique à la surveillance d'un réseau d'oléoducs couvrant des milliers de kilomètres, Telettra offre des systèmes appropriés, dont le matériel et le logiciel ont été élaborés dans l'entreprise : centraux électroniques privés, systèmes de lignes d'alimentation en énergie, systèmes de surveillance avec périphériques semi-intelligents, équipements de gestion de lignes, processeurs de données et interface. Ces produits et services spécifiques sont naturellement reliés, quand

▷ 224

The full range of Telettra's products: telecommunications in office, factory, banks, aqueducts, power stations, agriculture, defence and public telecommunications, of course, a wide range of microwave, optical fibers, coaxial cable installations, switching systems, are aimed at a large number of users.

La gamme entière des produits de Telettra : télécommunications pour les bureaux, les usines, les banques, les aqueducs, les centrales électriques, l'agriculture, la défense et, bien entendu, les télécommunications publiques : une large gamme d'installations par câbles, fibres optiques, et faisceaux hertziens offerte à un grand nombre d'usagers.

caciones es brillante para los sistemas integrados. Si "telemática" es una simbiosis de "telecom" e "informática", también el "sistema" deriva su vida de la vinculación de los soportes físico y lógico, y Telettra ha consagrado importantes recursos al desarrollo del soporte lógico que da vida a sus productos. Ahora se producen sistemas completos para centrales públicas con conmutación electrónica y redes privadas.

Una vez identificadas, mediante la planificación, "las probables demandas del mercado" el siguiente paso es decidir la mejor manera de proporcionar el producto o servicio. Tal vez lo mejor sea obtenerlo de proveedores del exterior; quizá fabricarlo en la empresa; de todos modos, se requerirá un elemento de investigación y desarrollo.

El término "lab-work" tiene un significado especial en Telettra, de acuerdo con la evolución histórica de la empresa. Conocida durante muchos años por su título original, "Telephone, Electronic and Radio Laboratories", sigue su tradición de dar prioridad a la tecnología.

"El esfuerzo de IyD de Telettra" puede describirse como una actividad que abarca prácticamente todos los sectores de la empresa, por lo que el acceso al cliente es particularmente rápido. Esta ventaja se debe al principio de la empresa fuertemente orientada al mercado. El contacto permanente con el mercado agudiza la visión del personal de laboratorio, que se enorgullece de adelantarse siempre a su tiempo, desarrollando a menudo series de productos de una nueva generación, incluso cuando comienzan a fabricarse los anteriores.

Uno de los mayores logros de Telettra es satisfacer la variable demanda del mercado. La empresa ha resultado a veces afectada, como cualquier otro fabricante de bienes de equipo, por los avatares de sus diversos mercados nacionales e internacionales. Los rápidos cambios de los ciclos de suministro y demanda, y los grandes condicionamientos financieros, han impuesto algunos reajustes desagradables, incluso en un sector tan clave como las telecomunicaciones. Telettra ha podido beneficiarse siempre de su estructura particular, y especialmente de su agilidad tecnológica, como gran fabricante basado en la electrónica, para adaptarse con rapidez a las nuevas exigencias del mercado. Como la propia electrónica, la empresa evoluciona velozmente, en las múltiples facetas, dispuesta siempre a consagrarse a nuevas tareas. Su identidad reside en sus ideas y en su movilidad.

Al proveer a mercados tan diversos, la empresa ha logrado, primero, distribuir ampliamente los riesgos comerciales y, segundo, un análisis fecundo de ideas entre un mercado y otro, que puede ser un gran venero de fuerza, sobre todo cuando se concibe con tecnologías que cambian rápidamente.

La presencia en su gama de productos de sistemas para los sectores público, privado y militar prueba "la orientación del mercado de Telettra".

Para el sector público de telecomunicaciones, que abarca millones de abonados, el catálogo de la empresa comprende sistemas múltiplex y en línea MFD de hasta 3600 y 10 800 canales, respectivamente; sistemas múltiplex y en línea de modulación por impulsos codificados (MIC) de hasta 7680 canales (565 mb/s); sistemas de transmisión por fibras ópticas de hasta 140 mb/s (1920 canales); sistemas de radioenlaces analógicos y digitales (de hasta 2700 y 1920 canales, respectivamente), y centrales de control por programa almacenado MIC y división en el espacio, incluidas las nodales vocales y de datos. Las nuevas centrales de conmutación electrónica de la red telefónica italiana utilizan productos de Telettra.

Para el sector privado, sumamente diverso, donde los requisitos varían desde la verificación de funcio-

▷ 225

Toda la gama de productos de Telettra: telecomunicaciones para oficinas, fábricas, bancos, acueductos, centrales eléctricas, agricultura, defensa y, claro es, telecomunicaciones públicas: una amplia gama de instalaciones de cables coaxiales, de fibras ópticas, de microondas y sistemas de conmutación para un gran número de usuarios.

quickly with market requirements — Telettra leads in the production of "customized" devices. For example, producing three thousand transceivers a year is already an achievement; even more remarkable is to meet the challenge of the market penetration of such a product, which involves its adaptation to a vast number of end user requirements. The problems presented may be topographic or demographic, they may involve traffic density or energy availability — whatever their nature, they require that a market-conscious manufacturer be able to see that products are items capable of being modified to suit the customer who pays for them.

The historical development of Telettra helps explain its consistent technological and commercial outlook and philosophy. During World War II Italy was a major battlefield but by 1946 reconstruction of the telecommunications network was begun. War had brought great technological advances, and the setting up of "Laboratori di Telefonia Elettronica e Radio" created a small but agile company ready to make an important contribution to this reconstruction. Using electronics from the start, Telettra was able to provide the telecom operating companies with innovative solutions, while maintaining compatibility with such existing installations as had survived the war or with the traditional systems being proposed again by older-established suppliers whose technology was less advanced. Among the innovations were automatic long-distance dialling and microwave radio links over sea.

Commitments to quality and reliability go hand-in-hand with advanced technology. These are two concepts with such an intimate relationship that their bonding under the digraph Q&R is an accepted industry convention. The concept is clear: built-in quality will translate itself into demonstrable reliability. Telettra goes further. Just as its R&D services are available to all sectors of the Company's organization, so is Q&R self-regulating and company-wide. Reporting directly to general management, it is involved not only in production engineering but in the whole design process, including evaluation of components and their part in the overall strategy. This progress-oriented concept of Q&R as a complete involvement of the entire company is characteristic of present-day industries which are planning ambitiously.

To achieve this involves a high level of investment in advanced equipment and in brainpower. Telettra's commercial solidity underpins its policy of expansion. And the returns on genuine Q&R thinking materialize in the form of customer satisfaction and loyalty. Telettra's Q&R team plays in the top league. For instance, at every stage of the 6,000 km coaxial cable project to connect the main centres in Libya, the Company has successfully satisfied the extremely demanding criteria laid down by the British Post Office inspectors appointed by the Libyan Posts and Telecommunications Department.

Effective technology transfer is basic company policy. Passing on development and manufacturing know-how to sister organisations throughout the world is paralleled by Telettra's attitude to scientific knowledge. She believes that only maximum openness and interchange can lead to fruitful scientific development. With this object in mind the company creates and maintains close contacts with universities and other centers of learning, and participates in conventions and symposia at national and international level.

Worthy of special note is its publication policy. This includes co-operation with established scientific journals, and its distribution, worldwide, of its own in-house publication "Telettra Review", a technical periodical which reports on work done in the Company's laboratories. The scientific standing of Telet-

▷ 226

cela est nécessaire, à toutes les possibilités offertes par les services de télécommunications publiques.

Le secteur défense demande un certain nombre de produits très spécifiques, des stations de radio HF transportables de grande puissance, des stations de radio mobiles de moyenne puissance, des téléphones multiplex et des systèmes de liaison par radio, de l'équipement télégraphique multiplex de basse capacité, et des modems FSK. Cette liste d'équipements est considérablement renforcée et amplifiée par les produits et les systèmes du secteur public et du secteur privé.

De par son orientation commerciale, et de par sa structure axée sur le progrès technologique, Telettra est au premier rang dans le monde pour la construction d'appareils « sur mesure ». Un exemple : la production et la vente annuelle de trois mille émetteurs-récepteurs adaptés à des conditions d'utilisation très diverses. Les problèmes qui se posent peuvent être d'ordre topographique ou démographique, ils peuvent tenir à la densité du trafic ou à la disponibilité d'énergie ; quelle qu'en soit la nature, ils exigent d'un fabricant conscient des besoins du marché la capacité de voir quels sont les produits qui pourront être modifiés conformément aux besoins du client. L'évolution historique de Telettra contribue à expliquer la philosophie de la Compagnie et la constance de son action dans le domaine technologique et commercial.

La création en 1946 des « Laboratori di Telefonia Elettronica e Radio » a permis de constituer une compagnie petite mais souple, prête à apporter une contribution importante à la reconstruction du réseau de télécommunication italien après la guerre. En utilisant l'électronique dès ses débuts, Telettra offrait aux compagnies exploitantes des solutions originales, tout en maintenant la compatibilité avec les installations qui avaient survécu à la guerre et avec les systèmes traditionnels que proposaient encore des fournisseurs mieux établis, mais dont la technologie était moins moderne. Parmi les innovations mentionnées, on comptait, notamment, le service téléphonique interurbain automatique et les liaisons à micro-ondes au-dessus de la mer.

L'adoption d'un standard de qualité et fiabilité (Q&F) va de pair avec l'application de la convention acceptée de l'industrie: la qualité se traduit par une fiabilité démontrable. Mais Telettra va encore plus loin. De même que les services de l'équipe de recherche et de développement sont à la disposition de tous les secteurs de l'entreprise, l'équipe « Qualité et Fiabilité » agit également de façon autonome dans toute la structure de Telettra. Responsable directement envers la direction générale, cette équipe participe non seulement aux études techniques de production mais aussi à tout le proccessus de conception, y compris l'évaluation des composants et de leur rôle dans la stratégie globale.

Maintenir une telle orientation vers l'avenir ne se fait pas sans un niveau élevé d'investissements en équipements modernes et en matière grise, mais une conception authentique de la fiabilité et de la qualité apporte des avantages, surtout la satisfaction et la fidélité des clients. Les critères de l'équipe Qualité et Fiabilité de Telettra sont d'un niveau très élevé. Par exemple, elle a réussi à satisfaire aux critères extrêmement rigoureux fixés par les inspecteurs de British Post Office, désignés par le Ministère libyen des postes et télécommunications pour évaluer l'installation de 6000 km de câble coaxial qui relie les grands centres de la Libye.

Un transfert efficace de sa technologie est une condition « sine qua non » des interventions de Telettra à l'étranger. Sa politique consiste aussi à communiquer les procédés techniques de conception et de fabrication à des organisations sœurs dans le monde entier. Telettra estime, en effet, que seul un maximum de communications et d'échanges peut contribuer à un développement scientifique fructueux. C'est pour-

▷ 226

Transfer of know-how to partners, to customers. Above, one generation instructs another; below, a Telettra engineer instructs young colleagues from 3 continents.

Transfert de savoir-faire aux partenaires, aux clients. En haut, une génération en forme une autre ; en bas, un ingénieur de Telettra instruit de jeunes collègues venus de trois continents.

nes de fábrica al control de supervisión de una red de gasoducto que abarca miles de kilómetros, los productos de Telettra comprenden soporte lógico y físico desarrollados por ella, centrales privadas electrónicas, sistemas portadores por línea eléctrica, sistemas de control de supervisión con equipo periférico semiinteligente, gestión de líneas, procesadores de datos y equipo de interfaz.

Orientada hacia el mercado, con una estructura empresarial fundada en el progreso, una amplia base de productos de vanguardia, y un esfuerzo flexible de IyD para atender rápidamente las necesidades, Telettra encabeza la producción de equipo "familiar". Por ejemplo, producir 3000 transceptores al año es ya un logro, pero todavía más notable es implantarse en el mercado de ese producto, que supone su adaptación a un gran número de exigencias de usuarios finales. Los problemas pueden ser topográficos o demográficos, entrañar la densidad de tráfico o la disponibilidad de energía; sea cual fuere su carácter, un fabricante consciente del mercado ha de tener presente la posibilidad de modificar su productos para adaptarlos al cliente que los paga.

El desarrollo histórico de Telettra sirve para explicar la coherencia de su política tecnológica y comercial.

Durante la Segunda Guerra Mundial, Italia fue un importante campo de batalla, pero en 1946 comenzaba la reconstrucción de la red de telecomunicaciones. La guerra había aportado grandes progresos tecnológicos, y el establecimiento de la "Laboratori di Telefonia Elettronica e Radio" creó una compañía pequeña pero ágil, dispuesta a contribuir considerablemente a esa reconstrucción. Usando desde el principio la electrónica, Telettra pudo proporcionar a las compañías de telecomunicaciones explotadoras soluciones nuevas, manteniendo la compatibilidad con las instalaciones que habían sobrevivido a la guerra o con los sistemas tradicionales propuestos otra vez por proveedores antiguos cuya tecnología era menos avanzada. Entre las innovaciones figuraban la marcación automática a larga distancia y los radioenlaces sobre el mar por microondas.

El respeto de la calidad y de la fiabilidad es inseparable de la tecnología avanzada: dos conceptos tan íntimamente relacionados que su unión con el diágrafo CyF es una convención aceptada en la industria. La noción es clara: la calidad de construcción se convierte en una fiabilidad demostrable. Telettra va más allá. Lo mismo que todos los sectores de la organización de la empresa disponen de sus servicios IyD, de igual modo CyF se regulan automáticamente y abarcan toda la empresa. La información directa a la dirección general no sólo comprende la ingeniería de producción, sino todo el proceso de diseño, incluida la evaluación de componentes y su parte en la estrategia global. En esta noción orientada hacia el progreso de CyF interviene toda la empresa.

Lograrlo supone un elevado nivel de inversión en equipo avanzado y talentos. La solidez comercial de Telettra sostiene su política de expansión. Y con esas CyF se obtiene un verdadero rendimiento: la satisfacción y lealtad de los clientes. El equipo de CyF de Telettra figura entre los primeros. Por ejemplo, en todas las etapas del proyecto de cable coaxial de 6000 km para unir los principales centros de Libia, la empresa ha logrado satisfacer los criterios, muy exigentes, fijados por los inspectores de British Post Office designados por el Departamento de Correos y Telecomunicaciones de Libia.

La transferencia efectiva de tecnología es una política básica de Telettra: transmitir los conocimientos de desarrollo y fabricación a organizaciones hermanas del mundo entero guarda paralelo con su actitud ante el conocimiento científico. Cree que sólo la apertura y el intercambio máximos pueden llevar a un desarrollo científico fructífero. Pensando en tal objetivo,

▷ 226

Transferencia de conocimientos a los asociados y a los clientes. Arriba: una generación forma a otra; abajo: un ingeniero de Telettra instruyendo a colegas jóvenes de tres continentes.

SUDAN	360 k
DJIBOUTI	249 k
MAINLAND FRANCE	243 k
SPAIN	240 k
MAINLAND ITALY	238 k
MAINLAND FRANCE	230 k
MAINLAND ITALY	140 k
THYRA (GR)	128 k
TYPICA	

tra Review is proven by the fact that abstracts are continually in demand by some of the world's best-known names in research, and the Company is happy to note that its free market policy leads to a progressive increase in the periodical's circulation.

The possibility for newly-established Telettra companies to have immediate access to a world-scale market has been a factor in their success. By the same token, the diversified product specializations and capabilities of these companies are available to the whole organization when major contracts are to be fulfilled. This two-way flow creates a synergism which gives the company special characteristics of entrepreneurial agility and independence.

Examples of specialization by member companies of the Group are provided by Telettra Española in Madrid, which developed and produced UHF and radio links; by ABC Telettra in Brasil, which supplies all open-wire line equipment and by Telettra Norge of Oslo, which specializes in the construction of private data channels on existing voice-frequency circuits. In addition to the benefits of such widely distributed specialization, this geographical spread ensures a most effective imformation feed-back on markets.

Telettra's policy of international collaboration is highly flexible and takes into consideration local political and economic realities. This has led, for example, to the decision to conclude a licensing agreement with an established national firm in Yugoslavia, and with local market leaders in the USA and Australia. These are proving mutually advantageous industrially and commercially.

▷ 227

quoi elle crée et entretient des contacts étroits avec des universités et d'autres établissements d'enseignement et participe à des réunions et colloques, au niveau national et international. Quant aux publications, elle coopère avec des revues scientifiques bien établies tout en distribuant, dans le monde entier, sa propre publication « Telettra Review », consacrée aux travaux effectués dans ses laboratoires.

La possibilité offerte aux compagnies « Telettra » récemment créées d'avoir un accès immédiat à un marché d'importance mondiale est un facteur de leur succès. Parallèlement, les spécialisations de la capacité de production diversifiée de ces compagnies sont à la disposition du groupe entier lorsqu'il s'agit d'exécuter des contrats particulièrement importants. Un exemple de coopération de ce genre est la production de liaisons à ondes décimétriques, utilisées pour des installations « clés-en-mains » très variées, qui sont toutes étudiées et construites par Telettra Española, à Madrid. Un autre est ABC Telettra au Brésil qui est le responsable de tous les équipements en fils aériens. Telettra Norge, à Oslo, est spécialisée dans la construction de voies privées pour données sur les circuits téléphoniques existants. Cette répartition géographique a aussi l'avantage de permettre la prise de décisions sur la base de données constamment mises à jour.

Telettra applique une politique souple dans le création des moyens de collaboration internationale. Les réalités politiques et économiques locales sont prises en compte, ce qui a amené la société à décider, par exemple, de conclure pour les opérations en Yougoslavie un accord de licence avec une firme nationale déjà établie. D'autre part, accords de licence

▷ 227

crea y mantiene estrechos contactos con universidades y otros centros de aprendizaje, y participa en convenciones y simposios a nivel nacional e internacional.

Merece la pena señalar su política de publicaciones, que comprende la cooperación con revistas científicas, y la distribución mundial de su propia publicación "Telettra Review", revista técnica con informes sobre los trabajos realizados en los laboratorios de la empresa.

La constante demanda de sus resúmenes por algunos de los investigadores más conocidos del mundo prueba el nivel científico de Telettra Review, y para la empresa es una satisfacción que, debido a su política de mercado libre, sus publicaciones se difundan cada vez más.

La posibilidad de que empresas nuevas de Telettra accedan inmediatamente a un mercado mundial es uno de los factores de su éxito. Del mismo modo, toda la organización dispone de las diversas especializaciones y capacidades de productos de esas empresas, cuando hay que atender importantes contratos. Este flujo bidireccional crea una magnífica oportunidad, que ofrece a la empresa características especiales, agilidad e independencia.

Como ejemplos de especialización de compañías miembros del grupo, cabe citar Telettra Española, de Madrid, que desarrolla y produce radioenlaces UHF: ABC Telettra, que suministra equipo de líneas aereas, y Telettra Norge, en Oslo, especializada en la construcción de canales privados de datos en circuitos de frecuencias vocales existentes. Además de los beneficios de esa especialización tan dispersa, la ex-

▷ 227

Microwave hops over land and sea; a speciality of Telettra's. A selection of installations including the longest hop in the world, over the Red Sea.

Des ondes hertziennes enjambant terre et mers : une spécialité Telettra. Voici une sélection de liaisons réalisées, parmi lesquelles la liaison la plus longue du monde, au dessus de la Mer Rouge.

Enlaces de microondas sobre la tierra y el mar: una especialidad de Telettra. Esta selección de instalaciones comprende el enlace mayor del mundo sobre el Mar Rojo.

0) \
3) \
5) \
2) \
0) \
6) \
3) \
-LAND

SAUDI ARABIA \
NORTH YEMEN \
CORSICA \
ALGERIA \
SARDINIA \
CORSICA \
MALTA \
CRETE

The policy of establishing branch offices ensures that there is an on-the-spot presence to serve all customers with the required closeness, and to intervene quickly and with constant contact when market conditions are favourable. The setting up of branch offices may sometimes lead the way to the establishment of a fledgling industry when local demands require it.

Another form of international co-operation is the Company's participation in consortia engaged on very large projects. A recent example is the 6,000 km coaxial line system in Libya where Telettra's partners in the project are all acknowledged leaders in their fields. Indeed, at the time of rapid market development, Telettra's policy is to make alliances, wherever suitable, with other operators in the field, in order to make the most of what today's technology offers. Examples are the agreements with a leading French manufacturer for private telecom networks, and with other major Italian operators in a program which will dominate the nation's public switching market. Private telecom and switching are seen as being particularly interesting areas as technologies increasingly converge. Representative though they are, these agreements are just examples of the Company's "alliance" orientation.

The introduction of new and extended telecommunications systems is shown elsewhere in this book as being associated with economic development and with improvement in the quality of life in many ways. Such changes are mostly an indirect effect; they arise at some future date; to believe that they will arise must often, at the time of deciding to introduce the new system, be an act of faith. The immediate and direct effect of the new system is more likely to be change for many individuals in their way of life — change which will be seen as a

avec les principales entreprises sur les marchés locaux aux Etats-Unis et en Australie, sont mutuellement avantageux, industriellement et commercialement.

La politique tendant à créer des succursales assure la présence sur place de Telettra, permet de suivre de près les besoins de tous ses clients et facilite une intervention rapide. Cela conduit parfois à la création d'une industrie nouvelle.

Une autre forme de coopération internationale est assurée par la présence de la société dans le cadre de consortiums intéressés à des projets très vastes. Comme, par exemple, le système en lignes coaxiales de 6000 km pour la Libye, dans lequel les partenaires de Telettra sont tous des entreprises de pointe dans leur domaine. En fait, lorsque le développement du marché est rapide, Telettra a pour politique de conclure des alliances avec d'autres exploitants, chaque fois que cela est opportun, afin de retirer le plus possible d'avantages de ce que les techniques actuelles peuvent offrir. A titre d'exemple: les accords avec un important constructeur français pour des réseaux privés, et ceux avec d'autres grands exploitants italiens dans le cadre d'un programme qui dominera le marché national des réseaux publics à commutation. Ce ne sont là que quelques exemples de la politique d'« alliances » de Telettra.

L'introduction de systèmes nouveaux et élargis de télécommunication est présentée ailleurs dans ce volume comme étant liée au développement économique et à l'amélioration de la qualité de la vie. Ces nouveaux systèmes dont l'adoption relève souvent d'un acte de foi, aura vraisemblablement pour effet immédiat de transformer le mode de vie d'un grand nombre de personnes, mais d'une manière indirecte et, parfois, avec une échéance assez lointaine. Par contre, ce changement est quelques fois perçu dans certaines régions comme une menace qui pèse sur les

pansión geográfica permite una información sumamente eficaz sobre los mercados.

La política de colaboración internacional de Telettra es muy flexible y tiene en cuenta las realidades políticas y económicas locales. Esto ha llevado, por ejemplo, a la decisión de concertar acuerdos de licencia con una firma yugoslava, y con líderes del mercado local en EE.UU. y Australia, que presentan ventajas mutuas, industrial y comercialmente.

La política de crear sucursales asegura la presencia en el terreno para servir a todos los clientes con diligencia, intervenir rápidamente y mantener un contacto permanente cuando las condiciones del mercado son favorables. La apertura de sucursales puede dar paso, a veces, a la creación de una nueva industria, cuando la demanda local lo justifica.

Otra forma de cooperación internacional es la participación de la empresa en consorcios que intervienen en grandes proyectos. Un ejemplo reciente es el sistema de línea coaxial de 6000 km, donde todos los asociados de Telettra en el proyecto son líderes reconocidos en sus sectores. En efecto, en momentos de rápida evolución del mercado, la política de Telettra es hacer alianzas, siempre que proceda, con otros operadores, a fin de fabricar la mayor parte de cuanto ofrece la tecnología actual. Ejemplos de ello son los acuerdos con un importante fabricante francés de redes privadas de telecomunicaciones, y con otras grandes empresas italianas en un programa que dominará el mercado de conmutación pública del país. La telecomunicación y la conmutación privadas se consideran sectores particularmente interesantes, puesto que las tecnologías convergen cada vez más.

Según se describe en otra parte de esta obra, los sistemas de telecomunicaciones nuevos y ampliados están asociados al desarrollo económico y al mejo-

▷ 228

▷ 228

▷ 228

threat, and indeed often will be a threat, to their present livelihood. The contractor who supplies and implements the new installations, although not responsible for the decision to do so, cannot escape entirely from some responsibility for the anxieties resulting from it. It therefore behoves such a contractor to play his part in allaying such fears and in relieving the causes for them. This he can probably best do by setting an example, by having exemplary conditions in his own house.

If the term "manpower" is no longer desired in the days of equal opportunity because of a possible hint of sexual discrimination, so also "human resources" is to be deprecated for its overtone of the exploiter's attitude to passive raw material, while to many ears "people", carries the taint of PR populism. So what term should be used to convey the notion that Telettra pays continuous attention to the person-to-company relationship at all the various managerial, research, production and commercial levels? An attention, in a world of rapid social and industrial change, which is intended to maintain and improve the excellence of these relationships.

This may be the manifestation of another Q&R syndrome: quality work-environment and continuing productive and commercial reliability. Much depends on the Company's awareness of how important the human factor is in an ultra-dynamic sector such as electronics, which requires inventiveness more than repetitive labour, job satisfaction rather than a mere clocking on and off.

Whatever the way of it, Telettra aims for a high percentage of well-qualified personnel and the Company organizes its production into small units, each responsible for an important part of the "life" of the product involved. And the customer gets the benefit of a policy which sets out to make the most of the "human capabilities" available.

moyens d'existence traditionnels. Bien qu'il ne soit pas responsable de la décision d'adopter de nouvelles installations, l'entrepreneur qui les construit et les met en œuvre ne peut échapper entièrement à un certain cas de conscience quant aux inquiétudes qu'il provoque. Il appartient donc à cet entrepreneur de jouer son rôle pour alléger les craintes et en éliminer les causes. La meilleure manière de le faire c'est souvent de donner l'exemple, en ayant des conditions de travail exemplaires dans sa propre entreprise.

Si le terme « Manpower », souvent traduit par « Travailleurs », n'est plus très souhaitable puisque l'on peut y voir une intention de discrimination entre les sexes, que les « ressources humaines » peuvent impliquer une attitude d'exploiteur face à une matière première passive, pour beaucoup de gens, le terme « peuple » est teinté de populisme. Quel terme utiliser, alors, pour exprimer l'idée que Telettra veille, en effet, constamment aux relations entre les individus et la Compagnie, et cela à tous les niveaux: direction, recherche, production et commerce. C'est là une politique qui, dans un monde en évolution rapide sur le plan social et industriel, vise à maintenir et à améliorer la qualité de ces relations. Peut-être est-ce là un autre indice de ce désir de qualité et de fiabilité: un milieu de travail de qualité conduit à une qualité de travail correspondante. La compagnie est consciente de l'importance du facteur humain dans un secteur particulièrement dynamique comme l'électronique, qui exige plus d'esprit d'invention que de travail répétitif, et apporte la satisfaction dans le travail (y compris la fierté pour les produits créés) plutôt qu'un pointage quotidiennement répété d'une fiche de présence.

Quoi qu'il en soit, Telettra cherche à s'assurer la plus grande collaboration possible de personnel qualifié et organise sa production en petits groupes, dont chacun est responsable d'une tranche de « vie » de la réalisation en cours. Finalement, le client qui est le bénéficiaire d'une politique qui vise à favoriser au maximum l'épanouissement constructif du génie humain des collaborateurs de l'entreprise.

ramiento de la calidad de la vida de todo tipo. Tales cambios tienen sobre todo un efecto indirecto; surgirán más adelante; creer que lo harán en seguida, en el momento de decidir la introducción del nuevo sistema, sería un acto de fe. Lo más probable es que el efecto inmediato y directo del nuevo sistema sea el cambio del modo de vida de muchos individuos, cambio que se considerará como una amenaza de su modo de vida actual, y lo será muchas veces. El contratista que suministra y aplica las nuevas instalaciones, aunque no sea responsable de la decisión de hacerlo, no puede eludir totalmente alguna responsabilidad de las inquietudes resultantes. Por tanto, le corresponde desempeñar su papel para mitigar esos temores y aliviar sus causas. La mejor manera de hacerlo sea dando el ejemplo, mediante condiciones ejemplares en su propia casa.

Telettra presta atención permanente a las relaciones personal-empresa en todos los niveles de gestión, investigación, producción y comercialización. Una atención, en un mundo de rápida evolución social e industrial, destinada a mantener y mejorar la excelencia de esas relaciones.

Puede ser la manifestacion de otro síndrome CyF: medio de trabajo de calidad y fiabilidad productiva y comercial continua. Depende mucho de la importancia que atribuya la empresa al factor humano en un sector ultradinámico como la electrónica, que requiere inventiva más que trabajo rutinario, satisfacción en el empleo (incluidos orgullo y placer en el producto), y no el mero hecho de figurar en nómina.

Sea como fuere, Telettra persigue el objetivo de un elevado porcentaje de personal bien calificado, y la empresa organiza su producción en pequeñas unidades, cada una responsable de una parte importante de la "vida" del producto correspondiente. Y el cliente se beneficia de una política establecida para sacar el máximo provecho de las "capacidades humanas" disponibles.

Telettra S.p.A. in Italy
Telettra S.p.A. abroad
Telettra S.p.A. total

Associated Company Italy
Telettra's foreign associated Companies
Telettra's associated Companies total

Company's total in Italy
Company's total abroad

Telettra (Italy)
Telettra española (Madrid)
Telettra norge (Oslo)
Telettra argentina (Buenos Aires)
abc Telettra (Rio de Janeiro)
Telettra industrial (Mexico)
Telettra swaziland (Mbabane)

Telettra: An international family of companies, working in harmony through five continents. More than two-thirds of Telettra's products and services are placed in markets outside Italy: a philosophy of creative understanding of customers' needs, leading to constructive and continuing co-operation.

Telettra : Une famille internationale d'entreprises qui travaillent ensemble sur cinq continents. Plus de deux tiers des produits et services de Telettra sont vendus hors d'Italie : une philosophie de créativité basée sur la compréhension des besoins de la clientèle menant à une coopération constructive et suivie.

Telettra: Un grupo internacional de empresas que trabajan a través de cinco continentes. Más de dos tercios de los productos y servicios se colocan en mercados del exterior de Italia: una filosofía de creatividad basada en la comprensión de las necesidades de los clientes, y que conduce a una cooperación constructiva y permanente.

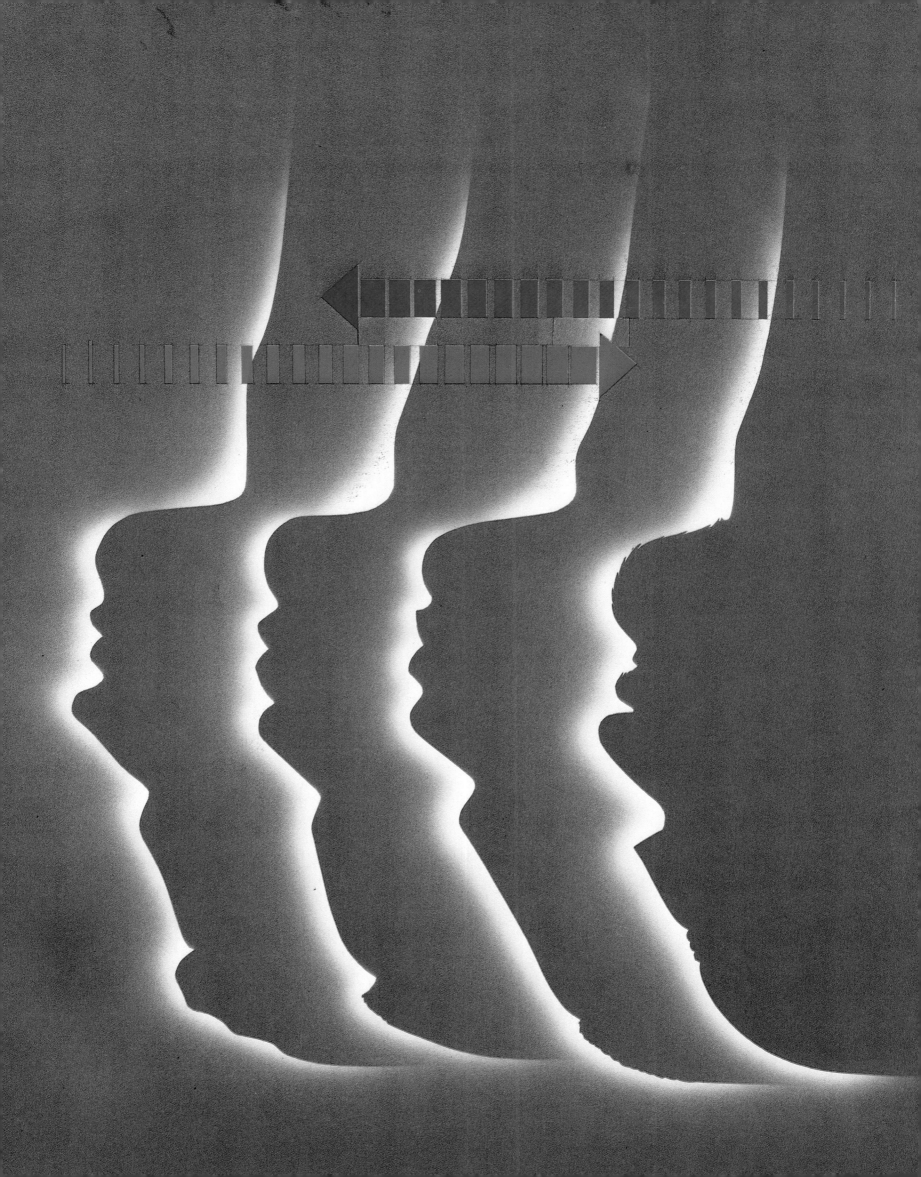

RADIO COMMUNICATIONS OF ALL TYPES depend upon highly abstract properties of nature, of the earth and its atmosphere. Telephone systems, television stations and computer networks only function as they do because information can be converted into energy and radiated through space. These natural properties have gradually been harnessed to a rapidly growing number of practical ends. Radio and television are used to inform, to entertain, to educate, to stimulate demand for goods and services. Two-way communication of voice, text and data have become an essential element in our life styles, used increasingly in the conduct of government, business and social relations. They are the neural system of our world.

Because of their vital importance, all countries are pressing claims, often conflicting, upon scarce radio frequencies and orbital positions. The resources required for communication purposes do not become depleted with use like most other natural resources, but they are limited and have to be shared. The key problem areas in the sharing include short wave frequencies; fixed satellite services; and broadcasting satellite services. Orbit/spectrum issues, however technical, ultimately raise political questions. Only political compromise, built on technical foundations, can reconcile:

— long-term, detailed, a priori planning to ensure universal access versus flexibility deemed essential to accommodate technical and economic change;

— simpler, more affordable technology versus spectrum-efficient, interference-avoiding, and sometimes more costly technology.

Developing countries acknowledge the shortcomings of a priori planning, but insist upon credible
⊲ 232

Plenary session of the World Administrative Radio Conference (WARC) of the ITU, at the Union's headquarters at Geneva.

QUEL QU'EN SOIT LE TYPE, les radiocommunications comme les autres richesses naturelles, dépendent de propriétés fort abstraites de la nature, de la Terre et de l'atmosphère. La téléphonie, la radio et la télématique fonctionnent uniquement parce que, grâce à certaines lois physiques, l'information peut être convertie en énergie et rayonnée dans l'espace. La radio et la télévision servent à informer, à enseigner, à simuler la demande de biens et de services. Les communications téléphoniques, ainsi que la transmission bidirectionnelle de textes et de données nous sont devenues indispensables à chacun, autant qu'aux pouvoirs publics et à l'industrie. Le réseau de communications est ainsi devenu le système nerveux du monde moderne.

En raison de l'importance des ressources en fréquences et en positions orbitales, chaque pays fait valoir des droits — souvent antagonistes — sur ce patrimoine de l'humanité toute entière.

Les fréquences et les positions orbitales ne s'épuisent pas comme les autres ressources naturelles, mais, simplement, leur nombre limité nécessite impérativement d'en partager l'usage. Ce n'est pas toujours facile en raison de la grande multiplicité des besoins en radiocommunications et en positions orbitales, pour les satellites. Ces derniers étant d'ailleurs eux-mêmes grands utilisateurs de fréquences.

Quelles que soient les difficultés inhérentes à la gestion technique de l'orbite géosynchrone et du spectre, celle-ci pose, en dernier ressort, des problèmes politiques. Seuls des compromis fondés sur des bases techniques peuvent en effet concilier :

— une planification détaillée et à long terme, établie a priori pour assurer normalement l'accès des pays en développement à ces facilités, et la souplesse jugée essentielle pour permettre l'évolution technique et économique ;
⊲ 232

Session plénière de la Conférence administrative mondiale de radiocommunications (CAMR) de l'UIT, au siège de l'Union à Genève.

TODAS LAS RADIOCOMUNICACIONES dependen de propiedades muy abstractas de la naturaleza, la Tierra y su atmósfera. Los sistemas telefónicos, las estaciones de televisión y las redes de computador funcionan como lo hacen porque la información puede convertirse en energía y radiarse a través del espacio. Esas propiedades naturales se han aprovechado para varios fines prácticos que aumentan rápidamente. La radio y la televisión se usan para informar, entretener, educar y estimular la demanda de bienes y servicios. La comunicación bidireccional de voz, texto y datos se ha convertido en un elemento esencial de nuestros modos de vida, empleados cada vez más en las relaciones gubernamentales, comerciales y sociales. Son el sistema neural de mundo moderno.

Debido a su vital importancia, todos los países solicitan con insistencia frecuencias radioeléctricas y posiciones orbitales escasas, a menudo en conflicto. Los recursos necesarios para las comunicaciones no se agotan con el uso, como la mayoría de los recursos naturales, pero son limitados y han de compartirse. Las áreas más problemáticas en este sentido son las frecuencias de ondas cortas; los servicios fijos por satélite; y los de radiodifusión por satélite. Las cuestiones de órbita y espectro, aunque técnicas, acaban por plantear problemas políticos. Sólo mediante un acuerdo político, sobre bases técnicas, puede reconciliarse:

— la planificación a priori detallada y a largo plazo para asegurar el acceso universal a la flexibilidad estimada esencial para acomodar el cambio técnico y económico;

— una tecnología más abordable y sencilla, que requiera menos espectro y evite la interferencia y, a veces, más costosa.
⊲ 233

Sesión plenaria de la Conferencia Administrativa Mundial de Radiocomunicaciones (CAMR) de la UIT, en la sede de la Unión, Ginebra.

THE RADIO FREQUENCY SPECTRUM OWERNEWHOPE A COMMON PROPERTY OF MANKIND

guarantees of access to both frequencies and satellite parking spots when needed. Industrial countries insist that flexibility must be maintained and argue that technological progress will very substantially reduce the call on scarce orbit/spectrum resources.

The usable radio frequency spectrum (see chart p. 234) ranges from a few thousand cycles (including AM or MW radio broadcasting) to a few thousand million cycles, including land-based microwave and satellite broadcasting. Transmissions at relatively low frequencies (AM/MW and shortwave/HF) bounce off the upper atmosphere and carry far beyond the horizon. Signals at these frequencies stray beyond national borders. Co-ordination of their use is required, for national as well as for international radio services.

Transmission at relatively high frequencies — very high (VHF), ultra high (UHF), super high (SHF), extremely high (EHF), and tremendously high (THF) connect only points in a "line-of-sight". Long distance transmissions on land use microwave repeaters. From geostationary earth orbit any point on earth, except near the poles, is in line-of-sight. Since, however, separation of the satellites is needed to avoid radio interference, the number of "orbital positions" which can be used for communications is limited. It is almost certainly inadequate to "house" every claimant at the stage of technology reached in the 80s, but the major increase in the power and capacities of future generations of satellites (including the likelihood of immense geostationary platforms) could radically improve the situation.

In addition to the requirements for communication purposes, there are other uses of the spectrum: "remote sensing" of the earth's surface is most efficiently performed if certain frequencies are kept free from communications. Radio astronomy, likewise, depends upon radio "silence" in key bands. There is also the possibility of interference from uses of microwaves in homes and factories and the problem of microwave congestion in certain areas.

In New York for example data transmission has become unsatisfactory due to overcrowding of very high frequency radio waves bands, so much so that several companies highly dependent on the transmission of large amounts of data have moved away from the city. To counter this, the Port Authority of New York and New Jersey, in partnership with stockbrokers Merrill Lynch, Pierce Fenner and Smith, Inc. are building a satellite reception center on relatively radio-frequency-free Staten Island. This "Teleport" will contain 17 earth stations providing a two-way link with the US domestic satellites, and eventually with satellites of other countries (see p. 188). They will be connected by optical cable to customers in the New York boroughs and adjoining major towns which have major telecommunications requirements.

From geostationary orbit, any satellite can access about one-third of the earth's surface. They can be designed to send a signal to the entire area or to concentrate signals on a small area. The difference will be in signal strength, relatively weak in the first instance, strong in the second. When the satellite signal is broadly diffused, earth stations must have large antennae and complex electronics; they are expensive both to acquire and to maintain. When the signal is strong, and narrowly focussed, smaller and simpler earth stations can be used, costing much less. The ultimate is an antenna 60-90 cm in diameter for home reception of satellite signals, costing only a few hundred dollars. In both cases, the job of the satellite is primarily the same: to receive a signal from an earth station, amplify it, convert its frequency and retransmit it to a receiving earth station. This is done by "transponders" in the satellite.

International arrangements surrounding access to earth orbit and use of frequencies for a growing diversity of satellite and terrestrial applications by a growing number of countries have become difficult to manage. At the last General World Administrative Radio Conference (WARC 79), there was a greater degree of

▷ 236

— une technique simple et bon marché, et une technique utilisant le spectre des fréquences d'une façon plus rigoureuse permettant d'éviter les brouillages, mais se révélant onéreuse.

Les pays en développement reconnaissent les inconvénients d'une planification a priori, mais ils tiennent à obtenir des garanties d'accès valables aux satellites sur l'orbite géosynchrone. Quant aux pays industriels, ils désirent maintenir la souplesse du système et prétendent que le progrès technique réduira considérablement la pression de la demande sur cette ressource limitée.

Le spectre des fréquences radioélectriques utilisables (voir tableau p. 234) s'étale de la fréquence de quelques milliers de hertz par seconde (notamment pour la radiodiffusion à modulation d'amplitude) à celle de plusieurs milliards de hertz (faisceaux hertziens à hyperfréquences, pour les réseaux de Terre et liaisons spatiales par satellites). Dans les bandes inférieures du spectre, ces émissions rebondissent sur la haute atmosphère et leur portée s'étend bien au-delà de l'horizon. Les signaux dépassent alors les frontières nationales et l'emploi de ces fréquences impose aux services nationaux une coordination internationale.

Les émissions faites dans les bandes de fréquences plus élevées (en ondes métriques, décimétriques, centimétriques et millimétriques) ne peuvent se propager qu'entre des points en ligne de visibilité directe. Pour assurer des liaisons en micro-ondes au-delà de l'horizon, il faut donc recourir à des relais-répéteurs. En revanche, pour un satellite placé sur l'orbite géosynchrone, tous les points situés sur la face apparente de la Terre, sauf au voisinage des pôles, se trouvent en visibilité directe. Cependant, le nombre des positions orbitales utilisables pour les radiocommunications est limité en raison de la nécessité d'éviter des brouillages radioélectriques nuisibles. En dépit du fait qu'actuellement il est pratiquement impossible de « loger » tous les demandeurs, on peut prévoir que les augmentations de puissance et de capacité des futures générations de satellites (y compris la probabilité d'immenses plateformes géostationnaires) vont modifier radicalement la situation.

L'utilisation du spectre ne peut cependant pas être réservée exclusivement aux communications. En effet, la « télé-exploration » de la surface de la Terre est facilitée lorsque certaines fréquences ne sont pas utilisées pour les radiocommunications. La radioastronomie a besoin, elle aussi, de zones de silence dans des bandes particulières. D'autre part, il importe aussi de tenir compte des perturbations induites par les fours ménagers à micro-ondes, ainsi que de la surcharge des bandes à hyperfréquences dans certaines régions.

A New-York, par exemple, l'encombrement de certaines bandes a rendu la transmission de données si difficile que de nombreuses sociétés, dont les activités en dépendent essentiellement, ont dû quitter cette ville. Pour lutter contre cet exode, la Port Authority de New-York et du New Jersey a entrepris, en collaboration avec les agents de change Merrill Lynch, Pierce Fenner and Smith, Inc. et Western Union la construction, à Staten Island, d'un centre de réception par satellite qui ne sera que relativement peu affecté par le brouillage radioélectrique. Ce « Téléport » disposera de 17 stations terriennes travaillant en liaison bidirectionnelle avec les satellites nationaux des Etats-Unis et avec divers satellites internationaux (voir p. 188). Il sera relié par des câbles à fibres optiques aux utilisateurs intéressés de toute l'agglomération new-yorkaise.

Tout satellite géostationnaire peut desservir environ un tiers de la surface terrestre. Il peut être conçu pour « arroser » la totalité de cette superficie, soit pour concentrer ses signaux sur une zone restreinte. Lorsque le signal d'un satellite est largement diffusé, les stations terriennes doivent être équipées de grandes antennes et d'un appareillage électronique complexe ; leur prix est plus élevé et leur maintenance est plus coûteuse. En revanche, un signal plus puissant et plus concentré permet l'utilisation de stations terriennes moins complexes et moins onéreuses. Les futures antennes de réception à domicile auront un diamètre

▷ 236

THE ITU 'WA

At the international level, orbit/spectrum issues are handled primarily through the ITU by means of World Administrative Radio Conferences (WARC), attended by representatives from Member nations. Held in 1929, 1947, 1959 and 1979, these intergovernmental conferences have as their principal function the revision of the ITU Radio Regulations, including the Table of Allocations of frequency bands.

The WARC of 1979 carried out a general review of the Radio Frequency Spectrum and associated provisions of the Radio Regulations. Specifically, in regard to the management of the Radio Frequency Spectrum and Satellite Orbits, WARC 79 made some very far-reaching decisions which will, when definitive — ie. ratified by the Governments concerned — facilitate and speed up the application of space technology.

● Warc for the planning of HF bands allocated to the broadcasting service - January/February 1984; October/November 1986

● Planning conference for the broadcasting service in the VHF band in Region 1 and certain countries concerned in Region 3 - October/November 1984

● Warc on the use of the geostationary-satellite orbit and the planning of space service - June/August 1985; June/August 1988

The primary change was the increasing role played by the developing countries in the organization, all determined to promote their telecommunications interests, often in disharmony and sometimes in direct conflict with those of industrialized countries.

WARC 79 made enormous increases in the allocation of the spectrum for all classes of services defined in the Regulations, to provide developing countries with allocations for future use whereas the USA and most Western nations wished to preserve existing IFRB registration/co-ordination procedures for assignment of frequencies in the HF and in the fixed satellite service. It passed resolutions which mandated the scheduling of future specialized WARCs to plan the use of those services on a global basis.

Specialized and Regional WARCs are held to deal with matters peculiar to a particular combination of telecommunications services or to one of the three ITU Regions. Recent examples have included the Space Communications WARC in 1971, and the Broadcasting Satellite WARC in 1977. An important conference planned by WARC 79 was the Western Hemisphere Broadcasting Satellite WARC scheduled in 1983. A High Frequency Broadcasting Satellite WARC has been scheduled in 1984 and a Space Services WARC for two sessions in 1985 and 1987, to determine assignments based on "overview considerations of assuring equitable access in practice".

Other ITU WARCs are convened to deal with specialized aspects of broadcasting, such as mobile telecommunications, satellite broadcasting, the use of particular frequency bands, or problems relating to certain countries or continents. One such conference, scheduled in 1986, is programmed to review and revise broadcasting regulations in Africa.

The schedule of conferences opposite includes preparatory sessions to ensure that the subjects are well documented and in good time.

RADIO AND SPACE CONFERENCES

'échelon international, les problèmes relatifs à l'orbite stationnaire et au spectre des fréquences sont traités prinlement par les Conférences administratives mondiales des ocommunications, CAMR, auxquelles participent les pays mbres de l'UIT. Ces conférences intergouvernementales tes en 1929, 1947, 1959 et 1979 ont pour tâche essentielle de ser le Règlement des radiocommunications de l'UIT, noment le Tableau d'attribution des fréquences.

a CAMR de 1979 a procédé à une révision générale du lement des radiocommunications et du spectre des frénces radioélectriques. En ce qui concerne particulièrement estion du spectre et les orbites de satellite, cette confée a pris d'importantes décisions lesquelles, une fois rati-s par les gouvernements intéressés, faciliteront et accélè-

A nivel internacional las cuestiones de la órbita y del espectro se tratan sobre todo por medio de la UIT, en Conferencias Administrativas Mundiales de Radiocomunicaciones (CAMR), a las que asisten los representantes de las naciones Miembros. La función primordial de esas conferencias intergubernamentales, celebradas en 1929, 1947, 1959 y 1979, es revisar el Reglamento de Radiocomunicaciones de la UIT, incluido el Cuadro de atribución de bandas de frecuencias.

La CAMR de 1979 procedió a la revisión general del espectro de frecuencias y disposiciones conexas del Reglamento de Radiocomunicaciones. Sobre la gestión del espectro de frecuencias radioeléctricas y órbitas de satélite, la CAMR 79 tomó algunas decisiones trascendentales que, cuando sean definitivas — una vez ratificadas por los gobiernos interesados —

Los países en desarrollo reconocen las deficiencias de una planificación a priori, pero insisten en garantías de acceso fiables a las frecuencias y a las porciones para colocar satélites, cuando lo necesiten. Los países industriales insisten en mantener la flexibilidad, y aducen que el progreso tecnológico reducirá muchísimo los requerimientos de los recursos de la órbita y el espectro.

El espectro de frecuencias radioeléctricas utilizable se extiende de varios miles de ciclos (incluida la radiofusión MA o por MW) a varios miles de millones de ciclos (incluida la radiodifusión por microondas con base en tierra y satélite, como se muestra en el recuadro de la pág. 234). Las transmisiones a frecuencias relativamente bajas (MA/ondas medias y cortas/decamétricas) se sirven de la atmósfera superior y van más allá del horizonte. Las señales en esas frecuencias rebasan las fronteras nacionales. Hay que coordinar su uso para servicios nacionales e internacionales de radiodifusión.

La transmisión en frecuencias relativamente altas — muy altas (VHF), ultraaltas (UHF), superaltas (SFH) y sumamente altas (EHF) — sólo conecta puntos en "visibilidad directa". Las transmisiones terrestres a larga distancia utilizan repetidores de microondas. Desde la órbita geoestacionaria (GEO), todo punto sobre la Tierra, excepto cerca de los polos, es de visibilidad directa. Pero, como hay que separar los satélites para evitar la interferencia, el número de "posiciones orbitales" en GEO para las comunicaciones es limitado. Es casi seguro inadecuado "acoger" a todo solicitante en la fase tecnológica de los años 80, pero el importante aumento de la potencia y las capacidades de los futuros satélites puede cambiar radicalmente la situación.

Además de las necesidades de comunicación, se hacen otros usos del espectro: la "teledetección" de la superficie de la Tierra se efectúa con gran eficacia si no hay comunicaciones en ciertas frecuencias. La radioastronomía depende igualmente del "silencio" radioeléctrico en bandas clave. El uso de microondas en hogares y fábricas, y el problema de la congestión de microondas en ciertas zonas, pueden dar lugar también a interferencia.

En Nueva York, la transmisión de datos es insatisfactoria debido a la saturación de ondas radioeléctricas de muy alta frecuencia, hasta el punto de que varias empresas que dependen mucho de la transmisión de grandes cantidades de datos han abandonado la ciudad. Para contrarrestar esta situación, la Port Authority of New York and New Jersey, en asociación con los agentes de bolsa Merrill Lynch, Pierce Fenner y Smith, Inc., está construyendo un centro de recepción por satélite en Staten Island, exento de frecuencias. Este *telepuerto* tendrà 17 estaciones terrenas que ofrecerán enlaces bidireccionales con satélites nacionales estadounidenses, y después con satélites de otros países. Estarán conectadas por cable óptico a los clientes de los barrios de Nueva York y a las principales ciudades circundantes con grandes necesidades de telecomunicaciones (véase pág. 188).

Desde GEO, todo satélite puede acceder a un tercio de la superficie de la Tierra. Pueden diseñarse para enviar una señal a una zona completa o para concentrar señales en una pequeña zona. La diferencia consistirá en la intensidad de la señal, relativamente débil en el primer caso, y fuerte en el segundo. Cuando la señal del satélite se difunda mucho, las estaciones terrenas habrán de tener grandes antenas y equipo electrónico complejo, cuya adquisición y mantenimiento son caros. Cuando la señal sea fuerte, y muy focalizada, podrán emplearse antenas pequeñas y más sencillas, y mucho menos costosas, hasta llegar a una antena de 60-90 cm de diámetro para recepción doméstica de señales por satélite, de un costo de varios centenares de dólares nada más. En ambos casos, el cometido del satélite es el mismo: recibir una señal desde una estación terrena, amplificarla, convertir su frecuencia y transmitirla a una estación terrena receptora. Esto lo hacen los "transpondedores" del satélite.

La géstion de los acuerdos internacionales sobre el acceso a GEO y el uso de frecuencias para un número cada vez mayor de aplicaciones de satélite y terrenales por un cre-

- Conference to review and revise the provisions of the final acts of the african VHF/UHF roadcasting conference, Geneva, 1963 - First half of 1987, for 3 weeks; September 1988

- Planning conference for the broadcasting service in the band 1605-1705 KHZ in Region 2 First half of 1986, for 3 weeks; Third quarter of 1988, for 4 weeks

- Conference to establish criteria for the shared use of the VHF and UHF bands allocated to fixed, broadcasting and mobile services in Region 3 - November 1987

- World administrative radio conference for mobile telecommunications - August/September 1987

- World administrative telegraph and telephone conference - December 1988.

- Plenipotentiary conference (beginning of 1989)

— Note - Preparatory seminars and Warc (Space Services) first half, 1985

nt la mise en oeuvre de la technologie spatiale. Les pays eñ eloppement s'efforcèrent de promouvoir leurs intérêts dans omaine des télécommunications.

n conséquence la CAMR 79 a augmenté considérablement attributions de spectre en faveur de toutes les catégories de vices définies dans le Règlement, afin de leur assurer des sibilités d'allotissement pour le futur, alors que les ts-Unis et la plupart des pays occidentaux désiraient mainr les procédures existantes d'enregistrement et de coordion par l'IFRB.

a Conférence a adopté des résolutions prévoyant la vocation de CAMR spécialisées et régionales qui auront r mandat de planifier à l'échelle mondiale l'utilisation de tions de spectre, notamment la bande des ondes décamélues et dans le service fixe par satellite, par les services ressés. Les CAMR spécialisées et régionales ont pour tâche raiter de sujets particuliers. Ce fut notamment le cas de la férence des radiocommunications pour la radiodiffusion par ellite de 1977. Quant à la CAMR de 1979, elle a décidé de voquer pour juin 1983 une Conférence de radiodiffusion par ellite pour l'hémisphère occidental. Une conférence de radiffusion à ondes décamétriques est prévue pour 1984 et une MR pour les services spatiaux se déroulera en deux sesıs, en 1985 et 1987 ; elle devra déterminer les attributions la base de considérations d'ensemble afin d'en assurer un ès équitable.

J'autres CAMR sont convoquées pour traiter d'aspects parliers de la radiodiffusion, notamment des services mobiles, la radiodiffusion par satellite, de l'utilisation de bandes de quences particulières ou de problèmes intéressant certains s ou continents déterminés. La conférence prévue pour 1986 a pour tâche d'examiner et de réviser la règlementation de la iodiffusion en Afrique.

e calendrier des conférences ci-dessus comprend les cycles udes préparatoires des CAMR organisées dans le but d'érer en temps utile la documentation nécessaire.

facilitarán y acelerarán la aplicación de la tecnología espacial.

El principal cambio consistió en el mayor papel de los países en desarrollo en la organización, decididos a fomentar sus intereses de telecomunicaciones, a menudo sin armonizar, y a veces en conflicto directo con los de los países industrializados.

La CAMR 79 aumentó mucho la atribución del espectro para toda clase de servicios definidos en el Reglamento, a fin de dar a los países en desarrollo atribuciones para el uso futuro, mientras EE.UU. y la mayoría de las naciones occidentales deseaban preservar los procedimientos existentes de registro y coordinación por la IFRB para la asignación de frecuencias en ondas decamétricas y en el servicio fijo por satélite. Aprobó resoluciones con el mandato de programar futuras CAMR para planificar el uso de esos servicios con carácter global.

Las CAMR se celebran para tratar de asuntos peculiares de servicios de telecomunicaciones o de una de las tres regiones de la UIT. Como ejemplos recientes, cabe citar la CAMR de Comunicaciones Espaciales de 1971, y la CAMR de Radiodifusión por Satélite en 1977. Una importante conferencia proyectada por la CAMR 79 es la CAMR sobre Servicios de Radiodifusión por Satélite para el hemisferio occidental, prevista para junio de 1983. Para 1984 se ha programado una CAMR de Radiodifusión por ondas decamétricas y una CAMR para Servicios Espaciales, en dos reuniones (1985 y 1987), con objeto de determinar asignaciones basadas en « consideraciones que aseguren un acceso equitativo en la práctica ».

Se han convocado otras CAMR de la UIT para tratar aspectos de radiodifusión, como telecomunicaciones móviles, radiodifusión por satélite, el uso de bandas de frecuencias particulares, o problemas relativos a ciertos países o continentes. Una de esas conferencias, prevista para 1986, va a examinar y revisar ła reglamentación de la radiodifusión en Africa.

El programa de conferencias que figura al margen comprende seminarios preparatorios para CAMR.

▷ 237

The overall frequency spectrum of the electromagnetic waves represented here includes, in increasing order of frequencies (or decreasing order of wavelengths), the following elements:
— the audible frequency spectrum,
— the radio frequency spectrum, also called Hertzian waves (named after Heinrich R. Hertz, 1857-1894),
— the visible frequency spectrum, or light, with, on either side, the invisible infrared and ultraviolet rays,
— the x-ray and the gamma ray spectrum.

The parts of the overall spectrum, (each also called "a spectrum" of the various categories of frequencies) have defined limits. This is particularly true of the "radio spectrum" used in telecommunications, which extends from a few kilohertz (kHz) to 3,000,000,000 kHz — variously expressed as 3,000,000 megahertz (MHz) cycles, or 3,000 gigaherz (GHz), hz corresponding to one cycle per second.

Useful radio waves can be produced in the upper audio frequencies up to about 300 GHz. The radio spectrum is divided into the 8 bands shown on the chart opposite. These frequency bands or divisions, officially numbered 4 to 11, accomodate all types of radio transmissions: maritime communications, shortwave radio, television broadcasting, microwave communications (terrestrial and satellite), and radar. An even higher band, EF12, ranging from 300 to 3,000 GHz, is being studied for its possible use.

Although the radio spectrum spans a very wide range of frequencies, not all of it is of equal value. For example, frequencies between 45 and 75 Hz could only be used by means of outsize aerial systems covering several miles.

At the other extreme, microwave signals are not reflected from the ionosphere, like most other radio signals, and their use is confined therefore to "line-of-sight" communications (whatever the distance). At certain frequencies within this range, signals are reflected by solid objects. This is, of course, the principle of radar.

The finite characteristics of the radio spectrum, and the ever growing demand for exclusive positions on it by broadcasters and other users, constitute a major problem, present ever since radio's early beginnings and continuing today despite a vast increase in the range of useful frequencies available. In their efforts to reduce congestion, engineers have succeeded first in extending the bandwidths (originally thought to be usable only from 10 to 15,000 kHz), second in reducing the frequency bandwidth needed for a given transmission and third in increasing the volume of information transmitted on a given bandwidth.

Intensive research in these directions is continuing but there is little doubt that the physical limits of the usable spectrum have almost been reached. Increases in the information carrying capacity of available frequencies (by various multiplexing techniques) remains the most promising avenue to still greater use. Optical communications, using lightwave frequencies (visible spectrum) through optical glass fiber and laser beams, hold out some hope of a substantial extension of the usable spectrum. However, in view of the inevitable explosive growth of communication requirements and the consequent expansion in demand for bandwidth frequencies, they will continue to be in short supply no matter how many ways engineers find to widen the usable spectrums.

Le spectre des ondes électromagnétiques représenté ici, en ordre croissant des valeurs de fréquences (ou décroissant des longueurs d'ondes), comprend les éléments suivants :
— le spectre des fréquences audibles,
— le spectre des fréquences radioélectriques ou spectre des ondes hertziennes (du nom de Heinrich R. Hertz, 1857-1894),
— le spectre visible, celui des ondes lumineuses limité à ses deux extrémités, respectivement par les rayons infrarouges et les rayons ultraviolets,
— le spectre des rayons X et celui des rayons gamma.

Il convient de noter que les différentes parties de l'ensemble du spectre des fréquences - représentant chacune "un spectre" d'une catégorie de fréquences déterminées - ont respectivement des limites bien définies. C'est notamment le cas du "spectre des fréquences radioélectriques" utilisé dans les télécommunications, lequel est compris entre quelques dizaines de kHz (kilohertz) et 3 000 000 000 kHz, soit autrement dit : 3 000 000 MHz (Mégahertz) ou 3000 GHz (Gigahertz), l'unité Hz correspondant à un cycle par seconde.

Depuis la limite supérieure des fréquences audibles jusqu'à environ 300 GHz, il est possible de produire des ondes radioélectriques utilisables. Le spectre radioélectrique se divise en 8 bandes représentées sur le diagramme ci-contre. Ces bandes ou gammes de fréquences, officiellement numérotées de 4 à 11, servent à tous les types de transmission radioélectrique : communications maritimes, radiocommunications à ondes décamétriques, radiodiffusion sonore et télévisuelle, communications en hyperfréquences (faisceaux hertziens de Terre et liaisons par satellite) et radar. On étudie même la possibilité d'utiliser la partie inférieure d'une bande de fréquences encore plus élevée, n. 12, comprise entre 300 et 3000 GHz.

A l'autre extrémité du spectre les signaux propagés par micro-ondes ne sont pas reflétés par l'ionosphère, comme la plupart des autres signaux radioélectriques. En conséquence, cette gamme d'ondes ne peut être utilisée que sur des liaisons en visibilité directe (quelle qu'en soit la longueur). Dans cette gamme, les signaux émis sur certaines fréquences sont réfléchis par des objets solides. C'est sur cette propriété qu'est fondé le principe du radar.

Le fait que le spectre des fréquences radioélectriques soit limité face à une demande sans cesse croissante, pose un problème majeur qui existait d'ailleurs depuis les débuts de la radiodiffusion et qui s'aggrave aujourd'hui en dépit de l'augmentation considérable de la gamme des fréquences utiles. Dans leurs efforts pour réduire l'encombrement du spectre, les ingénieurs sont parvenus tout d'abord à en étendre les portions utilisables; ensuite, ils ont réussi à réduire la largeur de bande nécessaire pour un type de transmission déterminé et, enfin, ils sont parvenus à augmenter le volume de l'information transmise dans une largeur de bande donnée.

La recherche se poursuit mais il est probable que les limites physiques du spectre utilisable soient quasiment atteintes. L'augmentation de la capacité de transmission de l'information des fréquences disponibles (par diverses méthodes de multiplexage) demeure la perspective la plus prometteuse. Les communications "optiques", utilisant des fréquences d'ondes lumineuses, dans le spectre visible, laissent espérer une extension substantielle du spectre utilisable. Toutefois, compte tenu de la croissance prévisible des besoins dans le domaine de la communication, et de l'explosion de la demande des fréquences qui en découlera, il s'ensuivra inévitablement une pénurie de moyens.

COSMIC RAYS ········· {

GAMMA RAYS ········· {

400 Mµ

X-RAYS ········· {

ULTRA-VIOLET RAYS ········ {

VISIBLE RAYS ·········

INFRA-RED RAYS ········· {

600 Mµ

HERTZIAN RAYS ··········· {
OR RADIO WAVES

LONG ELECTRICAL ··········· {
OSCILLATIONS

Streams of atomic nuclei of heterogenous extremely penetrating character that enters the earth's atmosphere from outer space at speeds approaching that of light and bombarding atmospheric atoms to produce mesons as well as secondary particles possessing some of the original energy

Very high frequency electromagnetic radiation, emitted by some radioactive elements

Electromagnetic radiation ranging from about 100 nm to 0.1nm (nano meter: one thousand millionth of 1 meter 10^{-9}) capable of penetrating non-metallic materials

Electromagnetic radiation in a frequency range between visible light and x-rays wavelengths shorter than 400 millimicrons to 5 millimicrons

Lightwave frequencies 400 to 600 millimicrons ($M\mu$): a millimicron equals one millionth of a millimeter

Electromagnetic radiation next to visible light extending down into microwave frequencies. Wavelength between 740 millimicron and 1 millimeter

THF	(tremendously high frequency) 300 to 3000 GHz	decimillimetric waves 1 to 0.1 mm	GHz, gigahertz (one thousand million cycles per second) Prefix: G = giga (10^9)
EHF	(extremely high frequency) 30 to 300 GHz	millimetric waves 10 to 1 mm	
SHF	(super high frequency) 3 to 30 GHz	centimetric waves 10 to 1 cm	
UHF	(ultra high frequency) 300 to 3000 MHz	decimetric waves 100 to 10 cm	MHz, megahertz (one million cycles per second) Prefix: M = mega (10^6)
VHF	(very high frequency) 30 to 300 MHz	metric waves 10 to 1 m	
HF	(high frequency) 3 to 30 MHz	decametric waves 100 to 10 m	
MF	(medium frequency) 300 to 3000 kHz	hectometric waves 1000 to 100 m	KHz, kilohertz (one thousand cycles per second) Prefix: K = kilo (10^3)
LF	(low frequency) 30 to 300 kHz	kilometric waves 10 to 1 km	
VLF	(very low frequency) 3 to 30 kHz	myriametric waves 100 to 10 km	

(audio frequencies) 16 to 37.000 Hz — corresponding to the audible sound by the human ear's frequency bands (best reception between 50 and 5.000 Hz)

Hz = Hertz = unit of frequency: one cycle per second

El espectro de frecuencias global de las ondas electromagnéticas representado aquí comprende, en orden creciente de frecuencias (o decreciente de longitudes de onda), los siguientes elementos:
— el espectro de frecuencias audibles;
— el espectro de frecuencias radioeléctricas, denominadas también ondas hertzianas (nombre derivado del físico alemán Heinrich R. Hertz, 1857-1894);
— el espectro de frecuencias visibles, o luminosas, y, en el otro lado, el de rayos infrarrojos invisibles y ultravioleta;
— el espectro de rayos X y rayos gamma.

Debe señalarse que las partes del espectro global tienen límites definidos. Así ocurre especialmente con el «espectro radioeléctrico» utilizado en telecomunicaciones, que se extiende desde unos cuantos miles de kilohertzios por segundo (kHz) a 3 000 000 000 kHz: varios expresados como 3 000 000 de megahertzios (MHz) o 3000 gigahertzios (GHz), por segundo.

En las audiofrecuencias superiores, hasta unos 300 GHz, pueden producirse ondas radioeléctricas. El espectro radioeléctrico se divide en las 8 bandas que se muestran en el gráfico. Esas bandas de frecuencias, numeradas oficialmente de 4 a 11, acomodan todos los tipos de transmisiones radioeléctricas: comunicaciones marítimas, radiocomunicaciones por ondas cortas, difusión de televisión, comunicaciones de microondas (terrenales y por satélite) y radar. Ya se está estudiando una banda todavía más alta, EF12, que va de 300 a 3000 GHz, para usarla en su gama de frecuencias más baja.

Aunque el espectro radioeléctrico abarca una amplia gama de frecuencias, su valor no es siempre el mismo. Por ejemplo, las frecuencias entre 45 y 75 Hz pueden usarse solamente mediante enormes sistemas de antenas de varios km.

En el otro extremo, las señales de microondas no se reflejan desde la jonosfera, como la mayoría de las otras señales radioeléctricas, y su uso se limita, pues, a las comunicaciones de «visibilidad directa» (a cualquier distancia). En ciertas frecuencias de esta gama, las señales se reflejan por objetos sólidos. Este es, naturalmente, el principio del radar.

Las características finitas del espectro radioeléctrico, y la demanda de posiciones exclusivas en el mismo por las empresas de radiodifusión y otros usuarios, que crece sin cesar, constituyen un importante problema, que existe ya desde los primeros días de la radio, y que perdura, a pesar del enorme aumento de la gama de frecuencias útiles disponibles. En sus esfuerzos por reducir la congestión, los ingenieros han logrado, primero, ampliar las anchuras de banda (al principio se pensaba que sólo podrían utilizarse de 10 a 15 000 kHz/s); segundo, reducir la anchura de banda de frecuencias necesaria para determinada transmisión, y tercero, aumentar el volumen de la información transmitida por una anchura de banda dada.

Prosiguen las investigaciónes, pero ya casi se ha llegado a los límites físicos del espectro utilizable. El sector más prometedor es el aumento de la capacidad de transmitir información por las frecuencias disponibles (mediante varias técnicas de multiplexación). Las comunicaciones ópticas, que utilizan frecuencias de ondas luminosas (espectro visible) a través de fibras de vidrio ópticas y haces láser, hacen abrigar esperanzas de aumentar sustancialmente el espectro utilizable. Sin embargo, en vista de la inevitable explosión las necesidades de comunicación, y de la consiguiente expansión de la demanda de frecuencias de banda ancha, seguirán a la zaga de la oferta, por muchos medios que hallen los ingenieros para ampliar el espectro disponible para las comunicaciones.

discord than in the earlier 1959 General WARC. The primary change has been the increasing role played by developing countries in the Organization, and their collective drive to promote their interests.

There is no doubt that to exploit fully the immense benefits of microwave broadcasting, industrialized countries will wish to use satellites in large numbers for increasingly precise operations. The US "wish list", prepared by the recently established FCC "Advisory Committee for the ITU", is for between 36 and 46 channels of Direct Broadcast Satellite service in 1985-86, between 51 and 121 in 1990-93, and between 68 and 205 by the year 2000. The relative isolation of the USA on the North American continent, however, combined with the directivity allowed by new antenna technology, appears to result in the USA having access to the entire usable geostationary arc for domestic telecommunications purposes, competing for this only with Canada and Mexico.

Most of the channels required by the USA would be for standard television service but some are earmarked for high definition TV and others for aural full-field teletext, video conferencing/slow-scan TV, electronic mail/facsimile, and document/data distribution. The FCC committee is also preparing the participation for the USA in the 1985 Space WARC which will be attended by virtually all developing nations. The purpose of the committee is to bring the private sector into the decision-making process.

The 1985 Space WARC (to be held in two sessions in 1985 and 1987) was demanded at the WARC 79 by Third World nations "to bring about more equitable institutional arrangements for use of the orbit/spectrum resource". These nations do not want to be prevented from meeting their most pressing needs — for basic telephone, telex and broadcast services nationwide by a lack of suitable facilities. For example, their planners may consider simpler, cheaper (sometimes more spectrum-hungry and interference-prone) technology to be most cost-effective for certain applications. The FCC committee admits that "forecasting the demand for a new service has always proved to be a hazardous undertaking" but nonetheless endorses the FCC's "preliminary view" that an evolutionary approach, determining allocation of orbit/spectrum facilities when required for a specific purpose by any country, is preferable to an a priori plan, under which orbital slots and frequencies would be apportioned among countries in advance, without regard to specific needs.

Salient among the considerations of orbit/spectrum planning, at the network level, is the work currently progressing towards the implementation of an integrated services digital network (ISDN). The ITU's CCITT are deeply involved in the development of the ISDN which likely to emerge as a viable system during the 1990s at the earliest.

The Secretary-General of the ITU, Richard E. Butler, speaking at a Unispace Forum in 1982, defined very clearly the purpose of regulations in the usage of the Radio Frequency Spectrum and satellite orbits as follows: "Generally speaking, the Regulations define the rules to be applied by Members in using the spectrum and orbit, as well as the rights and obligations resulting from this use. Hence, however simple they may be, regulations will inescapably have an impact on the application of national sovereignty by imposing restrictions on it, if only by limiting the freedom to use parts of the spectrum without taking into account other existing or planned uses". For this reason, while recognizing in its preamble "the sovereign right of each country to regulate its telecommunications", the Regulations annexed to the Convention contain "only the minimum of provisions absolutely essential for the efficient use of spectrum and orbit", adding that mutuality of interest and agreement reached in the Union enable Members to carry out the detailed planning and operation of services in their-day-to-day management of space and of the Radio Frequency Spectrum.

de 60 à 90 cm et leur prix ne dépassera pas quelques centaines de dollars. De toute façon, le satellite remplit toujours la même fonction : il reçoit de la Terre un signal, l'amplifie, le transpose en fréquence et le retransmet à la Terre au moyen de ses répéteurs.
Il est devenu de plus en plus difficile de réaliser des accords internationaux relatifs à l'orbite géosynchrone et aux fréquences requises pour divers types de communication par satellite nécessaires à un nombre croissant de pays. La dernière Conférence administrative mondiale des radiocommunications (CAMR) de 1979 a été beaucoup plus « dure » que la précédente qui s'était tenue en 1959 : les pays en développement s'y sont unis pour défendre leurs intérêts en matière de télécommunications.

Il ne fait aucun doute que, pour tirer le meilleur profit de la radiodiffusion à micro-ondes, les pays industriels voudront utiliser un nombre toujours plus grand de satellites, dans des buts précis. Aux États-Unis, le « Comité consultatif de la FCC » vient de dresser « une liste de desiderata/aspirations » qui portent sur l'allocation de 36 à 46 canaux de radiodiffusion directe par satellite en 1985-1986, de 51 à 121 en 1990-1993 et de 68 à 205 pour l'an 2000. La plupart des canaux revendiqués par les Etats-Unis sont destinés au service de radiodiffusion télévisuel normal, mais certains d'entre eux devraient être utilisés pour la télévision à haute définition et d'autres pour divers besoins tels que : télétext, téléconférence, TV à balayage lent, courrier électronique et fac-similé, ainsi que distribution de documents et de données. Le dit Comité prépare déjà la participation des Etats-Unis à la CAMR spatiale de 1985, à laquelle participeront presque tous les pays en développement, il cherche résolument à associer le secteur privé à la prise des décisions.

La CAMR spatiale de 1985 tiendra deux sessions, en 1985 et 1987. Les pays du tiers-monde ont demandé à la CAMR de 1979 de prévoir cette nouvelle conférence « pour établir des accords institutionnels plus équitables en ce qui concerne l'utilisation des ressources de l'orbite géosynchrone et du spectre ». Ils ne veulent pas se trouver empêchés de couvrir leurs besoins les plus urgents (téléphonie, télex, radiodiffusion) faute de moyens appropriés. Leurs spécialistes pourraient, en effet, envisager l'emploi de techniques plus simples et moins coûteuses mais plus « gourmandes » en fréquences et parfois plus sujettes aux brouillages. Quant au Comité de la FCC américaine, il reprend le point de vue préalablement exprimé par la FCC elle-même, selon lequel il est préférable d'appliquer une méthode évolutive en traitant les situations cas par cas, pour satisfaire les demandes des pays en matière de fréquences et d'orbite, plutôt que d'adopter un plan à priori, ne tenant pas compte des besoins spécifiques.

La planification de l'orbite et du spectre est essentiellement basée sur les travaux entrepris en vue de la réalisation d'un réseau numérique avec intégration des services (RNIS) qui devrait voir le jour au cours de la prochaine décennie.

M. Richard E. Butler, Secrétaire général de l'UIT, a déclaré en 1982 devant le Forum Unispace : « D'une manière générale, les règlements administratifs internationaux contiennent les dispositions que doivent appliquer les Membres pour utiliser l'orbite géosynchrone et le spectre, et celles définissant les droits et obligations découlant de cette utilisation. Il s'ensuit que — aussi simples soient-ils — ces règlements ont des incidences sur la souveraineté nationale car ils la limitent, ne fut-ce qu'en restreignant la liberté d'utilisation de certaines parties du spectre pour tenir compte des autres utilisations existantes ou prévues ». C'est pourquoi, si, dans son préambule, la Convention internationale des télécommunications reconnaît à chaque pays le droit de réglementer ses propres télécommunications, les règlements qui lui sont annexés ne contiennent que des dispositions minimales, rigoureusement indispensables à l'utilisation de l'orbite et du spectre. La communauté d'intérêts et les accords conclus au sein de l'Union permettent cependant aux Membres d'établir souverainement leur planification et d'exploiter leurs services, dans le cadre de l'effort quotidien de gestion commune de l'espace et du spectre des fréquences radioélectriques.

IFRB PROCEDUR
AND CLASSIFICATI

The procedures governing notification and registration of frequency assignments in the Master International Frequency Register may be broadly subdivided into the acts of co-ordination, notification, examination and registration.

In the 1950s and 1960s, the increased use of terrestrial systems (radio relay links) and of space radiocommunications, created a need to develop procedures for increased prior co-ordination of the use of frequencies and this has been a major preoccupation of the radio conferences convened by the ITU since 1963.

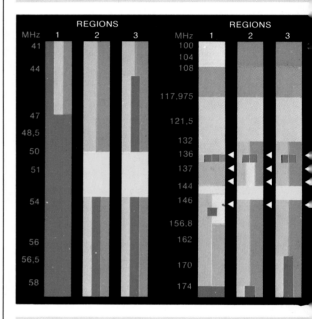

Radio Regulations RR1218 and RR1219 provide that the IFRB shall be notified of frequency assignments if:
a) the use of the frequency is capable of causing harmful interference to any service of another administration;
b) the frequency is to be used for international radiocommunication, or c) it is desired to obtain international recognition of the use of the frequency.

The Board examines the notice for its conformity with the Table of Frequency Allocations and the other provisions for the Radio Regulations and then assesses the extent to which the use of the frequency could cause interference. If the Board finds that there is a probability of such interference, the notice is returned to the notifying administration which then, normally, searches for an alternative frequency or modifies the characteristics of the station in such a way as to obviate the probable harmful interference. If the Board finds that there is little or no probability of harmful interference with existing entries of other administrations in the Master Register, the notices would normally receive a favourable finding. The particulars of the assignment are entered in the Master Register, accompanied by all relevant remarks, which establishes the legal status of the assignment vis-à-vis other existing and future assignments.

Initially the notification and registration procedures were developed as a means of ensuring that the agreed rules for the use of the spectrum were being respected by all governments. With the arrival of space techniques, insofar as the frequency bands shared between space and terrestrial radiocommunications are concerned, these procedures were confirmed and further developed to include the obligatory co-ordination of the use of frequencies prior to the notification and registration procedures for stations being put into service.

OR THE ALLOCATION, REGISTRATION OF RADIO FREQUENCIES BY REGIONS

procédures de notification et d'inscription des assignations
fréquence dans le Fichier de référence international des
uences peuvent se répartir en quatre étapes : coordination,
ification, examen et inscription. A la fin des années 50 et
dant les années 60, avec l'emploi croissant de systèmes de
e perfectionnés (faisceaux hertziens), et l'apparition des
ocommunications spatiales, il a fallu établir des procédures
inées à renforcer la coordination préalable de l'utilisation
fréquences. Cette question a été au centre des préoccupa-
s des conférences de radiocommunications convoquées par

Los procedimientos que regulan la notificación e inscripción de
asignaciones de frecuencias en el Registro Internacional de
Frecuencias se pueden dividir según se apliquen a las actividades de coordinación, notificación, examen e inscripción.

En los años 50 y 60, el mayor uso de sistemas terrenales
(relevadores radioeléctricos) y de las radiocomunicaciones espaciales, creó la necesidad de elaborar procedimientos de
coordinación previa de la utilización de frecuencias, lo que ha
preocupado mucho a las conferencias de radiocomunicaciones
organizadas por la UIT desde 1963.

ciente número de países es difícil. En la última Conferencia Administrativa Mundial de Radiocomunicaciones (CAMR 79) hubo mucho más desacuerdo
que en la CAMR general de 1959. El principal cambio es el mayor papel que desempeñan los países en
desarrollo en la organización, y su acción colectiva
para fomentar sus intereses.

No hay duda de que, para explotar plenamente los
inmensos beneficios de la radiodifusión por microondas, los países avanzados quieren utilizar un
gran número de satélites para operaciones cada vez
más precisas. La "lista de deseos" de EE.UU., pre-
parada por el « Comité Consultivo para la UIT » de
la FCC, comprende de 36 a 46 canales de servicio TV
DS en 1985-86, del 51 a 121 en 1990-93, y de 68 a 205
para el año 2000. Sin embargo, el relativo aislamiento de EE.UU. en el continente norteamericano,
unido a la directividad que permite la nueva tecnología de antenas, parece llevar a EE.UU. a acceder a
todo el arco geoestacionario utilizable para comunicaciones nacionales, compitiendo sólo con Canadá y
México.

EE.UU. necesita la mayoría de los canales para el
servicio de televisión normalizado, pero algunos se
asignan para TV de alta definición y otros para teletex aural de campo completo, conferencia/explora-
ción lenta TV, correo electrónico/facsímil, y distribución de documentos/datos. El comité de la FCC
está preparando también la participación de EE.UU.
en la CAMR espacial de 1985, a la que asistirán casi
todos los países en desarrollo. La finalidad del comité es introducir el sector privado en el proceso de
adopción de decisiones.

Los países del Tercer Mundo solicitaron en la CAMR de
1979 que en la CAMR espacial de 1985 (que se
celebrará en dos reuniones, en 1985 y 1987) « se
logren acuerdos internacionales más equitativos para uso de la órbita y del espectro ». Esos países no
quieren que se les impida atender sus necesidades
más apremiantes — telefonía, télex y radiodifusión
básicos — por falta de facilidades apropiadas. Por
ejemplo, sus planificadores pueden considerar que la
tecnología más sencilla, más barata (y también, a
veces, la que ocupa más espectro y es propensa a la
interferencia) es la más rentable para ciertas aplicaciones. La FCC admite que « la previsión de la demanda de un nuevo servicio ha sido siempre una
empresa arriesgada », pero, no obstante, apoya la
"opinión preliminar" de la FCC de que un enfoque
evolutivo, que determine la atribución de facilidades
de la órbita y del espectro cuando sea necesario para
determinado fin de un país, es preferible a un plan a
priori en el que las porciones y frecuencias orbitales
se distribuirían previamente entre países, sin tener en
cuenta necesidades específicas.

**Entre las consideraciones de la planificación de la órbita y del
espectro** a nivel nacional destaca la labor que conduce a la aplicación de una red digital de servicios
integrados (RDSI). El CCITT de la UIT interviene
mucho en el desarrollo de la RDSI, que probablemente sea un sistema viable en los años 1990.

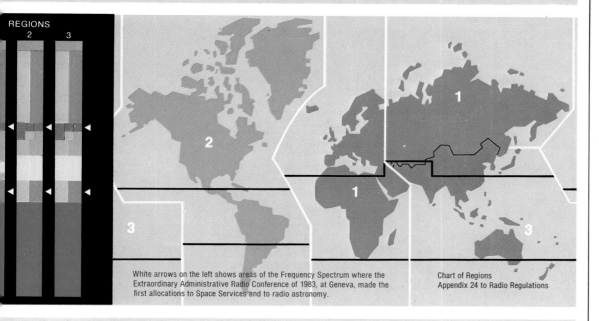

REGIONS
2   3

White arrows on the left shows areas of the Frequency Spectrum where the
Extraordinary Administrative Radio Conference of 1983, at Geneva, made the
first allocations to Space Services and to radio astronomy.

Chart of Regions
Appendix 24 to Radio Regulations

El Secretario General de la UIT, Richard E. Butler, hablando en el Foro Unispar en 1982, definió
con toda claridad el propósito de reglamentar el uso
del espectro de frecuencias radioeléctricas y las órbitas de satélites como sigue: « En términos generales, el Reglamento define las normas que han de
aplicar los Miembros en el uso del espectro y de la
órbita, así como los derechos y obligaciones resultantes de ese uso. De ahí que, por sencillo que pa-
rezca, la reglamentación repercutirá inevitablemente
en la aplicación de la soberanía nacional imponiendo restricciones, aunque sólo sea limitando la libertad de utilizar partes del espectro sin tener en cuenta
otros usos existentes o previstos ». Por tal razón, si
bien en el preámbulo del Convenio se reconoce « el
derecho soberano da cada país de reglamentar sus
telecomunicaciones », los Reglamentos anexos al
Convenio sólo contienen las disposiciones mínimas
absolutamente necesarias para el uso eficaz del espectro y de la órbita, agregando que la mutualidad
de intereses y el acuerdo alcanzado en la Unión
permite a los Miembros proceder a la planificación y
explotación detalladas de servicios en su gestión
diaria del espacio y del espectro de frecuencias.

depuis 1963. Conformément aux dispositions de l'article
uméros 1218 et 1219 du Règlement des radiocommunica-
, toute assignation de fréquence, sauf exceptions spéci-
, doit être notifiée à l'IFRB : a) si l'utilisation de la fré-
ce est susceptible d'entraîner des brouillages préjudicia-
à un service quelconque d'une autre administration ; b) ou
fréquence doit être utilisée pour des radiocommunications
nationales ; c) ou encore si l'on désire obtenir une recon-
sance internationale de l'utilisation de cette fréquence.
Comité examine si la fiche de notification est conforme au
eau d'attribution des bandes de fréquences et aux autres
ses du Règlement des radiocommunications ; il évalue en-
dans quelle mesure l'utilisation de la fréquence — dans
onditions notifiées — pourrait causer un brouillage préju-
ble au détriment du service assuré par les stations déjà
ites au nom d'autres administrations. Si le Comité conclue
e appréciable probabilité de brouillage préjudiciable, la
de notification est renvoyée à l'administration notificatri-
aquelle s'efforce alors habituellement de trouver une fré-
ce de remplacement ou de modifier les caractéristiques de
ation ; si le Comité estime faible ou nulle la probabilité, la
de notification fait en principe l'objet d'une conclusion
rable. Les caractéristiques de l'assignation de fréquence
mpagnées de toute observation pertinente) sont inscrites
le Fichier de référence qui définit le statut légal de l'assi-
on par rapport aux assignations existantes et futures.
ef, les procédures de notification et d'inscription ont été
lement établies pour faire en sorte que tous les Gouver-
nts observent les règles convenues pour l'utilisation du
re. Avec l'apparition des techniques spatiales, et dans la
re où cela concerne les bandes de fréquences partagées
les services de Terre, ces procédures ont été confirmées et
ues pour couvrir la coordination obligatoire de l'utilisation
réquences avant l'application des procédures de notifica-
et d'inscription applicables aux stations qui sont mises en
ce.

El Reglamento de la Radiocommunicaciones (RR1218 y
RR1219), prevé que se notificarán a la IFRB las asignaciones de
frecuencias: a) si la utilización de la frecuencia puede causar
interferencia prejudicial a un servicio de otra administración; b)
si la frecuencia se utiliza para la radiocomunicación internacional; o c) si se desea obtener el reconocimiento internacional
del uso de dicha frecuencia.

La Junta examinará si la notificación se conforma al Cuadro
de atribución de bandas de frecuencias y a las demás disposiciones del Reglamento de Radiocomunicaciones, y evaluará el
grado en que el uso de la frecuencia puede producir interfe-
rencias. Si la Junta concluye que la interferencia es probable,
se devuelve la notificación a la administración notificante que,
normalmente, busca una frecuencia alternativa o modifica las
características de la estación a fin de evitar la interferencia
perjudicial probable. Si la Junta concluye que la probabilidad de
interferencia perjudicial a estaciones de otras administraciones
inscritas en el Registro es escasa o nula, la notificación es
normalmente objeto de una conclusión favorable. Las características de la asignación, junto con las observaciones pertinentes, se inscriben en el Registro, que establece la condición
jurídica de la asignación respecto de las asignaciones existentes y futuras.

Se establecieron inicialmente los procedimentos de notificación e inscripción para que todos los gobiernos observaran
las reglas convenidas sobre la utilización del espectro. Al llegar
las técnicas espaciales, y en la medida en que ello afecta a las
bandas de frecuencias compartidas entre los servicios de ra-
diocommunicación espacial y terrenal, ha sido preciso confirmar y ampliar estos procedimientos para abarcar la coordinación obligatoria de la utilización de las frecuencias antes de
aplicar los procedimientos de notificación e incripción a las
estaciones que se ponen en servicio.

□

KEY PARTNERS IN PROGRESS
GOVERNMENTS, TELECOM ENTITIES
INDUSTRIES AND USERS

WHO ARE THE KEY PARTNERS in progress? And progress to what end? The answers to these questions are not always as clear as one would wish, often in fact confused and confusing. When we talk about progress in this state of the art volume on communications, we mean technological progress and progress towards a global system of telecommunications, a worldwide infrastructure which, utilizing technologies now maturing, will take us fully into the Information Age and maximize the benefits we derive from it.

This Information Age we conceive as an age of peaceful, fuller living, in which people will communicate more easily and more universally, know and understand one another better, share objectives and cooperate in reaching them. Information will be a "product" for the mind, conditioned and processed very much like we condition and process the food that sustains our bodies.

This global system, in its ultimate form the integrated services digital network (ISDN), involves the use of all technological advances reviewed here — radio, television, computers, space, integrated circuitry, optical transmission, digital communications, information storage, man-machine dialogue, and many other aspects of communications technology. One of the leading contributors to the thinking on this plane, Dr. Koji Kobayashi, quoted earlier in this book, spoke of "contributing to world peace by helping create an international communications network by which anyone anywhere in the world can talk to anyone else at any time". Only a few years ago it appeared a dream — even now two-thirds of the world have only skeletal telephone service — but

▷ 240

QUELS SONT DONC ces grands partenaires du progrès ? et pourquoi doivent-ils s'entendre ? Les réponses à ces questions ne sont pas toujours aussi claires qu'on le souhaiterait. Elles sont même souvent confuses et créent la confusion. Lorsque nous parlons de progrès dans le domaine des communications, nous entendons : progrès technique et progrès vers l'aménagement d'un système universel de télécommunications, une infrastructure mondiale mettant en œuvre des techniques en voie de maturation et nous transportant dans « l'ère de l'information ». Nous imaginons que cette ère sera celle de la paix et de la plénitude de vie, au cours de laquelle chacun pourra communiquer sans difficulté avec ses semblables, proches ou lointains, nous incitant ainsi à mieux nous connaître et à mieux nous comprendre, à reconnaître nos objectifs communs et à coopérer pour les atteindre.

Ce système global, généralement connu sous sa forme ultime comme le « réseau numérique avec intégration des services » (RNIS) implique l'utilisation de tous les progrès techniques passés en revue jusqu'ici. L'un des premiers à propager cette vision du futur est le Dr. Koji Kobayashi, PDG de NEC Corporation, pour lequel il importe désormais de « contribuer à la paix mondiale en aidant à la création d'un réseau international de communications grâce auquel chacun pourra, en quelque lieu qu'il se trouve, parler avec l'interlocuteur de son choix, à n'importe quel moment et n'importe où dans le monde ». Il a encore ajouté « toute l'humanité aurait alors la possibilité d'échanger et d'utiliser de l'information à n'importe quel moment et en tous lieux ». Il y a à peine quelques années cette idée semblait du domaine du rêve. Toutefois des progrès sont en cours et vont se poursuivre dans ce domaine, à condition que les pays

▷ 240

¿QUIENES SON LOS ASOCIADOS esenciales en el progreso? ¿Y progresar con qué fin? Las respuestas a estas preguntas no son siempre tan claras como sería de desear. Con frecuencia son confusas y desconcertantes. En este volumen sobre la ciencia actual de las comunicaciones, por progreso entendemos el tecnológico y el avance hacia un sistema global de telecomunicaciones, una infraestructura mundial que, utilizando tecnologías nuevas, nos llevará a la era de la información, que concebimos como una época de vida plena y pacífica, en que la gente comunicará con mayor facilidad y más universalmente, conociéndose y comprendiéndose mejor, compartiendo objetivos y cooperando para alcanzarlos. La información será un "producto" de la mente, condicionado y procesado casi como preparamos y procesamos los alimentos que sostienen nuestros cuerpos.

Este sistema global, conocido como red digital de servicios integrados (RDSI) entraña el uso de todas las tecnologías avanzadas consideradas: radio, televisión, computadores, espacio, circuitos integrados, transmisión óptica, comunicaciones digitales, almacenamiento de la información, diálogo hombre-máquina, y muchos otros aspectos. Uno de los principales contribuyentes al pensamiento en este plano, el Dr. Koji Kobayashi, ya citado, habla de « contribuir a la paz mundial ayudando a crear una red internacional de comunicaciones en la que todos puedan hablar desde cualquier parte del mundo con otros, en cualquier momento ». Esto parecía un sueño hace pocos años — incluso ahora, dos tercios del mundo disponen sólo de un servicio telefónico mínimo —, pero siguen los progresos, y continuarán — a condi-

▷ 241

This diagram of an Integrated Services Digital Network (ISDN) shows how subscribers are linked to each other and to processing, transit and other facilities via optical cable, as well as existing coaxial cables, microwaves towers or satellites.

Ce schéma d'un Réseau Numérique avec Intégration de Services (RNIS) montre comment les abonnés sont reliés entre eux et aux divers centres de traitement et de transit par câbles optiques, câbles coaxiaux, stations hertziennes ou satellites.

Esta estructura de la RDSI es la de cualquier región. El esquema muestra cómo están vinculados los abonados entre sí y a las unidades de tratamiento y de tránsito por cables ópticos, cables coaxiales, enlaces de microondas o satélites.

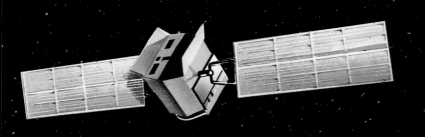

Transit communication processing center

Trunks optical, coaxial cable microwave, satellite

Transit communication processing center

Information processing center

Subscriber communication processing center

Subscriber communication processing center

Information processing center

Terminal connecting equipment

Terminal connecting equipment

mobile

Subscriber line (optical-fiber)

Subscriber line (optical-fiber)

Telephone set　Telex　Facsimile　Data terminal　Tele-meter　Tele-control　Video terminal

Video terminal　Tele-control　Tele-meter　Data terminal　Facsimile　Telex　Telephone set

Business or home telecommunication terminals

Business or home telecommunication terminals

progress is being made and will continue to be made, provided nations co-operate and partnerships are forged, until the ISDN is a reality.

The key partners in this endeavour are a diverse company of people and organizations, each with a specific contribution to make to the achievement of a global integrated network: the governments who regulate and finance; the telecom and broadcasting agencies who run and maintain the system; the manufacturers who supply the equipment, plus the researchers who have advanced the state of the art so far and so fast; the carriers who specialize in transporting the information and making it available; the companies who produce the end-user equipment; the banks which finance it all and, finally, the users who buy the services and make them a worthwhile endeavour. All this is shown graphically in the "Information Business" map on p. 26.

Some large enterprises combine several of these functions. The activities of some of these very large enterprises are examined more closely in the next section — "Master-builders in communications". Here we examine how far these various organizations combine successfully in the planning and execution of major projects, and in tackling the difficult and obdurate problem of the definition and adoption of international standards, which is one of the basic elements in successful co-operation.

A good illustration of combined effort, by private industry and a ministry of PTT, is provided by the profile of Saudi Arabia's construction of an integrated network, employing the latest techniques and tapping the resources of major manufacturers and contractors (see p. 244). Other examples of combined effort are contained in the descriptions of regional networks given in "Focus on World Development of Infrastructures and Network Integration" (see p. 70), where the ITU takes the lead in planning, co-ordinating and scheduling the building of regional infrastructures and in the training of local personnel.

Speaking at the Televent conference — a dialogue connecting Melbourne in Australia to Montreux in Switzerland — in July 1982 Richard Butler, Secretary-General of the ITU, commented that this event could not have taken place "without substantive agreements and understanding on the orderly application and fusion of the many scientific and technological advances... — governments, telecommunication administrations, common and specialized carriers, industry, scientific, technical and international organizations — all of which contribute to the result", namely to a "face to face" discussion between people on opposite sides of the earth. The ITU was described as the "forum to assist the harmonization and integration of techonology advances within the world of telecommunications".

Theodore F. Brophy, chief executive officer of GTE Corporation, considers that the ITU's role "will become even more vital in the coming years", especially in the furtherance of the adoption of international standards — "strong encouragement of the adaptation and applications, wherever appropriate, of such new technologies as SPC and digital" and the furtherance of the development of "a truly global network" continuing to unify the suppliers of the varied systems and "making certain that these systems are mutually compatible". Also "not to permit obsolete standards to block new technology" but to adopt standards of system architecture that will allow their orderly evolution.

International standards are not easy to define and rarely suit equally countries at varying stages of development and with radically different telecommunication requirements and traffic characteristics. Moreover some member countries house large powerful companies, all anxious to increase their share of world markets with systems of their own design. There is little doubt, however, that as suppliers, the industrial countries have an interest in developing multinational participation in a smooth and efficient international regulatory/standards setting process.

After the compatibility of systems and equipment, the most vital contribution of international standards

▷ 242

coopèrent et s'associent au cours des prochaines décennies, jusqu'au moment où le RNIS sera devenu une réalité.

Dans cette entreprise universelle, les grands partenaires sont les gouvernements qui établissent la réglementation et assurent le financement, les entreprises de télécommunications et de radiodiffusion qui exploitent et entretiennent les réseaux, les constructeurs et les fournisseurs d'équipements qui, en dehors de la fabrication et de la fourniture, accomplissent un travail de recherche considérable qui fait progresser la technique, les spécialistes dans la mise à disposition et le transport de l'information, les sociétés qui produisent les équipements terminaux, les banques qui financent l'ensemble et, bien sûr, les usagers eux-mêmes qui « achètent » des services et qui en définitive les mettent en valeur. Tout cela est indiqué graphiquement sur la carte-diagramme intitulée « Information Business » p. 26.

Un certain nombre de grandes entreprises combinent diverses fonctions. Les activités de certaines de ces firmes sont passées en revue plus loin, dans « Master-builders in Communications ». Examinons pour l'instant dans quelle mesure ces grandes organisations acceptent de s'associer, pour planifier et exécuter leurs grands projets, pour surmonter les obstacles et pour résoudre le problème ardu que représentent la définition et l'adoption de normes internationales.

Un bel exemple des efforts entrepris conjointement par l'industrie privée et les ministères des PTT, à l'échelon national, est celui donné par l'Arabie saoudite dans la construction d'un réseau intégré mettant en œuvre les techniques les plus récentes, ainsi que les ressources des grands constructeurs (voir p. 244), sans compter les autres exemples d'efforts entrepris en commun, cités dans les descriptions de réseaux régionaux (voir p. 70), et dans lesquels l'UIT joue un rôle pilote dans la planification et la coordination des opérations de construction des infrastructures régionales et dans la formation du personnel des pays concernés.

Parlant à la conférence "Televent" — dialogue entre Melbourne en Australie et Montreux en Suisse — en 1982, Richard Butler, Secrétaire général de l'UIT, a déclaré que : « de tels évènements n'auraient jamais pu se produire sans entente préalable, ni sans que des accords essentiels aient été conclus en ce qui concerne l'application et la fusion ordonnée de nombreuses innovations scientifiques et techniques auxquelles ont contribué les gouvernements, les administrations de télécommunications, les prestataires de services de communication, l'industrie, les milieux scientifiques et techniques et les organisations internationales. Ce sont toutes ces entités qui ont contribué au résultat: une discussion « face à face » entre des gens se trouvant aux antipodes de la terre. L'UIT a été décrite comme le forum mondial appelé à contribuer à l'harmonisation et à l'intégration des progrès techniques dans les télécommunications à l'échelle du monde entier ».

Theodore F. Brophy, PDG de GTE Corporation, estime que le rôle de l'UIT va devenir encore plus vital au cours des années à venir, spécialement pour susciter l'adoption de normes internationales et encourager fermement l'adaptation et l'utilisation, dans tous les cas où cela se justifie, de nouvelles méthodes telles que la commande par programme enregistré et la technique numérique, ainsi que pour promouvoir l'aménagement d'un réseau véritablement mondial, en continuant à inciter les fournisseurs à s'entendre, de manière à assurer la compatibilité réciproque de leurs différents systèmes sans que l'imposition de normes paralyse l'innovation.

Les normes internationales ne sont jamais faciles à définir, et conviennent rarement de façon égale à tous les 158 pays Membres de l'UIT, qui diffèrent par leur niveau de développement, leurs exigences en matière de télécommunications et leurs caractéristiques de trafic. En outre, de puissantes sociétés installées dans un certain nombre de pays s'efforcent de mieux se situer sur le marché mondial en fournissant des systèmes de leur propre conception. Toutefois, il est certain que les pays industrialisés, comme les fournisseurs, ont intérêt à favoriser une participation multinationale dans le cadre d'une procédure effi-

▷ 242

INTERNATIONAL ST

The establishment of international standards ensuring compatibility and effective interfacing between national networks is an obvious pre-requisite of success in establishing the ISDN. Ways must be found, therefore, to achieve this without stultifying innovation — always the danger of over-rigid standards — a none too easy task in a period of rapid technological change. Electronics has brought an increasing convergence in the modes of telecommunications, greatly facilitating integration, but also many new product opportunities, which in turn have brought about a proliferation of differentiated alternatives, outdistancing the present system of establishing standards.

This is well understood in the industry but commercial and other considerations often prevail. Theoretically, every designer, manufacturer, carrier, operator, is in favour of standardiza-

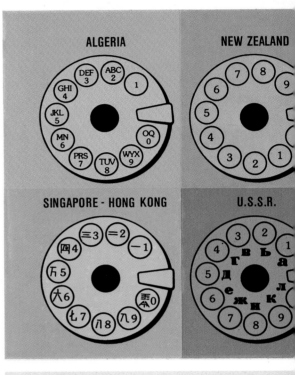

tion, provided it is "his" standard which is adopted. National network operators (PTTs) continue to impose each their own standards, to avoid complicating their infrastructure planning and maintenance, and to protect their home industries. Several industrial leaders have expressed their concern in recent years: William S. Anderson, Chairman of NCR Corporation, warned that in the task of linking computers and communications, for example, "the bridges we have built to date are inadequate... we see evidence of this in the proliferation of network architectures... as a result users face a bewildering array of communications choices". This was in 1981. In the same year John Whyte, engineer-in-chief of British Telecom, told a North American audience that "interface standards and interworking protocols should be established quickly wherever they are relevant to provide a structured framework within which innovation and further development can take place with confidence". He argued strongly that the innovator should be respected and ways found in which "his pioneering innovation can be protected and accomodated within emerging standards".

Progress is being made, largely through the efforts of the ITU's IFRB and the Consultative Committees, CCIR and CCITT. Considerable headway has been made, for example, in those vital areas currently under study: orbit/spectrum planning, ISDN requirements and high definition TV. Work is going on in many other areas necessarily, or as Dr. Koji Kobayashi, Chairman and Chief Executive of NEC Corporation of Japan told an American audience recently: "The accomplishment of a global computer and communication network will not just grow like Topsy, but must be thoroughly engineered to pre-determined standards".

...ption de normes internationales assurant la compatibilité ...terconnexion efficace des réseaux nationaux constitue un ...able impératif du succès de la mise en place du RNIS. Il ...ient cependant d'y parvenir sans paralyser les innovations, ...r permanent de normes trop rigides. Il s'agit donc là, ...tâche relativement ardue en période d'évolution accélérée ...technologie. L'avènement de l'électronique a favorisé la ...de convergence des différents modes de télécommunica-...et facilité considérablement leur intégration. Elle a égale-...suscité l'apparition de produits nouveaux qui, à leur tour, ...ngendré une prolifération de méthodes différentes qui ont ...ment débordé le système actuel d'établissement des nor-...Cela a été bien compris dans l'industrie mais ce sont ...ent des considérations commerciales ou autres qui préva-

El establecimiento de normas internacionales que aseguren la compatibilidad y la efectiva conexión entre redes nacionales es un requisito evidente para el éxito de la RDSI. Por tanto, hay que hallar la manera de lograrlo sin menoscabo de la innovación — el peligro constante de normas demasiado estrictas —, tarea nada fácil es un período de rápido cambio tecnológico. La electrónica ha aportado una mayor convergencia en los modos de telecomunicación, facilitando sobremanera la integración, pero también grandes oportunidades de productos nuevos, que han originado muchas alternativas, superando el sistema actual del establecimiento de normas.

Aunque esto se comprende bien en la industria, prevalecen a menudo consideraciones comerciales y de otro tipo. Teóricamente, todo proyectista, fabricante, empresa de comunicacio-

ción de que las naciones cooperen y se formen asociaciones, hasta que la RDSI sea realidad.

Los principales asociados en este empeño son un diverso grupo de personas y organizaciones, que han de aportar su contribución concreta para conseguir la red global integrada: los gobiernos, que reglamentan y financian; los organismos de telecomunicaciones y radiodifusión (CTT) que dirigen y mantienen el sistema, los fabricantes y proveedores de equipo, los investigadores, que han logrado un avance tan grande y tan rápido de la ciencia; las empresas que se especializan en transportar la información y facilitarla, las que producen el equipo para el usuario final, los bancos, que financian, y, por último, los usuarios, que compran los servicios y los convierten en algo valioso. Todo esto se muestra en el gráfico de la pág. 26.

Hay grandes empresas que combinan varias de estas funciones. Las actividades de algunas de esas enormes empresas se examinan con mayor detalle en la siguiente sección. Aquí analizamos cómo esas organizaciones se combinan en la planificación y ejecución de importantes proyectos y para abordar las dificultades del espinoso problema de la definición y adopción de normas internacionales, uno de los elementos básicos de la cooperación.

Un buen ejemplo del esfuerzo combinado, de la industria privada y una CTT nacional, lo ofrece el perfil de la construcción en Arabia Saudita de una red integrada, empleando las últimas técnicas y aprovechando los recursos de importantes fabricantes y contratistas (véase pág. 244). Otros ejemplos de esfuerzos conjuntos figuran en las descripciones de redes regionales, y en la sección de la pág. 70. La UIT se preocupa de la planificación, la coordinación y la programación de infraestructuras regionales, y de la formación de personal local.

Hablando en la conferencia Televent — diálogo entre Melbourne, en Australia y Montreux, en Suiza —, en julio de 1982, Richard E. Butler, Secretario General de la UIT, comentó que ese acontecimiento no hubiera podido tener lugar « sin acuerdos sustantivos y la comprensión acerca de la aplicación y fusión ordenada de muchos avances científicos y tecnológicos — gobiernos, administraciones de telecomunicaciones, empresas de comunicaciones comunes y especializadas, industria, científicos, técnicos y organizaciones internacionales — todos los cuales contribuyen al resultado », a saber, una discusión directa entre personas de lados opuestos de la Tierra. Se calificó a la UIT de « foro para ayudar a armonizar e integrar los avances tecnológicos con el mundo de las telecomunicaciones ».

Theodore F. Brophy, Jefe ejecutivo de GTE Corporation, considera que el papel de la UIT « será todavía más vital el año próximo », especialmente para fomentar la adopción de normas internacionales: « alentar fuertemente la adaptación y las aplicaciones, donde proceda hacerlo, de nuevas tecnologías como CPA y digitales », y estimular el desarrollo de una « red verdaderamente global », prosiguiendo la unificación de proveedores de los diversos sistemas y « comprobando que son mutuamente compatibles ». Asimismo, « no permitiendo que la nueva tecnología sea bloqueada por normas anticuadas » sino adoptando normas de arquitectura de sistemas que permitan su evolución ordenada.

No es fácil definir normas internacionales, y rara vez convienen por igual a los países en diversos grados de desarrollo y con necesidades de telecomunicaciones y características de tráfico radicalmente distintas. Además, en algunos países miembros hay empresas grandes y poderosas, todas deseosas de aumentar su parte en los mercados mundiales con sistemas de diseño propio. Mas no hay duda de que, como proveedores, los países industriales están interesados en desarrollar la participación multinacional en un proceso de reglamentación y fijación de normas sumamente eficaz.

Después de la compatibilidad de sistemas y equipo, la contribución más importante de las normas internacionales es, sin duda, simplificar los proble-

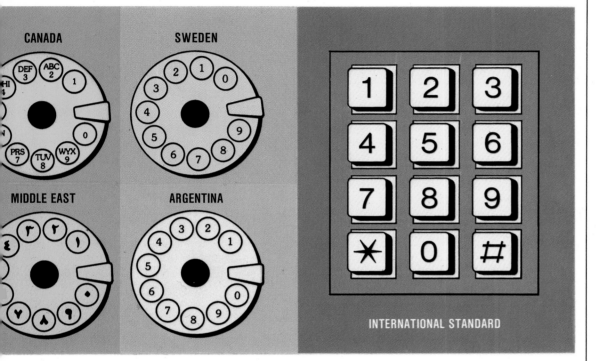

CANADA   SWEDEN
MIDDLE EAST   ARGENTINA
INTERNATIONAL STANDARD

Théoriquement, chaque constructeur, fabricant, diffuseur, ...itant, est favorable à la normalisation, pourvu que ce soit ... » norme qui soit adoptée. Les exploitants des réseaux ...naux (PTT) continuent à imposer chacun leurs propres ...es, afin d'éviter toute complications dans la planification ... maintenance de leurs infrastructures et pour protéger ... industries nationales.

... cours de ces dernières années, plusieurs dirigeants in-...iels ont exprimé leurs préoccupations à ce sujet.

...illiam S. Anderson, président de NCR Corporation a affirmé ...exemple : « les jonctions que nous avons construites jus-... sont inadéquates... nous en avons chaque jour la preuve ...la prolifération des architectures de réseaux... ayant pour ...tat de mettre les usagers dans l'obligation de faire un ...: entre une quantité extraordinaire de systèmes de ...munication ». Cette déclaration a été faite en 1981. La ...e année, John Whyte, ingénieur en chef de British Telecom, ...claré devant un auditoire nord-américain que « des normes ...rface et des protocoles d'interfonctionnement doivent être ...is rapidement chaque fois que cela s'impose pour établir ...adre structuré dans lequel les innovations et le dévelop-...nt futur pourront se réaliser dans la confiance ». M. John ...e a encore insisté fermement sur le fait qu'il importe de ...cter l'innovateur et de trouver les moyens « de protéger ...euvre de pionnier et de la mettre en valeur ».

...es progrès sont réalisés dans cette voie, principalement ...e aux efforts de l'IFRB et des Comités consultatifs — CCIR ...CITT — de l'UIT, notamment dans les domaines qui sont ...ellement à l'étude : planification de l'orbite géosynchrone et ...pectre utilisable par les satellites, besoins du RNIS et ...ision à haute définition. Les travaux sont en cours dans ...d'autres domaines encore.

nes o explotador es favorable a la normalización, a condición de que se adopte "su" norma. Los explotadores de redes nacionales (CCT) siguen imponiendo sus sendas normas, para evitar la complicación de la planificación y el mantenimiento de su infraestructura, y proteger sus industrias nacionales. En los últimos años, varios líderes industriales han expresado su preocupación.

William S. Anderson, Presidente de NCR Corporation, advirtió que, en la tarea de vincular los computadores y las comunicaciones, por ejemplo, « los puentes construidos hasta ahora son inadecuados... así lo prueba la proliferación de arquitecturas de redes... como resultado, los usuarios se encuentran ante opciones increíbles de sistemas de comunicaciones ». Esto era en 1981. El mismo año, John Whyte, ingeniero jefe de British Telecom, dijo ante un auditorio norteamericano que « deben establecerse rápidamente normas de interfaz y protocolos de interfuncionamiento dondequiera que ofrezcan un marco estructurado en que puedan realizarse con confianza la innovación y el futuro desarrollo ». Insistió en que debe respetarse al innovador y hallar la manera de « proteger su innovación y acomodarla a las nuevas normas ».

Se están haciendo progresos, sobre todo gracias a los esfuerzos de la IFRB y a los Comités Consultivos — CCIR y CCITT — de la UIT. Ya se ha avanzado mucho, por ejemplo, en las áreas vitales actualmente en estudio: planificación de la órbita y del espectro, requisitos de la RDSI y TV de alta definición. Se trabaja en muchas otras esferas necesarias, pues, como dijo hace poco ante un auditorio americano el Dr. Koji Kobayashi, Presidente y Jefe Ejecutivo de NEC Corporation de Japón: « La realización de un computador global y una red de comunicaciones no crecerá simplemente como Topsy, sino que debe concebirse totalmente para normas predeterminadas ».

▷ 243

is undoubtedly the simplification of maintenance problems. This is very much the manufacturers' concern since, due to the worldwide expansion of their activities and to the rapid advances in the state of the art, they have become much more intimately involved than formerly in the operating problems encountered by their customers.

The need for logistic support transcends by far the supply of spare parts and the execution of repairs. It now extends to providing the user of the equipment with the means and services which will enable him, at minimum cost and having regard to his specific environment, to use the equipment which he has procured and maintain it in good working order. It is a true and lasting partnership: it means the provision of clear operating and maintenance documents adapted to the user's capabilities, assistance in the definition of these capabilities, the supply of technical assistance and the training of the user's staff, the timely supply of spares and the execution of repairs, overhauls and enhancements as necessary. This is a vital need, even in industrialized countries — for example in the UK where the introduction of digital switching and optical transmission has required the assistance (to the system builders, installers and operators) of British Telecom's large R&D department. Integrated logistic support is already a key feature of the partnership of the vendor with his customer and will become even more so as the construction of the ISDN proceeds.

The magnitude of the problem has not escaped the manufacturers and it came as no surprise, therefore, that the ITU members assembled in Plenary Conference at Nairobi in 1982 instructed the Union to extend its technical assistance to developing countries to include the training of personnel. The maintenance problems so far encountered have confirmed the need for the Union's help, but also the need for logistic support by the manufacturers themselves.

The transfer of technology and of know-how is the other major aspect of partnership in the progress towards the realization of the ISDN. Developing countries are anxious to set up manufacturing facilities for some part of the range of the equipment they require. They have become deeply concerned about being kept on the fringes of the advance of technology and are now pressing for some involvement in the advance, leading to the production of their own technology. How this is taking place and with what results is discussed in the section on p. 340.

The earlier remark that the partnership situation between governments, telecommunication entities, industries and users was somewhat confused was based on the twin impacts of deregulation in some countries and of the entry of the computer industry in the markets for telecommunication equipment.

These recent developments have resulted in the entry of a multitude of new firms in world markets — broadcasters, narrowcasters, carriers, operators and manufacturers — each endeavouring to develop a range of activities adequate to win a satisfactory market share. Competition is certainly increasing but so is the diversity of products and systems being offered to users. The situation is therefore more confused and confusing and it will be some years before it stabilizes itself.

The user should benefit ultimately, and in the not-too-distant future. Mergers, joint ventures, partnerships, coalitions, understandings, will gradually bring order out of chaos in the developing information society. Many of the developing patterns of information processing and information usage require the association of diverse facilities and competences — progress in these directions will indeed need the strength of partnerships to bring it about.

cace de réglementation internationale et d'établissement de normes.

Après la compatibilité des systèmes et des équipements, la normalisation internationale doit impérativement porter sur la simplification des problèmes de maintenance. C'est là, une préoccupation capitale des producteurs étant donné que, en raison même de l'élargissement de leurs activités à l'échelle du monde entier et des progrès très rapides de la technique, ils sont impliqués plus étroitement que jamais dans les problèmes d'exploitation que rencontrent leurs clients.

Actuellement, le besoin d'appui logistique est encore plus vital que la fourniture de pièces de rechange et l'exécution de réparations. Cet appui consiste à fournir non seulement l'équipement, mais également les moyens et les services qui doivent permettre à l'utilisateur d'exploiter économiquement l'équipement qu'il a acquis et de le maintenir en bon état de fonctionnement. Il s'agit donc là, d'une association véritable et durable impliquant notamment la fourniture de documents clairs sur l'exploitation et la maintenance du matériel, la fourniture d'une assistance technique, la fourniture en temps utile de pièces de rechange, l'exécution des révisions et des améliorations nécessaires, et la formation du personnel de l'utilisateur.

C'est là, un impératif absolu, même dans les pays industrialisés. Ce fut d'ailleurs le cas au Royaume-Uni, où l'introduction de la commutation numérique et de la transmission par fibres optiques a exigé que le centre de recherche et de développement de British Telecom fournisse son assistance aussi bien aux constructeurs de systèmes, qu'aux installateurs et aux opérateurs. L'appui logistique intégré déjà une des caractéristiques fondamentales de l'association entre le vendeur et son client. Cette situation se confirmera d'une manière encore plus impérative lors de l'aménagement progressif du RNIS.

L'importance de ce problème n'a pas échappé aux constructeurs ou à leurs administrations et il n'est donc pas surprenant que les Membres de l'UIT réunis à la Conférence de plénipotentiaires de Nairobi, en 1982, aient décidé d'étendre l'assistance technique, que l'Union fournit aux pays en développement, aux domaines de la formation de personnel.

Le transfert de technologie et de savoir-faire est le dernier aspect de la collaboration à instituer, en vue de la réalisation du RNIS. Les pays en développement aspirent fortement, en effet, à produire eux-mêmes au moins une partie du matériel dont ils ont besoin. Ils sont en effet conscients d'avoir été maintenus jusqu'ici en marge du progrès technique et insistent de plus en plus à y être associés. Cette question est traitée dans « Development of human resources and technology transfer » (p. 340).

L'allusion faite au début de ce chapitre au sujet d'une certaine confusion sur le principe même de la collaboration entre les gouvernements, les organismes de télécommunications, l'industrie et les usagers se rapporte à une situation conditionnée en partie par la libéralisation décidée par certains pays, tels que les Etats-Unis, le Royaume-Uni et l'Italie, et, en partie par l'entrée de l'industrie de l'informatique sur le marché des équipements de télécommunication. Il s'agit notamment d'entreprises de radiodiffusion, de diffuseurs spécialisés, de prestataires de services de communication, d'exploitants et de fabricants cherchant chacun à déployer une série d'activités pour gagner une part satisfaisante du marché.

Pour le moment, la situation reste confuse et déconcertante ; il faudra attendre quelques années avant qu'elle s'éclaircisse et se stabilise. Les fusions, les entreprises communes, les associations, les coalitions, les ententes vont progressivement introduire de l'ordre dans ce chaos et c'est finalement l'utilisateur qui en bénéficiera. La mise au point de nombreux systèmes de traitement et d'utilisation de l'information exige la mise en commun de diverses facilités et compétences. Puor atteindre ce but, il sera indispensable de constituer des associations dynamiques et efficaces.

USSR
7

NORTH AM

8
FAR EAST

6
SOUTH PACIFIC

This map shows the numbering plan for the future worldwide automatic and semi-automatic telephone service. It is designed to take care of estimated telephone development beyond the year 2000. The plan was prepared by a study group of the CCITT and will be implemented gradually as administrations decide to introduce automatic and semi-automatic dialling.

The plan allots a number to each of eight large geographical zones, as shown on the map. Europe has been given two numbers, on account of the many countries in the area and the high density of telephones which would have made it impossible to limit the country identification to two digits, i.e. the zone number plus one. For example, Switzerland has the number of its zone, 4, plus its specific country identification, 1, making 41 the number for access to that country's network. The USSR is the only country which has a unique single digit number, 7, while the single digit number 1 is used by all the countries in North America.

To dial a complete world telephone number, it is necessary to dial as follows:
— international prefix (connecting the subscriber to his own country's international exchange);
— the country code (connection to the desired country's international exchange) and, within the desired country;
— the area code (connecting to a national telephone area);
— the number of the subscriber being called.

For example, the ITU headquarters are obtainable by dialling (a) the international exchange of the caller, (b) 41 for Switzerland, (c) 22 for Geneva and (d) 99 51 11 for the headquarters.

EPHONE NUMBERING ZONE PLAN

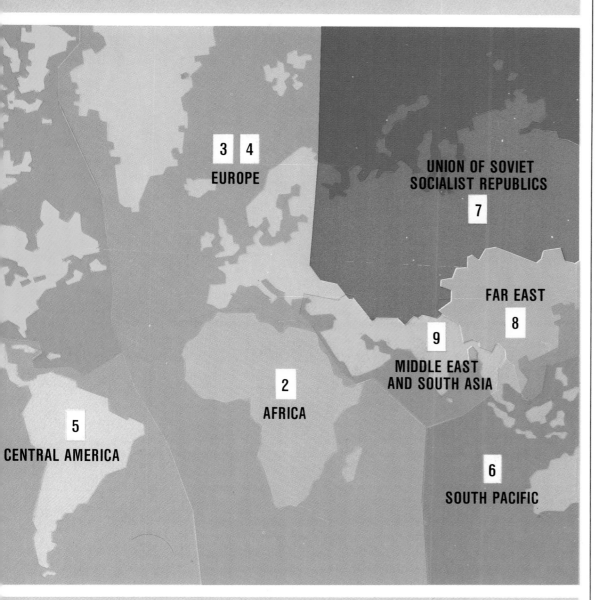

3 4 EUROPE

UNION OF SOVIET SOCIALIST REPUBLICS
7

FAR EAST
8

9

MIDDLE EAST AND SOUTH ASIA

2
AFRICA

5
CENTRAL AMERICA

6
SOUTH PACIFIC

arte ci-dessus représente le plan de numérotage du futur ice téléphonique automatique et semi-automatique mon- Préparé par une commission d'étude du CCITT, ce plan — : la mise en application est progressive — devra répondre besoins de la téléphonie au-delà de l'an 2000. Comme on le , un numéro est affecté à chacune des huit grandes zones raphiques. Toutefois, en raison du nombre important de s qui composent l'Europe, deux numéros sont attribués à e zone. Autrement, compte tenu de sa densité téléphonique, rait fallu plus de deux chiffres, en plus de celui de la zone, identifier chaque pays. Par exemple, la Suisse porte le éro de zone 4 et son indicatif de pays 1 ; le numéro d'accès n réseau est donc 41. L'URSS est le seul pays auquel a été bué un numéro de zone à un seul chiffre : 7 ; tandis que le re 1 est affecté à tous les pays de l'Amérique du Nord. our faire un numéro téléphonique mondial complet, il faut poser successivement :
le préfixe international (qui établit la liaison entre l'abonné centre international de son propre pays),
l'indicatif de pays (qui assure l'accès au centre internatio-u pays désiré), puis
l'indicatif interurbain (donnant accès au réseau interurbain andé) et
le numéro de l'abonné demandé.
ar exemple, le siège de l'UIT à Genève peut être obtenu en posant (a) le préfixe d'accès à l'international de l'abonné, 1 pour la Suisse, (c) 22 pour Genève et (d) 99 51 11 pour le e de l'UIT.

Este mapa muestra el plan de numeración del futuro servicio telefónico automático y semiautomático mundial. Está conce-bido para la evolución telefónica prevista después del año 2000. Preparado por una comisión de estudio del CCITT, se aplicará gradualmente, a medida que las administraciones decidan in-troducir la marcación automática y semiautomática.
El plan asigna sendos números a ocho grandes zonas geográficas, como muestra el mapa. A Europa se le han con-cedido dos números, porque la gran cantidad de países de la zona y la elevada densidad de teléfonos no hubieran permitido limitar la identificación de los países a dos cifras, es decir, el número de zona mas uno. Por ejemplo, Suiza tiene el número de zona 4, mas su identificación de país, 1, por lo que el número de acceso a su red es 41. La URSS es el único país con un solo número, el 7, mientras el 1 es utilizado por todos los países de América del Norte.
Un número telefónico mundial completo se marca como sigue:
— el prefijo internacional (que conecta al abonado con la central internacional de su país);
— el distintivo de país (conexión con la central internacional del país deseado), y, en el país deseado;
— el código de zona (que conecta con la zona telefónica nacional);
— el número del abonado solicitado.
Por ejemplo, la sede de la UIT, Ginebra, puede obtenerse marcando: a) la central internacional del abonado, b) 41, para Suiza, c) 22, para Ginebra, y d) 99 51 11 para la sede.

mas de mantenimiento. Esto es motivo de gran preocupación para los fabricantes, porque, debido a la expansión mundial de sus actividades y a los rápidos avances de la ciencia, intervienen mucho más íntimamente que antes en los problemas de ex-plotación que se plantean a sus clientes.
La necesidad de apoyo logístico excede con mucho al su-ministro de piezas de repuesto y a la ejecución de reparaciones. Ahora se proporcionan también al usuario el equipo, los medios y servicios que le per-miten, con un costo mínimo, y teniendo en cuenta su medio específico, utilizar el equipo adquirido y mantenerlo en buen estado. Se trata de una asocia-ción verdadera y perdurable: significa la provisión de documentos claros de explotación y manteni-miento adaptados a las capacidades del usuario, asistencia en la definición de esas capacidades, su-ministro de asistencia técnica y formación de perso-nal del usuario, abastecimiento oportuno de piezas y ejecución de reparaciones, revisiones y mejoras ne-cesarias. Esto es esencial incluso en países industria-lizados; por ejemplo, en el RU, donde la introduc-ción de la conmutación digital y la transmisión ópti-ca ha precisado la asistencia (a los constructores, instaladores y operadores de sistemas) del mayor departamento de IyD de British Telecom. El apoyo logístico integrado es ya un elemento clave de la asociación del vendedor con su cliente, y lo será todavía más cuando se construya la RDSI.
Los fabricantes no ignoran la magnitud del pro-blema, y no fue sorprendente, pues, que los Miem-bros de la UIT, reunidos en la Conferencia de Ple-nipotenciarios de Nairobi, en 1982, encargaran a la Unión que extendiera su asistencia técnica a los paí-ses en desarrollo, para incluir la formación de per-sonal. Los problemas de mantenimiento han confir-mado la necesidad de la ayuda de la Unión, pero también la de apoyo logístico de los propios fabri-cantes.
La transferencia de tecnología y conocimientos es el otro aspecto importante de la asociación en el avance hacia la realización de la RDSI. Los países en desa-rrollo ansían establecer instalaciones de fabricación para parte del equipo que necesitan. Les preocupa profundamente quedar al margen del avance tec-nológico, e insisten ahora en alguna participación en el progreso conducente a la producción de su propia tecnología. La evolución de esta situación y sus re-sultados se tratan en la pág. 340.
La afirmación anterior de que la asociación entre gobiernos, entidades de telecomunicaciones, indus-trias y usuario era un tanto confusa se debe al doble impacto de la liberalización en algunos países y de la entrada de la industria del computador en los mer-cados de equipo de telecomunicación.
Estos últimos hechos han dado lugar a la penetra-ción de una multitud de nuevas firmas en mercados mundiales — empresas de radiodifusión, de difusión limitada, telecomunicaciones, explotadores y fabri-cantes —, que tratan de desarrollar una gama de actividades adecuada para conquistar una parte sa-tisfactoria del mercado. La competencia es sin duda mayor, pero también lo es la diversidad de productos y sistemas que se ofrecen a los usuarios. Por tanto, la situación es más confusa y desconcertante, y tardará varios años en estabilizarse.
Mediante fusiones, empresas mixtas, asociaciones, coaliciones y acuerdos, se convertirá gradualmente el caos en orden, beneficiándose, en última instancia, el usuario. Para desarrollar muchas de las estructuras del tratamiento y uso de la información se necesita la asociación de diversas facilidades y competencias; y para avanzar en ese sentido se requerirán, sin duda, asociaciones.

□

SAUDI TELECOM

The Desert Speaks

The Story of Telecommunications in the Kingdom of Saudi Arabia

THE KINGDOM OF SAUDI ARABIA has adopted a system of Five-Year Plans for the comprehensive development of all its economic sectors. Realizing the vital role played by communications in the basic requirements and structural framework of the national economy and social well-being, telecommunications has been given a high priority. Thus, early plans were aimed at establishing an integrated national network, with secure links to the rest of the world.

Accomplishment of these plans was achieved within the guidelines that have been the foundation of the very existence of the Kingdom of Saudi Arabia, as part of the Arab nation. Saudi Arabia is guided by its mission, as a key part of the Arab nation, the Islamic community, and the global community. The overall goals of the plan are: to safeguard the values of Islam and the Holy Places, and to enforce and propagate its laws; to defend the homeland in order to maintain peace and stability for Saudi Arabia, the Middle East and the World; to continue the pursuit of a balanced development of economic resources in order to increase longterm fiscal security and preserve non-renewable resources from undue exploitation and depletion; to reduce the Kingdom's dependence on oil exports as the principle source of revenue; to raise the general health standard of the people and develop manpower through education and training; and to complete the Kingdom's essential infrastructure.

It is in these last two areas, in support of the Kingdom's other goals, and in support of general development, that the Ministry of PTT is most concerned.

▷ 246

LE ROYAUME D'ARABIE SAOUDITE a adopté un système de plans quinquennaux pour le développement général de tous ses secteurs économiques. Conscient de l'importance vitale des télécommunications pour le développement économique et social, il a donné une priorité absolue à ce secteur. Les premiers plans ont donc visé l'établissement d'un réseau national intégré permettant des liaisons sûres avec le reste du monde.

Ces plans ont été exécutés selon les principes directeurs qui sont à l'origine même de l'existence du royaume d'Arabie saoudite, élément de la nation arabe. L'Arabie saoudite est guidée par la mission qui lui incombe en sa qualité de composante essentielle de la nation arabe et de la communauté islamique, et vis à vis de la communauté mondiale.

Les objectifs généraux du plan tendent à protéger les valeurs de l'Islam et des Lieux saints, à faire respecter et propager ses lois, à défendre la patrie afin d'assurer la paix et la stabilité en Arabie saoudite, au Moyen-Orient et dans le reste du monde ; à poursuivre le développement harmonieux des ressources économiques du pays, afin d'assurer, à long terme, la sécurité financière et éviter une exploitation excessive, voire l'épuisement des ressources non renouvelables ; à rendre le Royaume moins tributaire des exportations pétrolières ; à relever le niveau sanitaire général de la population et à améliorer les qualifications de la main d'œuvre ; enfin, à achever les infrastructures essentielles du Royaume.

C'est sur ces deux derniers points — indispensables pour la réalisation des autres objectifs du Royaume et pour son développement en général — que se situe surtout l'action du Ministère des PTT.

Les télécommunications d'Arabie saoudite, exploitées par ce Ministère peuvent être considérées sous trois aspects : 1) l'infrastructure physique des télécommunications nationales en Arabie saoudite ;

▷ 246

EL REINO DE ARABIA SAUDITA ha adoptado un sistema de planes quinquenales para el desarrollo global de todos sus sectores económicos. Reconociendo el papel vital de la comunicación en las necesidades básicas y el marco estructural de la economía nacional y el bienestar social, se ha dado gran prioridad a las telecomunicaciones. Los primeros planes perseguían el establecimiento de una red nacional integrada, con enlaces seguros con el resto del mundo.

Estos planes siguieron las directrices básicas de la propia existencia del Reino de Arabia Saudita, como parte de la nación árabe. Arabia Saudita se guía por su misión, como elemento esencial de la nación árabe, la comunidad islámica y global. Los objetivos generales del plan son: proteger los valores del Islam y de los Santos Lugares, aplicar y propagar sus leyes; defender la patria para mantener la paz y la estabilidad del país, del Oriente Medio y del mundo; seguir desarrollando en forma equilibrada los recursos económicos, para aumentar la seguridad fiscal a largo plazo y preservar los recursos no renovables contra una explotación y un agotamiento indebidos; reducir la dependencia del Reino de las exportaciones de petróleo como principal fuente de ingresos; aumentar el nivel general de salud de la población, instruir más a los trabajadores, y completar la infraestructura esencial del Reino.

Estos dos últimos sectores, que sirven de apoyo a otros objetivos del Reino, y al desarrollo general, son los que más preocupan al Ministerio de CTT.

Puede considerarse que las telecomunicaciones de Arabia Saudita, a cargo del Ministerio de CTT, se dividen en tres categorías principales: 1) La infraestructura física de telecomunicaciones nacionales en

▷ 247

Saudi Arabia and its neighbour countries seen from a satellite: from the Red Sea, on the left, to the Arabian Gulf, on the right.

L'Arabie saoudite et ses pays voisins, vue d'un satellite : de la Mer Rouge, à gauche, au golfe d'Arabie, à droite.

Arabia Saudita y sus países vecinos vistos desde un satélite: desde el Mar Rojo, a la izquierda, hasta el Golfo Arábigo, a la derecha.

Saudi Arabian telecommunications operated by the Ministry of PTT can be considered in three major categories: 1) The physical infrastructure of national telecommunications in Saudi Arabia; 2) Operational activities and systems; 3) International cooperation.
On the physical infrastructure of national telecommunications, the mandate of the Ministry of PTT was to produce, over the period of the Second and Third Five-Year Plans, a quantum increase in the overall infrastructure and to update the entire system to a modern all-electronic network.

The Local Switching Network has increased from 177,000 lines in 1978 to one million lines of computerized switching capacity in mid-1982, serving some 283 communities. This will reach 1.2 million lines by the end of the Third Five-Year Plan.

Working lines increased from 126,000 in 1977, to 354,000 in 1980 and 710,000 in 1982. This growth is almost unprecedented in relative terms; in 1981, Saudi Arabia led all the nations of the world in working line growth.

The overall system will contain 212 local exchanges, 20 toll tandem exchanges with a capacity of 122,800 trunks, five international exchanges with a capacity of 11,000 trunks, and a total of 300 communities served by the equipment. Some 72 of these future exchanges will be in metropolitan areas, linked by 137 PCM (Pulse Code Modulation) junctions, five of which will be fiber optic cable junctions, the very latest technology available.

An Automatic Mobile Radio System with 11 radio base stations is now in existence, providing 3,000 customers with service from one of the most automated systems in the world.

In the future, 37 new radio base stations will allow 21,000 subscribers to have complete access to the national and international networks from their vehicles equipped with mobile telephones.

Coaxial Cable links Jeddah on the Red Sea via Makkah, Taif, Riyadh and Hofuf to Dammam on the Arabian Gulf. Most of the route is buried coaxial cable, and before its completion all long-distance telephone traffic had been carried by high-frequency radio. Originally carrying 1,800 telephone channels plus one for television, this coaxial link has been upgraded from 12 Megahertz (MHz) to 60 MHz, providing an additional 7,200 telephone channels.

Currently a South-North expansion is taking place. An additional 2,500 km route is underway between Riyadh, Taif, Makkah, Jeddah, Yanbu, Medina, Tabuk, Hallat Amman (Jordan border). This expansion will be on 12, 18, and 60 MHz systems providing 7,200 channels with two TV channels and data, telex, stereo FM and telephone services.

A national microwave network was started in June 1977. Completed within 30 months, this 10,000 km network (in the 4 and upper 6 GHz bands) provides 35,000 telephone channels and two colour TV channels, and branches out to provide telephone, telegraph, telex, radio and television services to most of the other major centers. The system consists of 300 microwave towers, and there are links to other countries. Eighty-two of the 300 stations are equipped with telephone drops and breakout points, and 54 with radio and TV drops, enabling the Kingdom to provide quick service to centers near the microwave route.

An expansion is currently underway to upgrade existing links and expand capacity to enhance the network further for high-speed data transmission.

The Kingdom's Domsat satellite network grew out of the need to supplement the ground-based network as work was proceeding on the Expansion Program.
▷ 250

2) les activités et les systèmes d'exploitation ; 3) la coopération internationale.
En ce qui concerne l'infrastructure physique des télécommunications nationales, le Ministère des PTT a été chargé de parvenir, au cours des deuxième et troisième Plans quinquennaux, à un accroissement quantitatif de l'infrastructure globale et de transformer tout le système en un réseau moderne entièrement électronique.

Le réseau local commuté est passé de 177 000 lignes en 1978, à 1 million de lignes à commutation électronique à la mi-1982, et dessert 283 localités. Ce réseau comprendra 1,2 million de lignes à la fin du troisième Plan quinquennal.

Les lignes en service ont progressé de 126 000 en 1977, à 354 000 en 1980 et à 710 000 en 1982. Cette progression est quasiment sans précédent dans les autres pays; en 1981, l'Arabie saoudite était en tête des pays du monde entier pour le taux d'augmentation du nombre des lignes en service.

L'ensemble du système comprendra 212 centraux urbains, 20 centraux interurbains en tandem d'une capacité de 122 800 circuits interurbains, 5 centres internationaux d'une capacité de 11 000 circuits, desservant au total 300 localités. Quelque 72 de ces futurs centraux seront installés dans les zones métropolitaines ; ils seront raccordés à 137 circuits de jonction MIC (modulations par impulsions codées), dont 5 en câble à fibres optiques, le plus récent perfectionnement technique mis sur le marché.

Un système de radiocommunications mobiles automatique reposant sur onze stations radioélectriques de base est déjà en service ; ce système, l'un des plus automatisés au monde, dessert 3000 abonnés.

Ultérieurement, 37 nouvelles stations radioélectriques de base permettront à 21 000 abonnés d'avoir accès à l'ensemble du réseau national et international à partir de postes téléphoniques mobiles.

Un câble coaxial de télécommunications est-ouest de 1600 km a été établi entre Djeddah sur la mer Rouge et Dammam sur le Golfe arabe via Makkah, Taïf, Riyadh et Hofuf. La plus grande partie de cette liaison est assurée par câble coaxial enterré ; jusqu'à son achèvement, la totalité du trafic téléphonique à longue distance était écoulée par des liaisons par faisceaux hertziens. Cette liaison par câble coaxial offrait à l'origine 1800 voies téléphoniques ; grâce à une augmentation de sa fréquence, qui est passée de 12 à 60 MHz, elle offre à présent 7200 voies téléphoniques de plus.

Une expansion est réalisée actuellement du sud vers le nord. Une nouvelle artère de 2500 km est en construction entre Riyadh, Taïf, Makkah, Djeddah, Yanbu, Médine, Tabuk et Hallat Ammar (frontière jordanienne). Elle se composera de systèmes à 12, 18 et 60 MHz qui fourniront 7200 voies avec deux canaux TV pour les services de données, de télex, de stéréo MF et de téléphone.

Un réseau national à hyperfréquences dont la construction a commencé en juin 1977 a duré 30 mois. Ce réseau de 10 000 km (exploité dans la bande des 4 GHz et dans la partie supérieure des 6 GHz) fournit 35 000 voies téléphoniques et deux canaux de TV en couleur et ses ramifications assurent des services téléphoniques, télégraphiques, télex, de radiodiffusion et de télévision à la plupart des autres grands centres. Il comprend 300 pylônes de micro-ondes et assure des liaisons avec d'autres pays. Sur 300 stations, 82 sont dotées de points de dérivation et d'interruption et 54 de points de dérivation pour la radiodiffusion sonore et télévisuelle, ce qui permet au royaume de fournir rapidement un service aux localités proches de l'artère à micro-ondes.

Le réseau à satellite Domsat du Royaume est né de la nécessité de compléter le réseau terrestre à mesure de l'exécution du programme d'expansion. Onze grandes villes du Royaume ont été provisoirement interconnectées par des stations terriennes transportables reliées au réseau national.
Le réseau régional et international comprend des liaisons à la fois régionales et inter-continentales. Les liaisons
▷ 250

Top: Remote desert earth station.
Bottom: An underground conduit being laid across the country to house the cables of the network.

En haut : Une station terrienne dans le désert.
En bas : Une canalisation souterraine en préparation pour recevoir les câbles qui traversent le pays.

Arabia Saudita; 2) Las actividades y sistemas operacionales; 3) La cooperación internacional.

En cuanto a la infraestructura física de las telecomunicaciones nacionales, el mandato del Ministerio de CTT consiste en lograr, en el Segundo y el Tercer Plan Quinquenales, un fuerte impulso de la infraestructura global, y actualizar todo el sistema, convirtiéndolo en una red moderna, totalmente electrónica.

La red de conmutación local pasó de 177 000 líneas en 1978 a un millón de líneas de capacidad de conmutación computadorizada a mediados de 1982, dando servicio a unas 283 comunidades. Para finales del Tercer Plan Quinquenal habrá 1,2 millones.

El número de líneas ha pasado de 126 000 en 1977 a 354 000 en 1980 y a 710 000 en 1982, crecimiento apenas sin precedentes en términos relativos; en 1981, Arabia Saudita iba a la cabeza del mundo en el aumento de líneas.

El sistema global tendrá 212 centrales locales, 20 centros de tránsito con capacidad para 122 800 enlaces, cinco centrales internacionales con capacidad para 11 000 enlaces, y el equipo dará servicios a 300 comunidades. Unas 72 de esas futuras centrales estarán en zonas metropolitanas, vinculadas por 137 sistemas MIC, cinco de ellos por cables de fibras ópticas, la tecnología más reciente.

El sistema automático de radiocomunicaciones móviles, con 11 estaciones de base, es el más automatizado del mundo, y da servicio a 3000 clientes.

En lo futuro, 37 estaciones de base más permitirán a 21 000 abonados acceder a la red telefónica nacional e internacional de servicios móviles.

Un cable coaxial enlaza Jeddah, en el Mar Rojo, con Dammam, en el Golfo Arábigo, pasando por Makkah, Taif, Riyadh y Hofuf. La mayoría de la arteria es de cable enterrado, y antes de terminarse todo el tráfico telefónico de larga distancia se cursaba por ondas decamétricas. Este cable coaxial, originalmente con capacidad para 1800 canales telefónicos y uno de TV, ha pasado de 12 MHz a 60 MHz, proporcionando 7200 canales telefónicos más.

Se está produciendo una expansión sur-norte. Se halla en construcción otra ruta de 2500 km entre Riyadh, Taif, Makkah, Jeddah, Yanbu, Medina, Tabuk, Hallat Ammar (frontera jordana). Esta expansión abarcará sistemas de 12, 18 y 60 MHz, con 7200 canales, y dos canales TV y datos, télex, MF estereofónica y servicios telefónicos.

En junio de 1977 se inició *una red nacional de microondas,* terminada en 30 meses; esta red de 10 000 km (en las bandas de 4 y más de 6 GHz) proporciona 35 000 canales telefónicos y dos canales TV en color, y puede prestar servicios telefónicos, telegráficos, télex, de radio y televisión a la mayoría de los demás centros principales. El sistema consta de 300 torres de microondas, y existen enlaces con otros países. De las 300 estaciones, 82 están equipadas con ramales de abonado y puntos de interrupción, y 54 con ramales de radio y TV, que permiten al Reino ofrecer rápidamente servicio a centros próximos a la ruta de microondas.

Está en marcha una expansión para mejorar los enlaces existentes y aumentar la capacidad, a fin de transmitir datos a gran velocidad.

La red de satélite Domsat del Reino surgió de la necesidad de suplementar la red basada en tierra, mientras se realizaba la expansión. Mediante estaciones terrenas transportables quedaron vinculadas temporalmente a la red nacional 11 ciudades importantes del Reino.

▷ 251

Arriba: Una estación terrena aislada en el desierto.
Abajo: Preparación de un conducto subterráneo para recibir los cables de la red nacional.

خدمات التلكس والهاتف السيّار

Telex and Mobile Telephone Service

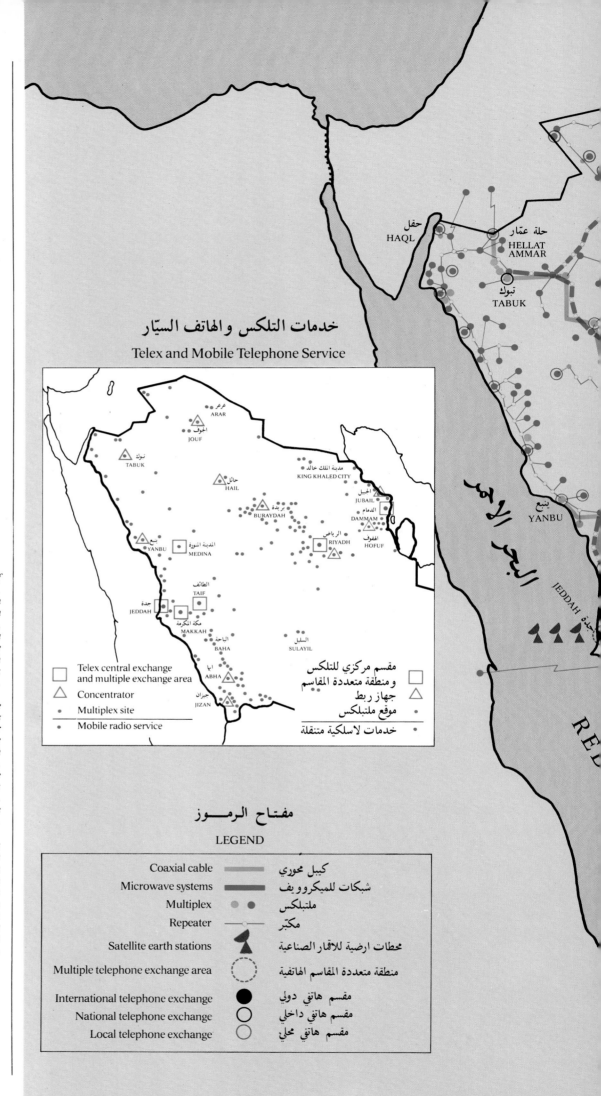

The geography of the most comprehensive network of telecommunications in what was a desert. Underground cables criss-cross the country from Jeddah, on the Red Sea, to Dammam and Al Khafi, on the Gulf, and northwards from Jeddah to Medina, Tabuk and Haql. This system is supplemented by a Kingdom wide microwave system and a satellite communications system based in Riyadh and Taif. Inset, on the left, is a map of the telex and mobile telephone service.

La géographie d'un réseau de télécommunications, le plus complet, dans ce qui était un désert. Des câbles souterrains traversent le pays de Jeddah sur la Mer Rouge, vers l'est, jusqu'à Dammam, et.Al Khafi sur le golfe d'Arabie, vers le nord, par Medine jusqu'à Tabuk et Haql sur la frontière.
Le réseau câblé est supplémenté par un système de micro-ondes transmises par satellites aux stations terriennes et relayées par des répéteurs. Encadré, à gauche, une carte des services de télex et de radiotéléphone mobile.

La geografia de la red de telecomunicaciones más completa en lo que era un desierto. Cables subterráneos atraviesan.el país desde Jeddah, en el Mar Rojo, hasta Dammam y Al Khafi, en el Golfo Árabigo, y hacia el norte de Jeddah a Medina, Tabuk y Haql, suplementados por un sistema de microondas transmitidas desde satélites a estaciones terrenas y retransmitidas por repetidores. A la izquierda, un mapa de los sistemas télex y telefónicos móviles.

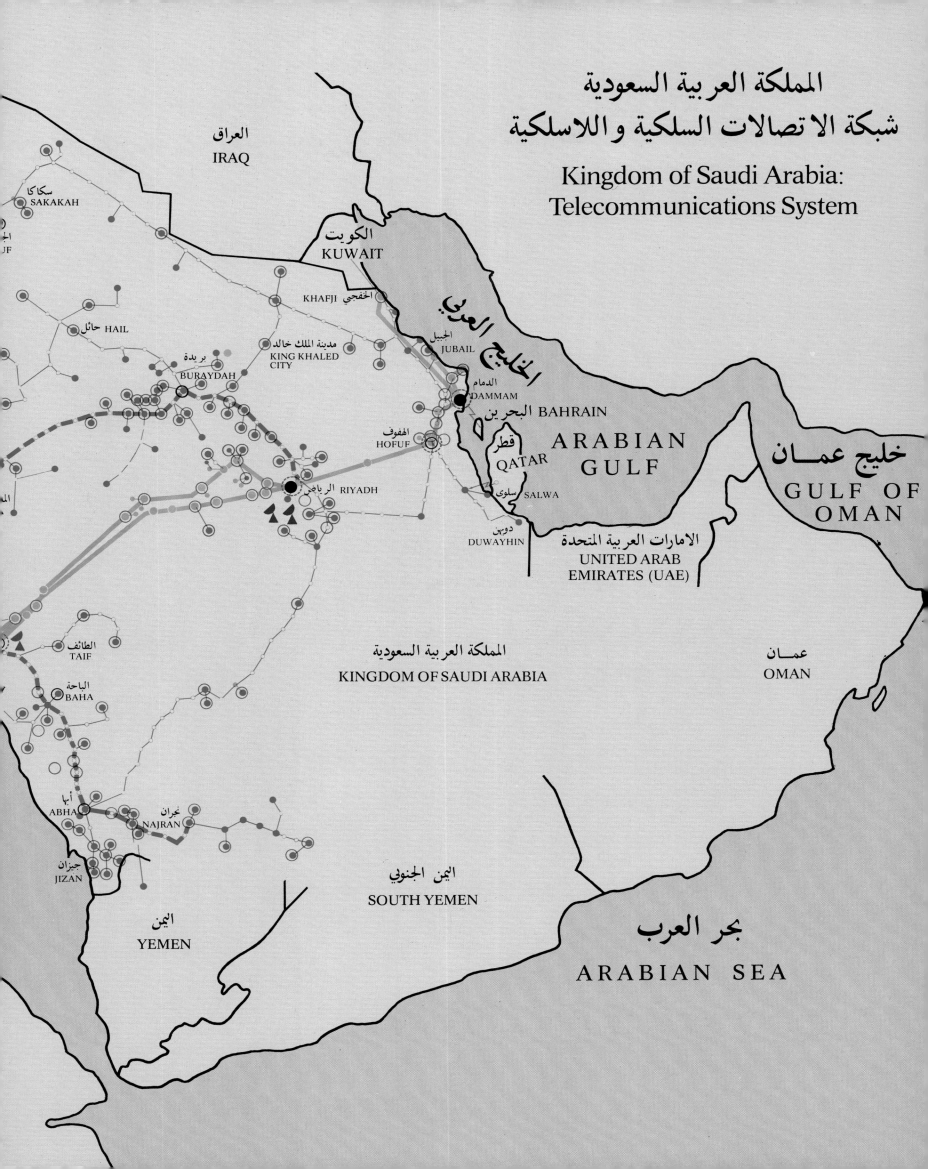

Eleven major cities in the Kingdom were temporarily linked together by transportable earth stations, which were tied to the national network.

The regional and international network comprises both regional and inter-continental links. The regional links to neighbouring Arab countries include:

— *Kuwait:* a network of coaxial cables between the Kingdom and Kuwait, with a capacity of 960 telephone channels. It was put into service in 1977.

— *Bahrain:* a microwave network has been established between the Kingdom and Bahrain with a capacity of 300 channels. Preparations are now underway to build a coaxial cable network along the sea bridge now under construction between the Kingdom and Bahrain.

— *Qatar:* a microwave network linking the Kingdom with Qatar has been built, with a capacity of 960 channels.

— *Sudan:* a microwave route having a capacity of 960 channels has been established linking the Kingdom with the Sudan across the Red Sea. This link is considered to be the longest link of its kind in the world (crossing a water barrier without repeater stations) since its length is 370 km from the station on the Saudi side to its corresponding station on the Sudanese side.

— *United Arab Emirates:* a microwave link has been established linking the Kingdom with the United Arab Emirates, having a capacity of 960 channels.

— *Yemen:* a microwave link is currently under construction to link the Kingdom with Yemen.

— *Jordan:* a coaxial cable network, supported by a microwave network, is currently under construction between the Kingdom and Jordan.

Satellite communications are playing an increasingly important part in the Kingdom's International Communications facilities. A significant event will be the launching, in 1984, of the *Arabsat* satellite. Saudi Arabia has contributed 26 per cent of the cost of the project. The total Arabsat project involves three satellites each with 26 transponders, providing 8,000 telephone circuits and seven TV channels.

For other international links the coaxial and microwave systems have been augmented by the extensive use of satellite communications. The Kingdom of Saudi Arabia is currently the world's 4th largest user of the Intelsat space segment. Two Standard A class earth stations in Riyadh and one in Taif operate with Intelsat satellites over the Atlantic and Indian oceans to provide inter-continental communications. The earth stations currently operate at a capacity of 1,600 telephone channels, providing direct dialing to 137 countries around the world. This system is also used to broadcast TV programs around the globe, providing service for the world's Islamic community.

Two further Standard A antennas are to be provided as part of the Jeddah earth station complex, due for completion in 1984. These will expand overall capacity to 2,500 telephone channels and beyond.

A coastal radio system has been inaugurated and provides 24-hour commercial ship-to-shore telecommunications for both the Red Sea and the Arabian Gulf. This system is capable of sending and receiving messages in Morse, radiotelephony, and radiotelex. The Kingdom is also planning for the introduction of maritime satellite service for ships at sea via the global Inmarsat system.

▷ 252

régionales avec les pays arabes voisins comprennent :

— *Koweït :* un réseau en câble coaxial à paires a été établi entre le Royaume et Koweït et mis en service en 1977 ; sa capacité est de 960 voies téléphoniques.

— *Bahreïn :* un réseau d'une capacité de 300 voies a été établi par micro-ondes entre le royaume et Bahreïn. On prépare actuellement la construction d'un réseau en câble coaxial le long du pont maritime en cours d'installation entre les deux pays.

— *Qatar :* un réseau de micro-ondes d'une capacité de 960 voies a été établi entre le Royaume et Qatar.

— *Soudan :* une artère à micro-ondes, d'une capacité de 960 voies a été construite entre le Royaume et le Soudan. Cette liaison qui franchit la mer Rouge est sans doute la plus longue du monde à traverser une voie d'eau sans stations de répéteurs : en effet, entre la station côté Arabie saoudite et la station correspondante côté Soudan, sa longueur totale est de 370 km.

— *Emirats arabes unis :* une liaison par micro-ondes d'une capacité de 960 voies a été établie entre le Royaume et les Emirats arabes unis.

— *Yémen :* une liaison par micro-ondes est en cours de réalisation entre le Royaume et le Yémen.

— *Jordanie :* un réseau à paires coaxiales, complété par un réseau de micro-ondes est en cours de construction entre le Royaume et la Jordanie.

Les communications par satellite jouent un rôle d'une importance croissante, et la mise en orbite, en 1984, du satellite *Arabsat* fera date dans l'histoire du Royaume. L'Arabie saoudite contribue pour 26% au coût de ce projet, qui porte au total sur trois satellites dotés chacun de 26 répéteurs/changeurs de fréquence et fournissant 8000 circuits téléphoniques et sept canaux de télévision.

Pour les autres liaisons internationales, les réseaux en câble coaxial et par micro-ondes ont été renforcés par le recours massif aux télécommunications par satellite. Le royaume d'Arabie saoudite occupe aujourd'hui la 4ᵉ place dans le monde parmi les utilisateurs des services spatiaux Intelsat. Deux stations terriennes de classe A, respectivement à Riyadh et à Taïf, sont en liaison avec les satellites Intelsat en orbite au-dessus des océans Atlantique et Indien pour assurer les communications intercontinentales ; d'une capacité actuelle de 1600 voies téléphoniques, elles permettent d'établir des communications en service automatique avec 137 pays. Ce système sert en outre à diffuser des programmes de télévision dans le monde entier et dessert ainsi la communauté islamique mondiale.

Deux autres antennes de classe A sont prévues dans le cadre du complexe de station terrienne de Djeddah, prévu pour 1984 ; elles porteront la capacité globale à 2500 voies téléphoniques, sinon plus.

Le système de radiocommunications côtières qui a été inauguré, assure 24 h sur 24 des radiocommunications commerciales navire/terre dans la mer Rouge comme dans le Golfe arabe. Le Royaume envisage par ailleurs la mise en œuvre d'un service maritime par satellite, dont les navires en mer pourront bénéficier grâce au réseau mondial Inmarsat.

La construction d'une liaison par câble sous-marin entre l'Asie du sud-est et l'Europe occidentale en traversant la région du Moyen-Orient est à l'étude. Il s'agit d'une ligne qui reliera Singapour à Marseille (France), en passant par Medan (Indonésie), le Sri Lanka, Djibouti, l'Arabie saoudite, l'Egypte et l'Italie. Djeddah sera le point d'aboutissement des sections vers Djibouti et l'Egypte. Une fois que ce système sera en service, l'Arabie saoudite en sera le principal utilisateur et le plus gros actionnaire.

Le service télex d'Arabie saoudite dessert 137 pays et compte déjà dans le Royaume plus de 15 000 lignes. Créé en 1979, il a été récemment associé au service téléphonique saoudien au titre de la première phase de la constitution de Saudi Telecom. L'Arabie saoudite a progressé du 160ᵉ rang en 1974 au 21ᵉ rang

▷ 252

One of the 120 m high microwave towers linking the Kingdom with the Sudan over the Red Sea. Top, on the right: The transmitting equipment of one of the 300 microwave towers of the Kingdom; and below, the National Network Center in Riyadh which monitors the condition of the entire Kingdom-wide system.

L'une des tours de 120 m de haut qui relient par faisceaux hertziens le Royaume au Soudan par dessus la Mer Rouge. En haut et à droite, l'émetteur-récepteur d'une des 300 tours micro-ondes du Royaume; en bas, le centre de contrôle national à Riyadh qui veille au bon fonctionnement du système.

Enlaces regionales con países árabes vecinos:

— *Kuwait*: se ha construido una red de cables coaxiales entre el Reino y Kuwait, con capacidad de 960 canales telefónicos. Entró en servicio en 1977.

— *Bahrein*: se ha establecido una red de microondas entre el Reino y Bahrein, con capacidad de 300 canales. Se hacen preparativos para construir una red de cables coaxiales a lo largo del puente que se está levantado sobre el mar entre el Reino y Bahrein.

— *Qatar*: se ha construido una red de microondas que une al Reino con Qatar, con capacidad de 960 canales.

— *Sudán*: se ha establecido una ruta de microondas que une al Reino con Sudán a lo largo del Mar Rojo, con capacidad de 960 canales. Este enlace se considera el más largo de su índole del mundo (cruzando una barrera de agua sin estaciones repetidoras), pues tiene 370 km, desde la estación del lado saudí hasta la correpondiente del sudanés.

— *Emiratos Arabes Unidos*: se ha establecido un enlace de microondas que une al Reino con los Emiratos Arabes Unidos, con capacidad de 960 canales.

— *Yemen*: se está construyendo un enlace de microondas para unir al Reino con Yemen.

— *Jordania*: se está construyendo una red de cables coaxiales, apoyada por una red de microondas, entre el Reino y Jordania.

Las comunicaciones por satélite revisten cada vez más importancia. Un acontecimiento histórico para el Reino será el lanzamiento, en 1984, del satélite *Arabsat*. Arabia Saudita ha contribuido al 26% del costo del proyecto, que comprende tres satélites, con 26 transpondedores cada uno, que proporcionarán 8000 circuitos telefónicos y siete canales TV.

Empleando más las comunicaciones por satélite, se han aumentado los sistemas coaxiales y de microondas para otros enlaces internacionales. El reino de Arabia Saudita es actualmente el cuarto usuario del mundo del segmento espacial Intelsat. Dos estaciones terrenas de norma A, instaladas en Riyadh y una en Taif operan con satélites Intelsat sobre los Océanos Atlántico y Pacífico, para proporcionar comunicaciones intercontinentales. Las estaciones terrenas funcionan actualmente a una capacidad de 1600 canales telefónicos, ofreciendo servicio automático a 137 países. Este sistema se usa también para difundir programas TV al mundo entero, prestando servicio a la comunidad islámica mundial.

Como parte del complejo de la estación terrena de Jeddah, en 1984 se terminarán otras dos antenas de norma A, con lo que la capacidad global será de 2500 canales telefónicos o más.

Se ha inaugurado un sistema de radiocomunicaciones costeras que permite la telecomunicación comercial ininterrumpida barco-costa en el Mar Rojo y el Golfo Arábigo. Con este sistema se pueden transmitir y recibir mensajes en Morse, radiotelefonía y radiotélex. El Reino proyecta también introducir un servicio marítimo por satélite para barcos en el mar, a través del sistema global Inmarsat.

Se está estudiando la construcción de un cable submarino para enlazar el Sudeste Asiático con Europa Occidental a través del Cercano Oriente. El sistema vinculará Singapur con Marsella, en Francia, pasando a través de Medan (Indonesia), Sri Lanka, Djibouti, Arabia Saudita, Egipto e Italia. Como punto de amarre para los circuitos con Djibouti y Egipto se propone Jeddah. Una vez realizado, Arabia Saudita será el principal usuario e inversor del sistema.

▷ 253

Una de las torres de 120 m de altura que unen por microondas el Reino de Arabia Saudita con Sudán, a través del Mar Rojo. Arriba, el transmisor/receptor de una de las 300 torres de microondas del Reino. Abajo, el centro de control nacional de Riyadh, que vela por el buen funcionamiento del sistema.

An intercontinental Submarine Cable project is currently under study to link South East Asia and Western Europe across the Middle East region. The system will be from Singapore to Marseilles in France, passing through Medan (Indonesia), Sri Lanka, Djibouti, Saudi Arabia, Egypt and Italy. Jeddah is the proposed landing point for the segments to Djibouti and Egypt. Once implemented, Saudi Arabia will be the largest user and investor in the system.

Saudi Arabia's Telex service reaches out to 137 nations. Telex lines had increased to over 15,000 by 1983. Saudi Telex was formed in 1979 and has recently joined with Saudi Telephone as a first phase in the formation of Saudi Telecom. Saudi Arabia has moved from 160th place in 1974 to 21st place in 1981 among the 180 countries around the world with telex service. Annual telex calls are more than 9 million, of which 60 per cent are international. Future projects will see a doubling of capacity to 30,000 lines. A bilingual teleprinter is now in use which prints in both Arabic and English and sets the standard for the industry.

A completely modern telegraph service is linked to 2,000 communities in the Kingdom. Full teleprinter capability is available, in both English and Arabic.

The operation of the complete communications system is the responsibility of the Ministry of PTT which established an operating arm — Saudi Telecom — now grown into a sophisticated technological entity with 15,000 employees. Fully deployed across the Kingdom, the Saudi Telecom organization is guided and assisted by the Headquarters staff in Riyadh through the most modern management techniques.

The telephone subscriber equipment available in the Kingdom has changed the face of telecommunications, both in terms of sophistication and quality. The following detailed statistics demonstrate both the nature and the magnitude of the change.

Number of Working Telephone Lines: over 800,000 working telephone lines, compared to 126,000 at the start of the Expansion Program.

Number of Lines Installed in 1981: 200,000 — a 60% increase in one year alone.

Installed Switching Capacity: 1,200,000 lines.

National Trunks Increase: domestic trunks have jumped 90-fold under the Program, to 90,000.

International Trunks Increase: international trunks have increased 15-fold since the start of the Program, to 1,800.

Number of Public Offices: Saudi Telecom now has 85 subscription offices Kingdom-wide, and 94 payment offices.

Public Coin Telephones Increase: the number of public coin telephones is now more than 3,800, covering 47 locations Kingdom-wide.

Modern Dialing: Saudi Arabia now has a uniform seven-digit number system across the Kingdom, with special three-digit emergency codes.

Direct Long-Distance Dialing: International Subscriber Dialing (ISD) is available to all subscribers, providing direct access to more than 137 countries; 90% of all long-distance calls are dialed by the subscribers themselves.

Key Indicators: Repair — 85% of all faults are repaired in less than eight hours.

Dial Tone — 99.8% of subscribers get immediate dial tone.

Operator Answer — 92% of callers get operator help within ten seconds.

Billing — 99.7% of bills are issued error-free.

Rates: the lowest equivalent rates of any nation.

Infrastructure development has been massive and equally rapid.

In 1978, Saudi Telecom had 34 buildings. The Buildings Program has since brought this to over 400,
▷ 254

en 1981 parmi les 180 pays offrant un service telex dans le monde. Plus de 9 millions de communications télex sont établies chaque année, dont 60% avec l'étranger. Les projets d'avenir portent sur le doublement de sa capacité, qui passera à 30 000 lignes. Un téléimprimeur bilingue est déjà en service : il imprime en arabe et en anglais et constitue et établit une norme pour l'industrie.

Le service télégraphique, ultra moderne, relie 2000 localités du Royaume. Il assure la transmission par téléimprimeur de messages, aussi bien en arabe qu'en anglais.

Pour exploiter son réseau, le Ministère des PTT a créé un organisme — Saudi Telecom — qui est à présent un organisme technique perfectionné employant 15 000 personnes. Couvrant la totalité du territoire du Royaume, Saudi Telecom est conseillé et administré par le personnel du siège social à Riyadh, qui applique les techniques de gestion les plus modernes.

Les équipements téléphoniques disponibles pour desservir les abonnés du Royaume ont bouleversé les télécommunications, aussi bien par leur modernité que par leur qualité. Les statistiques détaillées qui suivent montrent à la fois la nature et l'amplitude du changement.

Nombre de lignes gérées par Saudi Telecom : 800 000 lignes en 1982, contre 126 000 à l'instauration du programme.

Nombre de lignes installées en 1981 : 200 000, soit une progression de 60% en un an.

Capacité de commutation : 1 200 000 lignes.

Accroissement des circuits interurbains : les circuits interurbains ont été multipliés par 90 dans le cadre du programme, pour atteindre 90 000.

Accroissement des circuits internationaux : ces circuits ont été multipliés par 15 depuis le lancement du programme (1800 aujourd'hui).

Nombre de bureaux publics : Saudi Telecom dispose maintenant de 85 bureaux d'abonnement dans tout le Royaume, ainsi que de 94 bureaux de paiement.

Augmentation du nombre de publiphones : le nombre de publiphones dépasse à présent 3800 dans 47 localités du Royaume.

Numérotation moderne : l'Arabie saoudite a instauré un système de numéros à 7 chiffres, avec des codes de secours spéciaux à 3 chiffres.

Numérotation automatique de communications à longue distance : l'établissement de communications internationales en service automatique est offert à tous les abonnés et leur assure l'accès direct à plus de 137 pays ; 90% des communications à grande distance sont établies directement par les abonnés.

Caractéristiques principales : Réparations — 85% des dérangements sont réparés en moins de 8 h.

Tonalité de numérotation — 99,8% des abonnés reçoivent immédiatement cette tonalité.

Réponse de l'opératrice — 92% des demandeurs obtiennent une assistance de l'opératrice dans un délai de 10 secondes.

Facturation — 99,7% des factures sont établies sans erreur.

Tarification : les tarifs sont les plus bas du monde, à prestations égales.

Le développement de l'infrastructure a été vaste et également rapide. En 1978, Saudi Telecom possédait 34 immeubles. Le programme Bâtiments a porté ce nombre à plus de 400 : 16 grands immeubles administratifs, 114 bâtiments de central, deux centres modernes de formation professionnelle, 135 cabines téléphoniques internationales, 85 bureaux d'abonnement, 94 bureaux de paiement, 17 centres de réparations, ainsi que des entrepôts, des centres de construction et de réparation des installations et des ateliers de réparation des véhicules.

La formation programmée du personnel a fait l'objet d'une haute priorité. La productivité des 15 000 employés de Saudi Telecom a doublé en quelques années, grâce à un programme ambitieux de formation aux carrières de gestion et aux emplois techniques. Si on considère seulement l'année 1982, environ 6350 cadres saoudiens ont reçu une formation représentant
▷ 254

Above: An installation van at work near Abha.
Below: A Riyadh subscription office.

En haut: Une camionnette d'installation près d'Abha.
En bas : Un bureau de souscription à Riyadh.

El servicio télex de Arabia Saudita abarca 137 naciones. Ya hay más de 15 000 líneas télex. Saudi Telex se creó en 1979, y recientemente se ha unido a ella Saudi Telephone, en una primera fase para la formación de Saudi Telecom. Arabia Saudita ha pasado del 160° lugar en 1974 al 21° en 1981, entre los 180 países del mundo con servicio télex. Anualmente se realizan más de 9 millones de llamadas télex, el 60% de ellas internacionales. Los futuros proyectos permitirán duplicar la capacidad a 30 000 líneas. Se usa un teleimpresor bilingüe que imprime en árabe e inglés y establece la norma de la industria.

Un servicio telegráfico totalmente moderno vincula 2000 comunidades del Reino, con plena capacidad de teleimpresor en inglés y árabe.

Para explotar el sistema, el Ministerio de CTT creó una rama — Saudi Telecom — que se ha convertido en una sofisticada entidad tecnológica con 15 000 empleados. Desplegada por todo el Reino, Saudi Telecom es dirigida y asistida por el personal de la sede, en Riyadh, con las técnicas de gestión más modernas.

El equipo telefónico de abonado del Reino ha cambiado totalmente las telecomunicaciones, tanto en modernización como en calidad. Los siguientes datos muestran el carácter y la magnitud del cambio.

Número de líneas telefónicas: más de 800 000, frente a 126 000 al comenzar el programa de expansión.

Número de líneas instaladas en 1981: 200 000; 60% de aumento tan sólo en un año.

Capacidad de conmutación instalada: 1 200 000 de líneas.

Aumento de los enlaces nacionales: estos enlaces se han multiplicado por 90 durante el programa, pasando a 90 000.

Aumento de los enlaces internacionales: los enlaces internacionales se han multiplicado por 15 desde que comenzó el programa. Y suman ahora 1800.

Número de oficinas públicas: Saudi Telephone tiene ahora unas 85 oficinas de abonado en el Reino, y 94 oficinas de pago.

Aumento de teléfonos públicos: ya hay más de 3800 teléfonos públicos, instalados en 47 localidades del Reino.

Marcación moderna: Arabia Saudita dispone ahora de un sistema de siete cifras en el Reino, con códigos de emergencia especiales de tres cifras.

Marcación directa de larga distancia: todos los abonados disponen del servicio automático internacional, que permite acceder directamente a más de 137 países. El 90% de las llamadas a larga distancia las realizan los propios abonados.

Indicadores esenciales: *Reparación* — El 85% de las averías se reparan en menos de ocho horas.

Tono de marcar — el 99,8% de los abonados obtienen inmediatamente el tono.

Respuesta de la operadora — el 92% de los solicitantes obtienen ayuda de la operadora en 10 segundos.

Facturación — el 99,7% de las llamadas están exentas de errores.

Tarifas: las tarifas equivalentes más bajas de todos los países.

El desarrollo de la infraestructura ha sido enorme y mucho rápida. En 1978, Saudi Telecom tenía 34 edificios. El programa de construcción ha permitido aumentar esa cifra a más de 400, incluidos 16 grandes edificios administrativos, 144 de centrales, dos centros de formación modernos, 135 cabinas telefónicas internacionales, 85 oficinas de abonado, 94 oficinas

▷ 255

Arriba: Una camioneta de instalación trabajando cerca de Abha.
Abajo: Una oficina de abonados de Riyadh.

including 16 large Administration Buildings, 114 Exchange Buildings, two modern training centers, 135 international call cabines, 85 subscription offices, 94 payment offices, 17 repair centers, plus warehouses, installation repair and construction work centers, and vehicle repair facilities.

Manpower planning and training is accorded a high priority. The efficiency of the 15,000 employees of Saudi Telecom has doubled in the past few years. This was accomplished through extensive training efforts in both managerial and technical fields. In 1982 alone some 6,350 Saudi Managers received instruction totalling 327,900 man-hours. All Saudi managers receive individualized "career paths" designed to optimize their future development. Sixty-nine per cent of Saudi Telecom managers are Saudi Nationals.

Once the system has been installed, the creation of a disciplined management team will be the permanent result of the Expansion Program. The transfer of advanced technology permits Saudis to assume complete control of telephone operations. Training efforts range from the Telecommunications Institutes to Saudi Telecom own training programs. There are at present two Telecommunications Institutes: one in Jeddah and one in Riyadh. Three more are to be added: in Dammam, Abha and Al Jouf. These Institutes provide classroom education on telecommunications theory.

The Saudi Telecom program is job-oriented, with two large training centres providing hands-on training in over one hundred different courses, integrated with on-the-job training by expert advisors and a comprehensive set of Kingdom-wide documentation systems and procedures. Courses are also provided outside the Kingdom.

The National Network Control Centre is linked to the entire Saudi Arabian Telecommunications System and can supervise it electronically on giant computer-controlled display screens. Any fault in the network can be detected immediately and corrective action taken.

The computer data center is one of the most sophisticated computer systems in the Middle East. It was established to deal with the technical, operational, financial, commercial and administrative systems concerned with the communications network. The MoPTT's drive for even greater efficiency and utilization of limited national manpower resources has dictated a priority mandate for computerized mechanization.

A computer-assisted Directory Inquiry Center gives fast, free service for telephone directory information through a central network.

International cooperation in communication matters is secured through international agencies which Saudi Arabia actively supports. The Kingdom participates in the programs of the ITU and receives technical advice. It is also a major contributor to Intelsat, with a seat on the Board of Directors, and is the only Middle Eastern country to have its own category listed. Saudi Arabia is very involved in the development of the Arabsat project, being one of its largest shareholders. It also provides the location for the Arabsat headquarters. The project is being undertaken jointly by the 22 member countries of the Arab League, and will allow the Arab world to share its heritage as never before.

Saudi Arabia's special mission is to propagate the values of Islam. As Custodian of the Holy Places, Saudi Arabia broadcasts the holy ceremonies worldwide, providing religious comfort and support for hundreds of millions of followers.

In providing this service, and in establishing a world-class system for its citizens, the Kingdom makes full use of the latest in telecommunications equipment and techniques from advanced nations.

▷ 258

327 900 heures-hommes. Tous les cadres saoudiens bénéficient d'« itinéraires de carrière » destinés à optimiser l'avancement de leur carrière. Soixante-neuf pour cent des cadres de Saudi Telecom sont de nationalité saoudienne.

Une fois que le système sera installé, la création d'une équipe de direction disciplinée constituera un résultat durable du Programme d'expansion. Le transfert des techniques de pointe permet aux Saoudiens de prendre complètement en mains l'exploitation du téléphone. Les activités de formation professionnelle sont assurées à la fois par les Centres professionnels des télécommunications et par le biais des propres programmes de formation de Saudi Telecom. Il y a aujourd'hui deux centres professionnels, l'un à Djeddah, l'autre à Riyadh, auxquels s'ajouteront trois centres à Dammam, Abha et Al Jouf. Ces centres fournissent une formation pédagogique relative à la théorie des télécommunications.

Le programme de Saudi Telecom est adapté à un enseignement pratique : deux grands centres professionnels dispensent en effet une centaine de cours différents avec travaux pratiques, associés à une formation sur le terrain sous la direction de conseillers spécialisés et s'appuyant sur des systèmes et des procédures de documentation complets répartis dans tout le Royaume. Des cours sont également organisés à l'étranger.

Le centre de commande du réseau national est relié à l'ensemble du réseau de télécommunication d'Arabie saoudite qu'il surveille électroniquement sur des écrans géants à affichage informatisé. Toute défaillance du réseau est aussitôt décelée et les actions correctives sont aussitôt entreprises.

Un grand système informatique, un des plus perfectionnés et complexes du Moyen-Orient a été mis en place pour gérer les systèmes techniques, d'exploitation, financiers, commerciaux et administratifs qui concernent le réseau de télécommunications. Les efforts du Ministère des PTT visant à améliorer l'efficacité et à accroître l'utilisation des ressources limitées en personnel national l'ont conduit à donner la priorité à une mécanisation informatisée.

Un centre de renseignements d'annuaire piloté par ordinateur assure un service rapide et gratuit de renseignements d'annuaire par l'intermédiaire d'un réseau central.

La coopération internationale dans le domaine des communications est organisée par l'intermédiaire des agences internationales que l'Arabie saoudite soutient activement. En tant que membre de l'UIT le Royaume participe à ses programmes et reçoit des conseils techniques. Il contribue par ailleurs pour une part notable à l'Intelsat : il siège au conseil des Gouverneurs et parmi les pays du Moyen-Orient, il occupe une place privilégiée.

La mise au point du projet Arabsat est suivie de près par l'Arabie saoudite qui en est l'un des principaux actionnaires et qui abrite le siège de l'organisation Arabsat. Cette réalisation, qui a été entreprise en commun par les 22 pays Membres de la Ligue arabe, permettra au monde arabe de profiter beaucoup plus largement de son héritage.

L'Arabie saoudite a spécialement pour mission de propager les valeurs de l'Islam. En tant que gardien des Lieux saints, ce pays diffuse les cérémonies religieuses dans le monde entier afin que les centaines de millions de fidèles puissent bénéficier du réconfort et du secours de la religion.

Pour fournir ce service et mettre un système de niveau mondial à la disposition de ses ressortissants, le Royaume utilise au maximum les plus récents équipements et procédés réalisés dans les pays avancés en matière de télécommunications. Mais il recourt à ces services uniquement en faisant jouer la concurrence internationale sur la base du coût-rendement. De nombreuses firmes du monde entier ont ainsi participé à l'essor des télécommunications en Arabie saoudite, à savoir :

AT&T International (Etats-Unis) : programme pour l'expansion des réseaux en micro-ondes ;

▷ 258

Above, trainees, receive telex instruction in the Telecommunications Institute in Riyadh; below, an operator records service applications.

En haut, des stagiaires apprenant à se servir du telex à l'Institut des Télécommunications à Riyadh ; en bas, un opérateur enregistrant des demandes de service.

de pago, 17 centros de reparación, mas almacenes, centros de instalación, reparación y construcción, e instalaciones para la reparación de vehículos.

Se concede gran prioridad a la formación programada del personal. La productividad de los 15 000 empleados de Saudi Telecom se ha duplicado en unos años. En 1982 recibieron instrucción unos 6350 dirigentes saudíes, por un total de 327 900 horas-hombre. Todos los directores saudíes tienen «perspectivas de carrera» individuales, concebidas para optimar su futuro desarrollo. El 69% de los directores de Saudi Telecom son ciudadanos saudíes.

Una vez instalado el sistema, el resultado permanente del programa de expansión es la creación de un equipo de gestión disciplinado. La transferencia de tecnología avanzada permite a los saudíes asumir el control total de las operaciones telefónicas. La capacitación va desde los institutos de telecomunicaciones hasta los propios programas de formación de Saudi Telecom. Hay dos institutos: uno en Jeddah y otro en Riyadh. Pronto habrá tres más: en Dammam, Abha y Al Jouf. Estos institutos imparten cursos sobre teoría de las telecomunicaciones.

El programa de Saudi Telecom se orienta hacia el empleo, con dos grandes centros de formación que dispensan capacitación práctica en más de cien cursos, integrados con la capacitación en el empleo por expertos asesores y toda una serie de sistemas de documentación a escala nacional. También se imparten cursos fuera del Reino.

Un centro nacional de control de redes está vinculado a todo el sistema de telecomunicaciones de Arabia Saudita, y puede supervisarse electrónicamente en pantallas gigantes controladas por computador. Toda avería de la red puede detectarse inmediatamente, y tomarse medidas correctivas.

Se ha establecido *uno de los sistemas de computador más sofisticados* del Oriente Medio para tratar de los aspectos técnicos, operacionales, financieros, comerciales y administrativos relacionados con la red de telecomunicaciones. La actuación del Ministerio de CTT para aumentar la eficacia y utilización de los limitados recursos nacionales de mano de obra ha exigido la computadorización con carácter prioritario.

Un centro de consulta de guías con ayuda de computador proporciona rápidamente información gratuita a través de una red central.

La cooperación internacional de las telecomunicaciones se establece mediante organismos internacionales que Arabia Saudita apoya activamente. El Reino participa en los programas de la UIT y recibe asistencia técnica. Es también uno de los países que más contribuyen a Intelsat, con un puesto en el Consejo de Administración, y es el único del Oriente Medio cuya categoría se indica. Arabia Saudita participa en gran medida en el desarrollo del proyecto Arabsat, y es uno de sus mayores accionistas. También acoge a la sede de Arabsat. El proyecto lo realizan los 22 países miembros de la Liga Árabe, y permitirá al mundo árabe compartir su herencia en mayor grado que nunca.

La misión especial de Arabia Saudita es difundir los valores del Islam. Como guardián de los Santos Lugares, Arabia Saudita transmite las ceremonias sacras al mundo entero, reconfortando religiosamente a centenares de millones de personas.

Al prestar este servicio, y al establecer un sistema de categoría mundial para sus ciudadanos, el Reino utiliza plenamente el equipo y las técnicas de comunicaciones más recientes de los países avanzados.

▷ 259

Arriba: Cursillistas aprendiendo a manejar el télex en el Instituto de Telecomunicaciones de Riyadh; abajo, un operador registrando solicitudes de servicio.

The television broadcasting center of Habak Carabie.

La régie des émissions de télévision à Habak Carabie.

El centro de radiodifusión de televisión de Habak Carabie.

These services are obtained solely on the basis of cost-effective international competition. Saudi Arabia's telecommunications effort has been supported by many companies from all over the world, including:

AT&T International (USA): microwave expansion program;

Cable & Wireless (Great Britain): operation and maintenance of domestic satellite system;

Bell Canada (Canada): management and operations contract of total telephone system;

Philips (The Netherlands) and *L. M. Ericsson* (Sweden): equipment and outside plant contract;

Western Electric (USA): engineering and installation of microwave;

Dong Ah (Korea): placement of outside plant;

Telettra (Italy): supply and installation of microwave links;

Sirti (Italy): supply and maintenance of coaxial system;

Sartelco (Italy): maintenance of microwave system;

Siemens (FRG): supplies teleprinter and telex equipment;

Dete Con (FRG): operations and maintenance for telex system;

Arthur D. Little (USA): general advisors to MoPTT;

Norconsult (Norway): consultancy services;

PCR/Swedtel (Sweden), *Preece, Cardew and Rider* (England) and *Telecoms International* (Sweden): consultancy services for the original microwave network.

In addition to these companies, there are scores of domestic companies which participate in the effort, individually or jointly with foreign companies. Some of the most prominent are:

Beta: construction, installation and O&M work;

Gentec: construction, installation and O&M work;

CAP/SA: installation, operation and maintenance of computers;

DAR Okaz: printing of directories;

Binladen: telecommunications equipment, PBX;

MidMac: buildings contractors;

Al Mabani: buildings contractors;

Dallah-Avco: electro-mechanical maintenance.

Beyond this, hundreds of local contractors and companies supply manpower and material for one of the largest projects of its type in the world.

The Second and Third Five-Year Plans have already substantially achieved their goals, most of then ahead of schedule, due to the implementation of a Management by Objectives program. The physical infrastructure and — most important — the modern management systems are in place as planned by MoPTT. The Kingdom of Saudi Arabia can now offer its citizens a world-class telecommunications service.

On the base provided by the Third Five-Year Plan, the vast telecommunications network will be extended to hundreds more communities across the Kingdom. The number of working lines will soon pass the million mark. A new Automatic Mobile Telephone System will become the largest of its type in the world. The number of coin telephones will increase, and major telecommunications complexes will be completed. Modern management methods will bring the organization into the front ranks of the Kingdom's models of efficient organizations. The Ministry of PTT will continue to provide the public with the improvements and innovations necessary to keep the Kingdom's telecommunications system in the forefront of the global electronic community, through the future development of Saudi Telecom — an autonomous operating company with all telecommunications functions under one roof.

□

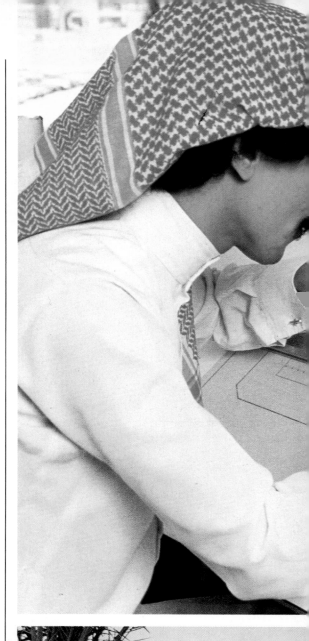

Cable & Wireless (Grande-Bretagne) : exploitation et maintenance du système à satellite du Royaume ;

Bell Canada (Canada) : contrat de gestion et d'exploitation de l'ensemble du réseau téléphonique ;

Philips (Pays-Bas) et *L.M. Ericsson* (Suède) : contrat pour les équipements et les installations extérieures ;

Western Electric (Etats-Unis) : ingénierie et installation des réseaux en micro-ondes ;

Dong Ah (Corée) : mise en place des installations extérieures ;

Telettra (Italie) : fourniture et maintenance des réseaux en micro-ondes ;

Sirti (Italie) : fourniture et maintenance du réseau en câble coaxial ;

Sartelco (Italie) : maintenance des systèmes de micro-ondes ;

Siemens (Rép. fédérale d'Allemagne) : fourniture de téléimprimeurs et d'équipements télex ;

Dete Con (Rép. fédérale d'Allemagne) : exploitation et maintenance du réseau télex ;

Arthur D. Little (Etats-Unis) : services d'expert-conseil général au Ministère des PTT ;

Norconsult (Norvège) : services d'expert-conseil ;

PCR/Swedtel (Suède), *Preece, Cardew and Rider* (Royaume-Uni) et *Telecoms International* (Suède) : services d'expert-conseil pour le réseau initial en micro-ondes.

Outre ces sociétés, des dizaines d'entreprises nationales contribuent à cet essor, individuellement ou en association avec des firmes étrangères ; citons parmi les plus importantes :

Beta : construction, installation et travaux d'exploitation et de maintenance ;

Gentec : construction, installation et travaux d'exploitation et de maintenance ;

CAP/SA : installation, exploitation et maintenance des ordinateurs ;

DAR Okaz : impression des annuaires ;

Binladen : équipements de télécommunications, autocommutateurs privés ;

MidMac : construction immobilière ;

Dallah-Avco : maintenance des équipements électro-mécaniques.

Enfin, des centaines d'entreprises locales fournissent la main d'œuvre et les matériaux nécessaires à la réalisation d'un des projets les plus ambitieux entrepris dans ce domaine dans le monde.

Les Deuxième et Troisième Plans Quinquennaux ont déjà atteint leurs objectifs, pour la plupart en avance sur les prévisions, grâce à la mise en œuvre d'un programme de Gestion par Objectifs. L'infrastructure physique et les systèmes de gestion modernes, d'une importance encore plus grande, ont été mis en place tels qu'ils avaient été conçus par le ministère des PTT. Le Royaume d'Arabie saoudite peut maintenant offrir à ses citoyens un service de télécommunication de classe internationale.

Sur la base définie par le Troisième Plan Quinquennal l'immense réseau de télécommunications sera étendu à des centaines d'autres communautés du Royaume. Les nombre de lignes en service dépassera bientôt le million et le nouveau système de radiotéléphone mobile automatique qui sera mis en service sera le plus important de son genre dans le monde. Le nombre de publiphones augmentera, et de grands complexes de télécommunications seront terminés. L'emploi de méthodes de gestion ultra-modernes amènera les PTT au premier rang des organisations les plus efficientes du Royaume.

Le Ministère des PTT continuera à fournir à son public toutes les améliorations et innovations nécessaires pour maintenir le système des télécommunications du Royaume au premier rang de la communauté mondiale de l'électronique, en assurant dans l'avenir le développement de Saudi Telecom, compagnie d'exploitation autonome assumant toutes les fonctions de télécommunications sous un seul toit.

□

Above: An architect lays out plans for telephone compounds; below, the headquarters building of Saudi Telecom in Riyadh.

En haut : Un architecte préparant des plans pour les complexes téléphoniques ; en bas, le siège de Saudi Telecom à Riyadh.

Esos servicios se obtienen sólo sobre la base de concursos internacionales, habida cuenta de la relación eficacia-costo. El esfuerzo de Arabia Saudita en las telecomunicaciones han sido apoyado por las principales compañías del mundo, y entre ellas:

AT&T International (EE.UU.): programa de expansión de las redes de microondas;

Cable & Wireless (RU): explotación y mantenimiento del sistema nacional por satélite;

Bell Canada (Canadá): contrato de gestión y explotación de todo el sistema telefónico;

Philips (Países Bajos) y *L.M. Ericsson* (Suecia): contrato de equipo e instalación exterior;

Western Electric (EE.UU.): ingeniería e instalación de microondas;

Dong Ah (Corea): establecimiento de instalación exterior;

Telettra (Italia): suministro e instalación de enlace de microondas;

Sirti (Italia): suministro y mantenimiento del sistema coaxial;

Sartelco (Italia): mantenimiento del sistema de microondas;

Siemens (Rep. Fed. de Alemania): suministro de teleimpresores y equipo télex;

Dete Con (Rep. Fed. de Alemania): explotación y mantenimiento del sistema télex;

Arthur D. Little (EE.UU.): asesoramiento general del Min. de CTT;

Norconsult (Noruega): servicios consultivos;

PCR/Swedtel (Suecia) - *Preece, Cardew and Rider* (RU) y *Telecoms Internacional* (Suecia): servicios consultivos para la red original de microondas.

Adémas de estas empresas, hay muchas compañías nacionales que participan en las actividades, solas o en empresas mixtas con compañías extranjeras. Algunas de las más importantes son:

Beta: construcción, instalación y EyM;

Gentec: construcción, instalación y EyM;

CAP/SA: instalación, explotación y mantenimiento de computadores;

DAR Okaz: impresión de guías;

Binladen: equipo de telecomunicaciones, CAP;

MidMac: contratos de construcción;

Al Mabani: contratos de construcción;

Dallah-Avco: mantenimiento electro-mecánico.

Además, centenares de contratistas y empresas locales suministran mano de obra y material para uno de los mayores proyectos mundiales de este tipo.

El Segundo y el Tercer Plan Quinquenal han alcanzado sus objetivos antes de lo previsto gracias a un programa de gestión por finalidades. Ya se ha establecido la infraestructura física y, lo que es más importante, los sistemas de gestión modernos, previstos por el Min. de CTT. El Reino puede ofrecer a sus ciudadanos un servicio de categoría mundial.

Sobre la base del tercer plan quinquenal, la vasta red de telecomunicaciones se extenderá a centenares de comunidades más del país. Pronto habrá en servicio más de un millón de líneas, y el nuevo sistema telefónico móvil automático será el mayor del mundo. Aumentará el número de telefónos públicos y se completarán importantes complejos de telecomunicaciones. Merced a métodos de gestión modernos, la organización de CTT figurará entre las más eficaces del Reino. El Ministerio de CTT seguirá proporcionando al público todas las novedades necesarias para mantener al Reino a la vanguardia de la comunidad mundial de la electrónica, con el futuro desarrollo de Saudi Telecom, empresa autónoma que abarca todas las funciones de telecomunicaciones.

□

Arriba: Un arquitecto preparando planos para complejos telefónicos; abajo, la sede de Saudi Telecom, en Riyadh.

MASTER-BUILDERS
WHO PE IN COMMUNICATIONS NEWHORIZONS
THE INTERNATIONAL SCENE

MASTER-BUILDERS IN TELECOMMUNICATIONS are firms with the experience and resources to operate as main contractors in the construction of infrastructures. There are only very few of them. Ideally, the attributes of a master-builder in telecommunications are the following :
— management resources to conduct major multi-million dollar projects in distant locations, involving the training and use of local personnel and the supply of integrated logistic support of network operation and maintenance;
— design experience of networks of proven operational soundness, and familiarity with interfacing problems, as well as great strength in the latest applicable technologies;
— R&D facilities equipped to develop and adopt requisite hardware and software;
— experience of network operation and management;
— proven competence in the management of large projects involving the use of substantial numbers of specialized sub-contractors;
— experience in managing projects away from base, in partnership with the telecommunications authority of the country concerned;
— ability to arrange project finance.

Two companies, both American, fully possess all these attributes. American Telephone and Telegraph (AT&T), with the longest and most widespread experience of network operation of any private firm (the Bell System), splendidly equipped also in manufacturing and network design know-how (Western Electric), and in research and development (Bell Laboratories). The other is GTE Corporation, the largest "independent" telecommunications operator

▷ 262

LES « MAITRES-CONSTRUCTEURS » en télécommunication sont très peu nombreux. Ce sont de grandes firmes avec les ressources et l'expérience requises pour opérer en qualité de maître d'œuvre dans la construction d'une infrastructure intégrale. Voici les critères qui, a des degrés divers, entrent en jeu dans une telle définition :
— compétence et ressources de gestion suffisantes pour diriger, souvent à des milliers de kilomètres de la base, de grands projets coûtant des centaines de millions de dollars, qui impliquent la formation et l'emploi de la main d'œuvre locale ainsi qu'un apport logistique et la maintenance ;
— connaissance approfondie de la conception des réseaux, des problèmes d'interface, de la fiabilité et de la maîtrise des techniques les plus récentes ;
— services capables d'adapter et de mettre au point le matériel et le logiciel requis ;
— expérience de l'exploitation et de la maintenance des réseaux ;
— capacité de contrôle de gestion et d'organisation d'équipes, comprenant des sous-traitants ;
— expérience dans la gestion de grands complexes dans d'autres pays assurée en étroites relations avec l'administration des PTT du pays client ;
— la capacité d'organiser le financement des projets.

Deux compagnies répondent parfaitement à ces critères : American Telephone and Telegraph, AT&T, qui possède à la fois l'expérience d'exploitation des réseaux (The Bell System), les moyens de fabrication de matériel (Western Eletric) et une grande organisation de recherche et de développement (Bell Laboratories). L'autre, GTE Corporation, est la plus grande exploitation de télécommunications « indépendante » des Etats-Unis avec capacité de production et de « R&D ». Une troisième

▷ 262

LOS GRANDES CONSTRUCTORES de las telecomunicaciones, empresas con experiencia y recursos para actuar como principales contratistas de las infraestructuras, son muy pocos. Los atributos ideales de un gran constructor son:
— recursos de gestión para realizar importantes proyectos de muchos millones de dólares en lugares lejanos, que entrañan la formación y el uso de personal local y el suministro de apoyo integrado para la explotación y mantenimiento de redes;
— profundo conocimiento del diseño de redes, problemas de conexión y aplicación de las técnicas más modernas;
— instalaciones de IyD, para desarrollar y adoptar el soporte físico y lógico necesario;
— experiencia en explotación y gestión de redes;
— capacidad para dirigir grandes proyectos, lo que supone el empleo de un considerable número de subcontratistas especializados;
— experiencia en dirección de proyectos en otros países, en asociación con la autoridad de telecomunicaciones correspondiente;
— capacidad para organizar la financiación de proyectos.

Sólo dos empresas, ambas americanas, poseen todos estos atributos. American Telephone and Telegraph (AT&T), con la mayor experiencia en explotación de redes (Bell System), magníficamente equipada para fabricar y diseñar redes (Western Electric) y para la investigación y el desarrollo (Bell Laboratories). La otra es GTE Corporation, la principal empresa de explotación de telecomunicaciones "independiente" de EE.UU., con amplias actividades de fabricación y de investigación en el país y en el extranjero. Una tercera, también americana, pero

▷ 263

The building blocks of
a worldwide network of communications:
the amalgam of equipments and services
constituting the wherewithal of a master-builder.

Les blocs de construction
d'un système universel de communications :
l'amalgame des équipements et des services
constituant l'arsenal d'un maître-constructeur.

Los bloques de construcción
de una red mundial de comunicaciones;
la amalgama de equipos y servicios constituyen
los recursos de un gran constructor.

in the USA, with extensive manufacturing and research activities in the USA and overseas. A third company prominent in this field, basically American, although with resources widely distributed worldwide, is ITT Corporation.

Several other companies have extensive experience of constructing major systems and the wherewithal to instruct their clients in operational and maintenance procedures but lack experience of network operation. They may nonetheless be described as master-builders: in Japan, NEC; in Canada, Northern Telecom; and in Western Europe: Ericsson, GEC Telecommunications, Plessey, Siemens, Thomson-CSF and CIT Alcatel (CGE Group). All these, however, derive their network experience from long intimate associations with their national telecommunications operating entities. NEC Corporation works hand in hand with Nippon Telephone and Telegraph and benefits from the latter's considerable experience of complex systems; Northern Telecom was until 1982 a member of the Bell Canada group companies and therefore very close to network operation and problems.

The Europeans are all in some measure "integrated" in the operational pattern of the national telecommunications service. GEC Communications and Plessey work with British Telecom, the operators of the national British network, and benefit from the latter's major investment in R&D. Siemens is the largest equipment manufacturer in Europe (3rd in the world) and, like the other European firms, works closely with the national PTT, the Bundespost. Thomson-CSF and CIT Alcatel work within the nationalized framework of French telecommunications and cooperate closely with the national PTT which, like its British counterpart, possesses a large R&D resource.

L.M. Ericsson is somewhat different from all the other in Europe or elsewhere. Its Swedish home-market is highly developed but small and Ericsson has grown into one of the major providers with the powerful assistance of the Swedish Telecoms International, Swedtel, which has long been active in promoting the export of Swedish telecommunications technology.

There are other companies which, though not fitting the description of "master-builders in telecommunications" given above, have extended their own experience by associating with other organizations whose activities are complementary to their own. For example, Italtel, the nationally-owned Italian supplier of telecommunications equipment and systems, with the GTE Corporation; CIT Alcatel and NV Philips. More of this type of alliance will certainly be concluded as the building of the ISDN progresses.

Another development of considerable importance is the entry into the communications industry of electronic engineering companies, such as IBM, Honeywell, Univac, DEC, Rolm and many others. Developments in this direction are discussed on p. 282.

The decision of several countries to deregulate and to allow the importation of foreign equipment and systems has intensified this process.

Other major new entrants during the past two or three decades are firms from the aerospace industries leaders among whom are the US firms Hughes Aircraft and Ford Aerospace, the French Aérospatiale and British Aerospace.

Hughes Aircraft who have recently become involved in the operation of satellite networks — as have IBM — are the world leaders in the design and construction of satellites and act as main contractors in the great majority of new projects spanning the 80s and 90s. In 1982 communications satellites built by Hughes accounted for over 70 per cent of all revenue-bearing satellites in use outside the Soviet Union's own network. On receipt of the order for five *Intelsat VI* satellites (with options for 11 more) the company formed a team of space technology firms including

▷ 264

compagnie, ITT Corporation, également américaine, est le deuxième fabricant de matériel du monde et possède une expérience considérable de la construction et de la conception de grands systèmes.

D'autres compagnies qui possèdent une longue expérience des grands projets et les resources nécessaires pour former le personnel des clients pour l'exploitation et la maintenance, mais qui n'ont pas d'expérience d'exploitation de réseau, peuvent cependant être considérées « maitres-constructeurs » : CIT Alcatel (groupe CGE) et Thomson-CSF en France, Ericsson en Suède, GEC Telecommunications et Plessey en Grande-Bretagne, NEC au Japon, et Siemens en République Fédérale d'Allemagne. Toutefois ces compagnies tirent leur expérience d'une association de longue date avec les PTT de leurs pays. NEC coopère étroitement avec Nippon Telephone & Telegraph (NTT) laquelle exploite le réseau japonais. Jusqu'en 1982, Northen Telecom était membre du groupe Bell Canada qui assure le service des télécommunications dans ce pays.

Les firmes européennes sont toutes plus ou moins "intégrées" dans le schéma opérationnel de l'administration nationale des télécommunications. GEC Telecommunications et Plessey travaillent avec British Telecom, qui exploite le réseau national britannique, et consacre d'importants investissements à la recherche et au développement. Siemens, le plus grand constructeur européen d'équipements de télécommunications, travaille en étroite liaison avec le « Bundespost » de la RFA, Thomson-CSF travaille dans le cadre nationalisé des télécommunications françaises, côte à côte avec l'autre grand constructeur, CIT Alcatel, et avec la Direction Générale des Télécommunications qui dispose d'importants services de recherche et de développement.

Ericsson diffère peu des firmes d'Europe ou d'ailleurs. Comme le marché suédois est très moderne mais restreint, Ericsson s'est donc tournée vers le marché mondial où elle est devenue l'un des principaux fournisseurs de systèmes avec l'aide puissante de Swedish Telecoms International (Swedtel), qui existe au niveau public pour promouvoir l'exploitation de la technologie suédoise.

Il existe d'autres compagnies qui, tout en ne répondant pas à la définition de « maître-constructeur » citée ci-dessus, ont étendu leur expérience en s'associant avec d'autres entreprises ayant une expérience et des activités complémentaires. Un exemple d'une telle association est celle d'Italtel, l'entreprise nationale italienne, avec GTE Corporation. Un autre est l'accord de coopération entre CIT Alcatel et NV Philips. D'autres associations de ce genre, se constitueront à fur et à mesure que la construction des systèmes régionaux et du RNIS progresse.

Un autre évènement de grande importance est l'entrée dans l'industrie de la communication des entreprises d'ingénierie électronique, telle que IBM, Honeywell, DEC, Rolm et bien d'autres. Cette évolution est examinée à la p. 282. Elle a été considérablement influencée par la decision de plusieurs pays de lever la réglementation et de permettre l'importation de systèmes et de matériel étrangers.

Une autre irruption de firmes importantes pendant les deux ou trois dernières décennies provient des industries aérospatiales, parmi lesquelles on trouve les firmes américaines Hughes Aircraft et Ford Aerospace, et les Européens Aérospatiale et British Aerospace.

Hughes Aircraft qui vient récemment de s'engager dans l'exploitation de réseau de satellites, comme l'a fait IBM parmi les constructeurs de matériel, maîtrise parfaitement la conception et la construction des satellites. En 1982, les satellites construits par cette firme représentaient plus de 70% des recettes apportées par les engins spatiaux , exception faite des satellites appartenant au réseau de l'URSS. Après avoir reçu commande de 5 satellites *Intelsat VI*, la compagnie a formé un consortium de spécialistes en technologie spatiale, comprenant SPAR Aerospace of Canada, Thomson-CSF, Messerschmidt-Boelkow-Blohm, British Aerospace, Selenia et NEC,

▷ 264

A microwave antenna for digital transmission perched on the Zugspitze, the highest mountain in the Federal Republic of Germany.

Une antenne de micro-ondes pour transmission numérique sur le Zugspitze, la plus haute montagne de la République Fédérale d'Allemagne.

con recursos muy dispersos en el mundo entero, y considerable experiencia en el diseño y construcción de infraestructuras, es ITT Corporation.

Pueden considerarse grandes constructores otras empresas con mucha experiencia en grandes proyectos y con recursos para formar al personal de los clientes en explotación y mantenimiento, pero no para la explotación de redes: en Japón, NEC; en Canadá, Northern Telecom, y en Europa Occidental, Ericsson, GEC Telecommunications, Plessey, Siemens, Thomson-CSF y CIT Alcatel (Grupo CGE). Sin embargo, todas ellas derivan su experiencia de las CTT de sus países. NEC Corporation trabaja con Nippon Telephone and Telegraph, y se beneficia de la gran experiencia de ésta en sistemas complejos; Northern Telecom fue hasta 1982 miembro del grupo de empresas Bell Canada, por lo que conoce muy bien la explotación y los problemas de redes.

Las europeas están todas "integradas" en cierto grado en la estructura operacional del servicio nacional de telecomunicaciones. GEC Communications y Plessey trabajan con British Telecom, que explota la red nacional británica, y se beneficia de las grandes inversiones de ésta en IyD. Siemens es el mayor fabricante europeo (3° del mundo) y, como los demás europeos, trabaja estrechamente con la Bundespost. Thomson-CSF y CIT Alcatel operan en el marco nacionalizado de las telecomunicaciones francesas y cooperan con la CTT nacional que, como su homóloga británica, explota grandes recursos de IyD.

L. M. Ericsson es algo distinta de todas las demás de Europa y otros lugares. Su mercado nacional sueco está muy desarrollado, pero es pequeño, y Ericsson se ha convertido en uno de los principales proveedores de sistemas de telecomunicaciones del mundo, con la poderosa ayuda de Swedish Telecoms International (Swedtel), que fomenta la exportación de la tecnología sueca.

Hay otras empresas que, si bien no corresponden a la definición de "gran constructor de telecomunicaciones" citada, han enriquecido su experiencia asociándose con otras cuyas actividades son complementarias. Por ejemplo, Italtel, proveedor estatal italiano de equipo y sistemas de comunicaciones, con GTE Corporation; CIT Alcatel y NV Philips. A medida que progrese la RDSI, se celebrarán más alianzas de este tipo.

Otro hecho de gran importancia es la entrada en la industria de comunicaciones de compañías de ingeniería electrónica, como IBM, Honeywell, Univac, DEC, Rolm y muchas otras. Esto se trata en la pág. 282. La decisión de varias países de liberalizar la industria y permitir la importación de equipo y sistemas extranjeros ha acelerado este proceso.

Otras industrias nuevas en este sector durante los 2 ó 3 últimos decenios proceden de la industria aerospacial, destacando las empresas americanas Hughes Aircraft y Ford Aerospace, la Aerospatiale francesa y British Aerospace.

Hughes Aircraft, que acaba de iniciar la explotación de redes de satélite — lo mismo que IBM entre los constructores de equipo —, va a la cabeza mundial en el diseño y construcción de satélites, siendo el principal contratista de la mayoría de los nuevos proyectos de los años 80 y 90. En 1982, los satélites de comunicaciones construidos por Hughes representaron más del 70% de todos los satélites que producen ingresos utilizados fuera de la red de la Unión Soviética. Al recibir el pedido de 5 satélites *Intelsat VI* (con opción para 11 más), la empresa formó un equipo de firmas de tecnología espacial, que comprende SPAR Aerospace of Canada, Thomson-CSF, Messerschmidt-Boelkow-Blohm, British Aerospace, Selenia y NEC Corporation, subcontratando cada una parte del trabajo bajo la dirección de Hughes. La empresa ha extendido sus actividades para cubrir las tecnologías de verificación y control de satélites desde estaciones terrenas. Ejemplo de ello es la cons-

▷ 265

Una antena de microondas para transmisiones digitales en la cumbre del Zugspitze, la montaña más alta de la República Federal de Alemania.

SPAR Aerospace of Canada, Thomson-CSF of France, Messerschmidt-Boelkow-Blohm of the FRG, British Aerospace, Selenia of Italy and NEC Corporation of Japan, each being sub-contracted part of the work under Hughes' direction. The company has extended its activities to cover the technologies of satellite monitoring and control from earth stations. An example of this was the construction of two satellite command centers, equipped with computer-controlled 13-meter dish antennae, for AT&T's first telecommunications satellite, *Telstar 3*. In recognition of his pioneering work in the design of geostationary telecommunication satellites, Hughes' Dr. Harold Rosen was awarded the Alexander Graham Bell medal by the US Institute of Electrical and Electronic Engineers.

Prerequisite of success for large projects involved in network development or expansion is an understanding of regional and national differences in approach and requirements. Some of the firms cited above, for example Siemens and NEC, who reached 3rd and 7th respectively as vendors of telecommunications equipment in 1982, have developed this to an uncommon degree.

Siemens has some of its products manufactured in 28 countries and is involved in numerous joint ventures with local companies to promote the transfer of technology to points of applications and usage.

NEC has local affiliates in 20 countries — including 13 in the developing stage — established "to contribute to host countries through a transfer of technologies, creation of new employment opportunities and the purchase of local parts and materials". The task of each affiliate is to "develop its area by tailoring products and services to meet specific customer requirements".

Another example of this approach is that of American Telephone and Telegraph, through their wholly owned subsidiary AT&T International, formed in 1980 to develop and market telecommunication products outside the USA. AT&T's notion of the telephone as "a social service which should be available to all" and the success it has had in harmonizing self-interest and social purpose are factors in the new company's approach to the development of their business outside the USA. The President of AT&T International, Robert Sageman, has stated that the possibility of additional partnerships or joint ventures, or of the establishment of foreign subsidiaries in which local investors will be invited to purchase equity, is basic to the company's concept of worldwide development.

These companies' concern for the effective transfer of technology to points of application and usage, and for establishing a working partnership with their clients which lasts beyond the end of projects — in fact as long as it is needed — is a vital element in the successful establishment and operation of an integrated world network.

It is this technological excellence, coupled with the ability to lead multinational teams and to promote harmony in the communality of effort which makes firms such as AT&T, IBM and Hughes excel. Interdependence, however, has practical working limits. IBM finds it necessary to extend their product range into digital switching, AT&T is manufacturing microprocessors and a widening range of computers, Hughes designs and builds sophisticated computer-controlled equipment. All three are deeply involved therefore in the development of very high speed integrated circuits (VHSIC) — such components being basic to their further development.

GTE Corporation, a company with similar attributes, is profiled in the pages that follow: a master-builder in the most modern and adaptive style, with experience in every area of telecommunications.

□

chacun travaillant en sous-traitance sous sa direction.

Hughes Aircraft a élargi son champ d'activité aux techniques de contrôle et de commande des engins spatiaux à partir des stations terriennes. Citons, à titre d'exemple, la construction de deux centres de commande de satellites, équipés d'antennes paraboliques guidées par ordinateur pour le premier satellite de télécommunications AT&T, *Telstar 3*, l'Institute of Electrical and Electronic Engineers des Etats-Unis a du reste décerné la médaille Alexander Graham Bell au Dr. Harold Rosen de Hughes Aircraft, l'un des pionniers dans le domaine des satellites géostationnaires de télécommunications.

L'appréciation des différences régionales et nationales, est une démarche essentielle au succès des grands projets de construction ou d'expansion de réseaux. Quelques unes des firmes citées, par exemple Siemens et NEC qui étaient respectivement au 3ème et 7ème rang mondial des constructeurs de matériel de télécommunication, ont développé une aptitude remarquable dans cette direction. Siemens construit son matériel dans 28 pays et participe à de nombreuses entreprises conjointes avec des firmes locales pour effectuer le transfert de technologie sur les lieux d'application.

NEC a des associés dans 20 pays, dont 13 sont des pays en développement, dans le but « de contribuer à un transfert de technologie, de créer de nouveaux emplois et de produire du matériel et des composants dans le pays client ». Chaque associé a pour tâche de « développer son marché en adaptant matériels et services aux besoins spécifiques de la clientèle ».

Un autre exemple de cette option à l'exportation est celui de AT&T qui a créé, en 1980, une filiale, AT&T International, pour développer et vendre du matériel de télécommunication hors des Etats-Unis. Pour AT&T, la notion même du téléphone conçu comme un « service disponible pour tous », et le succès indéniable qu'elle a obtenu en réalisant une conciliation harmonieuse de ses intérêts sont des facteurs déterminants pour la formulation de sa nouvelle politique d'expansion en dehors des Etats-Unis. Le président de AT&T International, Robert Sageman, a indiqué, par ailleurs, que la possibilité de nouvelles associations ou « joint ventures », ou même l'établissement de filiales à l'étranger dans lesquelles les investisseurs locaux seraient encouragés à prendre des participations, étaient un principe fondamental de la politique de développement mondial de la compagnie.

La préoccupation de ces firmes concernant le transfert de technologie aux endroits d'application et d'utilisation, ainsi que l'établissement d'une association de travail avec leurs clients au delà de la réalisation des projets, est un élément vital dans la conception et l'exploitation d'un réseau numérique avec intégration de services (RNIS).

C'est cette éminence technologique, jointe à la capacité de diriger des équipes multinationales et de promouvoir l'harmonie des efforts communs, qui explique pourquoi des firmes telles que AT&T, IBM et Hughes Aircraft réussissent à se développer dans la télécommunication. Mais l'interdépendance a ses limites. C'est pourquoi IBM envisage l'extension de sa production aux systèmes numériques de commutation, AT&T fabrique des microprocesseurs et un éventail toujours plus large d'ordinateurs, tandis que Hughes Aircraft conçoit des équipements complexes commandés par ordinateur. Les trois firmes étudient donc de très près la mise au point de circuits intégrés à très grande capacité, ces composants étant une condition essentielle du succès.

Les pages qui suivent présentent le profil de GTE Corporation : un maître-constructeur, dans le style le plus moderne et le plus souple, possédant une expérience qui s'étend à toutes les branches des télécommunications.

□

Above: The cable ship "Long Lines", the AT&T vessel especially fitted to handle the new types of submarine cable.
Below: British Telecom's Sea Dog, an underwater tracked vehicle used to bury, inspect and repair submarine cable at depths up to 300 metres.

En haut : Le navire câblier « Long Lines » de AT&T, spécialement équipé pour installer les nouveaux types de câble sous-marin.
En bas : Le tracteur sous-marin à chenilles Sea Dog, de British Telecom, qui enfouit, inspecte et répare les câbles jusqu'à 300 mètres de profondeur.

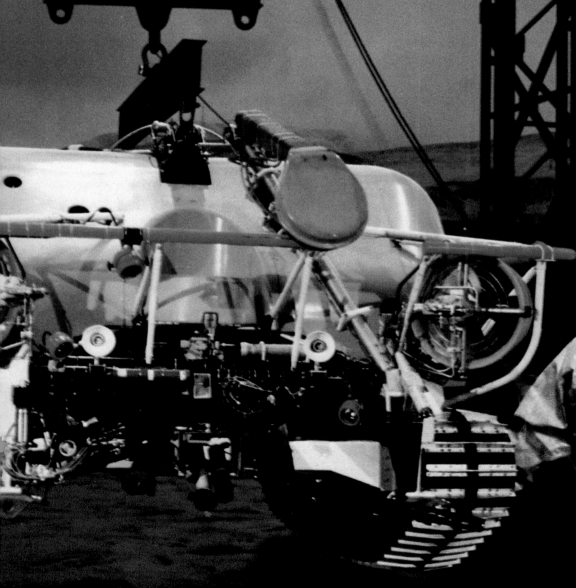

trucción de dos centros de mando de satélites, provistos de antenas parabólicas de 13 metros controladas por computador, para el primer satélite de telecomunicaciones de AT&T, *Telstar 3*. En reconocimiento de su labor de vanguardia en el diseño de satélites de comunicación geoestacionarios, el Institute of Electrical and Electronic Engineers de EE.UU. concedió al Dr. Harold Rosen, de Hughes, la medalla Alexander Graham Bell.

Un requisito del éxito de grandes proyectos de desarrollo y expansión de redes es la comprensión de las diferencias regionales y nacionales en cuanto a enfoque y necesidades. Algunas de las empresas citadas, por ejemplo, Siemens y NEC, que ocuparon el tercer y séptimo lugar como vendedores de equipo de telecomunicaciones en 1982, han elevado esto a un grado poco común.

Siemens fabrica algunos productos en 28 países y participa en numerosas empresas mixtas con compañías locales para fomentar la transferencia de tecnología. Un tercio de los empleados de la empresa están en el extranjero: 16% en países de Europa fuera de la RFA; sendos 5% en América Latina y Asia/Australia; 4% en América del Norte, y 2% en África.

NEC tiene asociados en 20 países — 13 de ellos en desarrollo — con el fin de contribuir a la transferencia de tecnología, la creación de nuevos empleos y procurar material y componentes fabricados localmente». La tarea de cada asociado es «desarrollar su mercado adaptando materiales y servicios a las necesidades de la clientela».

Otro ejemplo de este enfoque es el de American Telephone and Telegraph, a través de su propia filial AT&T International, creada en 1980 para desarrollar y vender productos de telecomunicación fuera de EE.UU. La noción de la empresa del teléfono como «servicio social del que todos deben disponer» y el éxito logrado al armonizar intereses propios y el fin social son factores de su nuevo enfoque para desarrollar actividades fuera de EE.UU. El Presidente de AT&T International, Robert Sageman, declaró que la posibilidad de nuevas asociaciones o empresas mixtas, o de crear filiales extranjeras en que se invitará a participar a los inversores locales, es fundamental para la noción de la empresa de desarrollo mundial.

La preocupación de esas empresas por la transferencia de tecnología a los puntos de aplicación y uso, así como el establecimiento de una asociación de trabajo con sus clientes, una vez terminados los proyectos — en realidad, durante el tiempo necesario —, es un elemento vital del éxito de una red mundial integrada.

Con esta superioridad tecnológica, y su capacidad para dirigir equipos multinacionales y fomentar la armonía y la comunidad de esfuerzos, empresas como AT&T, IBM y Hughes destacan como grandes constructores. Sin embargo, la interdependencia tiene sus límites. IBM ha de extender su gama de productos a la conmutación digital; AT&T está fabricando microprocesadores y una amplia gama de computadores; Hughes diseña y construye equipo controlado por computador sofisticado. Las tres participan, pues, en sumo grado en el desarrollo de circuitos integrados de muy alta velocidad (VHSIC), usando técnicas DAC, porque tales componentes son la clave de su éxito.

En las páginas siguientes figura el perfil de GTE Corporation, empresa con atributos similares: un gran constructor en el estilo más moderno y adaptable, con experiencia en todos los sectores de las telecomunicaciones.

□

Arriba: El cablero «Long Lines», barco de AT&T equipado especialmente para tender nuevos tipos de cables submarinos.
Abajo: El tractor submarino oruga, Sea Dog, de British Telecom, que entierra, inspecciona y repara los cables hasta una profundidad de 300 metros.

GTE Corporation

Master-Builder in Communications

A BOURGEONING "INFORMATION AGE" with extraordinary capabilities for serving the growing communications needs of countries, organizations and individuals is playing an integral role in hastening the pace of social and economic progress throughout the world.

The new age was created and is being shaped by the electronic and information technologies developed during the last two decades. Among its most important manifestations are the versatile new telecommunications systems and services appearing on the world's markets in greater numbers and in increasing diversity each year.

These innovative communications tools are producing quiet, yet revolutionary, changes in the ways people conduct their business, educate themselves, obtain a broad spectrum of vital public services and spend their periods of leisure. In sum, improved communications are contributing significantly to the economic and social progress of people everywhere.

Major forces are making for change in telecommunications. The American industry progressed at a steady yet modest pace for the first three-quarters of a century of its existence. Change came in a measured, orderly way because changes in technology, in the regulatory environment, in the economy and in society at large also occurred at a comparatively slow pace. During the last quarter-century, however the pace of change in telecommunications has quickened, giving birth to a host of new products and services. This has been due in large part to the push from technology: the introduction of many new technologies such as solid-state electronics, stored-program control computer techniques, digital transmission and switching, satellite communications and fiber optics.

▷ 268

L'AVÉNEMENT DE L'« ÈRE DE L'INFORMATION » apporte des moyens inimaginables, en moins d'une génération, pour satisfaire les besoins croissants en communications des pays, des entreprises et des individus et contribue ainsi à accélérer le rythme du progrès social et économique dans le monde entier.

Une nouvelle ère fut créée par les technologies de l'électronique et de l'information développées pendant les 70 dernières années, qui en déterminent le cours. Parmi ces manifestations, les plus importantes sont les systèmes et les services de télécommunications qui apparaissent en rapide succession et en nombre croissant chaque année.

Ces instruments novateurs de la communication produisent de profonds changements, presque inaperçus, mais en fait révolutionnaires, dans la façon dont les gens travaillent, s'instruisent, obtiennent une large gamme de services publics et se divertissent. En somme l'amélioration des communications contribue puissamment au progrès dans le monde entier.

De puissantes forces sont à l'œuvre et transforment l'industrie des télécommunications. Pendant trois quarts de siècle, depuis sa naissance, l'industrie américaine s'est développée régulièrement, mais à un rythme modeste. Ce fut une lente et prudente évolution, parallèle à celle de la technologie (dans son environnement de réglementation), de l'économie et de la société. En revanche, pendant le dernier quart de siècle, les changements se sont succédé à un rythme sans cesse accéléré et ont engendré une foule de nouveaux produits et de nouveaux services, ceci dû essentiellement à une forte poussée technologique — l'introduction du transistor dans les circuits électroniques, de l'ordinateur commandé par programme enregistré, de la commutation et de la transmission

▷ 268

LA NUEVA "ERA DE LA INFORMACIÓN", con extraordinarias posibilidades para atender las necesidades, cada vez mayores, de países, organizaciones e individuos, contribuye a acelerar el ritmo del progreso social y económico en el mundo entero.

El avance de la tecnología electrónica y de la información durante las dos últimas décadas ha creado y configura la nueva era. La aparición en los mercados mundiales de sistemas y servicios de telecomunicaciones nuevos y versátiles cuya cantidad y diversidad aumentan anualmente figuran entre sus manifestaciones más importantes.

Esos instrumentos innovadores de comunicaciones producen cambios suaves, pero revolucionarios, en la manera de llevar los negocios, instruirse, obtener una amplia gama de servicios públicos vitales y ocupar el tiempo libre. En resumen, la mejora de las comunicaciones contribuye grandemente al progreso económico y social en todo el mundo.

Las importantes fuerzas que cambian las telecomunicaciones. La industria americana progresó a un ritmo modesto pero constante los primeros 75 años. Sin embargo, en el último cuarto de siglo, las telecomunicaciones han evolucionado cada vez más rápidamente, dando origen a una multitud de nuevos productos y servicios, debido en gran parte al impulso de la tecnología: la introducción de muchas técnicas nuevas, como la electronica de estado sólido, las de computador con control por programa almacenado, la transmisión y conmutación digitales, las comunicaciones por satélite y las fibras ópticas.

Al mismo tiempo, los organismos estatales encargados de reglamentar las compañías telefónicas en EE.UU. han establecido nuevas políticas para encuadrar a la industria en un medio más competitivo y

▷ 269

One of the two satellites GSTAR due to be launched in 1984 by GTE, each capable of relaying simultaneously 30,000 conversations, or 300 teleconferences, or a combination of both.

L'un des deux satellites de communication GSTAR dont le lancement par GTE est prévu en 1984. Chacun d'eux est capable de relayer simultanément 30 000 conversations ou 300 téléconférences, ou une combinaison des deux.

Uno de los dos satélites de comunicaciones GSTAR, cuyo lanzamiento por GTE, está previsto para 1984. Ambos son capaces de retransmitir simultáneamente 30 000 conversaciones, o 300 teleconferencias o una combinación de ambas.

During this period, government agencies responsible for regulating telephone companies in the USA have been establishing new policies to move the industry into a more competitive, less regulated environment. This shift is opening new markets presenting new business opportunities to telephone companies, equipment manufacturers and others. These changes are having a marked impact not only on the industry and its customers but also on the US public in general.

Further change has been brought about by the steady upward trend in inflation in recent years, inducing higher costs and rising interest rates which have stimulated many companies, and telephone companies in particular — to adopt new approaches to pricing their goods and services, financing their operations and managing their assets and resources. The result: still more change.

A major force for change is provided by society itself. In the industrialized nations, better educated populations with increasing needs for information in larger quantities, in a variety of forms and on a more timely basis, are providing a more receptive, more sophisticated customer base for the communications systems employing the new technologies. Such systems play an important part in establishing a growing and healthy economy. In recent years, the demand for improved telecommunications networks and systems has spread to the less industrialized nations as well. As the worldwide telecommunications industry responds to society's strong pull, change will continue to occur rapidly.

GTE is ideally positioned and well equipped to make major contributions to the worldwide development of communications. The company's experience in telecommunications dates almost to Alexander Graham Bell's invention of the telephone in 1876. The GTE manufacturing operations trace their history back to 1881 when the Strowger Automatic Exchange was established in Chicago, Illinois, to manufacture dial-telephone switching systems. The telephone operations date to the birth in 1918 of a small telephone company in Wisconsin which became the first of many that eventually made up an extensive telephone organization. Today, the company maintains large research and development facilities, manufactures telecommunications equipment at 34 plants in the USA and seven other countries, and fields an experienced and capable marketing organization with a presence in many nations around the globe.

Planning is a major tool for the GTE manufacturing organizations and is based on a highly-developed approach employing technological, economic and other factors. The GTE telephone companies are experienced in forecasting population trends and movements and in utilizing such forecasts to identify needs for switching and transmission systems to accommodate growth and provide new services.

Considerable emphasis is placed on research and development. The company operates 40 laboratories employing some 3,000 scientists and engineers in the USA, Canada, Belgium and Italy. These facilities provide substantial "technology pull" to system conception and design and to the development of new and improved products in telecommunications as well as in GTE's other businesses. The marketing and service organizations maintain close contact with users and thereby contribute to creating the "market pull" which is so essential a component of a realistic, customer-oriented, development program.

GTE, Master-Builder par excellence, is among the small number of the world's telecommunications companies which possess the necessary attributes to fulfil the role of "Master-Builder in Communications". It is a member of that select group by virtue of long
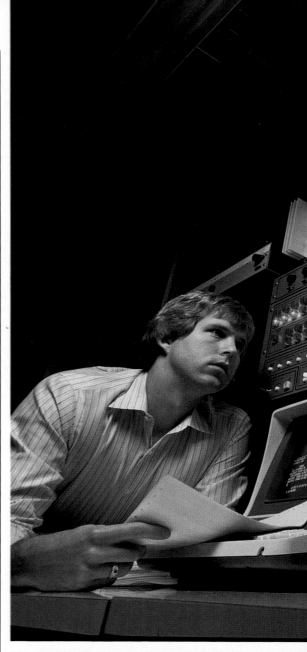

▷ 272

numériques, du satellite géostationnaire et des fibres optiques.

Dans cette même période les agences gouvernementales chargées de la réglementation des compagnies téléphoniques aux Etats-Unis ont adopté une nouvelle politique d'assouplissement de la réglementation pour laisser la concurrence jouer plus librement. Ce changement a ouvert de nouveaux marchés aux exploitants de réseaux téléphoniques, aux fabricants de matériel et à d'autres. Cette nouvelle orientation a eu des répercussions très profondes non seulement sur l'industrie et ses clients, mais aussi sur le grand public américain.

D'autres changements sont occasionnés par l'inflation persistante des dernières années. Les problèmes de la hausse des coûts et des taux d'intérêt ont incité de nombreuses sociétés, y compris les compagnies téléphoniques, à adopter de nouvelles politiques de prix, de financement et de gestion d'actifs et de ressources. Résultat : encore du changement.

L'évolution de la société est elle-même un important facteur de changement. Dans les pays industrialisés, le niveau général de l'éducation augmente et les populations exigent de l'information sans cesse plus abondante, diversifiée et immédiate, ce qui crée, pour les systèmes de communication utilisant les techniques de pointe, un marché à la fois plus réceptif et plus exigeant. La mise en place de ces nouveaux systèmes est un puissant facteur de croissance et de prospérité économique. Plus récemment, cette demande pour des réseaux et systèmes de télécommunications plus perfectionnés s'est étendue aux pays en développement. Dans la mesure où l'industrie mondiale des télécommunications répond à cet appel de la société, son évolution continuera à une vitesse accrue.

GTE est idéalement située et munie des moyens nécessaires pour contribuer puissamment au développement mondial des communications. Son expérience dans ce secteur remonte presque à l'invention du téléphone en 1876. Ses activités en tant que constructeur ont commencé en 1881, à Chicago, quand la société Strowger Automatic Exchange commença à fabriquer des systèmes de commutation automatiques. Son exploitation du réseau remonte à 1918, avec une petite compagnie téléphonique desservant la région. Elle fut suivie par beaucoup d'autres, constituant aujourd'hui une grande organisation téléphonique desservant des millions d'abonnés.

A l'heure actuelle GTE dispose d'une grande organisation de recherche et de développement, fabrique du matériel de télécommunications dans 34 usines aux Etats-Unis et dans 7 autres pays. Son organisation commerciale, très efficace et expérimentée, est présente un peu partout dans le monde.

Pour les entreprises de fabrication de GTE, la planification est un instrument-clé, ayant pour base une formule très complexe mettant en jeu des paramètres techniques et économiques, ainsi que d'autres facteurs. Les entreprises d'exploitation téléphonique de GTE, ont une vaste expérience en matière de prévision des tendances et des mouvements démographiques. Ils se servent de ces prévisions pour identifier les besoins futurs en systèmes de communication et de transmission, et pour tenir compte de la croissance attendue dans l'aménagement de leurs nouveaux services.

GTE accorde une grande importance aux activités de recherche et de développement. La société exploite, aux Etats-Unis, au Canada, en Belgique et en Italie, 40 laboratoires dans lesquels travaillent quelque 3000 personnes qualifiées. L'émulation scientifique et technique entretenue dans ces établissements permet à la société de maintenir son dynamisme dans la conception et la réalisation de produits nouveaux, et dans le perfectionnement des produits existants, de même qu'au niveau d'autres activités déployées par GTE dans le domaine des télécommunications.

▷ 272

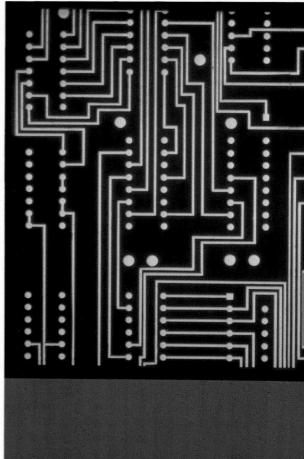

Above: Central control complex used to test lines and trunks for local base and remote units of the GTE 5 EAX family of switches. Below: Part of a circuit for GTE's line of digital switching systems, which interconnects the latest integrated circuits; vastly enlarged for inspection.

En haut : Système central de contrôle utilisé pour tester les lignes et les liaisons interurbaines des unités de la série GTD 5 EAX de GTE. En bas : Une section d'un circuit de commutateur numérique de GTE, qui rélie les plus récents circuits intégrés ; immensément agrandie pour inspection.

con menos restricciones. Esto abre nuevos mercados, que ofrecen más oportunidades comerciales a las compañías telefónicas, los fabricantes de equipo y otros.

La constante tendencia inflacionaria de los últimos años ha entrañado otros cambios. Los problemas originados por el aumento de los costos y de los tipos de interés a causa de la inflación han incitado a muchas empresas, en particular telefónicas, a adoptar nuevas políticas de precios de sus bienes y servicios, financiación de sus operaciones y gestión de sus activos y recursos. Resultado: más cambios.

La propia sociedad es una importante fuerza de cambio. En los países industrializados, la población, más instruida, precisa una información cada vez más abundante, diversificada y rápida, lo que crea una base más receptiva y exigente para los sistemas de comunicaciones que utilizan las nuevas tecnologías. Esos sistemas juegan un papel importante en el sano crecimiento de la economía. En los últimos años, la demanda de mejores redes y sistemas de telecomunicaciones se ha extendido a los países menos industrializados.

GTE está en una situación ideal, y bien dotada, para hacer grandes contribuciones al desarrollo de las comunicaciones mundiales. La experiencia de la empresa en telecomunicaciones data de 1876, en que Alexander Graham Bell inventó el teléfono. Sus operaciones de fabricación se remontan a 1881, en que la sociedad Strowger Automatic Exchange comenzó a fabricar en Chicago, Illinois, sistemas de conmutación telefónica automáticos. Las operaciones telefónicas comenzaron al crearse en 1918 una pequeña compañía en Wisconsin, que fue la primera de las muchas que acabaron constituyendo una amplia organización telefónica. Actualmente, la empresa tiene grandes instalaciones de investigación y desarrollo, fabrica equipo de telecomunicación en 34 plantas de EE.UU. y otros siete países, y tiene en muchas naciones una experimentada y capaz organización comercial.

La planificación es un importante instrumento de las organizaciones de fabricación de GTE, y se basa en métodos muy desarrollados que se sirven de factores tecnológicos, económicos y otros. Las compañías telefónicas de GTE prevén las tendencias y movimientos demográficos, y el uso de tales previsiones para conocer las necesidades de sistemas de conmutación y transmisión, a fin de adaptar el crecimiento y de prestar nuevos servicios.

Se insiste mucho en la investigación y el desarrollo. La empresa dispone de 40 laboratorios que emplean a unos 3000 científicos e ingenieros en EE.UU., Canadá, Bélgica e Italia. Esas instalaciones aportan un sustancial "impulso tecnológico" a la concepción y el diseño de sistemas y al desarrollo de nuevos productos y mejores en las telecomunicaciones y en otros sectores de GTE. Las organizaciones de comercialización y servicios mantienen estrecho contacto con los usuarios, contribuyendo así a crear el "impulso del mercado", elemento esencial de un programa de desarrollo realista destinado al cliente.

GTE, gran constructor por excelencia, figura entre las pocas empresas mundiales de telecomunicaciones que poseen los atributos necesarios para cumplir el papel de "gran constructor de comunicaciones". Su larga experiencia en planificación, desarrollo, fabricación, instalación y explotación de una amplia gama de sistemas de comunicaciones para los mercados mundiales le permiten figurar en ese selecto grupo.

La empresa, basada sólidamente en muchos decenios de experiencia en la industria mundial de telecomunicaciones, entra ahora con confianza en la era de la información, que evoluciona rápidamente y

▷ 273

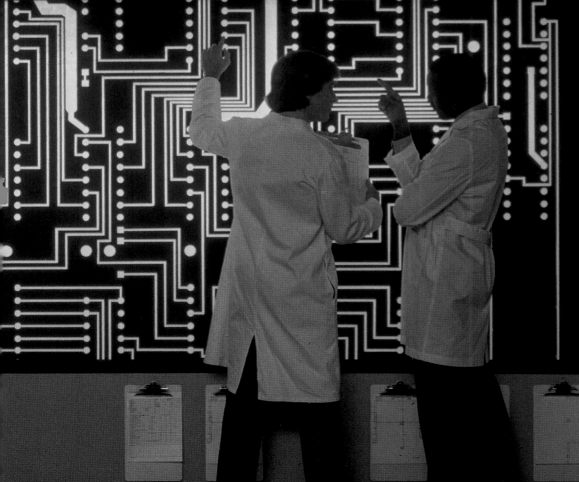

Arriba: Oficina central y sistema de control utilizados para probar las líneas y los enlaces interurbanos de las unidades de la serie GTD 5EAX de GTE.
Abajo: Parte de un circuito del sistema de conmutación digital de GTE, que une los «circuitos integrados» más recientes, muy agrandado para inspeccionarlo.

*Circuitry from a TP 3010 data concentrator
translates protocol transmitted from computers and
data terminals into internationally understood
CCITT X. 25 protocols for packet networks.*

*Eléments de circuit d'un concentrateur de
données pouvant traduire le protocole d'exécution
transmis par des ordinateurs et des terminaux en
protocoles CCITT X. 25 internationalement adoptés
pour les réseaux de transmission par paquet.*

*Elementos de un circuito de concentrador de datos
TP 3010 para convertir el protocolo de ejecución
transmitido por computadores y terminales de datos
en protocolos internacionales CCITT X.25 para las
redes de transmisión por paquetes.*

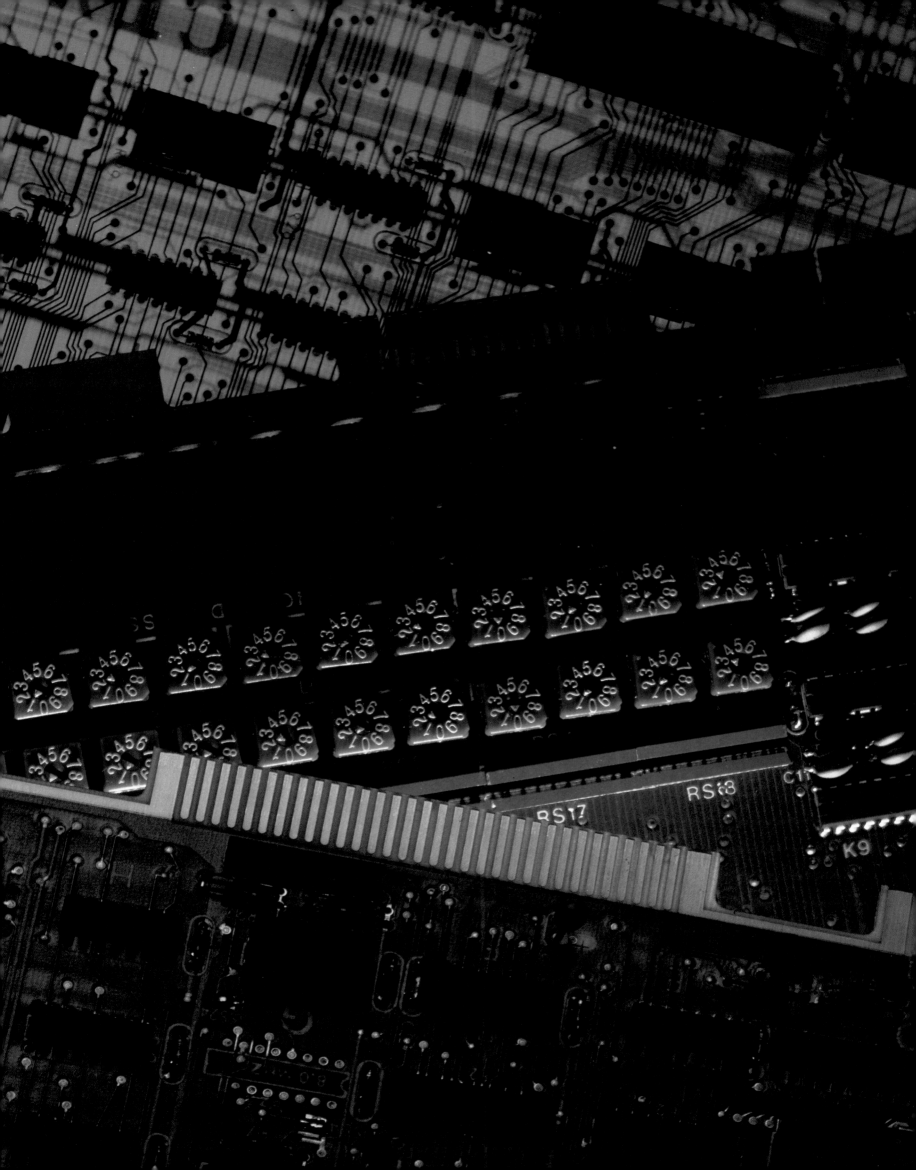

experience in planning, developing, manufacturing, installing and operating a broad spectrum of communications systems for the global markets.

With a foundation built solidly on many decades of experience in the telecommunications industry worldwide, the company is moving confidently into the swiftly-changing Information Age now emerging in many countries. It is demonstrating that it can capitalize on the marketing opportunities opening up in this new era and in this manner contributes widely to progress at every stage of industrial and social development. It typifies the humanization of self-interest and social purpose.

Much of its success is based on its ability to separate the truly promising technological trends from those that appear to offer potential but which, under experienced scrutiny, do not show the necessary signs of strength for the long run. The ability to recognize the meaningful technologies and incorporate them into the company's offerings, and to understand how they fit the requirements of customers at varying stages of development, is the mark of the Master-Builder.

Great emphasis is placed on the planning function and on-going planning processes to ensure that its products and services will meet customers' changing needs for both the near- and long-term futures. Because the implementation of future plans depends heavily on research and development, the company maintains extensive R&D facilities devoted to creating systems and techniques that will meet customers' needs more efficiently and cost-effectively.

GTE's manufacturing units in North and South America, Europe and the Far East have long been in the business of producing equipment to exacting specifications and to high standards of quality. The company also possesses expertise in the many technical disciplines needed to design large complex systems such as local and long-distance telephone switches, earth stations and entire communications networks and to "tailor" them to meet customers' particular needs. In addition, it is experienced in installing such systems, performing rigorous on-site testing programs, and training customers' employees in operation and maintenance procedures.

As a large multinational Master-Builder, GTE has enjoyed close working relationships with many customers representing private organizations, telephone administrations and other government agencies around the world. The company is also well-versed in helping customers develop plans for financing the purchase of large communications systems. It recognizes that finance is only too often a major factor affecting both the rate of change and the spread of technology worldwide.

Extensive facilities are available internationally. The company operates in 39 of the 50 States of the USA and in 18 other countries in North America, Latin America, Europe, the Middle East and the Far East. It is today a worldwide leader in developing, manufacturing and marketing telecommunications and electronic systems, products and services.

Three of the corporation's four business groups are engaged in telecommunications: GTE Communications Products, GTE Telenet Communications, and GTE Telephone Operations. The fourth, GTE Electrical Products, manufactures and markets lighting products and precision materials.

GTE Communications Products develops, manufactures and markets a broad line of telecommunications products and systems offering a wide selection of features and services based on state-of-the-art technologies. The group sells to both the regulated telephone industry and the unregulated market in the USA as well as to telephone administrations and

▷ 276

Son organisation commerciale et son service après vente maintiennent un contact étroit avec les usagers et interprètent ainsi les besoins du marché pour leurs collègues dans la R&D et la fabrication; ce qui constitue un élément vital dans la conception d'un programme de développement axé sur les besoins des consommateurs.

GTE. « Maître-constructeur en communications », est l'une des rares sociétés dans le monde des télécommunications qui puisse remplir le rôle de « maître-constructeur ». C'est grâce a sa longue expérience dans la planification, le développement, la fabrication du matériel et des systèmes, et dans l'exploitation des réseaux, que GTE fait partie de ce groupe select.

Forte d'une expérience dans les télécommunications de près d'un siècle, acquise dans le monde entier, GTE s'engage résolument dans l'Ère de l'information qui apparaît maintenant dans un grand nombre de pays. Elle est en train de démontrer qu'il est possible de saisir les opportunités qui se présentent dans les marchés du monde et de contribuer de cette façon au progrès à tous les stades de développement économique et social. Ainsi, est-il possible d'humaniser l'intérêt sectoriel en y associant un but social.

Une grande partie du succès de GTE est attribuable à son expertise dans l'identification des tendances technologiques qui offrent un vrai potentiel de développement. Cette disposition à reconnaître les technologies et à les intégrer dans la gamme des produits et services de la compagnie, et de les adapter aux besoins spécifiques de la clientèle, est la marque du vrai « maître-constructeur ».

L'importance donnée à la planification et au processus d'adaptation continuel des produits et des services aux besoins des clients, à la fois dans l'avenir immédiat et lointain, est considérable. Ensuite, la réalisation des plans dépend beaucoup de la recherche et du développement. GTE maintient des services R&D pour la mise au point de nouveaux dispositifs, systèmes et techniques qui répondent aux besoins des clients d'une façon plus efficace el plus économique.

Les usines de GTE dans le Nord et le Sud de l'Amérique, en Europe, et Asie sont habituées à produire du matériel de haute qualité. La compagnie possède également une maîtrise des disciplines requises pour la conception de grands ensembles tels que des réseaux de communication locaux et à grande distance, stations terriennes et réseaux entiers de communications, adaptés aux besoins précis des usagers. GTE a l'expérience nécessaire pour installer les systèmes, tester les programmes et former le personnel du client aux méthodes d'exploitation et de maintenance.

En tant que maître-constructeur, GTE est en étroites relations avec beaucoup de firmes privées, administrations téléphoniques et agences gouvernementales. Elle est bien placée pour aider ses clients à financer leurs installations, consciente que les difficultés de financement sont souvent une contrainte qui affecte à la fois l'évolution technologique et la pénétration des techniques nouvelles.

GTE est une organisation internationale, active dans 39 des 50 Etats des Etats-Unis et dans 18 autres pays en Amérique du Nord, en Amérique latine, en Europe, au Moyen-Orient et en Extrême-Orient. Elle est devenue un leader mondial dans le domaine des communications. Elle est structurée en quatre groupes : GTE Communications Products, GTE Telenet Communications, GTE Telephone Operations et GTE Electrical Products. Ce dernier fabrique et vend des produits d'éclairage et des matériels de précision.

GTE Communications Products développe, fabrique et vend une vaste gamme de produits et de systèmes de télé-

▷ 276

Above: Test on a sample of material prior to purchase, ensures it meets the highest standards of quality. All materials and components used in GTE equipment are tested both before and after purchase.
Below: Reliability test on printed wiring card. Tests are carried out after each plating, etching and wave soldering operation.

En haut : Test effectué sur un échantillon de matériaux. Tous les matériaux et composants utilisés par GTE sont testés avant et après l'achat.
En bas : Test de fiabilité sur une carte à circuit imprimé. Des tests sont exécutés après chaque opération de placage, de gravure et de soudure.

surge en muchos países. Con ello demuestra que puede capitalizar las posibilidades de comercialización que ofrece la nueva era, y contribuye así en gran medida al progreso en todas las etapas de la expansión industrial y social, simbolizando la humanización del propio interés y la finalidad social.

Gran parte de su éxito se basa en la capacidad de separar las tendencias tecnológicas realmente prometedoras de las que parecen ofrecer posibilidades, pero, sometidas a minucioso análisis, no muestran los indicios necesarios de fuerza a largo plazo. Uno de los rasgos del gran constructor es la aptitud para reconocer las tecnologías importantes e incorporarlas en los productos que satisfagan las necesidades de los usuarios en las diversas etapas de desarrollo.

GTE insiste mucho en la función de planificación y utiliza procesos continuos para que sus productos y servicios atiendan las necesidades cambiantes de los usuarios. Como la aplicación de los planes futuros depende mucho de la investigación y el desarrollo, la empresa mantiene grandes instalaciones de IyD para crear nuevos dispositivos, sistemas y técnicas que atiendan las necesidades de los clientes de manera más eficaz y rentable.

Hace mucho que los centros de fabricación de GTE en América del Norte y del Sur, Europa y el Lejano Oriente producen equipo que se ajusta a las rigurosas especificaciones y elevadas normas de calidad. La empresa domina también numerosas disciplinas técnicas necesarias para diseñar grandes y complejos sistemas, como conmutadores telefónicos urbanos y de larga distancia, estaciones terrenas y redes completas de comunicaciones, y para ajustarlos a las necesidades de los usuarios. Además, tiene experiencia en la instalación de esos sistemas, la ejecución de programas estrictos de pruebas prácticas, y la formación de personal del usuario.

Como gran constructor multinacional, GTE mantiene estrechas relaciones de trabajo con muchos clientes que representan a organizaciones privadas, administraciones telefónicas y otros organismos públicos del mundo entero. También está muy calificada para ayudar a los clientes a elaborar planes para financiar la compra de grandes sistemas de comunicaciones. Reconoce que la financiación suele ser un importante factor, tanto del ritmo de cambio como de la difusión mundial de tecnología.

GTE tiene grandes instalaciones en el mundo entero. Opera en 39 de los 50 estados de EE.UU. y en otros 18 países de América del Norte, América Latina, Europa, el Oriente Medio y el Lejano Oriente. Hoy día, es un líder mundial en el desarrollo, fabricación y comercialización de sistemas, productos y servicios electrónicos y de telecomunicaciones.

Tres de los cuatro grupos comerciales de la empresa se dedican a las telecomunicaciones: GTE Communications Products, GTE Telenet Communications y GTE Telephone Operations. El cuarto, GTE Electrical Products, fabrica y comercializa productos de alumbrado y materiales de precisión.

GTE Communications Products desarrolla, fabrica y comercializa una amplia gama de productos y sistemas de telecomunicaciones que ofrecen una gran selección de características y servicios a base de las tecnologías más avanzadas. El grupo vende a la industria telefónica reglamentada y al mercado libre de EE.UU., así como a administraciones telefónicas y otros clientes de Europa, América Latina, Africa y el Lejano Oriente. Muchos de los productos se ofrecen en más de una versión, para cumplir las normas norteamericanas de telecomunicaciones y las del CCITT y el CCIR adoptadas en otros países.

Entre los principales productos del grupo figuran sistemas de conmutación con control por programa

▷ 277

Arriba: Prueba de una muestra de material. Todos los materiales y componentes utilizados por GTE se prueban antes y después de comprarlos.
Abajo: Prueba de fiabilidad en una tarjeta de circuito impreso. Las pruebas se ejecutan después de cada operación de plaqueado, grabado y soldadura.

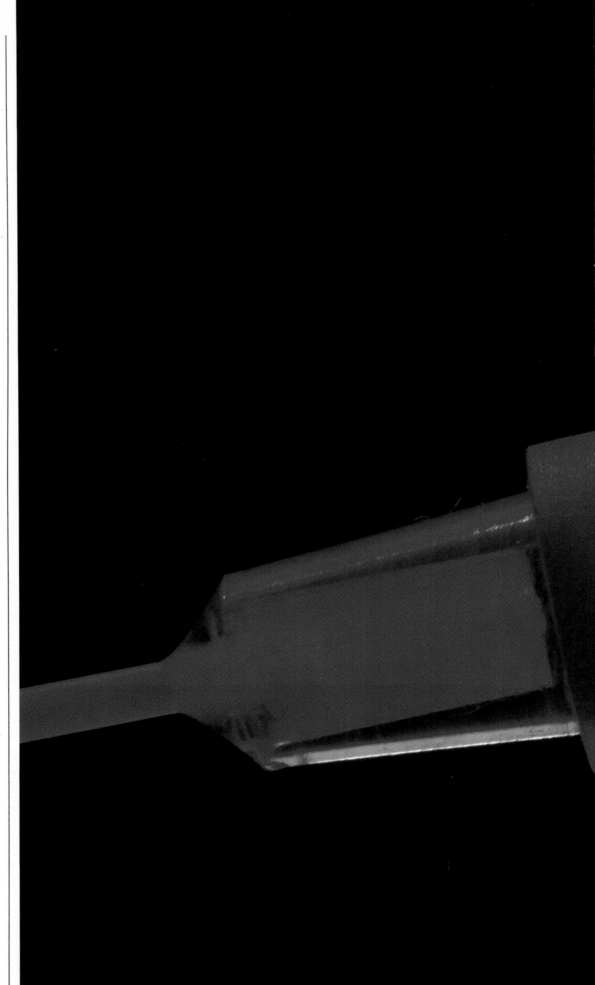

GTE's new "expanded beam lens connector"
used to link lengths of thread-like optical fibers in
optical systems. It is a two-piece plastic device with a
lens in each section that focuses the light signals
very accurately. The device can be taken
apart and reassembled in the field with no loss or
degradation of the optical signals.

Le nouveau « connecteur élargi des faisceaux
lumineux à lentilles » de GTE sert à relier de très
fines fibres optiques utilisées dans des systèmes de
communications. Le connecteur est composé d'un
dispositif en plastique divisé en deux, avec une lentille
dans chaque moitié qui focalise les signaux lumineux
avec une grande précision. Ce dispositif peut être
ouvert et réassemblé en chantier, sans perte ou
dégradation des signaux optiques.

El nuevo «conector expandido de haces luminosos de
lentes» de GTE sirve para vincular fibras ópticas
muy finas utilizadas en sistemas de comunicaciones.
El conector se compone de un dispositivo
de plástico dividido en dos, con una lente en cada
sección, que focaliza las señales luminosas
con gran precisión. El dispositivo puede desmontarse
y montarse en el lugar que se desee aplicarlo,
sin pérdida ni degradación de las señales ópticas.

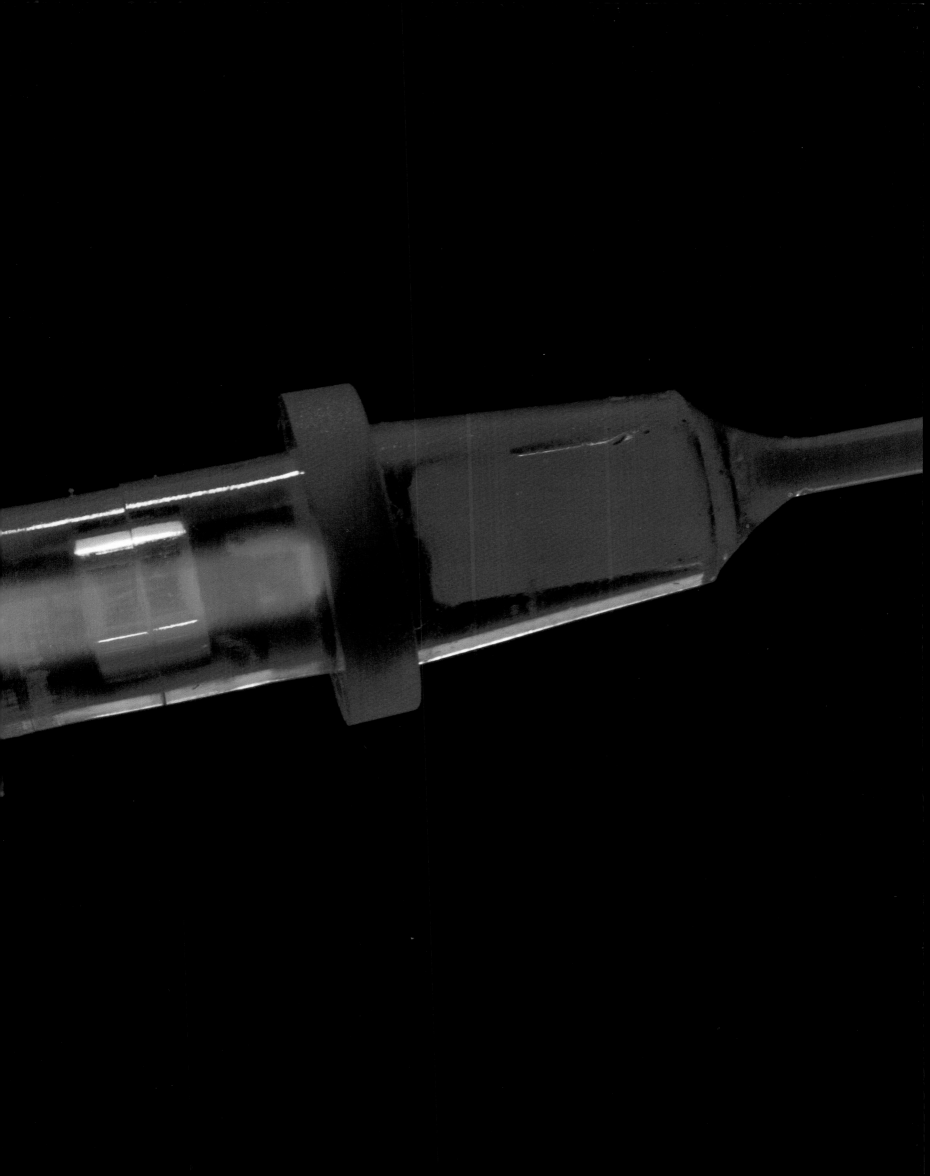

other customers in Europe, Latin America, Africa and the Far East. Many of the products are offered in more than one version to meet North American telecommunications standards as well as the CCITT and CCIR standards adopted in other countries.

Among the group's major products are stored-program-control switching systems designed to exacting requirements set by the US telephone industry, foreign telephone administrations and the ITU. These electronic switching systems are employed in local telephone exchanges as well as in the long-distance network. The most recent addition to the line is the GTD-5 EAX (electronic automatic exchange), fully digital and available in different modules so it can serve communities of various sizes as they grow in the future.

GTE Communications Products also manufactures digital PABXs (private automatic branch exchanges) which perform the switching function for the internal telephone systems of all sizes of business, government, educational and other customers. These systems are marketed to telephone companies and, when sold directly to customers, can serve as the cornerstones for private communications networks. The group also markets many types of terminal equipment, including key (multi-line) telephone systems, a large number of telephones for business and residential use and other business terminals.

In the field of transmission, GTE Communications Products develops, produces and sells a broad line of systems for carrying telephone calls, data traffic and video signals over cable, microwave radio and satellite links. An expanding array of state-of-the-art digital systems are contributing to the worldwide transition to digital technology, supplemented by an established line of analog transmission products. It is also a pioneer in the new, rapidly advancing field of fiber optics, providing various types of optical communications systems for telephone links in the USA and abroad.

GTE Communications Products has expanded significantly its capabilities for designing and producing large-scale integrated circuits for a variety of telecommunications applications. In recent years there has been increasing use of these small, reliable, low-cost devices in equipment throughout the telephone network. In addition, the group designs, supplies and installs large earth stations in the USA and abroad for service in domestic and international satellite communications networks.

GTE Telenet Communications, GTE's newest business, is a pioneer and leader in the high-technology field of "packet switching". Packet switching networks are a low-cost way of enabling dissimilar computers and terminals to communicate with one another. They also offer customers the means of transmitting large volumes of data from one location to another at rapid speeds. Telenet operates a public packet switching network which transmits data in the CCITT standard format, X.25, over leased lines to customers in the USA and in more than 40 other countries. The group also designs and provides these networks for customers' private use in North America, Latin America and Europe. Among the newer services provided is a data-base network (offered in co-operation with the American Medical Association) which supplies information on medical topics to hospitals, medical schools and physicians.

GTE Telephone Operations group is GTE's largest business. It provides telephone services and equipment under government regulation to some 12 million customer lines in portions of 31 states in the USA, in the provinces of British Columbia and Quebec in Canada, and in the Dominican Republic. In the USA, the 16 GTE telephone companies are moving into

▷ 280

communications, offrant un grand choix, et des services faisant appel aux techniques les plus récentes. Les clients comprennent tous les exploitants de réseaux téléphoniques dans le secteur réglementé et le secteur déréglementé aux Etats-Unis, ainsi qu'en Europe, en Amérique Latine, en Afrique et en Extrême-Orient. La plupart des produits sont fabriqués à la fois selon les normes nord-américaines et les normes établies par le CCITT et le CCIR adoptées par d'autres pays.

Parmi les principaux produits du groupe figurent des autocommutateurs à commande par programme enregistré, conformes aux exigences rigoureuses établies par l'industrie américaine du téléphone, les exploitants de réseaux à l'étranger et l'UIT. Ces systèmes de commutation sont utilisés dans les centraux urbains, interurbains et internationaux. La plus récente addition à la gamme est l'autocommutateur numérique GTD-5 EAX (electronic automatic exchange) disponible en différents modules. Le groupe fabrique également des autocommutateurs numériques pour usage interne PABX (private automatic branch exchanges) de toutes dimensions. Ces systèmes sont généralement vendus à des exploitants de réseaux, ou directement à des clients qui en font l'élément central de leur réseau privé. Il fabrique aussi, et commercialise, une gamme de terminaux, y compris des centraux multi-lignes à touches de commande, un grand nombre de téléphones pour bureaux et résidences, et d'autres terminaux.

Dans le domaine des transmissions GTE Communications Products met au point, fabrique et vend une gamme de systèmes pour la transmission d'appels téléphoniques, de données et d'images par câble, micro-ondes et relais par satellites. Un nombre croissant de systèmes numériques à technologie de pointe, complétés par une série bien établie de systèmes analogiques. Le groupe est également un pionnier dans le domaine très dynamique des fibres optiques, et fournit plusieurs types de systèmes à câbles optiques pour les transmissions téléphoniques aux Etats-Unis et à l'étranger.

GTE Communications Products a énormément agrandi ses capacités de conception et de production de circuits intégrés à grande échelle pour toutes sortes d'applications. Depuis quelques années l'utilisation de ces petits dispositifs, peu chers et très fiables a beaucoup augmenté dans tous les réseaux de télécommunications. En outre, le groupe conçoit et installe des stations terriennes de grande capacité aux Etats-Unis et à l'étranger.

GTE Telenet Communications, le dernier-né des groupes, est un pionnier et un leader dans le domaine de la technologie de pointe de la transmission par paquet. Cette méthode est une façon économique de permettre aux ordinateurs de conceptions différentes de communiquer entre eux. Elle permet également une transmission ultra-rapide de données. Telenet exploite un réseau de commutation par paquet qui transmet des données dans le format normalisé CCITT X. 25, par lignes louées à des clients aux Etats-Unis et dans 40 autres pays. Le groupe conçoit et fournit ce type de réseau pour usage privé en Amérique du Nord, en Amérique Latine et en Europe. Parmi les plus récents : un réseau d'information médicale pour hôpitaux, écoles de médecine et docteurs praticiens. Ce service est offert en collaboration avec l'American Medical Association.

GTE Telephone Operations est le plus grand des quatres groupes. Il fournit des services téléphoniques et du matériel, dans le cadre de la réglementation du FCC, à quelque 12 millions de lignes d'abonnés desservant une partie de 31 Etats des Etats-Unis, au Canada (Colombie britannique et Québec) et en République Dominicaine.

Aux Etats-Unis 16 filiales de GTE pénètrent dans des marchés de matériel et de services qui ont été déréglementés en 1983.

▷ 280

Top: A telephone worker completing the installation of an aerial line.
Middle: Cutting a narrow trench for a transmission cable.
Bottom: A GTE technician working in an underground structure filled with telephone cables.

En haut : Monteur complétant l'installation d'une ligne téléphonique aérienne.
Au milieu : Machine creusant une tranchée pour enterrer un câble de transmission.
En bas : Entretien de câbles téléphoniques souterrains par un technicien de GTE.

almacenado, diseñados con arreglo a requisitos fijados por la industria telefónica de EE.UU., las administraciones extranjeras y la Unión Internacional de Telecomunicaciones (UIT). Esos sistemas de conmutación electrónicos se usan en centrales telefónicas locales y en redes de larga distancia. La más reciente es la GTD-5 EAX (central automática electrónica) que utiliza la nueva tecnología digital y existe en distintos módulos, para dar servicio a comunidades de diverso tamaño, a medida que crezcan.

GTE Communications Products fabrica también CAP digitales (centralitas automáticas privadas) que realizan la función de conmutación en sistemas telefónicos internos de cualquier tamaño de empresas, instituciones gubernamentales, docentes y otros usuarios. Esos sistemas se comercializan a compañías telefónicas y, cuando se venden directamente a los usuarios, pueden servir de base para redes privadas. El grupo ofrece muchos tipos de equipo terminal, inclusive sistemas telefónicos de multilínea, un gran número de aparatos para uso comercial y residencial y otros terminales comerciales.

En materia de transmisión, GTE Communications Products desarrolla, produce y vende una amplia gama de sistemas para transmitir llamadas telefónicas, tráfico de datos y señales video por cable, enlaces de microondas y por satélite. La creciente serie de sistemas digitales modernos que contribuyen a la transición mundial hacia la tecnología digital se complementa con una gama establecida de productos de transmisión analógica. También figura entre los pioneros en el nuevo sector, en rápida expansión, de las fibras ópticas, proporcionando sistemas de comunicación ópticos de varias clases para enlaces telefónicos en EE.UU. y en el extranjero.

GTE Communications Products ha ampliado mucho su capacidad de diseño y producción de circuitos integrados en gran escala para varias aplicaciones telefónicas. En los últimos años ha aumentado el uso de esos dispositivos pequeños, seguros y económicos en equipos de toda la red telefónica. Además, el grupo diseña, suministra e instala grandes estaciones terrenas en EE.UU. y en el extranjero para dar servicio a redes nacionales e internacionales de comunicaciones por satélite.

GTE Telenet Communications, el grupo más reciente de GTE, es uno de los pioneros y líderes en materia de alta tecnología de la "conmutación por paquetes". Las redes de conmutación por paquetes permiten la comunicación entre sí, a bajo costo, de conmutadores y terminales distintos. También ofrecen a los usuarios el medio de transmitir grandes cantidades de datos de un lugar a otro, a gran velocidad. Telenet explota una red pública de conmutación por paquetes que transmite datos en formato normalizado del CCITT, X.25, por redes arrendadas a usuarios de EE.UU. y más de 40 países. El grupo también diseña y suministra esas redes para uso privado de clientes de América del Norte, América Latina y Europa. Entre los nuevos servicios del grupo figura una red de base de datos que suministra información sobre temas médicos a hospitales, escuelas de medicina y doctores. El servicio se ofrece en cooperación con la American Medical Association.

El grupo GTE Telephone Operations proporciona servicios y equipos telefónicos, sometidos a reglamentación gubernamental, a unos 12 millones de líneas de abonado en partes de 31 estados de EE.UU., en las provincias de Columbia Británica y Quebec, en Canadá, y en la República Dominicana. En EE.UU., 16 compañías de GTE comienzan a implantarse en los mercados de equipo y servicios liberalizados por el Gobierno Federal en enero de 1983.

Una dependencia del grupo Telephone Operations, GTE Satellite Corporation, y la American Te-

▷ 281

Arriba: Un operario telefónico termina el trabajo de instalación de una línea aérea.
En el centro: Un obrero abre una zanja en la que se enterrará el cable.
Abajo: Un técnico de GTE trabajando en una estructura subterránea por la que pasan numerosos cables telefónicos gruesos.

This computer-controlled call-switching system provides improved service for customers and cost savings for telephone companies. It is one of the many GTE switching systems in operation.

Ce système de commutation, commandé par ordinateur, fournit un service beaucoup amélioré pour les usagers et permet de réaliser des économies pour les exploitants téléphoniques. C'est l'un des nombreux systèmes de commutation automatiques de GTE actuellement en fonction.

Este sistema de conmutación de llamadas controlado por computador proporciona un servicio mucho mejor a los usuarios, y permite a las compañías telefónicas hacer economías. Es uno de los muchos sistemas de conmutación de GTE actualmente en funcionamiento.

rvice markets that were deregulat-
Government in January 1983.
elephone Operations group, GTE
ion, and the American Telephone
ompany (AT&T) jointly operate a
atellite network which is integrat-
national telephone network. The
 long-distance telephone voice
s specialized services that include
nd television transmission as well
ncing capabilities. GTE Satellite
lso provide customized voice, data
ission facilities to all 50 US states
AR satellite system which is sche-
operational in mid-1984. The new
parate from, and operated inde-
GTE/AT&T system.
ry, GTE Mobilnet Incorporated,
vative "cellular" mobile radio tele-
numerous US metropolitan areas.
roved form of mobile service proof channels to mobile telephones in
nd to wireless phones carried by
lings or in the open.
f the Telephone Operations group
es Corporation which sells Yellow
 and publishes some 900 telephone
iTE telephone companies, other
phone companies in the USA and
zations in several other countries.
ries are printed in six languages
an 30 million copies a year.
TE announced plans to enter the
-distance telephone business by
thern Pacific Communications
e Southern Pacific Company. The
called Sprint, serves some 425,000
microwave radio network extend-
5 million circuit-miles to virtually
 in the USA. The purchase also
ion of Southern Pacific Satellite
net) which plans to launch its first
satellites in 1984.
ment facilities are located in 40 R&D
 USA, Canada, Italy and Belgium.
 R&D programs incorporates the
s into the company's products in
nunications, lighting, and precision
lition, GTE operates a major re-
, GTE Laboratories, at Waltham,
here, a staff of scientists and engi-
programs involving advanced re-
uct development and new manu-
ues.
he 3,000 scientists and engineers
is to develop new products and
rove existing ones, thus providing
petitive, cost-effective product line
terest of communications users.
offers experience not only in design
 but also in analyzing the commu-
ments of customers ranging from
rge corporations with many loca-
nmunications units provide skilled
ng equipment on customers' pre-
g customers' personnel to operate
equipment once it is in service.
operation and maintenance, GTE
rience as an operator of large local
phone companies — its Telephone
p being the ninth largest such or-
World. In addition, the GTE ma-
have a well-earned reputation for
pport their products with high-
d enhancements that prolong their
ars after commissioning.
                                    □

v GTE XT300 action station, a fully
voice/data communication terminal
nagers and professionals with a need
or rapid, easy access to information.

Une unité du groupe, GTE Satellite Corporation,
exploite conjointement avec AT&T un réseau de
communications par satellite qui est intégré au réseau téléphonique national des Etats-Unis. Ce système assure des liaisons téléphoniques à grande distance et sert également pour la transmission rapide
de données, de la télévision et pour des services de
téléconférence. GTE Satellite Corporation va également fournir des liaisons personnalisées de téléphone, de données et d'images aux 50 Etats
des Etats-Unis par son nouveau système à satellite
GSTAR qui entrera en service en 1984. Le nouveau
système sera distinct et exploité séparément du réseau GTE/AT&T.
Une nouvelle unité du Groupe, GTE Mobilnet
Incorporated va exploiter dans plusieurs centres urbains des Etats-Unis le nouveau service de radiotéléphonie alvéolaire qui fournira des milliers de
liaisons pour des téléphones mobiles installés sur des
véhicules motorisés ou pour des téléphones sans fil
utilisés à l'intérieur des bâtiments.
Une autre unité du groupe, GTE Directories
Corporation, vend de la publicité dans les « pages
jaunes » et publie quelques 900 annuaires (30 millions d'exemplaires par an, imprimés en six langues)
pour les compagnies téléphoniques de GTE et d'autres exploitants de réseaux.
En 1982, GTE annonça ses intentions de se lancer
sur le marché des services téléphoniques interurbains aux Etats-Unis en achetant Southern Pacific
Communications Company à la Southern Pacific
Company. Le réseau interurbain « Sprint » dessert
425 000 abonnés par liaison à micro-ondes dans
presque toutes les villes des Etats-Unis (environ 74
millions km). La Southern Pacific Satellite Company
(Spacenet), qui lancera son premier satellite en 1984,
est incluse dans l'achat.
Les laboratoires de recherche et de développement: 40 établissements, situés aux Etats-Unis, au Canada, en
Italie et en Belgique, sont engagés dans un grand
nombre de programmes dont l'objet est de maintenir
GTE à la pointe de l'évolution des technologies des
communications, de l'éclairage, et du matériel de
précision.
La compagnie possède également une autre filiale : GTE Laboratories, située à Waltham Massachusetts, au sein de laquelle une importante équipe
de chercheurs et d'ingénieurs exécute des programmes de recherche de pointe, développe de nouveaux
produits et de nouvelles techniques de fabrication
dans plusieurs domaines technologiques.
La mission des 3000 chercheurs et ingénieurs de
GTE est de développer de nouveaux produits, de
nouveaux services et d'améliorer ceux qui existent,
pour que la compagnie soit toujours en mesure d'être
concurrentielle en termes de technique, de qualité et
de prix et qu'elle puisse satisfaire les besoins de sa
clientèle.
L'organisation de GTE offre une riche expérience, non
seulement dans la conception et la fabrication, mais
aussi dans l'analyse des besoins des clients, qu'ils
soient petits usagers ou grandes sociétés aux multiples succursales. Ses filiales spécialisées dans les
télécommunications disposent d'équipes capables
d'installer, n'importe quel matériel ou système, faire
les essais nécessaires, et former le personnel du client
pour qu'il puisse exploiter l'installation et la maintenir.
Dans les domaines de l'installation, de l'exploitation et de l'entretien du matériel, GTE tire également
parti de l'expérience acquise dans l'exploitation de
vaste réseaux téléphoniques, locaux et régionaux,
son Téléphone Operations Group se situant au 9°
rang mondial des exploitants de réseaux. Un autre
avantage considérable est la réputation acquise par
ses unités de fabrication pour assurer un service
après vente de haute qualité, et une modernisation
du matériel qui garantit de nombreuses années de
vie utile.
                                    □

Le nouveau poste de commande GTE
XT300, un terminal voix/données complètement
intégré, conçu pour les cadres ayant un besoin
d'accès rapide et facile à l'information.

lephone and Telegraph Company, explotan una red de satélites de comunicaciones integrada en la red telefónica nacional de EE.UU. El sistema proporciona canales vocales telefónicos de larga distancia, así como servicios especializados que comprenden transmissiones de datos y televisión a gran velocidad y posibilidades de videoconferencia. GTE Satellite suministrará también servicios especiales de transmisión de voz, datos e imágenes a los 50 estados del país por su nuevo sistema de satélite GSTAR, que comenzará a funcionar a mediados de 1984. El nuevo sistema será distinto del GTE/AT&T, y funcionará independientemente.

Una nueva filial, GTE Mobilnet Incorporated, ofrecerá en numerosas áreas metropolitanas de EE.UU. el nuevo servicio radiotelefónico móvil celular. Se trata de una versión mejorada del servicio móvil, con miles de canales a teléfonos instalados en vehículos motorizados y a teléfonos inalámbricos de los clientes en edificios o la calle.

Otra dependencia del grupo Telephone Operations es GTE Directories Corporation, que vende publicidad en las "páginas amarillas" y publica unas 900 guías para las compañías telefónicas de GTE, otras empresas telefónicas independientes de EE.UU. y organizaciones del ramo de otros países. Cada año se publican más de 30 millones de ejemplares de esas guías, impresas en seis idiomas.

A fines del 1982, GTE anunció su intención de dedicarse también a las operaciones telefónicas nacionales de larga distancia, adquiriendo Southern Pacific Communications Company a la Southern Pacific Company. El servicio interurbano, denominado Sprint, atiende a unos 425 000 clientes por una red de microondas que llega, a través de 70 millones km de circuitos a prácticamente todas las grandes ciudades de EE.UU. La transacción comprende también la adquisición de Southern Pacific Satellite Company (Spacenet), que proyecta lanzar sus primeros satélites de comunicaciones en 1984.

Las instalaciones de investigación y desarrollo se encuentran en 40 laboratorios de EE.UU., Canadá, Italia y Bélgica, cuya extensa gama de programas de IyD incorpora las tecnologías más recientes en los productos de la empresa para los sectores de comunicaciones, alumbrado y materiales de precisión. Además, GTE tiene en Waltham, Massachusetts, una importante filial de investigación denominada GTE Laboratories, donde un equipo de científicos e ingenieros realiza programas que abarcan la investigación avanzada, el desarrollo de nuevos productos y nuevas técnicas de fabricación en muchos sectores tecnológicos.

El objetivo de los 3000 científicos e ingenieros de GTE es desarrollar nuevos productos y servicios, y mejorar les existentes, para siguir atendiendo en forma óptima a los usuarios de comunicaciones con una gama de productos competitivos y rentables.

La organización de GTE ofrece experiencia no sólo en el diseño y la fabricación, sino también en el análisis de las necesidades de comunicaciones de los clientes, desde los pequeños usuarios a las grandes empresas con muchas oficinas. Las dependencias de telecomunicaciones proporcionan especialistas para instalar el equipo en los locales de los clientes y para formar a su personal en la explotación y mantenimiento, una vez en servicio.

En cuanto a la instalación, el funcionamiento y el mantenimiento, GTE puede aportar también su experiencia en la marcha de grandes compañías telefónicas locales y regionales: su grupo Telephone Operations ocupa el noveno lugar mundial en el ramo. Además, las unidades de fabricación de GTE gozan de una merecida reputación, debido a un servicio de postventa de la mayor calidad y al mejoramiento del equipo instalado, que permite prolongar durante muchos años su vida útil.

□

El nuevo centro de control GTE XT300,
terminal de comunicaciones voz/datos, totalmente
integrado, concebido para directores y
profesionales que necesitan acceder rápida
y fácilmente a la información.

COMMUNICATIONS INDUSTRY
A GREAT PACE SETTER
IN THE WORLD ECONOMY

THE COMMUNICATIONS INDUSTRY is a vast composite force, employing millions of people and enjoying a growth rate substantially higher than that of industry at large. The industry is today a major pace setter in the development of world industrial activity and this role promises to be even more of a determinant during the next century. The scale of operations is truly immense: estimates of the revenue of the world telecommunications entities put this at some US$ 88 billion in 1975 (nearly half of it in North America), over $ 175 billion in 1980, rising to $ 384 billion in 1990.

The major groupings within the industry are as follows:
— *the providers of telecommunications services:* telephone, telegraph, telex, electronic mail, videotex, distributed information processing, etc., sometimes referred to as telecommunication entities or carriers;
— *the manufacturers of equipment:* the telecommunications hardware which includes a wide range of computers and other electronic machines as well as switching, transmission and subscriber equipment;
— *the designers and producers of software:* supplied mainly by specialized firms but increasingly by the vendors of communications equipment;
— *the manufacturers of components, fittings, tools and specialized materials:* cable, integrated circuits, splicing and connecting tools, and a host of other essential "bits and pieces" without which telecommunications infrastructures and systems could not be built; and, finally;
— *the consultants and contractors* who build, expand and enhance telecommunication networks.

▷ 284

L'INDUSTRIE DES TÉLÉCOMMUNICATIONS est un vaste ensemble composite qui emploie des millions de personnes, réalise un taux de croissance bien supérieur à celui de l'industrie en général et se révèle un puissant stimulant d'activité industrielle dans le monde entier. Le revenu mondial des entreprises de service — la plupart sont des administrations — s'élevait à 88 milliards de dollars US en 1975 (près de la moitié en Amérique du Nord) à $ 175 milliards en 1980, et on estime qu'il s'élèvera à plus de $ 384 milliards en 1990.

Les principales activités de cette industrie peuvent être groupées comme suit :
— *les prestataires de services de télécommunication* : téléphone, télégraphe, télex, courrier électronique, téléinformatique, etc ;
— *des constructeurs d'équipement* : le matériel des télécommunications comprend tout ce qui est commutation, transmission, équipement d'abonnés, ainsi qu'une très large gamme d'ordinateurs, de terminaux et autres dispositifs électroniques ;
— *les producteurs de logiciel* : comprenant à l'origine des sociétés de service en informatique mais aussi, et de plus en plus, de fournisseurs de matériel ;
— *les fabricants de composants, d'accessoires, d'outils et de matériaux specialisés* : câbles, circuits intégrés, outillage pour épissures et raccords, et une foule d'autres composants essentiels à la construction de systèmes de télécommunication ;
— *les experts-conseils et entrepreneurs* qui s'occupent de la planification, construction, extension et modernisation des réseaux.

Les cinq éléments sont restés distincts, et donc identifiables, jusque vers les années 1970, mais ils le sont beaucoup moins maintenant. Les démarcations sont devenues floues et la concurrence s'est développée entre les fabricants traditionnels de matériel

▷ 284

LA INDUSTRIA DE LAS COMUNICACIONES es una vasta fuerza mixta, que emplea millones de personas, y su tasa de crecimiento es bastante más alta que la de la industria en general. Hoy marca la pauta del desarrollo industrial mundial, y su papel será aún más determinante el siglo próximo. Su escala de actividad es inmensa: según estimaciones de los ingresos de las entidades mundiales de telecomunicaciones, ascendía a 88 000 millones $ EE.UU. en 1975 (casi la mitad en América del Norte), más de 170 000 millones $ en 1980, y será de 384 000 millones $ en 1990.

Las principales partes de la industria son:
— *los proveedores de servicios de telecomunicaciones:* teléfono, telégrafo, télex, correo electrónico, videotex, procesamiento de información distribuida, etc., denominados a veces entidades o empresas de telecomunicaciones;
— *los fabricantes de equipo:* el soporte físico, que comprende una amplia gama de computadores y otros aparatos electrónicos, así como equipo de conmutación, transmisión y de abonado;
— *los diseñadores y productores de soporte lógico:* sobre todo casas especializadas, pero cada vez más vendedores de equipo;
— *los fabricantes de componentes, accesorios, instrumentos y materiales especializados:* cable, circuitos integrados, instrumentos de empalme y conexión, y una serie de otras "minucias y piezas" esenciales, sin las que no podrían construirse las infraestructuras y sistemas de comunicaciones; y, por último,
— *los consultores y contratistas:* que construyen, amplían y mejoran las redes de telecomunicación.

▷ 285

The robotic arm shown here is aiding in the assembly of electronic components in various tests at Western Electric's engineering research center near Princeton, New Jersey.

Le bras robotique que l'on voit ici est en train d'aider au montage de composants électroniques pendant des essais au centre de recherche de Western Electric à Princeton, New Jersey.

El brazo de robot mostrado aquí ayuda a montar componentes electrónicos durante las pruebas realizadas en el centro de investigación de Western Electric en Princeton, Nueva Jersey.

These several elements were fairly distinct and identifiable until well into the seventies but are now much less so. Boundaries have become blurred and competition for major markets has developed between the traditional suppliers of telecommunication equipment and the newcomers to the industry, principally electronic engineering and aerospace companies and providers of communication services.

There is also increasing competition between carriers, intensified in the USA by deregulation, by the entry of cable companies (television and other audio-visual services) and by that of microwave radio operators (satellite relays and mobile telephones). A similar process is taking place in other countries where the traditional monopoly of PTTs is being challenged, often with official encouragement or backing.

Another form of competition is arising in the private sector where telecommunications consultants and contractors are becoming a major factor. Subscribers are no longer forced to rely on their PTTs or equipment suppliers for the planning or installation of the facilities they require, the choice of equipment or the provision of software. How all this is developing is outlined further on p. 306.

The telecommunication equipment industry's development has been conditioned by its close relationship with the providers of telecommunication services. In most countries there are monopolistic authorities, publicly owned or publicly regulated. This has resulted in a very high concentration of the equipment supplying industry, with the four largest firms typically enjoying more than a 70 per cent share of their home market. In fact in 1981 the top four manufacturers in the world accounted for over half of the total sales of telecommunication equipment and the 13 largest (see the Table on p. 286) for over three quarters. Apart from Western Electric — whose activities were, until the early 1980s, largely confined to the USA — all these companies are substantially multinational in their operations, which explains why the sales of foreign-owned firms represent a significant proportion of total sales in some, mainly Third World, countries.

The concentration of the industry is the direct result of the presence of only one major customer in each country. The trend towards deregulation, particularly marked in the USA, Canada and the UK, will doubtless change this in time and may spread to other countries.

In most countries the service providers have found it more convenient to deal with only a few companies in order to procure systems and equipment that require lengthy development and major inputs of R&D, the latter being supplied in major part by the service provider or carrier itself.

A close relationship between customer and supplier was thus considered an essential element in the successful development of national telecommunication networks. Approved suppliers were given preferential access to the service providers' intentions and to necessary technical information. They were protected from foreign competition and benefited from an assurance of business based on an explicit or implicit quota system. The drawback of such a system is a tendency to insularity in innovation strategies, undue weight given to investment in obsolete technologies and the prevalence of a cost-plus mentality among suppliers.

In countries equipped with basic telecommunications infrastructures — 20 out of the 158 Member nations of the ITU account for 80 per cent or more of the world's investment in telecommunications — further growth and development is to be found as much in new products that plug into the existing network as in the technical improvement and expansion of the basic services.

Evidence of this is the phenomenal increase in the output of semiconductor devices and of products in which they are basic components. Production of digital PABXs, facsimile machines, word processors,

▷ 286

et les nouveaux venus dans l'industrie, notamment les firmes d'ingénierie électronique et aérospatiale.

Il existe également une concurrence croissante parmi les transmetteurs, intensifiée aux Etats-Unis par la dérégulation, due à l'entrée, en tant que prestataires de service, d'exploitants de réseaux câblés (télévision et autres services audio-visuels) et d'exploitants de réseaux micro-ondes (relais par satellite et téléphones mobiles). Un développement parallèle commence déjà dans d'autres pays où le monopole des PTT est mis en cause, parfois avec l'encouragement ou l'appui des gouvernements eux-mêmes. Une autre forme de concurrence se développe dans le secteur privé où les experts-conseils et les entrepreneurs deviennent un facteur important (v. p. 306).

Le développement de l'industrie de l'équipement des télécommunications a été conditionné par l'étroite relation de cette industrie avec les prestataires de services de télécommunications. Il existe, dans la plupart des pays, des monopoles, publics ou réglementés par l'Etat. Il en est résulté une très forte concentration de l'industrie de l'équipement. En fait, les quatre grands constructeurs du monde représentaient en 1981 plus de la moitié du total des ventes d'équipement de télécommunications (v. p. 286). En dehors de AT&T Western Electric, dont les activités étaient, jusqu'au commencement des années 1980, concentrées aux Etats-Unis, toutes ces compagnies sont essentiellement multinationales dans leur exploitation, ce qui explique pourquoi les fournitures effectuées par des firmes étrangères représentent une partie importante du total dans certains pays du tiers-monde.

La concentration de l'industrie est la conséquence directe de l'existence d'un seul grand client dans chaque pays. La tendance à la suppression de la réglementation, surtout aux Etats-Unis, au Canada et au Royaume-Uni, modifiera certainement cette situation et s'étendra peut-être à d'autres pays.

Néanmoins, jusqu'à présent, dans la plupart des pays, les prestataires de services ont estimé plus pratique de travailler avec quelques compagnies seulement, pour acquérir des systèmes et des équipements qui nécessitent une longue mise au point avec une part importante de R&D, généralement fournie par le prestataire de services lui-même.

Un étroite relation entre client et fournisseur a donc été considérée comme un élément essentiel du développement harmonieux des réseaux de télécommunications nationaux. Certains fournisseurs agréés bénéficient d'un accès préférentiel aux projets des prestataires de services et aux informations techniques nécessaires. Ils sont protégés contre la concurrence étrangère et assurés de réaliser un chiffre d'affaires fondé sur un système explicite et implicite de quotas. Les inconvénients d'un tel système, et il y en a, sont souvent une tendance à l'isolement dans les stratégies d'innovation, l'importance excessive accordée aux investissements dans des technologies périmées et la recherche de profits excessifs.

Dans les pays dotés d'infrastructures de base en matière de télécommunications, les systèmes croissent et se développent autant par les nouveaux produits qui s'intègrent dans les réseaux existants que par l'amélioration technique et l'extension des services de base. La concentration des efforts dans les pays industrialisés est notoire, car 20 des 158 pays membres de l'UIT représentent 80 pour cent des investissements mondiaux dans les télécommunications.

La preuve en est donnée par l'augmentation phénoménale de la production de dispositifs à semiconducteurs et des produits dans lesquels ces dispositifs entrent comme composants de base. La production d'autocommutateurs privés (PABXs), de machines de télécopie, de traitement de texte, d'enregistrement et de remise de messages, d'appareils vidéotex, d'imprimantes électroniques et, surtout, de micro-ordinateurs, enregistre des taux de croissance annuels qui dépassent de loin non seulement ceux des économies nationales mais aussi ceux de l'équipement de base des réseaux de télécommunications.

L'« insularité » des producteurs traditionnels d'équipement de télécommunications est mise en cause et les trois entreprises ultra-spécialisées — Western Electric, Ericsson et Northern Telecom — étendent toutes leurs activités aux produits électroniques tels

▷ 286

THE TREND TOWAR

The four "maps" (see p. 26) below show how deregulation and the relaxation of import controls are likely to impact on the telecommunications industry. On the left are shown (shaded areas) the probable market coverage of "deregulated" AT&T (above) and of an "unregulated" IBM (below). The area they both cover suggest a substantial amount of competition is likely. Similarly, on the right, the communications industries of Europe (top) and of Japan (bottom) cover very much the same wide areas.

The message is clear: competition will be worldwide and much fiercer than in the past, due, on the one hand, to deregulation and relaxation of import controls and, on the other, to the entry of powerful firms from the electronics, aerospace and other industries into what was hitherto a guarded preserve.

Boundaries of activities of a deregulated AT&T

Boundaries of activities of an unregulated IBM

quatre « cartes » montrent l'influence que la levée de la ...mentation et l'assouplissement des contrôles d'importa- ...exerceront vraisemblablement sur l'industrie des télécom- ...cations. A gauche, l'étendue probable des activités d'AT&T ...ment « libéralisée » et celles d'IBM « non réglementée ». ...ite, les télécommunications de l'Europe et celles du Japon, ... les vastes domaines se recouvrent.

...chevauchement des mêmes activités laisse présager ...e concurrence très sévère va se livrer dans le monde ...r. Elle résultera en partie de la libéralisation et de l'as- ...lissement des contrôles d'importation dans certains pays, ... partie de l'irruption de puissantes firmes électroniques, ...spatiales et autres, dans ce qui était jusqu'ici une « chasse ...ée ».

Los cuatro "mapas" siguientes indican la influencia que pueden tener en la industria de las telecomunicaciones la liberalización y la suavización de los controles de importación. La parte sombreada representa la probable extensión de las actividades de una AT&T "liberalizada" y una IBM "no reglamentada". El área que cubren ambas indica la posible competencia. Asimismo, a la derecha, las industrias de comunicaciones de Europa y de Japón abarcan prácticamente las mismas áreas.

La competencia será, pues, mundial y mucho mayor que en el pasado, debido, por un lado, a la liberalización y la suavización de los controles de importación, y, por otro, a la entrada de nuevas y poderosas firmas de las industrias electrónica, aeroespacial y otras en lo que era un terreno acotado.

Esos diversos elementos se distinguían claramente hasta los años 70, pero ahora ya no. Las fronteras son confusas y hay mucha competencia por los principales mercados entre los proveedores tradicionales y los nuevos, sobre todo las empresas de ingeniería electrónica y aeroespaciales, y algunos proveedores de servicios de comunicación.

También hay más competencia entre empresas, intensificada en EE.UU. por la liberalización, debido a la entrada, como proveedores de servicios, de empresas de redes de cables (TV y otros servicios audiovisuales) y de operadores de redes de microondas (enlaces de satélite y teléfonos móviles). El mismo proceso se inicia en otros países donde se pone en duda el monopolio de CTT, a veces con el estímulo o el apoyo oficial.

En el sector privado, donde consultores y contratistas son un factor importante, surge otra forma de competencia. Los usuarios ya no dependen de su CTT o sus proveedores de material para planificar y construir instalaciones, elegir equipo o soporte lógico. Estan tendencias se analizan el la pág. 306.

La evolución de la industria de equipo de telecomunicaciones ha estado condicionada por su estrecha relación con los proveedores de servicios de telecomunicaciones. En la mayoría de los países hay autoridades monopolistas, propiedad o reglamentación pública. Esto ha dado lugar a una enorme concentración de la industria que suministra equipo, correspondiendo a las cuatro empresas principales más del 70% de su mercado nacional. En efecto, en 1981, los cuatro mayores fabricantes del mundo absorbieron más de la mitad de las ventas totales de equipo de telecomunicaciones, y las 13 principales (véase el recuadro de la pág. 286) más de los tres cuartos. Aparte de Western Electric — filial de fabricación de equipo de AT&T — las operaciones de todas esas empresas son sustancialmente multinacionales, lo que explica por qué las ventas de firmas extranjeras representan una considerable proporción de las ventas totales en algunos países, sobre todo del Tercer Mundo.

La concentración de la industria es el resultado directo de la presencia de un importante cliente nada más en cada país. La tendencia a la libertad de comercio, acusada sobre todo en EE.UU., Canadá y el RU, cambiará esto sin duda con el tiempo, y podrá extenderse a otras naciones.

En la mayoría de los países, los proveedores de servicios han estimado más interesante tratar sólo con unas cuantas empresas, para suministrar sistemas y equipo que requieren un largo desarrollo y grandes aportaciones de IyD, la mayor parte por quien presta el servicio o la propia empresa.

La estrecha relación entre cliente y proveedor se ha considerado, pues, un elemento esencial para desarrollar con éxito redes nacionales de telecomunicaciones. Los proveedores autorizados tenían preferencia para conocer las intenciones de los proveedores de servicios y la información técnica necesaria. Estaban protegidos contra la competencia exterior y gozaban de una seguridad comercial basada en un sistema de cuotas explícito o implícito. Los inconvenientes de tal sistema son la tendencia al aislamiento en las estrategias de innovación, a no considerar debidamente la inversión en tecnologías anticuadas y la mentalidad de beneficio de los proveedores.

En países equipados con infraestructuras de telecomunicaciones básicas — 20 de los 158 países Miembros de la UIT representan el 80% o más de la inversión mundial en telecomunicaciones —, el desarrollo se acelerará, tanto en lo relativo a nuevos productos que se incorporan a las red existente como al mejoramiento técnico y a la expansión de los servicios básicos.

Así lo prueba el fenomenal aumento de la producción de dispositivos semiconductores y de productos en que son los componentes básicos. La producción de CAP digitales, aparatos facsímil, procesadores de texto, sistemas de grabación y entrega de

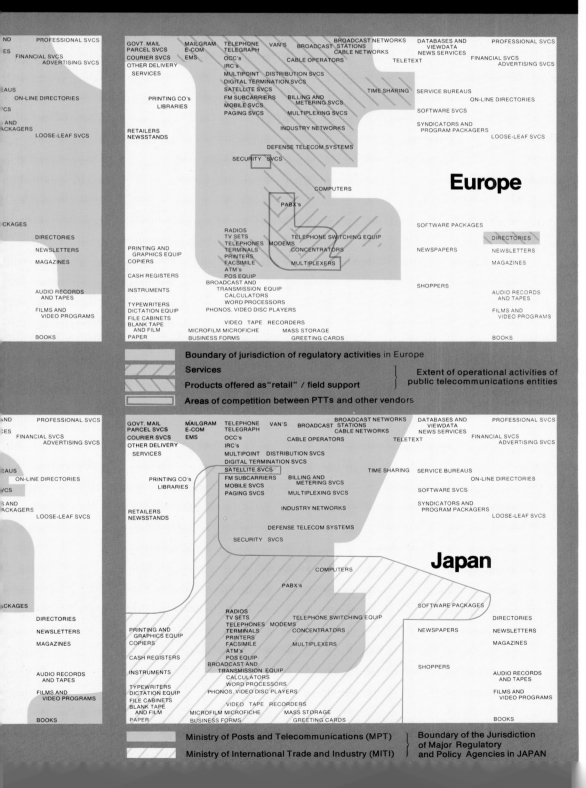

Boundary of jurisdiction of regulatory activities in Europe

Services

Products offered as "retail" / field support

Areas of competition between PTTs and other vendors

Extent of operational activities of public telecommunications entities

Ministry of Posts and Telecommunications (MPT)

Ministry of International Trade and Industry (MITI)

Boundary of the Jurisdiction of Major Regulatory and Policy Agencies in JAPAN

message recording and delivery systems, videotex units, electronic copiers, and above all, desk top and personal computers, is exhibiting annual growth rates far in excess not only of those of national economies but those of basic telecommunications network equipment.

The "insularity" of the traditional producers of this equipment is being shattered, and the three ultra-specialists — Western Electric, Ericsson and Northern Telecom — are all expanding into other electronic products just as computer, aerospace, office equipment and even carriers or service providers are expanding in telecommunications products. The telecommunication equipment industry's basic character is changing. It is becoming more broadly based and much more competitive.

Deregulation on the one hand and electronification of telecommunications on the other will impact deeply on industrial structures and product strategies. An attempt to show how this may develop has been made by the Center for Information Policy Research of Harvard University. The "Information Business Map" on pages 26 and 148 shows how the products and services supplied by the "Communications Industry" in its total new compass are related. Other maps of the same spread which could not be included in this book, delineate by approximate shading the situation of the various companies in the industry. The authors suggest that they are "useful tools for looking at the strategic positioning of individual corporations".

Maps showing the positions of a "deregulated AT&T" and an "unregulated IBM", on page 284, are certainly full of interest. Both companies are now free to enter previously regulated product or service areas and untrammelled by anti-trust actions. The IBM map includes products and services that the company offers outside the USA, PABXs, time sharing and service bureaus, some of its internal technological capabilities and its joint ventures with Aetna Life Assurance and Comsat (Satellite Business Systems SBS), with Mitel (integrated circuits and microprocessors) and with Rolm (mini-computers and PABXs). The deregulated AT&T covers practically the whole map areas of electronic products and services. Both have vast R&D facilities and both are working on the development of integrated circuits, broadband transmission systems and the automation of software production. IBM has a vital interest in integrated systems which include digital switching and transmission and in subscriber equipment, from interactive terminals with multiple access points to desk-top home computers.

Competition between AT&T and IBM is likely to develop essentially in the area of telephone subscriber equipment, i.e. private digital exchanges, "office of the future" type equipment, intelligent interactive terminals, personal computers and personal computer software, the demand for which is increasing so fast that it is unlikely to become a constraint on the expansion plans of either company.

The strength of both AT&T and IBM is derived from the depth and resourcefulness of their technological bases. Each was spending about US$ 2 billion on research and development in the early 1980s, and both command a broad range of technologies. Expenditure on this scale, amounting to about 6 per cent of turnover (AT&T, divested of its service operating companies, and IBM worldwide) is far in excess of the norm in the telecommunications equipment industry.

The concentration of the industry in highly industrialized countries, however, where basic telecommunications infrastructures exist and carry a high volume of profitable traffic, has not been altered. The revenue of the North American common carriers is estimated to account for over half the world total. A similar picture emerges from the analysis of equipment sales. The new entrants from the electronics, aerospace and office equipment industries have merely increased this geographical bias.

▷ 288

que les ordinateurs, le matériel aérospatial et les équipements de bureau. D'autre part, les prestataires de services commencent eux aussi à s'étendre dans la fabrication de produits de télécommunications. Le caractère fondamental de l'industrie de l'équipement est donc en cours de mutation ; elle élargit ses bases et devient beaucoup plus compétitive.

La levée de la réglementation, d'un côté, et l'entrée de l'électronique dans les télécommunications de l'autre, vont influencer profondément les structures des firmes et leur politique de produits. Une démonstration de la façon dont cela peut se produire a été faite par le centre de recherche pour une politique de l'information « Center for Information Policy Research » de l'Université de Harvard.

La présentation graphique des résultats de ces recherches (pp. 26 et 148), montre comment les produits et services de l'information sont reliés. D'autres « cartes » de même type, que le manque de place ne permet pas de reproduire, indiquent la position de plusieurs grandes firmes dans cette industrie. Les auteurs considèrent que ces « cartes » sont « un moyen utile de situer la stratégie de développement de chaque entreprise ».

On peut toutefois trouver à la page 284, d'autres « cartes » qui montrent le champ d'action d'AT&T libéralisée et d'IBM « non-réglementée » qui sont particulièrement intéressantes. Ces deux firmes américaines sont maintenant libres de pénétrer les secteurs du marché d'où elles étaient exclues par la réglementation de la FCC (Federal Communications Commission), sans être entravées par des actions gouvernementales contre le monopole (anti-trust).

La présentation d'IBM comprend aussi les produits et services que la firme vend en dehors des Etats-Unis, tels que autocommutateurs privés, centres d'ordinateurs à temps partagé, quelques unes de ses ressources technologiques internes, et ses actions communes avec Aetna et Comsat (Satellite Business Systems) et avec Mitel (circuits intégrés et microprocesseurs). AT&T « déréglementée » s'étend sur presque tous les produits et services sur la carte. Il y aura certainement de la concurrence entre AT&T et IBM, les deux géants de l'industrie américaine — il en existe déjà, mais essentiellement dans le domaine de l'équipement téléphonique d'abonnés, c'est-à-dire les centraux numériques privés, l'équipement de type « bureau du futur », les terminaux interactifs intelligents et les ordinateurs personnels, ainsi que pour le logiciel d'ordinateur personnel, dont la demande augmente si rapidement que cette concurrence ne risque guère de devenir une contrainte pour leurs plans d'extension.

Les deux compagnies AT&T et IBM tirent leur force de l'étendue et de la richesse de leurs bases technologiques. Chacune d'elles consacrait environ 2 milliards de dollars à la recherche et au développement au début des années 1980 et elles maîtrisent toutes les deux une large gamme de technologies. Les dépenses à cette échelle, qui s'élevaient à environ 6 pour cent du chiffre d'affaires (pour AT&T, sans ses compagnies d'exploitation de services, et pour IBM, sur le plan international) dépassent de loin la norme dans l'industrie de l'équipement, les fournisseurs ayant dû compter, en matière de conception de systèmes et de recherche et de développement, sur la capacité de leurs prestataires de services nationaux.

La concentration de l'industrie des télécommunications dans les pays hautement industrialisés où il existe des infrastructures de base qui assurent un gros volume de trafic rentable, n'a cependant pas changé. On estime que les recettes des exploitants nord-américains représentent plus de la moitié du total mondial. Une image semblable se dégage de l'analyse des ventes d'équipement. Les nouveaux venus des industries de l'électronique, du matériel aérospatial et de l'équipement de bureau n'ont fait qu'accroître ce déséquilibre géographique.

Le tableau ci-contre montre que, parmi les 13 principaux constructeurs d'équipement en dehors de l'URSS, 4 firmes nord-américaines représentaient 59 pour cent du montant total des ventes, 8 firmes d'Europe occidentale 37 pour cent, et 1 firme japo-

▷ 288

TURNOVER OF

Sales of telecommunication equipment by the 13 largest manufacturers in the world, showing these as a proportion of their total output*

The last column indicates the percentage of world sales accounted for by each firm.

Western Electric	United States
ITT	United States
Siemens	Fed. Rep. of Germany
L.M. Ericsson	Sweden
GTE	United States
Northern Telecom	Canada
NEC	Japan
Thomson Group	France
Philips	Netherlands
CGE (Cit Alcatel)	France
GEC	United Kingdom
Plessey	United Kingdom
Italtel	Italy
TOTAL	

* Estimates based on the hypothesis that the telecommunica
Source: Company annual reports and Fortune Magazine, May

A		B		B / A	B / Total B
Total sales		Total sales Telecommunications equipment			
US $ billion				%	%
1980	1981	1980	1981	1980	1980
12.03	13.01	12.03	13.01	100	32
18.53	17.31	6.04	5.48	33	16
17.56	15.29	5.05	4.60	29	13
2.88	3.20	2.88	3.20	100	7
9.98	11.03	2.20	2.20	22	6
1.76	2.14	1.76	2.14	100	5
3.94	4.82	1.45	1.68	37	4
8.64	7.83	1.63	1.91	19	4
8.28	8.38	1.33*	1.34*	16	4
18.36	16.96	1.29*	n.a.	7	3
10.82	10.10	0.75	0.78	7	2
1.97	1.96	0.79	0.85	40	2
0.59	0.62	0.59	0.62	100	2
15.34	112.65	37.79	n.a.	33	100

ment sales/total sales ratio did not vary for the firm concerned over the period 1976-1980.

st 23, 1982.

mensajes, aparatos videotex, copiadores electrónicos y, sobre todo, computadores de sobremesa y personales, presenta tasas de crecimiento anuales muy superiores no sólo a las de las economías nacionales, sino a las del equipo básico de redes.

La "limitación" de los productores tradicionales de este equipo desaparece, y los tres ultraespecialistas — Western Electric, Ericsson y Northern Telecom — se extienden a productos electrónicos como computadores, areoespaciales y equipo de oficina, e incluso las empresas o prestadores de servicio se dedican a productos de telecomunicaciones. Está cambiando, pues, el carácter fundamental de la industria del equipo de telecomunicaciones, que adquiriere una base mucho más general y más competitiva.

La libertad de comercio, por un lado, y la electronificación de las comunicaciones, por otro, repercutirán profundamente en las estrategias estructurales y de productos. El centro de Investigación de la Política de Información de la Universidad de Harward ha tratado de ver cómo sucederá esto. En el « Gráfico de la industria de la información » de las páginas 26 y 148 se muestra la relación entre productos y servicios. Otros gráficos, que no pueden incluirse, presentan la situación de las diversas empresas en la industria. Los autores de esos gráficos indican que se dispone de « útiles instrumentos para considerar la posición estratégica de las empresas ».

Los gráficos que muestran las posiciones de "una AT&T liberalizada" y "una IBM no sometida a control" tienen gran interés. Ambas empresas pueden dedicarse ahora a sectores de productos o servicios anteriormente vedados. El gráfico de IBM comprende productos y servicios que ofrece la empresa fuera de EE.UU., CAP, oficinas de compartición en el tiempo y servicios, algunas de sus capacidades tecnológicas internas, y sus. empresas mixtas con Aetna y Comsat (Satellite Business Systems SBS), con MCA (Discovision Associates) y con Mitel (circuitos integrados y microprocesadores). La AT&T liberalizada abarca prácticamente todos los sectores del gráfico de productos y servicios electrónicos. Ambas disponen de grandes instalaciones de IyD y trabajan en el desarrollo de plaquetas, sistemas de transmisión de banda ancha y automatización de la producción de soporte lógico. IBM tiene un interés vital en sistemas integrados que comprenden conmutación y transmisión digital, para la producción de terminales interactivos con puntos de acceso múltiple y la producción de computadores de sobremesa.

La competencia tendrá lugar, esencialmente, en el sector de equipo telefónico de abonado, es decir, centrales digitales privadas, equipo de tipo "oficina del futuro", terminales interactivos inteligentes y computadores personales y su soporte lógico, cuya demanda aumenta tan rápidamente que es improbable que suponga un obstáculo a los planes de expansión de ambas empresas.

La fuerza de AT&T e IBM se debe a los recursos y la profundidad de sus bases tecnológicas. En los primeros años 80, cada una gastó alrededor de 2000 millones $ en investigación y desarrollo, y dominan una amplia gama de tecnologías. Este nivel de gastos, que representa un 6% de la cifra de negocios (obteniéndolos AT&T de sus empresas de explotación de servicios, e IBM mundialmente) es muy superior a la norma en la industria de equipo de telecomunicaciones.

Sin embargo, la concentración de la industria en países muy industrializados, donde existen infraestructuras de telecomunicaciones básicas y se cursa un elevado volumen de tráfico rentable, no ha variado. Se estima que los ingresos de las empresas de telecomunicaciones americanas representan más de la mitad del total mundial. Y el análisis de las ventas de equipo presenta una situación análoga. Los recién llegados de las industrias electrónica, aeroespacial y

▷ 289

The Table on p. 286 shows that of the 13 major "traditional" equipment makers outside the USSR, four North American firms accounted for 59 per cent of total sales in 1981, eight West European firms for 37 per cent and one Japanese for the remaining 4 per cent. The entry of large electronic and office equipment producers such as Control Data, DEC, GE, General Dynamics, Harris Corp., IBM, Mitel, Motorola, Rockwell International, Rolm, 3M, Wang, Xerox from North America; Fujitsu, Matsushita, Mitsubishi and Toshiba from Japan, will substantially increase the size and strength of the industries of North America and South East Asia relative to that of Western Europe. The development of aerospace companies into communications, again mainly American — Ford Aerospace, Hughes and RCA — further increases this geographical lopsidedness.

The association of European firms with their American opposite numbers, already begun by British Aerospace, CIT Alcatel, Ferranti, Philips, Plessey and Thomson-CSF, is setting a trend likely to accentuate as competition develops. An on-going research program carried out by Arthur D. Little of Cambridge, Massachusetts, provides strong confirmation of the likelihood of increased competition. A recent report states that although the telecommunications sector continues to sustain a higher growth rate than most other sectors of the economy, several factors are combining to create great pressure on suppliers:

— development costs for high technology products, such as digital central office switching, have soared and are continuing to increase. They require amortising over high volume production and manufacturers are being forced to seek larger markets, thus intensifying competitive pressures;

— as boundaries between telecommunications, information processing and office systems become less distinct, the traditional telecommunications suppliers are facing new competitive situations. They must develop new product lines and be prepared to deal with a new set of competitors;

— the regulatory framework for telecommunications is in the process of change in several countries, allowing increased competition in common carriage and liberalizing the rules of equipment ownership. For the suppliers in these changing markets there will be a period of adjustment to a different set of buyers;

— newly industrialized countries have been revising their procurement policies and laws to favour in-country manufacturing. Suppliers are forced to meet the new requirements in order to retain their established markets with possible adverse impact on employment (and on economies of scale) in their home countries.

A.D. Little conclude that "in combination, we can expect that developments over the next few years will alter existing supplier/buyer relationships and drastically change the industry structure worldwide. Nevertheless we may be sure that the basic strength of the telecommunications suppliers will carry the industry and its vital services to new levels".

How these levels will be reached, when, and by which firms, is not easy to determine. The only certainty is that the industry's structure in the year 2000 will bear little resemblance to what it is today.

The profile of the 3M Company that follows is an example of how the activities of a major US company are directed to meeting the challenges facing the communications industry. The success of 3M is based on innovative research and development and a strong commitment to quality. The company is organized to identify emerging industry needs worldwide and to meet them.

naise les 4 pour cent restants. L'entrée sur le marché de grands producteurs d'équipement électronique et de bureau d'origine américaine ou japonaise tels que Control Data, DEC, GE, General Dynamics, Harris Corp., IBM, Mitel, Motorola, Rockwell International, Rolm, 3M, Wang, Xerox, d'une part, ainsi que Fujitsu, Matsushita, Mitsubishi et Toshiba, d'autrepart, augmentera considérablement la taille et la puissance des industries de l'Amérique du Nord et de l'Asie du Sud-est par rapport à celles de l'Europe occidentale. Le développement dans le domaine des télécommunications de compagnies aérospatiales, ici encore principalement américaines — Ford Aerospace, Hughes et RCA — ne fait que renforcer cette dissymétrie.

L'association de firmes européennes avec leurs homologues américains, déjà commencée par British Aerospace, CIT Alcatel, Ferranti, Philips, Plessey, Thomson-CSF, marque une tendance susceptible de s'accentuer avec le développement de la concurrence. Un programme de recherche mené actuellement par Arthur D. Little de Cambridge, Massachusetts, apporte une confirmation éloquente de la probabilité d'une concurrence accrue. Un récent rapport indique que le secteur des télécommunications continue à enregistrer un taux de croissance plus élevé que la plupart des autres secteurs de l'économie, mais que plusieurs facteurs se conjuguent pour exercer une forte pression sur les fournisseurs d'équipement :

— les dépenses de mise au point pour les produits de haute technologie, tels que les centraux de commutation numérique, ont fait un bond en avant et continuent à augmenter. Il faut qu'elles soient amorties par un volume de production élevé et les fabricants sont contraints de rechercher des marchés plus larges, ce qui renforce la concurrence;

— au fur et à mesure que les frontières s'estompent entre les systèmes de télécommunications, de traitement de l'information et de bureau, les fournisseurs traditionnels d'équipement de télécommunications affrontent de nouvelles situations de concurrence. Ils doivent mettre au point de nouveaux produits et être prêts à se mesurer à un nouveau type de concurrents;

— le cadre de la réglementation pour les télécommunications se modifie dans plusieurs pays, permettant une concurrence accrue dans le domaine de l'exploitation et libéralisant les règles de propriété de l'équipement. Il y aura pour les fournisseurs, dans ces marchés qui s'ouvrent, une période d'adaptation à une clientèle différente;

— les pays nouvellement industrialisés ont révisé leur politique d'achat et leur législation pour favoriser les produits intérieurs. Les fournisseurs sont obligés de satisfaire aux nouvelles conditions pour conserver leurs marchés établis, avec les conséquences néfastes qui en résultent pour l'emploi (et les économies d'échelle) dans leur propre pays.

A.D. Little conclut : « on peut prévoir que, globalement, la situation nouvelle modifiera, au cours des prochaines années, les relations fournisseurs/acheteurs existantes et transformera radicalement la structure de l'industrie dans le monde entier. On peut être assuré néanmoins que la force vive des fournisseurs d'équipement conduira l'industrie et ses services vitaux vers de nouveaux sommets ».

Il n'est pas facile de déterminer comment ces sommets seront atteints, quand et par quelles firmes. La seule certitude est que la structure de l'industrie en l'an 2000 ne ressemblera guère à ce qu'elle est aujourd'hui. Se maintenir au niveau du progrès technologique et des changements dans l'industrie mondiale des télécommunications présente, néanmoins, un grand défi aux fournisseurs d'équipement de télécommunications, à leur puissance technologique à leur capacité de marketing.

Le profil de 3M Company qui suit, est un exemple de la façon par laquelle les ressources d'une grande firme américaine sont mobilisées pour répondre au défi qui est lancé à l'industrie des communications. Le succès de 3M repose sur une capacité d'innovation dans sa recherche et développement, et sur l'importance vitale qu'elle attache à la qualité de ses produits. Cette firme est organisée de manière à pouvoir identifier les nouveaux besoins technologiques qui émergent dans le monde et de les satisfaire.

THE ITU WORLI

"TELECOM", the World Telecommunication Exhibition, is held every four years in Geneva, Switzerland. The Exhibition, sponsored and organized by the International Telecommunication Union in pursuance of Opinion No. 3 of the International Telecommunication Convention, Nairobi, 1982, covers all areas of telecommunications. The spirit of TELECOM, the world's largest and most prestigious communications and electronics exhibition, is firmly governed by the principle of international cooperation. Governments of ITU Member countries, private operating agencies, manufacturers of telecommunication systems, and telecommunication users, exhibit side by side.

The motive for instituting the TELECOM World Exhibitions lay in the rapid emergence of numerous new telecommunications services, the intensification of international exchange and the

Lausanne
Airport

resulting idea of providing a "world show-case". It provides Member countries an opportunity to make comparisons and hence makes it easier for them to decide which new telecommunications services to develop and which new systems and products to choose. The result of four-years of research and work by the 35 ITU/CCIR and CCITT study groups is reflected in the quadrennial exhibitions.

The ITU Plenipotentiary Conference held in Nairobi in 1982 endorsed the ITU Secretary-General's mandate to organize TELECOM exhibitions so that visitors from industrialized and developing countries could "familiarize themselves with the latest technological developments". In organizing the World Exhibitions, the ITU seeks to further world social and economic development through a constant increase in the density of the global telecommunications network and the development of an Integrated Services Digital Network (ISDN). While the World Telecommunications Exhibitions held in 1971 and 1975 focused on electromagnetic and crossbar switching systems, those held in 1979 and 1983 highlighted electronic switching and transmission systems and rural communications. Rural and mobile communications will no doubt be the highlights of future World Telecommunication Exhibitions.

In general they not only reflect the technical progress which has been achieved, but also reveal the successful outcome of the desire to work together in a worldwide international partnership. The TELECOM Exhibitions always provide a stimulus for the entire field of telecommunications, and are a constant source of new ideas. They provide the best focus on future telecommunication services. In assuming their organization the ITU has established a highly productive center for the exchange of ideas and opinions.

Thus, every four years in Geneva, is held the World Telecommunication Forum (see p. 54) attended by virtually all the heads of telecommunication entities and by leaders of industries, research establishments and financial organizations involved in the development of communications.

TELECOM" EXHIBITIONS IN GENEVA

ELECOM » est l'Exposition mondiale des télécommunications se tient tous les quatre ans à Genève en Suisse. Patronnée organisée par l'Union internationale des télécommunications T), elle couvre tous les secteurs des télécommunications. ECOM est l'exposition la plus grande et la plus prestigieuse monde dans le domaine des communications et est inspirée le principe essentiel de la coopération internationale. Les vernements des pays Membres de l'UIT, les exploitations vées, les constructeurs de systèmes et les prestataires aussi n que les utilisateurs de services y exposent côte à côte. L'origine de TELECOM fut « l'explosion de l'électronique », parition de nombreux nouveaux services, l'intensification s échanges internationaux et, en définitive, l'idée d'en amé er une « vitrine mondiale ». L'intention de l'UIT était d'offrir

"TELECOM", la Exposición Mundial de Telecomunicaciones, se celebra cada cuatro años en Ginebra, Suiza. Patrocinada y organizada por la UIT, de conformidad con el Ruego N° 3 del Convenio Internacional de Telecomunicaciones, Nairobi, 1982, abarca todos los sectores de telecomunicaciones. El espíritu de TELECOM, la mayor y más prestigiosa exposición de comunicaciones y electrónica del mundo, se rige firmemente por el principio de la cooperación internacional. En ella exponen juntos los gobiernos de los países Miembros de la UIT, las empresas privadas de explotación, los fabricantes de sistemas de telecomunicaciones y los usuarios.

La razón de las exposiciones mundiales TELECOM es la rápida aparición de muchos servicios de telecomunicaciones, la intensificación del intercambio internacional y la idea resul-

de equipo de oficina sólo han aumentado su extensión geográfica.

El cuadro de la pag. 286 muestra que de los 13 principales fabricantes de equipo « tradicional » fuera de la URSS, 4 empresas norteamericanas representaron en 1981 el 59% de las ventas totales, 8 empresas de Europa Occidental el 37%, y una japonesa el 4% restante. Con la llegada de grandes productores de equipo electrónico y de oficina, de origen americano o japonés, como Control Data, DEC, GE, General Dynamics, Harris Corp., IBM, Mitel, Motorola, Rockwell International, Rolm, 3M, Wang y Xerox de América del Norte; y Fujitsu, Matsushita, Mitsubishi y Toshiba, de Japón, aumentará sustancialmente el tamaño y la fuerza de las industrias de América del Norte y del Sudeste Asiático en relación con Europa Occidental. El desarrollo de empresas aeroespaciales, también americanas sobre todo — Ford Aerospace, Hughes y RCA —, amplia todavía más este desequilibrio geográfico.

La asociación de empresas europeas con sus adversarias americanas, iniciada ya por British Aerospace, Philips, Plessey, Thomson-CSF, establece una tendencia que tal vez se acentúe al intensificarse la competencia. Un programa de investigación en curso realizado por Arthur D. Little de Cambridge, Massachusetts, confirma la probabilidad de una mayor competencia. En un reciente informe se dice que, si bien el sector de las telecomunicaciones sigue sosteniendo una tasa de crecimiento más alta que la mayoría de los demás sectores de la economía, se combinan varios factores para ejercer gran presión sobre los proveedores:

— los costos de desarrollo de productos de alta tecnología, como conmutación digital de oficinas centrales, aumentan sin cesar. Hay que amortizarlos con un elevado volumen de producción, y los fabricantes se ven obligados a buscar mayores mercados, intensificando así las presiones competitivas;

— a media que las fronteras entre telecomunicaciones, procesamiento de la información y sistemas de oficina es menos clara, los proveedores tradicionales se encuentran ante otras situaciones competitivas. Han de elaborar nuevos productos y estar dispuestos a tratar con nuevos competidores;

— el marco reglamentario de las telecomunicaciones está cambiando en varios países, para que haya mayor competencia entre las empresas y liberalizar las reglas de propiedad de equipo. Los proveedores de esos nuevos mercados pasarán por un período de ajuste a distintas clases de compradores;

— los países recién industrializados están revisando sus políticas de adquisición y la legislación para favorecer la fabricación nacional. Los proveedores se ven obligados a atender las nuevas exigencias, para conservar sus mercados, con posibles repercusiones adversas sobre el empleo (y las economías de escala) en sus propios países.

A.D. Little concluyó: « en conjunto, es de esperar que la evolución de los próximos años altere la actual relación proveedor/comprador y cambie drásticamente la estructura de la industria en el mundo. Pero podemos estar seguros de que la fuerza básica de los proveedores de telecomunicaciones abrirá nuevos horizontes para la industria y sus servicios vitales ».

No es fácil determinar cuándo se alcanzarán esos horizontes, cómo y por qué empresas. Lo único cierto es que la estructura del año 2000 tendrá muy poco parecido con la actual.

El perfil que sigue, de 3M Company, es un ejemplo de cómo una gran empresa americana puede afrontar el desafío de la industria de telecomunicaciones. La base de su éxito es la investigación y el desarrollo y la calidad. La empresa está organizada para conocer las nuevas necesidades en el mundo entero, y atenderlas.

Geneva

s pays Membres l'occasion de faire des comparaisons et de permettre ainsi de décider plus facilement quels étaient les veaux produits, services, ou systèmes à mettre au point. résultats des recherches et des travaux des 35 commisns d'étude du CCIR et du CCITT, organismes permanents de T, sont également reflétés dans ces expositions.

a Conférence de plénipotentiaires de Nairobi, en 1982, a firmé le mandat du secrétaire général de l'UIT pour l'orgaation des expositions TELECOM, afin que les visiteurs se iliarisent avec les « derniers perfectionnements de la techue des télécommunications ». L'UIT n'a aucun objectif mmercial mais cherche plutôt à favoriser le développement ial et économique du monde en stimulant l'augmentation de ensité du réseau de communications et la mise en place d'un eau numérique avec intégration des services (RNIS).

lors que les expositions TELECOM de 1971 et de 1975 ient mis l'accent sur les systèmes de commutation électrognétique et crossbar, celles de 1979 et 1983 ont démontré à ois les progrès réalisés et les efforts à accomplir dans les naines de transmission et de commutation électroniques et s l'infrastructure des communications rurales. Les futures ositions TELECOM, mettront sans doute en évidence les mmunications rurales et mobiles.

d'une manière générale, ces expositions reflètent les progrès nniques accomplis, révèlent et encouragent la coopération cace sur le plan international, stimulant le progrès en révé-x ce qui a été accompli et ce qui reste à faire. Ils constituent neilleure présentation des services de télécommunications demain. En se chargeant de l'organisation des TELECOM, T a institué un grand centre productif d'échange d'idées et pinions.

'est ainsi qu'à l'occasion des TELECOM, a lieu tous les 4 , à Genève (voir p. 54), le « Forum mondial des télécommuations » : la plus grande conférence sur le développement des monde qui réunit, virtuellement, tous les hauts dirigeants administrations des PTT, de l'industrie, de la recherche et a finance concernés par le développement des communica-s.

tante de ofrecer una "muestra mundial". Ofrecen a los países Miembros la oportunidad de hacer comparaciones y, por ende, les facilita la decisión sobre el desarrollo de nuevos servicios de telecomunicaciones y la elección de nuevos sistemas y productos. El resultado de cuatro años de investigación y trabajo de las 35 comisiones de estudio del CCIR y del CCITT de la UIT se refleja en las exposiciones cuatrienales.

La Conferencia de Plenipotenciarios de la UIT, celebrada en Nairobi en 1982, sancionó el mandato del Secretario General de la UIT de organizar exposiciones TELECOM para que los visitantes de los países industrializados y en desarrollo puedan « familiarizarse con la última evolución tecnológica ». Al organizar las exposiciones mundiales, la UIT trata de fomentar el desarrollo social y económico del mundo, mediante el constante aumento de la densidad de la red global de telecomunicaciones y el desarrollo de una red digital de servicios integrados (RDSI). Mientras las exposiciones mundiales de telecomunicaciones celebradas en 1971 y 1975 se centraron en los sistemas electromagnéticos y de conmutación de barras cruzadas, las de 1979 y 1983 insisten en la conmutación electrónica, sistemas de transmisión y comunicaciones rurales. Las comunicaciones rurales y móviles serán sin duda los aspectos sobresalientes de las futuras exposiciones mundiales de telecomunicaciones.

En general, no sólo reflejan los progresos técnicos logrados, sino que revelan el satisfactorio resultado del deseo de trabajar juntos en una asociación internacional mundial. Las exposiciones TELECOM ofrecen siempre un estímulo a todo el sector de las telecomunicaciones, y son un venero constante de nuevas ideas. Constituyen la mejor presentación de los servicios futuros de telecomunicaciones. Al ocuparse de organizarlas, la UIT ha establecido un centro sumamente productivo para el intercambio de ideas y opiniones.

Así, cada cuatro años se celebra en Ginebra el "Foro Mundial de las Telecomunicaciones" (véase pág. 54), a las que asisten prácticamente todos los directores de entidades de telecomunicaciones, dirigentes de industrias e instituciones financieras que participan en el desarrollo de las comunicaciones.

□

3M Company

Providing Innovative Products and Services Around the World

FROM THE TINIEST COMPONENT to complex electronic networks, 3M contributions to communications are dynamic in nature, with a mix of products and systems that reflect the needs of the industry around the world.

Product innovation, offering significant customer benefits, has been a key factor in the growth of the company. Early in its history, 3M originated a number of unique products such as water resistant sandpaper, masking tape, and transparent tape that established a tradition of innovation based on customer needs.

During the past three decades a broad range of communication products and systems has been developed to meet customer requirements around the world. Manufacturers and communication companies use 3M products ranging from state-of-the-art microelectronic interconnects for integrated circuits to sophisticated electronic test and measurement equipment for communication networks. Others use the company's teleprinters, digital facsimile transceivers, broadband local area networks and related products to solve communication problems or to improve productivity.

Involvement with the customer remains a high company priority. Its international subsidiaries work closely with telephone and communication companies to promote understanding and proper use of 3M systems worldwide.

Supporting this close attention to customer needs is an equally strong commitment to research and development. 3M has more than 5,500 laboratory personnel that form a network of major laboratories in North America, Europe, Japan and Brazil. These laboratories, in addition to other development fa-
▷ 292

DYNAMIQUES PAR NATURE, avec une gamme de produits et de systèmes allant du plus petit composant aux réseaux électroniques les plus complexes, les contributions 3M répondent aux besoins industriels mondiaux.

Les produits nouveaux ont toujours constitué un facteur important de croissance pour 3M. Elle fut à l'origine de produits tels que le papier-émeri résistant à l'eau, le ruban de masquage et le ruban transparent, instaurant ainsi une tradition d'innovation basée sur son étude des besoins du marché.

Au cours des trois dernières décennies, une quantité de produits et de systèmes de télécommunication ont été mis au point. Les industries et les services de télécommunication du monde entier emploient des produits 3M, toujours en pointe du progrès, depuis les connecteurs microélectroniques pour circuits intégrés jusqu'aux appareils les plus perfectionnés de test et de mesure. D'autres firmes utilisent des téléimprimeurs de presse, des télécopieurs interactifs en fac-similé numérique, des réseaux locaux à large bande, ainsi que d'autres produits, pour résoudre leurs problèmes de communication ou pour améliorer leur productivité.

La concertation avec les usagers reste prioritaire. Les filiales de la Compagnie à l'étranger collaborent avec les entreprises de télécommunications à fin d'assurer une utilisation appropriée des systèmes 3M.

Les besoins de l'usager, sont étudiés dans les laboratoires de recherche et de développement implantés en Amérique du Nord, en Europe, au Japon et au Brésil qui emploient plus de 5500 personnes. Ces laboratoires, ainsi que d'autres unités R&D installées dans 31 pays, sont aussi utilisés comme centres de formation de personnel des télécommunications.
▷ 292

DESDE EL COMPONENTE MÁS PEQUEÑO hasta las redes electrónicas más complejas, la contribución de 3M a las comunicaciones es dinámica, con una mezcla de productos y sistemas que reflejan las necesidades de la industria del mundo entero.

La innovación de productos que ofrecen importantes beneficios a los clientes es un factor clave en el crecimiento de la empresa. Ya en sus primeros tiempos, creó una serie de productos únicos, como papel de lija resistente al agua, cinta enmascarante y cinta transparente, que establecen una tradición innovadora basada en las necesidades del cliente.

En las tres últimas décadas se ha desarrollado una amplia gama de productos y sistemas de comunicaciones para atender las necesidades de clientes de todo el mundo. Los fabricantes y las empresas de comunicaciones emplean productos de 3M, desde las interconexiones microelectrónicas más avanzadas para circuitos integrados hasta equipo de prueba y medición electrónica sofisticado para redes. Otros usan los teleimpresores de la empresa, transceptores de facsímil digitales, redes de zona local de banda ancha y productos conexos para resolver problemas de comunicación o mejorar la productividad.

La relación con el cliente sigue siendo una de las prioridades de la empresa. Sus filiales internacionales trabajan estrechamente con compañías telefónicas y de comunicaciones para fomentar la comprensión y el uso adecuado en el mundo de sistemas 3M.

Esta gran atención del cliente exige también un gran esfuerzo de investigación y desarrollo. 3M tiene más de 5500 empleados de laboratorio, en una red de importantes laboratorios en América del Norte, Europa, Japón y Brasil. Estos laboratorios, y las otras
▷ 293

A 25 times enlargement of a state of the art developmental interconnect by 3M for VLSI logic chips used in high speed computers is being inspected in the Electronic Products Laboratory.

Agrandissement de 25 fois d'un interconnecteur ultra-moderne conçu par 3M pour les VLSI utilisés dans les ordinateurs ultra rapides en cours d'inspection dans le Laboratoire des produits électroniques.

Ampliación en 25 veces de un interconector moderno concebido por 3M para los circuitos lógicos de integración en muy gran escala, VLSI, utilizados con computadores de gran velocidad, inspeccionado en el laboratorio de productos electrónicos.

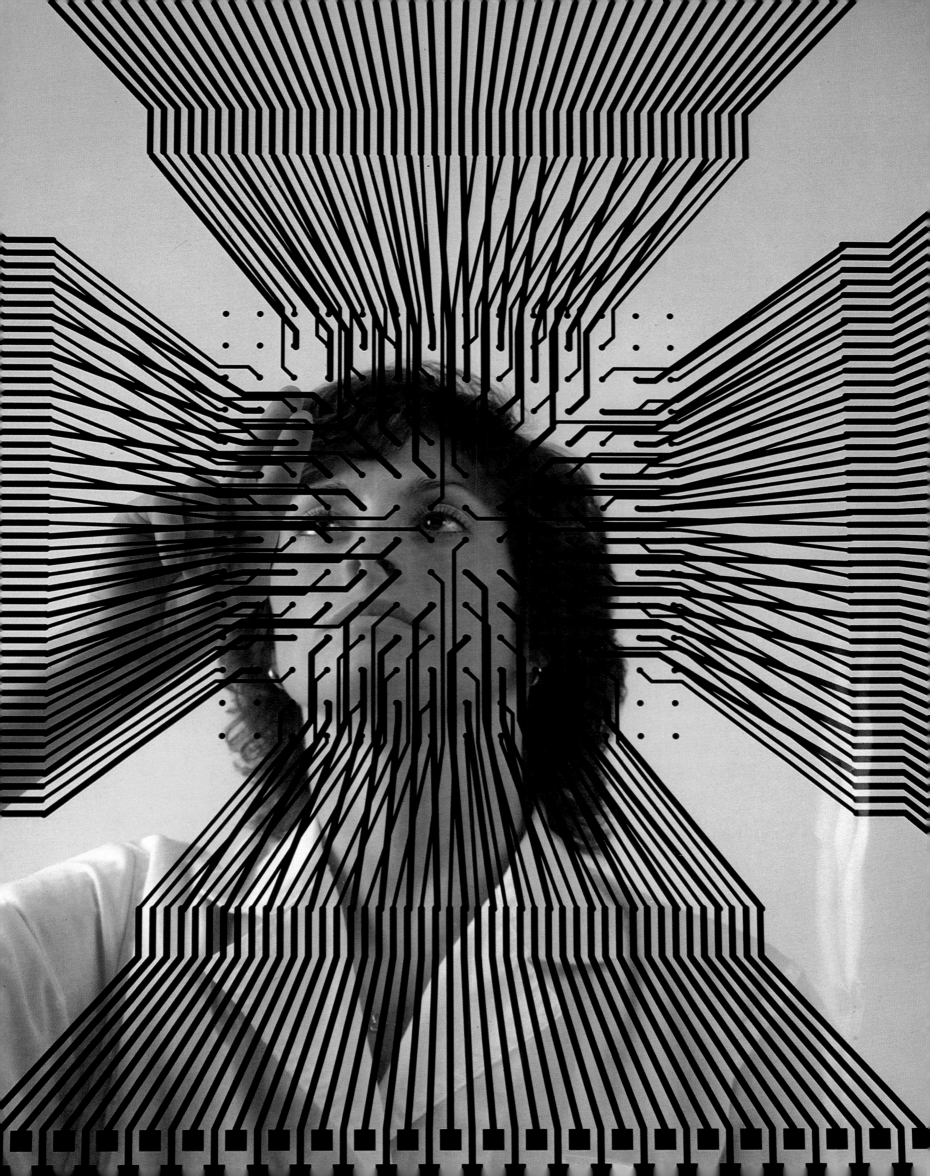

cilities in 31 countries, serve as training and instruction centers for telecommunication personnel worldwide.

A broad range of innovative products has been developed for use in the telecommunications industry. In 1958 the Scotchlok connector was introduced. It replaced the time-consuming strip and solder method of wire joining with a self-stripping U-contactor that combines cost effectiveness and reliability. Today it is a standard in the industry. From this innovative product has evolved a comprehensive approach to wire joining and terminating that meets telecommunication needs from individual wire pairs to complete building wiring systems:
— Scotchlok discrete connectors, used for joining many different types and sizes of wire.
— MS^2 (Modular System Splicing) connectors, using the same insulation displacement concept in a multiple contact form, for simultaneous joining of many wires at one time. Using standard color-code wire sorting, MS^2 connectors handle various indoor and outdoor cable jointing tasks.
— Factory-prepared jointing systems for large communication cables to reduce field wire handling.
— Developments in MS^2 connectors produced systems for wire termination at the telephone office, distribution points, and the user end of the cable. These products include both quick-connect and binding post terminals. Termination panels are made in sizes from 25-pair to thousands of pairs, and, if necessary, with pre-wired protector fields to prevent damage from electrical surges or lightning.

The concept of factory pre-connection has also been extended to termination fields, load coils, and switching equipment to reduce wire work for the user. Factory wiring makes use of color-coded cable preparation under controlled conditions for better productivity and accuracy.

Termination and jointing systems are supported by a line of approved pole-mounted and pedestal cabinets to secure and protect cable access points, terminations, and digital carrier equipment. Tools and procedures have also been developed for telephone companies to use in rehabilitation and maintenance of outdoor cable termination points, a major task for most companies.

Test devices for diagnostic field work on telephone cables of advanced design are produced by 3M. Portable Dynatel testers are used for the quick location and analysis of buried cable problems. Automated fault location and analysis saves labour, speeds repairs and reduces damage to the cable plant during maintenance. Telephone craftsmen use Dynatel testers to pinpoint broken cable sheath, shorted wire, or other cable faults in seconds, and to determine the depth of the cable below ground. Cable excavation and repair can be accomplished quickly without extensive search and without accidental damage to the remainder of the cable.

The recent acquisition of a manufacturer of electronic test and measurement equipment for the telecommunications industry will broaden 3M's test and measurement capabilities. This company, APC Industries, provides facilities products for cable and wire management in construction of communications lines and network products for remote test and measurement of telecommunications trunking facilities. One of APC's fundamental strengths is its in-depth technical understanding of communications network design employed in the USA and around the world.

▷ 296

Une large gamme de produits nouveaux, développée pour servir l'installateur et le personnel d'entretien des équipements de télécommunication, comprend un grand nombre d'outils et de matériaux.

Le connecteur « Scotchlok » lancé en 1958, a remplacé le laborieux procédé de détacher et de souder les fils à la main.

Le contacteur-U à déroulement automatique, devenu équipement standard dans l'industrie, a engendré toute une méthode de raccordement et de terminaison des câbles téléphoniques et répond à tous les besoins en matière de télécommunication, depuis la simple paire en câble jusqu'aux systèmes complets de câblage utilisés dans la construction, notamment :
— les connecteurs discrets Scotchlok pour raccorder les câbles de tous types et de toutes dimensions ;
— les connecteurs MS^2 « système d'épissure modulaire » pour le raccordement simultané d'un grand nombre de câbles, utilisant un code de couleur standard ;
— un système de raccordement préfabriqué pour les grands câbles de télécommunication, permettant de réduire les travaux de chantier et d'améliorer la précision du résultat ;
— les perfectionnements de connecteurs MS^2 pour têtes de câble dans les centraux téléphoniques, aux points de distribution et aux extrêmités chez l'abonné. Tous ces produits comprennent des dispositifs terminaux à montage et connexion rapides. Les panneaux de terminaison comprennent entre 25 paires et des milliers de paires et comportent, en cas de besoin, des champs protecteurs destinés à empêcher tous risques de dommages pouvant être causés par des surtensions ou par la foudre.

Le principe de la préfabrication des connexions s'applique aux terminaisons, aux bobines de charge et à l'équipement de commutation, et réduit le travail de câblage de l'utilisateur.

Les terminaisons et les raccordements sont contenus dans des coffrets montés sur des poteaux, afin de protéger les points d'accès au câble, les terminaisons et les équipements numériques à courants porteurs. Des outils et des procédés ont également été mis au point à l'intention des entreprises téléphoniques pour la réparation et la maintenance des installations terminales de câble montées à l'extérieur, tâches qui font partie du cahier des charges de la plupart de ces entreprises.

3M produit des appareils de diagnostic perfectionnés permettant d'identifier et de localiser les fautes sur câbles téléphoniques installés. Les appareils portatifs de contrôle Dynatel sont utilisés pour une « auscultation » rapide des câbles enterrés, permettant une localisation et une analyse automatique de défaillance qui permet d'accélérer les réparations et de réduire le risque de dégâts pendant les opérations de maintenance.

Les appareils de contrôle Dynatel sont utilisés pour déceler les ruptures de gaine, les courts-circuits et autres avaries, ainsi que pour déterminer la profondeur où se trouvent les câbles. Il est ainsi possible d'excaver et de réparer rapidement le câble sans avoir à effectuer de longues recherches et sans causer de dégâts au reste du câble.

L'acquisition récente d'une entreprise spécialisée dans la fabrication de matériel électronique pour l'industrie des télécommunications APC Industries, a augmenté les capacités de 3M dans ce domaine.

APC Industries fabrique une gamme de produits servant à la construction de réseaux câblés, ainsi que des appareils de test et de mesure pour les liaisons interurbaines. L'un des atouts de APC Industries est

▷ 296

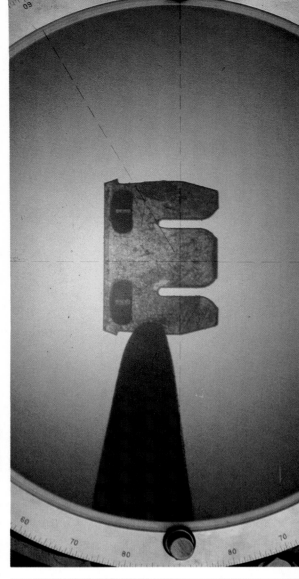

Top, left to right: An enlarged view of the insulation displacement "U" contact pioneered by 3M, shown on an optical comparator. Scotchlok U connectors for wire joining are examined by a laboratory technician in the Sumitomo 3M Laboratory, Sagamihara, Japan. Bottom, left to right: A two-compartment package for mixing and dispensing Scotchcast encapsulating resins is tested in the 3M Electrical Laboratories, GmbH, Hamburg, FRG. Re-enterable, water-resistant buried closures provide protection of service installations in all environments.

En haut, de g. à d. : Agrandissement d'un contact « U » de déplacement d'isolement conçu par 3M. Des connecteurs Scotchlok U pour la jointure des fils téléphoniques examinés au Sumitomo 3M Laboratoire à Sagamihara, au Japon. En bas, de g. à d. : Sachet plastique à deux compartiments utilisé pour mélanger et verser les résines à capsuler Scotchcast, testé dans les Laboratoires Electriques de 3M à Hambourg, RFA. Des cylindres ouvrables et réutilisables, résistants à l'eau, protègent les installations de service en toutes conditions.

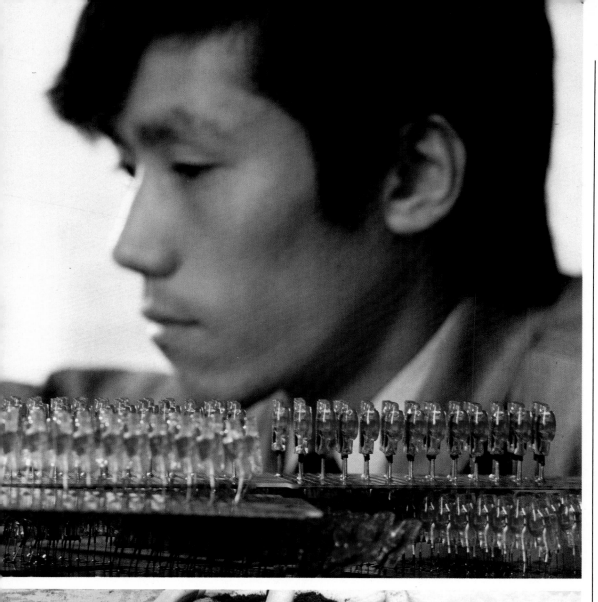

instalaciones de desarrollo en 31 países, sirven de centros de capacitación e instrucción para personal de telecomunicaciones en el mundo entero.

Se ha desarrollado una amplia gama de nuevos productos para uso de la industria de telecomunicaciones. En 1958 se introdujo el denominado conector Scotchlok, en sustitución del método de cinta y saldadura para empalmar circuitos, que requería mucho tiempo, por un contactor U autodesnudante que combina la rentabilidad y la seguridad, y es hoy norma en la industria. A partir de ese producto, ha elaborado un método global de empalme y terminación de conductores que atiende las necesidades de telecomunicaciones, desde pares individuales a sistemas de cableado de edificios completos:

— conectores discretos Scotchlok, usados para empalmar muchos tipos y tamaños de hilos;
— conectores MS² (empalme de sistemas modulares), que emplean la misma noción de desplazamiento de aislamiento en forma de contactos múltiples, para empalmar muchos hilos a la vez. Utilizando varios hilos de colores normalizados, con los conectores MS² se efectúan diversos trabajos de empalme de cables interiores y exteriores;
— sistemas de empalme preparados en fábrica para grandes cables de comunicación, a fin de reducir el trabajo sobre el terreno y de mejorar la precisión.

La evolución de los conectores MS² ha permitido realizar sistemas de terminación de cables en oficinas telefónicas, puntos de distribución y el usuario final del cable. Tales productos comprenden terminales de conexión rápida y de fijación. Existen paneles de terminación desde 25 pares a miles de ellos y, en caso necesario, con campos protectores precableados para impedir los daños debidos a sobretensiones o descargas eléctricas.

La noción de la preconexión en fábrica se ha ampliado a los campos de terminación, bobinas de carga y equipo de conmutación, para reducir la labor del usuario. En el cableado en fábrica se emplean cables codificados, controlándose las operaciones para mejorar la productividad y la exactitud.

Los sistemas de terminación y empalme se basan en una serie de cajas de pedestal y postes aprobadas para asegurar y proteger los puntos de acceso del cable, las terminaciones y el equipo de portadoras digitales. También se han desarrollado instrumentos y procedimientos para uso de las compañías telefónicas en la rehabilitación y mantenimiento de puntos de terminación de cable exteriores, una gran tarea para la mayoría de las empresas.

Los dispositivos para el diagnóstico sobre el terreno de cables telefónicos son productos sofisticados de 3M. Los dispositivos Dynatel portátiles se usan para localizar y analizar rápidamente los problemas de cables enterrados. Los especialistas emplean dispositivos Dynatel para detectar la rotura de la cubierta del cable, el hilo cortocircuitado y otras averías de cables en segundos, y determinar la profundidad del cable. Los trabajos de excavación y reparación de cables pueden realizarse rápidamente, sin daños accidentales para el resto del cable.

La reciente adquisición de un fabricante de equipo electrónico de prueba y medición de la industria de telecomunicaciones ampliará las capacidades de 3M en este sector. Esa empresa, APC Industries, fabrica cables conectores para líneas de comunicaciones y productos de redes para pruebas y mediciones remotas de facilidades de enlaces. Uno de los principales atributos de APC es su profundo cono-

▷ 296

Arriba, de izquierda a derecha: Ampliación de un contacto « U » de desplazamiento de aislamiento concebido por 3M, en un comparador óptico. Conectores Scotchlok U para empalmar hilos telefónicos, examinados por un técnico en el laboratorio de 3M de Sumitomo, Sagamihara (Japón). Abajo, de izquierda a derecha: Un saquito de plástico de dos compartimentos utilizado para mezclar y verter las resinas de encapsular Scotchcast, probado en el laboratorio eléctrico de 3M, GmbH, Hamburgo (RFA). Cilindros enterrados, que pueden abrirse, resistentes al agua, protegen las instalaciones de servicios en cualesquiera condiciones.

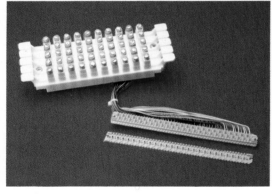

*The 4200 series cabinet is designed to house MS²
cross-connect systems, such as modular
hardware blocks and quick-connect modules,
plus carrier equipment or repeaters.*

*Une armoire de la série 4200 conçue pour contenir les
systèmes connecteurs-croisés MS², tels que les blocs
câblés modulaires et les modules de connexion
rapide, plus l'équipement porteur ou les répéteurs.*

*Un armario de la serie 4200 concebido para contener
sistemas de conectores cruzados MS², como bloques
de cables modulares y módulos de conexión rápida,
mas equipo portador o repetidores.*

3M expertise in chemistry has led to the development of clean, easy-to-use resins for encapsulation of telephone cables. Permanent and re-enterable resins are packaged in a two-part plastic bag with an internal seal that allows mixing and application without additional containers or tools. A family of proprietary jointing closures for protection of telephone cables and joint points above and below ground can be used with these encapsulants where extreme environmental protection is required. Closures range in size from small units for single wire pairs up to devices for several thousand pairs.

The company's basic strengths in tapes, insulations, connectors and compounds are augmented by sophisticated coating technologies, metallurgy, polymer chemistry, static control systems, fiber optics and other electronic and materials capabilities.

Building wiring systems and local area networks must meet a growing demand to handle voice, data, and video signals. 3M has developed two alternative systems.

One, the Voicedata paired wire network carries analog and low-speed digital signals in a flexible network that can be controlled and modified by the user at minimum cost with semi-skilled labour. A key element in these installations is a universal connector system, a series of connectors which can be assembled in a variety of ways for simple plug-to-plug interconnection of switching equipment, data devices and telephones.

▷ 297

sa connaissance technique approfondie des conceptions et des méthodes de construction de réseaux de télécommunication appliquées aussi bien aux Etats-Unis que dans le monde.

La maîtrise de 3M dans le domaine de la chimie lui a permis de mettre au point des résines propres et faciles à utiliser pour « encapsuler » les câbles téléphoniques.

Il existe une série de types de capsules (de marque déposée) pour la protection des raccords de câbles téléphoniques aériens et souterrains. Ces capsules sont généralement utilisées lorsqu'une protection renforcée contre l'environnement est requise. Leurs dimensions permettent de revêtir aussi bien de petites jonctions aériennes et souterraines que des raccordements de câbles à plusieurs milliers de paires.

La compétence de 3M en matière de bandes, d'isolateurs, de connecteurs et de produits dérivés, est renforcée par des techniques perfectionnées de revêtement, et un savoir-faire hautement spécialisé dans la métallurgie, la chimie des polymères, le contrôle de l'électricité statique, les fibres optiques et autres matériaux composants électroniques.

Construire des réseaux câblés et des réseaux locaux entraîne une demande croissante de systèmes de câblage, permettant d'aménager simultanément des signaux de sons et d'images, sous forme numérique ou analogique. 3M a mis au point deux systèmes, le Voicedata et le Vidéodata.

Le système Voicedata est un réseau mixte, en câbles à paires, pouvant transmettre indifféremment

▷ 297

cimiento técnico del diseño de redes de comunicaciones empleado en EE.UU. y en el mundo entero.

La pericia química de 3M le ha permitido desarrollar resinas puras de fácil uso para encapsular cables telefónicos. En una bolsa de plástico dividida en dos partes se envasan resinas permanentes y penetrables con un sello interno que permite la mezcla y la aplicación sin otros contenedores o instrumentos. Con estos encapsulantes puede usarse una serie de cierres de empalme registrados para la protección de cables telefónicos y puntos de empalme en líneas aéreas y subterráneas, cuando se requiere una extrema protección del medio. El tamaño de los cierres va de pequeñas unidades para pares de hilos aislados a dispositivos para varios miles de pares.

La gran fuerza de la empresa en cintas, aislamientos, conectores y compuestos aumenta merced a tecnologías de revestimiento sofisticadas, la metalurgia, la química de polímeros, sistemas de control estáticos, fibras ópticas, materiales y electrónica.

Los sistemas de cableado de edificios y redes locales han de atender cada vez mayor para cursar señales vocales, de datos y video. 3M ha desarrollado dos sistemas alternativos.

Uno, la red de pares de cables datos/voz, cursa señales analógicas y digitales a baja velocidad en una red flexible que puede controlarse y modificarse por el usuario con pocos gastos y personal semicalificado. Un elemento clave de estas instalaciones es el

▷ 297

Left: Static control wrist straps, shielding bags and floor mats from 3M protect electronic switching components during installation and maintenance. Center: Testing a circuit on the MS² high-density protection and distribution frame. From protected entrance terminal to station, building wiring needs for telecommunications, data and signal handling are met with 3M's voicedata paired network.

A gauche : Bracelets pour contrôle d'électricité statique, sacs de protection et revêtements de sol fournis par 3M pour la protection de composants de commutation électronique pendant l'installation et la maintenance. Au centre : Essai d'un circuit sur un cadre MS² de protection et distribution de haute densité. Depuis le terminal d'entrée protégée jusqu'à la station, la construction du câblage se fait avec le réseau à paire de 3M.

A la izquierda: Muñequeras de control estático, bolsas de protección y esterillas, fabricados con materiales de 3M para la protección de los componentes de conmutación electrónica. En el centro: Un instalador prueba un circuito en un cuadro MS² de protección y distribución de gran densidad. Desde el terminal de entrada protegido hasta la estación, la construcción del cableado se realiza con la red de pares voz/datos de 3M.

The other, the Videodata high-speed, multi-purpose communications network, uses coaxial cable and radio frequency equipment to handle simultaneously voice, data and video signals on a single coaxial cable. More than 250 systems for manufacturers, hospitals, military installations, educational institutions and communications companies, are in operation around the world.

Once this broadband network is in place, it can be modified or expanded easily at minimal cost. One coaxial cable can replace thousands of twisted wire pairs, reducing installation costs significantly and eliminating the need for large cable duct capacity within a building or multi-building complex.

The incorporation of microelectronic circuitry into telecommunications equipment has resulted in major advances in performance and reductions in size. However, as the use of microelectronics has expanded, the circuits and equipment have become more susceptible to degradation or failure from static electricity. As the leading supplier of static control products, 3M has worked closely with communications companies and equipment manufacturers, such as major PABX suppliers, in implementing comprehensive programs to protect components and equipment from static discharge. Products used in conjunction with such programs include conductive floor mats and work surfaces, grounding wrist straps, static shielding containers and ionizing air blowers.

The growing application of microelectronics to system and subscriber communication equipment has expanded the needs of equipment manufacturers for materials and components offering higher performance, reduced size and greater reliability. A number of innovative 3M products meet such requirements, and are being designed into new equipment by manufacturers.

▷ 300

des signaux analogiques et des signaux numériques à faible vitesse, très souple, facilement contrôlable ou modifiable par l'utilisateur.

Dans le câblage d'immeubles le Voicedata assure une grande souplesse depuis l'entrée protégée jusqu'à la station de l'usager, à un coût minimal avec de la main d'œuvre semi-qualifiée. L'un des éléments les plus efficaces de ce type d'installation est son système d'interconnexion universel d'une souplesse exceptionnelle.

Le Vidéodata est un système à transmission rapide et à usages multiples, utilisant un câble coaxial et un équipement à fréquences radioélectriques qui permet d'écouler simultanément les signaux analogiques et les signaux numériques de données et vidéo. Plus de 250 systèmes de ce type fonctionnent déjà dans le monde, notamment pour les besoins de fabricants, d'hôpitaux, d'installations militaires, d'instituts pédagogiques, d'entreprises de télécommunications, etc.

Une fois mis en place, ce réseau à large bande est facile et peux coûteux à modifier ou à développer. Un câble coaxial peut remplacer des milliers de paires torsadées, ce qui réduit sensiblement le coût d'installation, tout en supprimant la nécessité d'aménager des conduits de câble à grande capacité.

L'incorporation de circuits microélectroniques dans les matériels de télécommunication s'est traduite par des progrès appréciables en ce qui concerne la performance et la miniaturisation. Cependant, la généralisation de la microélectronique rend les circuits et le matériel plus fragiles et plus sujets à l'usure ou aux défaillances dues à l'électricité statique. En tant que pionnier dans la mise au point de produits anti-statiques, 3M a organisé, en collaboration avec les fabricants de matériel de télécommunications particulièrement affectés par l'électricité statique, tels que les grands constructeurs de centraux PABX, des

▷ 300

sistema de conector universal, una serie de conectores que pueden unirse en diversas formas, interconectando equipo de conmutación, de datos y teléfonos. El otro, la red de comunicaciones con fines múltiples datos/video a gran velocidad, usa cable coaxial y equipo de frecuencias radioeléctricas para tratar simultáneamente señales vocales, digitales, de datos y video. Ya funcionan en el mundo más de 250 sistemas para fabricantes, hospitales, instalaciones militares, instituciones docentes y empresas de comunicaciones.

Una vez instalada esta red de banda ancha, puede modificarse o ampliarse fácilmente con un gasto mínimo. Un cable coaxial puede sustituir a miles de pares trenzados reduciendo mucho los gastos de instalación y su necesidad de grandes conductos de cables en un edificio o un complejo de ellos.

La incorporación de los circuitos microelectrónicos al equipo ha supuesto grandes avances de rendimiento y reducción de tamaño. Sin embargo, a medida que se hace mayor uso de la electrónica, los circuitos y el equipo son más susceptibles de degradación o fallo a causa de la electricidad estática. Como principal proveedor de productos de control estático, 3M ha trabajado con compañías de comunicaciones y fabricantes de equipo, como importantes proveedores de CAP, en la aplicación de programas completos para proteger los componentes y el equipo contra las descargas estáticas. Esos productos comprenden esterillas y superficies de trabajo conductoras, muñequeras de puesta a tierra, contenedores de protección estática y ventiladores ionizantes.

En vista de la creciente aplicación de la microelectrónica a sistemas y equipo de comunicación de

▷ 300

Right: The Dynatel 710 series fault locator is one in a family of test equipment used to detect and analyze cable faults in seconds.

A droite : Le localisateur de failles de la série Dynatel 710, un équipement capable de localiser et d'analyser les failles en quelques secondes.

A la derecha: El localizador de averías de la serie Dynatel 710, equipo capaz de localizar y analizar los fallos en unos segundos.

Optical telecommunications cable by Western Electric is fabricated from light guide fibers laminated between two layers of a special 3M pressure-sensitive tape that maintains fiber alignment and helps prevent microbending.

Câble optique de télécommunications Western Electric fabriqué avec des fibres optiques laminées entre deux couches de bandes spéciales de 3M, sensibles à la pression, qui maintiennent l'alignement des fibres et empêchent les microcourbes.

Cable óptico de telecomunicaciones de Western Electric fabricado con fibras ópticas laminadas entre dos capas de cintas especiales de 3M, sensibles a la presión, que mantienen la alineación de las fibras e impiden las microcurbas.

For example, Scotchflex mass-terminated connectors and flat electronic cable are being incorporated into new automated switching systems. These mass-terminated cables and connectors save assembly time for the equipment manufacturer and assure long-term reliability for the customer.

Another company innovation, the data cartridge recording system, is used by electronic communication switching equipment manufacturers for program backup, preserving critical control programming for PABX systems against the possibility of power loss or mechanical failure.

The data cartridge tape system provides a compact, reliable, low-cost data storage alternative to half-inch computer tape. High capacity cartridge memories have proven very successful for storage of computer programs, communications messages, point-of-sale billing, automatic toll recording and many other applications.

Microwave materials, with precisely controlled dielectric constants and low loss characteristics, have been developed for the rapidly emerging microwave integrated circuit market with applications that include satellite communications, military guidance systems and state of the art high-speed computer logic circuitry. Additionally, 3M has been a major supplier for more than a decade of flexible circuit board material for the telecommunications market.

Reorganization into four business sectors was carried out by 3M in 1981 in order to improve its service to customers around the world. One of the four is the

▷ 301

programmes de recherche contre l'électricité statique dans les composants et les équipements. Parmi les produits inclus dans les programmes sont les matériaux conducteurs (tapis de sol et surfaces de travail) bracelets avec mise à la terre, coffrets anti-statiques, ventilateurs ionisants, etc.

L'utilisation de la microélectronique dans les systèmes et réseaux de télécommunications a augmenté les besoins des fabricants en ce qui concerne la performance, la miniaturisation et la fiabilité des matériels et des composants.

Les connecteurs à terminaison massive et les câbles électroniques plats « Scotchflex » sont incorporés à de nouveaux systèmes de commutation automatique. Ces composants épargnent du temps de montage et garantissent une fiabilité de longue durée à l'usager.

Le système d'enregistrement de données à cartouches, utilisé par les fabricants de matériels de commutation comme programme de rappel — protège la programmation de contrôle des systèmes PABX contre les risques d'interruption de l'alimentation électrique ou de défaillance mécanique.

Par rapport à la bande d'ordinateur de 12 mm, le système à cartouche permet d'enregistrer les données sous une forme compacte, facilement interchangeable, fiable et d'un prix modique. Grâce à leur grande capacité, les mémoires à cartouche se sont révélées efficaces pour le stockage de programmes informatiques, les messages en télécommunication, la facturation aux points de vente, l'enregistrement automatique des taxes, etc. Les matériels micro-ondes, à constantes diélectriques minutieusement contrôlées

▷ 301

abonado, los fabricantes de equipo tienen más necesidad de materiales y componentes de mayor rendimiento, menor tamaño y más seguros. Hay varios productos nuevos de 3M que cumplen esos requisitos, y los fabricantes los están diseñando en nuevo equipo. Por ejemplo, en sistemas de conmutación automatizados recientes se incorporan conectores y cable electrónico plano terminados en masa Scotchflex, que economizan tiempo de montaje y garantizan al usuario la fiabilidad a largo plazo.

Otra innovación de la empresa es el sistema con registro de cartuchos de datos, utilizado por fabricantes de equipo de conmutación electrónico para apoyar el programa, protegiendo la programación de control crítica de sistemas CAP contra la posibilidad de pérdida de energía o avería mecánica.

El sistema de cinta de cartuchos de datos permite almacenar datos en forma compacta, segura y económica, en lugar de la cinta de computador de media pulgada. Las memorias de cartuchos de gran capacidad son muy satisfactorias para el almacenamiento de programas de computador, mensajes de comunicaciones, facturación de puntos de venta, registro automático de tasas y muchas otras aplicaciones.

Se están desarrollando materiales de microondas, con constantes dieléctricas controladas con precisión y características de poca pérdida, para el mercado de circuitos integrados de microondas, con aplicaciones que comprenden las comunicaciones por satélite, los sistemas de guía militar y los circuitos lógicos de computador más avanzados. Además, 3M es un importante proveedor desde hace más de una década

▷ 301

Left: This patching cable harness of 11 Scotchflex connectors and a flat cable simplifies the interconnection of electronic switching equipment. Center: A GTE Automatic Electric PABX unit equipped with a 3M data cartridge drive undergoes its final tests.

A gauche : Un harnais de câble composé de 11 connecteurs Scotchflex et un câble plat simplifie les interconnexions des équipements de commutation électronique. Au centre : Le dernier essai d'une installation automatique privée (PABX) de GTE munie d'une cartouche de données 3M.

A la izquierda: Un arnés de cable de enlace compuesto de 11 conectores Scotchflex y un cable plano, instalado para simplificar las interconexiones del equipo de conmutación electrónica. En el centro: Ultima prueba de la instalación de una centralita automática privada (CAP) de GTE, provista de una unidad de cartucho de banda magnética de datos 3M.

Electronic and Information Technologies Sector which includes the major products and technologies serving the telecommunications market. In 1982 this Sector generated more than $ 2 billion in sales, approximately 30% of 3M's total sales worldwide.

The reorganization has enabled the company to optimize its research effort by grouping products and technical resources on the basis of related technologies. This was necessary because the technologies are highly complex and fast-moving and because customer needs are changing rapidly.

Focal point for sector research and development is the sector laboratory. It is responsible for maintaining positions on the leading edge of technologies key to the sector's business. The sector laboratory is typically working on research programs with lead times of 5 to 10 years. Additionally, it works with the operating divisions within the sector to broaden their technologies and to increase their base of scientific understanding. The division laboratories work with products and technologies that serve current customer needs. The sector laboratories exchange information with other sectors and with the Science Research Laboratory of Central Research which is dealing with new technologies and programs that may not develop into business opportunities for many years.

3M technologies include precision coatings, pressure-sensitive adhesives, electrical and electronic circuits and connectors, magnetic memories, films and backings, surface preparation and finishing, non-woven materials, signing, fluorchemistry, imaging, microspheres and microencapsulation, medical and surgical supplies and pharmaceuticals.

▷ 302

et à faibles caractéristiques d'affaiblissement ont été mis au point pour répondre au développement rapide du marché des circuits intégrés, utilisés pour les communications par satellite, systèmes de guidage militaire et circuits logiques ultrarapides d'ordinateurs. Depuis plus de dix ans, 3M est un important fournisseur de plaquettes souples pour circuits intégrés.

Une restructuration en quatre secteurs d'activités a été effectuée en 1981 par 3M, afin d'améliorer ses services à travers le monde. L'un de ces secteurs, celui de l'électronique et de l'informatique, qui inclue les principaux produits et technologies nécessaires au marché des télécommunications, a réalisé en 1982 environ 30% du total des ventes, soit plus de 2 milliards de dollars.

La réorganisation a permis la rationalisation de la recherche et du développement en regroupant les ressources par domaines industriels, ce qui s'imposait en raison de la complexité et de l'évolution rapide des techniques, et compte tenu des modifications soudaines des besoins des usagers.

Le « laboratoire de secteur » pour chacun des quatre secteurs est le point central de recherche et de développement : c'est à ce laboratoire qu'incombe le support pratique des positions d'avant-garde des techniques-clé avec des programmes de recherche d'une échéance de cinq à dix ans. Il collabore avec les divisions d'exploitation, lesquelles travaillent sur des produits et des techniques répondant aux besoins courants de l'usager en vue de développer leurs bases technologiques et scientifiques, et avec le laboratoire de recherche scientifique du « Centre de recherche » (Central Research), qui s'occupe de nouvelles technologies. Les « Laboratoires de division » et les « Laboratoires de secteur » échangent les informations entre eux.

▷ 302

de material de tarjetas de circuitos flexibles para el mercado de telecomunicaciones.

Para mejorar su servicio a los usuarios mundiales. 3M se reorganizó en cuatro sectores comerciales. El sector de la tecnología electrónica y de la información comprende los principales productos y tecnologías del mercado de las telecomunicaciones. En 1982, generó más de 2000 millones $ de ventas, alrededor del 30% de las ventas mundiales de 3M.

Con esa reorganización, la empresa optima su esfuerzo de investigación agrupando productos y recursos técnicos sobre la base de tecnologías conexas. Había que hacerlo porque las tecnologías son muy complejas y avanzan con rapidez, y las necesidades del cliente también cambian velozmente.

El punto central de la investigación y el desarrollo es el laboratorio del sector, encargado de mantener posiciones en las tecnologías clave de sus actividades. El laboratorio trabaja típicamente en programas de investigación con plazos de 5 a 10 años. Además, lo hace con las divisiones de explotación del sector para ampliar sus tecnologías y aumentar su base de conocimientos científicos. Los laboratorios de la división manejan productos y tecnologías destinados al cliente actual. Los laboratorios intercambian información con otros sectores y con el de investigación científica del servicio central, que trata de nuevas tecnologías y programas que pueden ofrecer oportunidades comerciales para muchos años.

Las tecnologías de 3M comprenden revestimientos de precisión, adhesivos sensibles a la presión, circuitos eléctricos y electrónicos y conectores, memorias magnéticas, filmes y soportes, preparación y acabado de superficies, materiales no tejidos, signatura, química de flúor, imágenes, microsferas y microencapsulado, material médico y farmacéutico.

▷ 302

Right: Appalachian State University uses a broad Videodata communications network from Interactive Systems/3M.

A droite : La Appalachian State University emploie un réseau de communications à large bande Vidéodata d'un Système interactif/3M.

A la derecha: La Appalachian State University emplea una red de comunicaciones de banda ancha Videodata de un sistema interactivo/3M.

Facsimile is an important means of rapidly transferring information in today's world of high-speed communications. It is the only office communication device that can be operated without special training to transmit information worldwide, regardless of form. In 1982 facsimile accounted for more than half of the electronic mail messages sent in the USA, and predictions are that it will be a central element in the growing trend toward electronic communication and office automation. Nearly two million facsimile transceivers are expected to be in use in the USA by 1985, with much of the growth coming from high-performance digital facsimile.

3M digital facsimile equipment provides high-speed transmission of documents, graphics and pictorial material. A page-long document can be transmitted in as little as 20 seconds and at a fraction of the cost of priority mail. Rapid transmission combined with automatic operation makes digital facsimile especially attractive. A major application for facsimile is internal business communications. For example, telephone operating companies use facsimile to transmit field service information from remote locations to a central computer for consolidation of maintenance records.

In the very near future, facsimile machines will possess optical character recognition capabilities with the ability to send as well as receive alphanumeric characters at faster transmission rates. Other benefits include the ability to process facsimile and text messages on the same machine, directing data to a computer teleprinter or another digital machine, in addition to a traditional facsimile receiver.

A portable teleprinter, the Whisper Writer, which can be used with standard telephone lines to send and receive text or serve as a remote computer terminal is another useful tool made by 3M for the electronic mail user. This system has several business communications applications including electronic mail, re-

---

3M fabrique deux dispositifs électroniques importants pour la transmission de la correspondance électronique, notamment le fac-similé numérique.

Le fac-similé est le seul moyen de transmettre l'information à travers le monde, quelle qu'en soit la forme ou la destination, sans qu'une formation préalable de l'utilisateur soit nécessaire.

En 1982, le fac-similé totalisait, à lui seul, plus de la moitié des messages transmis aux Etats-Unis par courrier électronique et il est prévu, qu'en 1985, près de deux millions d'émetteurs-récepteurs fac-similé seront en service. Cette progression sera due en grande partie à l'utilisation du fac-similé numérique à haute performance qui assure une transmission ultra rapide des documents écrits et du matériel graphique et illustré.

Dans un avenir très proche, les machines fac-similé auront la capacité de reconnaître optiquement les caractères et pourront émettre et recevoir des caractères alphanumériques à des vitesses plus élevées. Il sera possible de traiter sur une machine aussi bien les messages en fac-similé que les textes, et de diriger les données sur un téléimprimeur d'ordinateur ou sur toute autre machine numérique.

Le téléimprimeur portatif « Whisper Writer », qui peut être relié à une ligne téléphonique normale pour envoyer et recevoir des textes, est un outil très utile. Il peut aussi fonctionner comme terminal d'ordinateur. Les applications sont principalement dans le domaine de la communication commerciale, notamment le courrier électronique, l'accès aux bases de données et l'accès au réseau mondial TWX/Telex.

3M offre plusieurs autres produits dans le secteur des communications. Par exemple, un support d'enregistrement optique à trois couches, pour le stockage à grande capacité de l'information est actuellement en cours de mise au point dans les laboratoires de la société, à Saint-Paul, Minnesota.

La précision de ce système est telle que 50 000 pistes peuvent être placées sur un disque de 30 centimètres, et l'enregistrement de 70 à 150 bits peut tenir sur la largeur d'un cheveu.

▷ 304

El facsímil es un importante medio de transmisión rápida de la información en las comunicaciones actuales de gran velocidad. Es el único dispositivo de comunicación de oficina que puede manejarse sin formación especial para transmitir al mundo entero, en cualquier forma. El facsímil representó en 1982 más de la mitad de los mensajes de correo electrónico enviados en EE.UU., y se predice que será un elemento básico de la creciente tendencia a la comunicación electrónica y la automatización de oficinas. Para 1985 se espera utilizar cerca de dos millones de transceptores de facsímil, en gran parte debido al facsímil digital, de magníficos resultados.

El equipo facsímil digital de 3M permite la transmisión a gran velocidad de documentos, gráficos y material ilustrado. Un documento de una página puede transmitirse tan sólo en 20 segundos, y a una fracción del costo del correo urgente. La rapidez de transmisión, unida a la explotación automática, hace especialmente atractivo el facsímil digital. Una importante aplicación del facsímil son las comunicaciones comerciales. Por ejemplo, las empresas telefónicas lo utilizan para transmitir información de servicio desde lugares remotos a un computador central, para agrupar los registros de mantenimiento.

Los aparatos facsímil dispondrán muy pronto de capacidad de reconocimiento óptico de caracteres, con la posibilidad de enviar y recibir caracteres alfanuméricos a mayor velocidad de transmisión. Otras ventajas son la posibilidad de procesar mensajes de facsímil y texto en el mismo aparato, dirigiendo datos a un teleimpresor u otro aparato digital, además de un receptor facsímil clásico.

El teleimpresor portátil. Otro instrumento útil para el usuario del correo electrónico es un teleimpresor portátil de 3M, el Whisper Writer, que puede emplearse con líneas telefónicas para transmitir o recibir texto o actuar como terminal de computador remoto. Tiene varias aplicaciones comerciales, incluso el correo electrónico, el acceso a bases de datos re-

▷ 304

On the left: Access to the actuarial data via telephone lines with a Whisper Writer teleprinter simplifies preparation of client proposal by an agent for Federal Kemper Life Assurance Company.

Sur la gauche : L'accès aux données des actuaires par lignes téléphoniques avec un téléimprimeur Whisper Writer simplifie la préparation des propositions pour les clients de cet agent de Federal Kemper Life Assurance Company.

A la izquierda: El acceso a datos actuariales por líneas telefónicas con un teleimpresor Whisper Writer simplifica la preparación de las proposiciones para los clientes de este agente de la Federal Kemper Life Assurance Company.

On the right: A superintendent of a Superior Oil Company rig in the Gulf of Mexico transmits current well-head drilling information on a 3M digital facsimile transceiver.

A droite : Le responsable d'une plateforme de la Superior Oil Company, dans le Golfe du Mexique, transmet de l'information sur les opérations de forage en utilisant un émetteur/récepteur fac-similé de 3M.

A la derecha: El responsable de una plataforma de la Superior Oil Company, en el Golfo de México, transmitiendo información corriente sobre las operaciones de sondeo utilizando un transmisor/receptor facsímil de 3M.

mote computer database access and worldwide TWX/Telex network access.

Many of 3M's capabilities touch on products that interface with the telecommunications industry. One of these is a Tri-layer Optical Recording Medium for high-capacity digital storage of information, which is being developed in the Company's St. Paul laboratories. Precision is so exact that 50,000 tracks can be placed on a 12-inch disk and 70 to 150 bits can be recorded in the width of a human hair.

Image enhancement is another of the Company's capabilities which is peripheral to the telecommunications industry. The Comtal digital image processing system supports research and industry activity with high-speed processing techniques for multiple color spectral analysis, image enhancement, picture magnification, scaling, rotation and translation. It enhances images for improved visual effect, eliminates various forms of image degradation, reduces electrical noise and performs various mathematical calculations for image analysis. An internal processor performs all calculations in real time without dependence on a host computer.

These sophisticated capabilities are used in conjunction with communication signals for processing of satellite images as well as radio astronomy, military intelligence, remote agricultural analysis, geologic survey and cartographic applications, to name but a few.

High-speed digital image processing emphasizes the scope of the Company's communication technology, which ranges from tiny wire connectors and protective compounds to complex computer-based systems.

Continuing product development and refinement keeps 3M products in tune with ever-changing needs. Company resources insure that technology developed in one part of the world contributes to the satisfaction of unique needs in yet another part of the world. In communications, 3M innovation is worldwide.

□

L'amélioration de la qualité de l'image est encore l'une des spécialités de la compagnie 3M dans un domaine connexe des télécommunications.

Un système 3M de traitement numérique de l'image, le « Comtal » est un instrument très efficace dans la recherche et les activités industrielles. Cela est dû à son traitement à grande vitesse pour l'analyse spectrale « multicolore », l'amélioration de la qualité et du contraste des images, ainsi que leur agrandissement, leur repiquage, leur rotation et leur report ou « transfert ».

Ce système permet donc de rehausser la qualité de l'image et d'en améliorer l'effet visuel, en éliminant les diverses causes de dégradation et en réduisant le brouillage électrique ; un microprocesseur intégré effectue les divers calculs requis pour l'analyse de l'image, en temps réel, sans dépendre d'un ordinateur d'appoint.

Ces techniques perfectionnées sont appliquées à des signaux de communication pour le traitement des images transmises par satellite et également dans des domaines aussi divers que la radioastronomie, le renseignement militaire, l'analyse agricole à distance, l'étude géologique et l'établissement de relevés cartographiques.

Le traitement numérique à grande vitesse de l'image a élargi les capacités technologiques de la compagnie qui s'étendent des minuscules connecteurs et de leurs capsules protectrices jusqu'aux systèmes complexes centrés sur les ordinateurs. La mise au point permanente et le perfectionnement continuel de nouveaux produits maintient la production de 3M en harmonie avec les besoins en constante évolution.

Les moyens et les ressources dont dispose la compagnie 3M lui donnent l'opportunité d'employer des techniques mises au point dans une région déterminée pour répondre à des besoins uniques en leur genre qui se manifestent à l'autre bout du monde. C'est ainsi que, dans le domaine de la communication, les innovations de 3M ont une portée véritablement universelle.

□

motas por computador, y una red mundial TWX/télex.

Muchos de los productos de 3M corresponden a la industria de telecomunicaciones. Uno de ellos es un *medio de registro óptico de tres capas* para almacenamiento digital de información de gran capacidad, desarrollado por los laboratorios St. Paul de la empresa. La precisión es tal que en un disco de 12 pulgadas pueden colocarse 50 000 pistas y almacenar en la anchura de un pelo humano de 70 a 150 bits.

El mejoramiento de la imagen es otra de las actividades de la empresa relacionada con las telecomunicaciones. El sistema digital Comtal apoya las operaciones de investigación e industriales con técnicas de tratamiento de gran velocidad para análisis espectrales de color múltiples, mejoramiento de imágenes, magnificación, graduación, rotación y traslación. Mejora las imágenes para perfeccionar el efecto visual, suprime varias formas de degradación, reduce el ruido eléctrico y realiza diversos cálculos matemáticos para análisis de imagen. Un procesador interno efectúa todos los cálculos en tiempo real, sin depender de un computador anfitrión.

Esas capacidades sofisticadas se usan con las señales de comunicación para procesar imágenes de satélite, así como radioastronomía, inteligencia militar, análisis agrícolas a distancia, estudio geológico y aplicaciones cartográficas, por citar sólo unas cuantas.

El procesamiento digital de imágenes a gran velocidad subraya el alcance de la tecnología de comunicaciones de la empresa, que va desde conectores muy pequeños y compuestos protectores hasta sistemas complejos basados en computador.

Merced al constante desarrollo y perfeccionamiento de sus productos, 3M atiende unas necesidades que cambian sin cesar. Los recursos de la empresa permiten que la tecnología desarrollada en una parte del mundo contribuya a satisfacer necesidades únicas en otra. En materia de comunicaciones, la innovación de 3M es mundial.

□

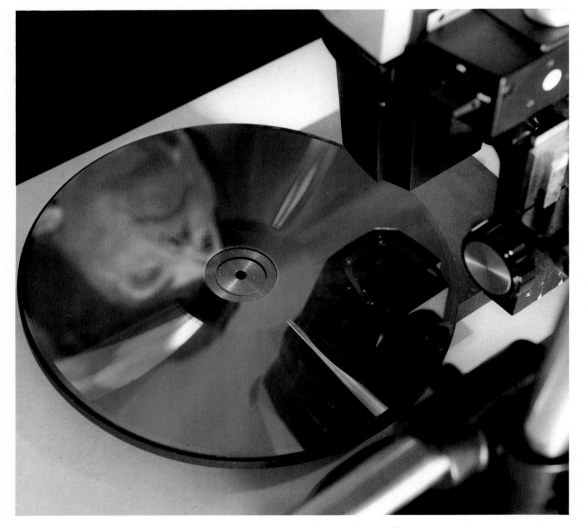

On the left: A high density recording disk, being developed by 3M, is inspected after prolonged exposure to high heat and humidity.

Sur la gauche : Un disque d'enregistrement de haute densité, en cours de développement par 3M, est inspecté après une longue exposition à une température et une humidité très élevées.

A la izquierda: Inspección de un disco de grabación de elevada densidad, que está desarrollando 3M, tras una larga exposición a gran temperatura y humedad.

On the right: A Comtal digital image processing system is used at the Laboratory for Applications of Remote Sensing, Purdue University, for analysis of satellite data to update land use maps.

Sur la droite : Un système Comtal de traitement numérique d'image est employé par le Laboratoire d'applications de lecture à distance de l'Université de Purdue, pour analyser des données de satellite afin de mettre à jour la cartographie d'utilisation des terres.

A la derecha: Un sistema Comtal de tratamiento de imagen utilizado en el laboratorio de aplicaciones de lectura a distancia de la Universidad de Purdue, para analizar datos de satélite, a fin de poner al día la cartografía de uso de las tierras.

CHANGING PATTERNS OF THE FAST-GROWING COMMUNICATIONS MARKETS

HORIZONS NEW POWER

THE EXPANSION OF THE TELECOMMUNICATIONS market shows little evidence of the worldwide economic turmoil of the past few years. Changes in the number of telephone stations (telephone handsets with a calling number connected directly or indirectly to the public switched network) remain the most readily available unit of measurement. Worldwide these increased by about 7 per cent per annum between 1979-1981 and Arthur D. Little estimates show a similar annual rate for 1982. The more industrialized countries are tending to grow less quickly, e.g. USA 3 per cent, and 5.5 per cent for the 20 countries with the biggest networks, although the USSR is an exception; Africa remains poorly represented among countries with the larger national networks.

Operating revenues worldwide of 170 billion US dollars in 1980 had approximately doubled since 1975 and may be expected to double again by 1990. Latin America, Oceania and Africa together account for only about 5 per cent of the total revenues; European revenues are expected to move well ahead of North American by the end of the decade. In several of the major markets tariffs have been lowered to reflect falling costs, but the rate of increase in telephone stations has been sufficient to produce a healthy growth in total operating revenues.

For the telecommunications market as a whole one can only use financial figures as a measure and here there are difficult problems of definition. Arthur D. Little has adopted a policy of defining the equipment market in terms of "shipments" as priced at the factory, i.e. excluding insurance, freight and on-site installation costs. The 20 countries with the

▷ 308

LE MARCHÉ DES TÉLÉCOMMUNICATIONS n'a pas été affecté par les mêmes turbulences que l'économie mondiale, au cours des années 1970 et 1980. Pour évaluer le développement de ce marché, l'unité de mesure la plus commode demeure le nombre des postes téléphoniques (appareils ayant un numéro relié au réseau public commuté) lequel a augmenté en moyenne de 7% pour l'ensemble du monde de 1979 à 1981 et les analyses de Arthur D. Little montrent un même taux de croissance pour 1982. Cette augmentation est toujours du même ordre dans les prévisions pour les années suivantes ; elle est cependant un peu plus faible dans les pays industrialisés, à l'exception de l'URSS (3% aux Etats-Unis et 5,5% dans les pays possédant les réseaux les plus importants). En Afrique, qui est loin derrière les autres continents à la fois en termes de densité et de croissance, peu de pays disposent de grands réseaux nationaux.

A l'échelle mondiale, les recettes d'exploitation ont à peu près doublé depuis 1975 pour atteindre 175 milliards de dollars en 1980. Elles devraient encore doubler d'ici à 1990. L'Amérique latine, l'Océanie et l'Afrique réunies ne représentent que 5% de l'ensemble de ces recettes. Quant à l'Europe, il est probable qu'elle dépassera largement l'Amérique du Nord avant la fin de la décennie. Malgré une réduction assez générale des tarifs, reflétant la baisse des coûts, les recettes ont progressé d'une manière substantielle en raison de l'augmentation du nombre des postes téléphoniques.

Seules les statistiques financières peuvent donner une idée des fluctuations du marché des télécommunications mais, dans ce domaine, il faut d'abord s'entendre sur les définitions. Selon Arthur D. Little, le matériel fourni est évalué « départ usine », compte non-tenu des frais d'assurance, de transport et d'installation. Pour les 20 pays possédant les réseaux les

▷ 308

LA EXPANSIÓN DEL MERCADO DE LAS TELECOMUNICACIONES no muestra el desorden económico mundial de los últimos años. La mejor unidad de medida sigue siendo la variación del número de teléfonos, que han aumentado en el mundo entero en un 7% anual entre 1979-1981; las estimaciones de Arthur D. Litte presentan una tasa anual similar para 1982. Los países más industrializados tienden a crecer a menor ritmo (por ejemplo EE.UU., 3%, y los 20 países con mayores redes, un 5,5%), aunque la URSS es una excepción; Africa sigue estando mal representada entre los países con grandes redes nacionales.

Los ingresos mundiales de explotación, de 170 000 millones $ EE.UU. en 1980, se habían duplicado aproximadamente desde 1975, y cabe esperar que se dupliquen de nuevo para 1990. América Latina, Oceanía y Africa representan juntas sólo un 5% de los ingresos totales; se espera que los ingresos europeos superen con mucho a los norteamericanos para finales del decenio. Las tarifas se han reducido en varios mercados principales para reflejar la disminución de los costos, pero el índice de aumento de aparatos ha sido suficiente para producir un saludable incremento de los ingresos totales de explotación.

Para el mercado de las telecomunicaciones en su conjunto, la única medida aplicable son las cifras financieras, lo cual plantea difíciles problemas de definición. Arthur D. Little ha adoptado la política de definir el mercado de equipo en términos de 'suministros' a precio de fábrica, es decir, excluidos seguro, flete y costos de instalación. Se estima que los 20 países con mayores redes telefónicas tenían unos gastos brutos de capital en sistemas de telecomunicaciones del orden de 78 600 millones $ en 1982, lo

▷ 309

A dazzling pattern of change in the Far-Eastern world.

Une configuration éblouissante de changement en Extrême-Orient.

La increíble configuración del cambio en el Lejano Oriente.

largest telephone networks are estimated to have gross capital expenditure for telecommunication systems in 1982 of about US$78.6 billion, which is an increase of some 7.4 per cent from 1981, that is rather more than the rate of growth in the number of telephone stations. These 20 countries account for approximately 83 per cent of the worldwide total. Shipments of equipment as defined were divided as 42 per cent in North America, 27 per cent in Europe and 25 per cent in Asia (including the USSR). It is projected that by 1987 Asia will exceed the European market in annual shipments.

The world market in telecommunication equipment represents about 30 per cent of the total output of electronics-based products and accounts for 10-15 per cent of world sales of electrical engineering products. About one-third of the telecommunication equipment sales consist of switching systems, one-third of transmission equipment, and one-eighth terminal equipment. The equipment industry to supply this market is itself highly concentrated; the top four manufacturers in the world account for over half the sales and the thirteen largest for over three-quarters.

The Plain Old Telephone Service (POTS), as Paul H. Henson, Chief Executive of United Telecommunications, Inc. called it some time ago, remains the backbone of the telecommunications market, but that market is already beginning to change in response to the new opportunities created by the new technologies. Not long ago virtually all telecommunication equipment went to major carriers. The ultimate users, whether companies or individuals, could have a telephone — and they could take it or leave it. Then the larger companies began to use more sophisticated ways of creating information and of communicating internally; soon they found the need to connect up all this with other parts of the company or with suppliers or customers outside. Telex was the first answer to this; then the data links. Now the pressure is on; the electronic office is a commonplace concept in firms of any size (see Box, p. 314) and even the smallest will have a computer or other electronic device creating ever more information and wanting to link up with outside respondents. So the number of users is going up; with increasing numbers goes increasing variety in their demands for services; and to meet increasing variety in demand there must be increased variety in supply.

The movement towards individual demand for tailor-made service can also be found in the area of personal services. Not only are "office" type requirements spreading into the home but there is a growing demand for selectively beamed television programs designed to provide the individual with educational or entertainment programs of his choice, coupled no doubt with suitably selected advertising. Such systems will be interactive so that the user's choice can be expressed; and once the expression of choice has started it cannot be doubted that it will develop more extensively and more insistently. The pressure to provide telephonic and TV programs via satellite in scattered or rural areas and in developing countries is in part a reflection of social conscience determined that nobody should be disadvantaged because of the place where he lives.

Yet we must never forget that the aspirations and activities of individuals are only elements in the total system. The information society, based upon the revolution in communications which makes it possible to transfer information and ideas quickly and cheaply across the world, holds the prospect of developing a truly international economy.

Western economies, at least, are likely to look to competition as a mechanism to stimulate the necessary reaction in the supply industry to the increasing variety of demand in the market and of technology to satisfy it. This may seem improbable in an industry which has the appearance, at least, of containing a series of protected areas and indeed, newly industrialized countries have been revising their procure-

▷ 310

plus importants, les investissements ont atteint environ 78,6 milliards de dollars en 1982 (+ 7,4% par rapport à 1981, un taux de croissance un peu plus élevé que celui des postes téléphoniques), ce qui représente 83% du total des investissements mondiaux. L'ensemble des livraisons de matériel se répartissait à raison de 42% pour l'Amérique du Nord, 27% pour l'Europe et 25% pour l'Asie (y compris l'URSS). En 1987, l'Asie devrait dépasser l'Europe.

Le marché mondial des équipements de télécommunication représente environ 30% de la production totale de matériel électronique et 10 à 15% des ventes mondiales de produits électrotechniques. Environ un tiers des ventes d'équipements de télécommunication est représenté par des systèmes de commutation, un tiers par du matériel de transmission et un huitième par des équipements terminaux. L'industrie des télécommunications est très concentrée : les quatre constructeurs les plus importants du monde s'en partagent la moitié, alors que les treize principaux en fournissent les trois quarts.

Le « bon vieux service téléphonique », comme l'appelait Paul H. Henson, administrateur de United Telecommunications Inc., constitue encore et toujours l'essentiel du marché des télécommunications ; toutefois, le marché a commencé à changer sous l'impact des nouvelles techniques, et les dispositifs électroniques, y compris les postes informatisés, les répondeurs automatiques et les unités de visualisation commencent à y occuper une place appréciable. Il n'y a pas si longtemps, les grandes entreprises officielles et privées de services publics étaient pratiquement les seuls acquéreurs de matériel de télécommunication. Quant aux utilisateurs, qu'il s'agisse de sociétés ou de particuliers, ils ne pouvaient obtenir que le téléphone ; c'était à prendre ou à laisser. Or, un beau jour, les grandes entreprises ont commencé à utiliser des moyens de communication plus complexes. Bientôt, elles éprouvèrent le besoin de relier leurs propres systèmes à leurs divers départements et à leurs filiales ou même d'établir des jonctions avec leurs fournisseurs et leurs clients. Ce fut d'abord le télex, puis la transmission de données. Aujourd'hui le mouvement est donné : la bureautique se banalise (voir p. 314). Plus le nombre des utilisateurs augmente, plus il devient impératif de faire face comme il convient à la diversité de la demande en matière de services.

Il existe actuellement une tendance à la fourniture de services « individualisés » répondant à des exigences personnelles. On constate non seulement que la bureautique envahit la sphère de l'habitation privée mais qu'il existe une demande croissante de programmes spécialisés permettant à l'usager de choisir à son gré des cours d'enseignement ou des émissions de divertissement, lesquelles seront certainement associées à des flashes publicitaires appropriés. A part l'introduction de tels systèmes, dits « interactifs » il convient d'insister sur l'effort entrepris pour apporter le téléphone et la télévision aux zones rurales ou faiblement peuplées et pour le généraliser dans les pays en développement, au moyen de liaisons par satellite. On se trouve là en présence d'une prise de conscience sociale imposant l'idée que nul ne doit être désavantagé en raison du lieu où il vit.

Pourtant, il ne faut pas oublier que les aspirations et les activités des gens ne sont jamais que des éléments de l'ensemble du système. La nouvelle société d'information est engendrée par la révolution en cours dans le domaine de la communication qui rend désormais possible le transfert instantané et économique de l'information et des idées. Ainsi, cette civilisation ouvre des perspectives débouchant sur l'instauration d'une véritable économie internationale dans laquelle les écarts entre les moyens de communications (et les niveaux de vie) des différents pays seraient beaucoup réduits.

Des pays industrialisés de l'Occident pourraient sans doute avoir recours à la concurrence en tant que mécanisme qui stimule l'offre face à la diversité croissante de la demande. Mais il est peu probable que cela se généralise dans une industrie qui contient toute une série de secteurs protégés. En fait les pays industrialisés de fraîche date, ont revisé leur politique d'im-

▷ 310

TOTAL WORL

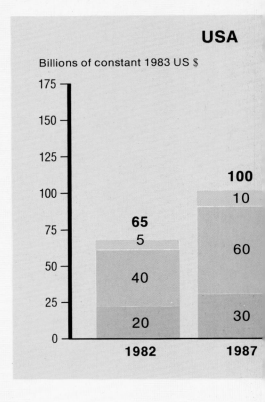

USA

Billions of constant 1983 US $

100
10

65
5
60
40
30
20

1982 **1987**

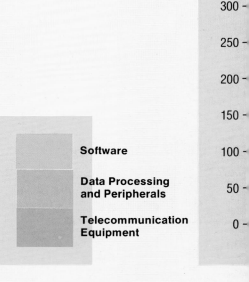

Billio

350 –

300 –

250 –

200 –

150 –

Software 100 –

Data Processing and Peripherals 50 –

Telecommunication Equipment 0 –

These estimates of demand, from a well-informed authoritative US source, show how the market for information products will evolve during the 1980s and beyond. Because of its economic size and heavy concentration of service industries, the US market will continue to represent between 40 and 50 per cent of world demand.

Traditional telecommunications products and their enhancements will experience healthy growth worldwide but even more so in countries other than the USA. However the demand for data processing and software will increase dramatically, especially as equipments installed on users' premises begin to embrace functions previously restricted to network products and as programs become more generally available.

NFORMATION PRODUCTS DEMAND

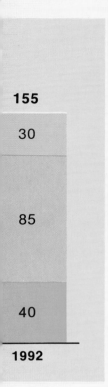

155

30

85

40

1992

OTHER COUNTRIES

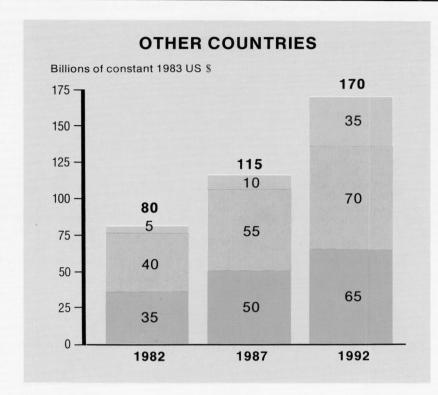

Billions of constant 1983 US $

	1982	1987	1992
Total	80	115	170
Top	5	10	35
Middle-top	40	55	70
Bottom	35	50	65

TOTAL WORLD

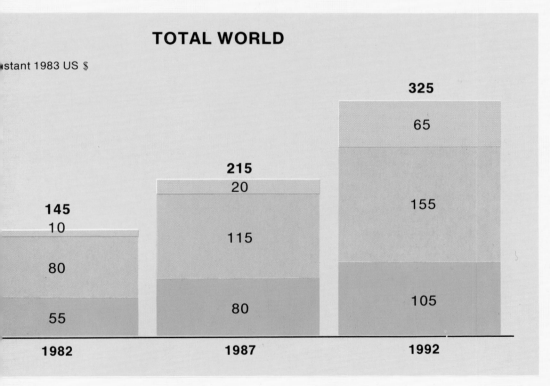

stant 1983 US $

	1982	1987	1992
Total	145	215	325
Top	10	20	65
Middle-top	80	115	155
Bottom	55	80	105

---

es prévisions, émanant d'une source américaine qui fait aurité, montrent comment le marché des produits de l'informan pourrait évoluer au cours des années 1980 et au-delà. En ison de son importance économique et de la forte concentran des industries de services, le marché des Etats-Unis ntinuera de représenter 40 à 50% de la demande mondiale.

Les produits de télécommunication traditionnels et leurs rfectionnements vont poursuivre leur progression ; quant à la mande de produits de télétraitement de données et de logiels, sa courbe de croissance sera exponentielle, dès l'instant ı les équipements installés chez les utilisateurs commencent à remplir les fonctions qui étaient précédemment onopolisées.

Estas previsiones, que proceden de una fuente estadounidense fidedigna, muestran la marcha del mercado de productos de información durante el presente decenio y después. Debido a su importancia económica y a la fuerte concentración de industrias de servicios, el mercado estadounidense seguirá representando del 40 al 50% de la demanda mundial.

Los productos de telecomunicaciones tradicionales crecerán fuertemente en el mundo entero, y en algunos países más que en EE.UU. Sin embargo, la demanda de tratamiento de datos y de soporte lógico aumentará espectacularmente, sobre todo cuando los equipos instalados en los locales de los usuarios comiencen a abarcar funciones limitadas anteriormente a las redes, y cuando se generalice el uso de los programas.

---

que supone un aumento del 7,7% desde 1981, algo más que la tasa de crecimiento del número de aparatos. Esos 20 países representan alrededor del 83% del total mundial. Los suministros de equipo definidos se dividieron así: 42% en América del Norte, 27% en Europa, y 25% en Asia (incluida la URSS). Se prevé que, para 1977, Asia superará al mercado europeo en suministros anuales.

El mercado mundial de equipo de telecomunicaciones representa alrededor del 30% de la producción total a base de electrónica, y del 10 al 15% de las ventas mundiales de productos de ingeniería eléctrica. Aproximadamente un tercio de las ventas de equipo de telecomunicación consisten en sistemas de conmutación, un tercio en equipo de transmisión, y un octavo en equipo terminal. La industria de equipamiento para proveer a ese mercado está muy concentrada; los cuatro principales fabricantes del mundo representan más de la mitad de las ventas, y los treinta mayores, más de los tres cuartos.

El « viejo servicio telefónico », como lo denominó hace algún tiempo Paul H. Henson, Jefe Ejecutivo de United Telecommunications, Inc., sigue siendo la base del mercado de telecomunicaciones, pero ese mercado comienza ya a cambiar debido a las nuevas oportunidades que crea la tecnología moderna. No hace mucho, prácticamente todo el equipo de telecomunicaciones iba a parar a las principales empresas. Los usuarios finales, ya fueran compañías o individuos, podían tener un teléfono, y tomarlo o dejarlo. Luego, las grandes empresas comenzaron a emplear medios más sofisticados de crear información y de comunicar interiormente; pronto sintieron la necesidad de conectar todo ello con otras partes de la empresa o con proveedores o clientes del exterior. La primera respuesta fue el télex. Luego, los enlaces de datos. Ahora continúa la presión; la oficina electrónica es una noción común en firmas de cualquier tamaño (véase el recuadro de la pág. 314), e incluso la más pequeña dispondrá de un computador u otro dispositivo electrónico que creará cada vez más información y deseará conectar con correspondientes del exterior. Por tanto, el número de usuarios aumenta, lo que conlleva una mayor variedad de demandas de servicios; y para atenderla tiene que haber un suministro más diverso.

La tendencia a la demanda individual de servicios especiales puede darse también en el sector de servicios personales. No sólo los requisitos de tipo "oficina" se extienden al hogar, sino que se analiza la creciente demanda de programas de televisión selectivos para ofrecer al individuo las actividades educativas y recreativas que elija, unidas a una publicidad seleccionada debidamente. Esos sistemas serán interactivos, para que pueda expresarse la selección del usuario; y una vez iniciada esa elección, no cabe duda de que se desarrollará más y con mayor insistencia. La presión para proporcionar programas telefónicos y TV vía satélite a zonas dispersas o rurales y de países en desarrollo es, en parte, un reflejo de la conciencia social de que nadie debe resultar desfavorecido a causa del lugar en que viva.

Pero no debemos olvidar que las aspiraciones y actividades de los individuos son sólo elementos del sistema total. La sociedad de la información, basada en la revolución de las comunicaciones que permite transferir información e ideas rápida y económicamente a través del mundo, entraña la perspectiva de una economía verdaderamente internacional.

Economías occidentales. Es probable que, al menos las economías occidentales, consideren la competencia como un mecanismo para estimular la reacción necesaria en la industria de abastecimiento a la variedad cada vez mayor de demanda en el mercado y de la tecnología para satisfacerla. Esto parece improbable en una industria que aparentemente contiene una serie de áreas protegidas, por lo que países recién industrializados revisan sus políticas y leyes sobre adquisición, a favor de la fabricación nacional. Los proveedores han de atender esas nuevas exigen

▷ 311

ment policies and laws to favour home manufacturing. Suppliers must meet these new requirements, and in this respect it seems that the movement is towards increased protectionism rather than increased competition.

Signs of liberalization of the market are becoming apparent particularly in some of the more industrialized countries. The Federal Communications Commission in the USA, has for many years actively encouraged competition within that country and many European suppliers are seeking to take advantage of that. Japan is taking steps to open its market, albeit on a limited scale, to imported equipment. The removal of the monopoly position of British Telecom is designed to allow some increased competition in common carriage and more especially to liberalize the sales of equipment ownership. This kind of change will mean that suppliers must adjust to different buyers, in much the same way as the breakdown in the distinction between traditional communications and information processing must lead to the forging of many new trading partnerships.

The movement towards deregulation goes along with liberalization of the market. The development of microwave radio and cellular telephony in the USA and the UK has been possible only after the relaxation of regulations. On the other hand the need to have systems which are compatible internationally brings pressure to settle standards. Standardization will have the same broad advantages and disadvantages in telecommunications as in any other industry. In addition to ensuring compatibility, it provides a basis for establishing quality in systems and their components, and it gives electronics manufacturers a necessary planning base and also a prospect of the economic advantages of long runs. The importance of high volume production to keep prices down is illustrated by OECD which estimates price levels in 1982: European prices of switching equipment were 60 to 100 per cent higher than in the USA, and those of transmission equipment 40 per cent higher; these differences are attributed in the main to high production levels. The advantages of high volume production are particularly pressing for an industry where rapid technological advance is seen to demand major research and development expenditure. The manufacturers seek ever larger markets.

The development of international technical standards has not so far kept pace with technological advance. There is a danger that all these factors will militate against competition. If the manufacturers do not see it that way, it certainly reduces the choice of alternative suppliers available to the buyer. A burgeoning of new industry, bristling with ideas of the best way to resolve its problems, must not allow its initiatives to be crippled. The battle over the market for viewdata equipment provided an example of the problems. Up to 1981, Canada, the FRG, Japan and the UK had all been developing different systems. By agreeing that year to merge their national standards into a European one they took an important step forward, creating a single market big enough to enable manufacturers to achieve significant production volumes. However, AT&T have their own design in North America; standardization requires the data bases of one to run on the terminals of the other; competition requires one to demonstrate that it is better than the other.

Central exchange, or switching systems together with transmission equipment account for roughly two-thirds of the telecommunication equipment market, which the OECD expects to grow by 50 per cent in the next five years because of the introduction of new generation systems. Here, surely, is a market to attract competitive suppliers. Indeed, in switching some sixteen major systems — developed at a total R&D cost which almost certainly exceeds US$6 billion — are competing for annual world sales of some US$12 billion, of which only about 20 per cent is

portation pour protéger les intérêts de leurs constructeurs locaux et favorisent ainsi la résurgence du protectionnisme, à l'encontre de la concurrence.

Des signes de libéralisation commencent à se manifester dans certains pays fortement industrialisés. Aux Etats-Unis, par exemple, la FCC encourage depuis plusieurs années la concurrence sur le plan intérieur et de nombreux constructeurs européens cherchent à en profiter. Le Japon prend certaines mesures pour ouvrir son marché à l'importation de matériel. La suppression du monopole de British Telecom a pour but de favoriser la concurrence entre les entreprises de télécommunication, de libéraliser et d'élargir les ventes d'équipements. Les fournisseurs devront donc s'adapter aux exigences de la clientèle. D'autre part, la distinction entre la communication traditionnelle et le traitement de l'information conduira à une rénovation des ententes et à la création de nouvelles associations commerciales.

La libéralisation signifie que les transactions commerciales cessent d'être assujetties à une réglementation. Aux Etats-Unis comme au Royaume-Uni, la radiotéléphonie mobile doit précisément son nouvel essor à cet assouplissement des règlements. Il n'en reste pas moins que la compatibilité des systèmes à l'échelle internationale impose une normalisation qui présente les mêmes avantages et les mêmes inconvénients que dans n'importe quelle autre branche industrielle. En garantissant la compatibilité et la qualité des systèmes, les normes donnent à l'industrie électronique une base de planification indispensable et la perspective d'avantages économiques à long terme.

La production de masse, permettant de maintenir les prix à un niveau raisonnable, a fait l'objet d'une étude de l'OCDE dans laquelle il est indiqué que les prix européens des équipements de commutation sont de 60 à 100% supérieurs à ceux des Etats-Unis tandis que pour le matériel de transmission, l'écart atteint 40% ; il est attribué à la différence des volumes de production. Ainsi, les avantages découlant de hauts niveaux de production présentent un intérêt particulier pour l'industrie, lorsque des progrès technologiques rapides imposent d'importantes dépenses de recherche et de développement et exigent la conquêtes de marchés toujours plus vastes.

L'élaboration de normes techniques suit difficilement le progrès. Il est évident qu'une industrie nouvelle, bouillonnante d'idées, ne peut se laisser arrêter dans son élan. La bataille qui s'est engagée sur le marché des équipements *viewdata* est un exemple de cette difficulté. Jusqu'en 1981, le Canada, le Japon, le Royaume-Uni et la République Fédérale d'Allemagne mettaient au point séparément leurs systèmes respectifs. En adoptant une norme européenne unique, elles ont créé un marché unifié de dimensions suffisantes pour assurer de grands volumes de production. De son côté AT&T a sa propre conception pour l'Amérique du Nord. Or, la normalisation exige que les bases de données puissent être utilisées indifféremment sur les terminaux de toutes les entreprises intéressées. La concurrence joue simplement sur la preuve qu'une conception est meilleure qu'une autre.

Les systèmes de commutation et de transmission représentent à peu près les deux tiers du marché des équipements de télécommunication, lequel devrait — selon l'OCDE — augmenter de 50% en cinq ans, en raison de l'apparition de nouveaux systèmes. En matière de commutation, 16 grands systèmes — dont la mise au point a coûté plus de 6 milliards de dollars — sont en concurrence sur un marché annuel de 12 milliards de dollars dont 20% seulement sont impliqués dans la concurrence internationale. Il semble donc que la majeure partie des transactions se déroule sur des marchés nationaux protégés. Pourtant, aucun de ces systèmes ne paraît véritablement rentable, de sorte que certains gouvernements pourraient être tentés d'élargir leur part du marché, en se tournant vers les pays en développement et en jouant sur les crédits à l'exportation ou sur d'autres procédés destinés à soutenir leurs constructeurs nationaux.

▷ 312

▷ 312

NEWSPAPERS

Publishers, broadcasters and other media companies have been repositioning themselves to deal with new ways of collecting, packaging and distributing information. The map opposite shows the kind of diversification by seven US companies generally classified as newspaper publishers: Dow Jones Co., Gannett Co., Harte-Hanks Communications, Lee Enterprises, New York Times Co., The Times Mirror Co. and The Washington Post Co. The map shows great variety in the diversification of newspaper groups but there is some focus of interest in the emerging market for cable/TV services and, more generally, in the direct-to-home news and information/data services. The loudspeaker and the screen are supplementing the printed word: they could be dominating in a decade.

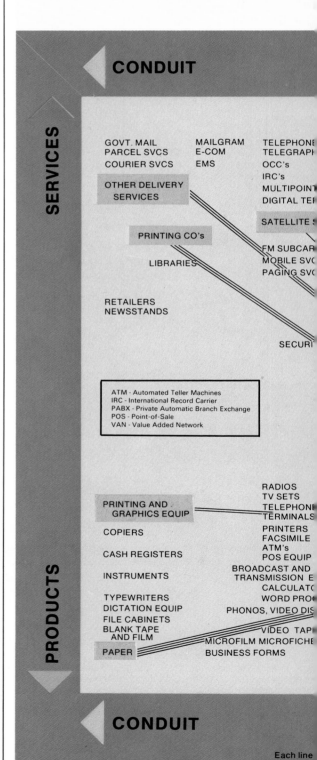

CONDUIT

SERVICES

GOVT. MAIL
PARCEL SVCS
COURIER SVCS

MAILGRAM
E-COM
EMS

TELEPHONE
TELEGRAPH
OCC's
IRC's
MULTIPOINT
DIGITAL TE

OTHER DELIVERY
SERVICES

SATELLITE S

PRINTING CO's

FM SUBCAR
MOBILE SVC
PAGING SVC

LIBRARIES

RETAILERS
NEWSSTANDS

SECURI

ATM - Automated Teller Machines
IRC - International Record Carrier
PABX - Private Automatic Branch Exchange
POS - Point-of-Sale
VAN - Value Added Network

PRINTING AND
GRAPHICS EQUIP

RADIOS
TV SETS
TELEPHONE
TERMINALS

COPIERS

PRINTERS
FACSIMILE
ATM's
POS EQUIP

CASH REGISTERS

BROADCAST AND
TRANSMISSION E
CALCULATO
WORD PRO
PHONOS, VIDEO DIS

INSTRUMENTS

TYPEWRITERS
DICTATION EQUIP
FILE CABINETS
BLANK TAPE
AND FILM

PRODUCTS

VIDEO TAP
MICROFILM MICROFICHE
BUSINESS FORMS

PAPER

CONDUIT

Each line

JRN TO TELECOMS FOR GROWTH

éditeurs de journaux, comme les autres industries et ser-
es de l'information, se re-situent par rapport aux nouvelles
thodes de recueillir, de présenter et de distribuer l'informa-
n. Cette carte-diagramme montre des stratégies de diversi-
ation adoptées par sept grands groupes de presse améri-
ns : Dow Jones & Co., Gannett Co., Harte-Hanks Communi-
ions, Lee Enterprises, New York Times Co., The Times Mirror
and The Washington Post Co. On peut noter une diversifi-
ion très variée de la part de ces groupes, mais aussi une
taine concentration sur le nouveau marché de l'information
ective câblée, et plus généralement sur celui de l'accès
ect par satellite à la télévision et aux services de télématique
égrés. L'audio-visuel supplémente aujourd'hui le mot
rimé : dans dix ans il pourrait le dominer.

Los editores de periódicos, las empresas de radiodifusión y
otras dedicadas a la información se han remodelado para
adaptarse a las nuevas formas de reunir, empaquetar y distribuir información. El gráfico muestra la diversificación de siete
grupos de prensa estadounidenses: Dow Jones Co., Jannett Co.,
Harte-Hanks Communications, Lee Enterprises, New York Times Co., The Times Mirror Co. y The Washington Post. Co. Este
gráfico de la «Industria de la información» muestra la gran
variedad de la diversificación de los grupos de prensa, pero
existe cierto interés en el nuevo mercado de los servicios por
cable/TV y, más generalmente, en los servicios de noticias
directas al hogar y de información/datos. El altavoz y la
pantalla son suplementos de la palabra impresa.

cias, y a este respecto parece que se tiende a intensificar el proteccionismo, en lugar de la competencia.
Hay indicios de liberalización del mercado, sobre todo en
algunos de los países más industrializados. La Federal Communications Commission de EE.UU. alienta
activamente la competencia en el país, desde hace
años, y bastantes proveedores europeos tratan de
sacar provecho de ello. Japón está tomando medidas
para abrir su mercado, aunque en grado limitado, a
la importación de equipo. La supresión de la posición monopolista de British Telecom está destinada
a impulsar algo la competencia entre las empresas
del sector, y más especialmente a liberalizar las ventas de equipo. Este cambio significará que los proveedores habrán de ajustarse a distintos compradores, lo mismo que la distinción entre comunicaciones
tradicionales y procesamiento de la información ha
de llevar a la creación de muchas asociaciones comerciales nuevas.

A la liberalización del mercado va unida la tendencia a suprimir controles. El desarrollo de las comunicaciones de microondas y la telefonía celular en
EE.UU. y el RU sólo ha sido posible después de
suavizar la legislación. Por otro lado, la necesidad de
disponer de sistemas internacionalmente compatibles influye en el establecimiento de normas. Las
ventajas y los inconvenientes de la normalización
serán los mismos en las telecomunicaciones que en
cualquier otra industria. Además de asegurar la
compatibilidad, ofrece una base para establecer la
calidad de sistemas y sus componentes, facilita a los
fabricantes de electrónica la planificación necesaria,
y brinda una perspectiva de las ventajas económicas
de las grandes series. La importancia de la producción en gran volumen para reducir los precios la
ilustran las estimaciones de la OCDE de que los
precios europeos de equipo de conmutación son un
60% más altos que en EE.UU., y los del equipo de
transmisión un 40%; estas diferencias de costo se
atribuyen sobre todo a los elevados niveles de producción, que son muy importantes para una industria donde se estima que el rápido avance tecnológico exigirá considerables gastos en investigación y
desarrollo. Los fabricantes buscan mercados cada
vez mayores.

La evolución de las normas técnicas internacionales no ha
seguido el ritmo del avance tecnológico. Existe el
peligro de que todos estos factores sean contrarios a
la competencia. Si los fabricantes no lo ven así, se
reducirá sin duda la elección de otros proveedores
para el comprador. La nueva industria, con abun-
dantes ideas sobre la mejor manera de resolver sus
problemas, no debe permitir que se frenen sus iniciativas. La batalla por el mercado de equipo de
videotexto ofrece un ejemplo de los problemas.
Hasta 1981, Canadá, el RU, Japón y la RFA habían
desarrollado sistemas distintos. Al acordar ese año
fusionar sus normas nacionales en una europea,
dieron un importante paso, creando un solo mercado
suficientemente grande para que los fabricantes
puedan producir en gran volumen. Sin embargo,
AT&T tiene su propio diseño en América del Norte;
la normalización exige que las bases de datos de uno
pasen a los terminales de otro; la competencia obliga
a demostrar que uno es superior a otro.

Las centrales principales o los sistemas de conmutación, junto con el equipo de transmisión, representan alrededor de los dos tercios del mercado
de equipo de telecomunicación, que la OCDE espera
crezca un 50% en los próximos cinco años, debido a
la introducción de nuevos sistemas de generación. Se
trata seguramente de un mercado que atraerá a proveedores competitivos. En efecto, conmutando unos
16 sistemas principales — desarrollados con un costo
total de IyD que rebasará sin duda los 6000 millones $ — compiten por unas ventas anuales mundia-
les del orden de 12 000 millones $, limitándose la
competencia internacional a un 20% nada más. Por
tanto, probablemente la mayoría sea sostenida por
mercados nacionales protegidos; así y todo, incluso
con sustanciales ventas en mercados nacionales,
puede dudarse de que la rentabilidad de muchos de
los sistemas sea satisfactoria. Por esta y otras razones,

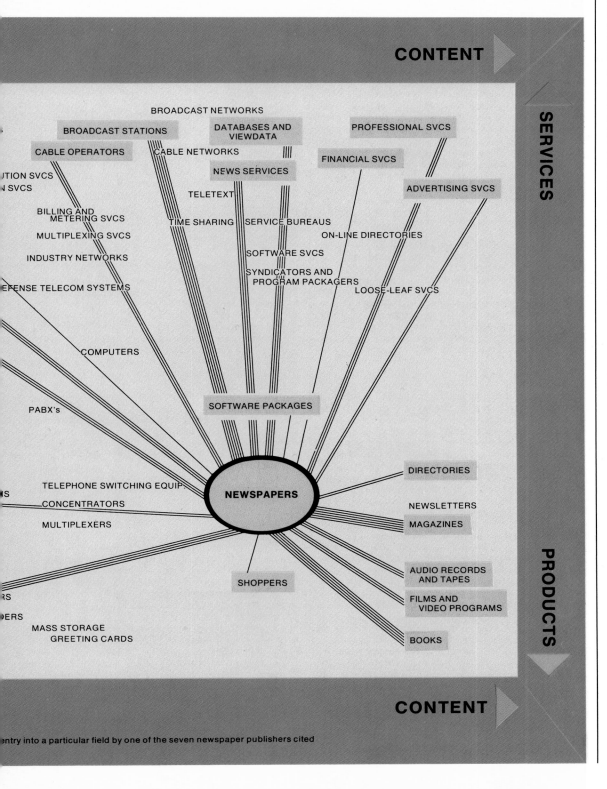

entry into a particular field by one of the seven newspaper publishers cited

▷ 313

open to international competition. Thus the majority of these are likely to be sustained by protected home markets; yet even with substantial home market sales it may be doubted whether many of the individual systems will yield a satisfactory return on investment. For this and other reasons some governments may be tempted to extend efforts to secure export contracts, expecially in the developing regions, by export credits and other devices in support of domestic manufacturers.

Each of the six regional markets has its own pattern of established competition, but the patterns must be expected to change and some signs of change can already be seen. In the USA the influence of deregulation is very powerful. The result of this is that even in the long-distance telephone market, AT&T is widely expected to lose its dominating 95-96% of the market; an AT&T official has even forecast that this share could fall to 50 per cent within five years, partly as a result of the divestiture of its local operating companies, partly because of new competitors, some using satellites. What the effect of this will be on tariffs and service to the user is much debated. Meanwhile, in the equipment market AT&T will compete with ITT, Siemens, GTE, and other established leaders, and overseas suppliers, especially European manufacturers, are hoping to increase their sales in the USA.

In the European market, apart from moves to deregulate in the UK as already mentioned, support for national manufacturers remains an important influence. However, the markets are by no means closed; for example, in West Germany, in addition to orders for EWS-Digital switching equipment from Siemens, the Bundespost has ordered PRA/D and System 12 exchanges from Philips and ITT respectively for a one-year evaluation program, after which the Bundespost will order production quantities of digital switching systems.

One way of overcoming the problem of national boundaries is the formation of joint ventures such as that announced in principle between AT&T and Philips to market electronic switching systems outside the USA. No doubt such a company will look to Asia, the Middle East and South America for most of its business. In these markets there will be plenty of competition from European and Japanese suppliers who have invested heavily to try and develop them. A recent OECD report indicated that most the OPEC contracts have now been awarded and demand in developing countries is expected to grow less strongly in the 1980s than in the previous decade.

Another emerging competitive pattern is the integration of the range of services offered by suppliers through reorganization, expansion or acquisition. Thus, an AT&T subsidiary, AT&T Information Systems, has been created to provide customer premises equipment, data communications processing and storage, and network management. This restructuring is expected to have widespread effects in the US telecommunications industry. Similarly, L. M. Ericsson has been expanding from its traditional telephone business to include the manufacture and marketing of office systems and products. The private office automation market may prove less liable to national politics, and so more open to choice on technical merit than public switching systems are. Other major telecommunications manufacturers are expected to make similar transitions.

It is not known yet if expenditures in the mature markets will shift most vigorously in the direction of non-voice services and facilities (e.g. teletex, electronic mail) or towards new technology to enhance existing telephone services such as fiber optic links. In the short term the telephone carriers' major investment must be in the replacement of analog equipment with digital systems and the expansion of their long-haul networks with fiber optic links.

□

Chacun des six marchés régionaux du monde a son propre style de concurrence mais il faut s'attendre à des changements qui s'annoncent déjà par des signes avant-coureurs. Aux Etats-Unis, l'influence de la libéralisation a été très puissante. Les mesures de levée de la réglementation ont eu pour conséquence même sur le marché téléphonique interurbain à grande distance. AT&T va certainement perdre sa position dominante qui pourrait tomber de 80% à 50%, au cours des cinq prochaines années, en partie à la suite du démembrement des ses sociétés locales d'exploitation et en partie en raison de l'arrivée de nouveaux concurrents dont un certain nombre utilisent des liaisons par satellite. Encore s'agit-il de savoir quelles vont être les répercussions de ces bouleversements sur les tarifs et les services. De plus, si AT&T est désormais autorisée à entrer en concurrence avec les grands constructeurs, tels que ITT, Siemens, GTE et d'autres encore, les constructeurs étrangers, notamment européens, espèrent bien, quant à eux, augmenter leurs ventes aux États Unis.

Sur le marché européen, en dehors des mesures de libéralisation précitées qui ont été prises au Royaume-Uni, l'appui assuré aux constructeurs nationaux demeure un élément important. Cela ne signifie nullement que les marchés sont fermés. Par exemple, en dehors des commandes d'équipements de commutation numérique EWS qui doivent être fournis par Siemens, la Deutsche Bundespost a commandé respectivement à Philips et à ITT des centraux PRA/D et System 12 à titre d'essai dans le cadre de son programme budgétaire annuel, après quoi elle placera des commandes pour le système ou les systèmes de son choix.

L'un des moyens de surmonter le problème des frontières nationales consiste à fonder des entreprises communes comme celles qui vont en principe lier AT&T et Philips, en vue de la commercialisation de systèmes de commutation électronique en dehors des États-Unis. Il ne fait aucun doute qu'une nouvelle société de ce type s'intéressera à l'Asie, au Moyen-Orient et à l'Amérique du Sud pour écouler la plupart de ses produits. Elle doit s'attendre à rencontrer sur ces marchés une forte concurrence de constructeurs européens et japonais qui ont investi lourdement pour les conquérir. Un récent rapport de l'OCDE indique que la plupart des contracts de l'OPEP ont déjà été octroyés, et que la demande des pays en développement va être nettement moins importante que pendant la décennie de 1970.

Un autre changement d'allure du marché est dû à l'intégration de la gamme des différents services offerts par les fournisseurs, par divers moyens de réorganisation, d'expansion ou d'acquisition. C'est ainsi que « AT&T Information Systems », filiale de AT&T, a été créée pour fournir des équipements jusqu'ici réservés au Bell System et pour assurer le traitement et l'enregistrement de données, ainsi que la gestion des réseaux. Cette restructuration devrait avoir des conséquences importantes dans l'industrie des télécommunications des Etats-Unis. De même, L.M. Ericsson a étendu ses activités téléphoniques traditionnelles pour s'engager dans la fabrication et la commercialisation de systèmes et produits de bureautique. Le marché privé de l'automatisation des travaux de bureau pourrait être moins assujetti aux politiques nationales et, en définitive, se révéler plus ouvert à une sélection sur la base des mérites techniques que ne le sont les systèmes de commutation pour les réseaux publics. Il est probable que d'autres fabricants importants suivront cet exemple.

On peut se demander si le marché s'orientera plus nettement en direction des services et des installations non téléphoniques (télétex, courrier électronique) ou de la nouvelle technologie qui tend à perfectionner les services téléphoniques en s'appuyant sur la technique de transmission par fibres optiques. A court terme, les services téléphoniques seront amenés à remplacer leurs équipements analogiques par du matériel numérique et à développer leurs réseaux interurbains en mettant en exploitation des liaisons à fibres optiques.

□

The plans of national expenditure on expansion or enhancement of telecommunications networks and facilities include:
Canada - With a fiber optic link (3,200 km), Canada is committed to a further high-capacity transmission system and more domestic satellite facilities.
Europe - In the Federal Republic of Germany: the Bundespost's "Bigfon" optical fiber network; a digital telephone switching scheme; four pilot cable television projects with experiments in Ludwigshafen and Munich and a cable service in Berlin and Dortmund. In France: CATV network expansion; electronic telephone directory and terminals, viewdata teletex services and telefax experiments. In the United Kingdom a privately owned public network to compete with some of the services provided by British Telecom; ten cities awarded pilot projects for cable

Enhanced Telephone

Fiber Optic Links

Digital Local Exchanges

Digital PBX and KTS

Cellular Radiotelephone

Air-ground Radiotelephone

television, starting with Liverpool and Glasgow. Racal Industries (UK) and Oak Industries (USA) form a joint venture to market cable television in Europe.
Japan - Nippon Telegraph and Telephone (NTT) which already provides a facsimile service over the public switched telephone network, plans a communications satellite for facsimile, teleconferencing, data banks, and other non-telephone services, cellular mobile radio telephones and improved telephone facilities (e.g. push-button telephone sets and residential keyphone systems).
United States - AT&T has begun service on a fiber optic link (Washington-New York-Boston) as well as a new series of satellites for television distribution service, video teleconferencing, and augmentation of the long-haul network. Other common carriers are expanding their satellite and data communications facilities to accomodate increasing voice and non-voice traffic.
USSR - Expenditures during the 11th Five Year Plan (1981-1985) are mostly for basic system elements rather than replacement of technology; expansion of satellite communications will continue at an increased rate.
Others - Brazil will expand its basic telephone facilities including a domsat project; Mexico will install digital switches and its own domsat network; The People's Republic of China is negotiating "technology transfer"; Korea and other countries will concentrate on basic equipment rather than high technology; Australia is planning a digital data network with packet switching, and its initial domsat system; a trans-Atlantic fiber optic cable "TAT-8" (3,570 miles), by a consortium of nations, will be laid in the 80s.

In the longer term the succesful meeting of new demand with further novel services will depend upon the industry's innovative flair and the skill and extent of its research and development effort. These efforts typically rely at present on close co-operation between the service providers and the equipment manufacturers, with the former paying a key role in initiating new effort and in subsidising the R&D of manufacturers.

With the limited role of private and export markets there has not been much scope for competition in equipment design. This may change with greater liberalization of the industry.

OEMAND WITH NOVEL SERVICES

s plans nationaux d'investissement dans les 20 marchés incipaux comprennent :

nada - Avec une liaison par câble optique de 3200 km, le nada s'oriente vers la transmission à large bande et vers le ais par satellite.

rope - En République Fédérale d'Allemagne : réseau sur fibres tiques « Bigfon » de la Bundespost ; la commutation télé- onique numérique ; des satellites de radiodiffusion directe et télécommunications ; quatre projets pilotes de télévision blée avec essais à Ludwigshafen et Munich et un service de ble à Berlin et Dortmund. En France, expansion de la télévi- n câblée, l'annuaire téléphonique électronique avec termi- ux ; services vidéotex/télétex et expérimentation du téléfax. x Pays-Bas, en Belgique et au Danemark, projet de législation

Los planes nacionales de inversión en los 20 mercados princi- pales comprenden:

Canadá - Con un enlace por cable óptico de 3200 km, Canadá se orienta hacia la transmisión de banda ancha y los enlaces por satélite.

Europa - En la RFA, red por fibras ópticas "Bigfon" de la Bundespost; la conmutación telefónica digital; satélites de ra- diodifusión directa y de telecomunicaciones; cuatro proyectos piloto de televisión por cable con pruebas en Ludwigshafen y Munich, y un servicio de cable en Berlín y Dortmund. En Francia, expansión de la TV por cable; guía telefónica electrónica y terminales; servicios videotex/teletex y experimentación de telefax. En Países Bajos, Bélgica y Dinamarca, proyecto de legislación para la televisión por cable privada. En Gran Breta-

Electronic Telephones	Electronic Mail
Multifeature Residential Telephones	High-speed Data Communications
Electronic Directories	Packet Switching
	Video Conferencing
Other New Services and Facilities	Wide-Area Radio Paging
	TV direct broadcast Satellites
Viewdata, Teletext, Videotex	Modernized Telegraph/Telex

Source: Arthur D. Little (WTIP).

r la télévision câblée privée. En Grande-Bretagne, un réseau lic à capitaux privés concurrencera certains services de tish Telecom ; projets de télévision câblée autorisés dans dix es, à commencer avec Liverpool et Glasgow.

on - NTT exploite déjà un service de télécopie sur le réseau télécommunications pour la télécopie, la téléconférence, les ques de données etc. ; des services radiotéléphoniques éolaires et des services téléphoniques complémentaires éliorés (par exemple, appareils à clavier et à mémoire).

ts-Unis - AT&T a commencé une liaison par câble optique ashington-New York-Boston, et opère avec une nouvelle série satellites pour la transmission de la télévision, la vidéo- nférence, et pour étendre le réseau à grande distance. D'au- s entreprises de télécommunications étendent leurs services satellites et de traitement des données pour répondre à la mande croissante en téléphonie et en télématique.

SS - Dans le cadre du onzième plan quinquennal (1981-1985) investissement sera principalement attribué à l'extension des eau, plutôt que sa modernisation : le développement des écommunications par satellite sera poursuivi.

tres pays - Le Brésil développera ses services téléphoniques, tamment par satellite ; le Mexique installera des commuta- urs numériques et établira son réseau Domsat ; la République pulaire de Chine négocie un « transfert de technologie » ; la rée et d'autres pays axeront leurs efforts sur les équipe- nts de base plutôt que les techniques de pointe ; l'Australie voit un réseau numérique avec commutation par paquets et pare son premier système Domsat. Un nouveau câble opti- e transatlantique « TAT-8 » de 5728 km, financé par un nsortium de nations, est prévu pour 1988.

A long terme la satisfaction d'une demande croissante pour utres nouveaux services dépendra de la capacité novatrice l'industrie et de l'excellence de ses efforts de recherche et de veloppement. Ceci dépend à présent dans une large mesure ne étroite collaboration entre prestataires de services et ricants d'équipements. L'ampleur très restreinte des dé- uchés dans le secteur privé ou dans les marchés d'exporta- n n'a guère encouragé l'innovation. Ceci pourrait changer ec la libéralisation des marchés industrialisés. Il est évident e le coût élevé et croissant de la recherche impose un rgissement des marchés et une plus forte concurrence.

ña, una red pública con capital privado competirá con ciertos servicios de British Telecom; proyectos de televisión por cable autorizados en 10 ciudades, comenzando por Liverpool y Glas- gow. Racal Industries (RU) y Oak Industries (EE.UU.) se han asociado para explotar la televisión por cable en Europa.

Japón - NTT explota un servicio de facsímil en la red telefónica pública con conmutación, y proyecta un satélite de comunica- ciones para facsímil, teleconferencia, bancos de datos y otros servicios no telefónicos; teléfonos radiocelulares y mejores servicios (aparatos de teclado y de memoria).

Estados Unidos - AT&T ha iniciado un enlace de fibras ópticas Washington-Nueva York-Boston, y explota una nueva serie de satélites para transmisión de televisión, videoconferencia, y para aumentar la red de larga distancia. Otras empresas ex- tienden sus servicios de satélites y tratamiento de datos para atender la creciente demanda de telefonía y telemática.

URSS - En el 11° plan quinquenal (1981-1985) las inversiones se destinarán, sobre todo, a ampliar la red, más bien que a modernizarla; proseguirá la expansión de las comunicaciones por satélite.

Otros - Brasil extenderá sus servicios telefónicos básicos, incluido un proyecto Domsat; México instalará conmutadores digitales y su propia red Domsat; la Republica Popular de China está negociando "transferencia de tecnología"; Corea y otros países se concentrarán en equipo básico en lugar de alta tecnología; Australia proyecta una red digital de datos con conmutación de paquetes, y su sistema inicial Domsat. En 1988 se tenderá un nuevo cable óptico transatlántico "TAT-8", de 5728 km, financiado por un consorcio de naciones.

A largo plazo, la atención de la nueva demanda con servicios modernos dependerá de la innovación de la industria y de la calidad y extensión de su investigación y desarrollo, en una estrecha cooperación entre proveedores de servicios y fabri- cantes de equipo, desempeñando los primeros un papel vital en el nuevo esfuerzo y en la subvención de la IyD de los fabrican- tes. Con el limitado papel de los mercados privados y de exportación, no hay muchas posibilidades de competencia en el diseño de equipo. Esto puede cambiar con la mayor liberaliza- ción de la industria. Es evidente que el elevado y creciente costo de la investigación impone la ampliación de los mercados y una mayor competencia.

algunos gobiernos pueden sentir la tentación de ampliar sus actividades para lograr contratos de ex- portación, sobre todo en regiones en desarrollo, me- diante créditos a la exportación y otras medidas para ayudar a los fabricantes nacionales.

Cada uno de los seis mercados regionales tiene su propia estructura competitiva, pero es de esperar que esas estructuras cambien, y ya se vislumbran algunos indicios.

En EE.UU., la influencia de la liberalización es muy fuerte. Como resultado, incluso en el mercado telefónico de larga distancia, lo normal es que AT&T pierda su parte dominante del 95-96%; un funciona- rio de AT&T ha previsto incluso que esa parte puede caer al 50% en cinco años, debido en parte al despo- seimiento de sus compañías de explotación locales, y en parte a los nuevos competidores, algunos de los cuales emplearán satélites. Se discute mucho del efecto que tendrá esto sobre las tarifas y los servicios al usuario. Entretanto, en el mercado de equipo, AT&T podrá competir con ITT, Siemens, GTE y otros líderes establecidos, a pesar de que los pro- veedores del exterior, sobre todo los fabricantes eu- ropeos, aumenten sus ventas en EE.UU.

En el mercado europeo, aparte de algunas medidas de libre comercio en el Reino Unido, como ya se ha dicho, el apoyo a los fabricantes nacionales sigue influyendo mucho. Sin embargo, los mercados no están cerrados; por ejemplo, en Alemania Occiden- tal, aparte de los pedidos de equipo de conmutación digital EWS de Siemens, la Bundespost ha solicitado centrales PRA/D y System 12 de Philips e ITT, res- pectivamente, para un programa de evaluación de un año.

Una manera de superar el problema de las fron- teras es la creación de empresas mixtas, como la anunciada, en principio, entre AT&T y Philips, para comercializar sistemas de conmutación electrónicos fuera de EE.UU. Sin duda, tal empresa orientará la mayoría de sus actividades hacia Asia, el Oriente Medio y América del Sur. En esos mercados habrá mucha competencia de proveedores europeos y ja- poneses que han hecho grandes inversiones y tra- tarán de desarrollarlas. Según un informe reciente de la OCDE, la mayoría de los contratos de la OPEP ya se han concedido, y se espera que la demanda en los países en desarrollo crezca menos en los años 1980 que en la década anterior.

Otra nueva estructura competitiva es la integra- ción de la gama de servicios ofrecidos por proveedo- res mediante la reorganización, la expansión o la adquisición. Así, la filial de AT&T, AT&T Informa- tion Systems, se ha creado para proporcionar equipo de locales de abonado, procesamiento y almacena- miento de datos, y gestión de redes. Se cree que esta reestructuración influirá mucho en la industria de las telecomunicaciones de EE.UU. Del mismo modo, L. M. Ericsson ha extendido sus actividades telefónicas tradicionales para abarcar la fabricación y comer- cialización de sistemas y productos de oficina.

El mercado privado de automatización de oficinas puede estar menos sometido a los políticos naciona- les y, por ende, más abierto a la elección por los méritos técnicos que los sistemas de conmutación públicos. Se espera que otros importantes fabrican- tes de telecomunicaciones sigan el ejemplo.

Todavía no se sabe si los gastos en los mercados se desplazarán con mayor fuerza en el sentido de los servicios y facilidades no vocales (por ejemplo, tele- tex, correo electrónico) o hacia nueva tecnología, para mejorar los servicios telefónicos existentes, co- mo enlaces de fibras ópticas. A breve plazo, las principales inversiones de las compañías se desti- narán a sustituir el equipo analógico por digital y ampliar sus redes de larga distancia con enlaces de fibras ópticas.

The electronic office is an example of a market lying in the overlapping area of the traditionally defined — and regulated — telecommunications industry, and the unregulated world of data processing. Forecasts early in the decade had the market quadrupling in size to something like US$ 18 billion in five years; but it seems to be developing more slowly than expected, and vendors tend to blame this on the customer as lacking a proper perception of need and potential.

A typical basic unit must include a work station with a computer terminal, screen, keyboard, and perhaps a telephone handset and printer, to provide the functions of data processing, drawing diagrams and sending messages. Storage will be needed, possibly very extensive and with quick retrieval. Except in the simplest applications it will almost certainly be based on an in-house information system; and the office will become a network of work stations each with a monitor and linked to each other and to the central data bank via a computer-based controller, providing quick and secure movement of information throughout the business; in short it will involve computer equipment as well, no doubt, as new office telephone exchange. Even with plunging prices of equipment all this costs money and in addition requires heavy investment in planning and organizing if it is to fit into an on-going enterprise and work effectively.

The most important attribute of an electronic office is the scope that it provides for innovation and creative management and the contribution it makes to increases in productivity. Innovation depends in the first place upon knowledge of what is possible and of the state of the art in the appropriate technology, both within the company and in the outside world. The technological information required for this can be stored and handled electronically; but it is not a dormant body of material, just to be drawn upon as needed; it is rather a dynamic quantity essential to the processes by which it is generated and to the future development and management of those processes.

With this potential, electronics, in the hands of suitably trained and lively managers, can extend the "office" function beyond the assembly of facts into the realm of their interpretation. The electronic office will not produce of its best if it is left to data processing experts to install it, just to automate existing office procedures. Electronics in the office will come into their own when their installation is directed by top managers who know what they want of them and understand what they can give.

The products and services most frequently included in the general concept of the "office of the future" are inscribed in the shaded area of the "Information Business" map on this page. These constitute something of a South-West to North-East diagonal, showing a contribution of "dumb" products and professional services — "the office of the past and present" — with the computer in the middle which might be viewed as a factor in reducing "dumb" products at one extreme of the diagonal and professional services at the other, much as "electronic publishing" might be a diagonal from the North-West to the South-East that could reduce the importance of printed matter at one end and mail or parcel services at the other.

The authors of the map, the Center for Information Research of Harvard University, consider such suppositions far from established by the mapping process but this type of presentation has the merit of being thought-provoking and a useful way of identifying trends in this complex world of electronics.

La bureautique est un exemple d'un marché qui s'étend à la fois dans le secteur traditionnel et réglementé de la télécommunication et dans le secteur non-réglementé du traitement des données et de l'information. En 1980 des prévisions chiffraient ce marché à 18 milliards de dollars US pour 1985, une croissance de 400% en 5 ans mais, en fait, ce développement a été moins rapide. Cela est dû, selon les commerciaux, à une perception insuffisante de la part des utilisateurs et de leurs besoins et du potentiel de l'informatique.

Un équipement de base doit comprendre un terminal d'ordinateur, un écran, une touche de commande et peut-être aussi un téléphone et un téléscripteur, pour assurer les fonctions de traitement de données de schématisation et d'envoi des messages. Une capacité de mémoire très grande sera sans doute nécessaire, assortie de moyens rapides d'extraction. Sauf pour les applications les plus sommaires, un tel équipement sera presque certainement intégré dans un système d'information interne et le bureau deviendra un réseau d'unités de travail, chacune avec son contrôle et reliées les unes aux autres, ainsi qu'à une banque centrale de données, en passant par un poste de contrôle informatisé. Le tout assurant un mouvement rapide et en toute sécurité de l'information dans l'organisation; en somme, le bureau informatisé comprendra des ordinateurs ainsi que de nouveaux types de centraux privés de commutation. Tout ça coûte cher, même en tenant compte de la rapide diminution des prix, et nécessite un gros effort de planification et d'organisation pour que l'ensemble soit bien intégré dans l'entreprise et fonctionne d'une manière efficace.

La contribution la plus importante de la bureautique est la possibilité qu'elle crée d'innover, d'améliorer la gestion et d'augmenter la productivité. L'innovation dépend, en effet, de la connaissance du possible, et du niveau de réalisation dans les technologies appropriées dans l'entreprise elle-même et à l'extérieur. L'information technologique peut être stockée et traitée électroniquement; mais il ne faut pas que ce soit de l'information statique à consulter quand le besoin s'en fait sentir ; c'est plutôt une quantité dynamique essentielle au développement et à la gestion du processus pour lequel elle avait été constituée.

Avec une telle potentialité, l'informatique maniée par des gestionnaires bien formés et imaginatifs - peut élargir la fonction bureautique, bien au delà de l'acquisition et le stockage de l'information, à celle de son interprétation. Mais l'installation d'un bureau informatisé ne doit pas être délégué à des experts extérieurs à l'entreprise qui se limiteraient à l'automatisation des procédures existantes. En fait, la bureautique ne peut pleinement se justifier que si elle est utilisée et dirigée par les cadres mêmes de l'entreprise qui devront savoir ce qu'ils veulent en obtenir et comprendre ce qu'elle peut leur apporter.

Les produits et services généralement inclus dans le « bureau du futur » sont inscrits dans la partie ombrée de la carte-diagramme ci-contre, avec l'ordinateur en position centrale. Ils forment une diagonale allant du Sud-ouest au Nord-est, une sorte de tapis qui laisserait autour de lui une sorte de poussière de produits et de services appartenant au « bureau du passé ».

Les auteurs de cette carte, le Centre de recherche sur l'information de l'Université d'Harvard, considèrent que les suppositions qui en découlent sont loin d'être établies, mais que ce type de présentation a le mérite de provoquer la réflexion et d'être un bon moyen d'identifier les tendances dans la compléxité du monde de l'informatique.

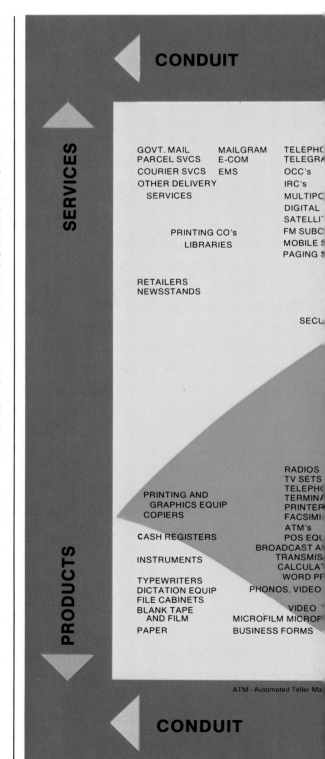

CONDUIT

SERVICES

GOVT. MAIL	MAILGRAM	TELEPHO
PARCEL SVCS	E-COM	TELEGRA
COURIER SVCS	EMS	OCC's
OTHER DELIVERY		IRC's
SERVICES		MULTIPC
		DIGITAL
		SATELLIT
PRINTING CO's		FM SUBC
LIBRARIES		MOBILE S
		PAGING S

RETAILERS
NEWSSTANDS

SECU

PRODUCTS

PRINTING AND	RADIOS
GRAPHICS EQUIP	TV SETS
COPIERS	TELEPHO
	TERMINA
	PRINTER
	FACSIMI
	ATM's
CASH REGISTERS	POS EQU
	BROADCAST A
INSTRUMENTS	TRANSMIS
	CALCULA
TYPEWRITERS	WORD PF
DICTATION EQUIP	PHONOS, VIDEO
FILE CABINETS	
BLANK TAPE	VIDEO
AND FILM	MICROFILM MICROF
PAPER	BUSINESS FORMS

ATM - Automated Teller Ma

CONDUIT

CTRONIC WORK PLACES"

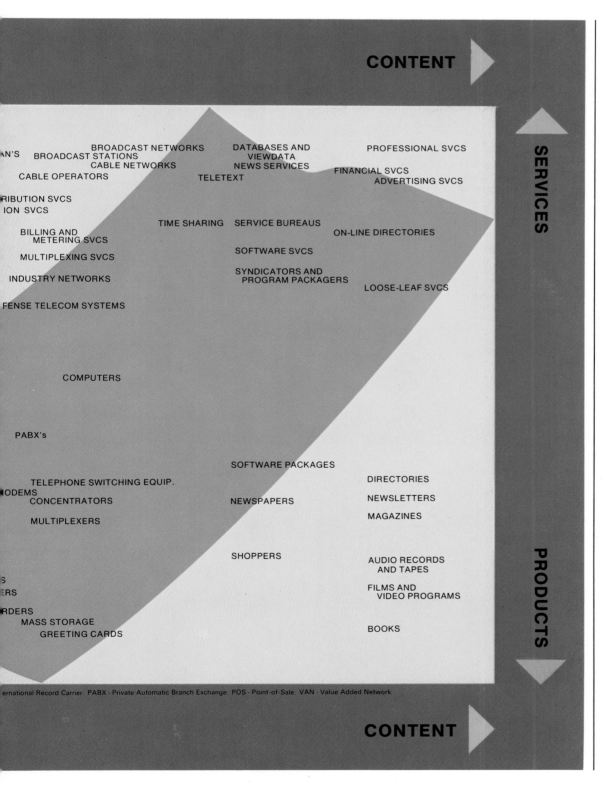

CONTENT

SERVICES

PRODUCTS

CONTENT

AN'S
BROADCAST NETWORKS
BROADCAST STATIONS
CABLE NETWORKS
CABLE OPERATORS
TELETEXT

DATABASES AND
VIEWDATA
NEWS SERVICES

PROFESSIONAL SVCS

FINANCIAL SVCS
ADVERTISING SVCS

RIBUTION SVCS
ION SVCS

TIME SHARING
SERVICE BUREAUS
ON-LINE DIRECTORIES

BILLING AND
METERING SVCS

MULTIPLEXING SVCS
SOFTWARE SVCS

INDUSTRY NETWORKS
SYNDICATORS AND
PROGRAM PACKAGERS
LOOSE-LEAF SVCS

FENSE TELECOM SYSTEMS

COMPUTERS

PABX's

SOFTWARE PACKAGES

TELEPHONE SWITCHING EQUIP.
DIRECTORIES

ODEMS
CONCENTRATORS
NEWSPAPERS
NEWSLETTERS

MULTIPLEXERS
MAGAZINES

SHOPPERS

AUDIO RECORDS
AND TAPES

FILMS AND
VIDEO PROGRAMS

RDERS
MASS STORAGE
GREETING CARDS
BOOKS

ernational Record Carrier. PABX - Private Automatic Branch Exchange. POS - Point-of-Sale. VAN - Value Added Network

La oficina electrónica es un ejemplo de mercado que se encuentra en el sector superpuesto de la industria de telecomunicaciones definida — y reglamentada — tradicionalmente y en el mundo no reglamentado del procesamiento de datos. A principios del decenio se previó ya la cuadruplicación del mercado, pasando a unos 18 000 millones $ en cinco años; pero parece que evoluciona con mayor lentitud, y los vendedores tienden a culpar de ello a los clientes, por carecer de una percepción adecuada de necesidades y potencial.

Una unidad básica típica ha de comprender una estación de trabajo con un terminal de computador, pantalla, teclado, y tal vez un teléfono con microteléfono e impresor, para procesar datos, trazar diagramas y transmitir mensajes. Será necesario el almacenamiento, quizá muy amplio y con rápida recuperación. Salvo en las aplicaciones más sencillas, seguramente se basará en un sistema de información interno; y la oficina será una red de estaciones de trabajo con sendos monitores, vinculadas entre sí y al banco central de datos a través de un controlador por computador, que proporcione un movimiento rápido y seguro de la información en toda la empresa; en resumen, comprenderá equipo de computador, así como, sin duda, nuevas clases de centrales telefónicas de oficina. Aunque los precios del equipo se reducen mucho, todo esto cuesta dinero y, además, requiere grandes inversiones de planificación y organización, si se quiere que corresponda a una empresa que funcione eficazmente.

El atributo más importante de la oficina electrónica son las posibilidades de innovación y gestión creadora que ofrece. La innovación depende, ante todo, de conocer lo que es posible y el estado de la ciencia en la tecnología apropiada. La información tecnológica necesaria puede almacenarse y tratarse electrónicamente; pero no es un material inactivo del que se echa mano cuando se necesita, sino más bien una cantidad dinámica esencial de los procesos en que se genera y del futuro desarrollo y gestión de esos procesos.

Con tales posibilidades, la electrónica, en mano de directores capacitados y activos, puede extender la función de la "oficina" más allá de lo que permite su interpretación. La producción de la oficina electrónica no será óptima si se deja a los expertos en tratamiento de datos que la instalen simplemente para automatizar los procedimientos actuales. El valor de la electrónica en la oficina se reconocerá solo cuando se ocupe de su instalación una alta dirección que sepa lo que quiere de ella y comprenda lo que puede aportar.

Los productos y servicios que figuran con más frecuencia en la noción general de la "oficina del futuro" se encuentran en la zona sombreada del gráfico "La industria de la información", en esta página. Constituyen algo así como una diagonal sudeste-nordeste. Muestra una contribución de productos "mudos" y servicios profesionales — "la oficina del pasado y del presente" — con el computador en el centro, que puede considerarse como un factor para reducir los productos "mudos" en un extremo de la diagonal y los servicios profesionales en el otro, lo mismo que una "publicación electrónica" puede ser una diagonal del noroeste al sudeste capaz de reducir la importancia de lo impreso en un extremo y de los servicios postales o de paquetes en el otro.

Los autores del gráfico, del Centro de investigación de la información de la Universidad de Harward, consideran que esas suposiciones distan de haberse establecido por el procedimiento cartográfico, pero esta presentación tiene el mérito de estimular ideas y de constituir un modo útil de identificar tendencias en este complejo mundo de la electrónica.

The Matrix displayed here is a file-gathering system ; a simplified method of categorizing, gathering, monitoring, and scrutinizing the latest developments in telecommunications media. A by-product of this codification scheme is the ability to build a hierarchy of information that can best serve as management decision inputs.

Looking along the Horizontal Axis - identified as "technologies". The definitions include:

— Telecommunications: viewed as traditional telephone services, basic services, information services or operator-assisted services.

— Computers: including developing products hand-held, programmable, portable, communicating terminals.

— Teletext: one-way broadcast information services for displaying pages of text and graphic material on the screens of adapted TV sets usually transmitted by using spare capacity in the broadcast TV signal. By means of a key pad, a user can select one page at a time for display from the cycle.

— CATV: Cable Television; giving access to private broadcast channels.

— DBTV: Direct Broadcast Television; using communications satellites to transmit signals directly to the home.

— Videotex: a two-way interactive service emphasizing information retrieval and capable of displaying pages of text and pictorial material on the screens of adapted TV sets.

Examining the vertical Axis - identified as "applications", the definitions include:

— General Consumer: the at-home, non-business uses to include entertainment, information and education.

— Small Business: persons whose businesses are operated from the home, or whose out-of-home locations have only one or two telephone lines.

— Large Business: firms employing five or more persons; or having multiple-site operations.

— Government: can be subdivided into federal, state or local; or by governmental departments.

— Special Interest: those groups that represent distinct and sizable, separate market segments, such as the handicapped and the farmers.

— Advertiser & Communications Professionals: added to the matrix to show how a special interest subset can gather information pertinent to the Communications profession.

Each receptacle in the Matrix is a "mix of functions", depending on the technology employed or the application addressed.

— Communication Carrier: the deliverers of the message, such as telephone companies, cable and satellite operators.

— Information Provider: the suppliers of the message. Can be segmented into free or paid information sources.

— Equipment Manufacturer: can be segmented into terminal, printer, computer, hardware or software suppliers.

— System Operators: companies that "package up" the elements identified above, able to provide add-on services such as record keeping, billing, security systems.

With the matrix established as a gathering file system, it should be used to collect information from diverse sources: the press, general business, specific trade and consumer sources, supplemented by symposiums, exhibits and conventions, and advertising materials. A matrix overlay can be developed identifying those sources representing the primary information input for each receptacle.

Next in importance is to establish a periodic review and "weeding out" process. For example, what is contained in weekly newsletters will often be found later, in expanded form, in special interest publications; materials presented at a symposium will probably be synopsized in the trade press, or made available as speech reprints; advertising material or publicity releases will be followed by application and case-history information. A formalized, on-going review can be used to gather more complete or more up-to-date information, on areas of specific interest. The establishment of an information hierarchy can help deal with the problem of "information float" — information float describes the delay between the time information appears and its availability in the level of detail needed.

"Weeding out" should be coupled with an identification of critical issues and information gaps. An increasingly important consideration which has already earned the label of **"meta-Information".** The sheer weight of facts describing new information technologies, procedures and systems has overwhelmed those undertaking analysis. Relevant facts overflow cognitive frameworks. We are at the point today where the understanding of how to use information is much more important than the ability to "get" it.

La matrice représentée ci-contre est un système d'établissement de fichier ; il s'agit d'une méthode simplifiée permettant le classement, l'assemblage, le suivi et l'examen des progrès réalisés dans le domaine des télécommunications. Un avantage de ce système est qu'il permet d'établir une hiérarchie des informations aptes à faciliter les décisions.

Dans l'axe horizontal intitulé : « technologie », on trouve :

— Télécommunications : considérées comme services téléphoniques traditionnels — services de base, de renseignements ou services requérant l'assistance de standardistes.

— Ordinateurs : comprenant les produits connexes tels que les terminaux de communication portatifs et programmables.

— Télétexte : services unidirectionnels de diffusion d'informations permettant l'affichage de textes ou de graphismes sur les écrans de télévision aménagés, généralement transmis par l'intermédiaire d'un canal vidéo disponible. Au moyen d'un bloc de touches, l'utilisateur peut sélectionner dans la mémoire une page à la fois pour l'afficher.

— CATV : télévision par câble, accès à des chaines privées.

— TVDS : télédiffusion en direct ; utilisation de satellites de communication pour la transmission dans les foyers.

— Vidéotex : un service en mode conversationnel dont le but principal est la recherche d'informations et qui permet l'affichage de textes et d'illustrations, transmis par ligne téléphonique, sur les écrans de télévision aménagés.

Dans l'axe vertical intitulé : « Applications », on trouve :

— Consommateur moyen : utilisation domestique, notamment pour les loisirs, l'information et l'enseignement.

— Petites entreprises : gérées à domicile, ou dont les locaux commerciaux n'ont qu'une ou deux lignes téléphoniques.

— Grandes entreprises : unités de plus de cinq personnes, ou dont les opérations sont réparties entre plusieurs locaux.

— Gouvernement : on peut subdiviser cette catégorie de manière géographique ou par ministères.

— Intérêts spéciaux : groupes de consommateurs représentant des marchés distincts, par exemple les agriculteurs.

— Spécialistes de la publicité et de la communication : ajoutés à la matrice dans ce cas précis pour montrer comment un sous-groupe d'intérêt spécial peut recueillir des informations intéressant les spécialistes de la communication en général.

Chaque plan mémoire de la matrice peut être identifié par un ensemble de « fonctions », selon la technique employée ou l'application recherchée.

— Transporteurs : publics ou privés, ils assurent le transport physique du message, tels que les services de télédistribution ou téléphoniques, et les systèmes de satellites.

— Courtiers en information : ils fournissent les informations: sources gratuites et sources payantes.

— Fabricants d'équipement : fabricants de terminaux, d'imprimantes, d'ordinateurs, de matériel ou de logiciel.

— Distributeurs : compagnies qui vendent les éléments mentionnés, plus des services complémentaires tels que tenue d'archives, facturation, et systèmes de sécurité.

Une fois la matrice établie, elle doit être utilisée pour rassembler des données provenant de diverses sources, telles que la presse, les informations recueillies à l'occasion de colloques, d'expositions et de conventions, ainsi que dans des matériels publicitaires. Une matrice de recouvrement peut être construite identifiant les entrées primaires pour chaque plan de mémoire.

A ce système de rassemblement des données, il faut associer un processus périodique de mise à jour et de tri. Par exemple, les informations contenues dans les bulletins hebdomadaires figureront souvent plus tard, plus détaillées, dans des publications spécialisées; les documents présentés lors d'un colloque seront probablement résumés dans la presse; les discours prononcés paraîtront plus tard dans leur intégralité.

Un examen continu et systématique peut permettre de rassembler des informations plus complètes ou plus à jour concernant un domaine d'intérêt particulier. On pourra ainsi limiter le volume et regrouper les informations pertinentes.

L'établissement d'une hiérarchie des informations peut aider à résoudre le problème du laps de temps qui peut s'écouler entre le moment où l'information est publiée et le moment où elle devient disponible sous une forme suffisamment détaillée pour satisfaire les besoins spécifiques de l'utilisateur. Tout en opérant le tri des informations, il convient d'identifier les points critiques, les raccordements et les lacunes. Cette notion, d'une importance fondamentale, a déjà reçu le nom de « méta-information ». Les analystes sont, en effet, submergés par le volume de la documentation. Pour que leur analyse soit valable, ils doivent abandonner l'idée qu'il leur suffit de « rassembler » tout ce qui existe. Les faits pertinents dépassent les cadres cognitifs. Nous avons atteint le stade où l'aptitude à utiliser l'information est beaucoup plus importante que la faculté de l'acquérir.

CLEARING HOUS
A SIMPLIFIED AP

Meta-Information is the synthesis of information gathered into more general and theoretical conclusions. It is "information about information". Essentially it is a means of identifying certain propositions, generalizations and principles out of an array of primary information sources that have been gathered on a particular subject. "Meta-Information" can serve as a value-added device — weak information can add up to strong conclusions, to higher levels of generalization.

It is accepted fact that information is accumulating at an exponential rate, outstripping meaning formation and that de-

MATRIX ESTABLISHED AS A GATHERING FILE SYSTEM

APPLICATIONS

General User and Consumer

Small Business

Large Business

Government

Special Interest

Advertisers and Communications Professiona

Fonctions of "suppliers"

cision makers have more and more of it which they do not know how to use. This is one method to deal with the information flood, to channel its energy to useful purposes ; to move from information to knowledge. "Coping with information on new forms of communications" is the subject selected to illustrate the method. The matrix and the research that underly it evolve from study in this area by Peter Eder.

OR INFORMATION ON INFORMATION
OACH TO HANDLING AND SYNTHESIS

méta-information est une nouvelle notion de synthèse d'in-mations provenant de sources diverses. En substance, c'est e méthode permettant d'identifier certaines propositions, néralisations et principes à partir d'un éventail d'informa-ns primaires rassemblées sur un sujet donné. Il s'agit 'informations sur l'information ». La « méta-information » nstitue une valeur ajoutée ; des informations ayant peu de leur en elles-mêmes pouvant mener par cette méthode à des nclusions importantes et à des niveaux de généralisation us élevés.

La metainformación es una nueva noción de síntesis de informaciones de diversas fuentes. En el fondo, es un método para identificar ciertas propuestas, generalizaciones y principios desde varias informaciones primarias reunidas sobre su tema. Se trata de "informaciones sobre la información". La "metainformación" constituye un valor añadido; informaciones con escaso valor intrínseco pueden llevar a conclusiones importantes y a mayores niveles de generalización.

Es indiscutible que las informaciones se acumulan a velocidad exponencial, por lo que acaban perdiendo todo significado.

TECHNOLOGIES →

TELECOMS VOICE IMAGE/DATA	COMPUTERS	TELETEXT	TV CTV/DBTV	VIDEOTEX
CC IP / EM SO	CC IP / EM SO	CC IP / EM SO	CC IP	CC IP / EM SO
CC IP / EM SO	CC IP / EM SO	CC IP / EM SO	CC IP	CC IP / EM SO
CC IP / EM SO	CC IP / EM SO	CC IP / EM SO	CC IP	CC IP / EM SO
C IP / EM SO	CC IP / EM SO	CC IP / EM SO	CC IP	CC IP / EM SO
CC IP / EM SO	CC IP / EM SO	CC IP / EM SO	CC IP	CC IP / EM SO
IP	CC IP / SO	CC IP	CC IP	CC IP / EM

CC Communication Carrier   **IP** Information Provider

EM Equipment Manufacturer   **SO** System Operator

l est incontestable que les informations s'accumulent à une esse exponentielle et que, de ce fait, elles finissent par dre toute signification. Les décideurs ont donc à leur dispo-on de plus en plus de connaissances, dont ils ne savent que e. Cette méthode permet de faire face à cet afflux d'infor-tions, de le maîtriser à des fins utiles et d'opérer le passage l'information à la connaissance. La matrice ci-dessus et la herche qui la sous-tend découlent d'une étude de Peter Eder.

Quienes deciden disponen, pues, cada vez de más conocimientos, que no saben utilizar. Este método permite hacer frente a ese aflujo de información, dominarlo con fines útiles y pasar de la información al conocimiento. La matriz anterior y la investigación en que se basa se derivan de un estudio de Peter Eder. Para ilustrarlo, nos referimos a un ámbito preciso: la asimilación de informaciones relativas a las nuevas formas de comunicación.

La matriz representada aquí es un sistema de establecimiento de fichero; se trata de un método simplificado para clasificar, reunir, seguir y examinar los últimos progresos de las telecomunicaciones. Una de las ventajas del sistema es que permite una jerarquía de informaciones que facilita las decisiones.

En el eje horizontal titulado "Tecnología", tenemos:
— Telecomunicaciones: consideradas como servicios telefónicos tradicionales: servicios de base, de información o asistidos por operador.
— Computadores: comprenden los productos conexos, como terminales de comunicación portátiles y programables.
— Teletexto: servicios unidireccionales de difusión de informaciones que permiten presentar textos o grafismos en pantallas de receptores de televisión, generalmente por medio de un canal video. Mediante una serie de teclas, el usuario puede seleccionar en la memoria una página cada vez para visualizarla.
— TVCA: televisión por cable; acceso a cadenas privadas.
— TVDS: televisión directa; uso de satélites de comunicación para la transmisión directa a los hogares.
— Videotex: servicio en modo conversación cuyo principal fin es la búsqueda de informaciones, y que permite visualizar textos e ilustraciones, tansmitidos por línea telefónica, en pantallas de receptores de televisión acondicionados.

En el eje vertical, titulado "Aplicaciones", tenemos:
— Cunsumidor medio: utilización en el hogar, sobre todo con fines recreativos, de información y enseñanza.
— Pequeñas empresas: las regentadas a domicilio, y cuyos locales comerciales están provistos de una o dos líneas telefónicas.
— Grandes empresas: las que emplean cinco personas o más, y operan en varios lugares.
— Gobierno: esta categoría puede subdividirse geográficamente o por ministerios.
— Intereses especiales: grupos de consumidores que representan mercados concretos: p. ej., incapacitados o agricultores.
— Especialistas de publicidad y de comunicación: agregados a la matriz, como ejemplo, para mostrar cómo un subgrupo de interés especial puede recoger información interesante para los especialistas de la comunicación.

Cada plano de memoria de la matriz es una mezcla de "funciones", según la técnica empleada o la aplicación.
— Transportadores: los que transportan los mensajes: compañías telefónicas, operadores de cable y satélite.
— Agentes de información: quienes suministran gratuitamente la información, o la venden.
— Fabricantes de equipo: fabricantes de terminales, impresoras, computadores, material o soporte lógico.
— Distribuidores: empresas que venden los elementos citados, y las que pueden proporcionar servicios complementarios, como archivos, facturación y sistemas de seguridad.

Una vez establecida la matriz, debe utilizarse para reunir datos procedentes de diversas fuentes, como la prensa, las informaciones obtenidas con motivo de coloquios, exposiciones o convenciones, así como de material publicitario. Identificando las entradas primarias para cada plano de memoria, puede construirse una matriz de recuperación.

A este sistema de reunión de datos hay que asociar un proceso periódico de puesta al día y clasificación. Por ejemplo, la información contenida en los boletines semanales figurará, en general, más tarde y en forma más desarrollada, en publicaciones especializadas. Los documentos presentados en un coloquio se resumirán probablemente en la prensa comercial, o los discursos pronunciados aparecerán después íntegramente. El examen continuo y sistemático puede permitir la recopilación de información más compléta o actualizada sobre una materia de interés especial. Así, se podrá limitar el volumen y reagrupar las informaciones pertinentes.

El establecimiento de una jerarquía de las informaciones puede ayudar a resolver el problema del tiempo que transcurre desde el momento que se publica una información hasta el que se dispone de ella con suficiente detalle para satisfacer las necesidades específicas del usuario.

Además de clasificar la información, conviene conocer los puntos críticos, las conexiones y las lagunas. Esta noción, de importancia primordial, ha recibido ya el nombre de **"metainformación"**. Los analistas están abrumados por el volumen de la documentación. Para que su análisis sea válido, deben abandonar la idea de que les basta "reunir" cuanto existe. Los hechos rebasan los marcos cognoscitivos. Hemos llegado a la fase en que la aptitud para utilizar la información es mucho más importante que la facultad de adquirirla.

DEEP INVOLVEMENT
IEWHOPENEWHO **OF MAN** RIZONSNEWPOWER
IN SYSTEMS THROUGH SOFTWARE

THE JOB OF SOFTWARE is to make the hardware perform. The top level manager knows what he wants of computers and understands what they can give him. For an effective system the expression of the need, its translation into software, and the capabilities of the hardware, must all work in unison.

In the beginning it was commonly thought that problems of production control would be an ideal area for computers. They appeared to be intellectually not too difficult but bedevilled by the sheer mass of figures requiring rather frequent, quick calculations. Many efforts were made but weaknesses soon became apparent; misunderstanding or, at least, mis-specification of the management problem; the clumsiness of the early computers themselves; but above all the software which failed to introduce the necessary versatility needed to provide good responses to on-going situations. The concept of versatility is fundamental to the modern development of software; not only is it apparent in interactive systems in which the computer does not just carry through monolithic calculations but can respond to fresh inputs or questions from the manager; but also fundamental to the structure of the industry itself.

Software may be for many the most difficult of the Information Age technologies to understand, often confused by strange names, acronyms, and obscure technical jargon. Fortunately for the manager, there is no more need to have a detailed knowledge of how it works in order to use it than there is to have detailed knowledge of how a telephone works in order to use that, or indeed of how one's own brain works.

Software's importance lies not only in its central function but in the amount of effort and resources it consumes. It is big business. Consider its position in

▷ 320

LE LOGICIEL SERT à faire fonctionner le matériel. Le gestionnaire de haut niveau sait ce qu'il attend des ordinateurs et comprend ce que ceux-ci peuvent lui apporter. Pour qu'un système soit efficace, l'expression des besoins, leur « traduction » en logiciel et les capacités du matériel doivent travailler à l'unisson.

Au début, on pensait que les problèmes de contrôle de la production seraient un domaine idéal pour les ordinateurs. Intellectuellement, ils ne paraissaient pas trop difficiles, mais embrouillés par une montagne de chiffres exigeant des calculs fréquents et rapides quoique fondamentalement simples. A la suite des nombreux efforts qui ont été faits pour généraliser l'usage de l'informatique, de nombreuses faiblesses sont vite devenues apparentes : un certain manque de compréhension, ou pour le moins une définition erronée du problème ; la maladresse des premiers ordinateurs peut-être ; mais avant tout l'insuffisance du logiciel qui ne pouvait introduire la souplesse nécessaire pour obtenir de bonnes réponses à des problèmes courants. L'introduction de la souplesse est une notion fondamentale dans le développement du logiciel. Cela est évident non seulement pour les systèmes interactifs, dans lesquels l'ordinateur ne se limite pas à faire des calculs monolithiques, mais cela est fondamental pour la structure de l'industrie des communications.

Le logiciel peut apparaître, pour beaucoup d'entre nous, la plus difficile à comprendre des techniques de l'âge de l'information — souvent obscurcie par d'étranges acronymes ou du jargon. Heureusement pour les gestionnaires, il n'est pas besoin de connaître le fonctionnement du logiciel, pas plus qu'on ne doit connaître le fonctionnement du téléphone pour pouvoir s'en servir, et moins encore, savoir comment le cerveau fonctionne pour penser.

L'importance du logiciel réside non seulement dans sa fonction centrale mais dans la quantité d'efforts et de ressources qu'il met en jeu. Il s'agit là d'un

▷ 320

EL COMETIDO DEL SOPORTE LÓGICO es que funcione el físico. El director de alto nivel sabe lo que quiere del computador y comprende lo que puede aportar. Para un sistema eficaz, la expresión de la necesidad, su conversión en soporte lógico y las capacidades del físico han de marchar al unísono.

Al principio, se pensaba que los problemas de control de producción serían un ámbito ideal del computador. No parecían difíciles intelectualmente, sino complejos por la gran cantidad de cifras que requieren cálculos bastantes frecuentes y rápidos. Se hicieron grandes esfuerzos, pero pronto aparecieron las debilidades: la incomprensión o, al menos, mala especificación del problema de gestión; la pesadez de los primeros computadores, pero, principalmente, el soporte físico que no introducía la versatilidad necesaria para responder debidamente a las situaciones. La noción de versatilidad es fundamental para el desarrollo moderno de soporte lógico; no sólo es aparente en sistemas interactivos, en que el computador no se limita a efectuar cálculos monolíticos, sino que puede responder a nuevas entradas o preguntas del director; también es fundamental para la estructura de la propia industria.

Para muchos, el soporte logico puede ser la tecnología de la era de la información más difícil de comprender, confundida a menudo por nombres extraños, acrónimos y una jerga técnica obscura. Afortunadamente para el director, su uso no requiere conocer con mayor detalle su funcionamiento que el de un teléfono, o el de su propio cerebro.

La importancia del soporte lógico no reside nada más en su función central, sino en la cantidad de esfuerzo y recursos que consume. Se trata de grandes

▷ 321

Facing the major problem of the Information Age: how to program the automatic production of software.

Implication profonde du génie de l'homme dans la création du logiciel.

Profunda intervención del genio humano en la creación de sistemas de soporte lógico.

the Bell System, for example. This gigantic enterprise has an enormous installation of technological apparatus to maintain and constantly enhance; yet in the Bell Labs 40 per cent of the technical staff work on software development and support.

The Bell System has some 3,000 software-controlled call-handling systems. For example, No.4 electronic switching system (4ESS), which handles toll calls, contains 1.4 millions lines of instructions; each year a half million or more lines of code are produced to offer new features or improvements. Fully half the programming in these systems is used to audit, correct and maintain their operations to reliability standards far more stringent, and with real-time volumes of information processed much higher, than is often required of normal commercial computer installations.

Bell Laboratories is constantly developing programming for microprocessors as these versatile chips find their way into a growing variety of equipment and products. To reduce the complexity of the software needed, efforts are being made to build into the chip hardware some of the software functions. Apart from these task-specific systems for operations support, switching and microprocessors, a significant amount of software is needed for giving users general access to computer or processor capabilities.

Other users of new information technology have, in proportion, similar problems. How can they best resolve these without massive internal resources? It is generally true that the installation of a new system is likely to involve a greater expense in software than in hardware; and with falling hardware costs the discrepancy is increasing. In the USA there is a well-organized services industry with over 500 members in the Association of Data Processing Service Organizations Inc. (ADAPSO). This organization forecasts that by 1986 the total US Computer Services market will exceed US$ 35 billion.

The composition of that total market is expected to be about 40 per cent in processing services and 30 per cent each in professional services and software products; the software will be the fastest growing, having increased from about 20 per cent in 1981. The services provided cover a very wide range as does the style of the companies. The largest of them will provide a wide range of services and turnover may exceed $500 million; others may specialize in particular services, or even in special aspects of such services, and may operate on a quite small scale. The important result in relation to software is that there are many companies which may, and do, develop specific application expertise; they are therefore well placed either to write special programs for individual customers within their area of application or to produce software packages where demand is appropriate.

A degree of separation of the software and hardware industries in the USA has been established over many years. It is instructive to see the way things are developing in Japan where such separation has begun only recently and hitherto much of the software has, in effect, been tailor-made or built into the hardware by the computer manufacturer. The Japanese government introduced, during the 1980s, a five-year project to encourage the software industry to develop multi-purpose packages and generally to produce versatile, less costly, kinds of software. The project has substantial government backing, in support of the efforts of the major corporations and of the independent, often small, software companies from whom a major contribution is expected.

The Japanese Ministry for Trade and Industry (MITI) is channelling $10.6 million in R&D funds mainly among the 2,000 independent software houses. Government guarantees are available for commercial bank loans for software ventures by small companies with limited assets (which commercial loans normally require). There are tax concessions on software revenues in their early life. Big corporations, e.g. Hitachi, are spinning off subsidiaries designed to be less bureaucratic. Skilled programmers

grand problème. Examinons, par exemple, comment il se présente chez AT&T. Cette gigantesque entreprise doit assurer la maintenance et l'amélioration constante d'énormes installations techniques ultra modernes. Neánmoins 40 pour cent des techniciens de Bell Laboratories travaillent à la mise au point du logiciel. Le Bell System a plus de 3000 systèmes de commutation qui sont programmés sur ordinateur. Par exemple, le système 4ESS, qui écoule les communications interurbaines, contient 1,4 million de lignes de code. Chaque année un demi-million de lignes de code ou plus sont produites pour améliorer les programmes en service.

Dans ces systèmes, la moitié de la programmation sert à vérifier, corriger ou maintenir leur fonctionnement dans des normes de fiabilité beaucoup plus strictes, et avec des volumes d'information traitée en temps réel beaucoup plus élevés, qu'il n'est généralement exigé des installations de type courant.

Bell met constamment au point de nouveaux programmes pour des microprocesseurs qui sont incorporés dans une diversité sans cesse croissante d'équipements et de produits. Afin de réduire la complexité des programmes, les fabricants cherchent à introduire certaines fonctions du logiciel dans le microprocesseur. En dehors de ces systèmes affectés spécifiquement à l'appui opérationnel, à la commutation et à l'introduction dans les microprocesseurs, une quantité considérable de logiciel est requise pour accéder aux fonctions des ordinateurs.

Les autres usagers des nouvelles techniques de l'informatique rencontrent des problèmes analogues. Comment peuvent-ils les résoudre sans disposer par eux-mêmes d'énormes ressources ? L'installation d'un nouveau système entraîne généralement des dépenses plus importantes pour le logiciel que pour le matériel et, compte tenu de la chute des prix de ce dernier, la disparité s'accroît. Aux Etats-Unis, il existe une industrie de services bien organisée groupant environ 500 membres au sein de l'Association of Data Processing Service Organizations Inc. (ADAPSO). Cette association prévoit qu'en 1986, aux Etats-Unis, le marché des services de l'informatique dépassera 35 milliards de dollars.

La répartition probable de ce marché sera environ : 40% pour les services de traitement d'information et de données et 30% chacun pour les services professionnels et le progiciel (software packages), ce dernier étant en très forte croissance.

L'industrie des services couvre une très large gamme de produits correspondant aux différents styles des entreprises. La firme la plus importante offre une grande diversité de services et son chiffre d'affaires pourrait dépasser 500 millions de dollars ; d'autres, généralement beaucoup plus petites, se cantonnent dans des services particuliers ou même dans certains petits créneaux. En fait un grand nombre de sociétés de service se spécialisent dans des programmes d'application bien déterminés et peuvent, dans leur secteur d'application, élaborer des programmes adaptés aux besoins spécifiques de leurs clients ou produire du progiciel.

Aux Etats-Unis, il existe, depuis plusieurs années, une certaine séparation entre l'industrie du logiciel et celle du matériel. Au Japon, cette séparation ne s'est manifestée que récemment, le logiciel étant auparavant en grande partie élaboré « sur mesure », ou directement incorporé au matériel par les constructeurs d'ordinateurs.

Pendant les années 1980, le gouvernement japonais a introduit un projet pour encourager l'augmentation de la production de logiciel, particulièrement celle de supports polyvalents et de programmes souples et peu coûteux. Le projet jouit d'un apport financier du gouvernement qui vient s'ajouter aux efforts réalisés à la fois par les grandes entreprises et les firmes indépendantes. Le ministère japonais du Commerce et de l'Industrie (MITI) a ainsi distribué 10,6 millions de dollars US (1982) de subvention à la production, principalement parmi les 2000 producteurs de logiciel indépendants. Il est également possible pour ces entreprises, la plupart petites et sans beaucoup de ressources financières, d'obtenir des garanties du gouvernement pour des prêts bancaires.

▷ 322

▷ 322

THE PRODUCTS AND
FOR FIRMS OF E

COMPUTER SERVICES INDUSTRY
15 YEARS OF EXPLOSIVE GR

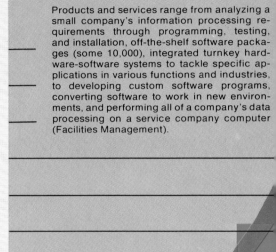

Products and services range from analyzing a small company's information processing requirements through programming, testing, and installation, off-the-shelf software packages (some 10,000), integrated turnkey hardware-software systems to tackle specific applications in various functions and industries, to developing custom software programs, converting software to work in new environments, and performing all of a company's data processing on a service company computer (Facilities Management).

1966   1971   1976   1981
(estima

Source : Association of Data Processing Service Organizations

These charts show how, during the 1980s in the USA, the number of businesses purchasing computer services and the revenues of software houses and other suppliers of these services are likely to grow. Focus Research Systems Inc. (chart on the right) estimates that the number of users will increase from less than half a million in 1980 to 1.2 million in 1985. The Association of Data Processing Service Organizations Inc., (chart on the left) expect the value of purchases of software and computer services to increase at an even faster rate, more than double in 5 years. Both trends are steeply upwards.

Ces diagrammes montrent la progression rapide — tout au long de la décennie 1980 aux Etats-Unis — du nombre des acquéreurs de services informatiques et le chiffre d'affaire des entreprises qui les fournissent. Focus Research Systems Inc. (à droite) estime que le nombre des utilisateurs s'élèvera de moins d'un demi million en 1980 à 1,2 million en 1986. ADAPSO (à gauche) prévoit que la valeur des achats de logiciel et de services informatiques augmentera à un rythme encore plus rapide : plus du double en 5 ans. Dans un cas comme dans l'autre, la courbe de progression est quasi verticale.

Estos gráficos muestran cómo crescerá probablemente en los años 80 en EE.UU. el número de empresas que adquirirán servicios de computador y los ingresos de las casas de soporte lógico y otros proveedores de esos servicios. Focus Research Systems Inc. (gráfico de la derecha) estima que el número de usuarios aumentará de menos de medio millón en 1980 a 1,2 millones en 1985. La Association of Data Processing Service Organizations Inc., ADAPSO (gráfico de la izquierda), espera que el valor de las adquisiciones de servicios de soporte lógico y computador aumenten a un ritmo aún mayor, más del doble en 5 años. Ambas tendencias son muy marcadas.

ERVICES OF THE SOFTWARE INDUSTRY
RY SIZE, IN EVERY KIND OF ACTIVITY

E USA

NUMBER OF BUSINESSES USING COMPUTER SERVICES IN THE USA

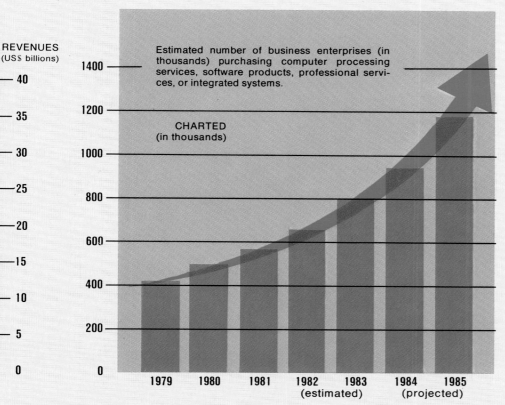

REVENUES
(US$ billions)

40
35
30
25
20
15
10
5
0

Estimated number of business enterprises (in thousands) purchasing computer processing services, software products, professional services, or integrated systems.

CHARTED
(in thousands)

1400
1200
1000
800
600
400
200
0

1979 1980 1981 1982 1983 1984 1985
(estimated) (projected)

86
ected)

Source : Focus Research Systems, Inc.

mmunications Services

Electronic funds transfer
Electronic mail
Data distribution
Distributed data processing
Computer conferencing

ta Bases

Econometric
Financial
Legal
Demographics
News
Etc.

tegrated Systems

Claims processing
Distribution
Legal
Auto supplies
Medical
Wholesale

nancial Services

Third party leasing of new systems

☐ Upgrading current systems (financing)
☐ Add-on equipment financing

Professional Services

☐ Analysis
☐ Design
☐ Programming
☐ Develop RFP
☐ Select hardware vendor
☐ Negotiate deal
☐ Hardware maintenance
☐ Facilities Management
☐ Software conversion
☐ Custom software
☐ Integrate system
☐ Test, install
☐ Audit system
☐ Evaluate system performance
☐ Training
☐ Software maintenance
☐ Documentation
☐ Design, development methodologie

Data Processing Services

☐ On-line conversational computing

☐ On-line application services
☐ Remote batch
☐ Overload computing, processing
☐ Access to special applications
☐ Batch
☐ Data storage
☐ Back-up computing
☐ Consulting

Software Packages

☐ Systems software
☐ Support software
☐ Applications software
  —accounting
  —banking
  —distribution
  —financial
  —insurance
  —manufacturing
  —payroll
  —purchasing
  —retail
  —wholesale
  —and many, many more
☐ Operating systems
☐ Utilities
☐ Data communications

negocios. Consideremos su posición en el Bell System. Esta gigantesa empresa tiene que mantener y mejorar constantemente una enorme instalación de aparatos tecnológicos modernos; sin embargo, en Bell Laboratories, el 40% de su trabajo técnico es el desarrollo y apoyo de soporte lógico.

El Bell System tiene unos 3000 sistemas de tratamiento de llamadas controlados por soporte lógico. Por ejemplo, el de conmutación electrónica N° 4 (4ESS), que cursa las llamadas interurbanas, contiene 1,4 millones de líneas de instrucciones; y anualmente, se producen medio millón o más de líneas de código para ofrecer nuevas características o mejoras. La mitad de la programación de esos sistemas se usa para verificar, corregir y mantener sus operaciones según normas de fiabilidad mucho más estrictas, y con volúmenes de información procesada en tiempo real mucho más altos, de lo que se requiere de las instalaciones normales de computadores comerciales.

Bell elabora constantemente programación para microprocesadores, a medida que esas plaquetas versátiles se implantan en una creciente variedad de equipo y de productos. Para reducir la complejidad del soporte lógico necesario, se trata de incorporar en el soporte físico de la plaqueta algunas de las funciones del lógico. Además de esos sistemas de tareas concretas para apoyo de operaciones, conmutación y microprocesadores, se requiere una considerable cantidad de soporte lógico, para que los usuarios accedan a las capacidades de computador o procesador.

Otros usuarios de nueva tecnología de la información tienen problemas análogos. ¿Cuál es la mejor manera de resolverlos sin recursos internos masivos? En general, la instalación de un nuevo sistema tal vez entrañe mayores gastos de soporte lógico que físico; y la diferencia aumenta al disminuir el costo del físico. En EE.UU. hay una industria de servicios bien organizada, con más de 500 miembros en la Association of Data Processing Service Organizations Inc. (ADAPSO). ADAPSO prevé que, para 1986, el mercado total de servicios de información del país rebasará los 50 000 millones $ y superará al de soporte físico.

Se espera que el desglose de este mercado total sea del orden del 40% en los servicios de procesamiento y del 30% en los profesionales y los productos de soporte lógico; éste es el que crecerá más, habiendo aumentado en 1981 en un 20%. Los servicios abarcan una amplísima gama, lo mismo que el estilo de las empresas. La mayor ofrecerá una gran serie de servicios, con una cifra de negocios que quizá rebase los 500 millones $; otras pueden especializarse en servicios particulares, o incluso en aspectos especiales de esos servicios, y operar en muy pequeña escala. Lo importante en relación con el soporte lógico es que hay muchas empresas que pueden desarrollar, y lo hacen, una pericia de aplicación específica; por tanto, están bien situadas para elaborar programas especiales para distintos clientes en su esfera de aplicación o producir conjuntos de soporte lógico cuando lo aconseje la demanda.

A lo largo de muchos años, se ha establecido cierto grado de separación en las industrias de soporte lógico y físico en EE.UU. Es instructivo observar cómo evoluciona la situación en Japón, donde tal separación ha comenzado, hace poco, pues el soporte lógico se realizaba especialmente o lo incorporaba al físico el fabricante del computador. Japón está en medio de un proyecto quinquenal para estimular a la industria de soporte lógico a desarrollar conjuntos con fines múltiples y, en general, a producir soporte lógico versátil y menos costoso. En 50% del proyecto está respaldado por el gobierno, que participa en los esfuerzos de las grandes empresas, y el importante papel que jugarán las compañías independientes, a menudo pequeñas, de soporte lógico es evidente.

El Ministerio de Comercio e Industria (MICI) de Japón está canalizando 10,6 millones $ en fondos de IyD, principalmente entre las 2000 casas de soporte lógico. Se dispone de garantías gubernamentales

▷ 323

are leaving large companies and setting up their own small companies and this in a country with strong traditional in-company loyalties. Women are being increasingly trained and employed as programmers and working from home. The picture everywhere is of entrepreneurial versatility creating a structure for the industry and working conditions suited to the versatility that is needed in the product.

The individual information system user has to choose how best to satisfy his software requirements. In the first place he can buy suitable software from the equipment supplier and this he will undoubtedly do so far as the supplier is able to provide it; the availability of suitable software is an important consideration in selecting one's system. But once the equipment has been bought the enthusiasm of the supplier to provide software may wane; in any case he is not in the business of writing specialized programs and so would probably be an economically inefficient source. The user may then rely on his own resources to write his own tailor-made programs; or he can go to a service software house either to write a tailor-made program or for a suitable package. In practice a mixed strategy is likely.

In-house, the user will be helped by the efforts of suppliers and software houses to produce generative aids to reduce the programming effort involved in developing and maintaining systems. An advance in this direction has been made, for example, with Burroughs LINC (Logic and Information Network Compiler), which is a software tool to assist in the development of comprehensive information systems by enabling business problems to be defined in business rather than programming language. Solutions to business information processing problems are generated automatically by the computer rather than through tedious programming techniques. That apart, a company may well feel that it needs to have some in-house programming skills if only to enable it to talk intelligently to outside software houses.

But programming skills are expensive and need to be kept fully and usefully employed for economic reasons and to avoid frustration. Furthermore, here as elsewhere, the gap between the costs of tailor-made and off-the-shelf goods is wide and increasing. To write and install a specialized program is likely to take several man-years; to buy and install a packaged equivalent, only a few man-months.

In this context it is interesting to note the emphasis Dr. Ian Ross, President of Bell Laboratories, places on the need to reduce the cost and increase the versatility of software. Speaking in 1983 he said "If you ask me the most dramatic breakthrough that I would like to see, it is not another transistor or another laser. It is a science of software, a dramatic breakthrough which would change the whole underpinning of the way we produce software".

Intensive research on software production methods is now under way in Bell Laboratories and elsewhere. Dr. Ross considers that his scientists now have some clues about where to start looking for a breakthrough, but when and where this will come was by no means clear when he spoke. Meantime, the demand for software continues to soar. The computer market research firm, INPUT, anticipated in 1983 that personal computer software only would have risen from US$ 945 million in 1982 to $ 6.7 billion in 1987. The versatility of the industry and the technology is making suitable package software increasingly available; the economy of it will make it increasingly used.

A major producer and user of software is the Control Data Corporation. The profile of the company, which follows, describes in some detail the application of computers to education and training. This, and other advanced applications of software and hardware technology, are basic to Control Data's considerable progress in recent years.

Une autre incitation prend la forme d'un allègement fiscal pour les entreprises de logiciel pendant les premières années de leur éxistence.

Les effets de ce projet se sont vite concrétisés et la production du logiciel a fait un bond en avant. Les grandes entreprises, telles que Hitachi, ont créé des filiales autonomes de petite taille ; des programmeurs expérimentés ont quitté des grandes sociétés pour fonder leurs propres entreprises ; un nombre croissant de femmes ont été formées pour la programmation avec la possibilité de travailler à domicile ; les grandes sociétés donnent des contrats aux petits spécialistes. De toute part, on constate que l'initiative et la souplesse gagnent le terrain et que les conditions de travail se façonnent à la grande variété et profonde spécialisation des produits. Il n'y a aucun doute qu'au Japon, comme ailleurs, l'évolution est vers une production croissante de progiciel.

L'utilisateur de logiciel peut choisir, pour satisfaire ses besoins, d'acheter ses programmes à son fournisseur d'équipement, lui-même, ou de acheter un progiciel adapté. En pratique une stratégie mixte des deux dernières possibilités est la plus probable, car le fabricant de matériel n'est généralement pas un spécialiste dans le secteur en question. Il fournira sans doute le logiciel initial, sa disponibilité étant un élément important dans le choix d'un système, mais il est peu probable qu'il se charge de l'entretenir ou de le moderniser. L'importance des spécialistes de progiciel adapté est donc capitale.

L'utilisateur d'un système d'information individuel sera aidé par des dispositifs générateurs de programmes que les fournisseurs d'équipement et les spécialistes de logiciel s'efforcent de produire afin de réduire l'effort de programmation qu'imposent la mise au point et la maintenance des systèmes. Un pas a été fait dans ce sens, par exemple avec le « Burroughs LINC » (Logic and Information Network Compiler), un instrument conçu pour la mise au point de systèmes informatiques complets, permettant de définir les problèmes en termes courants plutôt qu'un langage de programmation informatique. Les solutions de problèmes de traitement informatique sont ainsi fournies directement par l'ordinateur, sans passer par des techniques de programmation fastidieuses. Ceci dit, une entreprise peut estimer qu'elle doit disposer dans son personnel de spécialistes programmeurs, même si ce n'est que pour pouvoir négocier intelligemment avec des entreprises spécialisées.

D'ailleurs il faut reconnaître que les informaticiens coûtent cher et qu'ils deviennent vite frustrés s'ils ne sont pas pleinement occupés. Aussi, existe-t-il un grand écart croissant, entre le coût des programmes adaptés et celui des programmes standard. Un programme « fait sur mesure » peut demander plusieurs années/homme, alors que l'adaptation d'un programme standard ne demande que quelques mois.

L'importance de réduire les coûts et d'augmenter la versatilité du logiciel fut soulignée par le Dr. Ian Ross, président de Bell Laboratories. En 1983, il a déclaré : « Si vous me demandez quel est le progrès le plus souhaitable, de nos jours, je vous répondrai que ce n'est ni un nouveau transistor, ni un nouveau laser. Ce serait plutôt une science du logiciel, une innovation spectaculaire qui bouleverserait de fond en comble les méthodes de production du logiciel ».

Actuellement, des travaux de recherche intensifs sur les méthodes de production du logiciel sont en cours aux Bell Laboratories et ailleurs. Le Dr. Ross considère que ses chercheurs se trouvent déjà sur la voie de la solution espérée mais n'a précisé ni l'heure ni le lieu de l'évènement. Entre temps la demande de logiciel ne fait que s'accroître. La société INPUT spécialisée dans la recherche sur le marché des ordinateurs a prévu, en 1983, que le chiffre d'affaires concernant uniquement le logiciel destiné aux ordinateurs individuels passerait de 945 millions de dollars en 1982 à 6,7 milliards de dollars en 1987.

Control Data Corporation, dont le profil suit, présente l'intérêt d'être à la fois un très grand producteur et un très grand utilisateur de logiciel. L'informatisation de l'éducation et de la formation et d'autres applications très évoluées du logiciel, sont à la base de son succès.

□   □

FROM DATA PRO
PEOPLE AND

The basis of software is the programming language and the productivity of a program depends upon the language used. Programming languages progress from machine language, assembler language to high-level languages. A variety of languages is used for different applications. For example, the interpreter method (derived from early work by the Whirlwind Group of MIT) has done much to improve the efficiency of high-level language and is used in personal computers where simple programming is a prime requirement.

High-level languages have made programming easier but the

user must still speak to the machine in a language it understands. Machines can read characters and can now decipher handwriting. Progress is being made with machine recognition of ideographs (e.g. Chinese). For real partnership between man and machine however they should converse in a human language, or at least a kind of pidgin language (very high-level machine language). Computers which are capable of doing this, and which do not just process data but actually process knowledge, are sometimes referred to as "fifth generation". Such computers have functions of understanding meanings, making inferences, and learning, which approach human abilities and the realm of artificial intelligence.

Prior to the attainment of this man-machine dialoguing ability, however, remains the problem of finding a language suitable for microcomputer communications, regardless of type or make. A step to this end was taken towards the end of 1982 when 13 electronic companies, including DEC, National Semiconductor, Fujitsu and Siemens, endorsed the adoption of a standard language. However, the fact that Control Data, Honeywell, IBM, NEC and Sperry were not among the signatories may well signify that something bigger and better is on the way.

base du logiciel est le langage de programmation et la oductivité d'un programme dépend du langage utilisé. Les ages de programmation procèdent du langage machine au age d'assemblage et, de là, au langage de niveau supérieur. utilise divers langages pour différentes applications. Par emple, la méthode de l'interprète (dérivée des premiers tra- ux du groupe Whirlwind du MIT) a permis d'améliorer nsidérablement l'efficacité du langage de niveau supérieur ; e est utilisée dans les ordinateurs personnels, pour lesquels simplicité de la programmation est une exigence primordiale.

La base del soporte lógico es el lenguaje de programación, y la productividad de un programa depende del lenguaje utilizado. Los lenguajes de programación pasan del de máquina y del ensamblador al lenguaje de alto nivel. Se emplean diversos lenguajes para diferentes aplicaciones. Por ejemplo, el método de intérprete (derivado de los primeros trabajos del Grupo Whirlwind de M.I.T.) ha permitido en gran medida mejorar la eficacia del lenguaje de alto nivel, y se usa en computadores personales, donde la programación sencilla es un requisito primordial.

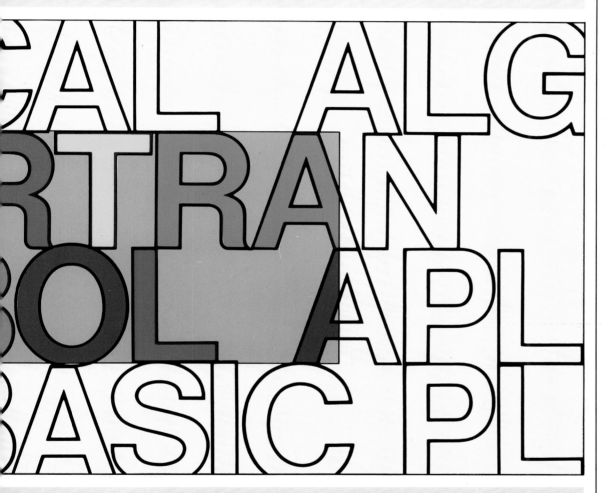

Néanmoins, l'utilisateur doit encore parler à la machine dans e langue qu'elle comprend. Les machines peuvent lire des actères et déchiffrer des manuscrits, et des progrès ont été lisés en ce qui concerne la reconnaissance des idéogrammes tamment chinois). Pour qu'il existe une véritable collabora- n entre l'homme et la machine, il faut que celle-ci soit able de converser en langage humain, ou du moins en un gage pidgin qui serait déjà un langage de machine de très t niveau. Les ordinateurs qui seront peut être capables de le e sont désignés comme étant de la « cinquième généra- n ». Ils ont des fonctions leur permettant de comprendre les nifications, les inférences et d'apprendre — ce qui se rap- che des capacités humaines. Toutefois avant d'atteindre ce stade du dialogue entre omme et la machine, il faut résoudre le problème du langage roprié pour les communications avec les différents cro-ordinateurs, quels qu'en soit le type ou le fabricant. Un nd pas a été franchi lorsque 13 compagnies électroniques, mi lesquelles DEC, National Semiconductor, Fujitsu et Sie- ns, ont adopté un langage normalisé. Toutefois, le fait que ntrol Data, Honeywell, IBM, NEC et Sperry ne figurent pas mi les signataires peut signifier que quelque chose de plus ortant se prépare.

Los lenguajes de alto nivel han facilitado la programación, pero el usuario tiene que hablar aún a la máquina en un lenguaje que comprenda. Las máquinas pueden leer caracteres y desci- frar ya manuscritos. Se avanza en el reconocimiento por má- quinas de ideogramas (por ejemplo, el chino). Para la asocia- ción real de hombre y máquina, deben conversar en un lenguaje humano o, al menos, en un lenguaje macarrónico (lenguaje de máquina de muy alto nivel). Los computadores capaces de hacerlo, y que no sólo procesan datos, sino realmente conoci- miento, se denominan a veces de « quinta generación ». Tales computadores tienen funciones de comprender significados, hacer inferencias y aprender que se aproximan a las capaci- dades humanas y al ámbito de la inteligencia artificial.

Sin embargo, antes de lograr esa capacidad de diálogo hombre-máquina, hay que resolver el problema de hallar un lenguaje adecuado para comunicaciones de microcomputador. A finales de 1982 se dio un paso en ese sentido, al apoyar 13 compañías de electrónica, incluidas DEC, National Semicon- ductor, Fujitsu Y Siemens, la adopción de un lenguaje normali- zado. CDC, Honeywell, IBM, NEC y Sperry no figuraban entre los firmantes, lo que puede muy bien significar que está en marcha algo mejor y más importante.

para préstamos de bancos comerciales a esas em- presas por pequeñas compañías con recursos limita- dos (que requieren normalmente préstamos comer- ciales). Al comienzo, los ingresos de soporte lógico gozan de desgravaciones fiscales. Las grandes em- presas, como Hitachi, crean filiales para reducir la burocracia. Los programadores calificados dejan las grandes empresas y fundan sus propias compañías pequeñas, y ello en un país con una fuerte y tradi- cional fidelidad a la empresa. Aumenta el número de mujeres formadas y empleadas como programado- res, y que trabajan en el hogar. En todas partes hay una versatilidad empresarial que crea una estructura industrial y condiciones de trabajo adecuadas a la variación necesaria del producto.

El usuario de sistemas de información tiene que elegir lo que mejor satisfaga sus necesidades. En primer lugar, puede adquirir soporte lógico adecua- do del proveedor del equipo, lo que hará mientras el proveedor pueda suministrárselo; la disponibilidad de soporte lógico adecuado es una consideración importante al elegir el sistema. Pero, una vez adqui- rido el equipo, el entusiasmo del proveedor puede decaer; en todo caso, no se dedica a escribir progra- mas especializados, por lo que sería quizá una fuente económica ineficaz. El usuario puede basarse en- tonces en sus propios recursos para elaborar sus programas especiales, o recurrir a una casa para que le prepare un programa especial o para un conjunto apropiado. Lo probable es la estrategia mixta.

Los proveedores y las casas de soporte lógico pueden ayudar al usuario a producir medios auxi- liares generativos para reducir el esfuerzo de prog- ramación que impone el desarrollo y mantenimiento de sistemas. Ya se ha avanzado en este sentido, por ejemplo, con Burroughs LINC (Logic and Informa- tion Network Compiler), instrumento de soporte ló- gico para coadyuvar al desarrollo de sistemas de información completos, permitiendo definir proble- mas comerciales en lenguaje comercial y no de programación. El computador genera automática- mente soluciones a los problemas de procesamiento de la información comercial, en lugar de las fasti- diosas técnicas de programación. Además, una em- presa puede estimar que necesita algunas aptitudes de programación interna, aunque sólo sea para ha- blar inteligentemente con casas de soporte lógico del exterior.

Pero las aptitudes de programación son costosas y hay que utilizarlas plena y útilmente por razones económicas, y para evitar la frustración. Y, como en otros aspectos, la diferencia entre el costo de pro- ductos elaborados especialmente y los comerciales es grande y se amplía. Para escribir e instalar un programa especializado tal vez se necesiten varios años-hombre; para adquirir e instalar un equivalen- te ya preparado, unos meses-hombre.

A este respecto, es interesante señalar la insisten- cia del Dr. Ian Ross, Presidente de Bell Laboratories, en la necesidad de reducir el costo y aumentar la versatilidad del soporte lógico. Hablando en 1983, dijo: « Si se me pregunta cuál es el avance más es- pectacular que yo desearía, no es otro transistor ni otro láser. Es una ciencia de soporte lógico, un paso increíble que cambiaría totalmente el método en que se basa la producción del soporte lógico ».

En Bell Laboratories y en otras partes se realiza una intensa investigación sobre métodos de produc- ción de soporte lógico. El Dr. Ross considera que sus científicos disponen ya de indicios para tal progreso, pero cuando hablaba no estaba claro cuándo se lo- grará ni dónde. Entretanto, la demanda sigue cre- ciento. La firma de investigación de mercados de computador, INPUT, adelantó en 1983 que sola- mente el soporte lógico de computador personal pa- sará de 945 millones $ en 1982 a 6700 millones $ en 1987.

Control Data Corporation, cuyo perfil sigue, pre- senta el interés de ser al mismo tiempo un gran productor y un gran usuario de soporte lógico. Esto, unido a otras aplicaciones tecnológicas del soporte lógico, constituye la base de su éxito.

□

⊞ CONTROL DATA

Control Data Corporation

Addressing Needs as Opportunities

TODAY, IN EVERY corner of the world, there is an insatiable demand for knowledge. Control Data has assembled a unique array of products and services that makes the company exceptionally well qualified to meet this need in the many ways it is manifest. For example:

— an engineer at a major automobile manufacturing plant in Germany designs an engine part on a terminal connected to a Control Data computer;

— an owner of a small business in Atlanta, Georgia, adds to his knowledge of marketing at a PLATO® terminal in a Control Data Learning Center;

— an American research scientist investigating nuclear fusion uses a Control Data computer to process data from a 12-trillion-watt laser system;

— government officials in a European country work with Control Data information consultants to develop a national property record system using advanced data base methods;

— a geophysicist at an oil company's offices in Norway consults a printout of seismic traces produced by a Control Data computer;

— company managers in Japan tap the power of a Control Data supercomputer over a data services network to get the answers they need to help run their businesses;

— a major Hong Kong bank uses a Control Data financial application system to help manage its foreign exchange operation;

— a small business entrepreneur in the Netherlands locates his office in a Control Data Business and Technology Center where he gets space, office services, and marketing assistance.

This is Control Data today, an international organization helping people and organizations solve

▷ 326

DE NOS JOURS, une demande insatiable de connaissances se manifeste partout dans le monde. Control Data a groupé un ensemble exceptionnel de produits et de services qui confère à cette société une qualification incontestable pour répondre à cette demande insatiable, sous toutes ses formes. Par exemple :

— un ingénieur d'une grande fabrique d'automobiles allemande conçoit une partie de moteur sur un terminal relié à un ordinateur de Control Data ;

— le propriétaire d'une petite affaire d'Atlanta, en Géorgie, parfait ses connaissances en matière de commercialisation, en concentrant son attention sur un terminal PLATO®, dans un centre d'enseignement de Control Data ;

— un scientifique américain, qui étudie la fusion nucléaire, utilise un ordinateur de Control Data pour traiter les données provenant d'un système laser à 12 000 milliards de watts ;

— des fonctionnaires d'un pays européen travaillent avec des informaticiens de Control Data à la mise au point d'un système national de registre foncier utilisant des méthodes informatiques spéciales ;

— un géophysicien consulte, dans l'un des bureaux d'une compagnie pétrolière norvégienne, le tracé d'une secousse sismique relevé par un ordinateur de Control Data ;

— les administrateurs d'une société japonaise mettent à contribution la puissance d'un super-ordinateur de Control Data sur le réseau des services de données, afin d'obtenir les réponses dont ils ont besoin pour exploiter rationnellement leurs affaires ;

— une grande banque de Hong Kong utilise un système d'applications financières de Control Data, pour faciliter ses opérations de change à l'étranger ;

— le directeur d'une petite société des Pays-Bas installe son bureau dans un des Centres d'Affaires et de Technologie de Control Data, où il dispose d'un local, de services de bureau et de l'assistance nécessaire pour ses opérations de commercialisation.

▷ 326

EXISTE EN TODOS LOS RINCONES del mundo una insaciable demanda de conocimientos. Control Data ha reunido una serie única de productos y servicios que la coloca en situación excepcional para atender tal necesidad en sus múltiples formas. Por ejemplo:

— un ingeniero de una fábrica de automóviles de Alemania diseña un parte del motor en un terminal conectado a un computador de Control Data;

— el propietario de una pequeña empresa de Atlanta (Georgia) mejora sus conocimientos de comercialización en un terminal PLATO® de un centro de aprendizaje de Control Data;

— un científico americano que investiga la fusión nuclear utiliza un computador de Control Data para procesar datos desde un sistema láser de 12 trillones de vatios;

— funcionarios de un país europeo trabajan con consultores de información de Control Data para desarrollar un sistema de registro de propiedad nacional aplicando métodos de base de datos avanzados;

— un geofísico consulta en la oficina de una empresa petrolera de Noruega una tabulación de huellas sísmicas producida por un computador de Control Data;

— directores de empresas japoneses utilizan la energía de un supercomputador de Control Data en una red de servicios de datos para dirigir sus operaciones comerciales;

— un importante banco de Hong Kong emplea un sistema de aplicación financiera de Control Data para dirigir sus operaciones de moneda extranjera;

— un pequeño empresario de Países Bajos ubica su oficina en un centro comercial y tecnológico de Control Data, donde obtiene espacio, servicios de oficina y asistencia para la comercialización.

▷ 326

The vast new vistas of computer applications.

Les horizons sans fin de la télématique.

Las enormes perspectivas del computador.

LI 6T
01 UP CRT RECV ACT
02 UP CRT XMIT
03 UP CRT RECV ACT
04 UP CRT XMIT
05 UP TTY RECV ACT 1550   0660   0666   0697   0805   0761   0656   1712 9* 5T
07 DM TTY RECV   0000   0000   0000   0000   0000   0001   0000   0000 9* 1M
08 UP TTY XMIT IDL 0359 0181   0159   0201   0417   0377   0463   0213 9* 4L
              40 (0000) 41 (0000)
09 DM TTY RECV   0000   0000   0000   0000   0000   0000   0000   0000 9* 1M
10 UP TTY XMIT IDL 0012 0003   0004   0004   0004   0005   0001   0004 9* 7T
              42 (0000) 43 (0000)
11 UP TTY RECV IDL 0000 0000   0014   0000   0000   0000   0000   0000 9* 8T
12 UP TTY XMIT IDL 0002 0014   39 (0000)
              44 (0000) 45 (0000) 0071   0067   0148   0183   0159   0074 9* 1T
13 UP TTY RECV ACT 0144 0101   0071   0055   0066   0145   0141   0131   0074 9* 1T
         TO= 0013   0000   0055   0066   0145   0141   0131   0089 3* 1M
15 UP TTY RECV ACT 0144 0000   0058   0070   0102   0189   0165   0099 3* 1M
         TO= 0016   0084   0058   0070   0102   0189   0165   0094 3* 1M
17 UP TTY RECV ACT 0159 0084   0088   0095   0177   0209   0136   0094 3* 1M
         TO= 0012   0113   0088   0095   0177   0136   0101   0094 3* 1M
19 UP TTY RECV ACT 0163 0113   0080   0057   0117   0136   0101   0094 3* 1M
         TO= 0022   0082   0080   0057   0117
21 UP TTY RECV ACT 0177 0082

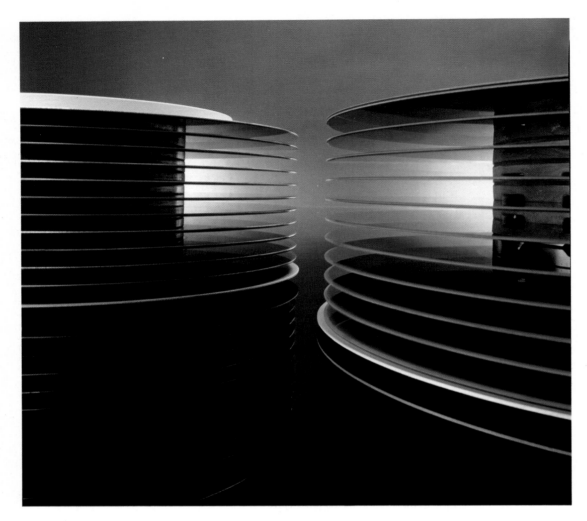

On the left: Disk packs for computer systems. Control Data also manufactures a complete line of cartridges, flexible disks, printer ribbons and other data processing products.

A gauche : Chargeurs de disques amovibles pour des systèmes d'ordinateurs. Control Data les produit pour optimiser les performances, avec en plus, une gamme complète de cartouches, de disques souples, de rubans d'imprimantes, ainsi que d'autres produits pour le traitement de données.

A la izquierda: Cargadores de discos amovibles para sistemas de computador. Control Data los fabrica para optimar el rendimiento, mas una gama completa de cartuchos, discos flexibles, cintas e impresores, así como otros productos para el tratamiento de datos.

On the right: Drill hole data analysis by a GeoCYBER workstation which functions on site both as a micro-computer and as an access terminal to data bases and applications from larger computer systems.

A droite : Analyse des données de forage, faite par un poste de travail GeoCYBER qui fonctionne sur le chantier à la fois comme micro-ordinateur et comme terminal d'accès aux banques de données et aux applications de grands systèmes d'ordinateurs.

A la derecha: Análisis de datos de un tres de sondeo, realizado por un puesto de trabajo GeoCYBER, que funciona in situ como microcomputador y termindl de acceso a bancos de datos y aplicaciones de grandes sistemas de computador.

problems by applying advanced technology. The company's goal is to help meet the fundamental needs that exist worldwide for higher productivity, better education, creation and distribution of knowledge, and more jobs, wherever the need for knowledge is the basic ingredient.

Central to its corporate strategy are the problem-solving capabilities of the computer and the ability of telecommunications technology to distribute computer power to every corner of the world. Combined with the technical and management skills of Control Data people and the company's financial resources, these converging technologies provide a foundation from which Control Data addresses the deepest social and economic problems in a wide range of cultural and economic settings.

Large-scale computer systems needed to solve complex engineering and scientific problems have been provided by Control Data for more than two decades. Continuing research and development has produced a steady stream of technological innovation which enabled the company to keep pace with even the most complex needs of business, industry, educational institutions and governments throughout the world. In recent years it has also developed minicomputer and microcomputer-based systems to meet the growing need for efficient, economical distributed processing.

Peripheral equipment offered by Control Data to the data processing and word processing markets constitutes one of the broadest selections available from a single source — everything from rigid disks and the latest flexible disks to software systems that help customers get more use out of their equipment. Also, computer manufacturers throughout the world buy more peripherals from Control Data than from any other independent supplier.

Control Data est aujourd'hui une organisation internationale capable d'aider aussi bien des personnes physiques que des organismes publics ou des entreprises privées, à résoudre leurs problèmes en appliquant des techniques de pointe. Son objectif est de continuer à répondre efficacement, dans le monde entier, à tous les besoins fondamentaux concernant : l'amélioration de la productivité, l'élévation des normes d'enseignement, l'élaboration et la diffusion des connaissances, ainsi que la création d'emplois, chaque fois que la connaissance se révèle comme l'élément indispensable pour atteindre ces buts.

L'efficacité de la stratégie de Control Data résulte de son aptitude à résoudre une foule de problèmes en mettant en œuvre l'informatique et les télécommunications, et en répercutant aux quatre coins du monde la puissance de ses ordinateurs. Cette dynamique convergente de l'informatique et des télécommunications, combinée avec les capacités techniques et administratives du personnel, et avec les ressources financières de la compagnie, constituent les fondements qui permettent à cette organisation de s'attaquer à des problèmes économiques et sociaux très complexes.

Les grands systèmes informatiques requis pour résoudre les problèmes techniques et scientifiques d'une grande complexité sont la spécialité de Control Data depuis plus de 20 ans. Des travaux de recherche, et de mise au point incessants, ont abouti à un flux régulier d'innovations techniques qui ont permis à la société de répondre, dans le monde entier, aux besoins multiples et très diversifiés des organismes commerciaux et industriels, des établissements d'enseignement et des gouvernements.

L'équipement périphérique fourni par Control Data dans le domaine du traitement de données et du traitement de texte représente une des plus grandes gammes provenant de la même source : depuis les disques rigides et les modèles les plus récents de disques souples, jusqu'au système logiciel, permettant aux usagers de tirer le meilleur parti de leur équipement informatique.

Esto es hoy Control Data: una organización internacional que ayuda al individuo y a las instituciones a resolver problemas aplicando tecnología avanzada. Su objetivo es satisfacer las necesidades esenciales del mundo en cuanto a mayor productividad, mejor educación, creación y distribución de conocimientos, y más empleos, siempre que el elemento básico es la necesidad de conocimientos.

En el centro de su estrategia global figuran las capacidades del computador para resolver problemas y la facultad de la tecnología de telecomunicaciones para distribuir potencia de computador a todos los rincones del mundo. Combinadas con las aptitudes técnicas y de gestión del personal de Control Data y con sus recursos financieros, esas tecnologías convergentes sirven de base para abordar los problemas sociales y económicos más agudos en una amplia gama de medios culturales y económicos.

Los grandes sistemas de computador requeridos para resolver los complejos problemas técnicos y científicos son la especialidad de Control Data desde hace más de 20 años. La investigación y el desarrollo constantes han producido una innovación tecnológica que permite a la empresa atender en todo momento las necesidades más complejas de las instituciones comerciales, industriales, educativas y gubernamentales del mundo. En los últimos años, también ha desarrollado sistemas a base de mini y microcomputadores para satisfacer las crecientes necesidades de tratamiento eficaz y distribución económica de la información.

El equipo periférico que ofrece Control Data a los mercados de procesamiento de datos y de texto es uno de los más amplios de una sola fuente: desde discos rígidos y los últimos discos flexibles hasta sistemas de soporte lógico, que ayudan al usuario a sacar más

▷ 327

▷ 327

▷ 327

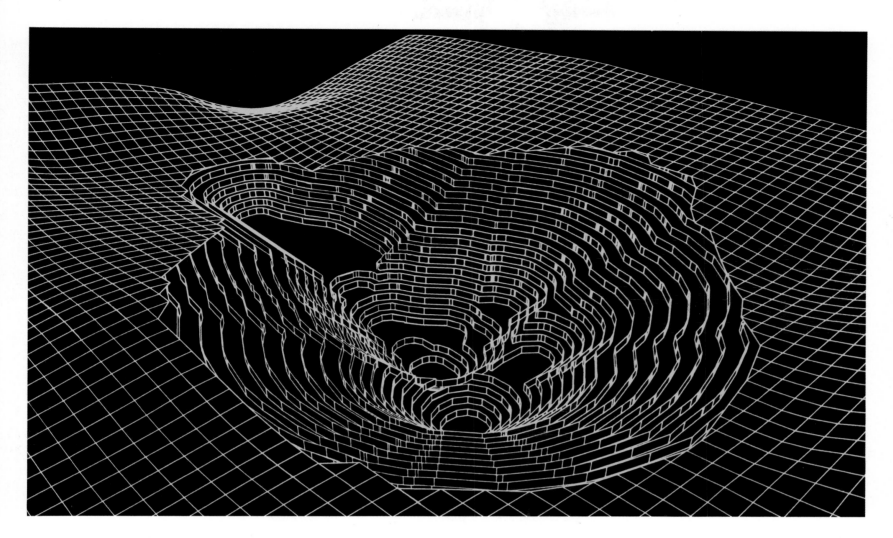

Worldwide data services networks provided by Control Data are used by organizations whose special computing requirements cannot be handled on in-house systems. CYBERNET ® Services provides remote computing facilities for a broad range of scientific and engineering applications. These services are available in the United States, Canada, South America, Europe, the Middle East, South Africa, Australia and Japan. Through satellite telecommunications, the power of "supercomputers" is available to users at each location.

Business applications are provided on a time-sharing basis to help managers plan, report, and analyze the course of their various businesses. The spectrum of business services includes financial modeling, corporate cash flow analysis, sales reporting and forecasting, salary and fringe benefits analysis, budget preparation, performance reports, trend analysis and profit projections. Extensive applications libraries include numerous industry-specific programs and a growing list of data bases.

Financial, insurance, and related services are provided by Control Data's subsidiary, Commercial Credit Company, to both large and small businesses as well as individuals.

Financial services offered outside North America range from leasing in France, Japan and Brazil to a full-service consumer and commercial finance company in the United Kingdom. Commercial Credit's international trading company provides basic marketing expertise and bartering facilities for organizations and countries seeking international outlets

Un réseau mondial de traitement de données est fourni par Control Data aux entreprises qui ne disposent pas du système informatique requis pour satisfaire leurs propres besoins. Les services CYBERNET ® offrent des facilités de « télécalcul » utilisable pour une multitude d'applications scientifiques et techniques, aux Etats-Unis, au Canada, en Amérique du Sud, en Europe, au Moyen-Orient, en Afrique du Sud, en Australie et au Japon. Grâce aux liaisons par satellite, les utilisateurs disposent sur place, chez eux, de la puissance des « super-ordinateurs » de Control Data.

Les services offerts aux entreprises sont fournis en partage de temps, pour faciliter aux dirigeants la planification, le compte rendu et l'analyse du déroulement de leurs affaires. L'éventail des services offerts comprend la modélisation financière, l'analyse des mouvements de trésorerie, l'état et les prévisions des ventes, l'analyse des salaires et des prestations annexes, la préparation du budget, les rapports d'activité, l'analyse des tendances et les prévisions de bénéfices. Des bibliothèques d'applications très complètes contiennent de nombreux programmes spécifiques pour les diverses branches industrielles et un répertoire de bases de données qui est régulièrement tenu à jour.

Des services financiers sont fournis par Commercial Credit Company, une filiale de Control Data. Ceux-ci comprennent une gamme très complète de services d'assurances et de services annexes offerts aux grandes comme aux petites entreprises, et même aux particuliers.

En dehors de l'Amérique du Nord, ces services financiers s'étendent du crédit-bail (en France, au Japon et au Brésil) à une société de financement complet pour les particuliers et le commerce (au Royaume-Uni). La société commerciale internationale dépendant de Commercial Credit offre des services d'experts en commercialisation et des facilités d'échange aux organismes et aux pays qui cherchent des débouchés internationaux pour leurs matières premières et leurs produits. Deux filiales de

provecho de su equipo. Los fabricantes de computadores del mundo entero compran también más equipo periférico de Control Data que de cualquier otro proveedor independiente.

Control Data presta servicios de datos a las empresa que no pueden atender internamente sus necesidades de computador. Los servicios CYBERNET ® ofrecen facilidades de computadorización remota para una amplia gama de aplicaciones científicas y técnicas. Se dispone de esos servicios en EE.UU., Canadá, América del Sur, Europa, Oriente Medio, Sudáfrica, Australia y Japón. Los usuarios de todas partes disponen de potencia de «supercomputadores» a través de comunicaciones por satélite.

Se ofrecen aplicaciones comerciales por compartición en el tiempo, para ayudar a los directores en la planificación, información y análisis de sus diversas actividades. La gama de servicios comerciales comprende modelos financieros, análisis de cash flow, información y previsión de ventas, análisis salariales y de prestaciones sociales, preparación de presupuestos, informes de resultados, análisis de tendencias y proyecciones de beneficios. Los gabinetes de amplias aplicaciones comprenden numerosos programas propios de la industria y una creciente lista de bases de datos.

Servicios financieros. La filial de Control Data, Commercial Credit Company, ofrece servicios financieros, de seguros y conexos, tanto a empresas grandes y pequeñas como a individuos.

Los servicios financieros ofrecidos fuera de América del Norte van desde el arriendo en Francia, Japón y Brasil a un consumidor de servicios completos y una empresa de financiación comercial en el Reino Unido. La compañía internacional de Commercial Credit suministra experiencia técnica en co-

▷ 330

▷ 330

▷ 331

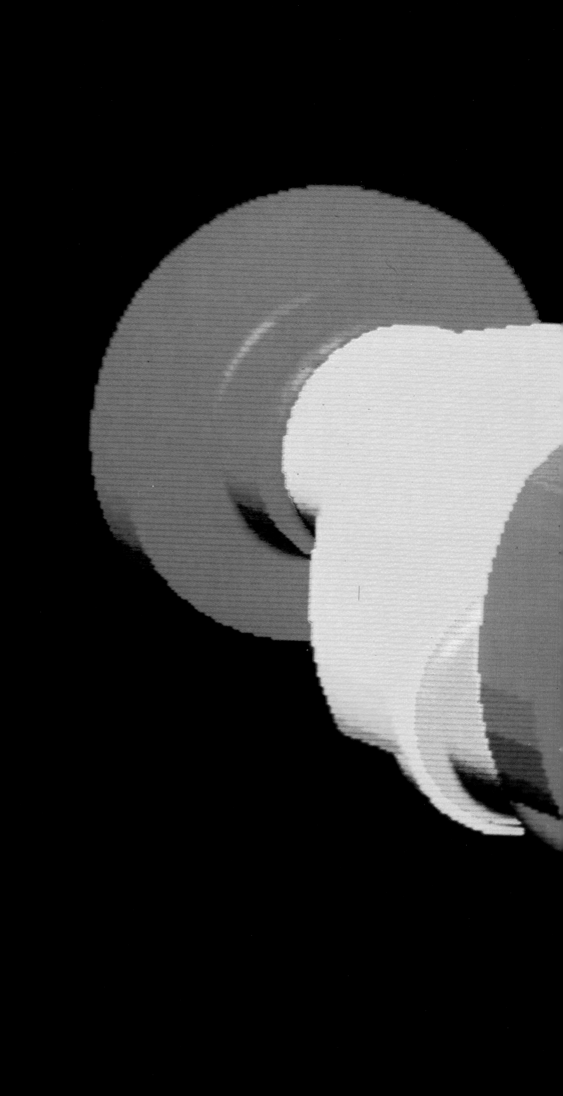

A computer terminal display of a crankshaft design created with the assistance of ICEM (Integrated Computer-Aided Engineering and Manufacturing).Using the geometric modeling capabilities of ICEM, design engineers create three-dimensional models of products and parts. These models can be turned and viewed from any angle on the computer screen. Such a capability aids both in perfecting the design and in creating manufacturing specifications.

Vue sur écran d'ordinateur, l'image d'un arbre vilebrequin, conçu et dessiné avec l'aide de ICEM (Integrated Computer-Aided Engineering and Manufacturing). En utilisant les capacités de modelage géométrique d'ICEM, les ingénieurs créent des modèles tridimensionnels de produits et de composants. Ces modèles peuvent être manipulés dans tous les sens sur l'écran de l'ordinateur. Cette capacité aide à la fois à perfectionner la conception et à créer des prescriptions de fabrication.

Presentación en pantalla de un árbol de cigüeñal realizado por ICEM (Integrated Computer-Aided Engineering and Manufacturing). Utilizando las capacidades de modelado geométrico de ICEM, los ingenieros crean modelos tridimensionales de productos y de componentes. Esos modelos pueden manipularse en todos los sentidos sobre la pantalla del computador. Su capacidad ayuda a perfeccionar la concepción y a crear prescripciones de fabricación.

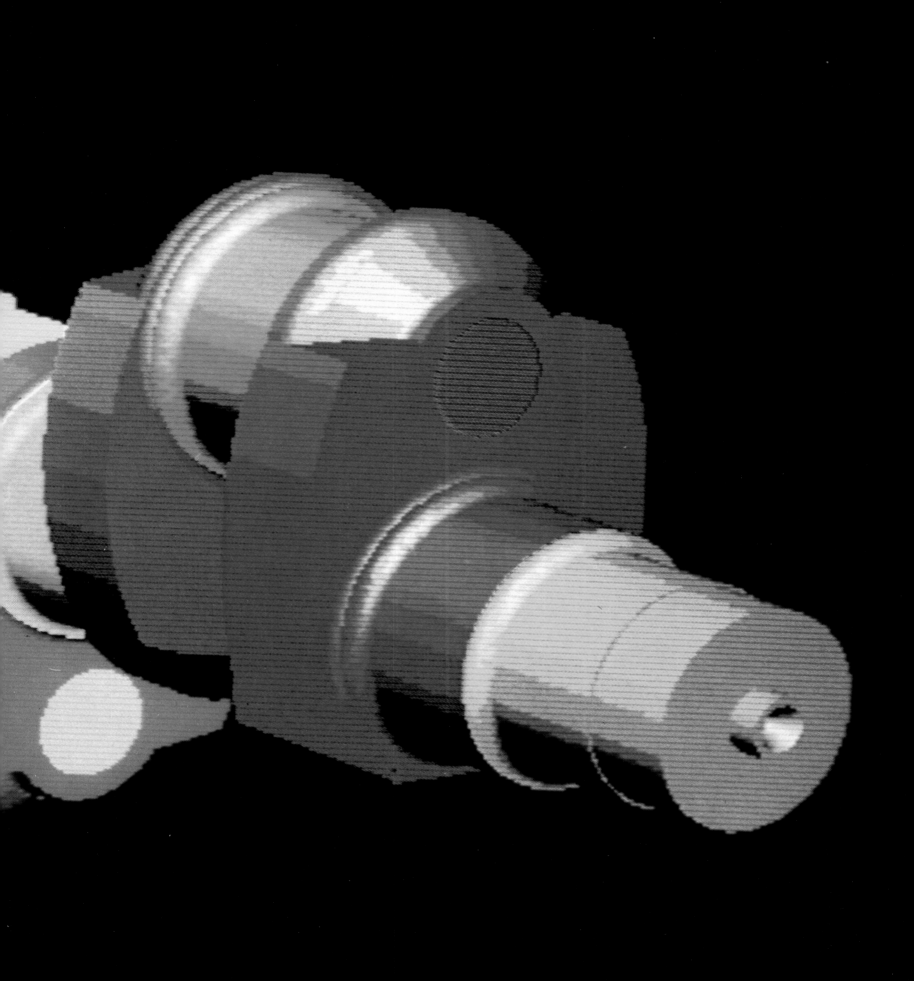

for their raw materials or finished goods. Two subsidiaries of Commercial Credit specialize in countertrade arrangements. Another subsidiary markets technology through an international network and a data base maintained on Control Data computers.

Computer-based education brings state of the art computer technology to bear on the learning process, resulting in an education system able to provide more accessible, affordable, high quality knowledge delivery and skills training.

Control Data's PLATO® computer-based educational system brings a comprehensive range of subjects within the reach of everyone. Remote delivery of PLATO instruction is made possible through telecommunications, providing an example of technologies converging to serve a fundamental need.

PLATO is serving the education and training needs of industries, businesses, educational institutions, governments and individuals throughout the world. Courses range from basic reading and mathematics to advanced upper-level college education and include a large and growing selection of specialty training and vocational courses, such as computer and medical technology.

The human resources of Control Data, strategically disposed around the globe, constitute the key to the company's success. These resources include thousands of specialists with consulting expertise in problem analysis, technology applications, management sciences, project management, education, and training.

This is why Control Data can assist its customers in many technical areas and in such diverse fields as mining, petroleum, weather, energy conservation, electric utilities, discrete and continuous process manufacturing, construction, engineering, communications and transportation. The following present a few examples of Control Data's expertise at work.

Computer-aided design and manufacturing services provided by Control Data are helping manufacturers improve productivity by making better use of their human resouces through a wide variety of automated design and production processes and training. ICEM (Integrated Computer-Aided Engineering and Manufacturing) provides an integrated answer to design and manufacturing problems, enabling the user to reduce production costs, cut the timespan from concept to marketable product, and improve the quality of the final product.

Oil exploration and production are activities whose success rate has been substantially improved by the use of Control Data's combination of computer systems, software, training courseware, and consulting know-how.

The company is a leading supplier of seismic data processing equipment and services to locate new petroleum resources. Specialized software, available on CYBER computer systems and through CYBERNET Services, assists petroleum engineers through such applications as:
— digital image processing using satellite photography;
— "well-logging" to determine oil and gas zones that warrant development;
— reservoir simulation to estimate reserves.

The mining industry is helped by Control Data in a similar fashion in identifying, exploring and developing new mineral properties. By combining its computer technology with mining industry expertise, Control Data offers an array of mine-planning and mineral-evaluation programs through either CYBER systems or CYBERNET Services. Each software package is

▷ 334

Commercial Credit sont spécialisées dans les échanges commerciaux fondés sur la compensation. Une autre commercialise les techniques par l'intermédiaire d'un réseau international et d'une base de données stockées dans des ordinateurs de Control Data.

Enseignement informatisé : Un système d'enseignement par ordinateur PLATO® applique à l'enseignement les techniques informatiques les plus récentes, ce qui a permis de mettre au point un système d'éducation capable de fournir des connaissances de grande qualité, tout en rendant celles-ci plus accessibles et plus économiques, et d'offrir une formation dans diverses branches professionnelles. La « fourniture » à distance de l'enseignement PLATO est possible grâce aux télécommunications. C'est là un exemple positif de la mise en œuvre d'une combinaison de techniques pour répondre à un besoin fondamental.

PLATO satisfait les besoins en matière d'enseignement et de formation professionnelle de l'industrie, des services publics, des entreprises, des établissements pédagogiques, des gouvernements et des particuliers dans le monde entier. La gamme des cours s'étend de la lecture élémentaire et des connaissances mathématiques de base aux disciplines universitaires, jusqu'au plus haut niveau ; elle comprend un choix toujours plus vaste de cours de formation professionnelle (notamment l'informatique médicale).

Les ressources humaines de Control Data postées dans le monde aux endroits stratégiques — des milliers de collaborateurs — sont les facteurs essentiels de son succès dans des domaines tels que l'analyse, les applications technologiques, la gestion scientifique, la mise en œuvre de projets, l'enseignement et la formation professionnelle. Grâce à la haute qualification de ses experts, Control Data peut apporter une aide efficace à ses clients, dans d'innombrables branches : le pétrole, la météorologie, la conservation de l'énergie, les services publics d'électricité, la construction, l'ingénierie, les communications et les transports. Ce ne sont là que quelques exemples des compétences disponibles chez Control Data.

La conception et la fabrication assistées par ordinateur sont des services offerts par Control Data pour aider les fabricants à améliorer leur productivité en rationalisant l'utilisation de leurs ressources humaines, grâce à divers procédés automatiques de conception, de production et de formation professionnelle.

L'exploration et l'exploitation du pétrole sont des activités dont la productivité a été fortement améliorée : grâce à une combinaison informatique dans laquelle sont associés le matériel, le logiciel, les cours de formation professionnelle et les services d'experts techniques, Control Data joue, dans le monde entier, un rôle important dans l'élévation des taux de réussite, aussi bien dans le domaine de la prospection que dans celui de la production du pétrole.

Les systèmes informatiques CYBER et les services CYBERNET, comportant un logiciel approprié, permettent d'apporter aux ingénieurs et aux prospecteurs de pétrole une assistance précieuse en leur fournissant notamment :
— le traitement numérique d'images en se servant des photographies prises par satellite ;
— les relevés de sondage permettant de déterminer les zones où se trouvent les gisements de pétrole ou de gaz dignes d'exploitation ;
— la simulation de réservoir pour évaluer les réserves.

L'industrie minière est assistée par Control Data d'une même façon pour identifier, pour explorer et pour mettre en valeur de nouveaux gisements minéraux. En combinant sa technologie informatique avec le savoir-faire de l'industrie minière, Control Data offre une gamme étendue de programmes de planification minière et d'évaluation des minéraux, grâce

▷ 334

CYBERMAN*, a computerized mannequin, demonstrates the interaction of people with new designs - without the expense and time required to build prototypes. (* Licensed under an agreement with the Chrysler Corporation).

CYBERMAN*, un mannequin informatisé montre les interactions des personnes avec de nouvelles conceptions de voitures, sans nécessiter les dépenses et le temps requis pour fabriquer des prototypes. (*Accord de licence avec Chrysler Corporation).

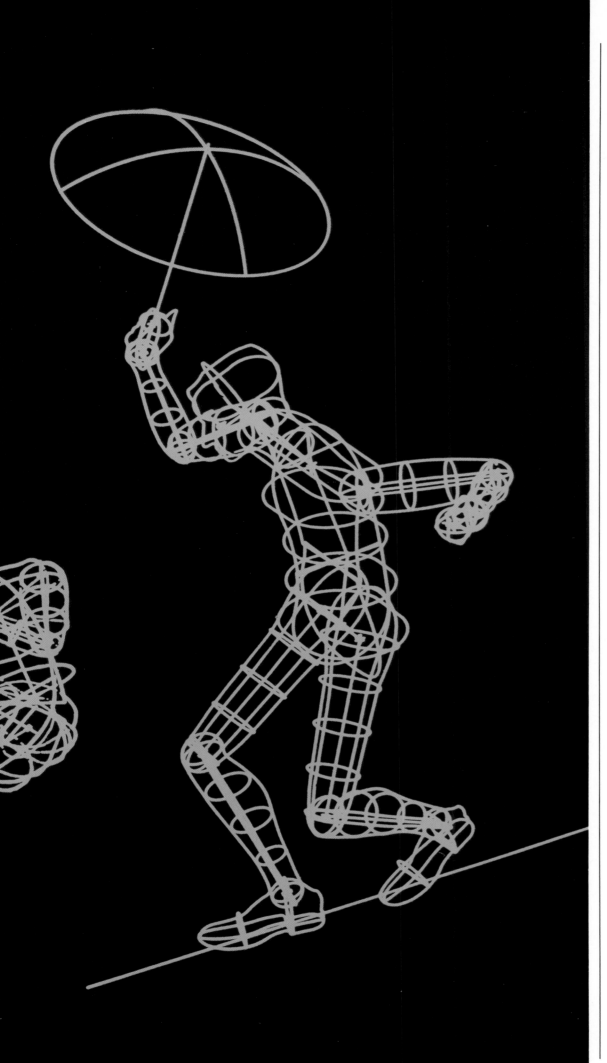

mercialización y facilidades de intercambio a organizaciones y países que buscan mercados internacionales para sus materias primas o productos terminados.

Dos filiales de Commercial Credit se especializan en operaciones extrabursatiles. Otra filial comercializa tecnología a través de una red internacional y de una base de datos mantenida en computadores de Control Data.

La educación basada en computador aporta la tecnología más avanzada para el proceso de aprendizaje, lo que supone un sistema educativo que permite impartir de manera más asequible y factible conocimientos de alto nivel.

El sistema PLATO® de Control Data pone al alcance de todos una gama de cursos muy completa. Las telecomunicaciones hacen posible la instrucción PLATO a distancia, que ofrece un ejemplo de tecnologías convergentes para atender una necesidad fundamental.

PLATO atiende las necesidades de instrucción y formación de industrias, empresas, instituciones docentes, gobiernos e individuos de todo el mundo. Los cursos abarcan desde lectura básica y matemáticas hasta instrucción superior de alto nivel, y comprenden una amplia y creciente selección de formación especializada y cursos profesionales, como tecnología de computador y médica.

Los recursos humanos de Control Data, distribuidos estratégicamente en el mundo entero, constan de miles de especialistas consultores en análisis de problemas, aplicaciones tecnológicas, ciencias de gestión, dirección de proyectos, instrucción y capacitación. Por eso, puede ayudar a sus clientes en muchas esferas técnicas y en campos tan diversos como minería, petróleo, meteorología, conservación de energía, servicios eléctricos, fabricación con proceso discreto y continuo, construcción, ingeniería, comunicaciones y transporte. Se trata de algunos ejemplos de la pericia en el trabajo de Control Data.

El diseño y fabricación asistidos por computador de Control Data ayuda a los fabricantes a mejorar la productividad utilizando mejor sus recursos humanos mediante una amplia variedad de procesos de diseño y producción automatizados, y de formación. Su solución ICEM (Integrated Computer-Aided Engineering and Manufacturing) responde a los problemas de diseño y fabricación, permitiendo al usuario reducir los costos de producción y el período entre la concepción y la comercialización, y mejorar la calidad del producto final.

La exploración y explotación del petróleo son actividades que han mejorado mucho con una combinación de sistemas de computador, soporte lógico, material didáctico y conocimientos consultivos. La empresa es uno de los principales proveedores de equipo y servicios de procesamiento de datos sísmicos para localizar nuevos recursos petrolíferos. El soporte lógico especializado que ofrecen sus sistemas de cómputador CYBER y sus servicios CYBERNET ayudan a los ingenieros del sector mediante aplicaciones como:

— procesamiento de imágenes digitales utilizando fotografías de satélite;
— «registro de yacimientos», para determinar las zonas de petróleo y gas que justifican la explotación;
— simulación de depósitos para estimar las reservas.

Industria minera. Control Data ayuda igualmente a la industria minera a identificar, explorar y desarrollar nuevos yacimientos. Con su tecnología de computador y su pericia en la industria minera, ofrece una serie de programas de planificación de minas y evaluación de minerales a través de los sistemas CYBER o los servicios CYBERNET. Cada conjunto de so-

▷ 334

CYBERMAN*, un maniquí computadorizado, demuestra las interacciones de personas con las nuevas concepciones, sin el gasto ni el tiempo requeridos para fabricar prototipos.
(* Patentado según un acuerdo con Chrysler Corporation.)

The CYBERNET worldwide data processing
network gives Control Data's customers at almost
any location access to the capabilities of large
computer systems and to the company's extensive
software application library. CYBERNET offers
business data processing as well as complex scientific
and engineering computing.

CYBERNET, réseau mondial de
télétraitement de données, donne aux clients de
Control Data, répartis presque partout, un accès aux
capacités des grands systèmes d'ordinateurs et
à l'immense bibliothèque d'applications de logiciel
que maintient Control Data. CYBERNET
fournit du traitement de données de gestion ainsi
qu'une informatique complexe pour
l'ingénierie et la recherche scientifique.

CYBERNET, red mundial de teletratamiento de
datos, proporciona a los clientes de Control
Data casi toda clase de accesos a las capacidades de
grandes sistemas de computadores y a la inmensa
biblioteca de aplicaciones de soporte
lógico que mantiene Control Data.
CYBERNET ofrece tratamiento de datos de
gestión, así como cálculos científicos y técnicos.

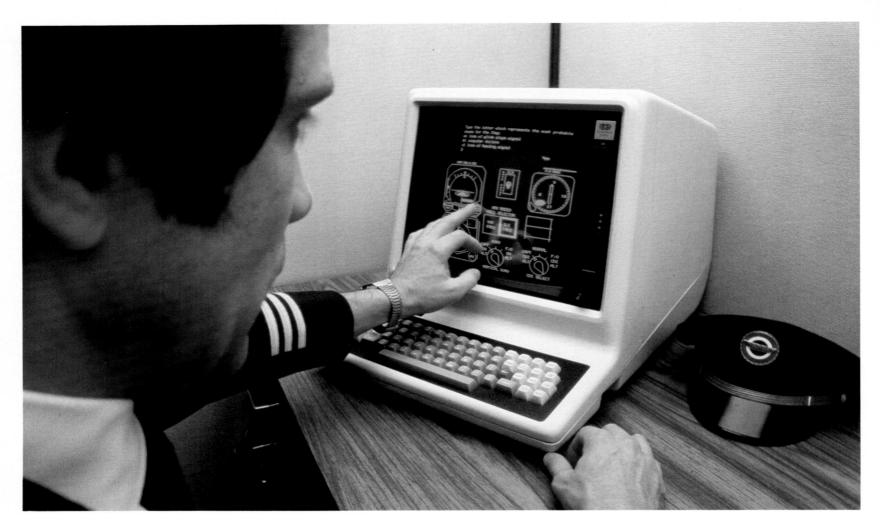

suited to a particular type of mineral deposit and can be easily updated during the life cycle of the mine — from ore reserve estimation through mine-planning and production scheduling to equipment operations simulation.

The weather forecasting services of Control Data are helping to meet the critical need for more accurate crop production predictions. Control Data is the acknowledged leader in supplying large-scale computers to major weather analysis centers around the world. The company's environmental specialists provide a whole range of capabilities, from basic research to the application of state of the art computer technology to specific environmental problems.

Electric power network control systems are supplied by Control Data to electric utilities. Coupled with real-time process control computers, the Control Data systems meet a utility's need for supervisory control and data acquisition, automation, generation control, security analysis and other real-time functions.

The company also provides a wide range of applications and technical expertise to train people to optimize and maintain power systems.

Education and training facilities equipped with one or more Control Data computers can satisfy virtually any requirement of an educational institution. The company's computer systems are installed in educational institutions for use in basic research, instructional time-sharing and administrative data process-
▷ 335

à son système CYBER ou à ses services CYBER-NET. Chaque logiciel est approprié à un type particulier de gisement minéral et peut facilement être mis à jour durant le cycle d'exploitation minière.

Le service de prévisions météorologiques de Control Data permet de satisfaire les besoins critiques en prévisions aussi précises que possibles de la production de céréales. Les spécialistes de l'environnement de la société maîtrisent diverses branches telles que la recherche fondamentale, aussi bien que les applications de l'informatique la plus moderne aux problèmes particuliers de l'environnement. La compagnie est le principal fournisseur d'ordinateurs géants des grands centres météorologiques.

La gestion de l'énergie électrique est un domaine dans lequel Control Data est également un important fournisseur de grands systèmes de contrôle des entreprises de génération et de distribution d'électricité. Associés à des ordinateurs de contrôle en temps réel, les systèmes de Control Data permettent de satisfaire les besoins des services publics, en ce qui concerne le contrôle de surveillance et l'acquisition de données, la commande automatique des générateurs, les études de sécurité et d'autres fonctions en temps réel. Control Data dispose d'une large gamme d'applications et de services d'experts, permettant d'assurer la formation professionnelle et la maintenance des centrales et des systèmes de distribution de l'énergie électrique.

Des moyens d'enseignement et formation professionnelle constitués par des systèmes informatiques de Control Data sont installés dans des institutions pédagogiques. Ils sont utilisés pour la recherche fondamentale, pour l'enseignement et pour le traitement des données administratives. Une telle installation
▷ 335

porte lógico corresponde a un tipo de yacimiento minero, y puede actualizarse fácilmente durante la vida útil de la mina; desde la estimación de las reservas, la planificación de la mina y la programación de la producción hasta la simulación de operaciones de equipo.

Los servicios de previsiones meteorológicas de Control Data ayudan a satisfacer las necesidades críticas de predicciones más precisas sobre la producción de cereales. Control Data es un líder reconocido en el suministro de computadores gigantes a importantes centros mundiales de análisis meteorólogicos. Y sus especialistas ofrecen una amplia gama de posibilidades, desde la investigación básica para la aplicación de la última tecnología de computador hasta problemas ambientales concretos.

Energía eléctrica. Control Data provee de grandes sistemas de control de redes de energía a compañías eléctricas. Acoplados a computadores de control de proceso en tiempo real, sus sistemas satisfacen las necesidades de las empresas en control de supervisión y adquisición de datos, control automático de generadores análisis de seguridad y otras funciones en tiempo real. La empresa proporciona una amplia gama de aplicación y de asistencia técnica para formar personal de optimización y mantenimiento de sistemas de energía.

Educación y formación. En las instituciones docentes se han instalado sistemas de educación y formación por computador de Control Data para la investigación basica, la compartición en el tiempo con fines de instrucción y el procesamiento de datos administrativos; uno o más computadores de Control Data
▷ 335

An airline pilot using the PLATO computer-based education facilities. PLATO offers business and industry employee training solutions that range from training nuclear plant-operators to teaching employees how to operate new equipment.

La méthode PLATO utilisée pour la formation d'un pilote. Ce système informatisé offre des programmations qui s'étendent de la formation des exploitants de centrale nucléaire à celle d'ouvriers d'usine.

El método PLATO utilizado para la formación de pilotos de aviación. El sistema informatizado ofrece métodos de programas que van desde la formación de operadores de centrales nucleares hasta la instrucción de obréros de fábrica.

ing and are capable of supporting a number of campuses distributed around a city or through a region. The often unpredictable mix of processing modes and application flowing concurrently into the computer center can be handled easily.

Some companies and universities with extensive education and training needs find it advantageous to install a system complete with on-site computer, terminals and PLATO software.

For other organizations, the most effective use of system is simply to install terminals and subscribe to the PLATO service. PLATO courses can also be delivered on microcomputers, independent of large computers.

Control Data Learning Centers offer individual and group training with PLATO education as the key element. Individual consumers use the Learning Centers for basic skills remediation in reading, mathematics, and language arts, as well as to learn new general and technical skills.

Each year, thousands of programmers, operators, data entry specialists, and technicians are trained at Control Data Institutes around the world, helping business and industry meet the growing need for skilled computer personnel.

Management assistance is provided by Control Data in support of small enterprise formation and development throughout the world. Products and services are available in six areas where small firms most often need help: technology, financing, management, education and training, marketing, and efficient access to necessary facilities and services.

▷ 338

comportant un ou plusieurs ordinateurs peut satisfaire pratiquement tous les besoins d'une institution d'enseignement et peut servir d'appui à un certain nombre de campus répartis aux alentours d'une ville ou dans une région. Les mélanges, souvent imprévisibles, de modes de traitement et d'applications arrivant simultanément dans un centre informatique posent des problèmes faciles à résoudre par des ordinateurs puissants.

Certaines firmes et universités ayant d'importants besoins en matière d'enseignement et de formation considèrent avantageux d'installer un système complet, composé d'un ordinateur, de terminaux et d'un logiciel PLATO. Pour d'autres, la méthode la plus rentable consiste à installer uniquement des terminaux et à s'abonner au service PLATO. Les cours PLATO peuvent être fournis sur micro-ordinateurs, indépendamment des grands ordinateurs.

Les centres d'enseignement de Control Data offrent des cours de formation individuelle et de groupe, fondés sur le système d'enseignement PLATO. Les utilisateurs individuels recourent aux centres d'enseignement pour se perfectionner dans les matières de base : lecture, mathématiques et langues, ainsi que pour acquérir de nouvelles connaissances générales ou techniques.

Chaque année, dans les Control Data Institutes (CDI) implantés dans le monde, sont formés plusieurs milliers de programmeurs, opérateurs, spécialistes de l'entrée de données, et techniciens, aidant ainsi le commerce et l'industrie à faire face aux besoins croissants d'informaticiens.

L'assistance à la gestion est fournie par Control Data aux petites entreprises pour favoriser leur développement dans le monde entier. Des produits et des ser-

▷ 338

pueden atender virtualmente todas las necesidades de un centro de enseñanza y servir de apoyo a varios campus distribuidos alrededor de una ciudad o a través de una región. La mezcla de modos de procesamiento y aplicación, con frecuencia imprevisible, que pasa al mismo tiempo al centro del computador puede tratarse fácilmente.

Algunas empresas y universidades con grandes necesidades de educación consideran ventajoso instalar un sistema completo con computador, terminales y soporte lógico PLATO in situ. Para otras, el uso más eficaz del sistema consiste simplemente en instalar terminales y abonarse al servicio PLATO. También pueden impartirse cursos PLATO con minicomputadores dependientes de computadores grandes.

Los centros de aprendizaje de Control Data ofrecen formación individual y en grupo; el elemento clave es la instrucción PLATO. Diversos usuarios se sirven de los centros de aprendizaje para perfeccionar sus conocimientos básicos en lectura, matemáticas e idiomas, así como para adquirir nuevos conocimientos generales y técnicos.

En los institutos mundiales de Control Data se forma anualmente a miles de programadores, operadores, especialistas en entrada de datos y técnicos, ayudando a las empresas y a la industria a satisfacer las necesidades de especialistas en informática.

Control Data proporciona asistencia de gestión a pequeñas empresas en todo el mundo, suministrándoles productos y servicios en seis sectores donde mayores son sus necesidades: tecnología, financiación, gestión,

▷ 338

A child learning basic skills on a computer terminal. Both children and adults learn basic mathematics, reading and language skills with individualized instruction from PLATO computer-based education.

Un enfant s'entraînant sur un terminal d'ordinateur. Enfants et adultes apprennent les mathématiques de base, la lecture et le perfectionnement de la langue au moyen de l'instruction individualisée fournie par PLATO.

Un niño entrenándose con un terminal de computador. Niños y adultos aprenden las matemáticas básicas, a leer y a perfeccionar los idiomas mediante la instrucción individualizada suministrada por PLATO.

NASDAQ, the second largest securities market in the USA. The National Association of Securities Dealers (regulator and owner / operator of NASDAQ) uses the Control Data PLATO Learning Center network to test and certify the qualification of the representatives of all its member firms.

NASDAQ, le deuxième marché de valeurs aux Etats-Unis. L'association nationale de courtiers en valeurs (organisation régulatrice et propriétaire / exploitant de NASDAQ) utilise le réseau du PLATO Learning Center de Control Data pour examiner et certifier la qualification des représentants de tous ses membres.

NASDAQ, el segundo mercado de valores más importante de Estados Unidos. La asociación nacional de agentes de bolsa (organización reguladora y proprietaria / explotadora de NASDAQ) utiliza la red del PLATO Learning Center de Control Data para examinar y certificar la calificación de los representantes de todos sus miembros.

In the United States, Control Data Business Centers offer combinations of services designed for the small business customer, including management and personnel training and marketing, accounting, insurance, and tax preparation assistance.

A strategy of establishing cooperative ventures is an important reason for Control Data's success. Combining the company's own resources with those of other corporations, non-profit organizations, and governments is an effective way to leverage limited resources and to establish a comprehensive response to a major need. Each organization brings its own capabilities and expertise to enhance the effectiveness of the program.

For example, Control Data participates in a series of joint ventures in peripheral equipment development and manufacturing. The largest of these ventures, Magnetic Peripherals, Inc., jointly owned with Honeywell and CII, makes disk memory devices. Computer Peripherals, Inc., jointly owned with NCR and International Computers (ICL) of Great Britain, makes tape drives. Control Data and its partners in Computer Peripherals, Inc. recently merged its printer manufacturing with Centronics Data Computer Corporation, creating one of the world's largest independent printer manufacturers.

The recently established Microelectronics and Computer Technology Corporation (MCC) is a significant step forward in sharing technology. MCC brings together a number of high-technology companies who are contributing to a research program that will advance the state of the art in computer architecture, computer-aided design and manufacturing, system and circuit chip packaging, and software.

Many of the problems associated with the acceleration of technology are international in character and must be resolved through cooperation on an

vices sont fournis dans chacun des six domaines où les petites firmes ont le plus souvent besoin d'aide : technologie, financement, gestion, enseignement et formation de personnel, commercialisation et accès efficace aux installations et aux services requis. »

Aux Etats-Unis, les « Business Centers » de Control Data offrent divers services conçus pour les petites entreprises clientes : formation des cadres et du personnel, assistance en commercialisation, comptabilité, assurances, préparation de déclarations fiscales et accès à toutes les services nécessaires.

Une politique d'implantation d'entreprises coopératives est un facteur important dans le succès de Control Data. La combinaison de ses propres ressources avec celles d'autres compagnies, d'organisations sans but lucratif et de gouvernements permet d'optimiser l'utilisation de ressources limitées et d'établir une base qui réponde bien à un besoin pressant. Chacun des participants y apporte ses propres capacités et son expertise pour renforcer l'efficacité du programme.

Voici quelques exemples : Control Data participe à une série d'entreprises communes pour la mise au point et la production d'équipements périphériques. La plus importante de ces entreprises : Magnetic Peripherals, Inc., qui appartient conjointement à Control Data, à Honeywell et à CII, fabrique des mémoires à disques. Computer Peripherals, Inc., contrôlé par Control Data, NCR et International Computers (ICL) de Grande-Bretagne, produit des dérouleurs de bande magnétique. Control Data, avec ses partenaires au sein de Computer Peripherals, Inc., a récemment regroupé son potentiel de production d'imprimantes avec celui de Centronics Data Computer Corporation, ayant ainsi créé un des premiers producteurs d'imprimantes au monde.

La création récente de la société Microelectronics and Computer Technology Corporation (MCC) marque une étape décisive dans le partage de la technologie. En effet, MCC groupe un certain nombre d'entreprises de haute technologie qui contribuent activement à la recherche des perfectionnements techniques essentiels en matière d'architecture

educación y formación, comercialización, y acceso eficiente a las facilidades y servicios.

En EE.UU., los centros comerciales de Control Data ofrecen combinaciones de servicios concebidos para pequeños clientes comerciales, incluidos gestión y formación de personal, comercialización, contabilidad, seguros, y asistencia en materia fiscal.

Una estrategia para crear empresas mixtas constituye una razón importante del éxito de Control Data. La combinación de sus propios recursos con los de otras empresas, organizaciones sin fines de lucro y gobiernos es una manera eficaz de aprovechar recursos limitados y de atender una importante necesidad. Cada organización aporta sus capacidades y conocimientos para mejorar la eficacia del programa.

Por ejemplo, Control Data participa en una serie de empresas mixtas para el desarrollo y fabricación de equipo periférico. La más importante de ellas, Magnetic Peripherals, Inc., propiedad conjunta de Control Data, Honeywell y CII, fabrica dispositivos de memoria en disco. Computer Peripherals, Inc., propiedad de Control Data, NCR e International Computers (ICL), de Gran Bretaña, fabrica arrastres de cinta. Control Data y sus asociados en Computer Peripherals Inc., fusionaron recientemente su fabricación de impresores con Centronics Data Computer Corporation, creando uno de los principales fabricantes de impresores independientes del mundo.

Microelectronics and Computer Technology Corporation (MCC), que acaba de crearse, supone un importante paso en la compartición de tecnología. MCC agrupa a varias compañías de alta tecnología, que contribuyen a un programa de investigación que avanzará la ciencia de la arquitectura de computadores, el diseño y la fabricación asistidos por computador, el empaquetado de plaquetas en sistemas y circuitos, y el soporte lógico.

Muchos de los problemas vinculados a la aceleración de la tecnología son internacionales y han de

▷ 339   ▷ 339   ▷ 339

international basis. The solution of these problems demands imagination, creativity and, above all, responsibility from those who are leading the way.
— A systems house in the United Kingdom improves the capacity and the price of its equipment by using Control Data peripherals.
— A government official in Sweden and a Control Data consultant develop plans for creating jobs.
— A meteorologist at a national weather center scans a forecast produced by a Control Data supercomputer.
— A small business owner in Singapore orders a supply of flexible disks from a local Control Data distributor.
— The president of a joint venture formed by a Jamaican company and Control Data puts the finishing touches on a proposal to train unemployed youth.
— Thousands of students, faculty members, and administrators on dozens of campuses in California tap the power of fifty Control Data computers welded into a statewide university computing network.

This is Control Data today — addressing society's major unmet needs as profitable business opportunities. With every need addressed more resources are assembled, more knowledge is acquired, and problem-solving capabilities are further developed. This, in turn, strengthens the company's ability to meet even greater challenges.

Control Data recognizes the inseparability of its own well-being from the well-being of the world economy, and is wholly committed to applying its knowledge-enhancing technologies to the needs of the world community.

des ordinateurs, de CAO et de FAO, de conditionnement de circuits intégrés, de microprocesseurs et de logiciel.

Bien des problèmes engendrés par les progrès techniques se posent à l'échelon international et doivent être résolus par voie de coopération.
— Un constructeur de systèmes du Royaume-Uni améliore la capacité et le prix de l'équipement qu'il produit à l'aide de périphériques de Control Data.
— Un fonctionnaire du gouvernement suédois et un expert de Control Data élaborent des plans pour la création d'emplois.
— Un spécialiste d'un centre national de météorologie analyse une prévision produite par un super ordinateur de Control Data.
— Le PDG d'une entreprise commune formée par une société jamaïcaine et Control Data finalise une proposition visant à assurer la formation de jeunes demandeurs d'emploi.
— Des milliers d'étudiants, de membres de l'enseignement universitaire, d'administrateurs de douzaines de campus californiens, mettent à profit la puissance de cinquante ordinateurs de Control Data concentrés en un réseau d'informatique universitaire pour l'ensemble de la Californie.

Aujourd'hui, la compagnie Control Data considère qu'elle a le devoir de déployer ses activités commerciales en vue de répondre à tous besoins importants de la société qui ne sont pas encore satisfaits. A cette fin, elle rassemble des ressources, acquière plus de connaissances et développe son aptitude à résoudre les problèmes. Elle augmente ainsi ses possibilités d'atteindre des objectifs encore plus ambitieux.

Control Data est consciente du fait que sa prospérité est inséparable de celle de l'économie du monde ; en conséquence, elle applique toute son énergie à faire bénéficier la communauté mondiale de ses techniques d'enrichissement des connaissances.

resolverse mediante la cooperación internacional. Su solución exige imaginación, creatividad y, sobre todo, responsabilidad de quienes marcan la pauta.
— Una casa de sistemas en el Reino Unido mejora la capacidad y el preciso de su equipo utilizando unidades periféricas de Control Data.
— Un funcionario gubernamental de Suecia y un consultor de Control Data elaboran planes para crear empleos.
— Un meteorólogo analiza en un centro nacional un pronóstico producido por un supercomputador de Control Data.
— El propietario de una pequeña empresa de Singapur pide discos flexibles desde un distribuidor local de Control Data.
— El presidente de una empresa mixta formada por una compañía jamaicana y Control Data da los últimos toques a una propuesta para formar a jóvenes desempleados.
— Miles de estudiantes, miembros de la facultad y administradores en docenas de campus de California utilizan la energía de 50 computadores de Control Data que forman una red computadorizada de las universidades del estado.

Esto es hoy Control Data, que satisface las principales necesidades de la sociedad como oportunidades comerciales rentables. Cada nueva necesidad le permite reunir más recursos, adquirir más conocimientos y desarrollar todavía más sus capacidades para resolver problemas. A su vez, esto la refuerza para hacer frente a desafíos aún mayores.

Control Data reconoce la inseparabilidad de su propio bienestar del de la economía mundial, y se consagra sin reservas a aplicar sus tecnologías para mejorar los conocimientos a las necesidades de la comunidad mundial.

DEVELOPMENT OF HUMAN RESOURCES
NEWHOPENEWHORI AND ZONSNEWPOWERNI
TECHNOLOGY TRANSFER

THE TRANSFER OF TECHNOLOGY, from where it is rooted and is developing to where it does not yet exist, has always proved difficult to do successfully. Like the transfer of plants from their place of origin to another terrain, adaptation is required, both from the receiving location and from the technology itself, to adjust to the differences which cannot be eliminated. Infinite precautions need be taken and certain conditions established. In the telecommunications field it is heartening to register the strong belief of some of its leaders that it can be done successfully and technology flourish away from its birthplace.

Talking to the US technical journal Telephony, Richard E. Butler, Secretary-General of the ITU stated that *the sharing of technology* is "an essential element in the realization of accelerated domestic telecommunications development" and that "people are beginning to realize that you can share technology". He quoted a proposition accepted by the Nairobi Plenipotentiary Conference that there should be an independent world telecommunications commission to examine and recommend "a range of methods both tried and untried for stimulating telecommunications development in the developing world using appropriate and proven technologies on which would serve the mutual interests of governments, operating companies, the public and special user groups in the developing world, and of public and private sectors in the developed world, and to lead to the progressive achievement of self reliance in the developing world and the narrowing of the gap between developing and developed countries". This view is shared by leaders in the telecommunications industry and does not lack support.

William C. Norris, Chairman and Chief Executive
▷ 342

LE TRANSFERT DE TECHNOLOGIE a toujours été très difficile. Pour transplanter les techniques du lieu où elles ont germé pour les faire prospérer sous d'autres latitudes, il est essentiel, comme pour les plantes, de veiller à leur adaptation, en prenant toutes les dispositions utiles pour aménager le terrain d'accueil afin qu'il corresponde d'aussi près que possible à la chimie et à la consistance du lieu d'origine, et à son climat et pour que la technique — comme la plante transférée — soit elle-même capable de s'adapter.

Ceci est presque toujours possible, mais il faut prendre beaucoup de précautions. Dans les télécommunications il est encourageant de trouver plusieurs leaders de l'industrie qui croient fermement que la technologie peut être transférée et trouver un nouvel épanouissement loin de son lieu de naissance. Dans une interview parue dans la revue technique américaine « Telephony », Richard E. Butler, Secrétaire-général de l'UIT affirme que *le partage de la technologie* est « un élément essentiel dans la réalisation du développement accéléré des télécommunications nationales ». Il cite une proposition acceptée par la Conférence plénipotentiaire de Nairobi ayant pour objet la création d'une commission indépendante mondiale des télécommunications chargée d'examiner et de recommander « une série de méthodes, éprouvées ou nouvelles, destinées à stimuler le développement des télécommunications dans le Tiers Monde, mettant en œuvre des techniques appropriées et éprouvées pour répondre aux intérêts communs des gouvernements, des entreprises publiques et privées de télécommunications, du public, de groupes d'utilisateurs particuliers du monde en développement, dans les secteurs publics et privés du monde industrialisé, aussi bien que pour conduire progressivement à l'autonomie des pays en développement et pour permettre ainsi de combler le fossé qui existe entre pays développés et pays en dévelop-
▷ 342

TRANSFERIR TECNOLOGÍA satisfactoriamente ha sido siempre difícil. Puede compararse a la transferencia de plantas de su lugar de origen a otro terreno. Se requiere adaptación del lugar receptor, para lograr la química, las condiciones y el clima del lugar de origen, y de la propia planta, para adaptarse a las diferencias subsistentes. Puede conseguirse, pero es preciso tomar infinitas precauciones y establecer ciertas condiciones. En el sector de telecomunicaciones es alentador comprobar la firme creencia de algunos de sus líderes de que puede lograrse, y que la tecnología florece en su nuevo lugar.

Hablando al Boletín Técnico de EE.UU., « Telephony », Richard E. Butler, Secretario General de la UIT, declaró que *la compartición de tecnología* es « un elemento esencial de la realización del desarrollo acelerado de las telecomunicaciones nacionales » y que « la gente comienza a comprender que puede compartirse ». Citó una proposición aceptada por la Conferencia de Plenipotenciarios de Nairobi de crear una Comisión Mundial de Telecomunicaciones independiente para examinar y recomendar una serie de métodos, incluso nuevos, para estimular el desarrollo de las telecomunicaciones en el mundo en desarrollo, mediante la utilización de tecnologías apropiadas y probadas, de modo que se sirva a los intereses de los gobiernos, las empresas de explotación, los grupos de usuarios públicos y especializados del mundo en desarrollo y los sectores público y privado del mundo desarrollado; se promueva la progresiva autosuficiencia del mundo en desarrollo y la reducción de la diferencia entre los países en desarrollo y los países desarrollados".

De alcanzarse ese objetivo, constituiría un avance decisivo en la transferencia de tecnología de los paí-
▷ 343

Translating the need of high technology business into personal skills.

Satisfaire le besoin de technologie de pointe par une formation appropriée.

Mediante una formación apropiada, se satisfacen las necesidades de alta tecnología.

Officer of Control Data Corporation, wrote in his *Technical Cooperation for Survival* series that "technical innovation is the well-spring of new jobs" and that "we need to minimize unproductive duplication (of research and development) and to share the resulting benefits through worldwide pooling of technological effort at all levels". Countering the notion that keeping innovation to oneself is essential in a competitive environment, Norris claimed that "concern for proprietor position now is rooted more in tradition than logic" and quoted a survey of Control Data professional employees' views on technology co-operation at the project level which uncovered "a deep conviction that it is highly advantageous".

Another powerful supporting voice is that of Robert E. Sageman, Chief Executive Officer of AT&T International. Speaking to his marketing staff on Establishing New Ventures in the International Marketplace he argued that "creating jobs and boosting local economy are frequently primary communications-related objectives, consistent with the growing recognition that industrial growth depends on good communications". Likewise, Theodore F. Brophy, President and Chief Executive Officer of GTE Corporation, speaking at the ITU Forum in 1979, underlined the importance of the Union's role in "promoting the furtherance of telecommunications development and the essential transfer of technology which is involved".

There is unquestionably a generalized desire to promote the development of an integrated global network and a great deal is being done to achieve this — by the ITU, the UNDP and several other international or national organizations, such as the United States Agency for International Development (USAID) and Swedish Telecoms International (Swedtel), a subsidiary of Sweden's state-owned telecommunications administration, Televerket. Some of these activities, especially those designed to provide technological assistance and training facilities, are outlined in this section. Nonetheless it is prudent to take stock of the situation relating to the transfer of technology as it was in the early 1980s, and to be clear as to the meaning of the words. It was defined by UNCTAD (The United Nations Conference on Trade and Development) as "the transfer of systematic knowledge for the manufacture of a product, for the application of a process or for the rendering of a service".

The technology transfer situation was investigated in 1982 by a team of scientists and management experts led by Don Hinrichsen, the Editor of *Ambio*, the environmental journal of the Royal Swedish Academy of Sciences. In a document entitled "The Transfer of Technology from North to South" the team stress the state of imbalance between industrialized and developing countries: "in spite of various attempts to stimulate North-South co-operation, the dichotomy between rich and poor grows even wider. Unfortunately, the technologies used to fuel the engines of development are becoming prohibitively expensive for most Third World countries. Although the direct cost of technology transferred is running at well over US$ 10 billion a year and is expected to rise to $ 40 billion in 1985, developing countries account for only $ one billion a year of the trade in technology which might increase to $ 6 billion". Moreover, the major slice of this goes to 6 countries (Brazil, Mexico, Argentina, India, Colombia and the Philippines) where most of the growth is confined to urban areas.

Research and development activity is a good indicator of the large gulf that exists between countries of the North and those of the South. In the 1970s, six countries — USA, USSR, FRG, Japan, France and the UK — accounted for nearly 85 per cent of the world's expenditure on R&D, and employed some 70 per cent of all research scientists and engineers. A similar picture emerged from a study by UNCTAD of the world's distribution of patents: only 6 per cent

▷ 344

pement ». Ce point de vue est partagé par plusieurs dirigeants de l'industrie des télécommunications.

William C. Norris, Chairman et directeur général de Control Data écrit dans sa série « Coopération Technique pour la Survie » que « l'innovation technique est une source vitale de nouveaux emplois » et que « nous devons minimiser le dédoublement improductif (de la recherche et du développement) et partager les résultats par la mise en commun des efforts technologiques à tous les niveaux ». Rejetant la notion d'exclusivité de l'innovation comme essentielle dans un environnement concurrentiel, Norris ajoute que « la préoccupation de la propriété technologique réside plus dans la tradition que dans la logique ».

Une autre voix puissante vient à l'appui de Richard Butler, celle de Robert E. Sageman, PDG de AT&T International. S'adressant à son équipe commerciale à propos du « Lancement de nouvelles entreprises sur le marché international » il affirme que « créer des emplois et activer les économies locales sont souvent des objectifs prioritaires étroitement liés aux communications, ceci découlant de la conviction croissante que le développement industriel dépend de bonnes communications ». Parallèlement, Theodore F. Brophy, PDG de GTE a souligné l'importance, dans son allocution au Forum de l'UIT en 1979, du rôle de l'Union dans la promotion du développement des télécommunications et du transfert des techniques que cela implique.

Il existe un désir incontestable et généralisé de promouvoir la mise en place d'un réseau mondial intégré et de nombreuses institutions internationales et nationales déploient de grands efforts en vue de la réalisation de cet objectif. Il s'agit de l'UIT, du PNUD, ainsi que de plusieurs autres organisations, telles que l'USAID (United States Agency for International Development) et Swedtel (Swedisch Telecoms International), une filiale de Televerket l'administration des télécommunications de la Suède. Certaines de ces activités sont citées plus loin. Néanmoins il est bon de revoir la situation comme elle se présentait au début des années 1980 en ce qui concerne le transfert de technologie et de bien établir la signification des mots. L'UNCTAD (The United Nations Conference on Trade and Development) les définit ainsi : « le transfert de connaissances systématiques pour la fabrication d'un produit, pour l'application d'un procédé, ou pour la prestation d'un service ».

La situation du transfert de technologie fut examinée en 1982 par une équipe d'ingénieurs et de gestionnaires menée par Don Henrichsen, rédacteur en chef de *Ambio*, le journal de l'Environnement publié par l'Académie des Sciences de Suède. Dans un document titré « Le Transfert de technologie du Nord au Sud » l'équipe souligne l'état d'extrême déséquilibre entre les pays industrialisés et les pays en développement : « malgré plusieurs tentatives de stimuler la coopération Nord-Sud, la dichotomie entre riches et pauvres s'élargit. Malheureusement, le coût des technologies nécessaires pour alimenter les moteurs du développement devient inabordable pour la plupart des nations du Tiers Monde. Quoique le coût direct de la technologie transférée s'élève à plus de 10 milliards de dollars par an (1982) et doit atteindre 40 milliards de dollars en 1985, les pays en développement n'obtiennent qu'un milliard de dollars par an de la valeur des transactions laquelle pourrait atteindre jusqu'à 6 millards ».

Les activités de recherche et développement sont une illustration frappante de l'abîme qui existe entre les nations du Nord et celles du Sud. Dans les années 1970 six pays — Etats-Unis, URSS, RFA, Japon, France et Royaume-Uni — constituaient presque 85 pour cent du total des dépenses mondiales sur le R&D, et employaient environ 70 pour cent des chercheurs scientifiques et des ingénieurs. Une situation analogue ressort d'un étude de l'UNCTAD sur la distribution globale des brevets: seulement 6 pour cent des brevets exploités en 1972 étaient détenus dans les

▷ 344

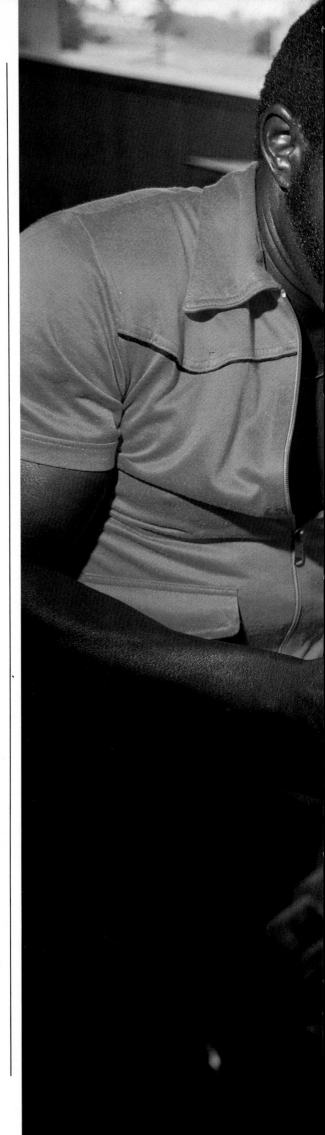

Liberian telecommunications workers receive hands-on training with 3M's MS² modular splicing systems as part of a program to rehabilitate the Liberian communication system.

Des employés de l'exploitation des télécommunications du Libéria s'entrainent avec le système d'épissure modulaire 3M-MS², lors d'un programme de réhabilitation du réseau téléphonique.

ses industrializados, donde nace, a los países en desarrollo, adonde ha de trasplantarse.

La opinión de Richard Butler es compartida por la industria de las telecomunicaciones, y apoyada.

William C. Norris, Presidente y Jefe Ejecutivo de Control Data Corporation, escribió en su *Technical Cooperation for Survival* que « la innovación técnica es la fuente de nuevos empleos » y que « hemos de minimizar una duplicación productiva (de investigación y desarrollo) y de compartir los beneficios resultantes mancomunando el esfuerzo tecnológico mundial a todos los niveles ». Refutando la noción de que guardar la innovación para sí es esencial en un medio competitivo, Norris dijo que « la preocupación por la propiedad está más arraigada en la tradición que en la lógica » y citó un estudio de opiniones de empleados profesionales de CDC sobre cooperación tecnológica que muestra « la profunda convicción de que es sumamente ventajoso ».

Otra autorizada opinión favorable es la de Robert E. Sageman, Jefe Ejecutivo de AT&T. Hablando a su personal de comercialización sobre la creación de nuevas empresas en el mercado internacional, adujo que « crear empleos e impulsar la economía local son con frecuencia objetivos primordiales de las comunicaciones, compatibles con el creciente reconocimiento de que el crecimiento industrial depende de buenas comunicaciones », y, en el contexto de la empresa mixta de AT&T en Irlanda, que es un medio de « convertir la necesidad de nuestras actividades tecnológicas en empleo para la población irlandesa ». Igualmente, Theodore F. Brophy, Presidente y Jefe Ejecutivo de GTE Corporation, hablando en el Foro de la UIT, 1979, subrayó la importancia del papel de la Unión para fomentar el desarrollo de las telecomunicaciones y la transferencia esencial de tecnología que supone.

No hay duda de que existe un deseo generalizado de fomentar el desarrollo de una red global integrada, y que ese objetivo se persigue en la UIT, el PNUD y otras organizaciones internacionales y nacionales, como la United States Agency for International Development (USAID) y Swedish Telecoms International (Swedtel), filial de la Administración estatal sueca, Televerket. Se subrayan aquí algunas de esas actividades, sobre todo las destinadas a prestar asistencia técnica y servicios de formación. Pero conviene tener en cuenta la situación relativa a la transferencia de tecnología a comienzos de los años 1980 y medir bien las palabras. La UNCTAD la definió como « la transferencia de conocimiento sistemático para la fabricación de un producto, la aplicación de un proceso o la prestación de un servicio ».

La situación de la transferencia de tecnología fue estudiada en 1982 por un grupo de científicos y expertos en gestión dirigidos por Don Hinrichsen, editor de *Ambio*, el boletín del medio de la Real Academia Sueca de Ciencias. En un documento titulado "La transferencia de tecnología del Norte al Sur", el grupo subraya el desequilibrio entre países industrializados y en desarrollo: « a pesar de varios intentos para estimular la cooperación Norte-Sur, la dicotomía entre ricos y pobres sigue aumentado. Lamentablemente, las tecnologías para alimentar los motores del desarrollo suponen un costo prohibitivo para la mayoría de los países del Tercer Mundo. Aunque el costo directo de la transferencia de tecnología es muy superior a 10 000 millones $ anuales, y se espera que pase a 40 000 millones en 1985, los países en desarrollo sólo representan 1000 millones anuales del comercio en tecnología, que pueden pasar a 6000 millones ». Además, la mayor parte va a 6 países (Brasil, México, Argentina, India, Colombia y Filipinas) donde la mayoría del crecimiento se limita a zonas urbanas.

La actividad de investigación y desarrollo es un buen indicador de la gran diferencia existente entre los países del Norte y del Sur. En los años 1970, seis países — EE.UU., URSS, RFA, Japón, Francia y RU — re-

▷ 345

Empleados de la empresa de telecomunicaciones de Liberia entrenándose con el sistema de empalme modular 3M-MS², como parte de un programa de restablecimiento de la red telefónica.

343

of the total exploited in 1972 were held in developing countries and only 1% by nationals of those countries. The rest were held almost entirely by multinational companies centered in five countries — the USA, the FRG, the UK, Switzerland and France.

In consequence, there is mounting pressure from Third World nations to obtain financial assistance from industrialized countries to build their own industrial infrastructures. The fact that they provide major markets for manufactured goods and services argues strongly in their favour. In 1980, developing countries accounted for over a third of US exports, 43 per cent of Japanese exports and over 40 per cent of European Economic Community (EEC) exports.

There is no doubt that the transfer of technology is the major problem confronting the telecommunications industry in its widest compass. This was stressed by Swedtel which was created in 1967 by the Swedish parliament for the express purpose of catering for the needs of developing countries seeking expert assistance in tackling their telecommunications expansion programs. Its managing director, Janne Blohm, considers that the two most important aspects of transferring technology were first to define what is needed and to provide the technology and technical assistance accordingly, and second to train local personnel: "the most critical task in the whole process is the development of the human resources". Blohm also argued strongly in favour of the transfer of the best, top-of-the-line technology, and the transfer not only of the technology, but of a complete organization staffed with local personnel at all levels.

Major training programs have been developed by the ITU and by Control Data which is promoting computer-based training (CAT) systems tailored to particular requirements. Both programs take into account the fact that telecommunications technology is changing rapidly, and that the realization of the ISDN involves not only the initial training of very large numbers of construction, operation and maintenance personnel but the extensive retraining of many thousands of maintenance engineers, previously trained in electromechanical switching techniques. The changing technology affects not only engineers involved with maintenance and installation but also telephone operators, traffic, marketing, commercial staff and, not least, the users.

The ITU training program Codevtel (Course Development in Telecommunications) was designed in the mid 1970s in co-operation with the UNDP and the support of experts seconded by Member nations and by leading equipment manufacturers. Codevtel follows the most up-to-date teaching principles and uses a standardized approach to the development of high quality training courses in every aspect of telecommunication installation, operation and maintenance. The program uses standard modules which are fitted to correspond to specific requirements in particular countries and has proved highly successful. It is laying a foundation for an international training development co-operative, so essential to the establishment of an integrated global network.

ITU technical co-operation is not limited to the provision of courses and training facilities. It has involved the entire setting up process of the regional and national networks as well as the development of the structure required for the operation and maintenance of the various systems and, more recently, the establishment of test and applied research centers. The activities of the ITU and the international co-operation that it stimulates are a key agent of transition to a global communication network, leading to a new global economic framework, to the building of national, administrative and financial capabilities and to the up-grading of human infrastructures in developing countries. The growing recognition in the industry of the importance of communications as a factor in national development could well prove decisive in bridging the still widening gulf between the industrialized North and the developing South.

□

pays en développement et seulement un pour cent par les nationaux de ces pays. Le reste était détenu presque entièrement par des compagnies multinationales situées dans 5 pays — Etats-Unis, RFA, Royaume-Uni, la Suisse et la France.

En conséquence, les nations du Tiers Monde exercent une pression de plus en plus grande pour obtenir de l'aide des pays industrialisés afin de bâtir leurs propres infrastructures industrielles. Le fait qu'elles constituent de grands marchés pour les produits et les services est un argument en leur faveur. En 1980 ces pays prenaient plus d'un tiers des exportations des Etats-Unis, 43 % de ceux du Japon et plus de 40 % de ceux de la CEE.

Il n'y a aucun doute que le transfert de technologie est un des grands problèmes de l'industrie des télécommunications dans sa plus grande étendue. Ceci fut souligné par Swedtel, qui fut créée en 1967 par le parlement suédois dans le but très précis de s'occuper des besoins des pays en développement. Le directeur général de Swedtel, Janne Blohm, considère que les deux aspects les plus importants du transfert de technologie sont, en premier lieu, la définition de ce qui est nécessaire et de fournir la technologie et l'assistance technique requise, et en deuxième lieu, la formation du personnel local : « la tâche la plus vitale étant le développement des resources humaines ». Blohm souligne fortement la nécessité de transférer non seulement la technologie mais d'une organisation complète faisant appel au personnel local à tous les niveaux.

Des programmes de formation ont été développés par l'UIT et par Control Data qui fournit des programmes de formation assistée par ordinateur (CAT) adaptés aux besoins particuliers de chaque pays. Les deux programmes tiennent compte du fait que la technologie des communications est en rapide évolution, et que la réalisation du RNIS nécessite non seulement la formation initiale d'un très grand nombre de personnels spécialisés dans la construction, l'exploitation et la maintenance, mais aussi le recyclage de milliers de techniciens de maintenance formés dans les techniques de commutation électro-mécanique. Le changement de technologie n'affecte pas seulement les techniciens affectés à la maintenance et à l'installation, mais aussi les opérateurs du téléphone, les personnels assignés aux études de marché, à la commercialisation, aux transports et, bien sûr, les utilisateurs.

Le programme de formation UIT Codevtel (Course Development in Telecommunications) fut conçu dans les années 1970 en coopération avec le PNUD et l'appui d'experts en détachement par les pays Membres et par les grands fabricants d'équipement. Codevtel est conçu suivant les principes d'enseignement les plus évolués et emploie une approche normalisée pour le développement de cours de formation de haute qualité pour chaque aspect de l'installation, de l'exploitation et de la maintenance des télécommunications. Le programme utilise des modules standards qui sont élaborés pour correspondre aux besoins spécifiques de chaque pays et a eu beaucoup de succès. Il a même créé une norme pour une méthode coopérative internationale de formation essentielle à la création d'un réseau mondial intégré.

La coopération technique de l'UIT ne se limite pas à pourvoir des cours et des moyens de formation. Elle implique également tout le processus d'implantation des réseaux régionaux et nationaux, ainsi que le développement de la structure nécessaire pour l'exploitation et la maintenance des divers systèmes et, plus récemment à l'établissement de centres d'essais et de recherche. Les activités de l'UIT et la coopération internationale qu'elles stimulent sont un élément fondamental dans la transition vers un réseau mondial de communications. La reconnaissance générale et croissante dans l'industrie de l'importance des communications en tant qu'agent de transition pourrait bien avoir une influence décisive dans la diminution de l'écart énorme et toujours croissant entre le Nord industrialisé et le Sud en développement.

□

East and West meet to solve their problems : the sharing of communications technology worldwide.

L'Orient et l'Occident se rencontrent pour résoudre leurs problèmes : un partage mondial de la technologie des communications.

presentaban casi el 85% del gasto mundial en IyD; y empleaban al 70% de todos los científicos e ingenieros. Un estudio de la UNCTAD sobre la distribución mundial de patentes presenta una situación análoga: sólo el 6% del total explotado en 1972 correspondía a países en desarrollo, y únicamente el 1% a nacionales de esos países. El resto casi lo acaparaban empresas multinacionales centradas en cinco países: EE.UU., RFA, RU, Suiza Y Francia.

Por tanto, lois países del Tercer Mundo presionan para obtener asistencia financiera de los industrializados, a fin de construir sus propias infraestructuras industriales. El hecho de suministrar importantes mercados para bienes manufacturados y servicios les favorece mucho. En 1980 fue a parar a esos países un tercio de las exportaciones de EE.UU., el 43% de las japonesas y más del 40% de las de la CEE.

No hay duda de que esa transferencia es el principal problema para la mayor expansión de la industria de las telecomunicaciones. Así lo subrayó Swedtel, creada en 1967 por el Parlamento Sueco para atender las necesidades de asistencia técnica de los países en desarrollo, al abordar la expansión de sus telecomunicaciones. Su Director General, Janne Blohm, considera que los dos aspectos esenciales de la transferencia de tecnología consisten, primero, en definir la necesidad y atenderla debidamente, y, segundo, formar al personal local: «la tarea más esencial en todo el proceso es el desarrollo de recursos humanos». Blohm se mostró firmemente partidario de transferir la tecnología más reciente, y no sólo eso, sino una organización completa con personal local a todos los niveles.

Programas de formación. La UIT y Control Data Corporation, que fomenta la capacitación asistida por computador (CAT) adaptada a las necesidades, han elaborado importantes programas de formación, teniendo en cuenta que la tecnología de las telecomunicaciones cambia rápidamente y que la realización de la RDSI no sólo exige la capacitación inicial de mucho personal de construcción, explotación y mantenimiento, sino la amplia reconversión de miles de ingenieros de mantenimiento, formados para técnicas de conmutación electromecánicas. El cambio no sólo afecta a los ingenieros de mantenimiento e instalación, sino también a operadoras, tráfico, comercialización y su personal y, por supuesto, a los usuarios.

El programa de capacitación Codevtel de la UIT se concibió a mediados de los años 1970 en cooperación con el PNUD y con el apoyo de expertos y de países miembros e importantes fabricantes de equipo. Codevtel sigue las últimas técnicas docentes y elabora cursos de capacitación de gran calidad en todos los aspectos de la instalación, explotación y mantenimiento de telecomunicaciones. El programa aplica módulos normalizados que se ajustan a las distintas necesidades de los países, y ha tenido gran éxito. Está sentando las bases de la cooperación internacional para el desarrollo de la capacitación, tan esencial para una red global integrada.

La cooperación técnica de la UIT no se limita a cursos y servicios de formación. Comprende procesos de redes regionales y nacionales, así como la estructura necesaria para explotar y mantener diversos sistemas y, últimamente, establecer centros de investigación de prueba y aplicada.

Las actividades de la UIT y la cooperación internacional que estimulan son esenciales para una red mundial de comunicaciones, tendiente a un nuevo marco económico global, a la creación de capacidades administrativas y financieras nacionales y al mejoramiento de las infraestructuras humanas en países en desarrollo. El creciente reconocimiento de la importancia de las comunicaciones como factor del desarrollo nacional puede ser decisivo para reducir las diferencias entre el Norte industrializado y el Sur en desarrollo.

□

Oriente y Occidente se encuentran para resolver sus problemas: la compartición de la tecnología mundial de las comunicaciones.

CIT ALCATEL

Compagnie Industrielle des Télécommunications

Communicating Today with the Technologies of Tomorrow

A PIONEER IN THE INTRODUCTION of digitalization in communications during the 1960s, the Alcatel Group provides complete systems required in to-day's networks of information transmission and processing. A member of the CGE Group, Alcatel incorporates CIT Alcatel and its subsidiaries active principally in the market for telecommunications and electronics. Its industrial know-how, plus its facilities for training, maintenance and technical assistance have made it the choice of countries wanting not only to enhance their telecommunications network but also to set up their own industry. In commissioning Alcatel these countries recognized the Group's lead in a number of techniques essential to highly developed systems of communications.

The Alcatel Group employs 40,000 people, more than 6,000 of these outside France. In 1982 its consolidated turnover was 12.4 billion French francs (ca. US$ 1.8 billion), nearly 30% of it outside France.

The international standing of CIT Alcatel rests on the excellence of its products in the sector of public telecommunications. The company began working on the construction of digital time-division exchanges as early as 1965. During the 1970s CIT Alcatel was one of the major participants in the accelerated development of the French national telephone network — the number of lines having quadrupled in ten years to nearly 20 million at the end of 1982 — and participated in setting up manufacture of time division switching centers outside France. Thus, having acquired the manufacturing licence for the E.10, Finland, Poland and Syria were able to start production with the assistance of CIT Alcatel in the design of installations, the training of personnel and the supply of intermediate products.

More recently, major contracts have been secured from Ireland and India under which industrial plants will be set up.

PIONIER DE L'INTRODUCTION des techniques numériques dans les communications dans les années 1960, le Groupe Alcatel est aujourd'hui en mesure de proposer, partout dans le monde, les systèmes permettant la constitution de réseaux modernes de transmission et de traitement de l'information. Le Groupe rassemble, au sein de la Compagnie Générale d'Electricité (CGE), CIT Alcatel et ses filiales intervenant principalement sur les marchés des télécommunications et de l'électronique.

Ses compétences industrielles, ainsi que ses moyens de formation, de maintenance et d'assistance technique, lui ont valu d'être retenu comme fournisseur par des pays qui, non seulement désiraient améliorer leur réseau de télécommunications, mais voulaient également mettre en place une industrie nationale. En faisant appel à son savoir-faire, ces pays ont reconnu l'avance d'Alcatel dans de nombreuses techniques indispensables aux systèmes évolués de communication. Employant 40 000 personnes, dont plus de 6000 hors de France, le Groupe a réalisé en 1982 un chiffre d'affaires consolidé de 12,4 milliards de francs hors taxes (ca. US$ 1,8 milliard) dont près de 3,7 milliards de francs hors de France.

La position internationale de CIT Alcatel a été acquise grâce à ses matériels destinés aux télécommunications publiques. Dès 1965, CIT Alcatel s'est engagé dans la réalisation de centraux de commutation temporels.

Dans les années 1970, tout en ayant été, en France, un des principaux artisans du développement accéléré du réseau national — le nombre de lignes téléphoniques installées a pratiquement quadruplé en dix ans, pour approcher vingt millions fin 1982 — CIT Alcatel a coopéré à la mise en œuvre de la production de centraux temporels à l'étranger. Ainsi, après avoir acquis la licence du E.10, la Finlande, la Pologne et la Syrie ont pu lancer sa fabrication en bénéficiant de l'assistance de CIT Alcatel : conception des installations, formation du personnel et fourniture de produits intermédiaires.

Ces dernières années, la compagnie s'est engagée à

COMO PIONERO EN LA INTRODUCCIÓN de técnicas digitales en las telecomunicaciones en los años 60, el Grupo Alcatel puede proponer en todo el mundo sistemas que permiten constituir redes modernas de transmisión y de tratamiento de la información. El Grupo reúne, en el seno de la Compagnie Générale d'Electricité (CGE), Cit Alcatel y sus filiales, que intervienen principalmente en los mercados de telecomunicaciones y electrónica. Debido a sus recursos industriales, y a sus medios de formación, mantenimiento y asistencia técnica, el Grupo Alcatel es el proveedor de países que no sólo desean mejorar su red sino también establecer una industria nacional. Al confiar en Alcatel, esos países reconocen su avance en numerosas técnicas indispensables para los sistemas sofisticados de comunicaciones.

El Grupo Alcatel emplea a 40 000 personas, más de 6000 de ellas fuera de Francia. En 1982, su cifra de negocios consolidada fue de 12 400 millones de francos (1800 millones $ EE.UU.), cerca del 30% fuera de Francia.

La situación internacional de CIT Alcatel se debe a la excelencia de sus productos en el sector público de telecomunicaciones. En 1965, CIT Alcatel emprendió la realización de centrales de conmutación temporales. En los años 70, además de ser uno de los primeros artesanos en Francia del desarrollo acelerado de la red nacional — el número de líneas telefónicas instaladas se cuadruplicó prácticamente en diez años, para acercarse a 20 millones a fines de 1982 —, CIT Alcatel cooperó en la instalación de centrales temporales en el extranjero. Así, después de adquirir la licencia del E.10, Finlandia, Polonia y Siria lanzaron su fabricación con la asistencia de CIT Alcatel: diseño de instalaciones, formación de personal y suministro de productos intermedios.

Ultimamente, la empresa se ha comprometido a

▷ 348

▷ 348

▷ 348

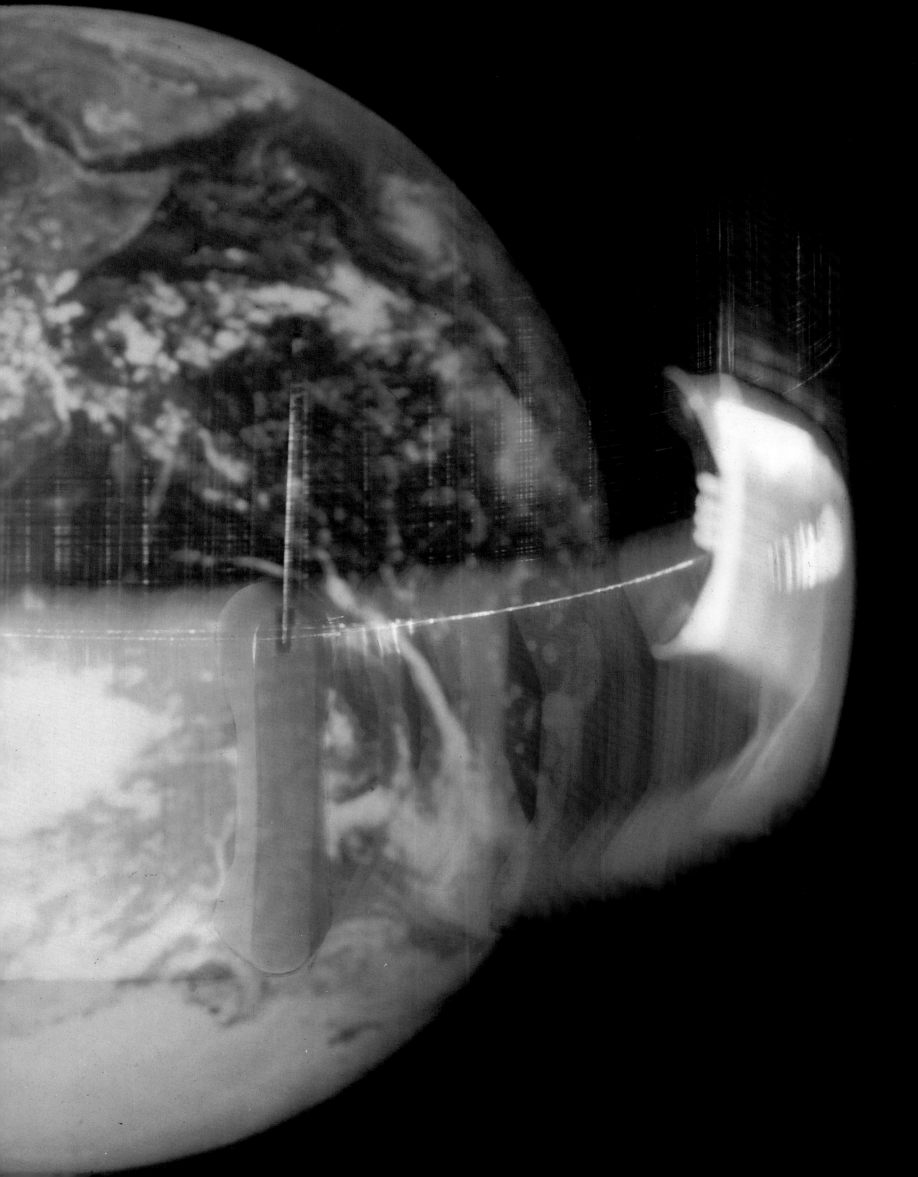

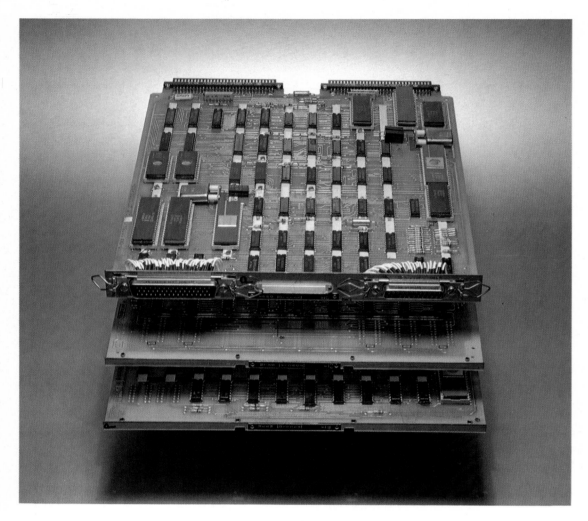

On the left: Cards for time-division exchange.

A gauche : Cartes pour central temporel.

A la izquierda: Tarjetas para centrales temporales.

On the right: Optical fibers,
a new transmission support.

*A droite : Les fibres optiques,
un nouveau support de transmission.*

*A la derecha: Las fibras ópticas,
un nuevo soporte de transmisión.*

CIT Alcatel signed a long-term supply contract with the Irish PTT Administration in 1981. As a result, it has set up an industrial subsidiary in Ireland, Telecom Alcatel, which will manufacture time-division switching systems to meet a major proportion of the requirement of Ireland. In the future, part of the output may be available for export markets.

In 1982, CIT Alcatel secured a long-term contract worth more than 3 billion francs from the Indian government. Under a cooperation agreement, CIT Alcatel will supply time-division switching equipment. After the transfer and adaptation of E.10 technology, the company will be closely involved in the creation of an Indian telephone industry, in particular through the construction of a plant to manufacture E.10 digital exchanges under licence. The Indian contract also covers technical assistance, know-how, supply of tooling and intermediate products and training of Indian personnel.

CIT Alcatel's American subsidiary TSS Alcatel has completed the major phase in the development of the E.10 FIVE system, a product in the E.10 family meeting US standards. The first exchanges have already been commissioned.

The performance of E.10 family systems have made CIT Alcatel the world leader in digital subscriber switching systems, with four million subscriber lines in service in 20 countries at the beginning of 1983 (over 35% of the world total) and more than 10 million subscriber lines on order or in service in 30 countries (approximately 30% of the world total).

Second generation time-division subscriber switching centers (E.10B) suit all modern telephone network configurations with a wide range of capacities. The new E.10S system is particularly well suited to satellite communications, videotex services and cellular radiotelephone systems.

mettre en place des usines en Irlande et en Inde, tout en fournissant les centraux nécessaires à l'amélioration rapide des réseaux de ces deux pays.

En Irlande, CIT Alcatel a signé, en 1981, avec l'Administration nationale des PTT, un contrat de fourniture à long terme. A la suite de cet accord, la compagnie a créé en Irlande une filiale industrielle, Telecom Alcatel, dont l'usine produira des systèmes de commutation temporelle destinés à couvrir une part importante des besoins de l'Irlande et éventuellement à être exportés.

En Inde, en 1982, CIT Alcatel a obtenu des autorités indiennes un contrat à long terme d'une valeur supérieure à 3 milliards de francs. Selon cet accord de coopération, CIT Alcatel fournira des équipements de commutation temporelle ; après transfert et adaptation de la technologie E.10, elle participera à la création d'une industrie nationale et notamment à la réalisation d'une usine de production de centraux numériques. Outre la vente de matériels et la cession de la licence E.10, ce contrat prévoit une assistance technique, des fournitures de savoir-faire, d'outillage et de produits intermédiaires, ainsi que la formation du personnel indien.

Aux Etats-Unis, TSS Alcatel, filiale de CIT Alcatel, a terminé la phase principale de développement du système E.10-FIVE, produit aux normes américaines de la famille E.10. Les deux premiers centraux sont entrés en service et la commercialisation en série a commencé en 1983.

Les performances enregistrées par les systèmes E.10 placent CIT Alcatel au premier rang mondial des constructeurs de centraux de commutation numérique d'abonnés avec, au début de 1983, 4 millions de lignes en service dans 20 pays (environ 35% du total mondial) et plus de 10 millions de lignes en commande ou en service dans 30 pays (environ 30% du total mondial).

Les centraux de commutation temporelle d'abonnés de deuxième génération, E.10B, peuvent s'adapter à toutes les configurations des réseaux téléphoniques modernes dans une très large gamme

instalar fábricas en Irlanda y la India, estableciendo al mismo tiempo las centrales necesarias para el mejoramiento rápido de las redes de estos dos países.

En Irlanda, CIT Alcatel firmó en 1981 con la Administración nacional de CTT un contrato de suministro de larga duración. A raíz de ese acuerdo, la compañía ha creado Telecom Alcatel en Irlanda, filial industrial, que producirá sistemas de conmutación temporal para atender una parte importante de las necesidades del país y quizá para la exportación.

En 1982, CIT Alcatel firmó otro contrato de larga duración con las autoridades indias por un valor superior a 3000 millones de francos. Según ese acuerdo de cooperación, CIT Alcatel proporcionará equipos de conmutación temporal; después de la transferencia y adaptación de la tecnología E.10, participará en la creación de una industria nacional y, sobre todo, en la realización de una fábrica de producción de centrales digitales con licencia. Además de la venta de estos materiales y la cesion de la licencia del E.10, este contrato prevé asistencia técnica, conocimientos técnicos, utillaje y productos intermedios, así como la formación de personal indio.

En EE.UU., TSS Alcatel, filial de CIT Alcatel, terminó la fase principal de desarrollo del sistema E.10 FIVE, el E.10 para las normas americanas. Las primeras centrales entraron en servicio, y la comercialización en serie está prevista para el año 1983.

Los resultados de los sistemas E.10 sitúan a CIT Alcatel en cabeza de los constructores mundiales de centrales de conmutación digital de abonados con 4 millones de líneas en servicio en 20 países a comienzos de 1983 (alrededor del 35% del total mundial) y más de 10 millones de líneas solicitadas o en servicio en 30 países (alrededor del 30% del total mundial).

Las centrales de conmutación temporal de abonados de segunda generación E.10 B pueden adap-

▷ 349

▷ 349

▷ 349

In this radiocommunications sector, CIT Alcatel and Philips signed in 1982 a worldwide agreement under which both companies will participate in the development, manufacture and marketing of a common system, CIT Alcatel having special responsibility for the switching centers. The agreement also provides for the standard utilized to be made available worldwide.

In the field of transmission equipment, the group is also highly successful. CIT Alcatel and les Cables de Lyon, another company in the CGE group, hold about a quarter of the world market for submarine telecommunications.

The CIT Alcatel digital transmission equipment range is one of the most comprehensive, and CIT Alcatel is currently the only company anywhere in the world to have constructed links operating at 560 Mbit/s.

In the field of satellite communications, CIT Alcatel and Thomson-CSF have set up the joint-venture, Telespace, which has already sold satellite telecommunication stations in a number of countries.

Large orders have been booked for optical communication equipment. The French PTT Administration has selected CIT Alcatel as the prime contractor for its planned optical fiber subscriber system. It has also awarded the company a contract for the submarine link between Corsica and the European mainland, in view of its unique combination of expertise in submarine links and optical transmission.

The high quality of the Group's transmission equipment has led to success in all parts of the globe. Orders are regularly received from the United States, where a marketing subsidiary has been set up. CIT Alcatel has also acquired shares in Lynch Communications Systems, an American company specializing in transmission products.

de capacités. Le nouveau système E.10S, base de la version américaine E.10-FIVE, est en outre particulièrement adapté aux télécommunications par satellite, aux services vidéotex interactifs et à la radiotéléphonie cellulaire.

Dans ce dernier domaine, CIT Alcatel et Philips ont conclu en 1982 un accord selon lequel les deux sociétés développeront, produiront et commercialiseront un système commun, CIT Alcatel prenant notamment en charge la réalisation des centres de commutation. Le standard utilisé pourra être mis à la disposition des administrations et des industriels intéressés, dans le monde entier.

Les matériels de transmission du Groupe lui valent également des positions notables. Ainsi, en liaisons sous-marines, CIT Alcatel associée aux Câbles de Lyon, autre filiale de la Compagnie Générale d'Electricité, détient environ le quart du marché mondial.

En transmissions numériques, sa gamme est l'une des plus complètes du marché et lui permet notamment d'être le premier industriel mondial à réaliser des liaisons à 560 Mbits/s.

En transmissions spatiales, CIT Alcatel a constitué avec Thomson-CSF un Groupement d'Intérêt Economique, Telspace, qui a vendu des stations terriennes pour satellites dans de nombreux pays.

En transmissions optiques, plusieurs commandes ont attesté la qualité des matériels du Groupe. Ainsi, l'Administration française des PTT a choisi CIT Alcatel comme maître d'œuvre de son futur « Système d'Abonnés sur Fibre Optique » ; misant sur les compétences conjuguées du Groupe en liaisons sous-marines et en transmissions optiques, elle lui a confié la réalisation de la liaison « Corse-Continent ».

Les équipements de transmission de CIT Alcatel lui ont permis de remporter des succès dans toutes les parties du monde. CIT Alcatel reçoit des commandes régulières des Etats-Unis où elle a créé une filiale commerciale ; elle y a également pris une participation dans la société Lynch Communications Systems, fabriquant des produits de transmission.

tarse a todas las configuraciones de las redes modernas, con una amplísima gama de capacidades.

El nuevo sistema E.10S, basado en la version americana E.10 FIVE, es además es particularmente apropiado para las telecomunicaciones por satélite, los servicios videotex interactivos y la radiotelefonía celular.

En este último sector, CIT Alcatel y Philips concertaron en 1982 un acuerdo para desarrollar, producir y comercializar un sistema común, asumiendo CIT Alcatel la responsabilidad de los centros de conmutación. La norma utilizada podrá ponerse a disposición de las administraciones y los industriales interesados del mundo entero.

Con su equipo de transmisión, el Grupo tiene también gran éxito. Así, en enlaces submarinos, CIT Alcatel, asociado a Cables de Lyon, otra filial de la Compagnie Generale d'Electricité, tiene más o menos la cuarta parte del mercado mundial.

En la transmisión digital, su gama es una de las más completas del mercado, y le permite ser el primer industrial mundial en realizar enlaces a 560 Mbit/s.

En transmisiones espaciales, CIT Alcatel ha constituido con Thomson-CSF una agrupación de interés económico, Telspace, que ha vendido estaciones de telecomunicaciones por satélite en muchos países.

En transmisiones ópticas, el número de pedidos confirma la calidad de los materiales del Grupo. Así, la Administración francesa de CTT ha elegido a CIT Alcatel como contratista para su futuro sistema de abonados por fibras ópticas; en razón de su competencia conjugada en enlaces submarinos y transmisiones ópticas, le ha confiado la realización del enlace Córcega-continente.

Su equipo de transmisión ha permitido a CIT Alcatel conseguir éxitos mundiales. Recibe pedidos regulares de EE.UU., donde ha creado una filial comercial; también participa en la sociedad americana

▷ 352

▷ 352

▷ 353

*Container (left) for time-division
exchange and its contents (right).*

*Conteneur pour central temporel
(à gauche) et son contenu (à droite).*

*Contenedor de central temporal (a la
izquierda) y su contenido (a la derecha).*

In the public telecommunication sector, including associated components, 1982 sales by the Alcatel Group amounted to approximately 5.5 billion francs before tax of which 1.5 billion francs came from countries outside France. Foreign orders exceeded 2 billion francs. 19,000 people are employed in this sector, of whom some 2,500 are located abroad.

The company's further progress will be founded on its achievements. Thus in the digital switching sector, the international success which the E.10B system will provide an exceptionally secure base. The same applies to the E.10S system in satellite telecommunications, videotex services and radio communications. The Group should be able to maintain its position in the world market for submarine links, for which new prospects are opening up through the introduction of optical fiber technology.

Finally, research and development work conducted over several years will enable CIT Alcatel to build equipment for optical fiber cable distribution systems and the integrated services digital network (ISDN). The Company is also deeply involved in the development of the next generation of universal switching centers, the functions of which will include image switching.

As part of the policy of diversification pursued by the Group since 1970, it has been expanding its activities in the "office automation" sector in which the various companies of the Group are complementary.

Telic Alcatel is the French market leader in private telephone systems and its export sales are expanding rapidly. The company reached a significant stage in its development in 1982 when the number of private electronic switching lines in service topped the million mark. Another of its major achievements is the first large-scale production of videotex terminals undertaken anywhere in the world. The company was able, in 1983, to turn out 1,500 terminals a day.

The combination of SMH Alcatel, Friden Alcatel and Roneo Alcatel offers a comprehensive range of physical mail handling equipment, designed and manufactured entirely within the Group. With a market share of approximately 15%, the combination is the world's second largest supplier of franking machines. Friden Alcatel, in the USA, is the second largest supplier of franking machines to the North American market. Roneo Alcatel has an international sales network supplied by three manufacturing plants in the UK, the FRG and The Netherlands.

The Group manufactures electronic mail products. CIT Alcatel produces high-performance telecopiers and printers. Sintra Alcatel manufactures electronics telex terminals equipped with a screen, and is active in the development of teletex terminals and flat display screens.

All these products are distributed through a marketing network covering 80 countries, with especially strong representation in North America and Europe. While this network is oriented towards the marketing of the Group's products, it is also used to market equipment from other companies, through cooperation agreements.

The Group has some 10,000 employees in the office automation sector, of whom some 3,000 work outside France. Office automation sales approached 3.5 billion francs in 1982, of which over 40% was exported.

In the "professional electronics" sector the Group's activities are, overall, on behalf of a number of large public sector clients. Defence and industrial electronic products and systems, and associated electronic data processing systems have been in production for many years. There is abundant expertise in a very wide range of disciplines: submarine warfare, military and civil radio communication, automatic control of industrial production plant, opto-electronics, etc...

▷ 356

Dans le secteur des télécommunications publiques et des composants associés, le Groupe a réalisé, en 1982, un chiffre d'affaires hors taxes d'environ 5,5 milliards de francs, dont 1,5 milliards de francs hors de France. Les commandes étrangères ont dépassé 2 milliards de francs. Les effectifs de ce secteur sont de l'ordre de 19 000 personnes, dont 2500 à l'étranger.

Au cours des prochaines années, l'expansion de CIT Alcatel prendra appui sur les positions acquises. Ainsi, en commutation numérique les succès internationaux du système E.10B constituent un atout exceptionnel ; il en est de même des applications nouvelles du E.10S aux télécommunications par satellites, aux services vidéotex et aux radiocommunications. En liaisons sous-marines, le Groupe doit maintenir sa part d'un marché mondial aux perspectives élargies par l'introduction des fibres optiques.

Grâce aux efforts de Recherche et Développement conduits depuis plusieurs années, CIT Alcatel pourra réaliser des systèmes de télédistribution sur fibre optique et des Réseaux Numériques avec Intégration de Services (RNIS). Elle a déjà engagé l'étude des futurs centraux de commutation universelle qui intégreront en particulier la commutation de l'image.

La diversification conduite depuis 1970 a permis au Groupe Alcatel de se développer dans la bureautique où interviennent différentes sociétés qui se complètent efficacement. Telic Alcatel se situe au premier rang sur le marché français de la téléphonie privée et ses exportations croissent rapidement.

En téléphonie privée, comme en téléphonie publique, les changements technologiques ont généralisé la commutation électronique. Telic Alcatel a franchi, en 1982, une étape importante en dépassant le million de lignes électroniques en service.

Il faut en outre souligner la performance industrielle réussie par Telic Alcatel en réalisant la première fabrication en série de terminaux vidéotex ; la société a actuellement une capacité de production de 1500 unités par jour. Ces terminaux, comportant un clavier et un écran, permettent de consulter des banques de données.

SMH Alcatel, Friden Alcatel et Ronéo Alcatel constituent un ensemble qui dispose, pour le traitement du courrier physique, d'une gamme complète de matériels et qui occupe le deuxième rang mondial du marché de la machine à affranchir avec environ 15% du total. Friden Alcatel, implantée aux Etats-Unis, est le deuxième fournisseur de machines à affranchir du marché nord-américain. Ronéo Alcatel, à partir de 3 usines en Grande-Bretagne, en République Fédérale d'Allemagne et aux Pays-Bas, dessert un réseau commercial international.

Le Groupe réalise des matériels de courrier électronique. CIT Alcatel produit des télécopieurs et des imprimantes de hautes performances. Sintra Alcatel fabrique des terminaux télex électroniques à écran, développe des terminaux télétex et des écrans plats.

Tous ces matériels bénéficient pour leur distribution d'un réseau présent dans 80 pays et particulièrement implanté en Amérique du Nord et en Europe. Si ce réseau est orienté vers la commercialisation des produits du Groupe, il est utilisé aussi, à travers des accords de coopération, pour la vente de matériels d'entreprises extérieures.

Le Groupe emploie près de 10 000 personnes en bureautique dont 3800 à l'étranger. Les ventes dans ce domaine ont approché 3,5 milliards de francs en 1982, dont près de 1,5 milliards de francs à l'étranger.

Les activités en électronique professionnelle du Groupe sont principalement tournées vers les grands clients institutionnels. Il réalise des produits et systèmes d'électronique militaire et industrielle, et l'informatique associée. Ses domaines de compétence sont vastes : lutte sous-marine, systèmes de contrôle, de conduite opérationnelle et d'aide au commandement, radiocommunications militaires et civiles, applications des automatismes à la production industrielle, optronique...

▷ 356

Top: Laying of a submarine telephone link.
Bottom: Repeater for submarine optical fiber link.

En haut : Mise en place d'une liaison téléphonique sous-marine.
En bas : Répéteur pour liaison sous-marine sur fibre optique.

Lynch Communications System, fabricante de productos de transmisión.

En el sector de telecomunicaciones públicas y componentes asociados, la cifra de negocios del Grupo en 1982 fue de 5500 millones de francos, 1500 de ellos fuera de Francia. Los pedidos extranjeros superaron los 2000 millones de francos. Emplea en este sector a unas 19 000 personas, 2500 en el extranjero.

Los próximos años, la expansión de CIT Alcatel se basará en las posiciones adquiridas. Así, en conmutación digital, el éxito internacional del sistema E.10B supone una base excepcional, lo mismo que las nuevas aplicaciones del E.10S a las telecomunicaciones por satélite, los servicios videotex y las radiocomunicaciones. En enlaces submarinos, el Grupo debe mantenerse en un mercado mundial con mayores perspectivas, merced a la introducción de las fibras ópticas.

Gracias a los esfuerzos de investigación y desarrollo de varios años, CIT Alcatel podrá realizar sistemas de teledistribución por fibras ópticas y redes digitales de servicios integrados (RDSI). Está estudiando a fondo futuras centrales de conmutación universal que abarcarán en particular la conmutación de la imagen.

La diversificación aplicada desde 1970 ha permitido al Grupo Alcatel extenderse en el sector de la "automatización de oficina", cuya eficacia complementan varias empresas del Grupo.

Telic Alcatel va a la vanguardia del mercado francés de la telefonía privada, y sus exportaciones aumentan rápidamente. La empresa aleanzó en 1982 una importante etapa, superando el millón de líneas electrónicas privadas en servicio.

Otro de sus grandes éxitos industriales es la primera fabricación mundial en serie de terminales videotex, con una capacidad de producción de 1500 unidades diarias. Estos terminales, compuestos de un teclado y una pantalla, permiten consultar bancos de datos.

Smh Alcatel, Friden Alcatel y Roneo Alcatel constituyen un conjunto que dispone de una gama completa de material para el tratamiento del correo físico, y ocupa el segundo lugar mundial del mercado de máquinas de franquear, con un 15% del total. Friden Alcatel, implantada en EE.UU., es el segundo proveedor de máquinas de franquear del mercado norteamericano. Roneo Alcatel da servicio a una red comercial internacional desde tres fábricas de Gran Bretaña, RFA y Países Bajos.

El Grupo fabrica material de correo electrónico. CIT Alcatel produce telecopiadoras e impresoras de gran rendimiento. Sintra Alcatel fabrica terminales télex electrónicos de pantalla, y desarrolla terminales teletex y pantallas planas.

Para la distribución de todos estos materiales existe una red en 80 países, implantada sobre todo en América del Norte y Europa. Aunque la red tiende a la comercialización de los productos del Grupo, también vende materiales de empresas extranjeras, mediante acuerdos de cooperación.

El Grupo emplea a casi 10 000 personas en el sector de automatización de oficinas, 3800 de ellas en el extranjero. Las ventas de este sector se acercaron a 3500 millones de francos en 1982, casi 1500 de ellos en el extranjero.

En electrónica profesional, las actividades del Grupo se orientan ante todo hacia grandes clientes del sector público, con productos y sistemas de electrónica militar e industrial, e informática asociada. Sus esferas son vastas, lo mismo que su gran experiencia en muchas disciplinas: submarinos bélicos, radiocomunicaciones militares y civiles, control automático de fábricas industriales, optoelectrónica, etc.

Sintra Alcatel, principal sociedad del sector, registra un fuerte crecimiento: sus ventas se han cuadruplicado en cinco años, rebasando los 1000 millones de francos en 1982. Su competencia en radioco-

▷ 356

*Arriba: Instalación de
un enlace telefónico submarino.
Abajo: Repetidor para enlaces
submarinos de fibras ópticas.*

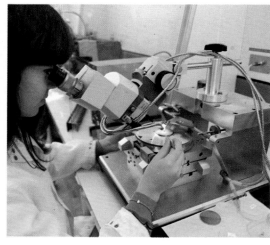

*Research laboratories of "Marcoussis"
and, right, laser diodes for optical
fiber transmission.*

*Laboratoires de recherches de « Marcoussis ».
A droite : Diodes laser pour
transmission sur fibre optique.*

*A la izquierda: Los laboratorios
de investigación de « Marcoussis ».
A la derecha: Diodos láser
para la transmisión por fibras ópticas.*

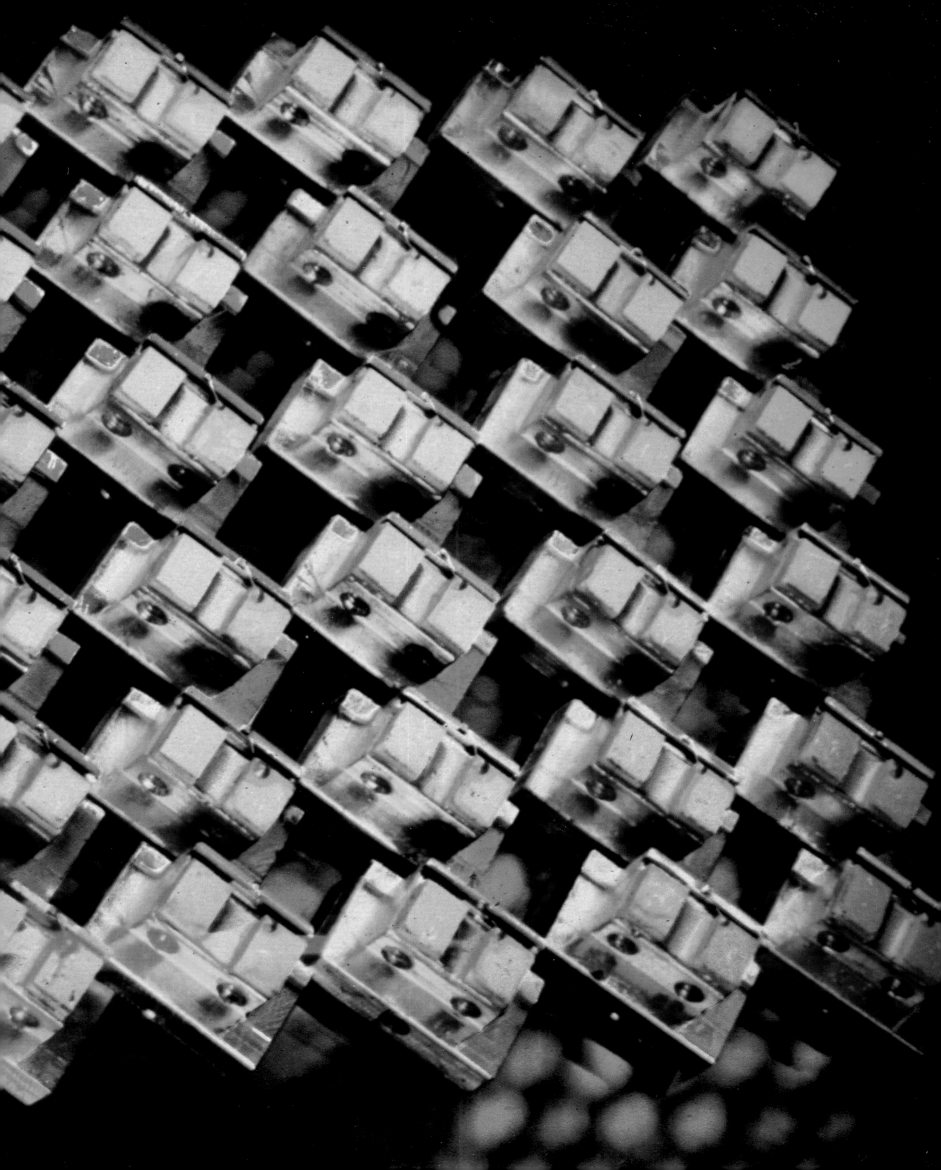

Sintra Alcatel, the main company in this sector, is expanding strongly : its sales have quadrupled in five years, and exceeded one billion francs in 1982. It has already been extremely successful with military and civil radio communication systems, and its expertise in this area is a major asset in the cellular radiotelephone market. The company has all the resources needed by a prime contractor in major military and civil projects: air defense systems, radio communications, etc.

The opto-electronics activities built around Cilas Alcatel are the way for new areas of activity integrating lasers into medical and industrial instrumentation. They will be a key factor in the future development of optical telecommunication systems.

With CGA Alcatel and its US subsidiary Alta Alcatel, the Group is among the leaders in automatic toll collection systems. Major orders booked in 1982 covered fare collection systems for the Hong Kong, Toronto and Baltimore underground railways and the highway system of Pennsylvania, USA. While continuing to consolidate its position in this field, CGA Alcatel is reinforcing its efforts in the application of automatic control to industrial manufacturing processes, banking operations and information storage systems.

Almost 6,000 employees work on professional electronics, and sales in this sector exceeded two billion francs in 1982.

Alcatel operates one of Europe's leading computer services networks. Of prime importance in France, it operates through subsidiaries in Spain, the Federal German Republic, Great Britain, Italy, Belgium and Switzerland.

The Group offers a complete range of services, from the provision of computing power through systems engineering to the production of a comprehensive range of software products.

▷ 357

Sintra Alcatel, principale société du secteur, connaît une forte croissance : ses ventes ont dépassé le milliard de francs en 1982, ayant ainsi quadruplé en cinq ans. Ses compétences en radiocommunications, qui lui valent d'importants succès dans les systèmes militaires et civils, lui permettent de renforcer les atouts du Groupe sur le marché de la radiotéléphonie cellulaire.

Sintra Alcatel peut assurer la maîtrise d'œuvre de grands programmes militaires et civils : systèmes de défense aérienne, sous-marins de gros tonnage, radiocommunications...

Le pôle optronique constitué autour de Cilas Alcatel prépare des activités nouvelles utilisant les lasers dans l'instrumentation médicale et industrielle notamment. Il constitue un appoint technologique décisif pour la réalisation des systèmes de télécommunications optiques.

Par CGA Alcatel et sa filiale aux Etats-Unis Alta Alcatel, le Groupe occupe des positions de premier plan sur le marché des péages automatiques. Ont été notamment reçues en 1982 des commandes pour réaliser les péages des autoroutes de Pennsylvanie et des métros de Hong Kong, de Toronto et de Baltimore. Tout en maintenant ses efforts sur ce marché des péages, CGA Alcatel renforce ses activités d'applications des automatismes aux processus industriels et bancaires et aux systèmes d'archivage.

Le secteur de l'électronique professionnelle emploie près de 6000 personnes et a réalisé, en 1982, des ventes supérieures à 2 milliards de francs.

En service informatique Alcatel a constitué un des premiers réseaux européens qui occupe une place de premier plan en France et dispose de filiales en Espagne, en République Fédérale d'Allemagne, en Grande-Bretagne, en Italie, en Belgique et en Suisse.

Le Groupe propose des services complets couvrant la mise à disposition d'énergie informatique, l'ingénierie des systèmes et la réalisation des logiciels les plus divers.

▷ 357

municaciones le permite aumentar sus posibilidades en el mercado de radiotelefonia celular.

Sintra Alcatel puede dirigir grandes programas militares y civiles: sistemas de defensa aérea, submarinos de gran tonelaje, radiocomunicaciones, etc.

El polo optrónico constituido en torno a Cilas Alcatel prepara nuevas actividades utilizando láseres en instrumentación médica e industrial, en particular. Es un factor clave en la futura realización de sistemas de telecomunicaciones ópticas.

Con CGA Alcatel y su filial en EE.UU., Alta Alcatel, el Grupo figura entre los primeros en el mercado de peajes automáticos. En 1982 se recibieron pedidos para los peajes de las autopistas de Pensilvania y de los metros de Hong Kong, Toronto y Baltimore. Además de sus actividades en ese mercado, refuerza las del control automático de procesos industriales, operaciones bancarias y archivo.

El sector de la electrónica profesional emplea a cerca de 6000 personas, y en 1982 sus ventas superaron los 2000 millones de francos.

Alcatel ha constituido una de las primeras redes europeas de servicios por computador, ocupa uno de los primeros lugares de Francia y dispone de filiales en España, la RFA, Gran Bretaña, Italia, Bélgica y Suiza.

El Grupo ofrece servicios completos que abarcan la disposición de energía de computador, ingeniería de sistemas y la realización del soporte lógico más diverso.

La red de telemática internacional de GSI Alcatel distribuye una serie de productos de nómina y gestión de personal, de servicio a los concesionarios de automóviles y al transporte por carretera, el turismo y los estudios de mercado.

▷ 357

"Minitel" videotex terminal.

Terminal vidéotex « Minitel ».

Terminal vidéotex « Minitel ».

Through its international telematics network, GSI Alcatel distributes a range of standard products including payroll and personnel management, services to automobile concessionaires and road transport operators, tourism and market research.

GSI Alcatel is also actively developing databank management systems for professional applications, with particular emphasis on economic and financial data, market analysis and specialist data (legal databanks, vehicle fleet management, etc. ...).

Sesa has received worldwide a claim for its data communication networks equipment, and has been successful in a number of international calls for tenders to supply such networks. It is extending its activities into the field of telematic products such as local networks, message systems and videotex services.

The software knowledge of the subsidiaries in this sector is used in close collaboration with other companies in the Group, especially in the definition of local networks and telecommunications architectures and in speech processing and optical character recognition.

The computer services companies employ some 3,500 people, and achieved sales of more than 1.3 billion francs in 1982.

As well as establishing that its telecommunications systems can be adapted without difficulty to a wide variety of public network configurations and common carriers policies, Alcatel has established a coherent industrial group which extends into office automation, professional electronics and computer services.

The Group is thus able to construct any type of communication network that may be required. Through the experience acquired and its major R&D activities Alcatel is ready to participate fully in the revolution in communications of the next decade: the integration of all network worldwide and an upsurge in optical transmission.

□

Le réseau télématique international de GSI Alcatel distribue des produits orientés notamment vers la paie et la gestion du personnel, le service aux concessionnaires automobiles et aux transporteurs routiers, le tourisme et les études de marchés.

En outre, GSI Alcatel développe activement la gestion des banques de données répondant à des besoins professionnels et portant principalement sur les données économiques et financières, l'analyse des marchés, et sur certaines informations spécialisées (données juridiques, parcs automobiles...).

Sesa, dont les compétences dans les réseaux téléinformatiques sont reconnues mondialement, a remporté de nombreux appels d'offres internationaux. Sesa se renforce dans les domaines des produits télématiques : réseaux locaux, systèmes de messagerie et services vidéotex.

Les compétences du secteur en génie logiciel sont notamment utilisées pour la définition des architectures de télécommunications et de réseaux locaux et pour le traitement de la parole et la lecture optique.

Les sociétés du secteur occupent environ 3500 personnes et ont réalisé, en 1982, un chiffre d'affaires supérieur à 1,3 milliard de francs.

Tout en prouvant que ses systèmes de télécommunications s'adaptent aux différentes configurations des réseaux publics et aux stratégies les plus diversifiées des organismes exploitants, Alcatel a construit un ensemble industriel cohérent qui étend ses activités à la bureautique, à l'électronique professionnelle et au service informatique.

Le Groupe peut ainsi proposer la réalisation complète de tous les réseaux de communication répondant aux besoins actuels. Par les travaux qu'il a réalisés, et par le volume des dépenses de recherche et développement qu'il engage chaque année, Alcatel est également prêt pour participer à la prochaine révolution des systèmes de communication, qui sera marquée, dans la prochaine décennie, par l'intégration générale des réseaux et par l'explosion des communications optiques.

□

Además, GSI Alcatel desarrolla activamente la gestión de bancos de datos para atender necesidades profesionales, sobre todo de datos económicos y financieros, análisis de mercados, información especializada (datos jurídicos, parques de automóviles, etc.).

Sesa, cuya competencia en las redes de teleinformática se reconoce mundialmente, ha ganado numerosas licitaciones internacionales. Intensifica sus actividades de telemática: redes locales, sistemas de mensajes y servicios videotex.

Los conocimientos de las filiales en soporte lógico se utilizan para definir arquitecturas de telecomunicaciones y redes locales, y para el tratamiento de la palabra y la lectura óptica.

Las empresas del sector ocupan a unas 3500 personas, y en 1982 realizaron una cifra de negocios superior a 1300 millones de francos.

Demostrando que sus sistemas de telecomunicaciones se adaptan a las distintas configuraciones de las redes públicas y a las estrategias más diversificadas de los organismos de explotación, Alcatel ha construido un conjunto industrial coherente que extiende sus actividades a la automatización de oficinas, la electrónica profesional y el servicio de informática.

Por tanto, el Grupo puede proponer el establecimiento completo de todas las redes de comunicaciones, respondiendo a las necesidades actuales. Los trabajos realizados y los gastos de investigación y desarrollo que efectúa anualmente permiten a Alcatel participar también en la próxima revolución de los sistemas de comunicación, que se caracterizará, en el próximo decenio, por la integración general de las redes y por la explosión de las comunicaciones ópticas.

□

Cellular mobile telephone.

Radiotéléphone en service.

Radioteléfono en servicio

PLANNING AND FINANCING
:WHOPENE EXPANSION OF WHORIZONSNEWPO
WORLD COMMUNICATIONS

INDUSTRIAL GROWTH NEEDS FINANCING. For telecommunications this is the more urgent because their growth is rapid and must accomodate a high rate of technological change. The usual pattern for the industry that has developed in most countries is for the service providers to be established monopolistic authorities (PTTs) related to a reasonably stable equipment supply oligopoly. Where basic infrastructures exist, further development of services may be found as much in new products that plug into existing networks as in technical improvements of the basic service. PTTs are often keen to extend their own interests into the manufacture of such new products, seeing this as a way of increasing their profits on their investment in the basic network. Governments, too, will be anxious to retain control over an industrial sector which is an instrument of public service and social policy and which has a vital role in the development of other sectors and in national security.

Business communities, on the other hand, as major user-beneficiaries, tend to press for development to be left to the free competition of the private sector in order to promote effectiveness, efficiency, and economy. Such competition at least in the manufacture and supply of equipment and ancillary services (such as software), which form the major part of the whole industry, can be not merely national but international since their products can be moved freely about the world, subject only to economic and political constraints. Thus the growth and· decay of the equipment industry may be left to the push and pull of world market competition — moderated as it will be by government pressures through low-cost financing and other incentives — and they will attract finance accordingly.

The installation and operation of infrastructures, however, is strictly geographically-related and is an integral part of each national economic and political scene. It is

LA CROISSANCE INDUSTRIELLE nécessite des moyens de financement. Pour les télécommunications, ce financement est d'autant plus urgent que leur développement est rapide et qu'elles doivent s'adapter au rythme élévé d'évolution technologique. Selon le schéma habituel que l'on retrouve dans la plupart des pays, les prestataires de services sont des monopôles établis (PTT) liés à un oligopole relativement stable pour la fourniture de l'équipement. Lorsqu'il existe des infrastructures, celles-ci continuent à se développer autant par les nouveaux produits qui s'intègrent dans les réseaux existants que par les améliorations techniques apportées au service de base. Les administrations des PTT sont souvent portées à étendre leurs activités à la fabrication de ces nouveaux produits, car elles y voient un nouveau moyen d'accroître le rendement de leurs investissements. Les gouvernements seront, eux aussi soucieux de conserver ce contrôle d'un secteur industriel qui est un instrument de service public et de politique sociale et qui joue un rôle essentiel dans le développement d'autres secteurs et dans la sécurité nationale.

Le monde des affaires, au contraire, en tant que usager/bénéficiaire principal, a tendance à exercer des pressions pour que le développement soit laissé à la libre concurrence du secteur privé afin de promouvoir l'efficacité, le rendement et l'économie. Une telle concurrence, au moins dans la fabrication et la fourniture d'équipement, de logiciel et de services auxiliaires ne peut être purement nationale ; elle doit être internationale, car les produits peuvent être utilisés librement dans le monde, sous réserve seulement de compatibilité et de contraintes économiques et politiques. Ainsi, l'industrie de l'équipement est soumise aux fluctuations de la concurrence mondiale, atténuée dans une certaine mesure par les pressions des gouvernements exercées à l'aide de crédits à faible taux et d'autres incitations.

L'installation et l'exploitation des infrastructures sont, elles, étroitement liées au gouvernement et font partie intégrante de l'environnement économique et poli-

EL CRECIMIENTO INDUSTRIAL requiere financiación. Para las telecomunicaciones esto es tanto más urgente cuanto que su crecimiento es rápido y ha de incorporar una elevada tasa de cambio tecnológico. Lo normal en la industria de la mayoría de los países es que quienes prestan el servicio sean autoridades monopolistas (CTT) relacionadas con un oligopolio de suministro de equipo razonablemente estable. Cuando hay infraestructuras básicas, el desarrollo de servicios puede hallarse tanto en nuevos productos conectados con redes existentes como en las mejoras técnicas del servicio básico. Las CTT se dedican también la fabricación de esos nuevos productos, por considerarlo una manera de aumentar los beneficios de su inversión en la red básica. También los gobiernos se mostrarán ansiosos por conservar el control del sector industrial, instrumento de servicio público y política social, y que desempeña un papel vital en el desarrollo de otros sectores y en la seguridad nacional.

Las comunidades comerciales, por otro lado, como principales usuarios-beneficiarios, tratan de que el desarrollo se deje a la libre competencia del sector privado, para fomentar la eficacia, la eficiencia y la economía. Esa competencia, al menos en la fabricación y suministro de equipo y servicio auxiliares (como el soporte lógico), que constituyen la mayor parte de toda la industria, no pueden ser meramente nacionales, ya que sus productos pueden desplazarse libremente por el mundo entero, sometidos sólo a condicionamientos económicos y políticos. Por eso, los altibajos de la industria de equipamiento pueden dejarse al tira y afloja de la competencia mundial — moderada por presiones gubernamentales mediante recursos de bajo costo y otros incentivos — y atraerán la financiación en consecuencia.

La instalación y explotación de infraestructuras tiene una relación estrictamente geográfica y forma parte de cada escena económica y política nacional. Conviene

▷ 360

▷ 360

▷ 361

convenient to consider industrialized and developing countries as two groups; but each country will have its own mixture of needs based upon its geography; population: economic, cultural, social, and political development: and availability of technical and managerial skills.

In industrial countries the growth of telecommunications tends to be self-financing, i.e. the user pays. This begs the question of deciding what is the right amount of investment — for who are the users and how much should each pay for what quality of service? For example, the cost of provision of telecommunication services, with existing technologies, is much higher per person in rural areas than in urban areas; or again, the costs for local and for long distance telephone calls is very different. In both these instances there is usually a suspicion of cross-subsidization (See Box opposite) between one category and the other. Cross-subsidization is easily justified as an element of social policy, to give everyone an equal service, when the principal carrier is a regulated — often state-owned — monopoly. The deregulation of AT&T must be expected to have a profound effect on such issues and consequently will be of the greatest interest to policy-makers in telecommunications not just in the USA but throughout the world.

These matters are not only a question of equitable allocation between users; they also affect, through the relationship of charges to costs, the total amount of cash flow generated internally to provide financing; and this financing has to provide not only for innovation, development, and growth, but also for replacement of equipment because of wear-and-tear or of obsolescence which is likely to be rapid. These are problems of self-regulated industry. It may be assumed that a supplier or carrier in such an industry is well able to balance the interests of its market and its profits to its own best advantage; but it cannot be expected to cater for markets which bring it no advantage unless it receives some form of grant from government or other source of social funds. Nor does state-ownership guarantee access to unlimited funds.

Every nation, however rich, is constantly preoccupied by the problems of balancing the use of available funds and resources between the many urgent social demands. Even a self-regulated industry may well be called upon by its government to contribute towards these other causes through taxes or in other ways; but financial self-sufficiency of efficiently managed telecommunications administrations with low operating costs is the likely way to success.

In developing countries it remains true that financial rates of return on telecommunication equipment can be high, see p. 362 where it is quoted that World Bank financed projects yield 13-35 per cent; so, high self-financing ratios can be attained, provided profits are retained. However, the amount of investment actually allowed is often insufficient to enable the industry to meet demand measured by any criterion. One reason for this lies in the high ratios of rural to urban populations, which can make any adequate cross-subsidy between them impracticable; this underlines the argument that market criteria based on users' revealed preferences or willingness to pay are fundamentally inappropriate in a developing country; this particular problem may be eased by the use of microwave or satellite systems which do not call for so much infrastructure to service scattered areas; see for example the Glodom system described on p. 82.

Other reasons for under-investment can be found in institutional and organizational constraints; in lack of technically skilled manpower, which is needed not just for installation but in the long-term for operations and, above all, for maintenance; and in a political feeling that other investments are more important. This last may be mistakenly encouraged by the fact that the ratio of invested capital to direct annual revenue is exceptionally high for telecommunications projects; many of the real benefits are in

▷ 362

tique des pays : chacun d'eux a des besoins divers fondés sur sa géographie, sa population, son développement économique, culturel, social et politique, et sur la disponibilité de techniciens et de personnel d'encadrement.

Dans les pays industrialisés, le développement des télécommunications tend à être autofinancé (c'est l'usager qui paie). Cela présuppose que l'on décide : 1) le montant adéquat des investissements ; 2) qui sont les usagers, et 3) combien chacun doit-il payer pour quelle qualité de service ? Par exemple, le coût de la fourniture de services est bien plus élevé par tête d'habitant dans les zones rurales que dans les zones urbaines ; ou encore, le coût des appels téléphoniques locaux et celui des appels téléphoniques à grande distance sont très différents. Il y a généralement dans ces deux cas une suspicion de subventions croisées (voir encadré ci-contre) entre une catégorie et l'autre. Le système de subventions croisées se justifie aisément en tant qu'élément social, pour assurer à chacun un service égal, lorsque le principal exploitant est une entreprise réglementée détenant un monopole. La dérégulation d'AT&T devrait avoir des répercussions profondes dans ce domaine. Elle est donc d'un grand intérêt pour les responsables des télécommunications non seulement aux Etats-Unis mais aussi dans le monde entier.

Ces considérations ne sont pas seulement une question de répartition équitable entre les usagers ; elles influent également, par la relation entre les revenus et les coûts, sur le montant des disponibilités à dégager pour assurer le financement lequel doit pourvoir non seulement à l'innovation, au développement et à la croissance, mais aussi au remplacement de l'équipement pour cause d'usure ou d'obsolescence. Ce sont là les problèmes d'une industrie soumise à sa propre réglementation. On peut supposer qu'un fournisseur ou un exploitant dans une telle industrie peut parfaitement équilibrer au mieux les intérêts de son marché et ses bénéfices à son propre avantage, à moins qu'il ne reçoive une forme quelconque de subvention. Le statut de société nationale ou de service public ne garantit pas non plus l'accès à des fonds illimités. Toute nation, aussi riche soit-elle, est constamment préoccupée par les problèmes que pose la répartition équilibrée des ressources disponibles entre les nombreux besoins sociaux. L'autosuffisance financière des organismes de télécommunication est probablement le seul moyen évident d'atteindre le succès.

Dans les pays en développement, le taux de rendement financier de l'équipement de télécommunications peut être élevé et de hauts rapports d'autofinancement peuvent donc être atteints, à condition que les bénéfices ne soient pas distribués. Cependant, le montant des investissements effectivement autorisés est souvent insuffisant pour permettre de répondre à la demande. Cela s'explique en partie par le rapport élevé des populations rurales aux populations urbaines qui peut rendre impossible entre elles tout système de subventions croisées. Ceci vient renforcer l'argument que les critères de marché fondés sur les préférences marquées ou la capacité de payer des usagers sont fondamentalement inadaptés dans un pays en développement. Ce problème particulier peut-être atténué par un nouveau concept de satellites (voir « Glodom » p. 82). Le sous-investissement s'explique également par les contraintes institutionnelles et organisationnelles, par la pénurie de personnel techniquement qualifié, qui est nécessaire non seulement pour l'installation mais aussi, à long terme, pour l'exploitation et surtout pour la maintenance. Il y a aussi le sentiment politique que d'autres investissements sont plus importants. Ce dernier peut être encouragé à tort par le fait que le rapport du capital investi au revenu annuel direct est exceptionnellement élevé pour les projets de télécommunications ; tandis qu'un grand nombre des avantages réels sont en fait indirects et donc peu évidents. Les études de l'UIT ont révélé des ratios d'avantages indirects par rapport à des avantages directs variant de 69 : 1 à 126 : 1, dans différents secteurs.

Les besoins en devises étrangères engendrés par les investissements des télécommunications, générale-

▷ 362

CROSS-SUBSID

In the early days of telecommunications, in those countries now regarded as advanced, the industry was dedicated not to rural areas but to urban areas where direct benefits, coupled with concentrated high-usage rates, permitted telecommunications to produce profits from which to operate and expand facilities.

Out of these profits it became possible to invest in the capital intensive infrastructures which, at least for traditional forms of telecommunications, were required to reach out long distances into rural and isolated areas, to provide a service where usage would be much less concentrated. Thus development has been based upon the concept of the "private good", i.e. telecommunications provide benefit to the user and profit arises out of the rate of return from the user as he pays for the benefit he has received.

Such an arrangement does not promote, and indeed may positively conceal, the concept of the "social good"; shifting the resource costs onto the user does not properly reflect the real need, only his capacity to pay; the idea that in a modern society everyone shall have the right and possibility to communicate and to join in the main streams of national activities then has to be imposed on the system by external pressures of a political nature.

So there exist systems which have been created to satisfy and to obtain profits from major cities and from interurban and perhaps international services. The rural services, where provided, are seen as involving a higher resource cost and lower receipts resulting in a much lower rate of return on investment. The rural customer appears as a poor relative, an object of charity, stigmatized under the name of "cross-subsidization". This is a dangerously facile attitude even in the strict context of the "private good". Individual customers will involve different costs and different receipts for a whole variety of reasons.

Rural customers as a group are likely to produce lower rates of return than urban ones as a group, the receipts from them may even be insufficient to cover the average costs of the system; but so long as the receipts from them exceed the direct costs of providing the service they are in fact contributing towards the economy or profitability of the system as a whole. In short they can claim to be not in receipt of a subsidy but as helping to create "collaborative surplus".

AC

The distinction between the profitable customer, the one who makes a contribution although below average, and the one that is an economic cost to the system, is an important one in considering methods and scale of finance. The first two, taken together, should attract commercial finance; the last requires social justification and must look to government or agency funding; these being limited the scale of the problem should not be exaggerated by including in this category commercially justified services.

Assessments of the kind commonly invoke innovative concepts such as cost/benefit analysis, but there are also fundamental problems of basic accounting practice. In 1979 Robert C. Scrivener of Northern Telecom Ltd. wrote of the existing equipment in many developed countries: "quite frankly, much of it should be discarded and replaced in the interests of operating efficiency and service quality". This need he attributed to past failure to accrue funds based on realistic rates of obsolescence.

Again, is it right to charge research and development costs — a heavy item in this fast-growing technology — against current receipts? The industry would appear to fund its growth to an unsual extent out of current income rather than by borrowing. These, and other aspects, can profoundly effect apparent profitability.

...TION OR COLLABORATIVE SURPLUS

A l'aube des télécommunications, leur développement fut concentré dans les zones urbaines des pays maintenant considérés comme avancés. Dans ces conditions, des taux d'utilisation élevés ont produit des bénéfices qui ont permis l'expansion de ces services à la fois à l'intérieur et en dehors de ces zones.

Il devint alors possible d'étendre les investissements aux infrastructures à forte densité de capital pour atteindre des zones rurales ou isolées, à petite concentration d'utilisateurs. La marge bénéficiaire sur l'ensemble suffisait.

Ce genre de développement est fondé sur le concept du « bien-être personnel », c'est-à-dire, que les télécommunications devaient procurer des avantages à l'usager pour lesquels il payait. Un tel système ne contribue pas à promouvoir, et il peut même éclipser, le concept du « bien-être social » : le fait de répercuter le coût du service sur l'usager ne reflète que sa capacité de paiement, pas ses besoins réels ou les besoins des autres. L'idée que, dans une société moderne, chacun doit avoir le droit, et donc la possibilité de communiquer et de participer aux grands courants des activités nationales, ne peut qu'être imposée par des pressions de nature politique.

Il existe donc des systèmes qui répondent aux besoins des grandes villes, assurent des services interurbains et internationaux. Les services ruraux, quand ils existent, produisent un taux de rendement inférieur, et l'usager rural fait donc figure de parent pauvre, objet d'une sorte de charité, découlant d'une certaine péréquation et stigmatisée sous le nom de « subvention croisée ».

Une telle attitude est dangereuse, même dans le contexte du « bien-être personnel », car pour de multiples raisons, les rapports coûts/revenus sont très variables d'un usager à un autre.

Les usagers ruraux, en tant que groupe, produisent un taux de rendement plus faible que les usagers urbains, également en tant que groupe, et les recettes risquent d'être inférieures aux coûts moyens de la totalité du système. Mais si les recettes qu'ils procurent sont supérieures au coût direct de la fourniture du service rendu, ils contribuent, en fait, à l'économie et à la rentabilité de l'ensemble. En résumé, les usagers ruraux peuvent affirmer qu'ils ne sont pas subventionnés, mais qu'ils coopèrent à la création d'un «surplus contributif».

En los albores de las telecomunicaciones, en los países considerados avanzados, la industria no se dedicó a las zonas rurales, sino a las urbanas, donde los beneficios directos, y las elevadas tasas de utilización, permitían a las telecomunicaciones producir beneficios para explotar y extender los servicios. Con ellos se podía invertir en las infraestructuras de gran densidad de capital requeridas, al menos en las formas tradicionales de telecomunicación, para llegar a las zonas rurales y aisladas remotas, y proporcionar un servicio donde el uso se concentraría mucho menos. Esa evolución se ha basado en la noción de « bien privado », es decir, que las telecomunicaciones benefician al usuario, obteniéndose un rendimiento de lo que el usuario paga por el servicio recibido.

Esto no fomenta la noción de « bien social », y en realidad puede encubrirla; el desplazamiento del costo de los recursos al usuario no refleja debidamente la verdadera necesidad, sino tan sólo su capacidad de pago; la idea de que en una sociedad moderna todos deben tener el derecho y la posibilidad de comunicar y de participar en las principales corrientes de las actividades nacionales ha de imponerse, pues, al sistema por presiones exteriores de carácter político.

Por tanto, existen sistemas creados para los servicios de las principales ciudades, así como interurbanos y quizá internacionales, y obtener beneficios de ellos. Se considera que los servicios rurales prestados suponen un costo de recursos más elevado y menores ingresos, por lo que el rendimiento de la inversión es mucho más bajo. El cliente rural es el pariente pobre, objeto de caridad, estigmatizado con el nombre de « subvención cruzada ». Se trata de una actitud fácil y peligrosa, incluso en el estricto contexto del « bien privado ». Los clientes individuales entrañarán costos e ingresos distintos, por una serie de razones. Los clientes rurales, como grupo, probablemente produzcan tasas de rendimiento más bajas que los urbanos, también como grupo; los ingresos que generan pueden incluso no bastar para cubrir el costo medio del sistema; pero mientras sus ingresos rebasen los costos directos de proporcionar el servicio, contribuyen en realidad a la economía o rentabilidad del sistema en su conjunto. En resumen, pueden afirmar que no reciben una subvención, sino que ayudan a crear un « excedente de colaboración ».

considerar a los países industrializados y en desarrollo como dos grupos; pero cada país tendrá su propia mezcla de necesidades basadas en su geografía, población, desarrollo económico, cultural, social y político, y su disponibilidad de personal técnico y de gestión.

En los países industriales, el crecimiento de las telecomunicaciones tiende a la autofinanciación, o sea, paga el usuario. Esto plantea la cuestión de decidir cuál es la cantidad de inversión acertada: ¿quiénes son los usuarios y cuánto deben pagar y por qué calidad de servicio? Por ejemplo, el costo de prestar servicios de telecomunicaciones, con tecnologías existentes, es mucho más alto por habitante en las zonas rurales que en las urbanas; o, una vez más, el costo de las llamadas telefónicas locales y de larga distancia difiere mucho. En ambos casos hay una sospecha de subvención cruzada (véase el recuadro) entre una categoría y otra. Esa subvención se justifica fácilmente como elemento de política social, para dar a todos el mismo servicio, cuando la principal empresa que lo presta es un monopolio reglamentado, frecuentemente estatal. Es de esperar que la libertad de comercio de AT&T tenga un profundo efecto sobre tales cuestiones y presente el mayor interés para las autoridades de telecomunicaciones, no sólo de EE.UU. sino del mundo entero.

No se trata únicamente de un asunto de distribución equitativa entre usuarios; afecta también, mediante la relación cargas-costos, a la cantidad total de dinero generado interiormente para la financiación; y esa financiación no sólo ha de atender la innovación, el desarrollo y el crecimiento, sino también la sustitución de equipo debido al deterioro o a la obsolescencia, que tal vez sea rápida. Son problemas de la industria autorreglamentada. Cabe suponer que un proveedor o empresa de tal industria pueda equilibrar los intereses de su mercado y sus beneficios en bien propio; pero no cabe esperar que se ocupe de mercados que no aportan ventajas, a menos que reciba algún subsidio del gobierno u otra fuente de fondos sociales. La propiedad estatal tampoco garantiza el acceso a fondos ilimitados.

Las naciones, aunque sean ricas, se preocupan constantemente por los problemas de equilibrar el uso de fondos y recursos disponibles entre las muchas demandas sociales urgentes. Incluso una industria autorreglamentada puede ser requerida por su gobierno para que contribuya a esas otras causas mediante impuestos u otras formas; pero el probable camino del éxito es la autosuficiencia financiera de administraciones de telecomunicaciones dirigidas eficazmente, con bajos costos de explotación.

En los países en desarrollo, las tasas de rendimiento financiero del equipo de telecomunicaciones pueden ser altas; véase la pág. 362, donde se dice que los proyectos financiados por el Banco Mundial produjeron del 13 al 15%, por lo que pueden alcanzarse elevadas tasas de autofinanciación, siempre que se conserven los beneficios. Pero la inversión realmente autorizada es con frecuencia insuficiente para que la industria atienda la demanda medida por cualquier criterio. Una de las razones es la elevada relación entre población rural y urbana, que puede impedir cualquier subvención cruzada entre ellas; esto refuerza el argumento de que los criterios de mercado basados en las preferencias o la disposición de los usuarios a pagar son fundamentalmente inapropiados en un país en desarrollo; tal problema puede facilitarse utilizando sistemas de microondas o satélite, que no requieren mucha infraestructura para dar servicio a zonas dispersas; véase, por ejemplo, el sistema Glodom descrito en la pág. 82.

Otras razones de inversión insuficiente son los condicionamientos institucionales y orgánicos; la falta de personal técnico calificado, no sólo necesario para la instalación sino para las operaciones a largo plazo y, sobre todo, para el mantenimiento; y el sentimiento político de que otras inversiones son más importantes. La elevada relación capital invertido/ingresos anuales directos en proyectos de telecomunicaciones puede alentar erróneamente a ello; muchos de los beneficios reales son indirectos y, por

...OUNTING FOR PROFIT

La distinction entre l'usager rentable, celui qui apporte une contribution, et celui qui constitue une charge pour le système, est importante lorsqu'on examine les méthodes et l'échelle de financement. Pris ensemble, les deux premiers doivent attirer le financement commercial ; pris seul, le dernier exige une justification sociale du recours aux fonds publics. Ceux-ci étant limités, il ne faut pas exagérer l'ampleur du problème en incluant dans cette catégorie des services commercialement justifiés.

Les évaluations de ce type impliquent des concepts nouveaux, tels que celui de l'analyse coût-avantages, mais elles soulèvent des problèmes fondamentaux de la comptabilité de base. En 1979, Robert C. Scrivener de Northern Telecom Ltd. écrivait à propos de l'équipement existant dans de nombreux pays développés : « Une grande partie de cet équipement doit être mise au rebut et remplacée dans l'intérêt de l'efficacité de l'exploitation et de la qualité du service ». Il attribuait cette nécessité à l'impossibilité qu'il y avait dans le passé de dégager des fonds suffisants, basés sur des taux d'obsolescence réalistes.

Là encore, est-il juste de mettre les dépenses de recherche et de développement, rubrique aujourd'hui très importante, au compte des recettes courantes ? L'industrie paraît financer dans des proportions anormales, sa croissance par les recettes courantes plutôt que par des apports de capital. Cette méthode, et d'autres, peuvent influencer la rentabilité apparente, et donc la politique de renouvellement des équipements.

La distinción entre el cliente rentable, el que hace una contribución, aunque sea inferior a la media, y el que supone un costo económico para el sistema, es importante al considerar los métodos y la escala de financiación. Los dos primeros, conjuntamente, deben atraer recursos comerciales; el último requiere una justificación social y la financiación por el gobierno o sus organismos; al ser limitados los recursos, no debe exagerarse la magnitud del problema incluyendo en esta categoría servicios justificados comercialmente. Esta clase de evaluaciones invoca normalmente nociones innovadoras como el análisis costo/beneficio, pero también existen problemas fundamentales de pácticas contables básicas. En 1979, Robert C. Scrivener, de Northern Telecom Ltd., escribía del equipo existente en muchos países desarrollados: « con toda franqueza, hay que descartar gran parte de él y sustituirlo en bien de la eficacia de la explotación y de la calidad del servicio ». Atribuía esta necesidad a que en el pasado no se han acumulado fondos basados en tasas de obsolescencia realistas.

Una vez más, ¿procede cargar los costos de investigación y desarrollo — un gran capítulo en esta tecnología en rápida expansión — a los ingresos corrientes? En tal caso, la industria financiaría su crecimiento en un grado inusitado con los ingresos corrientes en lugar de recurrir al préstamo. Estos y otros aspectos pueden influir mucho en una rentabilidad aparente.

▷ 363

fact indirect, and therefore not obvious. ITU studies have found ratios of indirect to direct benefits ranging from 69:1 to 126:1 in different sectors.

Foreign exchange requirements generated by telecommunications investment — typically 50-60 per cent of the total — are one of the key constraints. Many nations may lack the financial strength to take up commercially available funds for foreign exchange (e.g. supplier credits, foreign commercial bank and government loans and equity). Other sources open to them include bilateral aid and the development banks (World Bank, Inter-American Development Bank, Asian Development Bank) and the United Nations Development Program. Just as individual governments have tended to hold back, so the World Bank's support, and that of others, for telecommunications projects has tended to be lower than for many other sectors. The funds supplied for telecommunications compared with other sectors are shown opposite. The ITU Plenipotentiary Conference in 1982 urged that efforts be made to obtain a greater share of UNDP and other program resources.

Development funds of this kind need to allocate their resources just as much as governments do if telecommunications are to take their place as a basic social right. The criteria needed for telecommunications financing then must be the same as those used for development projects in, for example, food or health. These latter may secure long-term finance with exceptionally favourable terms (low interest rates, initial periods of moratorium). If similar terms were available for telecommunications perhaps more schemes could be started, at least to establish threshold services which could generate capital to finance extension. Comparability of criteria is not just in the interests of telecommunication development. Availability of telecommunications affects the needs for transport infrastructures, and vice versa; both affect agriculture; agriculture affects food; food affects health; communications affects the structure of health service required; and so on. No one program can be developed in isolation without causing imbalanced development. Each program is just a part of a highly interactive system.

The planning process, which must be preliminary to the application for finance, clearly calls for an understanding of all these interactions as well as for better measurement of the intangible, indirect, benefits of telecommunications themselves; many of these benefits do indeed arise from the interaction with other programs. Reference was made earlier to some of the many correlation studies that have been made. But the demonstration of more statistical connection is not enough; there is need for more extensive studies of cost/benefit and input-output nature, including the whole armoury of micro- and macro-economic analyses.

International links between different countries will include important regional schemes, such as Panaftel in Africa, and the South Pacific scheme, as well as global schemes. Investment needed is not great compared with that within individual countries and commercial financing is unlikely to be a constraint, though it is important to avoid too much concentration on links to the industrialized nations rather than direct links between the developing countries. The problems in achieving the necessary investment are likely to be organizational rather than financial, in ensuring compatibility between national administrations and systems (see for example the note about Standards p. 240) and in reconciling the individual national interests and priorities.

Many difficulties in international planning are attributable to the fact that the overall responsibility for the provision of international facilities is shared among a number of entities while the responsibility for service to the subscriber rests with the individual administration or carrier. It is essential that national control processes be compatible with the requirements of the international negotiation process between autonomous administrations.

ment 50 à 60 pour cent du total, sont l'une des principales contraintes. De nombreuses nations n'ont pas une capacité financière suffisante pour accepter des fonds en devises commercialement disponibles (crédits-fournisseur, prêts et fonds de banques commerciales étrangères et de gouvernements). Parmi les autres sources qui leur sont ouvertes figurent notamment l'aide bilatérale et les banques de développement (Banque mondiale, Banque interaméricaine de développement, Banque asiatique de développement), ainsi que les fonds dont dispose le Programme des Nations Unies pour le développement. De même que les gouvernements se sont, en général, montrés réservés, de même le soutien de la Banque mondiale (et d'autres banques) aux projets de télécommunications a eu tendance à être inférieur à celui de nombreux autres secteurs (voir ci-contre). La Conférence de plénipotentiaires de l'UIT de Nairobi, en 1982, a demandé instamment qu'une plus grande part des ressources du PNUD et d'autres programmes soit allouée aux télécommunications.

Les fonds de développement de ce type seront obligés de réviser les critères qu'ils appliquent à la distribution de leurs ressources si l'on veut que les télécommunications prennent leur place en tant que droit social. Ces critères devront être les mêmes que ceux qui sont appliqués pour le financement des projets de développement, par exemple dans l'alimentation, la santé ou le transport, pour que les télécommunications bénéficient de crédits à long terme à des conditions exceptionnellement favorables. Cela permettrait de lancer un plus grand nombre de projets. Le caractère comparatif des critères n'intéresse pas seulement le développement des télécommunications. Leur existence influe sur les besoins en infrastructures de transport et vice-versa ; les unes et les autres influent sur l'agriculture ; l'agriculture influe sur l'alimentation ; l'alimentation influe sur la santé ; les communications influent sur la structure des services de santé nécessaires, etc. Aucun programme ne peut être mis en œuvre isolément sans provoquer un déséquilibre du développement. Chaque programme n'est qu'une partie d'un système hautement interactif.

Le processus de planification, qui doit être préalable à la demande de crédits, exige naturellement que l'on comprenne toutes ces interactions et que l'on mesure mieux les avantages intangibles et indirects des télécommunications elles-mêmes ; beaucoup de ces avantages résultent en effet de l'interaction avec d'autres programmes. Il a été question plus haut de certaines études de corrélation qui ont été effectuées. Mais il ne suffit pas de démontrer l'existence de seules relations statistiques ; il faut encore effectuer des études plus approfondies du type coût-avantages et entrée-sortie, y compris toute la panoplie des analyses micro et macro-économiques.

Les liaisons internationales entre les différents pays font l'objet de programmes régionaux importants, tels que Panaftel en Afrique et le programme du Pacifique Sud, ainsi que de programmes mondiaux. Les capitaux investis ne sont pas importants, comparés à ceux qui doivent l'être à l'intérieur des pays et le financement commercial ne sera vraisemblablement pas une contrainte, bien qu'il soit important d'éviter une trop forte concentration sur les liaisons vers les pays industrialisés au détriment des liaisons directes entre les pays en développement. Les problèmes soulevés par les investissements nécessaires risquent de revêtir un caractère plus organisationnel que financier, car il s'agit d'assurer la compatibilité entre les administrations et les systèmes nationaux et de concilier les intérêts et les priorités des divers pays.

De nombreuses difficultés de la planification internationale tiennent au fait que la responsabilité globale de la fourniture de services internationaux est partagée entre plusieurs entités, tandis que la responsabilité du service à l'abonné incombe à chaque administration ou exploitant. Il est indispensable que les processus de contrôle national soient compatibles avec les exigences de la négociation internationale entre administrations autonomes.

ADAPTING I
NEW TELECOMMU

This graphic presentation of World Bank Loans over 5 years is striking evidence of the low priority accorded to investment in telecommunications in the countries receiving the Bank's financial assistence. But the scene is changing.

In a report published in 1982 the World Bank noted growing recognition of the support role provided by telecommunications "in areas for which information transfer and two-way communications are vital", and that there was a need to review the "financing and policy arrangements which have been followed". Telecommunications were spoken of as "a basic infrastructure

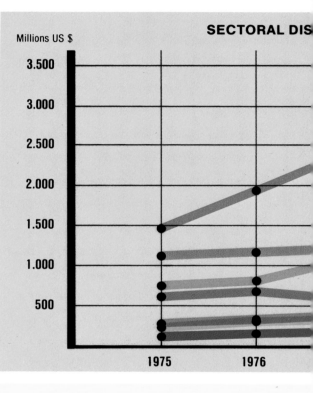

requirement for national development" and much evidence in support of this adduced from studies carried out by the ITU and the OECD, some jointly by the two organizations. Their general conclusion was that the direct benefits from telecommunications were only a fraction of the indirect benefits.

The World Bank's own review of the situation (as it prevailed in 1980/81) concluded that there was an urgent need to create awareness — in the national environments and, presumably, also among international investors — of the support role of telecommunications in activities dependent on quick and efficient information transfer. These included transportation, agriculture, social services and, more especially perhaps, education. Frequently lacking, they remarked, is "the recognition of the value of the new telecommunications" for the achievement of fundamental national objectives. These appeared to be, the Bank report argued, "a need to take at least account of communication requirements at the planning stage of development projects"

More studies are doubtless needed to adapt investment priorities and to establish a cohesive global program of telecommunications infrastructure development. Several regional projects, however, have made substantial headway under the leadership and with the technical assistance of the ITU. Many obstacles remain to be overcome, especially shortages of funds and of local skill, but real progress is being made, and the incrementum is increasing.

...ESTMENT PRIORITIES TO THE
...NICATIONS TECHNOLOGY PERSPECTIVE

Cette présentation graphique des prêts de la Banque Mondiale pendant les années 1975-80 démontre d'une manière frappante la basse priorité donnée aux investissements dans les télécommunications par les pays qui bénéficient de l'assistance financière de la Banque. Mais la situation est en train de changer.

Dans son rapport publié en 1982 la Banque souligne la reconnaissance croissante du rôle essentiel des télécommunications « dans les secteurs où le transfert de l'information et les communications interactives sont vitaux » et conclue qu'il

Este gráfico de los préstamos del Banco Mundial durante cinco años muestra claramente la escasa prioridad concedida a la inversión en telecomunicaciones en los países que reciben ayuda financiera del Banco. Pero la situación está cambiando.

En un informe publicado en 1982, el Banco Mundial señala el mayor reconocimiento del papel de apoyo de las telecomunicaciones «en zonas en que la transferencia de información y las comunicaciones bidireccionales son vitales», y que es necesario revisar «los acuerdos de financiación y políticas seguidos». Se ha calificado a las telecomunicaciones de «infraestructura

tanto, no evidentes. En los estudios de la UIT se observan relaciones de beneficios indirectos a directos que varían de 69:1 a 126:1 en diferentes sectores.

Las necesidades de divisas generadas por la inversión en telecomunicaciones — normalmente del 50 al 60% del total — son uno de los principales condicionamientos. Muchas naciones pueden carecer de recursos para consagrar fondos comerciales disponibles a divisas (por ejemplo, créditos del proveedor, banco comercial extranjero y préstamos y patrimonio del gobierno). Entre otras fuentes figuran la ayuda bilateral y los bancos de desarrollo (Banco Mundial, Banco Interamericano de Desarrollo, Banco Asiático de Desarrollo) y el Programa de las Naciones Unidas para el Desarrollo. Lo mismo que los gobiernos tienden a abstenerse, el apoyo del Banco Mundial (y de otros) para proyectos de telecomunicaciones tiende a ser inferior al de muchos otros sectores. En el gráfico se muestran los fondos asignados a este sector, en comparación con otros. La Conferencia de Plenipotenciarios de la UIT de 1982 instó a tratar de obtener una parte mayor de recursos del PNUD y de otros programas.

Estos fondos de desarrollo han de asignarse como lo hacen los gobiernos, si se quiere que las telecomunicaciones ocupen su lugar como derecho social fundamental. Los criterios para su financiación han de ser, pues, los mismos que se aplican en proyectos de desarrollo de alimentación o sanidad, por ejemplo. Estos pueden contar con una financiación a largo plazo en condiciones muy favorables (bajos tipos de interés, períodos de moratoria iniciales). Si se aplicaran condiciones análogas a las telecomunicaciones, tal vez pudieran iniciarse más sistemas, al menos para primeros servicios que generan capital para financiar la extensión. La comparación de criterios no es favorable a los intereses del desarrollo de las telecomunicaciones. Cuando existen, influyen en las infraestructuras de transporte, y viceversa; ambas afectan a la agricultura; la agricultura a la alimentación; la alimentación a la salud; las comunicaciones a la estructura de los servicios sanitarios requeridos, etc. Ningún programa puede realizarse aisladamente, sin desequilibrar el desarrollo. Cada programa forma parte de un sistema interactivo.

El proceso de planificación, que ha de preceder a la financiación, exige, sin duda, la comprensión de todas estas interacciones, así como de una evaluación mejor de los beneficios intangibles, indirectos, de las propias telecomunicaciones; muchos de ellos se derivan de la interacción con otros programas. Ya se ha hecho referencia a algunos de los múltiples estudios de correlación efectuados. Pero no basta con demostrar una mayor relación estadística; se necesitan estudios más amplios de costo/beneficio e insumo-producto, incluido el conjunto de análisis micro y macroeconómicos.

Los enlaces internacionales entre países comprenderán importantes sistemas regionales, como Panaftel en Africa, y el del Pacífico Sur, así como sistemas globales. No se necesitan grandes inversiones, si se comparan con las de algunos países, y no es probable que la financiación comercial sea un obstáculo, si bien es importante para evitar la excesiva concentración en enlaces con las naciones industrializadas en vez de enlaces directos entre países en desarrollo. Quizá los problemas para lograr la inversión necesaria sean de tipo orgánico, y no financiero, a fin de asegurar la compatibilidad entre administraciones y sistemas nacionales (véase la nota sobre normas, pág. 240) y conciliar los distintos intereses y prioridades nacionales.

Muchas dificultades de la planificación internacional se atribuyen a que la responsabilidad global de la provisión de facilidades internacionales la comparten varias entidades, en tanto que la responsabilidad de servicio al abonado la asume la administración o empresa correspondiente. Es esencial que los procesos de control nacional sean compatibles con los requisitos del proceso de negociación internacional entre administraciones antónomas.

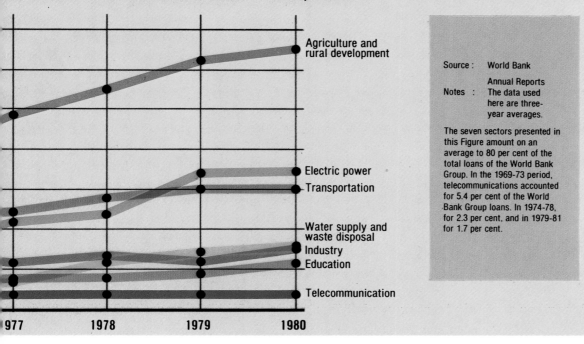

...BUTION OF WORLD BANK GROUP LOANS, 1975-1980

Agriculture and rural development

Electric power

Transportation

Water supply and waste disposal

Industry

Education

Telecommunication

...977   1978   1979   1980

Source :   World Bank

Notes :   Annual Reports
The data used here are three-year averages.

The seven sectors presented in this Figure amount on an average to 80 per cent of the total loans of the World Bank Group. In the 1969-73 period, telecommunications accounted for 5.4 per cent of the World Bank Group loans. In 1974-78, for 2.3 per cent, and in 1979-81 for 1.7 per cent.

existe un fort besoin de réviser « les dispositions financières et politiques en cours ».

La Banque considère les télécommunications « une infrastructure fondamentale du développement national » et cite en confirmation les études effectuées par l'UIT et l'OCDE séparément et parfois conjointement par les deux organisations. La conclusion générale est que les avantages directs procurés par les télécommunications ne sont qu'une fraction des avantages indirects.

L'analyse par la Banque Mondiale de la situation existante en 1980/81 révèle un besoin pressant de faire prendre conscience — à la fois par les autorités nationales et par les investisseurs internationaux — du rôle de soutien vital qu'exercent les télécommunications pour les secteurs qui dépendent d'un transfert d'information rapide et efficace. Ce qui manque le plus souvent, conclue le rapport, est la « réalisation de la valeur des télécommunications modernes » pour atteindre les objectifs nationaux. Il est évident, dit-il, « qu'il est nécessaire, pour le moins, d'évaluer les besoins en moyens de communications au stade de planification des projets de développement ».

D'autres études sont indubitablement nécessaires pour adapter l'ordre des priorités d'investissement et pour établir un programme global et cohérent de développement de l'infrastructure des communications. Plusieurs projets régionaux ont pourtant bien avancé sous la conduite et avec l'assistance technique de l'UIT. Beaucoup d'obstacles restent à surmonter, surtout le manque de fonds et de compétence technique locale, mais de vrais progrès ont été accomplis et l'accélération se maintient.

básica necesaria para el desarrollo nacional», y así lo confirman los estudios realizados por la UIT y la OCDE, algunos conjuntamente. Su conclusión general es que los beneficios directos de las telecomunicaciones son sólo una fracción de los indirectos.

En su propio análisis sobre la situación (1980-81), el Banco Mundial llega a la conclusión de que es indispensable que los medios nacionales y, presumiblemente, también los inversores internacionales, reconozcan la necesidad de las telecomunicaciones para apoyar actividades que dependen de la transferencia de información rápida y eficaz. Estas comprenden: transporte, agricultura, servicios sociales, y, tal vez más concretamente, educación. Observan que, con frecuencia, «no se reconoce el valor de las nuevas telecomunicaciones» para lograr objetivos nacionales fundamentales. Según el Banco Mundial, esto se debe «a la exigencia de tener al menos en cuenta las necesidades de comunicaciones al planear proyectos de desarrollo».

Sin duda, se requieren más estudios para adoptar prioridades de inversión y establecer un programa global cohesivo de desarrollo de la infraestructura de telecomunicaciones. Sin embargo, varios proyectos regionales han conseguido ya notables avances, con la dirección y la asistencia técnica de la UIT. Todavía hay que superar muchos obstáculos, sobre todo de falta de fondos y calificaciones locales, pero los progresos son cada vez mayores.

"**Communications is an inexhaustible resource,** an ever-growing technology which can greatly enhance the use of all the earth's resources, natural, human and economic. Through a vast array of communication techniques mankind is able to accumulate, organize, and transmit, information on a worldwide scale. Therefore, the harmonious and well-balanced development of an ever-closer-knit world communications network is a major historical event in keeping with the emergence of a collective awareness among mankind as a whole. Following its development, no-one should any longer be isolated from the national or international community. Communications should be a right and not a privilege".

Those words were spoken by Richard E. Butler, Secretary-General of the ITU, at the opening of World Communications Year 1983. This volume has attempted to present a picture of some of the prizes to be gained and of the means available to gain them as well as marking some of the areas of greatest difficulty and need.

The nations with a strong economic and industrial base are well advanced in the provision, use, manufacture, and processing of information and, perhaps most important of all, have technically trained and comprehending manpower. But the unbalanced distribution of services throughout the world is illustrated by the fact that 15 per cent of nations have 90 per cent of the world's telephones and TV receivers. And the physical problem to be overcome in some countries is shown by the calculation that some 80 per cent of Africa's population of 304 million live in rural areas; if a target were set to provide telephones so that everyone could reach a telephone within one hour (walking) a large proportion of the telephones would serve fewer than 100 people.

Those countries at present in a less developed state may have one advantage: they do not have obsolete equipment and infrastructures to replace with modern and more efficient equipment. So they may, with help, move forward directly to the installation of the latest and most modern technology which is also the most adapted for their needs.

« **La communication est un avoir inexhaustible,** une technologie en développement constant, permettant d'améliorer considérablement l'utilisation de toutes les ressources terrestres, qu'elles soient naturelles, humaines ou économiques. En faisant appel à une gamme étendue de techniques de communication, l'homme est désormais capable d'accumuler, d'organiser et de transmettre l'information à l'échelle du monde. En conséquence, le développement harmonieux et bien équilibré d'un réseau mondial de communications toujours plus dense est un évènement historique majeur, qui correspond à l'émergence d'une prise de conscience collective de l'humanité dans son ensemble. Lorsque l'aménagement de ce réseau sera achevé, nul ne devrait plus se sentir isolé de la communauté nationale ou internationale. La possibilité de communiquer doit être un droit et non un privilège. »

Ces paroles font partie de l'allocution inaugurale prononcée par M. R. E. Butler, Secrétaire général de l'UIT, pour l'ouverture de l'Année mondiale des communications 1983. Dans le présent ouvrage, on a tenté de mettre en évidence les avantages considérables qu'offrent les communications, ainsi que les moyens disponibles pour tirer profit de ces avantages, tout en signalant les domaines dans lesquels se rencontrent les difficultés les plus grandes et les besoins les plus pressants.

Les nations dotées d'une base économique et industrielle solide sont les mieux placées pour fournir, pour utiliser et pour traiter l'information et, ce qui est peut-être le plus important, sont les mieux nanties en main d'œuvre technique spécialisée et polyvalente. Il faut encore remarquer que la répartition très inégale des services est clairement illustrée par le fait que 15% seulement des pays disposent de 90% des appareils téléphoniques et des récepteurs de télévision actuellement en service dans le monde. De plus, certains problèmes géophysiques et démographiques doivent être résolus dans de nombreux pays. Cela est notamment démontré par le fait que les 80% de la population de l'Afrique, qui compte 304 millions d'habitants, vivent dans des zones rurales. Si l'on se fixait comme objectif d'aménager les services téléphoniques de telle manière que n'importe qui soit en mesure d'atteindre un appareil téléphonique en une heure de marche au maximum, une forte proportion des appareils téléphoniques existants servirait à moins de cent personnes.

Les pays qui se trouvent actuellement à un stade de développement élémentaire peuvent en retirer au moins un avantage : étant donné qu'ils ne disposent pas d'installations, ni d'infrastructures périmées, qu'il serait nécessaire de remplacer par un équipement moderne plus efficace, ces pays peuvent, s'ils sont aidés, s'équiper en adoptant d'emblée la technologie de pointe la plus avancée qui est, aussi, la plus appropriée à leurs besoins.

Digital communications systems
and interactive terminals bring the
Information Age to our doorsteps.

Les systèmes de télématique
nous apportent l'ère de l'information
aux portes mêmes de nos foyers.

«La comunicación es un recurso inagotable, una tecnología creciente que puede incrementar grandemente la utilización de los recursos naturales, humanos y económicos de la Tierra. Por medio de un amplio abanico de técnicas de comunicación, la humanidad puede acumular, organizar y transmitir información a escala mundial. En consecuencia, el desarrollo armonioso y equilibrado de una red mundial de comunicaciones cada vez más tupida constituye un importante acontecimiento histórico paralelo a la aparición de una conciencia colectiva en la humanidad en su conjunto. Tras este desarrollo, nadie estará aislado de la comunidad nacional o internacional. Las comunicaciones deben ser un derecho y no un privilegio».

Estas palabras fueron pronunciadas por el Sr. R.E. Butler, Secretario General de la UIT, en la apertura del Año Mundial de las Comunicaciones, 1983.

En este volumen se ha tratado de dar una idea de parte de lo que puede conseguirse y de los medios de que se dispone para ello, así como de destacar algunos de los sectores de mayor dificultad y necesidad.

Las naciones con una fuerte base económica « industrial » se encuentran muy avanzadas en la provisión, uso, fabricación, y, quizá lo más importante, personal técnicamente capacitado y completo. Pero el hecho de que el 15% de los países dispongan del 90% de los teléfonos y aparatos de TV del mundo ilustra la desequilibrada distribución de los servicios en el planeta. Y el problema físico que ha de superarse en algunos países se muestra calculando que alrededor del 80% de la población africana, de 304 millones, vive en zonas rurales; si se fijara el objetivo de proporcionar teléfonos de manera que todos pudieran disponer de un aparato en una hora (andando), una gran proporción de los teléfonos serviría a menos de 100 personas. Los países que se encuentran en la fase de menos adelantados pueden tener una ventaja; no han de sustituir equipo e infraestructuras anticuados por equipo moderno y más eficiente. Por eso, si se les ayuda, pueden avanzar directamente hacia la instalación de la tecnología más reciente y moderna, que es también la más apropiada para sus necesidades.

Los sistemas de telemática nos ofrecen
la integración en la sociedad de la información
a la propia puerta de nuestras casas.

NEW HORIZONS NEW POWER NEW HOPE

Art direction, graphic presentation and book layout: G. L. Franco ● Artwork ▪ Cover by F.H.K. Henrion, MBE, ▪ pp. *29, 65* and *319* by Stanislaw Fernandes ▪ p. *239* by Alessandro Lanzavecchia ▪ p. *39* by Jeffery Schrier ▪ p. *101* by Murray Tinkerman ▪ Charts by Gustave Gerno ▪ Cartography of the planisphere, pp. *72-73*, specially elaborated by Istituto Geografico De Agostini Novara ● The photographs and illustrations were created, selected or made available through the courtesy or with the assistance of ▪ American Telephone and Telegraph Company, pp. *21-22, 24-25, 29, 39, 59, 65, 68, 71, 85, 86-87, 88-89, 90-91, 92-93, 94-95, 96-97, 98-99, 101, 102-103, 106-107, 123, 124-125, 212-213, 283, 286-287, 307, 344-345, 364-365* ▪ CIT Alcatel, pp. *347, 348-349, 350-351, 352-353, 354-355, 356-357* ▪ Control Data Corporation, pp. *10-11, 31, 44-45, 322-323, 325, 326-327, 328-329, 330-331, 332-333, 334-335, 336-337, 338-339, 366-367* ▪ GTE Corporation, pp. *30, 31, 209, 260, 267, 268-269, 270-271, 272-273, 274-275, 276-277, 278-279, 280-281, 341* ▪ Harvard University, Program on Information Policy Research, pp. *26-27, 148-149, 284-285, 310-311, 314-315* ▪ International Telecommunication Union, pp. *36-37, 40-41, 49, 52-53, 66-67, 76-77, 80-81, 82-83, 236-237, 288-289, 362-363* ▪ ITT Corporation, pp. *60-61, 108-109, 124-125, 129, 130-131, 132-133, 134-135, 136-137, 138-139, 140-141, 142-143* ▪ NEC Corporation, pp. *12-13, 15, 30, 145, 146-147, 151, 152-153, 154-155, 156-157, 158-159, 160-161, 162-163, 164-165* ▪ Saudi Telecom, pp. *245, 246-247, 248-249, 250-251, 252-253, 254-255, 256-257, 258-259* ▪ Siemens AG Communications Group, pp. *111, 112-113, 114-115, 116-117, 118-119, 120-121, 124-125* ▪ Telettra SpA, pp. *214-215, 216-217, 218-219, 220-221, 222-223, 224-225, 226-227, 228-229* ▪ Thomson-CSF Communications, pp. *171, 197, 198-199, 200-201, 202-203, 204-205, 206-207, 210-211* ▪ 3M Company, pp. *291, 292-293, 294-295, 296-297, 298-299, 300-301, 302-303, 304-305, 342-343, 358* ▪ US National Aeronautics and Space Administration, pp. *168-169, 170, 245* ▪ Western Union Corporation, pp. *62-63, 166, 175, 176-177, 178-179, 180-181, 182-183, 184-185, 186-187, 188-189, 191* ● Photographers ▪ Roberto Bosan, pp. *364-365* ▪ Alain de Ferron, pp. *8, 172-173, 231* ▪ International Photo, pp. *344* top ▪ Dick Luria, pp. *344* bottom ▪ Vincent Nanfra, pp. *102-103* ▪ John Pemberton, pp. *59, 71* ▪ Jake Rajs, pp. *24-25* ▪ Michel Tcherenkoff, pp. *286-287* ▪ Roger Tully, p. *283* ▪ Mike Yamachita, p. *307*. Printed by Istituto Geografico De Agostini Officine Grafiche Novara, Italy, October 1983.